The New Engineering Contract
A Legal Commentary

By
Arthur McInnis BA, LLB, BCL, LLM, PhD FCIArb

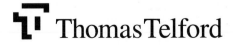

Thomas Telford

Published by Thomas Telford Publishing, Thomas Telford Ltd, 1 Heron Quay, London E14 4JD.
URL: http://www.thomastelford.com

Distributors for Thomas Telford books are
USA: ASCE Press, 1801 Alexander Bell Drive, Reston, VA 20191-4400, USA
Japan: Maruzen Co. Ltd, Book Department, 310 Nihonbashi 2-chome, Chuo-ku, Tokyo 103
Australia: DA Books and Journals, 648 Whitehorse Road, Mitcham 3132, Victoria

First published 2001

Also available from Thomas Telford Books
Civil Engineering Construction Contracts, 2nd edition. ISBN 07277 2785 0
The NEC Engineering and Construction Contract: A user's guide. ISBN 07277 2750 8
NEC and Partnering: The guide to building winning teams. ISBN 07277 2955 1

A catalogue record for this book is available from the British Library

ISBN: 0 7277 2961 6

Typeset by MHL Typesetting Ltd, Coventry
Printed and bound in Great Britain by MPG Books Ltd, Bodmin, Cornwall

To Debora, Whitney and Tristan

Foreword

Publication of this book is a very welcome event for the engineering and construction industries worldwide. The New Engineering Contract is becoming more widely used every day and it is a valuable development that there is now a comprehensive, intelligent and objective legal commentary upon it to which users of the NEC and potential users can refer.

I had the privilege of leading the team which identified the need for the NEC more than fifteen years ago and which went on to design and draft the documents that are now governing the management of so many projects. We knew that our task was to break the mould and produce something which would free those who wanted to manage their projects better from the anachronistic practices and constraints which the traditional standard forms of contract imposed. We also foresaw that the result would attract criticism from some lawyers. Unfortunately, much of the criticism has been parochial and some of it has been plainly ill-founded.

In his thorough and perceptive research, culminating in this book, Arthur provided a much needed tool. We now have the authoritative legal analysis that has addressed the criticism and will underpin the use of the NEC by managers and their legal advisers. Arthur clearly understands the management process and recognises its challenges. The book speaks clearly to lawyers and managers in terms which both will readily absorb. I foresee that it will rapidly become the standard legal work on the NEC – the modern Hudson. But there will be two big differences. McInnis on the NEC will be used by managers as well as by lawyers and it will be used in the avoidance of disputes much more than in the conduct of them.

Martin Barnes

Acknowledgments

I wish to express my deepest appreciation to Dr Julian D.M. Lew for his counsel, judgment, support and patience throughout.

I also wish to thank Dr Martin Barnes for his interest and enthusiasm which came without qualification during the entire project.

Finally, I would like to thank David Hay for gracious editorial assistance as well as Muruga Perumal and Bernadette Donnelly for their assistance in preparation of the original bibliography, and at Thomas Telford, James Murphy for shepherding the work through commissioning and Alasdair Deas and Stephen Nixey for their final editing.

Editorial note

In this book, identified or defined terms are occasionally capitalized or italicized for emphasis and placed in italics to indicate this. This commentary has not adopted capitalization and italicization as it is used throughout the New Engineering Contract (NEC) except in quotations.

Contents

Appendix

Bibliography of Abbreviated Works   632

Cases   640

Index   658

1. Introduction

The evolution of standard forms of contract in building and engineering has been haphazard. Over time, divergent aims and interests among various constituencies that use standard forms have hampered systematic development and design. Many standard forms appear to lack clearly defined design objectives and to disregard modern principles of risk allocation and project management. One result has been widespread criticism of standard forms for failing to meet the needs of the construction industry. The introduction of the New Engineering Contract (NEC) is a specific response to this criticism. The NEC introduces a new systematic approach to contracting which is multidisciplinary in nature and fully interlocked in form. The NEC is intended by its supporters to be more flexible and easier to use than any current leading traditional standard forms of contract. The NEC drafters assert that these features reduce adversariality and disputes. The NEC seeks to achieve this aim primarily through co-operative management techniques and incentives built into the NEC's procedures. In summary, this commentary analyses and evaluates these and related claims of innovation. It examines the background to the NEC, its design objectives, structure, procedures and likely judicial interpretation to determine whether it improves upon the traditional standard forms of contract. The conclusion reached is that the NEC does make a significant contribution to the development of standard forms of contract, addresses many of their shortcomings and offers one of the best models for their future design.

The commentary begins by introducing traditional contracts[1] as exemplified by the RIBA/JCT form of contract and its latter day engineering counterparts. P. D. V. Marsh has written: '[t]he New Engineering Contract (the NEC) is a fundamental departure from the traditional forms of contract'. This commentary also considers what this means and the implications which flow from it. In general, the term 'traditional' forms of contract is often used in the literature although it is not a term of art. According to one partial classification by Michael

---

[1] MARSH, P. D. V. *Contracting and Engineering for Construction Projects*, 4th edn. Gower, Aldershot, 1995. See also MURDOCH, JOHN and HUGHES, WILL. 'Traditional General Contracting'. In *Construction Contracts: Law and Management*, 2nd edn. E & FN Spon, London, 1996, pp. 29–45.

O'Reilly, under the form of project organization criterion, contracts may be further divided according to whether they are traditional, management contracting or construction management.[2] The contracts referred to here principally for comparison are the ICE 6th, FIDIC 4th and JCT 80 forms which are measure and value in respect of the engineering forms, and often lump sum in respect of the building form, according to this classification. In general references in this commentary to JCT 80 refer to the contract as amended and prior to the release of JCT 98. The JCT 98 form is based on the 1980 edition with amendments to 1 to 13 and 15 as well as corrected versions of 14, 16, 17 and 18 which seek to bring the form into compliance with the passage of the Housing Grants, Construction and Regeneration Act 1996 (HGCRA).

In contrast to these traditional forms of contracting newer or 'non-traditional' forms of contract may also be noted and compared to the NEC provisions. These forms are those often associated with the ACA/BPF, GC/Works series and now the NEC. In terms of project organization the NEC system of contracts most closely corresponds to the construction management model but may display characteristics of each individual type of form; for reasons that are discussed elsewhere this is held out as advantageous.

The focus will then turn to the development of the NEC and the principles underlying its preparation. Special attention will be given to the drafting objectives for the NEC and what support in the relevant literature exists for them. Chapter 4 will examine the NEC system of contracts as a whole. Central to the operation of the NEC are the new roles and responsibilities for those using the system and all their aspects are developed in Chapter 5. Throughout these early chapters, but in particular, in the commentary upon the NEC clauses which follows them, the NEC system of contracts will be used as the exemplar for a non-traditional form in comparison with and in contrast to traditional forms. The commentary is not about the choice of standard form *per se* within either the group of traditional or non-traditional forms but rather upon the NEC itself relative to and in juxtaposition with them.[3]

The NEC is examined in detail with an analysis of each clause in the contract against relevant jurisprudence or case law.[4] The emphasis is upon

---

[2] O'REILLY, MICHAEL. *Civil Engineering Construction Contracts*. Thomas Telford, London, 1996, pp. 3–7.

[3] See generally on the choice of form TURNER, ALAN *Building Procurement*, 2nd edn. Macmillan Press, Basingstoke: 1997, pp. 51–104; SMITH, NIGEL J. (ed.). *Engineering Project Management*. Blackwell Science, Oxford: 1995, pp. 188–209; and *Central Unit on Procurement. Contract Strategy Selection for Major Projects*. Guidance Note 36. HM Treasury, London: June 1992, all discussing in general advantages and disadvantages of various modes of procurement.

[4] The absence of judicial interpretation of NEC provisions themselves is seen as a weakness by some commentators, e.g. KNOWLES, R. The NEC: A User's Guide, *Chartered Quantity Surveyor*. June 1991, **8**; and CORNES, DAVID L. The Second Edition of the New Engineering Contract. *International Construction Law Review*, (1996), **97** who sees case precedents as 'the basis for proper legal construction of contracts'.

English case law, with occasional references to Australian and Canadian case law. The emphasis in this regard is more in keeping with recent British authors as well as the inherent difficulties in addressing the volume of American authority.[5] In this regard and in so far as possible principles of general application are portrayed as such without qualification. If the principle is intimately associated with the wording of a particular form of contract a reference to the form is also routinely included. However, it must be noted that this is but a general guide to assist in a reading of the text of the NEC for, in the construction context, it is almost always possible to override a given principle of law by the express terms of the contract and the meaning of cases too may change over time.[6]

In addition to seeking to understand the relationship of the NEC to existing case law much of the recent theoretical work in the project management literature will be introduced to test the NEC against some of its principal tenets and which the NEC drafters say the form respects. In short, the NEC will be tested on three bases: theoretical, jurisprudential, and doctrinal to seek to determine what contribution the form makes to address the problems associated with traditional contractual models and to support the conclusions which are drawn. There are, of course, also problems affecting the construction industry that are beyond the scope of this commentary and which standard forms of contract as a whole do not purport to address. These types of issues, such as cyclical, discontinuous and low demand, inadequate investment in training, research and development in industry, and the industry's poor public image must be left to one side.[7]

The conclusion will be set out in Chapter 15 at the end of the commentary and the view will be expressed that the NEC makes a significant contribution toward the progressive evolution of standard forms of contract, addresses many of the traditional forms shortcomings, and offers one of the best models for their future development, direction and design.

The commentary also contains four appendices. The first appendix shortly lists relevant reports which have been compiled on the construction industry; while the remaining appendices illustrate a sample works information checklist, an adjudication table to portray more clearly the role adjudication plays in relation to dispute avoidance and resolution as well as sample tribunal clauses.

---

[5] FURMSTON, PROFESSOR MICHAEL. Some Thoughts on the Uses of Commonwealth and United States Cases. *Construction Law Yearbook*, 1995, **13**, 18–19.

[6] See ANSON, WILLIAM R. Some Notes on Terminology in Contract. *Law Quarterly Review* 1891, **7**, 337–345 on how the meaning of a term can change over time with interpretation.

[7] See COX, ANDREW and THOMPSON, IAN. *Contracting for Business Success.* Thomas Telford, London, 1998, p. 22.

2. Critique of traditional forms and the need for change

It has been a depressing experience to re-read previous reports to the Government, including those of Sir Harold Emmerson (1962) or the Banwell Committee (1964). Many of the problems which they tackled still persist a generation later.

Sir Michael Latham.
Constructing the Team

The construction industry today may be understood through the wide range of reports written during the last 50 or so years (see Appendix 1). Very often these reports have referred to themselves selectively and occasionally. The same pattern of references can be seen in other reports with only similar selective and occasional references.[1] However, the piecemeal nature of these references obscures the very strong similarities most of the reports share. This absence of an overview of the myriad problems affecting the industry which have so often been touched upon in only an ad hoc manner has persisted until very recently. That is, however, until the publication of *A Bridge to the Future*. This report,[2] published under the authorship of three leading construction researchers, Roger Flanagan, Ian Ingram and Laurence Marsh, under a project task force, through the Reading Construction Forum, has now collated reviews of the performance, procedures, practices, problems and opportunities presented during these last five decades to provide a clear picture of their reappearance. Under some nine heads (Technology, Organization, People, Efficiency, Preconstruction, Competitive tendering, Site management, Legal/contractual, and Payment) as well as forty-six subheads, points are laid out. In this way, at least in so far as these points are concerned in the historical context, clear conclusions can be drawn about what points have been identified in the successive reports which are said either to plague or improve the industry. It does not mean that each point should be accepted without question. Many recommendations are controversial within one or more segments of industry. This is not surprising when the industry itself

---

[1] See e.g. FRANKS, J. *Building Procurement Systems*, 2nd edn. CIOB, Ascot, 1990, s 1.
[2] FLANAGAN, ROGER, *et al. A Bridge to the Future. Profitable Construction for Tomorrow's Industry and its Customers.* Thomas Telford, London, Reading Construction Forum, Reading, 1998.

admits of so many different views although it can be said that each one has at least some recognition or measure of support. Proponents on either side of these issues may then choose to support their position with whatever evidence they may have as well as show today how the point still remains valid or relevant. This in large part is what the researchers of *A Bridge to the Future* have done themselves in support of their case for better supply chain management and closer integration with the design team, exploiting information technology and reshaping peoples' and organizations' relationships. The focus on supply chain management and relationships, in the latter case 'power relationships', has also received recent attention by other researchers.[3] The same approach can be taken in this book particularly with respect to one head identified by the researchers, the legal/contractual, which comprises the focus of this commentary. The legal/contractual head itself was considered in *A Bridge to the Future* under three further sub-heads: increased litigation/arbitration, increased claims and variations, and prompt payment – claims and variations.

A significant part of many of these past reports has dwelled upon the merits and demerits of industry standard forms of contract. The debate as shown above actually goes back much further. Thus, Sir William McKenzie writing at the time of the introduction of a draft 1928 standard form of contract said:

> It is my considered opinion that it is difficult to measure the advantages that will flow from the general adoption of this Standard Form of Contract. The elimination of uncertainties and ambiguities and the certainty introduced by a standardisation on fair and just lines in clear and simple language must necessarily create confidence throughout the Building Industry; and I cannot doubt will, by reason of equitable and known conditions, result in closer prices and in reducing building costs.[4]

Additional advantages have been held out to pertain to the reduction of transaction costs and time savings,[5] serving as a sound practical basis for negotiations in the best interests of all the parties[6] and ideally even the public, according to Mocatta J. in *Birmingham Association of Building Trades Employers Agreement*.[7] In short the advantages of standard forms

---

[3] See COX, ANDREW and TOWNSEND, MIKE *Strategic Procurement in Construction: Towards Better Practice in the Management of Construction Supply Chains.* Thomas Telford, London, 1998; and COX, ANDREW and THOMPSON, IAN. *Contracting for Business Success.* Thomas Telford, London, 1998, albeit without sharing the same analysis.

[4] CLOSE, HOWARD A. *The Evolution of the RIBA Form of Contract.* NFBTE, London, 1952, p. 11.

[5] SWEET, JUSTIN. Judging Contracts: Some Reflections on the Third International Construction Law Conference. *International Construction Law Review*, 1994, 413, 430.

[6] See PIKE, ANDREW. Preface to *Practical Building Forms and Agreements.* E & FN Spon, London, 1993.

[7] MOCATTA, J. *Birmingham Association of Building Trades Employers Agreement* [1963] 2 All ER 361.

often resolve themselves into questions of efficiency.[8] Standard forms of contract are able to address important aspects of complex legal arrangements as well as provide the means to correct unsatisfactory legal rules[9] and industry practices.[10] Justin Sweet argues that standard forms are vital for three separate reasons in that they:

- provide a consensus as to allocating risks and responsibilities, remedies and administrative practices;
- make the negotiation process more efficient and less costly; and
- are a useful connector between different entities acting together on a project.

With standardization comes familiarity and familiarity is often held out as advantageous. It is said that familiarity should make compliance with the form easier and that previous court cases may aid in their interpretation. Lord Hoffman has described interpretation to be 'the ascertainment of the meaning which the document would convey to a reasonable person having all the background knowledge which would reasonably have been available to the parties in the situation in which they were at the time of the contract'.[11] However, familiarity as a perceived advantage favours existing over new forms even when practice has shown that parties are adept at adjusting to a standard form as it becomes more generally accepted.[12] It is probable that the extent of the usage of forms has an important effect on norms within the industry as well. Todd D. Rakoff, for example, has referred to the influence of the American Institute of Architects Standard forms contracts given the large number of sales of those forms and their dominant place in American industry.[13] Similar arguments could be put forward based upon the past sale of JCT forms.[14] The position here is that new forms of contract, such as the NEC, are influencing norms in new ways today.

---

[8] See CULLEN, ALLEN. Standard Conditions of Contract in the Building and Construction Industry. *Building and Construction Law*, June 1993, 92–94 referring to the efficiency argument as put forward and accepted by the Australian Trade Practices Commission in their consideration of standard forms; as well as in the Australian report *No Dispute: Strategies for Improvement in the Building and Construction Industry*. National Public Works Conference, National Building and Construction Council, 1990.

[9] See SWEET, n. 5 above, 434 referring to *Paradine* v. *Jane* (1647) Aleyn 26 and *Taylor* v. *Caldwell* (1863), Sydney, p. 3 B & S 826.

[10] JUSTIN, SWEET, n. 5 above.

[11] Lord Hoffman, *Investors Compensation Scheme Ltd* v *West Bromwich Building Society* [1998] 1 WLR 896, 912 (HL).

[12] JUSTIN, SWEET, n. 5 above.

[13] RAKOFF, TODD D. Social Structure, Legal Structure, and Default Rules: A Comment. *Southern California Interdisciplinary Law Journal* **3**, 1993: 25–26. See on the domination of JCT forms of contract: Davis, Langdon and Everest. Contracts in Use: A Survey of Building Contracts in Use During 1995. *Construction Law Journal* **13**, 1997: 297.

[14] *Ibid.*, p. 297.

In the absence of familiarity one of the most trenchant problems with respect to standard forms of late has become the vast number of them in use. The result for contractors is to have made it seemingly all but impossible to appreciate their implications. Clive Priestley has noted, for example, that the National Association of Lift Contractors has encountered some 150 forms of contract.[15] Professor Max Abrahamson has said that the situation resembles a 'jungle'.[16] As a result of the proliferation of forms it has been stated that '[i]t is inevitable, therefore, that many members of the industry are carrying out their duties with little or no understanding of the main building contract and their role within the contract'.[17] As long as ten years ago there were already said to be over thirty 'standard' conditions of contract which reflected different allocations of risk.[18] Some would argue we have reached a critical juncture.

> The development of construction contract forms stands at a watershed: the old forms are losing their influence; instead of orderly change, the existing institutions are being outflanked by the introduction of new forms and new systems; and the institutions are tending to respond by promoting more and more diverse forms of their own. The volume of activity in the production of standard forms is unprecedented. These facts demonstrate a clear need for a collective body of learning on the subject of construction contracts which is accessible and relevant; and an equally clear need for a considered appraisal of the policies which might govern change.[19]

It is also somewhat ironic that although many complain about the contents of the JCT forms their familiarity is still seen as an advantage. It has been succinctly, if cynically put by Andrew Pike who remarked '[t]he great

---

[15] PRIESTLEY, CLIVE. *British Construction: In Pursuit of Excellence*, a report to Sir Christopher Foster, chairman of the Construction Industry Sector Group. (Business Round Table, London, February 1994), p. 45 and citing *UK Lift and Escalator Industry*, p. 33.

[16] ABRAHAMSON, M. W. *et al.* introducers, DROBIG, K. N., reporter. FIDIC Conditions of Contract for Work of Civil Engineering Construction, Fourth Edition. *Proceedings of the Institution of Civil Engineers* **84**, part 1, August 1988, p. 821–836, 836.

[17] *Building Britain 2001*. Centre for Strategic Studies in Construction, University of Reading, Reading, 1988, p. 24.

[18] McGOWAN, PAUL H. *et al. Allocation and Evaluation of Risk in Construction Contracts*, Occasional Paper 52, CIOB, Ascot, 1992, citing FELLOWS, R. F. Development of Standard Forms of Building Contract in Britain. *Proceedings of an International Workshop on Contractual Procedures on 6 April 1989 at the University of Liverpool* by the Chartered Institute of Building. CIB, Liverpool, April 1989, p. 1, n. 3.

[19] UFF, PROFESSOR JOHN. Origin and Development of Construction Contracts. In *Construction Contract Policy, Improved Procedures and Practice* (eds UFF, JOHN and CAPPER, PHILLIP). Centre of Construction Law and Management, King's College, London, 1989, p. 5.

majority of the provisions of the JCT forms are reasonable and acceptable, if somewhat incomprehensible'.[20] An equally ambivalent endorsement is made by Ray Cecil who wrote:

> [t]he client will enter into the building contract on your advice. If anything is wrong with that contract, the client will try to blame you. You might find yourself spending days explaining the subtle nuances of JCT 80, but it is a standard form and it is unlikely that you would be faulted for recommending its use.[21]

The same has been said about the leading American private forms, for instance, the American Institute of Architect documents, and thus, even though there are complaints about given forms, their familiarity is still seen as a positive factor.[22] However, this argument has been questioned and the benefits said to derive from the fact that the JCT forms are, at least, in widespread use is, as Duncan Wallace has noted, 'a total non sequitur [for w]hile a standard form used as widely as possible is obviously desirable, it is far better to have no standard form than a bad standard form'.[23] Overall there is a very high level of dissatisfaction among clients in the construction industry with existing standard forms of contract. In one recent survey by Thompson, Cox and Anderson, it was suggested that only 6% of clients are fully satisfied with existing standard forms of contract.[24]

Perceptions of drafting bodies and either their fairness or representativeness are important. Seeking to be perceived in a positive way, a particular drafter may pursue the endorsement of user groups. This was the approach that FIDIC once used but has now forgone. With regard to the NEC the ICE seeks no endorsements, as it believes that the value of the endorsements is outweighed by the costs of obtaining them in terms of time and control. However, Justin Sweet sees this affecting trust and confidence in the form.[25] The role of those involved in the process should thus be an important consideration in determining what use, if any, should be made of a standard form. Thus, in considering the standard forms, it is prudent to have regard to the standing of the bodies under whose aegis the forms are sanctioned, recommended or issued. It is also wise to consider

[20] PIKE, ANDREW. *Practical Building Forms and Agreements*. E & FN Spon, London, 1993, p. 2.
[21] CECIL, RAY. *Risk Management for Architects*. RIBA Indemnity Research, London, 1992, p. 17.
[22] SWEET, JUSTIN. Standard Construction Contracts: Some Advice to Construction Lawyers. *Construction Law Journal* **7**, 1991, p. 13.
[23] WALLACE QC, PROFESSOR I. N. DUNCAN. *Construction Contracts: Principles and Policies in Tort and Contract*. Sweet & Maxwell, London, 1986, p. 502.
[24] THOMPSON, I., COX, A. and ANDERSON, I. Contracting Strategies in the Project Environment. *European Journal of Purchasing and Supply Management* **4**, March 1998.
[25] SWEET, JUSTIN, see n. 5 above, p. 435.

whether or not the forms are agreed documents, and if so agreed by whom and for whom.

Drafting bodies too may be remote from both practice and users in industry. In part this is the issue of how close the form should be to existing industry versus practice where practice in industry should move. Professor John Uff QC has stated:

> [t]he process of developing an adequate framework of new contracting systems should ideally be iterative and progressive.[26]

This is a problem that existed in the first moves toward the standardization of forms of contract;[27] therefore, mechanisms need to be in place to see that a proper balance is struck. One means of achieving this is through consultation with the prospective users and drafting bodies are increasingly using this tool. The drafters of the NEC originally released a Consultation Document or test edition prior to releasing the First Edition of the form. Likewise recently FIDIC released consultation or test editions of their latest forms.

One of the most strident critics of standard forms and the JCT forms of contract in particular is Professor I. N. Duncan Wallace QC. In texts and articles, as well as from his authoritative position as editor of *Hudson's*, Wallace has unrelentingly and critically condemned both the specific content as well as underlying policies behind them. In one damning critique of the 1963 RIBA form Wallace sets out 19 ways in which he regards the form as defective either on grounds of obscurity or policy. Wallace adds:

> It must not be thought that the criticisms of the forms which I have made in this article are exhaustive. A problem can be found in literally every line of text of the RIBA forms. The real criticism to be made of the forms are their almost total disregard for the reasonable commercial interest for the employer, their unnecessary obscurity, and their immutability in the face of criticisms.[28] ... They are of a length and complexity which renders them wholly incomprehensible to the layman, and a trap even for a skilful lawyer who has no previous experience in this field.[29]

Although Wallace's critique is made of the 1963 form he also notes that most of the criticisms can equally be made with respect to the 1980 form

---

[26] UFF QC, PROFESSOR JOHN, see n. 19 above, p. 10.

[27] See CLOSE, HOWARD A. *The Evolution of the RIBA Form of Contract.* NFBTE, London, 1952, p. 14.

[28] WALLACE QC, PROFESSOR I. N. DUNCAN. n. 23 above, p. 521.

[29] WALLACE QC, PROFESSOR I. N. DUNCAN. n. 23 above, p. 521. Some of Professor Wallace's criticisms are muted but not overcome in a paper by the late Donald Keating QC, delivered at King's College in London on 21 February 1990 and published in modified form in the Alwyn Waters Memorial Lecture: the Making of a Standard Form. *Construction Law Journal* **11**, 1995, p. 175.

as well.[30] Similarly, John Burkett writes: 'JCT 84 is really an updated version of the old 1963 form but still contains many of the [same] problems'.[31] Wallace also looks critically at the ICE 5th form in *Hudson's Building and Engineering Contracts*[32] and although acquitting the form of 'deviousness', a charge he levelled clearly at the RIBA/JCT form, he still finds much to criticize about the ICE form. Wallace takes his criticisms of the ICE form further in *Construction Contracts: Principles and Policies in Tort and Contract*[33] where Wallace has updated and expanded upon some of these criticisms in relation to measured price manipulation; price-plus philosophies; unmerited claims for additional payments; inadequate defective work remedies; nominated sub-contracts; and delay and liquidated damages. The problems attendant upon payment are dealt with subsequently.[34] The high regard in which Wallace's opinions are held was lately underscored when the House of Lords paid tribute to his contribution in shaping their views in the *Beaufort Developments* case.[35]

These criticisms reappear again and again with respect to the JCT forms including the views of judges. For example, Edmund Davies LJ in *English Industrial Estates Corporation* v. *George Wimpey & Co Ltd* referring to 'the farrago of obscurities which go to make up the RIBA contract', or that of Sachs LJ in *Bickerton* v. *North West Metropolitan Regional Hospital Board* saying it was 'unnecessary, amorphous and tortuous ... [and] lamentable that such a form ... should be so deviously drafted with what in parts can only be a calculated lack of forthright clarity', Danckwerts LJ also speaking in *Bickerton* and saying that the form 'has produced problems which have given this Court, as well as other courts in the past, difficulties of interpretation which defy the experienced intelligence of counsel concerned with these matters, and even more the efforts of the courts concerned'.[36] Criticisms of the traditional standard forms, primarily those of the JCT, may be outlined in a number of respects.

---

[30] WALLACE QC, PROFESSOR I. N. DUNCAN, n. 23 above, p. 538; and *Construction Contracts: Principles and Policies in Tort and Contract*. Sweet & Maxwell, London, vol. 2.

[31] BURKETT, JOHN. Building Contracts, *Arbitration*, 1989, 212.

[32] *Hudson's Building and Engineering Contracts* 11th edn. Sweet & Maxwell, London, 1994.

[33] *Construction Contracts: Principles and Policies in Tort and Contract*, see n. 30 above, pp. 547–558.

[34] WALLACE QC, PROFESSOR I. N. DUNCAN. Appendix 1 – The Pre-Latham Contractual and Legal Background. Following his article An Emperor without Clothes – Latham and the DOE. In *Contemporary Issues in Construction Law Vol II, Construction Contract Reform: A Plea for Sanity*, UFF QC, JOHN. Construction Law Press, London, pp. 262–269.

[35] *Beaufort Developments (NI) Ltd* v. *Gilbert-Ash (NI) Ltd* (1998) CILL: 1386.

[36] *Hudson's*, vol. 1, 338 citing Davies LJ in *English Industrial Estates Corporation* v. *George Wimpey & Co Ltd* [1973] 1 Lloyd's Rep 118 at 126; Sachs LJ in *Bickerton* v. *North West Metropolitan Regional Hospital Board* [1969] 1 All ER 977 at 989, CA and Danckwerts LJ at 996.

Length and complexity

Traditional contractual systems, based on JCT agreements, are being questioned and challenged owing to the increase in the size and complexity of building projects; the increase in service systems as a proportion of the project; the increase in major specialist contractors who not only contract but also design intricate parts of the project; and the need for fast-track building for commercial reasons.[37]

Language

The proliferation of forms has been criticized in various terms and calls have been made to 'supersede the existing JCT forms of contract and to introduce simpler forms, as used in other EC countries and in the chemical and offshore industries. Standard forms should be rationalized into a few key versions, with provisions which are much more balanced and fair between the parties and are written in plain English'.[38]

Revisions

...[E]ach time there is a drastic revision or even a simple one prospective users must study the new edition or revisions carefully to see whether it should be used and if changes need to be made. These reviews are costly. Also court decisions which interpret language of standardized contracts lose their precedent value if language changes are made ... [f]requent revisions of standard contracts can also create distrust in the competence of the entity that makes the standard contract. Failure to issue new editions if there are drastic changes in practice or in law is a sign of unresponsiveness. But generally frequent new editions are a sign of incompetent preparation.[39]

Amendments

Admirable though they are, the basic trouble with Standard Forms is that they never quite meet the unique situation of a particular contract. Consequently every time the standard form does not suit a particular set of circumstances amendments are made which in turn give employment to barristers in trying to interpret what was meant and frequently what was never intended in the first place so that further revisions are necessary. As a result we have had successive editions in 1931, 1939, 1963 and 1980, each longer than the last *but in essence containing the same provisions*.[40]

---

[37] PRIESTLEY, CLIVE, n. 15 above, p. 45.
[38] *Ibid. Restructure to Win*, paragraph 2.18.
[39] SWEET, JUSTIN, n. 5 above, p. 431.
[40] BURKETT, JOHN, n. 31 above, p. 212 (emphasis added).

Lack of interface

In the introduction to the first volume of the then newly launched *Building Law Reports*, the editor writes: '[t]he form in use between main building contractors and subcontractors is of entirely different authorship, and the two have not much more in common than chalk and cheese'.[41] The JCT forms share little as a family and thus one can point to a lack of *interface* across the main contract options as well, for instance JCT 80 against JCT IFC 84 or JCT MW. While the situation has improved, subcontracts in use with JCT main contract forms are at best *compatible* rather than *back-to-back*.

Problems of interpretation

In *Amalgamated Building Contractors Ltd* v. *Waltham Holy Cross UDC*, Denning LJ described the RIBA (pre-JCT) form as resembling a 'legislative code' which gave rise to interpretation problems as courts were generally precluded from considering the intentions of the JCT drafters, most of which was unpublished in any event. In *Peak Construction (Liverpool) Ltd* v. *McKinney Foundations Ltd*, Salmon JL also indirectly criticized the form remarking:

> Indeed, if a prize were to be offered for the form of building contract which contained the most one-sided, obscurely and ineptly drafted clauses in the United Kingdom, the claim of this contract could hardly be ignored, even if the RIBA form of contract was amongst the competitors.[42]

The JCT forms are also questioned on the basis that they lead to claims in practice and this objection is at the centre of Wallace's criticisms.

> The real criticisms of the RIBA forms of contract are two-fold. In the first place, they contain within their complicated and obscure provisions, which no layman can possibly understand, the seeds of many claims by the contractor in respect of matters known and ascertainable at the time of contracting on the one hand, or in respect of matters more properly, as a matter of both law and commonsense, the responsibility of the contractor. The result is that the employer is tendered an apparently attractive price ... which is likely to be materially exceeded in the event, though the extent of the excess is quite unpredictable and depends largely on the aggressiveness of the contractor in exploiting the contract provisions ... In the second place, a contract of this type, particularly one where obscurities make possible the presentation of claims for additional payment, is grossly unfair to the efficient contractor who

---

[41]   At page vii in an editorial entitled The Standard Building Contract Forms referring to the JCT forms of contract.

[42]   *Amalgamated Building Contractors Ltd* v. *Waltham Holy Cross UDC* [1952] 2 All ER 452, CA. *Peak Construction (Liverpool) Ltd* v. *McKinney Foundations Ltd* (1970) 1 BLR 111, CA.

tenders a realistic price, and who is not in the habit of either advancing or arbitrating and litigating such claims.[43]

Similarly, and after referring to the 'disparate body' of JCT membership, John Burkett says of JCT 80 that:

> the end result is that some, but mercifully not all contractors can now put in a tender which bears no relation to what they intend to be paid and the real purpose of the contract is relegated to being a vehicle for a complex game of chess, involving hours of time on both sides which would be better spent in producing a satisfactory building.[44]

In *Building Britain 2001*, a report prepared by the Centre for Strategic Studies in Construction at the University of Reading, the present situation in terms of forms of contract in the United Kingdom was described as 'confusing and wasteful'.[45] Later, in the same report the authors stated: '[t]he JCT Standard Form (currently JCT 80) has undoubtedly led to much money and time being wasted on mud-slinging and back-protecting within the building industry'.[46] More general criticisms point to the absence of accessible background materials and clearly articulated drafting objectives. However, there are guidance notes which are now issued as well as a JCT *Newsletter*. While many of these criticisms are made with respect to the JCT forms many of them are fundamental and thus can equally be made with regard to other leading traditional forms such as those of the ICE and FIDIC as well as those prepared by their counterparts in other jurisdictions.

The perceived shortcomings of the JCT forms reach far beyond Britain to countries which have closely followed them in drafting their own local standard forms. Thus, for example the late Professor Vincent Powell-Smith has written '[t]he Asean region as a whole must, it is submitted, break free of the fetters imposed by the standard forms of contract inherited from Europe and evolve forms of its own'.[47] Moves have been underway to recast the forms of contract in other jurisdictions. For instance, Standards Australia has developed a standard suite of contracts for use in Australia. The first of the new standard conditions of contract was published in May 1995 in the series as the AS4300-1995 Design and Construct Contract. Other jurisdictions are following this trend.[48]

It should be emphasized that these criticisms are not simply referring to objections over the wording of, for example, particular conditions or the

---

[43] WALLACE QC, PROFESSOR I. N. DUNCAN, n. 23 above, p. 503.

[44] n. 31 above, p. 212.

[45] See n. 17 above, p. 23.

[46] *Ibid.*, p. 24.

[47] POWELL-SMITH, PROFESSOR VINCENT. *Journal of Malaysian and Comparative Law*, 27. Cf Prof. Powell-Smith. An ASEAN Region Standard Form of Construction Contract? *International Construction Law Review*, 1992, 384.

[48] See on the other contracts then proposed to be included PILLEY, JOHN L. Topic of Interest. *Building and Construction Law* **12**, 1996, 2.

drafting choices which have been made with regard to them, but far more basic qualities of the forms relating to structure, philosophy and ease of use. Many of these fundamental criticisms actually refer to the assumptions currently underlying these forms. Wallace writes as follows:

> [t]he forms in both industries [building and civil engineering and referring to the RIBA/JCT and ICE 5th] as they have currently evolved, have been progressively designed to produce the lowest possible and most apparently attractive tendered price, with the maximum provisions making possible additions to that price of uncertain extent during the course of the construction period – it may fairly be said that the contract price under both forms represents little more than a 'best possible scenario' price, and that for practical purposes they are 'price-plus' contracts.[49]

Thus with the emphasis increasingly upon value for money[50] this objective underlying these traditional forms has been undermined and yet no allowance has been made for the shift in opinion.

Some of the fundamental problems of traditional standard forms have attracted greater attention than other problems; one that has already been raised concerns amendments. The issue of amendments to standard forms has proven particularly contentious over time. Historically, and with reference to the early RIBA form, contention existed not only regarding the substance of amendments but also the procedures to agree upon them; first, with debate over the outcomes and then with the procedures whereby the results would be achieved. Apart from the difficulty in arriving at agreement on amendments when operating within a consensus body such as the JCT there is also the quite separate issue of the effect on the users. This issue was highlighted not long ago when the National Specialist Subcontractors Council issued an ultimatum to the JCT that it would only stay on as a member if a wide ranging review of its constitution and activities were carried out that could lead to increased participation by subcontractors in the drafting process.[51] Notwithstanding the Council's views over time one 'inevitable consequence has been to increase steadily the length and complexity of the contract'.[52] Andrew Pike writes:

> ... it is sometimes rather difficult correctly to identify by reference the relevant up-to-date JCT document, in view of re-printing,

---

[49] *Hudson's*, vol. 1, p. 332.

[50] See COLLINS, S. and PASQUIRE, C. *Effect of Competitive Tendering on Value in Construction*, RICS Research Paper Series 2, no. 5, February 1997, offering evidence that certain procedures associated with compulsory competitive tendering adversely affect value.

[51] See RIDOUT, GRAHAM. Specialists' Pressure Forces JCT Review. *Contract Journal*, 18 August 1999, 1. See also LEWIS, SIMON. So That's Agreed, Then? *Building*, 26 June 1998, 38.

[52] GUEST, PENNY. Building Accord. *Building*, 25 June 1993, 34, quoting John Sims, buildings consultant and arbitrator. PIKE, ANDREW. *Practical Building Forms and Agreements*. E & FN Spon, London, 1993, pp. 13–14.

amendment, correction which takes place from time to time ... [and as] amendment and correction may occur during reprinting, as well as by numbered JCT Amendments.[53]

Looked at from a distance it also seems incongruous that while members of the JCT approve the forms themselves some members still recommend amendments on a universal basis in their own constituencies' interests.[54] Other concerns arising from heavily amended forms pertain to exacting unfair commercial advantages when it has been alleged that some amendments are attributable to parties capitalizing upon freedom of contract and economically superior bargaining positions to exact the unfair commercial advantages. Still further concerns arise from the sheer number and scope of amendments, their effect in contradicting assumptions underlying the document as a whole toward both risk allocation and the nature of the transaction itself, and the increased chance of misunderstandings. In fact, the scale of the amendments effectively results in reducing the standard forms to no more than model forms at best with a consequent loss of some of the benefits deriving from standardization.[55] The Latham Report too recognized the pitfalls of unbridled amendments and thus recommended regarding the NEC that no amendments be permitted to the core clauses.[56]

These criticisms of their traditional forms of contract as well as a coincidence of other factors eventually drove both the JCT and Conditions of Contract Standing Joint Committee ('CCSJC') belatedly to begin to consider and offer new forms of contract and other procurement modes. The CCSJC currently consists of nine members, three from each of the Institution of Civil Engineers, the Association of Consulting Engineers and the Federation of Civil Engineering Contractors. In this regard it has strong parallels to the Engineers Joint Contract Documents Committee (EJCDC) in the United States comprising representatives from the American Society of Civil Engineers, American Consulting Engineers Council, and National Society of Professional Engineers.

Richard F. Moore has looked at some of the factors that were both relevant and served to precipitate this change. Moore, writing for the

---

[53] *Ibid.*

[54] KLEIN, RUDI. Is JCT Up to the Job? *Building*, 29 March, 1996, 36.

[55] See GREENWOOD, DAVID J. *Contractual Arrangements and Conditions of Contract for the Engagement of Specialist Engineering Contractors for Construction Projects.* CASEC, Newcastle, the University of Northumbria at Newcastle, noting a study undertaken on amendments to standard forms and citing as examples: *Abuses of Standard Forms of Contract and Sub-contract*, A Report prepared by a Working Party of the National Joint Consultative Committee. *Building*, 13 February 1991, unpublished; and *Domestic Sub-contracting: Fair Play Benefits the Client*, CASEC, 1986. See also HUXTABLE, P. J. C. *Remedying Contractual Abuse in the Building Industry.* CIOB, Ascot, 1988, Technical Information Service 99.

[56] *Constructing the Team, Final Report of the Joint Review of Procurement and Contractual Arrangements in the United Kingdom Construction Industry.* HMSO, London, July 1994, the 'Latham Report'.

CIOB in *Response to Change – the Development of Non-traditional Forms of Contracting*[57] attributes the pressure for change to several factors, notably: recession during the 1970s, client dissatisfaction with project performance, and contractors seeking ways to improve their positions. General contractors faced with unexpected falls in demand shed directly employed labour and turned to specialist labour and labour and plant suppliers. This in turn contributed to the role of specialist contractors in the overall construction process. Those trends, as Moore notes, coupled with others, including the reluctance of many firms to trim managerial staff, created ideal conditions for contractors both to maintain and expand their market share through new managerial products and new contractual arrangements.[58] It was inevitable that this would lead to a larger role in the design of construction products up to and including new design and build forms. Management contracting and construction management were but two further means to advance the contractors' goals. In looking at these non-traditional forms of procurement one factor then stands out; these new forms were a *contractor response* to a particular set of circumstances. It was thus a shift away from the dominant role the professions have held historically in shaping traditional forms of contract over time. To some within industry the move is retrograde and when considered alongside the implementation of many of the Latham Report proposals only serves to further marginalize the architectural and civil engineering professions.[59]

The JCT and CCSJC have been significantly discredited following the Latham Report. Although their forms have been held out as consensus documents, the absence of true client representation as well as the disproportionate influence the RIBA enjoyed for many years considerably weakened their contract offerings. Professor Phillip Capper made a similar point in the context of highlighting industry challenges:

> [t]he challenge to the construction industry and its advisers is not so much the NEC's suitability as a contract (about which most expressed doubts are ill-founded or exaggerated), but rather how effectively existing practices can mould to the change of attitude and openness to new approaches that the NEC demands. So many of the industry's present participants have been trained from their infancy in the particular practices of the ICE and JCT forms that these have gained a significance far beyond contractual provision.[60]

[57]   MOORE, RICHARD F. *Response to Change – the Development of Non-traditional Forms of Contracting*. CIOB, Ascot, 1984. Occasional Paper 31, 3. See also COONEY, E. W. Contracts in the Postwar Building Industry. *Construction History*, 1987, **3**, 1987, 115–124; and SPIERS, G. S. *The Standard Form of Contract in Times of Change*. CIOB, London, 1983.

[58]   MOORE, RICHARD F., n. 57 above 3.

[59]   This theme is taken up in particular by WALLACE QC, I. N. DUNCAN, in An Emperor without Clothes, see n. 34, 150–152.

[60]   CAPPER, PROFESSOR PHILLIP. A Lawyer's View. In *Launch Seminar on The New Engineering Contract Launch 2nd Editions: Proceedings of a conference in London on 3 October 1995* by the Institution of Civil Engineers. Thomas Telford, London, 1995, 2.

The JCT has been slow to take up of the reforms suggested by Latham. For example, the JCT only released the amendments that JCT 80 required to comply with the HGCRA 1996 on 30 April 1998, just one day before the legislation came into force. The delay in conforming to the Housing Grants Construction and Regeneration Act 1996 provisions perhaps also suggested that neither body was willing to lead in implementing the Latham recommendation or collaborating on a new model form. Rudi Klein wrote at the time: '[t]o some extent, their [RIBA and BEC] desire to hang on to their traditional influence has bedevilled the JCT's progress towards making its forms more relevant to the needs of the industry today'.[61]

Perhaps in part in response to some of this criticism the JCT has lately moved to reshape itself. Thus, as from 1 May 1998, a new body has been at work – JCT Ltd. While the changes are to be welcomed they are too little too late in the view of Rudi Klein who has written: '[a]n opportunity has been missed for creating a dynamic and responsive body in which the industry's major players would have equal input and which would be producing families of documents for all procurement routes and all types of construction'.[62] The changes to the JCT were also diminished by the antagonism shown by members toward each other and, as Klein also noted at the same time, 'because JCT Ltd came about after nearly four years of ill-tempered wrangles under the old Joint Contracts Tribunal'.[63] However, it should be noted that the JCT 98 exceeded the minimum requirements expected for a construction contract to comply with the HGCRA 1996 by adopting some of Latham's other assumptions for a modern form of contract that were not enshrined in the legislation; one obvious omission in this regard was the recommendation that an express duty to deal fairly with each other in an atmosphere of mutual co-operation be included. In this respect the JCT has drawn a line under its *own* co-operation in implementing Latham's reforms.

In conclusion, the traditional forms of contract in use today perpetuate a legacy of Victorian construction problems.[64] The reliance upon nineteenth century commercial precedents in particular 'leases but without regard to the problems and situations on a building site and situations on a building sites with which, of course, the building contracts should have been concerned to deal'[65] has exacerbated the problem as well as further removed the traditional forms from industry's present needs. The reliance on leases is understandable when one notes that most

[61] KLEIN, RUDI. Is JCT Up to the Job? *Building*, 29 March 1996, 36.
[62] KLEIN, RUDI. New JCT of Limited Use. *Construction News*, 11 June 1998, 31. See also BINGHAM, TONY. Overhauling Formal Logic. *Building*, 7 July 1995, 30.
[63] KLEIN, RUDI, see n. 62 above.
[64] See UFF QC, PROFESSOR JOHN. The Place of Law and the Role of Construction. *The Centre of Construction Law and Project Management Lecture: delivered to the Society of Construction Law on 4 October 1988*. London: 1988, 3–4 and UFF QC, PROFESSOR JOHN, see n. 19 above, 5–7.
[65] *Hudson's*, vol. 1, 462.

of the lawyer's early formulary work related to land law.[66] If one were
tempted to forgive these shortcomings in the drafting of building contracts
on the ground that Wallace's revelation is of recent origin then perhaps
the views of Alfred A. Hudson writing closer to the time may give pause.
In 1891 Hudson opined:

> the building contract is often drawn by the engineer or architect
> himself, or rather, it is a contract made up by him of traditional, and
> often inconsistent and mutually destructive stipulations, in use by
> some person on whom he relies, or consists of conditions of various
> kinds which seem to have been handed down for years, often put
> together by the engineer or architect in various combinations,
> producing various legal results, of more beneficial interest to the
> lawyer than to the building owner.[67]

The final word on the historical record comes lately from the Reading
Construction Forum who have remarked that:

> [t]wo things are especially striking about the past 800 years of
> building history. The first is that at no time has there been
> widespread use of a single or a standard method of procuring
> buildings; time and again people have tried new ways as a result of
> their dissatisfaction with previous methods. The second is how little
> the problems have changed over the years, and how regularly the
> same ones crop up.[68]

---

[66] PRAUSNITZ, O. *The Standardization of Commercial Contracts in English and
Continental Law*. Sweet & Maxwell, London, 1937, pp. 8–9. It is also telling that the
first edition of the leading work by Alfred Emden was entitled in full *The Law Relating
to Building Leases and Building Contracts, The Improvement of Land by, and the
Construction of, Buildings with a Full Collection of Precedents of Agreements for
Building Leases, Building Leases, Contracts for Building, Building Grants, Mortgages,
and Other Forms with respect to Matters Connected with Building Together with the
Statutes Relating to Building with Notes and the Latest Cases under the Various
Sections and a Glossary of Architectural and Building Terms*. Stevens and Haynes, Bell
Yard, Temple Bar, London, 1882.

[67] HUDSON, ALFRED A. *The Law of Building and Engineering Contracts and of the
Duties and Liabilities of Engineers, Architects and Valuers: With an Appendix of
Precedents and an Appendix of Unreported Cases*. Waterlow and Sons, London Wall;
Stevens and Haynes, Bell Yard, London, 1891, 3. RIMMER, E. J. The Conditions of
Engineering Contracts. *ICE Journal*, February 1939, Paper 5203, **2**, 3 also uses the word
'peculiarities' to refer to a range of circumstances that differentiate engineering
contracts from other contracts. Rimmer's view merits considerable weight as a former
editor of *Hudson's* and also co-author with Michael Hoare of *The Standard Form of
Building Contract. Being a Critical Annotation of the New Form of Building Contract
Issued in 1931 under the Sanction of the RIBA & the NFBTE and a Guide to its Use*.
The National Builder, London, 1931.

[68] FLANAGAN, ROGER *et al.*, see n. 2 above, p. 13.

3. New Engineering Contract principles

At the heart of the NEC is a new creed that Project Management techniques can be successfully written into a main contract to produce more co-operation, more efficiency and fewer disputes. There is also, of course, the implicit assumption that the terms of the contract can affect the way in which the contractor performs the work. The boldness of the new approach cannot be overstated.

Professor John Uff QC,
'Figaro on ICE – the ICE 6th Edition and the New Engineering Contract'

Development of the New Engineering Contract
The Institution of Civil Engineers

The background to the NEC began formally in 1985. It was during that year that the Council of the Institution of Civil Engineers approved the following recommendation from the Legal Affairs Committee: 'to lead a fundamental review of alternative contract strategies for civil engineering design and construction with the objective of identifying the needs for good practice'.[1] The recommendation reveals much about the ICE's thinking at the time and ultimately, in a comparison to the NEC system that resulted, how far they moved and the leadership role that evolved. David H. Williams said of BAA's early use of the NEC in a similar vein that 'leadership is about not allowing ignorance of what is new to create fear of the unknown'.[2] By undertaking the review the ICE moved away from conditions of contract as merely rules[3] to the much larger issue of

---

[1] Guidance notes, First Edition, 1.
[2] WILLIAMS, DAVID H. Using the NEC: A Client's View. In *New Engineering Contract Conference Proceedings in Hong Kong, 28 November 1994*. Asian Law Journal, Hong Kong, 1994, 6.
[3] See generally ATIYAH, P. S. and SUMMERS, ROBERT S. *Form and Substance in Anglo-American Law: A Comparative Study of Legal Reasoning, Legal Theory, and Legal Institutions*. Clarendon Press, Oxford, 1987, on the nature and role of rules (71–75) and on the importance of flexibility (75–87).

procurement.[4] The language of the recommendation is somewhat imprecise and it is unclear what the drafters wished to improve upon. For instance, was the new form to be an improvement on the ICE conditions of contract or separate altogether? It may be noted that the ICE conditions, as well as several other forms, were closely considered in preparing the new form of contract.[5] Ultimately, it would appear that the then concurrent preparation of a Sixth Edition of the ICE conditions along with the NEC suggests it was not to be an improvement on that form but the drafting of a new form of contract altogether. Professor John Uff QC has pointed out one of the essential differences between the two forms: '[t]he ICE conditions of contract proceed on the basis that each side looks to its own interest. The NEC seeks to focus the interest of both parties on the project. If this is successful it will have been a remarkable achievement'. Professor Uff has also written: '[I]t would be hard to imagine a greater contrast between two forms intended to fulfil a similar purpose. The ICE has presented users with a remarkable range of choice between well-tried tradition and undiluted radicalism'.[6] Guy Cottam described the contract as an 'entirely fresh approach to contract conditions for the construction industry'.[7] Andrew Bolton did not see radicalness as an impediment to success[8] and Paul H. McGowan and others wrote: 'NEC is a radical new approach to the management of risk in today's industry. It has avoided the option of "a new variation on an old theme" and makes a major step towards shrinking risk'.[9] The information section of the *Construction Law Journal* referred to the contract as both 'innovative' and 'revolutionary'.[10] The limitations on how far one could move from the ICE conditions themselves without altering them beyond recognition and perhaps losing the benefit of the experience which has been gained using them was understood by the working group that took on the task.

---

[4] See FRANKS, J. *Building Procurement Systems.* CIOB, Ascot, 1984; FRANKS, J. with HARLOW, PETER. *Building Procurement Systems A Client's Guide*, 3rd edn. CIOB, Ascot, Addison Wesley Longman, Harlow, 1998; TURNER, A. *Building Procurement*, 2nd edn. Macmillan, Basingstoke, 1997; FERRY, D. *The Organisation of Procurement.* Thomas Telford, London, 1991; and GORDON, M. C. Choosing Appropriate Construction Contracting Methods. *Journal of Construction Engineering* 1994, 10 (1), 196–210. See on the regulatory regime and compulsory competitive tendering, LINDRUP, G. (ed.), *Butterworths' Public Procurement and CCT Handbook.* Butterworths, London, 1997.

[5] See discussion below.

[6] UFF QC, JOHN. Figaro on ICE – the ICE 6th Edition and the New Engineering Contract. *Construction Industry Law Letter*, 1991, 653, 654.

[7] COTTAM, GUY. The Contract to Suit All Occasions. *Construction News*, 27 May 1993, 14.

[8] BOLTON, ANDREW. Clear Way Forward. *New Civil Engineer*, 1 April 1993, 20.

[9] McGOWAN, PAUL H. *Allocation and Evaluation of Risk in Construction Contracts*, Occasional Paper 52, CIOB, Ascot, 1992, 7. See also for another short comparison of the NEC and ICE 6th by UFF, and WEDDEL. Contracts Compared. *New Civil Engineer*, 31 January 1991, 12–13; and for a critical review CHAPPEL, D. New Contract. *Architects' Journal*, 5 June 1991, **193** (20), 53–55.

[10] *Construction Law Journal*, 1991, **7**, 266.

This is a particularly appropriate time to introduce a flexible, multipurpose contract form. The alternative, to follow the proliferation of different forms, would be damaging in a number of respects. It would particularly confuse tendering contractors, with the risk of a heightened incidence of disputes ... the development of variants of the ICE Conditions of Contract to provide for minor works and for design and build contracts have necessitated detailed departures from the familiar text in a large number of clauses. It has proved impossible[11] to confine the differences to a discrete block of clauses, as has been achieved in the New Engineering Contract.[12]

This comment, apart from the three specific drafting objectives referred to, has been encapsulated in the following aim:

The NEC Engineering and Construction Contract (ECC), (previously the New Engineering Contract) has been developed to meet the current and future needs for a form of contract to be used in engineering and construction generally, which is an improvement on existing standard contracts in a number of ways.[13]

The project, first of all, was in the nature of a review. The task was to survey the alternative contract strategies for civil engineering *design and construction*. Appendix two of the *Specification and Partial Draft for a New Style Conditions of Contract*[14] indicates that the following standard forms were reviewed:

- ICE 5th;
- FIDIC 3rd and then current FIDIC Electrical and Mechanical;
- IChemE Process Plants (lump sum and cost-reimbursable);
- I Mech E/I E E; and
- Bovis Ltd's then Management Agreement.

Appendix one added J. W. Bazalgette, *Metropolitan Main Drainage and Intercepting Works, Specification (1863–1869)*; and *Standard Method of Measurement – Draft for Discussion* to the list.[15] It may be observed that

---

[11] Cf the work of the JCT and the steady increase in the number of their standard form agreements. See generally LOOSEMORE, MARTIN. Dealing with Unexpected Problems – Do Contracts Help? A Comparison of the NEC and JCT 80 Forms. *Engineering, Construction and Architectural Management*, 1994, **1** (2), 115.

[12] The New Engineering Contract: Need For and Features. Thomas Telford, London, 1991, 4. See also the comments of Dr Barnes reported following a meeting with the Hong Kong Institute of Engineers: More on the New Engineering Contract. *Hong Kong Engineer*, January 1992, 7.

[13] Guidance notes NEC, 1.

[14] BARNES, DR MARTIN. *Specification and Partial Draft for a New Style Conditions of Contract*. Martin Barnes Project Management, Deloittes, London, December 1986, p. 61.

[15] BAZALGETTE, J. W. *Metropolitan Main Drainage and Intercepting Works, Specification (1863–1869)*; and *Standard Method of Measurement – Draft for Discussion*. RICS and BEC, London, 1984.

the ICE at that time had one of the two principal forms in use in the industry with its ICE Fifth Edition conditions of contract. Of that Fifth Edition form I. N. Duncan Wallace QC, said 'I can truthfully say that it is the most difficult standard form which I have ever reviewed'.[16] The drafters indicate that the review of these forms was intended to ensure the comprehensiveness of the specification. The inclusions and omissions from this list are both significant. With regard to inclusions the electrical and mechanical forms confirm that the intention was the new style conditions would be more broadly applicable than civil engineering forms alone; while the regard to a management agreement suggests the importance that management would also have. Significantly absent from the list are building forms. The discussion of the Consultation Document and successive editions of the New Engineering Contract confirms that the drafters were more informed by civil engineering and electrical and mechanical engineering forms throughout than any building forms. This need not be a weakness if the engineering precedents themselves were capable of application to building situations. The willingness to look across traditional contractual boundaries may present other advantages. From a project management perspective no divide does, in fact, exist and all of these forms would be grouped together.[17]

Dr Martin Barnes and the First Specification

Agreement was reached on the preparation of a specification for a new style contract and in July 1986 Martin Barnes Project Management was commissioned to lead the drafting. Professor Justin Sweet has observed that this process differs from that pursued by most professional associations drafting standard contracts:

> ... the NEC was prepared in a different way. What struck me most was that the work was delegated to a group of compensated consultants The principal drafting was done by people with a bent toward management, rather than legal or professional specialists. This had a significant influence on the way the contract was drafted.[18]

The principal in that organization at the time was Dr Martin Barnes.[19] The NEC is synonymous with and clearly has been influenced by Dr Barnes'

---

[16] WALLACE QC, I. N. DUNCAN. *The ICE Conditions of Contract Fifth Edition A Commentary.* Sweet & Maxwell, London, 1978, p. v.

[17] See LOCK, DENNIS. *Project Management*, 4th edn. Gower, Aldershot, England, 1988, 2. See also WOODWARD, JOHN F. *Construction Project Management, Getting it Right First Time.* Thomas Telford, pp. 14–29.

[18] SWEET, PROFESSOR JUSTIN. Standard Contracts for Design and Construction: Comparisons and Advice. *Construction Law Yearbook*, 1994, 30, 31.

[19] At that time Martin Barnes Project Management had a relationship with Deloitte Haskins & Sells.

work during his 35 years in industry.[20] In particular, the NEC reflects much of Dr Barnes' work in two respects: the development of the British Property Federation (BPF) form and his writing on risk. With regard to Martin Barnes' work in drafting the BPF form it has been remarked:

> ... reference is made to the British Property Federation system as a radical new approach to construction project management, founded on a review of risk allocation. Having been responsible for designing the BPF system, we would like to draw attention to the fact that it has two elements of risk consideration. Not only is the traditional risk allocation changed, but measures are included aimed at an overall reduction of risk. The new system is based on the principle that if the *total amount* of risk to be carried by contractors can be reduced by more foresight in the conduct of a project they will not be averse to accepting a longer list of risks which make up the total.[21]

John Uff[22] has also made the connection between the introduction of a new style of contract and the earlier work that was carried out by the BPF.[23] Dr John Perry of the Project Management Group at the University of Manchester Institute of Science and Technology assisted Dr Barnes[24] along with others referred to here.

---

[20] Some of Barnes contributions include (with THOMPSON, P. A. in the first instance) *Civil Engineering Bills of Quantities*, Report 34, CIRIA, London, 1971; Towards Simpler Contracts, with Barnes himself as one of the introducers and reported by BARBER, J. N. in *Proceedings of the Institution of Civil Engineers*, part 1 June 1986, **80**, 818–821; How to Allocate Risks in Construction Contracts. *International Journal of Project Management*, 1993, **1**, 24; and the *CESMM3 Handbook*. Thomas Telford, London, 1994.

[21] PERRY, J. G. and HAYES, R. W. Risk and its Management in Construction Projects. *Proceedings of the Institution of Civil Engineers*, part 1, June 1986, **80**, 757–764, 758–759, remarks attributed to Martin Barnes and Andrew Norman.

[22] UFF QC, JOHN, see n. 6 above, 654. See for a critique of the ICE 6th Edition: VALENTINE, D. G., The ICE 6th Edition – An Opportunity Bungled. *International Construction Law Review*, 1992, 509; and VALENTINE, D. G. How Not to Draft a Contract. *International Construction Law Review*, 1992, 526; and see also SWEET, PROFESSOR JUSTIN. Standard Contracts for Design and Construction, 42, who critiqued the absence of persons from different legal systems, such as civilian jurisdictions, with knowledge of other contracting practices and law, particularly when the NEC form was intended to be used in international transactions.

[23] See generally for favourable reviews when introduced, WATERS, B. The BPF System. *Building*, December 1984, 25–30; DAVIES, C. The BPF System: The System in Action. *Building*, June 1984, 31–33; and DAVIES, C. The BPF System: No Going Back. *Building*, June 1984, 28–29; KNOWLES, R. BPF Agreement – a reprieve for the BQ. *Chartered Quantity Surveyor*, August 1984, 19; LLOYD, H. The BPF System: consultants architects back the system. *Building*, June 1984, 30.

[24] MEng, PhD, CEng, FICE, MAPM; currently Beale Professor and Head of the School of Civil Engineering at the University of Birmingham.

The specification listed the main functions that the clauses of the new form were to perform and set out the principles upon which it was to be based. During the preparation of the document it became clear that the aims could not be achieved by modifying any existing set of conditions of contract as the extent of change would be unmanageable and the end product unrecognizable as an offspring. A proposed structure for the new form was included in the specification.[25]

The specification was first submitted to the Legal Affairs Committee in December 1986[26] and thereafter presented publicly in September 1987.[27] Consultations followed beginning in November 1987 and culminating in a decision by the Council in June 1988[28] to develop a new style of contract through a small working group comprising and representing members of the ICE, contractors, consulting engineers and employers (listed in Appendix 2). The work of the working group was extended with additional funding from Thomas Telford, which has published the NEC documents throughout[29] and on behalf of the ICE who are the copyright holders. In contrast to this copyright in the ICE 6th form is held by not only the ICE but the Association of Consulting Engineers (ACE) and the Federation of Civil Engineering Contractors (FCEC).

Professor Justin Sweet, one of the leading commentators on American construction law,[30] has often underscored the important role of the drafting or sponsoring body. To be successful, there is a:

> ... need for a standard contract to be seen as the product of a broadly based group not captured or dominated by one segment of the industry. Trust in the good faith of the drafters, their willingness to be fair to potential users and belief in their technical competence are vital to the success of any standard contract.[31]

---

[25] PERRY, JOHN G. The New Engineering Contract: Principles of Design and Risk Allocation. *Engineering, Construction and Architectural Management*, 1995, **2** (3), 197, 198.

[26] See BARNES, DR MARTIN. *Specification and Partial Draft for a New Style Conditions of Contract.* Martin Barnes Project Management, Deloittes, London. December 1986.

[27] See BARNES, DR MARTIN. *ICE New Style Contract. Summary and Response to Comments Received.* Martin Barnes Project Management, Deloittes, London, February 1987. See also BILL, PETER. Barnes Storms Another Contract. *Building*, 18 September 1987, 32–33.

[28] BARNES, DR MARTIN. *Specification for a New Style of Contract.* Martin Barnes Project Management, Deloittes, London, June 1987.

[29] Thomas Telford Services Ltd, 1 Heron Quay, London E14 4JD.

[30] See generally *Sweet on Construction Industry Contracts*, 2nd edn. Wiley, New York, 1992, and SWEET, JUSTIN. *Legal Aspects of Architecture, Engineering, and the Construction Process*, 5th edn. West Publishing Co, St Paul, 1994. He reflects on the American Institute of Architects (AIA) form in The American Institute of Architects: Dominant Actor in the Construction Documents Market'. In *Comparative Studies in Construction Law: The Sweet Lectures*, (ed.) ODAMS, A. M., Construction Law Press, London, 1995, pp. 73ff.

[31] SWEET. Judging Contracts: Some Reflections on the Third International Construction Law Conference. *International Construction Law Review*, 1994, pp. 414–415.

In 1989 the specification was extended to include a compatible sub-contract, guidance notes and flow charts of the procedures. Conditions in other forms of contract contain their own procedures; however, they have not usually been reduced diagrammatically to flow charts. The flow charts[32] were an integral part of the drafting process. Dr Barnes stated that: '[t]he NEC was designed by first deciding how the parties should manage their interactions. The resulting procedures were set out as flow charts. These were checked, refined and simplified as a main input to the draughting of the contract'.[33] Some criticism of the procedures, however, has been raised on the basis that failure to follow them correctly can result in loss of entitlements.[34]

The Consultation Document

A consultative edition ('Consultation Document') of the NEC was first published in January 1991.[35] The consultation period lasted approximately two years. During this time comments were invited and received from about 200 organizations and individuals and in many cases discussed with them. The results of the consultation were described as 'dominantly favourable to each of the areas of innovation which characterize the New Engineering Contract'.[36] The experiences in using the NEC on a number of projects of differing sizes in various jurisdictions including the United Kingdom, Hong Kong[37] and South Africa were also considered. Andrew Baird has written how many of the changes between the First and Second Editions of the form were attributable to South African experience in use of the form.[38] Statistics

---

[32] See *Access to Justice: Final Report to the Lord Chancellor on the Civil Justice System in England and Wales* by the Right Honourable Lord Woolf, Master of the Rolls. HMSO, London, July 1996, for an interesting example of the use of flow charts, Annex IV, 370 showing a standard timetable to track cases. See generally ZUCKERMAN, A. A. S. *The Reform of Civil Procedure: Essays on 'Access to Justice'*. Clarendon Press, Oxford, 1996.

[33] BARNES, DR MARTIN. The New Engineering Contract – An Update. *International Construction Law Review*, 1996, 89, 90.

[34] See ATKINSON, D. The NEC Contract: 'Fatally Flawed. *Tunnels & Tunnelling*, 1995, **27** (6), 46–47.

[35] See BARNES, M. The New Engineering Contract. *International Construction Law Review*, 1991, 247. See also NUNN, D. Civilised New World (on paper). *Contract Journal*, 24 January 1991, 10–11; MAGURIAN, G. H. New Civil Engineering Contract. *Civil Engineering Surveyor*, 16 May 1991, 18–20; and WEBSTER, M. New Engineering Contracts. *Civil Engineering Surveyor*, 16 September 1991, 34–37.

[36] BARNES, M. News of the New Engineering Contract, *International Construction Law Review*, 1993.

[37] See *New Engineering Contract Conference Proceedings in Hong Kong, 28 November 1994*. Asian Law Journal, Hong Kong, 1994; and HALLIDAY, JOHN. Use of the New Engineering Contract in Hong Kong. *Engineering, Construction and Architectural Management*, 1995, **2** (4), 307.

[38] See BAIRD, ANDREW. The New Engineering Contract – A Management Summary for Plant Industry Users, 1995, *International Construction Law Review*, 1994, 114; and BAIRD, ANDREW. Pioneering the NEC System of Documents. *Engineering, Construction and Architectural Management*, 1995, **2** (4), 249.

on use in the UK are compiled by the NEC Users' Group. The Group was launched in January 1994. The Group's first newsletter, Spring 1994, stated that by that time more than 700 contracts had been let using the NEC around the world with the majority in the UK. Subsequent usage of the form under the First and Second Editions has increased substantially since then. The UK NEC Users' Group maintains a website at http://www.t-telford.co.uk/nec/ usergrp.html http://www.t-telford.co.uk/Nec that provides updates on usage. These comments and this experience as well as the normal process of revision informed the development of the First Edition of the NEC that was released on 30 March 1993.

The First Edition
The First Edition of the NEC was published in 1993 and members of the working group which developed the Consultation Document played the leading role in the preparation of the First Edition. While the form was named 'the New Engineering Contract', the first page of the contract describes it as 'a form of contract for engineering and construction projects'. Thus, the multidisciplinary intent behind the form was underscored at the outset although not as dramatically as would eventually be the case with a subsequent name change under the Second Edition. Thomas Telford Services Ltd published the First Edition form and the ICE's familiar coat of arms adorns the soft front covers.

The Second Edition
The Second Edition of the NEC documents was produced by the ICE through its New Engineering Contract Panel[39] and published in November 1995. The November 1995 publication itself is a reprint of the publication of the Engineering and Contract form that was released some three months earlier. The remaining forms in the series were released in November 1995, June 1998, and July 1999. All the forms clearly indicate on the cover the November 1995 release. A series of minor amendments were made to the original publication and are summarized again on the inside of the cover sheet to the ECC form. These amendments are discussed when relevant below.[40] With regard to the changes introduced by the Second Edition to the First Edition Martin Barnes states that most were 'adopted as a result of experience in use and are many but minor. In almost all cases they are intended to improve clarity, not to change function or meaning'; however, this comment does not apply to the rewriting of the insurance and termination provisions, which were 'given a comprehensive textual overhaul'.[41]

---

[39] See list of members in Appendix 2.
[40] It may be noted that a number of typographical errors in the publication remain notwithstanding the reprint. No further mention will be made of these errors unless viewed as material. See for a note of these printing errors VALENTINE, D.G. The New Engineering Contract: Part 1–a New Language. *Construction Law Journal*, 1991, **12**, 305, 312.
[41] BARNES, DR MARTIN, see n. 33 above, 94.

Some comparisons may be made between the First and Second Editions. Initially the First Edition was considerably shorter than the Second Edition.[42] For the most part the increase in length in the Second Edition was fairly uniform across all of the clauses and all of the pages. Thus there were 59 pages in the First Edition and 70 pages in the Second Edition. There are some differences in continuity of the pagination. For instance, the Second Edition uses the inside front cover while the First Edition does not. In addition, the Second Edition contains a helpful index that the First Edition does not. This adds a total of five pages to the overall length of the document. This increase in length and the change in bond or paperweight add to the feeling that the Second Edition is a far more substantial document than the First. The First Edition is also not as striking in presentation as the Second Edition. Thus the fonts for the clause numbering and marginal notes are smaller scale than those in the Second Edition. This has the effect of reducing the visual impact of the form but, subjectively, facilitates reading.[43] Two clauses in particular underwent significant revision: core clause 8 on risks and insurance and core clause 9 on disputes and termination. These changes, as well as others, are referred to here occasionally to support possible interpretations upon the wording of the clauses. The First Edition has the same number of main options and core clauses but a lesser number of secondary option clauses than the Second Edition. Thus, secondary option clauses U, V and Y have now been added. Both the Schedule of Cost Components (SCC) and Shorter Schedule of Cost Components (SSCC) contain the same number of clauses as in the Second Edition although once again they tend to be slightly longer. Parts one and two of the Contract Data follow the same format as in the Second Edition. Once again, the parts are shorter than the First Edition reflecting the lesser number of secondary option clauses and significant changes to the core clause on risks and insurance. The increases in length referred to here are of course reflected across the merged versions for each of the main options. The guidance notes are also shorter in the First Edition than in the Second Edition by 42 pages. Clearly the drafters must have felt that additional explanation of the contract could be given in a substantially expanded version of the guidance notes. Much of this difference in length is attributable to the number of appendices that have been added to the Second Edition. Thus the First Edition is without the Sample Form of Tender, Sample Form of Agreement, model tender assessment sheet and notes, worked example of

---

[42] See HAYWARD, D. who has remarked on the brevity of the First Edition in Stripped to the Core. *New Civil Engineer*, 24 January 1991, 20–21. See also BOLTON, A. Clear Way Forward. *New Civil Engineer*, 1 April 1993, 20.

[43] Typography and factors such as kerning, format, font, and spacing are increasingly being considered in contract design, drafting and layout. See for research in this area WHEILDON, C. *Type and Layout: How Typography and Design Can Get Your Message Across – or Get in the Way*. Strathmore Press, Berkeley, California, 1995; KRONGOLD, S. Writing Laws: Making them Easier to Understand. *Ottawa Law Review*, 1992, **24**, 495.

the Contract Data, meteorological office notice and Sample Trust Deed with supporting schedules present in the Second Edition.

The NEC system of contracts reproduces each of the six main options for procurement in a separate book or merged version in addition to the Engineering and Construction Subcontract (ECSC). Each book or merged version contains all of the core clauses (both core clauses and option clauses in the language of the black book) that are relevant to the respective individual main option. The development of new forms for the NEC system of contracts was endorsed in the Latham Report.[44] The amended Second Edition is the longest of the three versions of the NEC at approximately 10 000 words.

Currently the drafting committee is working on the Third Edition of the NEC primarily to bring the form into line with the Housing Grants, Construction and Regeneration Act.

In addition to but apart from the above procedures additional documents have been prepared and can be considered part of the NEC system of contract documents: the Professional Services Contract (PSC), the Adjudicator's Contract (AC), a Supply Contract and Short Contract. The PSC and AC were originally sold separately from a boxed Second Edition of the NEC but nevertheless formed part of the NEC system. The decision to prepare the two contracts was originally taken by the ICE and a drafting team chaired by Mr Peter Higgins.[45] The drafting team[46] reported to the NEC Contract Panel. A Consultation Document was released in 1992. Comments were received and the publication of both contracts took place in 1994. Second Editions of both the PSC and AC were subsequently released and now form part of the boxed set. All the contract documents in the NEC may also be purchased individually. This extends to each of the merged main options as well.

It is significant that the same drafting objectives were followed for all the documents in the NEC contract system. Systems theory proceeds from and upon the basis of defining general objectives at the outset and then only applying them in specific cases. Both the PSC and AC, however, may be used with other model conditions of contract and the PSC has been used as a model for reformed and unified conditions of engagement for other forms.[47] It may be noted that the Department of Trade and Industry, in *Professional Liability Report, Report of the Study Teams,*

---

[44] Latham Report, paragraph 5.20(6), 40. See on adoption of Latham's recommendations in the NEC: PROCTOR, NIGEL. The Engineering and Construction Contract (Second Edition). *Construction Law*, 1995, **6** (5), 163–166; SAUNDERS-WILLIAMS, J. The Contract with Eyes on Latham. *Construction Manager*, 2 February 1992, 25–26; and DAWN, TOWN. Contract Cure? *Electrical Review*, 25 November–8 December, 1994, 22–24.

[45] Mr Higgins was then Director of Contracts at Travers Morgan Consulting Group.

[46] In addition to Peter Higgins, the drafting team included F. Griffiths of the Chartered Institute of Purchasing and Supply, and M. Coleman of the Association of Project Managers. Dr Martin Barnes advised on co-ordination with the NEC.

[47] See New CIC Contract for Consultants. *Contract Journal*, 28 September 1995, 12.

recommended unified conditions of engagement as early as 1989.[48] The PSC is being used as a model for other forms. Shortly after it was released it was used by the Construction Industry Council (CIC) to draft a new multidisciplinary professional services contract. The CIC contract is funded by the Department of the Environment and to this extent the form could be said to have some official support. The importance of unified conditions of engagement is underscored given the multitude of consultants on site and the inherent risk of conflicts in their roles, duties and responsibilities.[49]

Initially, usage of the NEC in 1995 was 3% of large clients[50] and 4% of small clients[51] with JCT taking a commanding 95% share.[52] It has been estimated that as of February 1998 some 6 000 contracts have been let using the NEC mostly in the United Kingdom with associated subcontracts totalling approximately 200 000 and that approximately 70% of the contracts let with the ECC use the ECSC according to Ernest J. Bayton.[53] Denise Chevin first noted that early results on some of the NEC projects were mixed; notably when Mowlem Northern Civil Engineering used the NEC on a sewage treatment facility at Leeming Bar and experienced problems with the compensation event procedure; conversely BAA reported no problems on work using the form; Bovis working with BAA also endorsed the form.[54] Use of the NEC on the Leeming Bar works was also commented on by Ken Lumb.[55] There have been those who have been waiting on the results of others' use before committing to use the form.[56] While the overall number of contracts let is not exceedingly large there

[48] The Department of Trade and Industry. *Professional Liability Report, Report of the Study Teams.* HMSO, London, 1989, 10.

[49] See generally *Code of Practice for Project Management for Construction and Development* 2nd edn. CIOB, Ascot; Longman, Harlow, 1996, p. 7; and for a discussion of the distinction between 'conflicts' and 'disputes': FENN, PETER, LOWE, DAVID and SPECK, CHRISTOPHER. Conflict and Dispute in Construction. *Construction Management and Economics,* 1997, **15**, 513–518.

[50] For example, turnover over £10 million.

[51] For example, turnover less than £10 million.

[52] Customer Services – a poll conducted by Gallup for the journals *Building* and *Property Week* of some 400 clients and reported in *Building,* 28 July 1995, 26–30 at 27. See generally on the JCT forms POVEY, P. J., WAKEFIELD, R. and DANAHER, K. *Walker-Smith on the Standard Forms of Building Contract.* Charles Knight Publishing, London, 1998.

[53] BAYTON, ERNEST J. FRICS, FCIOB, Thomas Telford course tutor for the NEC, estimate made at Thomas Telford Training Course. An Introduction to the Engineering and Construction Contract. A course given at Altrincham on 3 March 1998. Thomas Telford Training, London, 1998.

[54] CHEVIN, DENISE. No Claims Bonus. *Building,* 12 August 1994, 16–17.

[55] LUMB, KEN. Legal Arguments – New Engineering Contract. *Building,* 23 April 1993, 34.

[56] WILDGOOSE, IAN. Institution of Civil Engineers: New Engineering Contract First Edition – A Management Perspective. *Construction Law,* August/September 1993, 328, 331.

were also delays in taking up other forms such as ICE 5th,[57] JCT 80, and FIDIC 4th.[58] Donald Keating QC noted that because JCT 80 was so unpopular when first introduced many continued to use JCT 63 for years even though JCT 80 maintained many of the same principles as JCT 63 until substantial amendments were made in 1987.[59] In fact, Mike Gibson has compared the arrival of the NEC to JCT 80 when that appeared.

> For a while people rejected it and wouldn't use it. It was too new –
> too unknown. They even photocopied JCT 63 and used that when
> the forms weren't available any more. It took a long time for the
> industry to move over to the new form. Whatever its theoretical
> merits, the NEC is going to have to face the same practical
> drawbacks of industry caution and inertia, and the tendency to stay
> with the familiar.[60]

The NEC, as noted, has been taken forward by the ICE through Thomas Telford. Support has also been given to, and the contract system has been promoted through, an NEC Users' Group. The NEC Users' Group is both a support service for those employing the NEC as well as a means to promote its use. The United Kingdom Group is managed by Thomas Telford and supported by the ICE. Memberships are purchased on an annual basis according to three levels: gold, silver, and bronze. The levels broadly reflect varying degrees of usage and benefits. Benefits will include delivery of the NEC *Newsletter*, a designated number of calls to the Helpline, and discounts at annual seminars and workshops. It may be noted that South Africa also has an NEC Users' Group.[61] This can raise issues of perception, however, on the part of potential users of the contract system toward the fairness of the drafting entity. Justin Sweet notes that certain standard forms are 'identified' with one sector of the industry. To meet or seek to overcome any perception of identification with one sector and possibly unfairness towards others as a result prompts certain drafting organizations to seek the endorsement or approval of various user groups.[62] This was the

[57]   See ABRAHAMSON, MAX W. introducer and POWNALL, A. J., reporter. Experience of the Fifth Edition of the ICE Conditions of Contract. *Proceedings of the Institution of Civil Engineers*, part 1, 1976, 563–566.

[58]   LYONS, M. BETH. The Role of the Consulting Engineer in Developing Country Construction Under the FIDIC Form of Contract. *Law and Policy in International Business*, **26**, 1994, 273, n. 3 citing a telephone interview with Charles Molineaux, partner Wickwire Gavin PC 24 February 1994. FIDIC 3rd was replaced by FIDIC 4th in 1994.

[59]   KEATING QC, DONALD. Alwyn Waters Memorial Lecture: the Making of a Standard Form. *Construction Law Journal*, 1995 **11**, 170, 171.

[60]   MOORE, MARK. One Good Form Deserves Another. *Contract Journal*, 7 September 1995, 28 at 29 quoting Mike Gibson.

[61]   BAIRD, ANDREW. Pioneering the NEC System of Documents, see n. 38 above, 249.

[62]   For example, DOM/1 is published and approved by the Building Employers Confederation as well as approved by the Confederation of Associations of Specialist Engineering Contractors, the Federation of Associations of Specialist Engineering Contractors, and the Federation of Building Specialist Contractors; FIDIC 4th has been

approach which FIDIC once used but has now forgone. With regard to the NEC the ICE seeks no express endorsements, as it believes that the value of the endorsements is outweighed by the costs in terms of time and control in the actual drafting. However, the counterpoint to this once again, is that without endorsements, trust and confidence in the document may be adversely affected.[63] Even when you have non-profit drafting organizations such as FIDIC it has been noted by John Bowcock that 'the sale of documents [still] makes a useful contribution to its revenue'.[64] However, Justin Sweet sees the competition as advantageous and notes that the mere *entry* of the NEC in the market as a viable alternative to the traditional standard forms will *improve* the quality of all standard forms.[65]

Constructing the Team

The most significant factor influencing and hastening the publication of the Second Edition was the release of the final report by Sir Michael Latham, *Constructing the Team*,[66] commonly referred to as the Latham Report. Sir Michael Latham, gave his support to the NEC approach in strong terms in two ways. First, he outlined his position generally as assumptions on what an effective form of contract in modern conditions should contain.[67] Secondly, Latham noted that the NEC respected almost all of these assumptions. He then set out what alterations were required to bring the NEC fully into line with them.[68] It is submitted that this endorsement has already had an influence on the overall acceptability of the NEC. Latham's position, and the fact that his support for the NEC came in one of the most far-reaching reviews of the construction industry in the United Kingdom in 30 years[69] is also significant and has to be borne in mind when trying to judge the future status of the NEC. The importance of Latham's assumptions for a modern form of contract and the recommendations that he made regarding the NEC in particular

approved by various organizations including the Associated General Contractors of America (AGCA), the International Federation of Asian and Western Pacific Contractors' Association (IFAWPCA) and the Inter-American Federation for the Construction Industry (FIIC).

[63] SWEET, JUSTIN, see n. 31 above, 435.

[64] BOWCOCK, JOHN. The FIDIC Contract Forms: The Present and Future. *The Patrick McCreight Memorial Lecture: a paper given in London on 7 November 1995* by the Society of Construction Law. Society of Construction Law, London, 1995, 6.

[65] SWEET, JUSTIN, see n. 31 above, 436.

[66] *Final Report of the Joint Review of Procurement and Contractual Arrangements in the United Kingdom Construction Industry.* HMSO, London, July 1994; and the foreword to the 2nd edn of the NEC. The 'team' metaphor has been invoked before, e.g. HAMILTON, B. A Team Effort. *New Builder*, July 1990, 18.

[67] Latham Report, paragraphs 5.18, 37. VALENTINE, D. G., n. 40 above, 306, n. 5 restates the term rather as 'requirements'.

[68] Latham Report, paragraphs 5.20, 39–40.

[69] Since the *Report of the Committee on Placing and Management of Contracts for Building and Civil Engineering Work.* HMSO, London, 1964, or the 'Banwell Report'.

underscore important features of the Second Edition of the NEC form. In his report Latham concluded: '5.19 The New Engineering Contract contains virtually all of these assumptions of best practice, and others, which are set out in the core clauses, the main and secondary options'.[70] However, he also added a caveat to his support in the series of alterations he recommended to be made for the NEC to comply fully with the principles he had set out.[71] The NEC Contract Panel stated that the Second Edition was fully informed by the suggestions. The foreword to the Second Edition states: 'This Second Edition includes ... the changes recommended in the Latham report in order that the New Engineering Contract should comply with the principles for a modern contract set out in the report and that it should be entirely appropriate for wide use'.

Latham and the NEC

Latham's recommendations with respect to the NEC can be summarized as follows:

- Change the name of the NEC to the 'New Construction Contract'.
- Add a secure trust fund as a core clause.
- Review the payment periods.
- – Amend core clause 1 to affirm the parties intend a fair and reasonable agreement with each other to undertake the project in a spirit of mutual trust and co-operation.
  - Amend core clause 1 to affirm the parties will trade fairly with each other and with their subcontractors and suppliers.
  - Strengthen core clause 16.3 to make it clear that 'win-win' solutions to problems will be devised in a spirit of partnership.
  - Add identical wording to the core clauses in the subcontract document.
- – Add an express provision to core clause 1 that either party to the contract will not amend the form.
  - Mandate for the main contractor to use only the NEC subcontract when using a formal contract and not amend any core clauses.
  - Usage by both the main contractor and subcontractor of identical secondary option clauses unless both parties agree to changes.
  - Agreement by subcontractors to the same measures in sub-subcontracts.
- – Prepare a full matrix of consultants' and adjudicators' terms of appointment that interlock with the main contract.
  - Prepare standard tender documents and bonds.
  - Amend the adjudication procedures as needed to bring them within the principles in Chapter 9 of his report.
- Prepare a simpler and shorter minor works document.[72]

---

[70] Latham Report, paragraphs 5.19, 39.
[71] Latham Report, paragraphs 5.20, 39–40.
[72] Latham Report, paragraph 5.20 (footnotes omitted).

The Latham Report can thus be used as one benchmark against which this book can both assess the 'modern' form of contract as well as judge the NEC. However, while Latham can be used as a touchstone not all commentary on either the recommendations in the report or the means of implementation has been positive. An extensive and forceful critique is set out by contributors to *Contemporary Issues in Construction Law.*[73] Most of the contributors focus their attention on the introduction of compulsory adjudication under the Housing Grants, Construction and Regeneration Act; however I. N. Duncan Wallace QC emphasizes many more issues.[74] One difference of the Latham Report from previous industry reviews such as the *Simon Report*, or the *Banwell Report* was the extensive implementation machinery that was set up under the auspices of the Construction Industry Board and 13 working groups. Professor John Uff writes in this respect:

> [t]his closely organised implementation machinery has involved all sides of the industry and has succeeded in locking itself into the group of industry bodies, some of whom have conveniently re-grouped for this purpose ... Rightly or wrongly, this impressive implementation system appears to have succeeded in silencing most of the potential critics of Latham and at the same time creating an impression of wide support throughout the industry.[75]

Many critics of Latham have focused upon his methodology arguing it was unrealistic,[76] lacking a theoretical foundation,[77] or failing to identify the driving force of self-interest.[78] Hence the views of critics of the Latham approach, where relevant to the issues under discussion here, must be and have been taken into account in judging certain aspects of the NEC contract system. Apart from Latham there are also well-known

[73] *Contemporary Issues in Construction Law, Vol II Construction Contract Reform: A Plea for Sanity.* (ed. UFF QC, JOHN). Construction Law Press, London, 1997.

[74] WALLACE QC, I. N. DUNCAN. An Emperor without Clothes – Latham and the DOE. In Contemporary Issues in Construction Law Vol II, Construction Contract Reform: A Plea for Sanity (ed. UFF QC, JOHN). Construction Law Press, London, 1997.

[75] UFF QC, PROFESSOR JOHN. *The Building of Construction Law.* A paper presented at the Tenth Annual Construction Conference on 19 September 1997, by the Society of Construction Law and the Centre of Construction Law and Management. King's College, London, 1997, 5. A different perspective on the Latham Report also worth noting is Paul Bick's look at the broader based Australian statutory intervention: Statutory Reform of Aspects of Construction Law in Australia. *Construction Management and Economics.* 1997, **15**, 549–558.

[76] COX, ANDREW and TOWNSEND, MIKE. *Strategic Procurement in Construction.* Thomas Telford, London, 1998, p. 106.

[77] McDERMOTT, P. and QUINN, B. Latham Causes Conflict – Institutional Development in the UK Construction Industry. *Journal of Construction Procurement*, 1995, **1** (2), 150–164.

[78] UFF, JOHN and ODAMS DE ZYLVA, MARTIN (eds). *New Horizons in Construction Law.* Construction Law Press, London, 1998, p. 8.

commentators who have written extensively on the modern standard form of construction contract.[79] In this regard, Professor Justin Sweet, who sometimes uses the term 'standard contracts' for prototype contracts that are used in construction, has reflected on the techniques that can be used to judge contracts. Some of Sweet's techniques involve assessing a contract against criteria that include congruence, completeness, clarity, coherence, workability and efficiency which can also be used as benchmarks against which the NEC can be judged.[80] Other commentators have added clarity, conciseness, completeness, internal consistency, practicality, fairness, effect on quality, effect on cost, effect on schedule, and effect on safety when judging contracts.[81] However, the elaboration of some aspects of the criteria with reference to provisions common to the NEC and traditional standard forms is omitted here as their consideration is at best a neutral factor.

Naming the contract

The NEC renamed its principal contract document in the Second Edition. This change is again attributable to a recommendation in the Latham Report that suggested the NEC be renamed the 'New Construction Contract'.[82] There appear to have been others who in fact had a prior claim to the name 'New Construction Contract', notably Max Abrahamson. Professor Abrahamson was a member of the original working group for the NEC and has also developed an alternative contract system with this appellation. The NEC Contract Panel chose 'The Engineering and Construction Contract' for the Second Edition instead although it is still referred to as an 'NEC document',[83] in part to reflect the contract's roots in the engineering sector. However, it may have been intended to call the contract the 'New Style Contract', which is how it was referred to by Martin Barnes in September 1988.[84] John D. Allen, quotes Martin Barnes on the naming of the contract as follows:

> If you ask, is the NEC an effective building contract, or an engineering contract, the answer is that it is both. When we started to design it, our brief was to design a contract that could be used for

[79] SWEET, PROFESSOR JUSTIN. Standard Construction Contracts, 8.

[80] SWEET, JUSTIN, n. 31 above, 414.

[81] BUBSHAIT, ABDULAZIZ A. and ALMOHAWIS, SOLIMAN A. Evaluating the General Conditions of a Construction Contract. *International Journal of Project Management*, 1994, **12** (3), 133–136.

[82] Latham Report, 39; and see the foreword to the 2nd edn NEC. See ABRAHAMSON, MAX. Risk, Management, Procurement & CCS. In (eds. UFF, JOHN and ODAMS, A. MARTIN). *Risk Management and Procurement in Construction*. Centre of Construction Law and Management, London, King's College, 1995, pp. 375–392. Abrahamson is best known for his *Engineering Law and the ICE Contracts*, 4th edn. Applied Science Publishers and Elsevier Science Publishers, London, 1979.

[83] See BARNES, DR MARTIN, n. 33 above, 92–94.

[84] BARNES, MARTIN. The Role of Contracts in Management. In *Construction Contract Policy*, (eds UFF and CAPPER), p. 119.

any kind of construction or engineering project. Partly because it was sponsored by the Institution of Civil Engineers we ended up calling it the New Engineering Contract, but it was designed to be used across the whole range.[85]

Michael Latham, on the change of name, has written: 'I am particularly pleased to see that the NEC principal contract is to be called the "Engineering and Construction Contract", emphasizing that it can be used across the whole spectrum of projects'.[86] D. G. Valentine has pointed out the term 'NEC' does not appear in the First Edition although it forms part of a heading in the Second Edition.[87] It may be remarked for the sake of consistency that the use of the acronym NEC should perhaps become NECC for 'New Engineering and Construction Contract' and so as to match the change in name of the forms.

The name of the document is not entirely beside the point. It serves to signal to the building (construction) and engineering sectors that the document is intended for both sectors. In the past there has been a *de facto* separation of these two sectors partly through the forms that each sector has preferred, especially at the domestic level. Typically the engineering sectors have preferred ICE forms, while the building sectors have preferred JCT forms. The RICS *Contracts in Use* survey 1996 revealed 85% of all building contracts used a JCT form which comprised 76% of the market by value.[88] In the international context the FIDIC form has achieved a high level of acceptance in both building and engineering work. The FIDIC form evolved from an earlier version of the ICE Conditions. The relationship between the two forms has not always been easy. I. N. Duncan Wallace QC is an astute observer in this regard:

> it is apparent that they [the FIDIC drafters] evidently considered and studiously avoided, all the principal difficulties (and indeed innovations) in the Fifth Edition, as well as a number of anomalies in the Fourth Edition ... which have been swept away, quite rightly, in the Fifth Edition, but which are retained unchanged in the 1977 FIDIC contract.[89]

Later, Wallace remarked, this time referring to ICE 4th after noting that the FIDIC form had been modelled on it, that:

[85] ALLEN, JOHN D. NEC – is it the Answer to Latham's Prayers? *Construction News*, 23 February 1995, 12.

[86] LATHAM, MICHAEL, publisher's flyer. Thomas Telford, London, 1995.

[87] VALENTINE, D. G., see n. 40 above, 310.

[88] See generally on the JCT forms of contract, POVEY, P. J., WAKEFIELD, R. and DANAHER, K. *Walker-Smith on the Standard Forms of Building Contract.* Charles Knight Publishing, London, 1998; and CHAPPELL, DAVID. *Understanding JCT Standard Building Contracts*, 5th edn. E & FN Spon, London, 1998.

[89] WALLACE QC, I. N. DUNCAN. *The ICE Conditions of Contract Fifth Edition: A Commentary.* Sweet & Maxwell, London, 1978, p. 1.

from an international point of view, I consider, far too closely, since it contains a whole host of specifically domestic English provisions or legal concepts, often couched in language which, even by English standards, must be regarded as archaic and obscure in the extreme.[90]

The separation referred to above has been less pronounced in engineering. Thus, for example, unlike the membership of the RIBA and RICS until comparatively recent times, members of the ICE were never precluded from working for contractors. John Uff has written how '[t]he polarisation between consultants and contractors at one time threatened to impede efficiency in developing new contract arrangements.'[91] In practice the result was many engineers working for contractors and, indeed, vice versa, with civil engineering contractors setting up civil engineering practices.[92] The NEC once again clearly shows that artificial divisions between the sectors need not be perpetuated and through its multidisciplinary approach to the works stands as natural inheritor of both traditions. It may be noted that other factors, such as substantial civil engineering components in many building projects, have been moving the two sectors closer together.[93] These developments should be encouraged as there never was any significance in law between the two terms. Both building and engineering contracts have at times been regarded as contracts for work and materials. It may be noted that some of the resistance to a 'Construction Contracts Bill' was attributed to the fact that building or construction and engineering contracts have not been seen in a separate category.[94] An interesting experiment in *multidisciplinarity* is given by D. R. Culverwell, in a paper published in 1986. The paper grew out of the author's experience on a major public works project in Hong Kong for a Light Rail Transit line that combined one set of contract conditions for the civil, building and electrical and mechanical work.[95]

NEC drafting objectives
The importance of clearly articulated drafting objectives for a new standard form has been underscored with the release of the NEC. Few recent standard forms have set out their drafting objectives so clearly from

[90] WALLACE QC, DUNCAN I. N. *The International Civil Engineering Contract, A Commentary on the FIDIC International Standard Form of Civil Engineering and Building Contract.* Sweet & Maxwell, London, 1974, Supplement 1980, p. 1.

[91] UFF QC, JOHN. The Place of Law and the Role of Construction. The Centre of Construction Law and Project Management Lecture: delivered to the Society of Construction Law on 4 October 1988. London, 1988, pp. 3–4.

[92] SHILSTON, ALAN. The Obligation to Co-operate: What does this Involve?, a paper given at a joint meeting of the Society of Construction Law and the Society of Construction Arbitrators on 2 June 1992. London, 1992, p. 8.

[93] *Ibid.*

[94] See Latham Report, 84, recommendation 25, paragraph 8.9.

[95] CULVERWELL, D. R. Civil, Building, Electrical and Mechanical Works Combined. A paper given to the Society of Construction Law on 7 January 1986. London, 1986.

the outset as the NEC, with the exception of the GC/Works/1 3rd.[96] The stated objectives for the design of the NEC were to make improvements under three main headings: flexibility, clarity and simplicity, and stimulus to good management. Robert J. Smith writes that 'there is a very high benefit-to-cost ratio in dealing with contractual risk through improving contract clarity and contract administration practices'.[97] Justin Sweet has noted with reference to the NEC that it is both novel and difficult to apply drafting principles in the creation of a standard form.[98] In addition to these general objectives a series of more specific design objectives or principles were also developed. These design objectives have been set out by John Perry[99] and revolve around:

- a choice of contract strategy;[100]
- varying levels of contractor design;[101]
- a choice of specific risk allocation in the secondary options;[102]
- maximum use of core clauses;[103]
- separate roles for key tasks;[104]
- motivations for collaborative working;[105]
- tight response periods;[106]
- specific rules for decisions;[107]
- early warning of potential problems;[108]
- one procedure to compensate for change/risk;[109]
- advance quotations for compensation events;[110]
- compensation events to be based on actual cost and current programme;[111]

---

[96] See BREWER, GEOFF. GC Works/1, Edition 3: Its use in Practice. *Construction Law*, August/September 1992, 87. See generally on the GC Works series of contracts CURTIS, PINSENT. Synopsis of the GC/Works/1,2,3,4 Contract Documentation. *International Construction Law Review*, 1997, 596.

[97] SMITH, ROBERT J. Allocation of Risk – The Case for Manageability. *International Construction Law Review*, 1996, 555.

[98] SWEET, JUSTIN, see n. 31 above, 428.

[99] PERRY, JOHN G, see n. 25 above, 200.

[100] See discussion main options.

[101] See discussion clauses 11.2(15), 14.1, 20.2, 21, 22.1, 23.1, 27.1, 60.1(1) and M1.1 ECC.

[102] See discussion secondary option clauses.

[103] It is recommended by the drafters that the core clauses be used unamended.

[104] For example, the separation of the roles of Project Manager, Supervisor, and Adjudicator.

[105] See e.g. clauses 10.1, 13, 16, 25, 26.3, 31.1, 31.2, 32.1, 36, 61.3, 61.5, 63.4 ECC.

[106] See e.g. clauses 13.3, 13.4, 13.5, 16, 17.1, 31.1, 31.3, 32.2, 35.2, 35.4, 36.2, 43.2, 45.1. 50, 51, 61, 62.3, 62.5 ECC.

[107] See e.g. clauses 16.4, 60.1(7), 61.1, 62.3, 63.4, 64.1 ECC.

[108] See clauses 11.2(29), 11.2(30), 16, 32.1, 61.5, 63.4 ECC.

[109] See discussion compensation events.

[110] See discussion quotations for compensation events.

[111] See again discussion compensation events.

- programme to include methods and resources;[112] and
- speedy dispute resolution.[113]

The first three principles were described, again by Perry, as the 'central components of the design' of the NEC.[114]

The NEC is drafted in the present tense. This technique has been criticized with some good reason.[115] However, there are other considerations that may be mentioned, in particular the effect of an obligation that is 'always speaking'. The drafting of obligations in the present tense suggests that they are continuous. At a minimum this will require an adjustment as to how many parties may view their obligations. Continuing obligations it may be argued are one potential means of overcoming the reluctance of parties to report or address a matter, speedily. The NEC strives to identify and address issues at the earliest possible moment and when it is hoped the consequences will be least felt. The bias in the NEC is that notice is better given late than not at all and that this obligation, like many others under the contract, continues throughout performance of the contract.

Flexibility
Flexibility is one of the main articulated drafting objectives for the NEC. In general, a flexible form is intended to be a responsive form – one that takes into account and responds to ever-changing needs. The flexibility of the drafting has been singled out as providing two advantages by Professor Andrew Cox and Ian Thompson; namely a variety of contractual approaches to risk apportionment depending upon the contingent circumstances of each project; as well as managing the relationship with the contractor.[116] The flexibility of the ECC is said to derive from four principal factors:

- The contract system is intended for engineering and construction work across traditional disciplines such as civil, electrical, mechanical and building work.
- The contract system can be used whether the contractor has some design responsibility, full design responsibility or no design responsibility.
- It provides all the normal current options for types of contract such as competitive tender, target contracts, cost reimbursable contracts and management contracts.
- It can be used in the United Kingdom and other countries.[117]

---

[112] See clauses 31.2, 32.1, 35.3 and 54.2 ECC.
[113] See discussion disputes and termination.
[114] PERRY, JOHN G., see n. 25 above.
[115] See for example VALENTINE, DONALD. The New Engineering Contract – Drafting Defects. In *Contemporary Issues in Construction Law, Vol II Construction Contract Reform: A Plea for Sanity* (ed. UFF QC, JOHN). Construction Law Press, London, 1997, pp. 98–100.
[116] COX, ANDREW and THOMPSON, IAN. *Contracting for Business Success.* Thomas Telford, London, 1998, p. 171.
[117] Guidance notes, NEC, 1.

At the outset an observation may be made regarding competitive tender noted in the third factor; that is, it can be a limitation on the realistic management of risk. Professor Phillip Capper states:

> [t]he pressure is always on those bidding for contracts to keep their tender prices as low as possible, which can put both them and their clients at great financial risk if things go wrong. When some provision has been made for eventualities, it is often buried in the total bid. This hinders the effective management of risk and militates against a systematic and equitable basis of payments.[118]

Some other aspects of these factors may also be briefly expanded upon. Initially it can be remarked that there have been traditional divisions within the construction industries, which have typically been identified as: building and civil engineering; the construction and erection of structural work; electrical and mechanical works and shipbuilding. While the NEC makes no claims to be applicable to shipbuilding it does hold out its applicability to the other industries. This is novel particularly given the bifurcation in much building and civil engineering work and the respective sectors separate conditions of contract. The NEC, it would seem, focuses thus not on what *divides* the industry but on what *unites* it; for example, traditional roles, specialist contractors and suppliers, employer procurement options, and in this regard is seeking to lead the vanguard of new multidisciplinary forms. Perry and Hoare make the point that it is not just the proliferation of forms that is problematic in industry but their proliferation *across* different disciplines. Multidisciplinary projects today necessitate cross-disciplinary forms.[119]

The NEC seeks to remove the lines of demarcation across the building, engineering and process plant industries in simple ways. Both the IChemE Process Plant Contracts, referred to as the Red Book (suitable for lump sum contracts) and Green Book (suitable for lump sum contracts) were reviewed by the drafters and would have influenced the drafting. However, the Process Plant Contracts arguably have a somewhat different focus than many building and some engineering contracts. David Wright would put the distinction this way:

> the industry uses contracts which concentrate upon whether the Plant will make the right product, rather than what the Plant will be ... [while the] principal RIBA and ICE Conditions are concerned with the problems of ensuring that the Contractor has built something which is totally in accordance with the design required

---

[118] CAPPER, PROFESSOR PHILLIP. Management of Legal Risks in Construction. A paper given to the Society of Construction Law at a meeting in Wales on 21 September 1994, 12.

[119] PERRY, J. G. and HOARE, D. J. Contracts of the Future: Risks and Rewards. In *Future Directions in Construction Law. Proceedings of the Fifth Annual Conference of the Centre of Construction Law and Management*, King's College, London, 1992, 81–97.

by the Purchaser ... and the problems of monitoring the way that work is carried out ...[120]

This difference in *emphasis* and what is said to be insufficient attention having been given to the performance aspect of the NEC conditions has been raised.

Perhaps the most significant change in demarcation, which is also discussed elsewhere, is the removal of the term 'engineer' from the conditions. Although a considerable amount of building work benefits from engineers' participation, (and vice versa with the involvement of architects in certain aspects of engineering work), engineers remain closely associated with engineering work. Remove the engineer from the conditions and the conditions lose their most obvious feature as an engineering form. The point is that the NEC drafters have consciously adopted an industry or *sectorally neutral* approach in their drafting. The intent is to encourage use of the form across all construction industries.

As remarked above it has always been open to employers to deal with a contractor either directly or through consultants. This option has existed both in relation to construction and to design. The latest formal expression of one of these routes, which have largely been seen as alternative to each other, is the design and build contract. A contribution of the NEC in this regard is to underscore that design and construction are a continuum and that responsibility may vary along that continuum from zero to 100%. Even with a 100% contractor design role the employer retains approval nevertheless under clause 21.[121] Design and build, as a mode of procurement, is growing in popularity among clients according to some surveys and with the publication of the NEC may be given further impetus. For example, one poll suggested an increase in design and build procurement versus the RICS *Contracts in Use* survey 1996 which showed a slight decline in the use of design and build from a high point in 1993.[122] Different reasons may be given as well in explanation of the changes, with one survey noting that client preferences conflict with those of architects who perceive design and build as reducing quality and design innovation.[123]

The choice of six main options plus the option of further choices, notably formal construction management, is a significant innovation in

---

[120] *An Engineer's Guide to the Model Forms of Conditions of Contract for Process Plant.* Institution of Chemical Engineers, Rugby, 1994, p. 5. The Institution of Chemical Engineers also publishes another model form, the Yellow Book (suitable for subcontracts). See generally on the various conditions MacFARLANE K. *The IChemE Conditions of Contract Compared* Thomas Telford, London, 1995.

[121] See YEANG, FIONA. Fixed Price Design and Build Contracts: Risk Allocation and Analysis. *International Construction Law Review*, 1996, 300, 301.

[122] Gallup Customer Services Poll. *Building*. 28 July 1995, 27.

[123] See AKINTOYE, A. and FITZGERALD, E. Design and Build: A Survey of Architects' Views. *Engineering, Construction and Architectural Management*, 1995, **2** (3), 27. See lately (eds ROWLINSON, STEVE and McDERMOTT, PETER). *Procurement Systems in Construction: A Guide to Best Practice.* E & FN Spon, London, 1998.

the presentation of standard forms. For example, FIDIC has lately released design and build conditions, the FIDIC Orange Book 1st; as well as broadened the choice available under the existing FIDIC 4th conditions with a 1996 Supplement. The 1996 Supplement contains three principal amendments to the 4th Edition including providing for payment on a lump sum basis instead of just a bill of quantities basis.

The choice of options may be influencing other drafting bodies to widen the procurement choices they make available. A construction management strategy[124] may be arranged by appointing a construction management contractor as the project manager who would then advise the employer on the placing of trade contracts under any of the other six main options. Reference has been made above to how the NEC contract system generally resembles construction management overall, more so than traditional contracts when classified according to project organization. The NEC, once again, would not have been able to achieve this breadth unless the drafters focused upon what was common to these various modes of procurement rather than what was unique to them. By focusing on commonality in a small number of core and option clauses it has been possible to achieve this diversity from a drafting standpoint. Flexibility through the use of optional clauses allows for individual variations. The various options also present significant choice in terms of their respective payment mechanisms. One final feature that also introduces flexibility is the choice available through the use of parts one and two of the Contract Data. The result of this flexibility is a high degree of customization available to the parties as well as freedom of action.

Flexibility both as itself and as a norm has also been equated with judicial discretion.

> Legal rules and principles are of three kinds ... [the] third class is, in a sense, the most important class of all, and the rules and principles composing it may properly be described as formulae for judicial discretion. The primary axiom of the formula for judicial discretion may be stated thus: the formulation of a principle that has no meaning in itself maximizes the flexibility of the law. Where there is some uncertainty, there is some flexibility, and where the uncertainty is total, the flexibility is commensurate.[125]

The deliberate choice of the drafters to achieve a high degree of flexibility may entail a trade-off for certain employers who do not have to consider a wide range of options in deciding on the most appropriate contract strategy. Professor Phillip Capper states:

---

[124] See on how construction management differs from project management HARRIS, F. and McCAFFER, R. *Modern Construction Management* 4th edn. Blackwell Scientific, Oxford, 1995; and JONES, E. Construction Management and Project Management – the Differences in Structure and its Impact on Project Participants. *International Construction Law Review*, 1993, 348–365.

[125] GRUNFELD, C. Reform in the Law of Contract, *Modern Law Review*, 1961, **24**, 73–74.

[i]t is a peculiar characteristic of construction projects, that they often proceed despite high degrees of uncertainty ... The norm has been traditionally to postpone addressing uncertainties, leaving enormous discretion to be exercised in the future by those administering the contract. *The management of construction risks will be better achieved by more pro-active contractual strategies.*[126]

The NEC assumes a process in arriving at the appropriate contract strategy and the choice of strategy is based upon the matching and optimum allocation of risk. This assumption departs from the basis upon which many clients or employers actually choose their contract system – be that simply 'official policy' or 'normal practice'. In one important survey carried out for the Chartered Institute of Builders, M. J. Bresnen concluded: '... most clients (62%) classified the type of contractual system used as official policy or normal practice, suggesting a consistency of approach regardless of variations between the projects'.[127] In contrast to these clients, take, for example, an employer who is well informed. If the employer's interests are optimized with a management contract then main option F should be favoured. The critical issue might then become whether the employer is better served with a generally worded or specifically worded management contract. Thus, the choice may be between main option F and, say, JCT 81. This example enables the benefits of flexibility to be examined in a different and broader light.

Clarity and simplicity

The New Engineering Contract has introduced some plain English into the world of contracts. A contract is an agreement between two or more parties to do something. Clarity of language in which the contract is written is vital if roles are to be understood and risk apportioned in the manner intended. Time alone will test whether plain words will survive in a litigious system where lawyers and advisors will demand alterations from a standard form to protect their clients' interest.[128]

Ann Minogue neatly sums up the views toward the wording of the form when it was first launched in 1993.

[The] NEC was greeted by the legal profession with a sort of stunned silence. The concept of a form written in what appeared to be plain English and in the present tense was a difficult one for business which lives by words and the many nuances thrown up by their interpretation.[129]

[126]   CAPPER, PROFESSOR PHILLIP, see n. 118 above.
[127]   BRESNEN, M. J. *et al. Performance on Site and the Building Client.* CIOB, Ascot, 1990, Occasional Paper 42, 12.
[128]   *Construction Law*, August/September 1993, contents page.
[129]   MINOGUE, ANN. On the NEC Road Forward. *Construction Legal Times Supplement*, May 1996, 7. See generally DEVLIN, PATRICK. The Relation Between Commercial Law and Commercial Practice. *Modern Law Review*, 1951, **14**, 249; and FRIDMAN, G. H. L. Construing Without Constructing a Contract. *Law Quarterly Review*, 1960, **76**, 521.

However, as Minogue notes, there was an evolution in views toward the contract and silence turned to approval followed by cautious criticisms. With the publication of the Second Edition, she writes: '[t]aken as a whole, however, the NEC is now coming of age as an imaginative and valuable contract form'.[130] These observations are telling. First of all it may be noted that the criticism has muted. Secondly, it is now the details of the contract system which are receiving the attention rather than simply the wording. Without wishing to prejudge the outcome of this research it would appear the NEC may have begun to play a significant role in reshaping attitudes within industry – and perhaps not simply attitudes toward new forms of contract but attitudes towards change itself. Two studies into the perceived clarity of the NEC, one by Jon Broome[131] and one by S Rhys Jones,[132] rank the NEC very highly compared to other standard forms of contract.

The NEC, in fact, is said to be drafted in 'ordinary language'.[133] However, the term 'plain English' does appear in the 'Introductory note for Subcontractors from the Users' Group'. The use of the term 'ordinary language' is novel and for the most part proponents supporting the use of simpler language refer instead to 'plain English' or 'plain language'. These latter two terms have often been used interchangeably since the very beginning of the move toward simpler language in legal drafting[134] and continue to be so used today. The plain language movement has been taken furthest in the United States where plain language statutes are now common.[135] While no formal plain language law is in force in the United Kingdom, Gyles Brandreth MP did present a Plain Language Bill to the House of Commons on 8 December 1992 dealing with consumer contracts, consumer credit contracts and housing contracts. In this commentary the term 'ordinary language' will be equated to and used interchangeably with both 'plain English' and 'plain language'. The meaning for 'plain language' can be that given to the term by the Alberta Government. The Alberta Government describes plain language in this way:

---

[130] MINOGUE, ANN, see n. 129 above, 7.
[131] See BROOME, J. C. A Comparison of the Clarity of Traditional Construction Contracts and of the New Engineering Contract. http://www.reading.ac.uk/kcshuwill/arcom/jonbroome.html.13 January 1999.
[132] See RHYS JONES, S. The Influence of Law, Language & Perception on Conflict in the Construction Industry. MSc dissertation, Centre for Construction Law and Management, King's College, London, 1992.
[133] Guidance notes, NEC, 2.
[134] MELLINKOFF, PROFESSOR DAVID authored the seminal text in the area, *The Language of the Law*. Little, Brown, Boston, 1963.
[135] See generally FELSENFELD, C. An Overview of the Plain English Movement for Lawyers. *Michigan Bar Journal*, 1983, **62**, 941; HATHAWAY, G. H. Plain Language Laws. *Michigan Bar Journal*, 1983, **62**, 945; (1983): 147; THOMAS, RICHARD. Plain English and the Law. *Statute Law Review*, 1985, 139; GOLDSTEIN, BERNARD H. Plain Language – Ten Years after: Some Reflections on its Basic Assumptions. *New York State Bar Journal*, 1989, **61**, 38.

> Plain language is language that communicates clearly and effectively. It is the opposite of complicated, confusing, obscure language. Plain language does not have to be unravelled to be understood – it is clear and concise. Plain language uses words and expressions that are familiar to readers, and presents information in a logical order using a straightforward writing style. It is good, standard English written with the needs of the reader in mind. It allows the reader to receive the writer's message with ease.[136]

Many of the objectives of the plain English or plain language movement are the same as those of the NEC drafters in using ordinary language. Martin Cutts,[137] one of the leading United Kingdom proponents of plain English describes it as '[t]he writing and setting out of essential information in a way that gives a co-operative, motivated person a good chance of understanding the document at first reading, and in the same sense that the writer meant it to be understood'.[138] Cutts has also set out a number of guidelines that are relevant to the composition of texts and contracts.[139] These guidelines can be compared to certain objectives of the NEC drafters:

- *Over the whole document, make the average sentence 15 to 20 words.*[140] The drafters sought to keep sentence length below 40 words per sentence as a general principle but in practice this cap has been exceeded on occasion; particularly in those instances where a series of bullet points is used.
- *Use words the readers are likely to understand.* This point has been contentious in the NEC. While most commentators would concede that the contract contains much ordinary language it is also argued that some certainty is lost in the replacement of so-called 'terms of art' in the industry; for example, the replacement of 'claims' with the phrase 'compensation events'. It is also argued that the legal certainty associated with past court rulings construing familiar words and phrases under other forms has been lost by omitting reference to them. Hence the issue in the case of the NEC in this regard is what terms are

---

[136] Writing in government? Make it plain language. Consumer and Corporate Affairs, EDMONTON, ALBERTA. 1991, p. 1. See generally for an introduction to the topic ASPREY, MICHELE M. *Plain Language for Lawyers*, 2nd edn. Federation Press, Sydney, 1996; DICK, ROBERT C. *Legal Drafting in Plain Language*, 3rd edn. Carswell, Scarborough, 1995; EAGLESON, ROBERT. *The Case for Plain Language*. Plain Language Centre, Canadian Law Information Council, Toronto, Ontario, 1988; DAVIES ROBERTS, PHILIP. *Plain English: a User's Guide*. Penguin Books, London, 1988; GOWERS, SIR ERNEST. *The Complete Plain Words* Penguin Books, London, 1987.

[137] CUTTS, MARTIN. *The Plain English Guide*. Oxford University Press, Oxford, 1995, and *Lucid Law*. Plain Language Commission, Stockport, 1994. Many other well-known proponents of plain English are members of 'Clarity', a movement to simplify legal English, whose patron is Lord Justice Staughton.

[138] CUTTS, MARTIN, see n. 137 above, 3.

[139] CUTTS, MARTIN. Plain English in the Law. *Statute Law Review*, 1996, **17**, 50, 56.

[140] Guidance notes, NEC, 2.

readers more likely to understand and in what context? The point does not admit of an easy answer and clearly persuasive arguments can be mounted on either side. It may be noted with a touch of irony that Lord Woolf proposed in *Access to Justice* that the word 'claims' replace all methods for starting a case and the word 'claimant' replace 'plaintiff'. Those recommendations became law on 26 April 1999.[141]

- *Use only as many words as are really needed.* Once again, it was an express objective of the drafters to reduce overall word content in comparison to other forms. However, it may be noted that word totals have increased from that in the Consultation Document through the First and later Second Edition. Thus there is a tendency, reflected in other forms e.g. the JCT 80 amendments, to grow over time – perhaps without necessarily adding to the overall clarity in the form.

- *Prefer the active voice unless there is a good reason for using the passive voice.* Drafting in the present tense has largely overcome the use of the passive voice in the NEC although D. G. Valentine would add that this is at the expense of clarity in terms of upon whom obligations are imposed.[142]

- *Use the clearest, crispest, liveliest verbs.*

- *Use vertical lists to break up complicated text.* Bulleted lists are a feature of the NEC.

- *Put points positively when you can.* This point both operates and does not operate in the NEC. Thus, while many points are put in affirmative terms, again in part attributable to drafting in the present tense, the form also uses negative and double negative wordings. These negative formulations are common regarding the giving of reasons by the project manager and add points of possible uncertainty.

- *Reduce cross-references to the minimum.* Cross-references have all but been eliminated. While this does make the form easier to read it has also been subjected to criticism as giving rise to occasional uncertainty.[143]

The 'ordinary language' objectives of the drafters are intended to be fulfilled through greater 'clarity and simplicity'. An early elaboration by Martin Barnes on three ways in which standard forms could be simplified was set out in 1986 as follows:

> (a) express the responsibilities of the parties more simply, perhaps with some rearrangement of the allocation of risk and responsibility (b) incorporate management procedures into the contract, so that it is clearly management based (c) avoid legalistic words, style and layout.[144]

---

[141] LORD WOOLF. *Access to Justice: Final Report to the Lord Chancellor on the Civil Justice System in England and Wales.* HMSO, London, July 1996, paragraph 13, 275.

[142] VALENTINE, D. G., see n. 40 above, 308–309.

[143] See generally EGGLESTON, BRIAN. *The New Engineering Contract, A Commentary.* Blackwell Science, London, 1996.

[144] BARNES, DR MARTIN. *et al.* Towards Simpler Contracts. BARNES *et al.* introducers. Reported by BARBER, J. N. In Proceedings of the Institution of Civil Engineers, June 1986, **80**, part 1.

While few would argue with these aims, there is a counter-argument that arises. The classic counter-argument to the aim of simpler expression is that it must not be achieved at the expense of or take precedence over legal certainty.

Brian Eggleston, has raised the issue in this way:

> But for legal interpretation of the contract the problem is not so easily solved ... and the application of legal precedents from traditional forms of contract written in conventional drafting style can only be surmised; which raises the question, has the NEC sacrificed legal certainty in pursuit of a new order? There are certainly some who feel that discarding conventional drafting amounts to discarding the accumulated contractual wisdom of generations. Throwing the baby out with the bathwater is how one eminent construction lawyer has put it.[145]

Richard Winward would appear to agree: '[t]he desire to move away from "lawyers jargon" into simple English has the potentiality of moving the contract away from the certainty of precedent into the uncertainty of interpretation'.[146]

Criticism of new forms is often the case on their introduction but Darryl Royce has noted: '[e]xperience has shown that new forms of contract, like new Acts of Parliament, should be considered at length before they are rejected out of hand ...'.[147] Several years after the introduction of the NEC a debate hosted by the Society of Construction Law tested the motion '[t]his House believes that the New Engineering Contract does not meet the foreseeable needs of the Construction Industry'. In the vote on the motion following the debate the result was 48 in favour, 53 against, with 4 abstentions.[148] Different views on the value of legal precedent in shaping standard forms may also be referred to. Thus, for instance, H. A. Palmer, has suggested that common law traditions according to which standard forms of contract were built on by interpretation furthered the resolution of ambiguities and uncertainties; however, Max Abrahamson has contradicted this view and said he *disagreed* that interpretations of the contract resolve uncertainties.[149]

---

[145] EGGLESTON, see n. 143 above, p. 3.

[146] WINWARD, RICHARD. Do Construction Contracts Benefit the Parties? In (eds UFF, JOHN and LAVERS, ANTHONY), *Legal Obligations Construction Revised Conference Proceedings.* Centre of Construction Law and Management, King's College, London, 1992, p. 113. David Chappell also recommends that the Professional Services Contract not be used as a basis for the engagement of architects because the 'simple language' might leave architects legally exposed: 'Contract Spreads Confusion'. *Architects' Journal*, 1994, **200** (20), 52–53.

[147] ROYCE, DARRYL. Tugging at the Contract: Some Preliminary Reflections on the JCT Intermediate Form of Building Contract. *Construction Law Journal*, 1984–85, **1**, 97.

[148] BELL, SIMON, in the information section, New Engineering Contract: Plague or Panacea? *Construction Law Journal*, 1995, **11**, pp. 247, 248.

[149] BARNES, DR MARTIN *et al.*, see n. 144 above, 818–821.

Abrahamson has supported his view with reference to the few interpretations of the ICE 5th form and the fact that judicial interpretations are often changed by the drafting committees revising the conditions in any case. This is certainly the case with some of the most recent changes in ICE 7th. More recently, Professor Abrahamson, writing with Jeremy Winter, has come out strongly in favour of 'purposeful intention' as the best means of interpretation; that is: '[f]ull benefit of law that concentrates on the parties' intentions and treats contracts as purposeful plans for action; with Guidance Notes and Disc admissible as evidence but not competing with the contract words'.[150]

However, while 'legal certainty' has been associated with formal legal expression, and underscored by the doctrine of precedent, the argument has increasingly been criticized, particularly by advocates of plain language in drafting. For reasons which are discussed in Chapter 6 it is submitted that one cannot state that legal precedent, traditional forms of contract, and conventional drafting style alone *equate with legal certainty*. A recent legislative example where legal precedent, tradition and convention were overturned was the passage of the UK Arbitration Act 1996. This subject is outside the scope of this book.

Notwithstanding differences of view over the value of legal precedent it may be noted that NEC drafting follows modern drafting practice and conventions in a number of respects. For example, the European Union tenders on occasion for legal guides to be drafted in plain language and as from 1995 most standard form consumer contracts in the European Union are required to be written in 'plain, intelligible language'.[151] In addition, by comparison to the Revised Statutes of British Columbia 1996 all sections were renumbered to replace previous decimal additions. Significantly, 'must' replaces 'shall' and this change has now become the standard in Canadian plain language drafting.[152] The change to replace decimals provides an interesting comparison because of the same debate surrounding various standard forms of contract.[153]

The clause numbering in the ECC is arranged in nine sections in single column format. A format division of the conditions into nine core sections was first used in IFC 84 and later adopted by JCT 87. Commenting on the format in general Tony Blackler *et al.* write: '[t]his is a welcome standardisation and it is to be hoped that Sections will soon become so

---

[150] ABRAHAMSON, MAX and WINTER, JEREMY. New Contract Systems – Permanent Change or Fashion? *The Building of Construction Law*. A paper presented at the Tenth Annual Construction Conference on 19 September 1997, by the Society of Construction Law and the Centre of Construction Law and Management. King's College, London, 1997.

[151] See e.g. OJ 1993 C70/14; Unfair Terms in Consumer Contracts Regulations 1994, and Council Directive 93/13/EEC (OL J 095, 21 April 1993). See generally DALBY, J. *EU Law for the Construction Industry*. Blackwell Science, Oxford, 1997.

[152] Under the Interpretation Act, RSBC (1996), section 2.

[153] See e.g. JONES, GLYN P. who is a harsh critic of decimalized numbering in JCT 80: see *A New Approach to the 1980 Standard Form of Building Contract*. The Construction Press, Lancaster, 1980.

familiar that, for instance, any clause within Section 4 will automatically be recognized as relating to payment'.[154] While the NEC format headings are not identical to these the rationale of promoting familiarity across the NEC family of forms remains the same; unfortunately some of this benefit is being lost in the Second Edition of the PSC and AC.

The first numeral or digit is the number of the section for the respective clause. This same principle applies to main options and core clauses. The numerals or digits number the paragraphs in each clause after a decimal point. The guidance notes adopt the convention of referring to paragraphs as clauses; this convention, or that of referring to them as subclauses is adopted here.[155] To facilitate cross-referencing among the main options where a clause or paragraph (subclause) is used in more than one main option the same numbering sequence is used. Thus clause 21.2 will be the same in every main option in which clause 21.2 appears. Changes would be made so far as required in the Engineering and Construction Subcontract (ECSC) form. However, the clause numbering may not be consecutive.[156] The secondary option clauses are numbered separately and preceded by a letter for each option clause. An appendix in the guidance notes illustrates the relationship of main option clauses and paragraphs (subclauses) and core clauses and secondary option clauses.[157] The main options are listed consecutively and alphabetically, thus main options A to F; however, the secondary options are not. Hence the secondary options omit the letter prefixes O, W, X and Y. This may simply be the result of changes to the lettering in successive editions of the contract. The Consultation Document added two secondary options: P (advanced payment bond), which was to be used only with the advanced payment to the contractor secondary option itself (option J), and T (VAT and sales tax), and omitted the current secondary options for T (changes in the law), U (The Construction (Design and Management) Regulations 1994), and V (trust fund). It would appear that no significance would attach to either the order or the letter prefixes. However, the use of letter prefixes may give rise to some confusion in at least one respect: as only one of the first six main options will be chosen, so too might one assume that one or more of the secondary option clauses are mutually exclusive. The omission of certain letter prefixes, occasional gaps in the numbering of subclauses and the replacement of bullets or numbered decimal places with letters in the SCC detracts from the logic and occasional symmetry of the forms.[158]

The clause numbering of the ECC is open to question in another respect. It has been implied that the drafters adopted bullet points in an effort to reduce the number of numbered clauses and subclauses. Ernest J.

---

[154] *Rowe & Maw. JCT Management Contract*, 7–8.
[155] It may be noted that there is uncertainty associated with choice that has more generally been commented on by VALENTINE, D. G., see n. 40 above, 311.
[156] See e.g. clause 11.2 in the various main options for examples.
[157] Guidance notes, NEC, 107–112.
[158] See VALENTINE, D. G., n. 40 above, 305.

Bayton has suggested that the technique the drafters seemed to have used was to insert a bullet point typically when lists were involved or a full stop where the sentence length exceeded 30 words.[159] The result may make reading the clauses easier in one respect but also more difficult in others. Thus it is not possible to be as precise as is desirable when referring to the clauses themselves; in addition, references become more difficult when successive bullet point drafting is employed apparently to indicate subclauses.[160] A conventional alternative to this drafting style would have been to use further numbering or a combination of numbers and letters. It would also have been open to the drafters to drop one tens' unit. Future editions of the NEC may have to revisit this issue.

There are a number of other demonstrably verifiable features of the NEC that would suggest that the drafters have achieved a greater measure of clarity and simplicity than other comparable leading standard forms. Thus, for instance, there are fewer clauses used as a general rule than under other forms. The sentences are generally shorter although commentators have questioned the brevity of the wording (drafting).[161] The use of guidance notes, recommended by Latham,[162] as well as the use of flow charts, both facilitate understanding and, it is submitted, clarity and simplicity. Simpler and more generally worded language that is less industry specific should facilitate translations. From the drafters' point of view as well '[i]t is arranged and organised in a structure which helps the user to gain familiarity with its contents'.[163] These features would appear to support the claims of a clearer and simpler form of contract. However, others disagree, in particular regarding new terminology.

A. A. Kwakye states:

> [a]lthough the intention of the authors of the NEC standard form of contract is to make the contract simple, the opposite is achieved as many of the clauses are obscure ... [and] [o]wing to the obscurity of meaning of some clauses, their diverse legal interpretation is likely to open the floodgates to contractual claims.[164]

Michael Ludlow has this to say on the likelihood of litigation over the language used:

> This is inevitable with a new, lengthy, document the brief for which was to take a blank sheet of paper and start from first principles, and which endeavours to find common wording for uses which cover

---

[159] BAYTON, ERNEST J., see n. 53 above. See also VALENTINE, D. G., n. 40 above, 305.

[160] See e.g. clauses 11.2(30) and 80.1 ECC.

[161] CLARKE, J. R. NEC – Thoughts and Questions. *Civil Engineering Surveyor*, July/August 1993, 14; and BOOTH, S. The 'New' NEC. *Civil Engineering Surveyor*, April 11 1993.

[162] Latham Report, paragraph 5.18(4), 37. Guidance notes were officially published with the ICE 6th edn by the CCJSC in 1993.

[163] Guidance notes, Consultation Document, 1.

[164] KWAKYE, A. A. *Construction Project Administration in Practice*. Addison Wesley Longman, Harlow, CIOB, Ascot, 1997, p. 105.

many permutations of choice of risk allocation and procurement routes.[165]

Three rejoinders may be put to these views. First, it could be said that there is no proof that new terminology is any more conducive to disputes than old language that has become complex over time. Secondly, the language may not be so new. Rather, it can be found to have established meanings in related disciplines; for instance project management. Thus the drafting may be viewed more in terms of bringing these meanings to the attention of a wider audience than has previously been the case.[166] Thirdly, in paragraph 5.18(4), 37 the Latham Report called for 'easily comprehensible language' in its assumptions for a modern form of contract, and as this aspect was not addressed again specifically in relation to the NEC, it can be argued that the NEC satisfied this assumption.[167]

Clarity, to be meaningful, may have to be defined in relation to a given audience. In this regard the NEC is also not traditional compared to most other standard forms. Justin Sweet sets out potential audiences for whom the contract must be clear. However, while each audience has a potential interest in clear language Sweet's preferred audience to be addressed is 'those who must live with it, that is, those involved in the performance' of the contract; that is architects, engineers, quantity surveyors, construction managers, superintendents and key employees of contractors.[168] Professor Sweet's recommendation in this regard contrasts with the audience chosen by the drafters of traditional standard forms. Thus the audience that has traditionally been chosen is '[p]ersons outside the contracting entities who must resolve or help the parties resolve claims or disputes, such as judges, arbitrators or mediators'.[169] The NEC, once again, is not traditional. It has chosen its intended audience from among those who must administer the contract rather than from those who are outside the contractual chain. It has been shown that it is not just communication that is a problem in construction but communication *in relation to* the contract.[170] If the contract is not understood it will inhibit effective communication between the parties. Thus contracts must be clearly drafted so that the information they contain and how parties may use the contracts to facilitate the exchange of new information are understood by those parties.[171] To close on this topic the view of Martin Barnes may be reiterated: '[i]f the contract

---

[165] LUDLOW, MICHAEL. Resolving Disputes under United Kingdom Construction Contracts through Alternatives to Litigation: Controlling the Cost. *Arbitration and Dispute Resolution Law Journal*, 1995, 13.

[166] VALENTINE, D. G. has criticized the move away from traditional language in the NEC in that it requires a new vocabulary to be learned: n. 40 above, 305.

[167] See Latham Report, paragraph 5.20, 39–40.

[168] SWEET, JUSTIN, n. 31 above, 419.

[169] *Ibid.*

[170] HIGGIN, G. and JESSOP, N. *Communications in the Building Industry: The Report of a Pilot Study.* Tavistock Publications, London, 1965.

[171] See generally FISHER, NORMAN and LI YIN, SHEN. *Information Management in a Contractor: A Model for the Flow of Data.* Thomas Telford, London, 1992.

draughtsman understood clearly how risks arose, he would be able to draught simpler conditions'.[172] Legal jargon, it may be noted has been observed to be a barrier to accurate risk assessment.[173]

Stimulus to good management

The New Engineering Contract represented a radical departure from the time-hallowed principles that, despite ever-increasing length, have underlain all earlier editions of the ICE Conditions. The New Engineering Contract involved an act of faith namely, that the application of project management techniques will improve the adversarial nature of contracting.[174]

Project management should axiomatically be important in the construction process because construction after all involves projects that need to be managed. In fact, there is a greater imperative for 'management' in construction than in many other forms of commercial organization because of its unique characteristics. The unique characteristics of construction centre around the number of participants and the complexity of their respective tasks. Stephen W. Mak puts it this way. 'A construction project is an engagement over different points in time of several organisations such as consultants, contractors, subcontractors and suppliers, with a client system that is organisationally complex.'[175] Hence, the 'management' itself may be construed as coming from all these organizations. However, insignificant attention has been paid to management in construction until very recently.[176] This is at odds with the tremendous growth in the application of management theories to other industries.[177]

The NEC drafters always intended that the new form should be a stimulus to good management and Perry describes this as 'the most important characteristic of [the] NEC'.[178] Martin Barnes too notes the contrast of the NEC in this regard to traditional forms. 'The management of projects has become a science with its own set of rules, techniques and words which are not even mentioned in the existing standard forms.'[179] Professor John Uff QC has noticed this gap and how 'low key' traditional management techniques have been.

---

[172] BARNES, DR MARTIN *et al.*, see n. 144 above, 818.

[173] WOODWARD, S. J. Vital Importance of Risk Management. *Construction Law*, April/May 1994, 13–14.

[174] STRINGER, GEORGE. The Future Role of Standard Forms of Contract. In *Future Directions*, p. 115.

[175] MAK, STEPHEN W. Risk Analysis in Construction: A Paradigm Shift from a Hard to Soft Approach. *Construction Management and Economics*, 1995, **13**, 387.

[176] There are some exceptions: see e.g. OXLEY, R. and POSKITT, J. *Management Techniques Applied to the Construction Industry*, 5th edn. Blackwell Science, Oxford, 1996.

[177] See ROBBINS, S. P. *Management*, 3rd edn. Prentice-Hall, Englewood Cliffs, 1991, pp. 30–59, and GRIFFIN, R. W. *Management*, 3rd edn. Houghton Mifflin, Boston, 1990, see n. 25 above, pp. 29–55.

[178] PERRY, JOHN G., see n. 25 above, p. 200.

[179] BARNES, DR MARTIN *et al.*, see n. 144 above, 818.

The impact of management on contract documents has been minimal in some cases; and in others, attempts to incorporate the provision of management have stopped at the level of specifying services, with no clear definition of duty being undertaken, and no effective sanction against non-performance. There is a clear need to examine conditions of contract to ascertain their relevance and usefulness in areas of management.[180]

Continuing in this vein, in the same paper, Uff wrote that:

[m]anagement is now a well established, complex, multi-faceted subject which impinges in a large variety of ways on construction projects and contracts. Its impact is largely ignored, avoided or simply missed in most conventional construction contracts.[181]

Uff also added a call to arms for the legal profession to recognize the role of project management as follows:

the demands and achievements of project management must be taken into account in drawing up both construction and professional services contracts, if the legal profession is to perform any useful function in the construction process.[182]

In fact, the 'impinging' typically occurs across a very broad spectrum in construction. Thus John F. Woodward[183] has been able to list the following areas that are amenable to management and which may be elaborated upon.

Scope
The scope of an NEC project would be defined by both core and main option clauses, in particular relevant identified and defined terms in core clause 1, the Contract Data, and the works information.

Procurement
Procurement is understood in the broadest possible terms through use of the main option clauses A to F.

Planning and progress
For example, the flow charts, as well as communications, early warning and programme provisions are central to progress and planning in the NEC and would pertain here.

---

[180] UFF, JOHN. Overview: The Place of Management in Construction. *Management and Construction Law.* A one-day seminar on 23 March 1990 by the Centre of Construction Law and Management. King's College, London, 1990, 3.

[181] *Ibid.*, 17.

[182] *Ibid.*

[183] WOODWARD, JOHN F. What Has to be Managed in a Project. In *Construction Project Management, Getting it Right First Time.* Thomas Telford, London, 1997, pp. 30–48 and referring to TURNER, J. R. *The Handbook of Project-Based Management.* McGraw-Hill, London, 1993, p. 30.

Time
The NEC system of dating, express time periods and delays for communications and actions, early warning, programming, take over, acceleration, payment, and compensation event provisions are all directly relevant to the issue of time from a project management perspective.

Cost
Cost is dealt with in meticulous detail through the defined term 'Actual Cost', clause 52 and the cost of components outlined in both the Schedule of Cost Components (SCC) and Shorter Schedule of Cost Components (SSCC).

Quality
The subject of 'quality' is addressed principally through core clause 4 on testing and defects.

People
People are the subject of express provision in clause 24 and statements with regard to named people are also given in parts one and two of the Contract Data.[184]

Risk
Risk is dealt with articulately in the NEC primarily by providing a choice of allocation of risks in the various main options, as well as certain core and secondary option clauses. The theoretical basis for assigning risk is to allocate the risks to the party best able to manage, estimate and carry them.[185]

Project success/failure
The *success* or *failure* of a project is dependent upon a wide range of variables including many of the variables separately included in this list by Woodward. P. J. Duffy has compiled a list of *success factors* in project management, which include: project definition, user involvement, appropriate project organization, realistic programme with defined stages, identification and management of risk, cost plan and contingency management, suitable contract strategy, quality assurance, project control, and project review.[186]

---

[184] See generally MARTIN, A. S. and GROVER, FRED. *Managing People.* Thomas Telford, London, 1989.

[185] Some relevant individual clauses with express risk allocations include clauses 60, 80, 81, 84, 85, 86 and 87 ECC.

[186] See generally MORRIS, P. W. G. and HOUGH, G. H. *Preconditions of Success and Failure in Major Projects.* Technical Paper 3. Major Projects Association, Oxford, 1986. DUFFY, P. J. Project Performance Auditing. *Management and Construction Law,* 3–4. See recently, CHAN, Dr ALBERT P. C. Measuring Success for a Construction Project. *The Australian Institute of Quantity Surveyors – Refereed Journal,* 1997, **1** (2), 55.

Facilities

Facilities are addressed separately in the form in numerous clauses.[187]

The relevance of the list to not only construction contracts but to the NEC in particular can thus be demonstrated. Apart from success factors potential obstacles may also be noted. John Rooke and David Seymour have specifically identified the legal profession as one possible barrier to success of the NEC.

> A more easily apparent source of resistance to the NEC is the legal profession. We have observed that the legal culture attempts to pre-empt disputes by predicting their likely outcomes. The putative culture of the NEC attempts the same thing by promoting good management practice. Given this contrast, the choice may be seen as one between pursuing an argument about techniques of good project management, in order to avoid problems arising, or an argument about contract law, to enable problems which have already arisen to be settled equitably. We have suggested that lawyers naturally tend to focus on the latter; they have no special expertise to enter into debate about the former. Thus, it is unsurprising that those lawyers whose comments we have reviewed do not address the principles of the NEC.[188]

The failure of the construction industry to adopt more readily more modern management methods is also a potential barrier to success. Some of the lessons that have been learned in relation to the manufacturing sector have had attention drawn to them in the strongest possible terms. Thus, in a recent *Statement on the Construction Industry*, the Royal Academy of Engineering[189] has called for swift action to stem the erosion in the competitive position of the industry relative to other sectors.

The key to the introduction and reinforcement of sound management practices in the NEC, in contrast to most of the traditional standard forms, is the procedures[190] that the contract calls for. A. A. Kwakye sees this as an advantage for the form: '[t]he NEC standard form of contract provides for detailed procedures for managing construction project risks as they occur'. These procedures reinforce the fundamental principles of project management which are inherent in the NEC. The *Code of Practice for Project Management for Construction and Development* describes project management thus:

> [p]roject management is an emergent professional discipline which separates the management function of a project from the design and

---

[187] See e.g. clauses 33.2, 40.2, 42.1, and 60.1(16) ECC.

[188] ROOKE, JOHN and SEYMOUR, DAVID. The NEC and the Culture of the Industry: Some Early Findings Regarding Possible Sources of Resistance to Change. *Engineering, Construction and Architectural Management*, 1995 **2** (4), 303–304.

[189] Royal Academy of Engineering. *Statement on the Construction Industry.* Royal Academy of Engineering, London, 1996.

[190] KWAKYE, A. A. see n. 164, above, 105.

execution functions. Management and design may still be combined on small projects and be performed by the leader of the Design team. For larger or more complex projects the need for separate management has resulted in the evolution of project management.[191]

This is an inherent part of the NEC.

The NEC stands in contrast to the view that a 'contract should be left in the drawer'.[192] The form is to be used and the procedures it sets out followed. The most important of those principles may be listed as follows:[193]

- foresight applied collaboratively mitigates problems and reduces risk;
- clear division of function and responsibility improves accountability[194] and motivation; and
- people will be motivated[195] to play their part in collaborative management if it is in their commercial and professional self-interest to do so.

There are many examples of the use of management techniques grounded in these principles which come out in the NEC including the following: choice of contract strategy in procurement;[196] independent adjudication;[197] incentives for the project manager to manage both unforeseen events as well as uncertainties;[198] variable and clear risk alternatives in contract strategy;[199] early warning procedures;[200] programme

---

[191] The *Code of Practice for Project Management for Construction and Development*, 3. Questions are still raised about project management: see e.g. WATERHOUSE, ROGER A. Project Management – Buzz Word or Professional Discipline. *Construction Law Journal*, 1993, **9**, 96; and in explanation of the questions HEREDIA, R. de. Barriers to the Application of Project Management Concepts outside Entrepreneurial Systems. *International Journal of Project Management*, 1993, **11** (3): 131–134.

[192] For example, '... the best jobs are when the contract never comes out of the drawer': Penny Guest. Building Accord. *Building*, 25 June 1993, 35 quoting Sid Clarworthy, Surveying Director Lindum Construction. See BARNES' comments as well on this topic in: The Role of Contracts in Management. In *Construction Contract Policy* (eds UFF and CAPPER), p. 119; and see also the Latham Report, seeming to acknowledge that there is a sentiment in industry that contracts will be left in the drawer during successful projects, paragraph 5.16, 36.

[193] PERRY, JOHN G., see n. 25 above, 201.

[194] See generally on the relationship between the two: LEONG, C. Accountability and Project Management: A Convergence of Objectives. *International Journal of Project Management*, November 1991, **9** (4), 240–249.

[195] See generally REISS, GEOFF. *Project Management Demystified: Today's Tools and Techniques*, 2nd edn. E & FN Spon, London, 1995, pp. 174–176.

[196] See discussion main options.

[197] See clauses 10, 11.2(2), 51.3, (90, 91, 92, unamended and amended 2nd ECC) and 93 ECC.

[198] See discussion Project Manager.

[199] See again discussion main options and guidance notes.

[200] For example, under clause 16 ECC.

provisions;[201] compensation events addressing time and cost risks in one core clause;[202] co-operative management;[203] incentives in cost reimbursable main options C, D, E and F;[204] designation of key people;[205] and clear relationships between tenders and information provided to tenderers.[206]

In summary, while the NEC drafting objectives may be examined in the abstract, a definitive view cannot be taken until there have been more empirical results on which to assess them. Professor Andrew Cox and Ian Thompson state:[207]

> Performance, as the determinant of success, needs to be quantifiable in order that the practitioner knows upon which criteria it is based and how that is measured. Thus the NEC may have successfully achieved its three principal objectives [flexibility, clarity and a stimulus to good project management], but ... [effectively] remains untested as very little performance data has been published.[208]

It can be expected that as experience with the form increases additional empirical data upon the form's performance will become available and scrutinized. Brian Eggleston has written:

> [r]eports from early users of the NEC suggest that improvements in project management are being achieved and that job satisfaction for those involved is somewhat better than with traditional contracts. But most early users of the NEC do admit that they are either enthusiasts or willing pioneers and it is probably too early to say how the NEC will fare in general practice.

The first observation supported by research has become available on the operation of the NEC with the recent publication of Jon Broome's work entitled *The NEC Engineering and Construction Contract: A User's Guide* looking into how the contract system operates on the jobsite.[209]

---

[201] See discussion on the programme.

[202] That is core clause 6 ECC.

[203] See clauses 10.1, 25.1, 26.3 ECC and discussion in Chapter 5.

[204] Notably through the definitions of 'Actual Cost' and 'Fee' as well as the contractor's share provisions. It is noteworthy that the Banwell Report paragraph 9.22 recommended incentive payments over damages clauses in building contracts.

[205] That is under clause 24.1 ECC and see also part two of the Contract Data.

[206] See discussion tendering.

[207] COX, PROFESSOR, ANDREW and THOMPSON, IAN. Is the NEC Going to Succeed? – An Examination of the Engineering and Construction Contract (Alias the NEC 2nd Edition). *International Construction Law Review*, 1996, 327.

[208] *Ibid.*

[209] EGGLESTON, BRIAN. The New Engineering Contract, A Critique of the Second Edition. 1995, 13-CLD-10-04, at 05. BROOME, JON. *The NEC Engineering and Construction Contract: A User's Guide.* Thomas Telford, London, 1999.

Role integration

As a system the NEC is intended to integrate and govern consistently the various roles and duties of those involved in construction projects. The Latham Report recommends in part that an effective form of contract 'clearly defines the roles and duties of all involved. . .'.[210] What are some of the roles and contractual relationships that may arise in a typical project configuration? They would include the following:

- employer and contractor in the Engineering and Construction Contract (ECC);
- contractor and subcontractor(s) in the Engineering and Construction Subcontract(s) (ECSC(s));
- employer and project manager and/or designers and/or supervisor in the PSC(s);
- employer and contractor jointly and adjudicator in the AC; and
- contractor and subcontractor jointly and adjudicator in the AC.

This is but one of the more likely project configurations that could pertain although clearly more diverse contractual relationships and arrangements are also possible. Thus roles may be combined; in-house employees of the employer may fulfil certain of the professional services roles; subcontractors themselves may enter into PSCs and otherwise.[211] The Professional Services Contract differs from the provisions in the ECC. One reason for some of the differences may be to reflect the fact that the PSC was intended to be used with other forms of contract. Dr Martin Barnes states: '[t]he professional services contract is directly linked to the management processes in NEC, but we have drafted it so that it can still be used even if the main document is not being used for the work'.[212] Irrespective of the configuration the essential point to take is that the NEC is designed to operate on a fully interlocking[213] basis. This, once again, is held out as a major difference from other standard forms and one of the principal advantages of the NEC. The absence of significant differences between the main and subcontract forms is one aspect of a true interlocking form. Dr Martin Barnes has written:

> [t]he text of the subcontract differs from the main contract only in the names of the parties and in a few details in the areas of payment and notice periods, insurance requirements and title to equipment, plant and materials.[214]

---

[210] Latham Report, paragraph 5.18(3), 37.
[211] See THOMPSON, N. Building New Role Models. *Construction News*, December 1993, 14.
[212] ALLEN, JOHN D. NEC – is it the Answer to Latham's Prayers? *Construction News*, 23 February 1995, 13 quoting Dr Martin Barnes.
[213] See Latham Report, paragraph 5.18(3), 37.
[214] BARNES, DR MARTIN, see n. 33 above, 90.

The uniqueness of the NEC is also in how it has affirmed the importance of interlocking conditions across consultants' terms of engagement. John Uff and Nerys Jefford write:

> It is particularly important that co-ordination and consistency should be achieved between related contracts, not simply between main contracts and subcontracts, but also between these contracts and the terms of appointment of the relevant professionals who are to issue certificates and adjudicate upon the matters which give rise to the certificates.[215]

The importance of clear associations founded on good co-operative relationships will serve to reduce the potential number of claims themselves.[216] The clarity of the relationships is facilitated in the NEC by an approach having been adopted that defines the roles of those involved in terms of the actions and decisions they take rather than simply who they are and thus what one assumes about their respective positions.

Separation of the engineer's functions

The professionally qualified engineer has played a central role in consecutive editions of both the ICE and FIDIC conditions of contract. One reason for this has been engineers' involvement in designing works that would then be constructed using one of these forms. Before the ECC could develop in the way in which it has there had to be first recognition of the possibility (if not advisability) of the separation of the traditional design and supervisory roles of the Engineer. Once there was recognition of this possibility it was only then a small step to further divide the engineer's adjunct roles as *de facto* project manager and adjudicator. These steps were taken to their logical conclusion in the NEC. Edward Corbett has described the change to the role of the engineer in the NEC as fundamental.

> There are significant changes to the NEC. Most importantly for present purposes, the role of the engineer has been fundamentally altered, dividing his functions between the supervisor, the project manager and the adjudicator, all of whom are mentioned in the contract, and the designer, who is not. The term engineer is not used.[217]

Moves toward these changes can be seen in some of the new roles that other standard forms had begun to introduce by the time the First Edition of the NEC was released and which A. R. Parish has noted as well as other changes which were taken into account by the NEC drafters such as the

---

[215] UFF, JOHN and JEFFORD, NERYS. European Harmonisation in the Field of Construction. *International Construction Law Review*, 1993, 126.

[216] WORBY, G., TYLER, A. H. and HARRIS, F. C. Management of Claims. *Building Technology and Management.* July/August 1985, 23–25.

[217] CORBETT, EDWARD. FIDIC 5th or a New Style Red Book? *International Construction Law Review*, 1993, 289.

greater reliance on specialist engineering services, joint working overseas, and the trend toward design and build construction at the time.[218]

Affirming contractor design

Most of the leading standard forms assume a traditional contracting arrangement.[219] By this the employer commissions the design of the works through an architect or engineer and any specialists working with them and then invites tenders from contractors on the basis of their design. The contractor is often the sole point of responsibility for the construction of the works from the employer's point of view. Thus subcontractors will contract only with the contractor although direct forms of subcontract between the employer and subcontractor do occur.[220] The contractor will often have to assume that the design is complete although in practice this is very often not the case. The traditional contracting arrangement thus presupposes that the contractor has no responsibility for the design of the works. The contractor's role is principally to complete the works according to the design commissioned.

The traditional forms of building contract have for the most part isolated contracting arrangements involving contractor led design and construction. It has instead been engineering forms and newer forms of building contract[221] that have conceded or accepted the design role of contractors.[222] The BPF system was one of the first standard forms to concede express design responsibility to the contractor; now, however, JCT 98 may be modified by the use of the Contractor's Designed Portion Supplement. The Supplement substantially reproduces many of the provisions included in JCT 81 – the JCT Design and Build form. Some of these newer forms of contracting, which are variably referred to as design and build, turnkey or package deal contracts, have been the exception rather than the rule insofar as the numbers of contracts let. The hallmark of these procurement methods has been single point responsibility of the contractor toward the employer for both design and construction, notwithstanding that the contractor may in turn have subcontracted a portion or all of the design work in fact. When design responsibility is not clearly allocated it may arise in other ways; for instance, by undertaking supervision of work.[223]

---

[218] Some of the changes were use of the 'employer's agent' in JCT 81, 'supervising officer' in GC/Works/1 3rd and even 'project manager' in GC/Works/1 3rd: PARISH, A. R. The Changing Role of Consultants. In *Management of International Construction Projects.* Proceedings of a Conference in London on 14 and 15 November 1984 by the Institution of Civil Engineers. Thomas Telford, London, 1984, 120–124.

[219] See JCT 80, JCT MW, IFC 84, ICE 6th, ICE MW, and FIDIC 4th.

[220] See discussion of nomination below.

[221] See on JCT 81 HACKETT, JEREMY. *Design and Build: Uses and Abuses.* Lloyd's of London Press, London, 1998.

[222] See the discussion in Chapter 8 below and see e.g. FIDIC 4th clause 7.2 on permanent works designed by the contractor.

[223] *Brunswick Construction Ltd* v. *Nowlan* (1974) 21 BLR 27, 49 DLR (3d) 93.

The issue of design responsibility may illustrate the problems inherent in the choice of the best form to govern a project. It may be taken as given that a contractor will have some degree of design responsibility even if only insofar as the fact that others' designs are under his or her control throughout. Very often the contractor will of course have a larger role than this. The problem is determining at what point, as design responsibility increases, should the employer move from a form that assumes a small design role for the contractor, e.g. ICE 6th, to a form that assumes a large or comprehensive design role, e.g. ICE Design and Construct 1992 or JCT 81. The question cannot be answered with any certainty. In addition, because each of these forms makes other assumptions dependent upon the extent of that design role, there are almost certainly going to be cases when it is inappropriate. In part, and for these reasons, the NEC seeks to overcome the dichotomous choices that these other forms present by setting out drafting assumptions which are consistent with any size of design role on the part of the contractor.

Risk allocation

It is now accepted that the choice of contract or procurement strategy can be understood and the project managed in terms of risk. The acceptance is evidenced in official government publications such as those of the Central Unit on Procurement[224] regarding risk management and recently the Health and Safety Executive's commissioning of a study on behalf of numerous government departments, represented as the Interdepartmental Liaison Group on Risk Assessment (ILGRA) to develop a set of principles for effective 'risk communication'.[225] Risk management grew out of the late 1960s and early 1970s as a means of analysing the probability of scheduled dates being over- or underrun. This development has taken place over the last three decades. Dr Peter Morris writes that risk management has now become a recognized if somewhat 'arcane' area of construction expertise involving distinct phases: risk identification, risk analysis and assessment, and risk management.[226] R. F. Fellows sees risk management as involving four primary steps: risk identification; risk quantification; risk allocation; and risk response.[227] The subject of 'risk management' is sufficiently defined to be the subject of a British Standard, BS 4778, 1979 defining the term as '[t]he process whereby decisions are made to accept a known risk or hazard or to eliminate or

---

[224] Central Unit on Procurement. *Managing Risk and Contingency for Works Projects.* HM Treasury, Central Unit on Procurement, London, August, 1993, guidance note 41; *Introduction to the Management of Risk.* HMSO, Government Centre for Information Systems, London, 1993; and Central Computer and Telecommunications Agency. *Management of Project Risk.* HMSO, London, 1994.

[225] Health and Safety Executive, press release, 25 February 1997, HSE.

[226] MORRIS, DR PETER. Current Trends in the Organisation of Construction Projects. In *Future Directions*, p. 181.

[227] FELLOWS, R. F. *The Management of Risk* (ed. HARLOW, PETER). CIOB, Ascot, 1996, Construction Paper 65.

mitigate it'. Today, of course, risk analysis extends far beyond construction.[228]

However, despite this understanding, most traditional forms of contract have made almost no allowance for risk in their conditions and very few cases ever address the subject.[229] Most standard form contracts will rather deal with risk allocation, and to a small degree risk response, e.g. liquidated damages. Not long ago a leading figure in both contract and construction law, Professor Michael Furmston, wrote that he doubted whether any of the traditional standard forms were guided by modern principles of risk allocation.[230] Morris has remarked upon the close association between risk management as understood in these terms and the NEC. He states: '[t]he results [of risk management] ... are now slowly beginning to become incorporated in some legal forms – the New Engineering Contract being the best and most obvious example'.[231] In more general terms Morris has forecast that risk management will become more common on projects in the future.[232] Several of the NEC drafters have led in this development and are recognized as pioneers of risk theory in relation to construction contracts, in particular, the work of Barnes,[233] Abrahamson,[234] and Perry and Hayes.[235] Barnes, for example, in a survey of who had published the most papers in the leading *International Journal of Project Management* between 1983 and 1992, was the twelfth most frequently published author.[236] Abrahamson's principles for risk allocation too have been picked up and elaborated upon with weightings in Australia by a Joint Working party examining the Australian construction industry: *No Dispute: Strategies for Improvement in the*

---

[228] See e.g. *Risk Analysis, An International Journal*, and an official publication of the Society for Risk Analysis. Plenum Press, New York and London.

[229] One exception to this is the case of *Photo Production Ltd* v. *Securicor Transport Ltd* [1980] AC 827, [1980] 1 All ER 556, HL.

[230] FURMSTON, PROFESSOR MICHAEL. The Liability of Contractors: Principles of Liability in Contract and Tort. In LLOYD, HUMPHREY (ed), *The Liability of Contractors*. Centre for Commercial Law Studies, Queen Mary College, Longman, London, 1986, p. 13.

[231] MORRIS, DR PETER, see n. 226, above, 191.

[232] MORRIS, PETER W. G. *The Management of Projects*. Thomas Telford, London, 1994, p. 291.

[233] See in particular by BARNES, MARTIN. How to Allocate Risks in Construction Contracts. *International Journal of Project Management*, 1983, **1**, 24–28.

[234] ABRAHAMSON, MAX. Risk Management. *International Construction Law Review*, 1984, 241. Other commentators refer to the work of these individuals together as well: see e.g. O'REILLY, MICHAEL. Risk, Construction Contracts and Construction Disputes. *Construction Law Journal*, 1995, **11**, 343.

[235] See notably, COOPER, D. and CHAPMAN, C. *Risk Analysis for Large Projects: Models, Methods and Cases*. John Wiley, Chichester, 1987; and FLANAGAN, R. and NORMAN, G. *Risk Management and Construction*. Blackwell Scientific Publications, Oxford, 1993.

[236] BETTS, MARTIN and LANSLEY, PETER. International Journal of Project Management: a Review of the First Ten Years. *International Journal of Project Management*, 1995, **13** (4), 207–217.

Building and Construction Industry.[237] Perry and Hayes have been equally influential in much of their writing.[238]

In an early paper of Barnes, the author credits C. A. Erikson with perhaps the first work showing that aspects of the science of risk analysis could be applied to construction and engineering contracts.[239] Erikson used a two-fold division of risk classification: contractual risk and construction risk. With respect to contractual risk Erikson wrote:

> [c]ontractual risks arise primarily from the interaction among different parties to the construction process. Contractual risk is introduced through lack of clarity, absence of perfect communication between the parties involved, and problems of timeliness in contract administration. These risks expose both the owner and contractor to uncertainties which may increase both parties' costs. Contractual risks are not risks to be shared; however, the owner can reduce them by improving contract clarity and contract administration. The cost of reducing contractual risk may be small relative to cost of the uncertainties, efficiencies, and delays which contractual risk creates.[240]

Erikson went on to define construction risk as follows:

> [c]onstruction risk arises from factors such as weather, differing site conditions, acts of God, resource availability etc. Construction risk is inherent in the work itself and would be present even if one company with perfect internal communication performed all of the construction process functions itself. Although construction risks may be reduced, they are primarily managed by assigning them to one or more of the parties involved. This assignment should consider factors such as comparing the differing utility functions of each of the parties, maintaining contractor incentives, and

---

[237] *No Dispute: Strategies for Improvement in the Building and Construction Industry.* National Public Works Conference, National Building and Construction Council, Sydney, 1990.

[238] PERRY, J. G. and HAYES, R. Risk and its Management in Construction Projects. *Proceedings of the Institution of Civil Engineers*, part 1, June 1985, 77: 499–552. See also HAYES, R. The Risks of Management Contracting. *Chartered Quantity Surveyor*, December 1985, 197–198; PERRY, J. G., HAYES, W. Risk Management for Project Managers. *Building Technology and Management*, August/September 1986, 8–11; HAYES, R. W. *et al. Risk Management in Engineering Construction.* Science and Engineering Research Council, Thomas Telford, London, 1987 (eds THOMPSON, P. A. and PERRY, J. G.); *Engineering Construction Risks: A Guide to Engineering Construction Risks: A Guide to Project Risk Analysis and Risk Management.* Science and Engineering Research Council, Thomas Telford, London, 1993.

[239] BARNES, MARTIN. Risk Sharing in Contracts, Civil Engineering Project Procedure in the EC. *Proceedings of a Conference* held at Heathrow on 24 January 1991 by the Institution of Civil Engineers (ed. COX, P. A.). Thomas Telford, London, 1991, 7.

[240] ERIKSON, C. A. Risk Sharing in Construction Contracts. PhD dissertation, University of Illinois, 1979, 6.

determining which party can best control the risk or influence the severity of the loss.[241]

P. A. Thompson and J. G. Perry also refer with approval to the work of D. B. Ashley and C. E. Porter.[242] Professor John Perry has recently[243] summarized the principles[244] for risk allocation in the NEC from earlier work, such as the conclusions of a report of proceedings of a conference on Construction Risks and Liability Sharing held by the American Society of Civil Engineers, in which it was agreed that risks belonged with those parties who were best able to evaluate, control, bear the cost and benefit from their assumption; that many risks and liabilities are best shared; and that every risk has an associated and unavoidable cost that must be assumed. The summary by Perry is as follows.

- Risks should be allocated to the party most able to control them.
- Risks which are outside the contractor's control should usually be allocated to the employer.
- Risks should not be allocated to a party who may be unable to sustain the consequences if the risk occurs. (The flip side of this statement could be that the more capable party should bear the risk. Michael O'Reilly explains: '[t]his is because in a highly interactive contractual setting such as occurs for most construction contracts, significant risks being carried by one party represent significant risks to the other', e.g. insolvency threatens completion for both parties so why put it out of ones control?).[245]
- Risk allocation should encourage good management by the party who carries the risk.
- The party who is not carrying the risk should be motivated to manage the consequences of the occurrence of the risk in an effective and equitable way. (O'Reilly again explains 'motivation' in this way: '[t]his means that its allocation to a particular party should have the effect of motivating that party to deal with it in the most effective and efficient way, e.g. can influence magnitude and control the effects of the risk once it has occurred').[246]

---

[241] *Ibid.*

[242] *Engineering Construction Risks*, (eds) THOMPSON, P. A. and PERRY, J. G., 32, n. 61 and 62 respectively; ASHLEY, D. B. *Construction Project Risk Sharing.* Construction Institute, Stanford University, Palo Alto, 1977, Technical Report 220; and PORTER, C. E. Risk Allocation in Construction Contracts. MSc thesis, UMIST, 1981.

[243] PERRY, JOHN G., see n. 25 above, 204–205. Cf PERRY, J. G. and HOARE, D. J. Contracts of the Future, at 87–88 setting out almost identical principles several years earlier.

[244] Volume II, American Society of Civil Engineers, 1979, held in Scottsdale, Arizona, US, 24–26 January. These principles are reproduced with approval by FELLOWS, R. F., *The Management of Risk* (ed. HARLOW, PETER). CIOB, Ascot, 1996, Construction Papers 65, 6, citing PERRY, J. G. and HOARE, D. J. once again Contracts of the Future, 81–97.

[245] O'REILLY, MICHAEL, see n. 234 above, 346.

[246] *Ibid.*

- Where the impact of a risk is small – either in terms of its size relative to other risks or in terms of the party's ability to sustain the consequences of its occurrence – the parties tend to become indifferent to the way it is allocated.

Perry has stated that the first three principles generally governed the NEC drafters' decisions on risk allocation while the last three principles influenced the design of other procedures to try to achieve appropriate motivations for good management.[247] While these were the principles the drafters followed, larger interests in their approach to the work also motivated them. Thus, the

> general philosophy on which . . . [the] NEC is based is that it should serve the long-term interests of the engineering construction industry and its clients, and that this is most likely to be achieved or facilitated by risk allocations and procedures for risk assessment which are equitable.[248]

Risk assessment is an integral part of risk management as described here and the NEC drafters have focused upon risk allocation as part of the risk management process. Risk assessment itself, however, is a highly technical area comprising a wide variety of techniques and concepts which include the following:

- failure mode and effects analysis;
- fault tree analysis and event tree analysis;
- hazard and operability study;
- cost benefit and risk benefit analysis;
- human reliability analysis;
- risk perception techniques;
- sensitivity analysis;
- Monte Carlo simulation; and
- expert systems.[249]

The well-being of the industry itself is a factor that must not be forgotten. It has been referred to as one of the first factors to take into account by one of the NEC Panel members, Max Abrahamson. He introduced it as a factor with this statement:

> In this intense focus of attention upon the distribution of risk between client and contractor there are a number of factors that should be taken into account in deciding contractual arrangements with a view to encouraging co-operation and goodwill between the parties during the currency of the contract.

He then wrote under the heading 'The maintenance of a healthy construction industry':

> The client should bear in mind the need to foster a comprehensive and capable construction industry in order that there remains a pool

---

[247] See n. 25 above, 205.
[248] *Ibid.* 204.
[249] WHITE, DIANA. Application of Systems Thinking to Risk Management: A Review of the Literature. *Management Decision*, 1995, **33** (10), 35–45.

of experienced and financially stable contractors ready for future work. The short term philosophy of driving as hard a bargain as possible on a contract may be counter-productive in creating an atmosphere of hostility which generates an excess of claims and a reluctance to tender for further work.[250]

Thompson and Perry have written that this risk allocation in the NEC is an advance over earlier models or standard forms of contract as it:

- requires the employer to choose a preferred contract strategy which should bring attention to the differences in the allocation of risk between various strategies;
- contains a standard risk allocation between employer and contractor and permits a tailored application of special risks;
- defines a single procedure for compensating the contractor when a risk occurs; and
- is designed to be simpler to read and understand than most other standard forms.[251]

These principles of risk allocation have been applied throughout the NEC and in particular with respect to key risks surrounding insurance, termination, and compensation events.

There are various reasons for the growing interest in risk management that may be put forward,[252] for instance, the interest in business failures in the 1980s and the growth in non-traditional contracting as a result of which the financial sector is also having an impact upon risk allocation. Thus, as knowledge of risk management increases financiers look more closely to see that risks are properly allocated before supporting requests for funding.[253] There are also new approaches in the financial sector.[254] Changing attitudes have also played a part as bodies have become more proactive toward the management of risk. For example, the ICE and the Institution and the Faculty of and the Institute of Actuaries recently embarked on the development of a risk management handbook through a joint working party to evaluate and control risk in major projects.[255]

---

[250] ABRAHAMSON, MAX and CURTIS, BERNARD. Collaborative Risk Distribution for Construction Contracts. *Management and Construction Law*, 8.

[251] THOMPSON, P. A. and PERRY, J. G., see n. 242 above, p. 36.

[252] See O'REILLY, MICHAEL, n. 234 above, 343–344.

[253] See *Allocation of Insurance Related Risks and Costs on Construction Projects*. University of Texas, Austin, Construction Industry Institute, Austin, 1993, p. 1.

[254] CAPPER, PROFESSOR PHILLIP, see n. 118 above, 11. Cf John Uff QC: '[m]odern funding arrangements with their high interest charges and risk premiums are, less flexible [than standard forms] ...'. Overview: The Place of Management in Construction. *Management and Construction Law*, 23.

[255] The Institution of Civil Engineers and the Faculty and Institute of Actuaries. *Risk Analysis and Management for Projects*. Thomas Telford, London, 1998. See also Construction Industry Institute. *Allocation of Insurance Related Risks and Costs on Construction Projects*. University of Texas, Austin, 1993, p. 1 and KANGARI, R. Risk Management Perceptions and Trends of US Construction. *Journal of Construction Engineering and Management*, 1995, **121**, 422–42 who have also noted the change in attitudes.

Contracting practices are also better today than previously.[256] There is new found attention being paid to cost-to-benefit ratios.[257] This was confirmed in a 1997 survey that suggested increasing numbers of small construction projects were using risk management to cut costs and reduce mistakes.[258] Changing attitudes toward the relationship between risk and project management may also be counted[259] if only because 'researchers in construction management have latched on to risk as providing a framework which is conceptually elegant and intellectually satisfying'.[260] Lastly, the Latham Report has put risk on the political agenda and at the forefront of much of the general debate as well.[261] David Greenwood and Rudi Klein write that:

> [t]he underlying theme of the Latham Report is that current practices are open to criticism on three counts: that the allocation of risks is normally considered too little and too late; that risks are in many cases improperly allocated; and that some of the risks imposed are totally unacceptable and unnecessary.[262]

These commentators go on to outline some of the reasons for poor payment practices in the construction industry including contract terms that inhibit payment (e.g. retention, set-off, and pay-when-paid); many creditors being outside the direct chain of payment; and risks of insolvency. The point was underscored again in the Latham Report when it recommended that the most effective form of contract should include a 'choice of allocation of risks, to be decided as appropriate to each project but then allocated to the party best able to manage, estimate and carry the risk'.[263] Several of Latham's assumptions for a modern contract are satisfied with regard to the risk allocation provisions in the NEC.[264]

There are four common methods of dealing with risk: avoidance, abatement, retention and transfer.[265] Risk management operates on

---

[256] See DERING, C. and CAPPER, PROFESSOR PHILLIP, n. 118 above.

[257] SMITH, ROBERT J., see n. 97 above, 564.

[258] See SAVVAS, ANTONY. Risk is Factor for Smaller Projects. *Contract Journal*, 3 September 1997, 5.

[259] See e.g. CHEUNG, SAI ON. Risk Allocation: An Essential Tool for Construction Project Management. *Journal of Construction Procurement*, 1997, **3** (1), 16–27; FLANAGAN, R. and NORMAN, G. *Risk Management and Construction*; and more generally OXLEY, R. and POSKITT, J. *Management Techniques Applied to the Construction Industry*, 5th edn. Blackwell Science, Boston, 1996.

[260] O'REILLY, MICHAEL, see n. 234 above, 343–344.

[261] GREENWOOD, DAVID and KLEIN, RUDI. Security of Payment in the Light of the Latham Report: An Opportunity to Remove Unacceptable Risks? *Construction Law Journal*, 1995, **11**, 255.

[262] GREENWOOD, DAVID and KLEIN, RUDI, see n. 261 above, 255.

[263] Latham Report, paragraph 5.18(6), 37.

[264] See Latham Report, paragraph 5.18(2), (6), (7) and (12), 37.

[265] SMITH, ROBERT J. 550 citing, n. 5, MASON G. E. *A Quantitative Risk Management Approach to Selection of Construction Contract Provisions*. University of Texas at Austin, The Construction Institute, Austin; Department of Civil Engineering, Stanford

several levels under the NEC. At one level it operates in the choice of main option or contract strategy. It also operates through the choices the employer makes in part one of the Contract Data and the secondary option clauses. The main options all allocate risk differently across a general spectrum. At one end of the spectrum, under main options A and B, the financial risk is borne largely by the contractor. This follows from the prices being agreed between the parties save otherwise, e.g. compensation events. Under main options C and D, the target contracts, the financial risks are shared between the parties in an agreed proportion. Under main options E and F, cost reimbursable contracts, the financial risk is assumed disproportionately by the employer. Each of the options offers incentives.[266] The incentives are offered for agreeing to the allocation of risk in the chosen proportions. This approach stands apart from comments of those who are critical of incentive options in existing forms.

> The incentives in the typical modern contract are wrong: contractors are penalized (i.e. get no benefit) for doing good work and are given incentives to do poor work. Much of this is due to the terms of engagement to which people are nonetheless willing to subscribe.[267]

Similarly, in the NEDO report *Faster Building for Industry*:

> [i]t is not the form of contract which primarily determines whether targets are met, but the attitudes of the parties, to which the form of contract may contribute. The standard form of contract offers penalties for delays but not incentives for speed. Industry and customer should look for ways of sharing the benefits for improved performance.[268]

The same and associated risks have also been addressed in the following way:

University, Palo Alto, April 1973, Technical Report 173, 26–61. It may be noted that Mason was considered in a review of the literature on risk by ERIKSON, C. A. Risk Sharing in Construction Contracts. PhD dissertation, University of Illinois, 1979 which in turn influenced Martin Barnes.

[266] Cf clause 52 of GC/Works/1 3rd which entitles the contractor to make recommendations and proposals to reduce the cost of the work or maintenance of the project and which could entitle the contractor to 50% of any savings.

[267] PRIESTLEY, CLIVE. *British Construction: In Pursuit of Excellence.* A Report to Sir Christopher Foster, Chairman of the Construction Industry Sector Group. Business Round Table, London, February 1994, p. 44 and citing HOKE, T. and SPACKMAN, C. J., unpublished correspondence.

[268] National Economic Development Office. *Faster Building for Industry.* HMSO, London, 1983, p. 4. See generally on the economic basis for and importance of incentives LAFFONT, JEAN-JACQUES and TIROLE, JEAN. *A Theory of Incentives in Procurement and Regulation.* MIT Press, Cambridge, Mass, 1993; and in construction ABU-HIJLEH, S. F. and IBBS, C. W. Schedule-based Construction Incentives. *Journal of Construction Engineering and Management,* 1989, **115**, 430–433; and STUKHART, G. Contractual Incentives. *Journal of Construction Engineering and Management,* 1984, **110**, 34–42.

Every risk has an associated price – visible or hidden. Visible costs appear in project bids as contingency or insurance cost and can be compared. Onerous contract conditions promote hidden costs. Hidden costs (in terms of time and money) ... include: (a) the cost of restricted bid competition; (b) the cost of increased claims/ disputes; (c) the cost of replacing a lesser quality contractor who is more likely to unknowingly accept a grossly inequitable risk allocation; and (d) the cost of harbouring an adversarial owner-contractor relationship in terms of final product quality, expeditious change order processing, reputation, and ultimate project income.[269]

By comparison it may be noted that FIDIC too has moved toward greater recognition of the role of conditions in the allocation of risk and according to John Bowcock:

[a]n important conclusion which is emerging from the work done by the task group to date is that the text of the conditions for a particular contract arises primarily from the allocation of risk rather than from the physical type of works. It is therefore probable that the new books will be structured around the allocation of risk.

This has in fact taken place with the release of the new suite of contracts.[270]

One of the most significant attenuations to the agreed allocation of risk coming out of the NEC is its use of a 'compensation event procedure'. The compensation event procedure plays a central role in reallocating risks, essentially time and cost risks, in certain cases. A transparent means of addressing the probable cases, which the NEC has set out as compensation events, is an important aspect of the form, and operates almost as if it were a risk register. A 'risk register' is a means of recording and controlling the risk management process. In its simplest form it will describe the risk and deal with possible risk reduction or mitigation measures. At one level the risks are those stipulated and they are dealt with in one regard by the compensation event procedures.[271] Recognition that such cases as those identified as compensation events are very likely to arise is a mature or prudent approach when surveys suggest, for example, that a large percentage of all projects finish over budget[272] and late. Thus the Construction Clients' Forum has indicated that 58% of

[269] ASHLEY, DAVID B. *et al. The Impact of Risk Allocation and Equity in Construction Contracts: An Overview of Indemnification, Consequential Damages, Differing Conditions & Delay Claims, A Report to the Construction Industry Institute.* The University of Texas, Austin, November 1988, pp. ii–iii.

[270] BOWCOCK, JOHN, see n. 64 above, 8–9.

[271] See GODFREY, PATRICK S. and HALCROW, SIR WILLIAM AND PARTNERS LTD. *Control of Risk A Guide to the Systematic Management of Risk from Construction.* CIRIA, London, 1996, 42–44; see also WILLIAMS, T. M. Using a Risk Register to Integrate Risk Management in Project Definition. *International Journal of Project Management*, February 1994, 17–22.

[272] Gallup, see n. 122 above, 27.

clients reported their projects were late, 32% said the work was over budget and 90% reported defects.[273]

Perry and Hoare argue that the NEC will not only reduce individual risks but *total risk* also. This statement is made on two grounds.

> Firstly that part of the total risk arises from the wrong choice of contract strategy. Secondly, that another part of the total risk arises from unfamiliarity with a particular standard form and from misunderstanding and misinterpretation of the text, often exacerbated by substantial amendment to a standard form in an attempt to apply it to specific situations or circumstances for which it was not designed.[274]

In summary, risk is key to the design and successful use of the NEC. According to one of the NEC's proponents, Andrew Baird,[275] users of the NEC gain a better understanding of the role of contract conditions, risk allocation and responsibility and contract strategy than under other forms of procurement.[276] In practice early research into the use of the form has tended to confirm this although it has also suggested that clients are still not fully utilizing all of the main options available to them to achieve their objectives.[277] These are of course very important goals if they can be established.

The role of co-operation at law and the NEC

The role of co-operation in the NEC is arguably the most important principle underlying the operation of the contract system and the one with potentially the most profound implications for it as a whole. Classical contract theory assumes the parties perform their contracts as agreed. Parties are contractually bound to perform according to the terms of the contract. Each party may insist upon their rights subject only to the law. There is no additional obligation or duty to co-operate in the performance in classical contract theory. However, in practice, the courts have insinuated duties to co-operate into parties' agreements through a variety of devices including the general rules of interpretation of documents and implication of terms or gap fillers. Leaving aside general rules of interpretation, courts will enforce not just the terms parties have expressly

---

[273] See RIDOUT, GRAHAM. Clients Frustrated at Industry Performance. *Contract Journal*, 14 April 1999, 1. In Gallup at 27 respondents said approximately 30% of all projects finish over budget and 31% of all projects finish late.

[274] PERRY, J. G. and HOARE, D. J., see n. 119 above, 85.

[275] Mr Baird is a consultant to Eskom, a large South African company and the world's fifth largest electrical utility, and a member of the NEC panel. Eskom was one of the first clients to use extensively the NEC outside of the United Kingdom. Eskom's use of the NEC has fostered the development of both the short contract and the maintenance forms of contract in the NEC.

[276] BAIRD, ANDREW. The New Engineering Contract, see n. 38 above, 116.

[277] See BROOME, JON C. and PERRY, JOHN G. Experiences of the Use of the New Engineering Contract. *Engineering, Construction and Architectural Management*, 1995 **2** (4), 275, 284.

agreed to but also the terms that can logically be implied from those express terms.[278] Logic, however, is not a strict limiting factor and there are many other cases where the law admits of and invokes implied terms. Glanville Williams wrote: '[j]udges are accustomed to read into documents and transactions many terms that are not logically implied in them'. Williams gives examples from areas of the law including the sale of goods, landlord and tenant, and master and servant.[279]

'Implied terms' is the nomenclature used here although it 'covers a number of dissimilar notions'[280] According to Edwin W. Patterson, other terms used have included 'implied conditions', 'constructive conditions', 'conditions implied in law', and 'conditions implied-in-fact'.[281] Patterson also deserves credit for a very early use of the term 'gap filler' which has become synonymous with implied terms. 'Constructive conditions of exchange are gap-fillers; they operate in the absence of language in the contracts which contradicts the construction'.[282] The terms 'gap fillers' and 'default rules' are used synonymously with implied terms here. Lately, Lord Steyn has written in this regard that: '[o]ften the expectations of the parties would be defeated if a term were not implied, e.g. sometimes a contract simply will not work unless a particular duty to co-operate is implied ... Such terms operate as default rules'.[283] A. L. Corbin, in a very early article, noted courts 'supply the gap and allocate the risk of loss in accordance with reason'.[284]

Implied terms
One conventional analysis of implied terms proceeds by classifying terms according to whether they are implied by custom, law, or for some other reason.[285] Whilst this is the 'conventional' analysis it is remarkable upon

---

[278] See e.g. for cases on the distinction between implication of terms versus interpretation of express terms: *Aspdin* v. *Austin* (1844) 5 QB 671; *Re Cadogan & Hans Place Estate Ltd, Ex p Willis* (1895) 11 TLR 477, CA; *Williams* v. *Burrell* (1845) 1 CB 402; 14 LJCP 98; 135 ER 596; and *A E Farr Ltd* v. *The Admiralty* [1953] 2 All ER 512, [1953] 1 WLR 965.

[279] WILLIAMS, GLANVILLE. Language and the Law-IV. *Law Quarterly Review*, 1945, **61**, 384, 398.

[280] *Halsbury's Laws of England*, 4th edn reissue, vol. 9(1), paragraph 778.

[281] PATTERSON, EDWIN W. Constructive Conditions in Contract. *Columbia Law Review*, 1942, **42**, 903–907.

[282] *Ibid.*, 913.

[283] LORD STEYN. Contract Law: Fulfilling the Reasonable Expectations of Honest Men. *Law Quarterly Review*, 1997, **113**, 441–442.

[284] CORBIN, A. L. Recent Developments in the Law of Contracts. *Harvard Law Review*, 1937, **50**, 465 noting courts '... supply the gap and allocate the risk of loss in accordance with reason'.

[285] *Halsbury's Laws of England*, 4th edn reissue, vol. 9(1), paragraph 778ff. The Halsbury classification is also adopted in *Luxor (Eastbourne) Ltd* v. *Cooper* [1941] AC 108 at 137, HL, and was endorsed lately in *Scally* v. *Southern Health and Social Services Board* [1992] 1 AC 294, [1991] 4 All ER 563, HL. The three-fold classification has been critiqued by PHANG, A. Implied Terms in English Law – Some Recent Developments. *Journal of Business Law*, 1993, 242. Cf the four-fold classification of Justice Byrne in Implied Terms in Construction. *Building and Construction Law*, 1995, **11**, 6.

closer examination how seriously this analysis is also questioned. Thus, in *Halsbury's*, it is stated:

> [i]t would be misleading to think of the implication of terms simply on the basis of an inquiry into the intention of the parties in a particular case. Over the course of time, there has been a convenient tendency to group those terms which are likely to be imported by reason of the particular *relationship* between the parties ... the real issue in any particular case may be into what classification the contract in question falls; the question may therefore become one of the *relationship* of the parties rather than their intention.[286]

The particular relationships are well known; for instance, in the sale of goods, employment, or construction. The attention given to the nature of the relationship between the parties for deciding which terms will be implied is wholly consistent with the importance attributed to relationships[287] in a theoretical sense here.[288] The point was made by Lord Denning some 20 years ago in *Shell UK Ltd* v. *Lostock Garage Ltd*.[289] Lord Denning spoke of two categories of implied terms: a first category that 'comprehends all those relationships which are of common occurrence'; and a second category made up simply of 'those cases which are not within the first category'.[290] The importance of Lord Denning's categories for present purposes is his inclusion of the 'contractor for building works' in a relationship of common occurrence. It is interesting that Lord Denning did not describe a second party in this respect as he did in setting out his other relationship examples, e.g. seller and buyer, owner and hirer. While it would thus seem logical to 'imply' the employer as the other party in the relationship there is no reason that it could not also be

---

[286] *Halsbury's Laws of England*, 4th edn reissue, vol. 9(1), paragraph 779 (emphasis added and footnotes omitted); others agree: see e.g. COOTE, B. Contract Formation and the Implication of Terms. *Journal of Contract Law*, 1993, **6**, 51.

[287] See generally KLIEM, RALPH I. and LUDIN, IRWIN, S. *The People Side of Project Management.* Gower, Aldershot, 1995.

[288] Three decisions are referred to in support in *Halsbury's Laws of England*, 4th edn reissue, vol. 9(1), paragraph 779, n. 4: *Lister* v. *Romford Ice and Cold Storage Co Ltd* [1957] AC 555 at 576, [1957] 1 All ER 125 at 132, HL, per Viscount Simonds; *Morgan* v. *Ravey* (1861) 6 H & N 265; and *Re Chappell, ex parte Ford* (1885) 16 QBD 305 at 307, CA, per Lord Esher MR. Similarly, CARTER, J. W. and FURMSTON, M. P. Good Faith and Fairness in the Negotiation of Contracts Part II. *Journal of Contract Law*, 1995, **8**, 93, 116 and ns. 148 and 150 make the same point with reference to Australian authority; namely *Hospital Products Ltd* v. *United States Surgical Corp* (1984) 156 CLR 41; and *Shepherd* v. *Felt and Textiles of Australia Ltd* (1931) 45 CLR 359: '[i]t is strongly arguable that these are terms implied in law from the nature of the relation rather than terms implied in fact to make the particular agreements work'. See also *Robb* v. *Green* [1895] 2 QB 1; and *House of Spring Gardens Ltd and Ors* v. *Point Blank Ltd* [1984] IR 611.

[289] *Shell UK Ltd* v. *Lostock Garage Ltd* [1977] 1 All ER 481, [1976] 1 WLR 1187, CA.

[290] *Shell UK Ltd* v. *Lostock Garage Ltd* [1977] 1 All ER 481 at 487–488, [1976] 1 WLR 1187 at 1196–1197, CA, per Lord Denning MR.

said to extend to the contractor and subcontractor relationship as well. In relationships in Lord Denning's first category the implied terms 'are not founded on the intention of the parties, actual or presumed, but on more general considerations'.[291] Conversely, in relationships in the second category the terms are implied on the basis of imputed intention.

Returning to *Halsbury's* classification of implied terms, after consideration of both terms implied by custom and terms implied by law, this conclusion is made:

> The conclusion would appear to be that terms implied by law are not happily described as 'implied terms': they are rather duties which (frequently subject to a contrary intention) are imposed by the law on the parties to particular types of contract. In deciding whether to create such duties, the courts tend to look, not to the intention of the parties, but to considerations of public policy.[292]

Thus, it has been stated that the move from implying terms on the basis of intention to implying terms on the basis of the *relationship* or common practice results in implication as a matter or rule of law.[293] Glanville Williams has written in this regard:

> it is a matter of taste whether [certain] implied terms ... be styled implied terms or rules of law. They are in fact merely rules of law that apply in the absence of an expression of contrary intent: whether we choose to call them implied terms or not is simply a matter of terminology.[294]

Lord Tucker in *Lister* v. *Romford Ice and Cold Storage Co Ltd* has said that terms are implied at law because 'they have become attached in the course of time to certain classes of contractual relationships...'.[295] Many commentators have long since made this point that intent is but a fiction.[296] In the construction context the use of implied terms to found agreement has been approved and disapproved by commentators. Thus the Honourable Mr Justice Byrne strongly critiques the intrusion of the courts in this practice.[297] Perhaps of more interest is Justice Byrne's fear

---

[291] *Shell UK Ltd* v. *Lostock Garage Ltd* [1977] 1 All ER 481 at 487, [1976] 1 WLR 1187 at 1196, CA, per Lord Denning MR citations omitted.

[292] *Halsbury's Laws of England*, 4th edn reissue, vol. 9(1), paragraph 781 (n. omitted).

[293] *Halsbury's Laws of England*, 4th edn reissue, vol. 9(1), paragraph 781, text to n. 36–38.

[294] WILLIAMS, GLANVILLE, see n. 279 above, 404 (ns. omitted).

[295] Lord Tucker in *Lister* v. *Romford Ice and Cold Storage Co Ltd* [1957] AC 555, HL, at 594.

[296] The history of the use of the *fiction* of intent as a guise for judicial construction is set out by FARNSWORTH, E. A. Disputes over Omissions in Contracts. *Columbia Law Review*, 1968, **68**, 862ff with examples and references to other leading commentators including: WILLIAMS, GLANVILLE, see n. 279 above, 401; CORBIN, A. L. Conditions in the Law of Contract. *Yale Law Journal*, 1919, **28**, 743–744; and FULLER, LON. Legal Fictions. *Illinois Law Review*, 1930, 369.

[297] The Hon. Mr Justice Byrne, 6.

that it is so widespread that the practice is now giving way to acceptance that the law itself has a role to play in both the formation and content of commercial contracts.[298] If one accepts this position, and indeed there is support for the routine implication of a wide variety of terms in construction contracts, then it would seem that it is less the traditional tests that govern than broader questions of policy.

John Redmond, on the other hand, takes the position that the practice shows 'the creativity of the courts in introducing implied terms into contracts, whilst pretending that they are merely discovering terms that were there all the time'.[299] Commenting on the implied duty to warn in two cases[300] Redmond states:

> it is difficult to accept that the duty to warn was in reality necessary[301] for the contract to work. After all in both cases the buildings were built, albeit defectively. The implied term was really not necessary to achieve a building but sensibly distribute the risk and liability to those who the judge felt truly responsible.[302]

Thus, for Redmond, the implied term serves as another risk allocation tool that the courts can use, albeit still maintaining the underlying reasonableness that is so closely associated with the practice.[303]

There are other reasons and bases upon which terms are implied. It is a process of development and reflects both values and the historical context. Just over 100 years ago Justice Holmes set forth a rationale in his view which still has the ring of truth to it today.

> You can always imply a condition in a contract. But why do you imply it? It is because of some belief as to the practice of the community or of a class, or because of some opinion as to policy, or in short, because of some attitude of yours as a matter not capable of exact quantitative measurement, and therefore not capable of founding exact logical conclusion.[304]

Implication may also be understood from an historical perspective. John Uff QC has stated:

> The conclusion is inescapable from the traditional wording of these contracts [referring to present day United Kingdom standard forms]

---

[298] The Hon. Mr Justice Byrne, 6, 7.

[299] REDMOND, JOHN. Creative Implication: Implied Terms in Construction Contracts. A paper given to the Society of Construction Law in London on 4 July 1995.

[300] *Equitable Debenture Assets Corpn Ltd* v. *William Moss Group Ltd* (1984) 2 Con LR 1; *Victoria University of Manchester* v. *Hugh Wilson & Lewis Womersley* (*a firm*) (1984) 2 Con LR 43.

[301] Recalling the necessity argument for implying terms from *The Moorcock* (1889) 14 PD 64, CA.

[302] REDMOND, JOHN, see n. 299, above, 6.

[303] *Ibid.* Redmond draws upon other commentators with a similar view and cites both WILSON, STEVE and RUTHERFORD, LESLIE from Design Defects in Building Contracts: a Contractor's Duty to Warn. *Construction Law Journal*, 1994, **10**, 6.

[304] HOLMES, JUSTICE O. W. The Path of the Law, *Harvard Law Review*, 1897, **10**, 466.

that the lawyers commissioned to draft the early contracts were probably Chancery pleaders, with the experience of leases but without any knowledge of the practical or commercial problems and situations on a building site with which, of course, the building contracts should have been concerned to deal. The result is that certain critically important problem areas concerned with price have been traditionally ignored by the draftsmen and so left for implication by law.[305]

Turning from this background and these general considerations with regard to the first two bases upon which terms are implied, namely custom and law, it falls to consider the third basis for implication as it is in this category that discussion of the subject of co-operation itself is often found.

The subject of co-operation and what duties may arise in this regard through the implication of terms is normally discussed under two headings: co-operation; and not to prevent completion (or perform-ance).[306] These two headings are sometimes discussed in relation to what is called a *positive* duty and a *negative* duty in English case law. Samuel J. Stoljar writes that the:

> basic requirement of co-operation must be stated in two parts. (1) Reduced to its lowest terms, the general duty to co-operate becomes but a duty not to prevent or hinder the occurrence of an express condition precedent upon which the performance of the promisor depends ... (2) On the other hand, the requirement of co-operation may turn into a distinctly positive duty, that is a duty to take all such necessary or additional steps in the performance of the contract that will either materially assist the other party or will generally contribute to the full realization of the bargain.[307]

Hudson's refers to two duties as well one of which is referred to as the 'prevention principle' and later to both the 'prevention principle' and 'co-operation' as implied terms.[308] *Keating on Building Contracts* discusses

---

[305]   UFF, JOHN. Control of Disputes within the Contract Framework. *Future Directions in Construction Law.* Proceedings of the Fifth Annual Conference of the Centre of Construction Law and Management. King's College, London, 1992.

[306]   PATTERSON, EDWIN W., 929, n. 281 gives himself credit for this distinction, referring to his earlier works: *Cases on Contracts II*, 1935, 266, Constructive Conditions of Cooperation or Non-Prevention: Judicial Freedom of Implying Conditions in Contracts. *Recueil d'Etudes sur les Sources du Droit en l'Honneur de Francois Geny.* Librairie du Recueil Sirey, Paris, 1935, vol. 2, 393; cf STOLJAR, SAMUEL J. Prevention and Co-operation in the Law of Contract. *Canadian Bar Review*, 1953, **31**, 231, n. 3. Others too have adopted the distinction e.g. MAY, SIR ANTHONY. *Keating on Building Contracts*, 6th edn. Sweet & Maxwell, London, 1995, pp. 52–56.

[307]   STOLJAR, SAMUEL J. *ibid.*, 231.

[308]   *Hudson's Building and Engineering Contracts* (ed. WALLACE, IAN DUNCAN), 11th edn. Sweet and Maxwell, London, 1994, vol. 1, p. 96 and later at pp. 568–569.

these implied terms under two headings: 'co-operation' and 'not to prevent completion'.[309] Similar references to positive and negative duties can also be found in American case law and thus *Williston on Contracts* provides in part:

> Where the necessary event is peculiarly within the power of the promisee, the obligation of the promisor is conditional on the promisee's bringing the event to pass; and if the contract is bilateral there is an implied obligation on the part of the promisee that he will bring the event to pass. Thus, wherever the cooperation of the promisee is necessary for the performance of the promise, there is a condition implied in fact that the cooperation will be given, and if the contract is bilateral there is an obligation to give it.[310]

One of the clearest articulations of the different foundations for these two duties is given in *Mona Oil Equipment & Supply Co Ltd* v. *Rhodesia Railways Ltd.*[311] In the *Mona Oil* case Mr Justice Devlin referred specifically to two principles: co-operation and prevention.

> *Mackay* v. *Dick* ... contains two separate and independent propositions, one enunciated by Lord Blackburn, and the other by Lord Watson, and there is a danger of misunderstanding them if, as in the headnote to the case, they are combined into one ... Lord Blackburn says nothing about prevention. The principle he enunciates may be put succinctly, as Viscount Simon, LC put it in *Luxor* (*Eastbourne*) v. *Cooper* ... saying that where co-operation is necessary, it is implied that it is forthcoming ... The second proposition, based on the opinion of Lord Watson, advances a stage further and gives the plaintiff in appropriate cases an additional form of relief. If the breach of the implied term prevents the plaintiff from performing a condition binding on him, he is to be taken as having fulfilled that condition, and, if the condition is one on which his right to payment depends, he may sue for damages. That these propositions are distinct is shown by the fact that Lord Blackburn's reasoning does not involve the second at all. His construction of the contract does not require it ... Lord Watson ... proceeded on a different construction of the contract and so invoked the principle I have stated. He rested it on well established doctrine ... and not on any implication in the contract. The formulation of the implied term in cases of this class depends, in my judgment, on the necessity for co-operation. Without co-operation the contract would lack business

---

[309] *Keating on Building Contracts* (ed. MAY, THE RIGHT HON. SIR ANTHONY), 6th edn. Sweet and Maxwell, London, 1995, pp. 52–56.

[310] *Williston on Contracts*, 3rd edn, vol. 6, section 887: WILLISTON, SAMUEL. *Williston on Contracts: A Treatise on the Law of Contracts*, 3rd edn by JAEGER, WALTER H. E. Baker, Voorhisy, Mount Kisio, 1957–1978.

[311] *Mona Oil Equipment & Supply Co Ltd* v. *Rhodesia Railways Ltd* [1949] 1 All ER 1014 (KB).

efficacy, and this class of case is, therefore, simply an exemplification of the general principle ... I can think of no term that can properly be implied other than one based on the necessity for co-operation. It is, no doubt, true that every business contract depends for its smooth working on co-operation, but in the ordinary business contract, and apart, of course, from express terms, the law can enforce co-operation only in a limited degree to the extent that it is necessary to make the contract workable. For any higher degree of co-operation the parties must rely on the desire that both of them usually have that the business should get done.[312]

According to Justice Devlin the 'co-operative' principle would be implied when necessary; but not the 'preventive' principle which instead could be supported by reference to the judgment given and authorities cited by McCardie J in *Colley* v. *Overseas Exporters*.[313] Hence prevention was a matter of law in Justice Devlin's view.

J. F. Burrows varies the above two-fold classification and prefers to examine co-operation under two broad headings: interference with enjoyment of subject matter, and interference with performance of promises.[314] With regard to this second head Burrows adopts a further subdivision as follows:

[t]he cases will be classified according to whether party B is blamed for having done a positive act obstructing party A, or whether he is being blamed for sitting back and not actively helping. The distinction, then, is between a duty not positively to obstruct and a duty to co-operate actively.[315]

Burrows duty not to obstruct is examined both under the heading of 'total prevention' as well as 'mere hindrance'. Relying upon this classification building contract cases would be more likely to arise under the second heading.

---

[312] *Mona Oil Equipment & Supply Co Ltd* v. *Rhodesia Railways Ltd* [1949] 1 All ER 1014, 1017–1018 (KB) per Mr Justice Devlin.

[313] *Colley* v. *Overseas Exporters* [1921] 3 KB 302 (KB) distinguished *Mackay* v. *Dick* (1881) 6 App Cas 251, HL, on the basis that it was decided under Scottish law and before passage of the Sale of Goods Act 1893. Mr Justice McCardie: 'Although, as I have said, *Mackay* v. *Dick* ... turned on Scotch law yet I think that that principle is equally well settled in English law. It is frequently asserted in well-known text books based on English law [after referring to several texts continued] ... the principle moreover has been frequently applied by the Courts and is illustrated by *Braithwaite* v. *Foreign Hardwood Co* ... *Sprague* v. *Booth* ... [and] *Kleinert* v. *Abosso Gold Mining Co* ... (at 308–309). See generally GUEST, PROFESSOR A. G., *Benjamin's Sale of Goods*, 5th edn., Sweet & Maxwell, London, 1997.

[314] BURROWS, J. F. Contractual Co-operation and the Implied Term. *Modern Law Review*, 1968, **31**, 390.

[315] *Ibid.*

Prevention
Lord Asquith, from *William Cory & Son Ltd* v. *London Corporation*, is often credited with one of the leading statements of what has occasionally been shortened and referred to as the 'prevention principle':

> The claimants argue that it is an implied term of every, or almost every, contract between A and B ... that A shall not prevent or disable B from performing the contract and vice versa ... In general, no doubt, it is true that a term is necessarily implied in any contract whose other terms do not repel the implication, that neither party shall prevent the other from performing it, and that a party so preventing the other is guilty of a breach.[316]

The issue of whether the prevention amounts to a breach of contract is also assumed for example in *Stirling* v. *Maitland and Boyd*.[317] The *Stirling* case involves a somewhat different obligation to maintain conditions within one's control; thus Cockburn CJ said:

> If a party enters into an arrangement which can only take effect by the continuance of a certain existing state of circumstances, there is an implied engagement on his part that he shall do nothing of his own motion to put an end to that state of circumstances under which alone the arrangement can be operative.[318]

Others who have commented upon the issue include Vaughan Williams LJ in *Barque Quilpué Ltd* v. *Brown* who said: 'in this contract, as in every other, there is an implied contract by each party that he will not do anything to prevent the other party from performing the contract or to delay him in performing it';[319] Lord Watson in *Sailing Ship Blairmore Co Ltd* v. *Macredie* who said: '[t]he rule of law applicable to contracts is that neither of the parties can by his own act or default defeat the obligations which he has undertaken to fulfil, or escape those obligations by offering to the other party an indemnity which is not that which the other party contracted to accept';[320] and Griffiths CJ in *Marshall and anor* v. *Colonial Bank of Australia* who said: 'all contractual relations impose upon the parties a mutual obligation that neither shall do anything which is calculated to hamper the other in performance of the contract on his part'.[321]

---

[316] *William Cory & Son Ltd* v. *London Corporation* [1951] 2 KB 476 at 484, [1951] 2 All ER 85 at 88, CA, per Lord Asquith.

[317] *Stirling* v. *Maitland and Boyd* (1864) 5 B & S (Eng) 840, 852.

[318] *Stirling* v. *Maitland and Boyd* (1864) 5 B & S (Eng) 840, 852.

[319] VAUGHAN WILLIAMS LJ in *Barque Quilpué Ltd* v. *Brown* [1904] 2 KB 264 at 271–272, CA.

[320] Lord Watson in *Sailing Ship Blairmore Co Ltd* v. *Macredie* [1898] AC 593 at 670–608, HL.

[321] *Marshall and anor* v. *Colonial Bank of Australia* (1903–1904) 1 CLR 632 at 647 per Griffiths C. J.

Both Patterson and Stoljar examine the early cases[322] upon which the implied duty of prevention rests. Stoljar is the more critical of the two commentators with regard to the foundation for the duty: '[i]t will ... be shown that these views [in the early decisions] are not altogether true and are perhaps based on too narrow an interpretation of the earlier decisions'. It may be noted that many of the early decisions involve penal bonds. In contrast to some of these early decisions, however, a much stronger basis for the principle can be seen in a series of early building cases.[323] Stoljar states that the:

> modern theory of prevention stems from another line of sixteenth and seventeenth century decisions dealing with the lessor-lessee relation in what were the earliest examples of building leases ... which were later to be neatly summarized by Comyns and which thus became the starting-point for subsequent development.[324]

The 'building cases' were one of five categories of cases or relationships that Stoljar looked at and that also included commission cases, employment cases, notice cases, and sale of goods cases. Among the building cases or examples that Stoljar lists there are the failures of a building owner to give immediate possession of the building site;[325] to supply requisite plans[326] or materials[327] in time; or the owner's unjustifiable interference in the course of construction.[328]

A similar rule has been discerned by Nagla Nassar in cases involving international arbitrations.[329] Nassar, who has undertaken a major study into long-term international commercial transactions focusing in particular on arbitration awards,[330] *Sanctity of Contracts Revisited: A Study in the Theory and Practice of Long-Term International Commercial Transactions*, has concluded that in one:

> category of cases where implementation of the contract has already commenced the party refusing to cooperate in the implementation of

---

[322] PATTERSON, EDWIN W., 931; and STOLJAR, SAMUEL J., 231 – see n. 306 above.

[323] STOLJAR, SAMUEL J. 234, n. 11.

[324] *Ibid.*, 236–237 (ns. omitted).

[325] *Ibid.*, 237, n. 27 citing *Holme* v. *Guppy* (1838) 3 M & W 387. See also *Lodder* v. *Slowey* [1904] AC 442, HL; and *Amalgamated Building Contractors* v. *Waltham Cross UDC* [1952] 2 All ER 452, CA.

[326] *Ibid.*, 238, n. 27 citing *Roberts* v. *Bury Improvement Commissioners* (1870) LR 5 CP 310.

[327] *Ibid.*, 238, n. 28 citing *Macintosh* v. *The Midland Counties Rly Co* (1845) 14 M & W 387 and *Holme* v. *Guppy* (1838) 3 M & W 387.

[328] *Ibid.*, 238 citing *Russel* v. *Da Bandeira* (1862) 13 CBNS 149.

[329] NASSAR, NAGLA. *Sanctity of Contracts Revisited: A Study in the Theory and Practice of Long-Term International Commercial Transactions*. Martinus Nijhoff Publishers, Dordrecht, 1994.

[330] ICC award in case 4761 of 1987 (1987) 114 JD Int's (Clunet) 1012, 1016–1017; and also appearing in an English translation at *International Construction Law Review*, 1989, 334.

the contract at issue has been held to be in breach of that contract. One is expected to use his best efforts to carry out the contractual project, and not to interfere with the contractual environment in a way that may hinder performance.[331]

Cases involving prevention may also be referred to, thus Nassar once again writes:

> Disputes involving obstruction of performance shed even more light on the extent to which cooperation is required. Contracting parties are required to refrain from any conduct that would obstruct the contract's implementation under two factual scenarios. Included under the first category are cases where the non-cooperative conduct impedes the commencement of the contractual project[332]... The second category of cases comprises instances where the implementation of the contract has already commenced ... In these and other cases,[333] the party refusing to cooperate in the implementation of the contract at issue has been held to be in breach of that contract. One is expected to use his best efforts to carry out the contractual project, and not to interfere with the contractual environment in a way that may hinder performance.[334]

Thus, both doctrine and jurisprudence on prevention provide considerable guidance on construing one aspect of the duty of co-operation. The second aspect of co-operation in a positive sense may now be turned to.

Co-operation

The classic statement of the requirement for co-operation in contracting comes from Lord Blackburn in *MacKay* v. *Dick*:

> I think I may safely say, as a general rule, that where in a written contract it appears that both parties have agreed that something shall be done, which cannot effectually be done unless both concur in doing it, the construction of the contract is that each agrees to do all that is necessary to be done on his part for the carrying out of that thing, though there may be no express words to that effect. What is the part of each must depend on the circumstances.[335]

Another case, *Hamlyn & Co* v. *Wood & Co* held that the question of whether in any situation an implication ought to be made must depend on the particular facts of the case, and that the construction of one contract in this respect affords little or no guidance for the construction of another.[336]

---

[331] NASSAR, see n. 329 above, 162, ns. 62, 63, and 64, case citations omitted.

[332] NASSAR, see n. 329 above, 162, n. 59 citing ICC award in case no 6230, *Subcontractor (UK)* v. *Main Contractor (Austria)* (1992) 17 Yearbook Comm Arb 164, 169.

[333] NASSAR, see n. 329 above, 162, n. 64, case citations omitted.

[334] NASSAR, see n. 329 above, 162.

[335] *MacKay* v. *Dick* (1881) 6 App Cas 251 at 263, HL.

[336] *Hamlyn & Co* v. *Wood & Co* [1891] 2 QB 488; [1891–94] All ER Rep 168, CA.

It has also been stated in *obiter*, that there 'is, of course, no general rule that terms cannot be implied into a standard form contract. The same principles apply to standard form contracts as they do to negotiated contracts.[337] On this authority an argument can be made that similar considerations apply when construing the NEC.

Several observations must be made. *MacKay* v. *Dick* involves the sale of goods as many later cases do that raise the principle. It is noteworthy that it was decided on appeal under Scots law and thus was heavily influenced by civil law traditions. The case was also heard before codification of sales law in the United Kingdom. Lord Blackburn relied upon a very early case decided in 1469 for the principle he formulated and then described as one of 'obvious good sense and justice'.[338] His Lordship's principle presupposes a requirement of co-operation and the duty itself is not expressly mentioned. The duty was derived from an interpretation of the contract and as an implied promise. It has since been considered[339] and applied[340] in a wide variety of cases.

Another English case that is often cited as authority for a duty of co-operation is *Luxor (Eastbourne) Limited* v. *Cooper*.[341] However, this case, involving a principal agent, in fact distinguished *MacKay* v. *Dick*.[342] It was held in *Luxor* on the facts of the case that no implied term of co-operation arose. Viscount Simon LC was unable to view the implication of the term sought as 'necessary'. Viscount Simon LC stated:

> I am unable to regard the suggested implied term as 'necessary'. The well known line of authorities, of which *Mackay* v. *Dick* is a leading example, do not, in my opinion, lead to the conclusion drawn from them by the majority of the Court of Appeal in *Trollope & Sons* v. *Martyn Brothers*.[343]

However, this *obiter* remark of Viscount Simon is followed nevertheless and routinely cited in support of the duty, perhaps because Viscount Simon LC also said in *Luxor*: '…generally speaking, where B is employed by A to do a piece of work which requires A's co-operation … it is implied that the necessary co-operation will be forthcoming'.[344] The

---

[337] KAPLAN J in *Jardine Engineering Corp Ltd & Ors* v. *Shimizu Corp* [1992] 2 HKC 89 (HC). On this authority an argument can be made that similar considerations apply when construing the NEC.

[338] *MacKay* v. *Dick* (1881) 6 App Cas 251 at 264, HL.

[339] For example, *City of Dublin Steam Packet Co* v. *R* (1908) 24 TLR 657; *Sprague* v. *Booth* [1909] AC 576, PC; *Harrison* v. *Walker* [1919] 2 KB 453; *Colley* v. *Overseas Exporters* [1921] 3 KB 302; *United States Shipping Board* v. *Durrell* [1923] 2 KB 739; and *Mona Oil Equipment & Supply Co* v. *Rhodesia Rlys Ltd* [1949] 2 All ER 1014.

[340] For example, *Kleinert* v. *Abosso Gold Mining Co* (1913) 58 Sol Jo 45; and *Saunders* v. *Ernest A Neale Ltd* [1974] 3 All ER 327.

[341] *Luxor (Eastbourne) Ltd* v. *Cooper* [1941] AC 108 HL.

[342] *MacKay* v. *Dick* (1881) 6 App Cas 251, HL.

[343] Viscount Simon LC, *Luxor (Eastbourne) Ltd* v. *Cooper* [1941] AC 108 at 118, HL.

[344] Viscount Simon LC, *Luxor (Eastbourne) Ltd* v. *Cooper* [1941] AC 108 at 118, HL.

importance of the dictum has not gone unnoticed by Alan Shilston who writes, referring to Viscount Simon's dictum:

> the importance of this dictum, to a construction industry practitioner, continually reasserts itself … [it represents] the underlying ethos of what contracting is all about is revealed. Yet it has frequently struck me as surprising that this essential piece of background fabric to the recognised standard forms of contract has never been set down in expressed language.[345]

Shilston's statement, perhaps no less significant today, should still be qualified given the express references to co-operation now made not only in the NEC but also the JCT Management Contract. John Gilbert, in fact, would equate the management contract itself with one essential criterion, namely 'co-operation'.[346] Clause 1.4 of the JCT Management Contract provides: 'The Management Contractor shall upon and subject to the Conditions co-operate with the Professional Team as stated in Appendix 1'. Tony Blackler *et al.* have commented: '[t]he legal duty of co-operation on the part of the Management Contractor constitutes the fundamental legal difference between management and traditional contracting'.[347] Unlike under traditional contracting arrangements Blackler *et al.* construe clause 1.4 as imposing a very clear and positive obligation upon the management contractor to co-operate and even initiate activity.

The *Luxor* case illustrates one of the two principal means by which implied terms are either justified or not in any given case; namely, by reason and necessity. These two control measures in effect permit almost any result to be logically supported. Hence, from *Bull* v. *Robison*[348] 'any warranty implied by the law must be a reasonable warranty, and cannot be one which is physically impossible to comply with'. The link to impossibility in this regard is also important for it shows the way in which the term is used to attenuate the harshness of absolute obligations. Patterson, referring to cases such as *Holme* v. *Guppy* and *Russel* v. *Da Bandeira*, although not *Bull* v. *Robison* concludes that:

> such cases recognize a much milder variety of prevention by the obligee as excusing performance of the obligation to pay a penalty for delay indicates the ascendance of the principle of co-operation over the principle that obligations are to be literally fulfilled.[349]

This follows from Patterson's observation that implied conditions are often discussed in one of three contexts: 'exchange, co-operation, and

---

[345] SHILSTON, ALAN, see n. 92 above, p. 2.
[346] GILBERT, JOHN, in the information section, A Personal View from the Touchline – The JCT Management Contract. *Construction Law Journal*, 1988, **4**.
[347] *Rowe & Maw, JCT Management Contract*, 38.
[348] *Bull* v. *Robison* (1854) 10 Exch 342; 156 ER 476 at 477 per Baron Alderson.
[349] *Holme* v. *Guppy* (1838) 3 M & W 387; *Russel* v. *Da Bandeira* (1862) 13 CBNS 149; *Bull* v. *Robison* (1854) 10 Exch 342; 156 ER 476; PATTERSON, EDWIN W. 932 n. 281 and see also n. 306, 137.

frustration'. *Keating on Building Contracts* similarly, uses 'three different senses' for implied terms: one of which 'a vital change of conditions' equates with frustration.[350]

Reasonableness, as well, serves as the foundation or otherwise of numerous implied terms that, in construction contract cases, often centre upon notice, care and skill, duration, and money.[351] With regard to the second criterion of necessity, although referred to in *MacKay* v. *Dick*,[352] the requirement is most closely associated with *The Moorcock*.[353] Clear statements of the principle have also been expressed in *Trollope & Colls Ltd* v. *North West Metropolitan Regional Hospital Board*,[354] and *BP Refinery (Westernport) Pty Ltd* v. *President, Councillors and Ratepayers of the Shire of Hastings*.[355] The emphasis here is upon necessity although the tests in these cases are also put forward in terms of 'business efficacy'; and in the case of *Shirlaw* v. *Southern Foundries* MacKinnon LJ formulated a test in terms of an 'officious bystander' also.[356] The *BP Refinery* case could also arguably be put forward as an example of a combination of all of these tests; in particular, Lord Simon's formulation of the test to be applied from *BP Refinery* has been relied upon by Judge Bowsher QC in *J & J Fee Ltd* v. *Express Lift Co Ltd* (1993).[357] These tests are employed predominantly in the common law and not the civil law. For example, in French civil the use of the technique of implied terms as understood by the common law does not exist, although article 1135 of the Civil Code obliges the parties to the extent that obligations arise from equity, custom and statute.[358]

It is noteworthy once again that implication of the term must be both necessary and reasonable. The common law test for implication of terms, focusing as it does upon necessity and reasonableness, is similar in these

---

[350]   *Keating* 49, n. 12.

[351]   See *Halsbury's Laws of England*, 4th edn, reissue, vol. 9(1), paragraph 787 for specific examples. Assistance on the meaning of *reasonableness* is also given in many cases including: *Wells* v. *Army & Navy Co-operative Society Ltd* (1902) 2 Hudson's BC 4th edn 346; 86 LT 764; and *Neodex* v. *Swinton and Pendlebury BC* (1958) 5 BLR 38. See generally COLE, JUSTICE T. R. H. The Concept of Reasonableness in Construction Contracts. *Building and Construction Law*, 1994, **10**, 7.

[352]   *Mackay* v. *Dick* (1881) 6 App Cas 251, HL.

[353]   *The Moorcock* (1889) 14 PD 64, [1886–90] All ER Rep 530, CA, per Bowen LJ. The case has been considered and applied in dozens of other cases in Commonwealth jurisdictions.

[354]   *Trollope & Colls Ltd* v. *North West Metropolitan Regional Hospital Board* [1973] 2 All ER 260 at 267–268, [1973] 1 WLR 601 at 609, HL, per Lord Pearson.

[355]   *BP Refinery (Westernport) Pty Ltd* v. *President, Councillors and Ratepayers of the Shire of Hastings* (1977–78) 16 ALR 363, 52 ALJR 20, PC.

[356]   *Shirlaw* v. *Southern Foundries (1926) Ltd* [1939] 2 KB 206, [1939] 2 All ER 113, CA, per MacKinnon LJ at 227 and 124.

[357]   Judge Bowsher QC, in *J & J Fee Ltd* v. *Express Lift Co Ltd* (1993) 34 Con LR 147.

[358]   COHEN, HÉLÈNE. French Construction Law: A Comparative Approach. *Construction Law Journal*, 1997, **13**, 75, 88.

ways to the considerations that have been found to be relevant in international arbitral jurisprudence. Nagla Nassar puts forward a test based upon this jurisprudence that a duty of co-operation will be found to exist when certain considerations are met.[359] In short Nassar's test posits that parties in a contractual relationship exercise their rights in a legitimate way, one that takes into account the parties' interests as well. However, interests protected must be substantial and they may be weighed against the norms in the relationship including commercial norms. Decisions not to co-operate must be prudent, neither unreasonable nor unnecessary and a defaulting party must be able to justify the action taken not solely on the basis of a contractual entitlement: neither reasonableness[360] alone nor even convenience alone is sufficient.[361] However, the courts vacillate as to how much emphasis they wish to place upon either of these requirements, although lately necessity has held sway. Thus in *Spring* v. *Guardian Assurance Plc* Lord Woolf, after setting out the circumstances supporting the implication of a term in an employment relationship, said:

> it is necessary to imply a term into the contract that the employer would, during the continuance of the engagement or within a reasonable time thereafter, provide a reference at the request of a prospective employer which was based on facts revealed after making those reasonably careful inquiries, a reasonable employer would make.[362]

Burrows sees necessity in particular imposing a significant limitation upon the duty.

> the law is not prepared to go much further. While it goes a little beyond absolute 'necessity' – as to be sensible it must – it stops short of demanding co-operation merely because it would be reasonable. The English law does not require a degree of conduct equivalent to the Roman 'good faith'.[363]

While this view can be acknowledged the theoretical framework outlined here for the NEC is postulated in terms of not only primarily co-operation – the express statement thereof in clause 10.1 – but also good faith and

---

[359]   See NASSAR, n. 329 above, 164—167.

[360]   *Lazarus* v. *Cairn Line of Steamships Ltd* (1912) 106 LT 378; 28 TLR 244; *Reigate* v. *Union Manufacturing Co (Ramsbottom) Ltd* [1918] 1 KB 592, [1918–19] All ER Rep 143, CA; *Re Comptoir Commercial Anversois and Power, Son & Co* [1920] 1 KB 868, [1918–19] All ER Rep 661, CA; *Liverpool City Council* v. *Irwin* [1977] AC 239, [1976] 2 All ER 39, HL; *George Hawkins* v. *Chrysler* (1986) 38 BLR 36, CA.

[361]   *Re Nott & Cardiff Corpn* [1918] 2 KB 146, 118 LT 487; on appeal sub nom *Brodie* v. *Cardiff Corpn* [1919] AC 337, HL.

[362]   *Spring* v. *Guardian Assurance Plc* [1994] 3 All ER 129, HL, per Lord Woolf at 179.

[363]   BURROWS, J. F., n. 314 above, 404. Burrows' 'best illustration' of this tendency comes from *Mona Oil Equipment Co* v. *Rhodesia Railways Ltd* [1949] 2 All ER 1014 at 1018 per Devlin J.

fairness *impliedly* influencing the interpretation and application of the form. Other views can also be put forward. Thus, some writers very carefully *equate* co-operation and good faith. Dr Malcolm Clarke,[364] for example, takes a statement of the rule of good faith in American law (that 'neither party to an agreement may do anything to impede performance of the agreement or to injure the right of the other party to receive the supposed benefit'),[365] which it may be noted looks similar to the 'prevention principle' and is framed in negative terms, along with a well-known quotation from *Southern Foundries (1926) Ltd* v. *Shirlaw* (that 'there is a "positive rule of the law of contract that conduct of either [party] which can be said to amount to ... bringing about the impossibility of performance is itself a breach" '),[366] and recombines them to arrive at the formulation of the duty to co-operate given by Lord Blackburn in *MacKay* v. *Dick*.[367] Clarke then adds, with reference to *Halsbury's*, that 'the proposition has also been restated as a duty of co-operation'.[368] Similarly, Carter and Furmston expressly equate the modern doctrine of good faith in Australian law[369] to an earlier narrower version of co-operation. 'The traditional perspective on the principle, [good faith] and the slightly narrower versions formulated in *Stirling* v. *Maitland* and *Mackay* v. *Dick* ... is co-operation in performance'.[370] Lastly, Collins writes in 'the United States lawyers describe the duty of co-operation during performance as the obligation to perform in good faith'.[371] Hence, even apart from an argument that good faith, or good faith and fairness or fair dealing, could be implied in the NEC in many situations, the express reference to co-operation alone might suffice to import the notion.

A strong argument can also be made that the express obligation to co-operate in clause 10.1 takes future cases involving the NEC out from under narrower interpretations which have implied the term effectively as

---

[364] CLARKE, DR MALCOLM. The Common Law of Contract in 1993: Is There a General Doctrine of Good Faith? *Hong Kong Law Journal*, 1993, **23**, 318.

[365] *Ibid.* 318, 331 n. 87 citing US *Surgical Corp* v. *Hospital Products International Pty Ltd* [1982] 2 NSWLR 766, 800 which was referring to the law of New York and Connecticut.

[366] *Southern Foundries (1926) Ltd* v. *Shirlaw* [1940] AC 701 at 717, HL, CLARKE, DR MALCOLM, n. 364 above, 318, 331, n. 88. It is submitted that there is merit in this analysis even if Clarke may have drifted into a third category of implied terms, namely 'frustration' according to some other authors: see e.g. *Keating*, 49 n. 12.

[367] *Mackay* v. *Dick* (1881) 6 App Cas 251 at 263, HL.

[368] CLARKE, DR MALCOLM, 331 n. 89: 'They appear to be equated by the citations employed in support in, for example, Halsbury's Laws of England 4th edn, vol 9 para 359. Later, in the article, Clarke concludes: 'during performance, parties must not sabotage the contract by refusing a basic level of co-operation', 341.

[369] CARTER, J. W. and FURMSTON, M. P., see n. 288 above, part II, 116 citing, among other decisions, *Secured Income Real Estate (Australia) Ltd* v. *St Martin's Investments Pty Ltd* (1979) 144 CLR 596, 607; and *Renard Constructions (ME) Pty Ltd* v. *Minister of Public Works* (1992) 26 NSWLR 234.

[370] *Ibid.*, 116, n. 154.

[371] COLLINS, HUGH. *The Law of Contract*, 2nd edn. Butterworths, London, 1993, 304.

one necessary only to ensure the fulfilment of preconditions to performance.[372] In this regard, on one view, the duty to co-operate has been said to be *negative* rather than *positive*. J. F. Burrows states: '[t]he distinction, then, is between a duty not positively to obstruct and a duty to co-operate actively'.[373] The duty to co-operate on another interpretation could be said to operate either as an adjunct to or a substitute for the finding of any fiduciary relationship. The importance of clause 10.1 in both its ability to make use of co-operative jurisprudence but at the same time to circumvent any limitations inherent in an implied term approach cannot be overstated. It is also consistent with the views of commentators who argue convincingly for the court ordered enforcement of express obligations to co-operate but not their implication.[374] The suggestion being made here to seek to leave open both the express and implied bases upon which a duty to co-operate can be founded has had a recent judicial endorsement. Thus, in *Maidenhead Electrical Services Limited* v. *Johnson Control Systems Limited* a duty to co-operate was implied in the parties' relationship notwithstanding an express contractual provision requiring co-operation as well.[375]

There are other bases that can be put forward for a far-reaching role for co-operation based upon express reference in the NEC. Thus, once again, from the *Mona Oil* case, Mr Justice Devlin clearly distinguished this case: '... apart, of course, from express terms, the law can enforce co-operation only in a limited degree to the extent that it is necessary to make the contract workable';[376] and so too has Nassar, whose work is especially important because of her close examination of international arbitral jurisprudence.[377]

> To what extent does international commercial practice acknowledge the right to demand joint contractual operation – or, to what extent does it permit a party to put his own interests ahead of those of his partner and the contractual relationship? ... Cases seldom expressly propose a general unrestricted duty to cooperate. One of the few exceptions is the ICC award in case no 2291 ... Tribunals have been

---

[372] For example, *Mackay* v. *Dick* (1881) 6 App Cas 251, HL; *Luxor (Eastbourne) Ltd* v. *Cooper* [1941] AC 108, HL; *Barque Quilpué Ltd* v. *Brown* [1904] 2 KB 264; *London Borough of Merton* v. *Stanley Hugh Leach Ltd* (1985) 32 BLR 51; and *Allridge (Builders) Ltd* v. *Grand Actual Ltd* (1997) 55 Con LR 91.

[373] For example, BURROWS, J. F., n. 314 above, 396.

[374] GOODARD, DAVID. Long-Term Contracts: A Law and Economics Perspective. *New Zealand Law Review*, 1997, 423, 450; and SCOTT, R. E. A Relational Theory of Default Rules for Commercial Contracts. *Journal of Legal Studies*, 1990, **19**, 606–615.

[375] *Maidenhead Electrical Services Ltd* v. *Johnson Control Systems Ltd* (1997) 15-CLD-10-01, Official Referee per Recorder Knight QC.

[376] DEVLIN J., *Mona Oil Equipment & Supply Co Ltd* v. *Rhodesia Railways Ltd* [1949] 1 All ER 1014 at 1018 (KB).

[377] On this subject Nassar also draws upon the work of Burrows, see n. 314 above, 390; and SCOTT, R. E., Conflict and Cooperation in Long Term Contracts. *California Law Review*, 1987, **75**, 2005, 156, n. 37 in Nassar among others.

more ready to enact a duty to cooperate where there is a contractual provision to that effect.[378] ... Similar positions have been adopted by other arbitral tribunals with respect to a variety of contracts. The Iran–US Claims Tribunal, in particular, supported this position on several occasions, where it was held that a contracting party cannot unreasonably refrain from approving the legitimate requests or expectations of the other party. This proposition is especially valid in cases where there are prior approval, or coordination clauses.[379]

In at least two of the cases Nassar refers to, the duty to co-operate was discussed in terms of good faith.[380] Once again, this willingness on the part of the tribunals to equate the two notions is significant in the way in which it opens up consideration of the good faith jurisprudence construing the duty of co-operation. This is an important link between the concepts.

Nassar recognizes at least one limitation under traditional contract doctrine and jurisprudence, however, and that is when express co-operation clauses are construed as agreements to agree and, as such, are potentially unenforceable.[381] However, rather than pursue that line of inquiry, Nassar, consistent with the theoretical framework developed here, declares this need not be the case if one accepts the following rationale and a relational perspective:

> The same [unenforceability] is not true under a relational approach, where a contract is not necessarily an all-encompassing set of by-laws, but is often merely a framework for the parties' relationship. The relational conceptualisation is not undermined when some of the contractual aspects are left for future consultation and collaboration between the parties, so long as the agreement is sufficiently defined and not totally vague ... international arbitral practice supports the relational approach ...[382]

Turning away from these issues of characterization the subject of co-operation can also be considered in another important respect: explication of the rules on the allocation of risk.

---

[378] NASSAR, n. 329 above, 157, n. 41, refers here to the ICC award in case 4761 of 1987 (1987) 114 JD Int'l (Clunet) 1012, 1016–1017; and also appearing in an English translation at *International Construction Law Review*, 1989, 334 involving an engineering subcontractor's request for a price increase.

[379] NASSAR, n. 329 above, 156–157.

[380] *Ibid.*, n. 329 above, referring to ICC award in case 2291 of 1975 (1976) 103 JD Int'l (Clunet) 989, 991; and ICC award in case 4761 of 1987 (1987) 114 JD Int'l (Clunet) 1012, 1016–1017.

[381] *Ibid.*, 158. See also PATERSON, JEANNIE MARIE. The Contract to Negotiate in Good Faith: Recognition and Enforcement. *Journal of Contract Law*, 1996, **10**, 120, who sets out and critiques four reasons why courts have refused to recognize a contract to negotiate in good faith, including contracts to contract.

[382] *Ibid.*, 159.

Patterson has considered the issue taking as his starting point that the requirement of co-operation, when implied,[383] can impose duties additional to those in the contract. There were then, at the time he was writing and as there are today, many examples of implied obligations in building and construction cases. It was these instances that Patterson construed as arising through implied co-operation. The duty varied and could be satisfied, in some cases, by the exercise of due diligence, while not in others. Of these latter cases he wrote:

> the requirement of co-operation is an allocation to the co-operator of the risk of the occurrence or non-occurrence of a certain event, in which case the requirement is not satisfied by his exercise of diligence. Similarly, the refusal to construct a requirement of co-operation may be regarded as an allocation of risk to the obligee …[384]

Patterson relies upon a dicta of Justice Learned Hand in support: 'It is of course true that, with certain exceptions not here important, an obligor takes the risk of whatever will prevent his performance, but that does not include prevention by the obligee himself'.[385] Patterson also develops certain boundaries for risks, which are determined by the requirement of co-operation. Thus, in the first instance, events which the 'co-operator' assumes the risk for, which may include their non-occurrence, are those which assist the other party to the contract to perform his obligations. In the second instance, the co-operator takes the risk for events over which he has a substantial measure of control.[386] By focusing on early American case law Patterson has been able to demonstrate the application of these risk allocation principles through two examples involving the adequacy of plans and specifications (design) and soil conditions.[387] In the same way today, clause 10.1 should operate to impose additional duties upon the parties depending upon the proper allocation of the risk. Indeed, the striking similarity of language between Patterson's articulation of these risk allocation rules and those underpinning risk allocation in the NEC dramatically call for it.

In summary, the NEC itself with its detailed framework for the allocation of risk has already provided a means for determining the

---

[383] Implication here could be either by constructive condition or implied promise using his terminology: PATTERSON, EDWIN, W., n. 306 above, 903.

[384] Ibid., 935–936.

[385] Ibid., 935–936, relying on Justice Learned Hand in Overbury v. Platten, 108 F (2d) 155, 157 (CCCA 2d 1939), 935 n. 155.

[386] Ibid., 935–936.

[387] Ibid., 936. Cf English cases with regard to 'design': Independent Broadcasting Authority v. EMI Electronics and BICC Construction (1980) 14 BLR 1; Viking Grain Storage v. T H White Installations Ltd (1985) 33 BLR 103; and Basildon District Council v. J E Lesser (Properties) Ltd [1985] QB 839, [1985] 1 All ER 20; and with regard to 'soil conditions': Roberts v Bury Improvement Commissioners (1870) LR 4 CP 755; LR 5 CP 310; and Freeman & Son v. Hensler (1900) 64 JP 260, 2 Hudson's BC 4th edn, 292.

parties' obligations. Clause 10.1, in the context of and in conjunction with this framework, can be used to define how and in what respects the parties must also co-operate. However, it is to be expected that situations will arise in construing the NEC where it will be unclear upon whom a particular risk is imposed or even the extent to which it should be borne if it is to be shared. In such a case further consideration would have to be given to the issue of how the parties should fulfil their duty to co-operate. The theoretical basis for the NEC posited here presupposes a relational view of the parties and, consistent with that view, norms will be important in determining their respective obligations. The most important norms in this regard, as has been seen, remain those premised upon co-operation, fairness and good faith.

Subcontracting

The NEC assumes that subcontracting normally occurs. With this assumption two important drafting objectives may be examined in turn. First, in the NEC the subcontract conditions of contract are almost fully back-to-back; and secondly, there is no nomination of Subcontractors.

Back-to-back conditions

The NEC interface between the main options conditions and the subcontract conditions is meticulously addressed with back-to-back wording. While there are other families of interconnected or back-to-back standard forms of contract, and even occasional reproduction of language from one contract group to another, there is no comparable uniformity. For example, in the FCEC form, under clause 1(1), unless otherwise provided or where the context requires, all words and expressions used in the FCEC form are to be given the same meaning as in the ICE 6th. However, while consistent terminology may be set out as a drafting objective across forms that are intended to operate back-to-back, omissions can occur. In this regard, modern drafting principles have not been consistently employed. The result is that one cannot be sure that where a different style of drafting or different terminology has been used a different interpretation or result was *intended*. This does not assist in the interpretation of the various groups of contracts. The NEC has seen this shortcoming and moved to address it. No other family of standard forms has elevated the principle of back-to-back drafting to one of such cardinal importance. Brian Eggleston writes in this regard:

> [t]he NEC engineering and construction subcontract (the NEC subcontract) takes this trend to the limit in that it is precise duplication of the main NEC contract with little more than the names of the parties changed. It is, so far as contractual provisions go, a complete match of the main contract. It is however, drafted in such detail that it is virtually independent of the main contract. It stands therefore as a subcontract which is fully back-to-back with the main contract but which, unusually, does not rely on the

examination of the terms of the main contract to give effect to its provisions.[388]

While it has been noted[389] that much detail will of course be left to the works information in setting out the contractor's and subcontractors' obligations, this is the current situation with many specifications in traditional general contracting. The NEC, however, is not holding out overcoming this potential source of inconsistency according to the principle of back-to-back contracts but only those that have arisen between main and subcontract provisions in traditional general forms. Hence it should not be a criticism that one problem is addressed still leaving one problem when 'two problems' were always apparent.

Today there is increasing sophistication on the part of commentators and some members of the judiciary in how contractual obligations are determined and assessed. In this regard, subcontracting in the construction industry has come in for special attention when occasionally referred to as 'hybrid' or 'network' contracting.[390] Hybrids are said to form an intermediate area between organizations and markets. There is some interest in the topic of hybrid or network contracts.[391] Network contract systems have been looked at from both positive and negative perspectives. From an economic point of view they are perceived to offer the advantages of increased flexibility, efficiency, lower transaction costs and innovation.[392] However, network contracts can also lead to opportunistic behaviour, loss of responsibility and artificial shifting of risks.[393] Examples with regard to the shifting of risks concern safety and ecological issues. Some commentators have thus expressed the need for new laws to address network contracts[394] because in the construction industry knowledge of others' contractual rights can give rise to enforceable obligations. Collins writes in this regard that:

---

[388] EGGLESTON, n. 143 above, 273.

[389] *Ibid.*, 275.

[390] TEUBNER, GUNTHER. Piercing the Contractual Veil? The Social Responsibility of Contractual Networks. In *Perspectives of Critical Contract Law.* (ed.) WILHELMSSON, THOMAS, Dartmouth, Aldershot, 1993.

[391] See e.g. COLLINS, HUGH., n. 371 above, 124ff; ADAMS, JOHN N. and BROWNSWORD, ROGER. Privity and the Concept of a Network Contract. *Legal Studies*, 1990, **10**, 12; COLLINS, HUGH. Independent Contractors and the Challenge of Vertical Disintegration to Employment Protection Laws. *Oxford Journal of Legal Studies*, 1990, **10**, EASTERBROOK, FRANK H. The Corporate Contract. *Columbia Law Review*, 1989, **89**, 1416.

[392] MacMILLAN, KEITH and FARMER, DAVID. Redefining the Boundaries of the Firm. *Journal of Industrial Economics.*, 1979, **27**, 277; JARILLO, CARLOS J. On Strategic Networks. *Strategic Management Journal*, 1988, **9**, 31; POWELL, W. WALTER. Neither Market nor Hierarchy: Network Forms of Organization. *Research in Organizational Behaviour*, 1990, **12**, 295.

[393] See COLLINS, HUGH. Ascription of Legal Responsibility to Groups in Complex Patterns of Economic Integration. *Modern Law Review*, 1990, **53**, 731–744.

[394] TEUBNER, GUNTHER, see n. 390 above, 230, references omitted.

cases concerning networks place severe strain on the classical principles for the ascription of responsibility. The dilemma confronting the law is that although it is contrary to principle to ascribe contractual responsibility without consent, in the context of a network this result may appear to conform to the intentions of the parties and represent a fair allocation of the risk.[395]

Fairness in the allocation of the risk has been seen to be a factor in the incidence of disputes.[396] Collins uses case law[397] to illustrate that courts have often failed properly to take account of networks although he also points out that that may be changing with the courts adopting a more sophisticated approach. For example, in *Norwich City Council* v. *Harvey*[398] the court referred to the terms of the main contract to determine the obligations of a third-party subcontractor. This issue, often discussed in terms of the incorporation of terms by reference, is significant for fully interfacing contract systems such as the NEC. Under some contracts the subcontractor is deemed to have notice of all main contract provisions save prices.[399] Back-to-back contract systems better lend themselves to network analysis than non-back-to-back systems. It has been noted that the NEC was the first United Kingdom construction industry main standard form contract to match a subcontract.[400] Michael Latham observed: 'the New Engineering Contract ... provid[es] a full matrix of documentation for clients'.[401] In this regard fully back-to-back contract systems offer an advantage, assuming all the parties are aware of their terms, over one-off or bespoke forms on a project that involves subcontracting arrangements. While drafting organizations such as the JCT and Conditions of Contract Standing Joint Committee (CCSJC) have not moved to fully integrated conditions of contract across alternative procurement strategies there have been moves, once again, to release more forms and standardize some of their wordings.[402] The near fully

---

[395] See SMITH, G. A. See Beyond ADR – Dispute Resolution in the Construction Industry through Realistic Contract Risk Allocation. In *The Organization of Management of Construction: Shaping Theory and Practice*, (eds LANGFORD, D. A. and RETICK, A). E & FN Spon, London, see n. 390 above, 1996, vol. 2, pp. 881–890, n.1 references omitted listing survey results of specific causes of construction disputes.

[396] COLLINS, HUGH, 126.

[397] COLLINS, HUGH, 124–128.

[398] *Norwich City Council* v. *Harvey* (1988) 45 BLR 14, [1989] 1 ALL ER 1180, CA referred to by COLLINS, HUGH, 127.

[399] For example, article 1.1 DOM/1, and clause 3(1) FCEC.

[400] ALLEN, JOHN D. NEC – is it the Answer to Latham's Prayers? *Construction News*, 23 February 1995, 12–13.

[401] LATHAM, MICHAEL. Answering the Call to Action. *Building*, 7 October 1994, 26.

[402] Lately the CCJSC released the Second Edition of the ICE MW form. In the guidance notes to the form under the heading 'Principal Changes From the First Edition of the Conditions of Contract for Minor Works' some six clauses were standardized with wording in the ICE 6th and/or ICE Design and Construct form with a further clause harmonized with wording in the ICE 6th and ICE Design and Construct form.

interlocking or interfacing nature of the ECC and ECSC in the NEC better positions the form to account for new trends such as network analysis and systems analysis.[403]

No nomination or naming

Nomination and *naming* subcontractors are two means whereby the employer designates who will perform a subcontract or specialist trade role. The practice of nomination in particular has been controversial. Keating states: '[t]he system [of nomination] is an ingenious attempt to give the employer the benefit of two opposing concepts'.[404] It has remained a practice because it is still one means by which the employer retains a measure of control over the process of subcontracting. Important issues have arisen over the responsibilities of the parties in nomination situations. One well-known case involving nomination resulted in amendments to JCT 80.[405] The result has been a move away from the system of nomination and turns toward other procedures. Professor John Uff QC states: 'the burdens thus imposed upon employers can be seen to have created a backlash resulting in employers and their advisers avoiding nomination where possible and adopting other contractual devices, such as giving the contractor a choice between a limited number of specified subcontractors'.[406] Naming is one example of such an alternative procedure, as is the procedure of 'approval' in the NEC. As a result of these problems associated with nomination all subcontractors in the NEC should be considered to be 'domestic' for the sake of comparisons.

In contrast to other forms, the BPF form and IFC 84 use 'named subcontractors'[407] in place of 'nominated Subcontractors'. Under the BPF system the subcontractors and suppliers are *named* in the invitation to tender to the main contractor and the contractor is told whether they are to be invited to tender for a portion of the work. Under IFC 84, the specification, schedules of work or contract bills may describe work for pricing by the subcontractor to be executed by a named person as subcontractor.[408] JCT 80 in fact includes a very similar mechanism in

---

[403] See CHECKLAND, P. *Systems Thinking, Systems Practice.* John Wiley, Chichester, 1981.

[404] *Keating*, see n. 309 above, p. 178.

[405] See *North-West Metropolitan Regional Hospital Board* v. *TA Bickerton & Son Ltd* [1970] 1 All ER 1039, [1970] 1 WLR 607, HL; and for comments on the case: WALLACE QC, PROFESSOR I. N. DUNCAN. *Construction Contracts: Principles and Policies in Tort and Contract.* Sweet and Maxwell, London, pp. 329–354; and clause 35.24 JCT 80.

[406] UFF QC, PROFESSOR JOHN. Standard Contract Terms and the Common Law. *Construction Law Journal*, 1993, **9**, 108.

[407] See clauses 3.3.1 and 3.3.2 IFC 84. The forms used in conjunction with IFC 84 include the NAM/SC and ESA/1. See JONES, NEIL F. and BERGMAN, DAVID. *A Commentary on the JCT Intermediate Form of Building Contract*, 2nd edn. BSP Professional Books, Oxford, 1990, p. 6 for details on the IFC naming procedure.

[408] Clause 3.3.1 IFC 84.

clause 19.3. Thus work in the contract bills to be priced by the contractor may have to be carried out by persons *named* in a list annexed to or included in the bills, provided by the employer, and from which the contractor must select the subcontractor. While the right of the contractor is to have sole discretion to select from the list, either party may add to the list. Once selected the subcontractor is treated as a domestic subcontractor. Naming under IFC 84 may be effected by statements in the tender documents requiring the work to be carried out by a named person or by architect's instructions that a provisional sum be allowed for work to be carried out by a named person. Again, under IFC 84, and as in JCT 80, the contractor retains a right to object reasonably to the named subcontractor.[409] The sanction for failing to comply with the naming procedure in IFC 84 is a ground for termination[410] and in this regard more closely resembles the ECC provisions[411] than other JCT provisions that do not.[412] For some commentators the difference in naming versus nominating may be more apparent than real.

> It is to be regretted that the JCT has seen fit to imply that the traditional arrangement of the employer reserving the right to him to specify who carries out certain sub-contracted works has not been followed with respect to the 1984 form. A rose, after all, by any other name would just as sweetly smell, and the nature and function of the sub-contractor is very much the same, whether he be 'named' or 'nominated'.[413]

Another approach to nomination can be seen in the ENAA 1992 *Model Form of Contract for Process Plant Construction*. It retains nominated subcontractors in the main form but has omitted them from the provisions in the ENAA alternative form. One reason for retaining nomination provisions in these forms is that many countries in which the form can be expected to be used would require nominated subcontractors to be employed in order to develop local industry.[414] Despite perceived shortcomings over the system of nomination or naming subcontractors, its persistence is testified to by the belated introduction of named contractor provisions for JCT 81 in February 1988. Thus the JCT clearly

---

[409]   Clause 3.3.2(c) IFC 84.

[410]   Clause 7.1(d) IFC 84.

[411]   Clause 95.2 (R13) ECC.

[412]   For example, clause 27 JCT 80.

[413]   ROYCE, DARRYL, see n. 147 above, 97. Cf FIDIC 4th, which refers collectively to specialists, merchants, tradesmen and others who have been nominated or selected or approved by the employer or engineer as 'nominated Subcontractors', clause 59.1.

[414]   See JAYNES, GORDON L. Turnkey Contracts: Japan's Model Forms. *International Construction Law Review*, 1993, 258–259 for further details of the ENAA's justification for retention of the nomination system; and see generally FURYUA, KUNIHIKO. ENAA Revised Model Form of Contract (1992 edn). *International Construction Law Review*, 1993, 8.

felt a need, presumably reflecting a demand, to set out the rights and responsibilities of the parties when named subcontractors were referred to in the employer's requirements. Although less extensive than the named subcontractor provisions under IFC 84, and much less so than the nominated subcontractor provisions in JCT 80, they still comprise ten subclauses in the contract.[415]

---

[415] See on the potential for uncertainty in pre-designating subcontractors under the GC/Works/1 form *Rackline Limited* v. *The National Library of Wales* (1997) CILL 1268.

4. New Engineering Contract system

Construction is the most visible of industries and conducts its affairs almost totally in the public arena The manner of execution and rate of progress of the building process frequently forms a public spectacle, and the commercial practices and contractual relationships are the subjects of undisguised professional and amateur scrutiny. The final product of the industry stands, almost without defence, against the searching examinations of a diverse body of interested parties comprising users, owners, occupiers, neighbours, and the general public, all of whom believe they have a legitimate entitlement to espouse a view.

David Baldry,
Building the Image – A Study of the Performance Factor

General

The choice of a construction contract has very wide implications for the delivery of products in society. With recognition of these implications have come calls for increasing accountability of the industry in reports such as *Trust and Money*[1]. For example, *Setting New Standards – A Strategy for Government Procurement* focuses upon key elements of 'value for money'.[2] Government strategy and latterly policy have been significantly impacting upon procurement issues. Thus tender and contract documentation, incentives, ongoing productivity, risk assessment including insurance and indemnity, and management of contracts post-award are all being influenced. While industry has thus withstood calls for change in the past the likelihood of this continuing decreases with each passing day. Sir Michael Latham neatly summarized the new influences

---

[1] See e.g. *Trust and Money, Interim Report of the Joint Government/Industry Review of Procurement and Contractual Arrangements in the United Kingdom Construction Industry.* HMSO, London, December 1993. The Latham Report followed in July 1994. See also POWELL, M. *Choice Between Trust and Distrust in Building.* CIOB, Ascot, 1993, Construction Paper 25.

[2] *Setting New Standards – A Strategy for Government Procurement.* HMSO, London, May 1995. See generally on value for money, *Contract Management*, guidance note 61. HM Treasury, Central Unit on Procurement, London, May 1991.

shaping the construction industry from benchmarking to risk[3] in *Constructing the Team*. Many of these influences such as supply chain management – value management – process mapping – whole life costing – post-project evaluation trace their origins to management theory and they can be expected to grow.[4] Others too have noted the importance of re-engineering basic business processes themselves in the construction industry and in particular borrowing from other sectors.

The re-engineering of basic business processes to provide 'lean', rapid and effective performance is now commonplace throughout other industries but rarely occurs in construction. These more advanced business techniques must be introduced as a matter of urgency, applying and capitalizing on the experience and knowledge gained in other sectors. Procurement is an important part of this. Thus, in Technology Foresight, *Progress Through Partnership 2 Construction* of five main obstacles to progress in the construction sector, one of them referred to 'procurement procedures and standard specifications used by large organizations and government which are often a disincentive to innovation'.[5] Many of the trends once only discussed prospectively are now here; for example, in procurement from optimized project strategies to minimize costs, as well as value engineering, risk analysis, partnering, and joint ventures, as innovations likely to contribute to raising performance and efficiency in the construction industry in the future.[6] The position taken here is that the NEC has contributed to their fruition. It is argued here that the increasing prominence of the NEC has *encouraged* more wide-ranging discussion and views on contract strategy, risk analysis, and project-specific documentation in the context of a standard form than before. It is also contended that a wider range of stakeholders in industry now better understands these views. Others have hinted at this: '[t]his approach has been pioneered by the New Engineering Contract...'.[7] While the authors

---

[3] See RAMABADRON, RAMAMURTHY *et al.* Benchmarking and Project Management: A Review and Organizational Model. *Benchmarking for Quality Management & Technology*, 1997 **4** (1), 47–58.

[4] See the United Kingdom Government White paper *Setting New Standards – A Strategy for Government Procurement.* HMSO, London, 1995.

[5] Technology Foresight, *Progress Through Partnership 2 Construction.* Office of Science and Technology, HMSO, London, 1995, 16. See also on the future issue in relation to construction: SIMMONDS, P. *A Digest of International Technology Future Studies for Construction.* Office of Science and Technology, HMSO, London, 1994; and BETTS, M. and WOOD-HARPER, T. Re-engineering Construction: A New Management Research Agenda. *Construction Management and Economics*, 1994, **12** (6), 551. See generally CRAIG, R. W. *Procurement Law for Construction and Engineering Work and Services.* Blackwell Science, Oxford, 1999.

[6] See generally *Managing Construction in the 90s. Profiting from Trends and Innovation.* Proceedings of a conference in London during October 1993. School of Business and Industrial Management, London, 1993.

[7] KENNEDY, JOHN and DAVIES, ROGER, preface to *Future Directions in Construction Law.* Proceedings of the Fifth Annual Conference of the Centre of Construction Law and Management. King's College, London, 1992, p. iv.

of this book thought at that time it was perhaps too early to judge the overall performance of the NEC in these regards, the contribution of the NEC to these trends can now be better judged.

The importance of 'contract strategy' or the broader issue of procurement was recognized in an early Business Roundtable Report in 1982.[8] The NEC drafters understand this importance and have thus adopted a flexible approach to the issue. The drafters have accomplished this through the promotion of a 'schedule of options' for the employer. The brief introduction to this accomplishment in the Engineering and Construction Contract begins: '[t]he strategy for choosing the form of contract starts with a decision between six main options, one of which must be chosen'.[9] The use of options in this manner is consistent with the recommendation in the Latham Report, paragraph 5.18(3) that an effective form of contract be 'suitable for all types of project and for any procurement route'. On one view 'the NEC provides a comprehensive option system by which a civil engineering contract can be tailored to a particular project'.[10] Options A to F are listed and followed by this statement: '[t]he following secondary options should then be considered. It is not necessary to use any of them. Any combination other than those stated may be used'. While this is the extent of the advice given regarding contract strategy in the ECC itself it must be read, of course, with the guidance notes. Significantly, the guidance notes summarize the key factors the drafters believe to be relevant to contract strategy:[11]

- who has the necessary design expertise;
- whether there is particular pressure to complete quickly;
- how important is performance of the complete works;
- whether a certainty of final cost is more important than lowest final cost;
- where a risk can be best managed;
- what total cost is tolerable for the contractor;
- how important is cross-contract co-ordination to achievement of project objectives; and
- whether the employer has good reasons for selecting specialist contractors or suppliers for parts of the work.

In theory, following consideration of these factors, the most appropriate contract strategy will be chosen. The strategy chosen may entail use of one or more of the main options depending upon the nature of the project.

---

[8] *Contractual Arrangements: A Construction Industry Cost Effectivenesss Report.* Business Round Table, London, 1982, see more recently *Contract Strategy Selection for Major Projects*, guidance note 36. HM Treasury, Central Unit on Procurement, London, August, 1993. See lately ROWLINSON AND MCDERMOTT, *Procurement Systems in Construction: A Guide to Best Practice.*

[9] ECC 1.

[10] HIBBERT, STEPHEN. Commercial and Legal Consequences of Risk Taking and Risk Sharing. *Building and Construction Law*, 1993, **8**, 190.

[11] Guidance notes NEC 12.

It may also entail significant decisions ranging in character from design to testing and commissioning. Failing to choose the most appropriate contract strategy can be costly. John G. Perry has written:

> [c]ontracting practices are growing more complicated and few items have more impact on the cost of the project than the contractual arrangements. The returns can be impressive. A representative sample of major owners and contractors estimates that the way construction contracts are written can add about 5% to the cost of typical projects.[12]

This approach of the NEC has been endorsed as one means of rationalizing the number of forms and improving communications in industry. The endorsement emanates from research that was carried out in furtherance of a prototype authoring system for drafting ad hoc construction contracts as opposed to standard forms. The NEC on this view stands somewhere between a simple database of clauses and traditional standard forms that offer no clause choices.

> To overcome the manifest problems of poor communication, which already exist because of the proliferation of contract forms and amendments thereto, we believe a database of clauses should be adopted in a similar way to the core clauses identified in the New Engineering Form of Contract (1993). For our experimental purposes we are utilizing clauses of the New Engineering Contract, because that contract offers the advantage of core clauses, regardless of procurement option, composed in a simple, straightforward style. A data base of clauses, together with an explanatory and tracing facility that enables the parties to identify how the contract is constructed, will substantially improve communication.[13]

In general there are no limitations upon the documents that may comprise an engineering or construction contract. Broadly these may include the following: articles of agreement, general conditions, special conditions, appendices, schedules (e.g. of rates), bills of quantities, plans and drawings, specifications, programmes, method statements, employer's requirements, contractor's proposals, and contract sum analyses.[14] In the

---

[12] PERRY, JOHN G. The New Engineering Contract: Principles of Design and Risk Allocation. *Engineering, Construction and Architectural Management*, 1995, **2** (3), 203–204. See also PERRY, J. G. and HOARE, D. J. Contracts of the Future: Risks and Rewards. In *Future Directions*, see n. 7 above, p. 83 citing *Contractual Arrangements: A Construction Industry Cost Effectiveness Project Report*. Business Roundtable, New York, October 1982; and NEDO. *Faster Building for Industry* HMSO, London, 1983.

[13] HIBBERD, P. R. *et al.* Intelligent Authoring of Contracts. In *East meets West*. Proceedings of CIB W 92 Procurement Systems in Hong Kong, 4–7 December 1994, by the Department of Surveying, Hong Kong University. Department of Surveying, Hong Kong University, 1994, 115, 118.

[14] Under the PSC the consultant will retain copies of the drawings and specifications: see clause 13.5 PSC. Cf FIDIC 4th clause 1.1(b) (i) which also includes any letter of acceptance or contract agreeement.

NEC the documents comprising the tender would be expected to include any instructions to tenderers, the (form of) tender, part one and part two of the Contract Data, any bill of quantities, works information, site information, and any health and safety plan.[15] In the NEC the documents comprising the contract are: the schedule of Contract Data; the *conditions of contract* in the core clauses and the optional clauses (both main option clauses and secondary options) relevant or chosen; the works information; the *activity schedule* and the tender. The phrase 'conditions of contract' is undefined in the ECC but includes the core clauses and relevant secondary option clauses according to the meaning given to it in part one of the Contract Data; in this respect it is an identified term.[16] Option Z provides additional conditions of contract stated in the Contract Data and may also form part of the contract documents. The parties must ensure that such additional options once intended are in fact delivered upon in the contract or they risk them being omitted.[17] It may be expected at a minimum that such additional conditions could comprise any of those that one finds, for example, in other standard forms.

The 'New Engineering Contract System' comprises forms of procurement and terms of engagement for consultants. One definition of a 'system' may be given as follows: 'a set of elements connected together which form a whole showing properties which are properties of the whole, rather than properties of its component parts'.[18] The use of the term 'system' to describe the NEC thus seems appropriate with common elements across its various main options as well as interlocking forms. Some prefer to use the term 'suite' of contracts also.[19] Other examples of a systems approach to contract drafting in this regard would be the British Property Federation System, and more recently the documentation in the Electrical Contractors' Association Specialist Engineering and Construction Contract system, or 'SEACC'. The system components may be set out as follows.

- The Engineering and Construction Contract.
- The Engineering and Construction Subcontract.
- The Professional Services Contract.
- The Adjudicator's Contract.

---

[15] Guidance notes NEC 17. Cf the FIDIC Orange Book 1st part I which, in addition to a definition of the 'contract' in clause 1.1.1.1, contains a helpful definition in clause 1.1.6.1 of the 'construction documents'.

[16] The interchangable use of this phrase as well as 'clauses' in the NEC has been criticized by VALENTINE, D. G. The New Engineering Contract: Part 1 – a New Language. *Construction Law Journal*, 1991, 12, 311.

[17] See e.g. *Mitsui Babcock Energy Ltd* v. *John Brown Engineering Ltd* (1996) 51 Con LR 129.

[18] CHECKLAND, P. *Systems Thinking, Systems Practice.* John Wiley, Chichester, 1981, p. 3.

[19] See CARRICK, D. NEC Suite of Contracts Part 2: The Black Book. *Civil Engineering Surveyor*, November 1997, 23.

- The Plant Contract.
- The Short Contract.

At present a Maintenance Contract is also being prepared. In addition to these documents the system also comprises flow charts and guidance notes. The ECC is at the foundation of the system and is the focus of this commentary. In fact, many of the conditions in the other contracts or terms of engagement are identical to those in the ECC or simply differ only insofar as the circumstances require (or *mutatis mutandis*). However, for completeness these documents are introduced below and reference will also be made to the other documents in the system where appropriate. The ECC is set out as a series of main options.

Engineering and Construction Contract
The ECC is divided into five 'schedules of options' (as described on the contents page of the form).

(1) Core clauses.
(2) Main option clauses.
(3) Secondary option clauses.
(4) Schedule of Cost Components and Shorter Schedule of Cost Components.
(5) Contract Data.

The contract conditions are set out in the core clauses, main option clauses and secondary option clauses and vary according to preference and method of procurement strategy selected. The main option clauses pertain specifically to the contract strategy or method of procurement. The secondary option clauses permit further refinement of the obligations between the parties and the agreed allocation of risk. The core clauses are the contract terms common to all of the methods of procurement in the contract system and across the main option clauses. In practice only one of six available main options will be selected as part of the contract conditions. In contrast, no secondary option clauses may be added to the mix of agreed contract conditions or indeed all of the secondary option clauses may be added save limited exceptions. Appendix 1 of the NEC guidance notes contains detailed tables on the clause numbering and applicable options for a given contract strategy or set of conditions.

The reference to main options and core clauses and secondary option clauses raises the question of comparison of general and special conditions. The view put forward here is that no analogy should be drawn in this regard for several reasons. First, the ECC does not adopt a precedence or hierarchy of documents clause and thus, subject to the core clauses, all clauses will presumably be read together to determine their meaning. Secondly, new language is used. Thirdly, option Z makes reference to 'additional' conditions of contract and thus it is always open to the parties to adopt special conditions as 'additional' conditions if they wish. Finally, the works information, site information and parts one and two of the Contract Data alternatively permit the parties to address certain aspects of what may comprise special conditions subject matter under other forms. However, some common characteristics may still be argued. Thus, it is also the intention that the FIDIC general clauses, those conditions in part I of the contract, be of universal application, while those conditions in part II are intended to be of specific application only. Similarly, as with the NEC core clauses, it is recommended that the FIDIC 4th part I clauses not be amended. Precedence of documents clauses may operate unexpectedly for the parties, for instance, in *Drake and Scull Engineering Ltd* v. *J Jarvis and Sons plc*[20] where a precedence of documents clause in one set of standard conditions resulted in another set of standard conditions being ruled ineffective to the extent they were in conflict.

Core clauses

The core clauses in the ECC are headed as follows.

- 'General'.
- 'The *Contractor's* main responsibilities'.
- 'Time'.
- 'Testing and Defects'.
- 'Payment'.
- 'Compensation events'.
- 'Title'.
- 'Risks and insurance'.
- 'Disputes and termination'.

Main option clauses

The main options are also set out and will be returned to below in greater detail.

- Main option A – priced contract with activity schedule.
- Main option B – priced contract with bill of quantities.
- Main option C – target contract with activity schedule.
- Main option D – target contract with bill of quantities.
- Main option E – cost reimbursable contract.
- Main option F – management contract.

The NEC publishes the main options together in one book as well as individual merged versions in different coloured contract books. The one book that contains all relevant clauses in respect of each main option has a black cover and has occasionally been referred to as the 'Black Book'.[21] Each merged version contains all the relevant clauses as well as any

---

[20] *Drake and Scull Engineering Ltd* v. *J Jarvis and Sons plc* (1996) 58 Con LR 39.

[21] See O'REILLY, MICHAEL. *Civil Engineering Construction Contracts*. Thomas Telford, London, 1996, p. 311. As an aside the colour of the book became noticeably darker in the Second Edition of the form and at least one commentator had referred to the single book as the 'grey book', see BARBER, JOHN. The Foresight Saga – A Tale of Quality.

relevant schedules of options for the respective main option. This enables the clauses and options to be read together as a whole in one document. The merged versions also contain any incidental amendments that are required to the wording to accommodate each respective main option. The availability and range of options open in the use of the NEC is said to facilitate teamwork by giving the employer a choice over contract strategy and allocation of risk.[22]

Priced contract with activity schedule – main option A
The priced[23] contract is one of the three principal main options that comprise the six described main options that may be employed under the NEC. 'Principal' is used here in relation to the division of the six main options into:

- priced contracts in A and B;
- target contracts in C and D; and
- cost reimbursable contracts in E and F.

It may be combined with either an activity schedule or bill of quantities. The activity schedule is novel in standard forms and one of the first forms to use activity schedules to replace bills of quantities was the BPF/ACA contract in the BPF system. The activity schedule is in effect a list of operations (activities) which the contractor intends to perform in carrying out the works.[24] It is one means of assessing interim payments, which was endorsed in the Latham Report. It was that the aim of using such new means of assessing interim payments 'should be to phase out the traditional system of monthly measurement or remeasurement' while also noting, consisent with not only practice in industry but with the NEC main options still employing bills of quantities that 'meanwhile provision should still be made for it'.[25] Depending upon the number of activities, computers and software can often be profitably involved in their preparation and administration. One 'rule of thumb' is that where more than 100 activities are involved a computer and software is warranted.[26] In contrast to a bill of quantities which uses individual rates the activity schedule uses lump sums. The activities may also be used for pricing and their total will equate with the price to be paid to the contractor for the works as a whole and as defined under the option. The activity schedule may be made a contract document and serve as or in addition to the

---

[22] KWAKYE, A. A. *Construction Project Administration in Practice*. Addison Wesley Longman, Harlow; CIOB, Ascot, 1997, p. 105.

[23] The Consultation Document, 7 originally referred to main options A and B as 'conventional' contracts.

[24] See discussion below.

[25] Latham Report paragraph 5.18(8), 37.

[26] See generally LOCK, DENNIS. Resource Scheduling. In *Gower Handbook of Project Management*, 2nd edn. Gower, Aldershot, 1994, pp. 311–328. See generally REISS, GEOFF. Choosing Project-Planning Software. In *Project Management Demystified Today's Tools and Techniques*, 2nd edn. E & FN Spon, London, 1995, pp. 177–186.

programme. In the absence of such an express provision the activity schedule would not be given contractual effect.[27] Although both main options A and C utilize activity schedules they serve different purposes. Thus, in main option A the activity schedule is used to assess payments to the contractor while in main option C it is used only to assess compensation events and to determine the contractor's share.

Priced contract with bill of quantities – main option B

The priced contract with bill of quantities is also a main option. The bill of quantities comprises individual items or entries of work and quantities, which may be priced in turn by the contractor.[28] Measurement is thus an integral aspect of the main options with bills and differs from the compensation event procedure.

> Early experience with the bill of quantities has demonstrated that a clear head is required in order to appreciate the difference between the remeasurement of quantities for items of work already described in the bills, (which is paid at bill rates) and the valuation of compensation events for new (usually additional) work which is paid for at actual cost plus fee.[29]

In both main options B and D the method of measurement for the works will be stated in the Contract Data. In the United Kingdom the RICS Standard Method of Measurement of Building Works, 7th edition will be the pre-eminent choice, but other standards may be used especially in other countries.[30] It seems from information obtained through the NEC Users' Group that United Kingdom contractors still like bills and prefer to use them even if only to determine pre-tender activity schedules if they are using main options A or C.[31] However, some view traditional bills of quantities as no longer an ideal part of procurement systems as they are out of step with current requirements.[32]

Target contract with activity schedule – main option C

Main options C and D comprise target contracts. The British Property Federation is one of the first to promote target contracts. Martin Barnes, who was involved in drafting forms in the BPF system, has long been a

---

[27] See clause 54.1 ECC.
[28] See discussion below.
[29] BAIRD, ANDREW. The New Engineering Contract – A Management Summary for Plant Industry Users. *International Construction Law Review.* 1994, 121.
[30] Royal Institution of Chartered Surveyors. *SMM 7: A Code of Procedure for Measurement of Building Works.* RICS, London, 1988, cf clause 13.5 of JCT 80 referring expressly to SMM 7th edn.
[31] See WILLIAMS, DAVID H. Using the NEC: A Client's View. In New Engineering Contract Conference Proceedings in Hong Kong, 28 November 1994. Asian Law Journal, Hong Kong, 1994.
[32] For example, HART, VICTOR A. Trade Package Approach to Construction Procurement. *Architects and Surveyors Institute Journal*, 1996, **7** (5), 33–34.

critic of traditional bills of quantities.[33] Some of the reasons behind the introduction of new forms of contract, in particular target cost contracts, have been investigated and it was concluded that it was to improve time, cost and quality performance of contracts as well as to apportion the risk differently.[34] No definition of 'target contract' is given in the NEC; rather the term reflects a sharing of the financial risk in attaining the parties agreed price for the works. Scott would describe a target contract as a 'risk sharing contract'.[35] The parties to target contracts also share a strong financial motivation to pursue common objectives. The variables of time, cost and quality are also the main concerns of the employer or client in procurement decisions.[36] One important common objective is increased profit which modelling has shown can be achieved using incentives or a bonus system in a target contract.[37] In the way target contracts provide additional incentives for exceptional performance, two of Latham's characteristics for a modern form of contract are also satisfied.[38] John Barber, however, is cautious about the relationship between risk allocation and motivation: 'Whether a contract can be framed effectively to provide specific and intended motivation is a moot point' although he seems to concede some role for motivation through the conditions of contract when he later writes:

[b]ut in so far as motivation can be achieved by the conditions of contract, there is one essential prerequisite. Those persons who are to be motivated must first be aware of the contents of the form of contract and must understand its implications ... and understanding must exist before the contract is entered into ....'[39]

---

[33] See BARNES, N. M. L. and THOMPSON, P. A. *Civil Engineering Bills of Quantities.* CIRIA, London, 1971, Report 34.

[34] CHAN, A. P. C. and LAM, P. T. I. Construction Management: A New Role to Building Contractor. *Proceedings to the First International Conference Changing Roles of Contractors in the Asia Pacific Rim.* In Hong Kong on 9–10 May 1994. Hong Kong, 1994. See on target cost contracts, TRENCH, D. *On Target – A Design and Manage Target Cost Procurement System.* Thomas Telford, London, 1991.

[35] SCOTT, ROBERT E. Risk Distribution and Adjustment in Long-Term Contracts. In *The Complex Long-Term Contract Structures and International Arbitration* (ed. FRITZ NICHLISCH). C F Muller Juristischer Verlag, Heidelberg, 1987, pp. 60–63. See generally on the subject of risk, GODFREY, PATRICK S. and HALCROW, SIR WILLIAM and Partners Ltd. *Control of Risk A Guide to the Systematic Management of Risk from Construction.* CIRIA, London, 1996, Special Publication 125.

[36] FARROW, J. J. and MAIN, FRASER R. *Use and Abuse of the Code of Procedure for Single Selective Tendering.* (ed. HARLOW, PETER). CIOB, Ascot, 1996, Construction Paper 70.

[37] See MURPHY, P. J. Pricing Strategy for Target Incentive Contracts. *Building Economist*, March 1994, 5–8.

[38] Latham Report, paragraphs 5.18 (2) and (12), 37.

[39] BARBER, JOHN. The Foresight Saga – A Tale of Quality.

A target contract may be the most appropriate form of contract strategy when the full extent of the work remains undefined at the time of contracting. The parties agree to a target price for completion of the works inclusive of the actual cost as defined in the contract plus all other costs, overheads and profits to be covered by the contractor's fee as defined. Thus, in effect, the contractor agrees to perform the work for a targeted prime cost against which both increases and decreases are shared with the employer.[40] Target contracts are similar to cost reimbursement contracts with regard to this sharing but differ in the procedures involved. Under the ECC the contractor is reimbursed for agreed costs as the work progresses to completion but there is no assessment of the contractor's share until completion itself. Two main reasons were given for this choice by the drafters.

- The tendered prices are not likely to provide a realistic forecast of cash flow and be comparable with the interim payments as they are calculated under the contract.
- The forecast prices are likely to be extremely uncertain at the early stages of the contract and would also be distorted by assessment of compensation events.[41]

With regard to cash flow Geoffrey Briscoe writes:

> [a] particularly important area of financial control for the construction firm is cash flow forecasting and the need to ensure that the firm does not run out of cash resources before the completion of its projects. The relatively high number of bankruptcies recorded in the construction sector testifies to the importance of cash flow to the building firm. Cash is a critical component of working capital, but it is the *timing* of the cash flow which is of paramount importance in an activity with so many potential cash flow inflows and outflows.[42]

Thus the drafters are saying that the level of uncertainty in determining the contractor's share of savings or excess compared to the target is too great during the works to warrant doing. Target cost contracts have been applied between main contractor and employer and have worked well according to some commentators. 'The benefit of a target cost approach is that the relationship begins to change. Teamwork begins to replace the more common adversarial and claims-conscious attitudes'.[43]

---

[40] See discussion under clause 53.

[41] Guidance notes NEC on clause 53.4 ECC, 55.

[42] BRISCOE, GEOFFREY. *The Economics of the Construction Industry*. B. T. Batsford Ltd, London, CIOB, Ascot, 1988, pp. 252–253 (original emphasis).

[43] HELMSLEY, ANDREW. Incentives for Teamwork. *Building*, 12 January 1996, 25. See for an overview of the organizational development issues in teamwork, DYER, WILLIAM G. *Team Building: Current Issues and New Alternatives*, 3rd edn. Addison Wesley Longman, Reading, 1995.

Target contract with bill of quantities – main option D

A target contract may also be employed as a main option with a bill of quantities to price the works rather than an activity schedule.[44] Although both main options B and D utilize bills they serve different purposes. Thus in main option B the bill of quantities is used to assess payments to the contractor while in main option D it is used only to assess compensation events and to determine the contractor's share.

Cost reimbursable contract – main option E

A cost reimbursable contract is suggested in certain circumstances including the following.[45]

- When there is inadequate definition of the work at the time of tender.
- There is work of exceptional complexity.
- The work involves technical innovation or again exceptional complexity.
- In other situations which involve major unquantifiable risks to the contractor.
- There is some recurrent work.

In general, there are different types of cost-based contract incentives: fixed-price firm contract incentives, cost-plus contract incentives, and cost reimbursable contract incentives. The fixed-price firm contract incentive pays the contractor a base rate plus or minus the incentive or disincentive amount normally coupled with a cost ceiling to cap the maximum liability of the contractor. The cost-plus contract incentive imposes a cap on the amount of incentives that may be paid to the contractor coupled with a minimum payment in the event of cost overruns. The cost reimbursable contract incentive leaves sole financial risk with the employer. Incentive provisions may be referable to different types of criteria as well and thus may utilize cost, schedule or performance indicators in assessments.[46] Perry and Thompson have written how targets are a valid and practicable means of providing incentives and controls and note that they may be applied to time, cost and quality criteria also.[47]

Under the NEC a cost reimbursable contact may be chosen using main option E. Under the ECC version of a cost reimbursable contract the contractor receives actual cost as defined plus an agreed fee to cover

---

[44] See discussion above on main options B and C.

[45] PERRY, J. G. and THOMPSON, P. A. *Target, and Cost-reimbursable Construction Contracts: A Study of Their Use and Implications*, CIRIA, London, 1982, CIRIA Report 85, (formerly CIRIA Report 56), 7–10.

[46] See ABU-HIJLEH, S. F. and IBBS, C. W. Schedule-based Construction Incentives. *Journal of Counstruction Engineering and Management*, 1989, 430–443; and STUKHART, G. Contractual Incentives, 34–42. See generally *Incentives in Procurement Contracting*. TIROLE, JEAN and LEITZEL, JIM (eds), Westview Press, Boulder, 1993.

[47] PERRY, J. G. and THOMPSON, P. A. n. 45 above, 10–12.

overhead and profit etc. The ECC permits different percentages for design overheads and working area overheads to be agreed in part two of the Contract Data. This practice has other precedents[48] and recognizes that overheads can differ considerably. The fee is calculated by applying the contractor's fee percentage to the defined actual cost.[49] In general cost components that are not listed in the SCC are included in the fee; however, there is also some flexibility with regard to individual rates which are set out and agreed in the SCC. The definitions of 'Actual Cost' in the ECC are important and facilitate clarity. In contrast ICE 5th used the term 'cost' 70 times without definition, thus leaving the parties to come to their own understanding of the meaning of the term. While this approach seems to leave the contractor with little incentive to economize, given that the contractor's fees will rise with the actual cost, the provisions on disallowance of costs serves to mitigate at least some aspects of this.[50] These provisions may be contrasted with other forms of cost reimbursable contracts. For instance, the JCT Fixed Fee Form of Prime Cost contract fixes the fee as a lump sum in advance and thus provides an incentive to the contractor to complete on time and thereby reduce overall overhead and other costs in relation to the project costs as a whole.

Management contract – main option F
The NEC includes a form of management contract in main option F. Management contracting is a relatively new phenomenon in construction. Some research carried out involving measures of project performance suggests that management contracting performs significantly better than traditional contracting with regard to factors involving time and project complexity.[51] Management contracting developed in the building industry although its use was also recommended for civil engineering projects.[52] The typical management contract involves a management contractor assuming overall supervisory, co-ordination and management roles during construction. Although very early in terms of the research that has been carried out, greater co-ordination on construction projects appears to hold out economic benefits and minimizes the costs of changed conditions.[53] The employer contracts with the management contractor who in turn subcontracts all works or enters into one main contract with a main

---

[48] See e.g. clauses 4.4.1 and 4.6 in the appendix of JCT/MT.
[49] See clauses 11.2 and 50 ECC. See JONES, GLYN P. *A New Approach to the ICE Conditions of Contract.* The Construction Press, Lancaster, 1975, vol. 1.
[50] See discussion clause 11.2(29), (30) ECC.
[51] NAOUM, G. Critical Analysis and Cost of Management and Traditional Contracts. *Journal of Construction Engineering and Management*, 1994, **120**, 687.
[52] *Management Contracting.* CIRIA, London, 1983, CIRIA Report 100, 23 based on research carried out by HAYES, R. W. *et al.*, 1995.
[53] O'BRIEN, WILLIAM J. *et al.* An Economic View of Project Coordination. *Construction Management and Economics*, 1995, **13**, 393–400. The FIDIC Orange Book 1st clause 4.4, parts I and II deal with co-ordination expressly.

contractor who in turn subcontracts all or a portion of the works.[54] Unlike traditional subcontracting the management contractor will normally not assume any responsibility toward the employer for subcontractor defaults.[55] Under the ECC management contract the contractor agrees to manage the contractor's design and the construction and installation of the works.[56] The contractor will not generally be expected to assume any construction responsibilities. Thus the contractor will ordinarily subcontract all design, construction and installation of the works according to the works information.[57] As with the cost reimbursement contract main option, the contractor will be paid actual cost as defined and the fee as agreed.[58]

Management contracting may be contrasted with construction management which the NEC specifically provides for by appointing the project manager as the construction manager. As a means of classifying forms of contract according to project organization the NEC also most closely resembles overall construction management, as distinct from traditional and management contracting project organizations.[59] In this case the employer could appoint the construction management contractor as the project manager. Hence, like traditional construction management, the contractor would not assume any responsibility for the actual construction work but would fulfil a management role instead. This would leave the employer in a position to contract directly with a specialist contractor using any of the preferred main options. In construction management the employer will contract directly with all specialist and trade contractors[60] while concurrently employing a construction manager for supervisory, co-ordination and management roles during construction. The construction manager will have responsibility for the construction work. This is accomplished by appointing the construction management contractor as the project manager.[61] The contractor will then advise the employer in turn on contracting through specialist and trade contractors using any of the NEC main options. The functions that the construction manager fulfils are similar to those of the management contractor. In both

[54] See generally *NJCC Code of Procedure for Selection of a Management Contractor and Works Contractors*. National Joint Consultative Committee for Building, London, 1991.

[55] See generally PRICE, JENNIE. *Sub-contracting under the JCT Standard Forms of Building Contract*. MacMillan, Basingstoke, 1994.

[56] Clause 20.2 ECC.

[57] See clause 20.2 ECC.

[58] See clauses 11.2 and 50 ECC.

[59] See O'REILLY MICHAEL, n. 21 above, pp. 3–7 and discussion in Chapter 3 above. See generally CURTIS, B. *et al. Roles, Responsibilities and Risks in Management Contracting*. CIRIA, London, 1991, CIRIA Special Publications 81.

[60] See the Latham Report, paragraph 4.14, 23 here on the use of term specialist and trade contractors in preference to subcontractors.

[61] See generally *Construction Management: Selection and Appointment of Construction Manager and Trade Contractors*. RIBA Publications, London, 1994, RIBA guidance note 8.

forms of contracting the construction manager's and management contractor's obligations are determined contractually.[62]

Other options

There are numerous others forms of contracting that may be referred to, even though they are not as common as those discussed above. For the most part these other forms of contract combine one or more features of either traditional or the newer forms of contracting; for instance design, construct and manage; design and manage; design and construction management etc.

Secondary option clauses

In addition to the selection of a main option the ECC also requires consideration of 15 additional matters. These matters are grouped together under the heading 'secondary option clauses'. Although initially confusing,[63] the fact that not all clauses are used does not pose any real problems. The choice of whether to use these options is left to the employer in the first instance. The selection of any secondary option clause should be identified in part one of the Contract Data. The employer's choice is, of course, dependent upon agreement by the contractor as well.

The secondary options ultimately allow the parties themselves to be the drafters and to make many of the choices which might otherwise have been made for them in other standard forms which then often necessitate amendments. The optional clauses are in essence different solutions for the parties. Justin Sweet writes of the topic in terms of the ability to customize a contact.

> If the standard contract makes it difficult to customize, to accommodate it to nonstandard arrangements, this reflects adversely on the standard contract and will limit its use. The NEC dealt with this by the use of core unchanging provisions, with the possibility of attaching optional clauses dealing with various topics. Other techniques are blank spaces, such as in provisions dealing with payment and retention ... The easier to customize the better the standard contract.[64]

---

[62] See generally FRYER, B. *Practice of Construction Management*, 3rd edn. Blackwell Science, London, 1997; PIKE, ANDREW. Construction Management and the JCT Contracts. *International Construction Law Review*, 1992, 476; JONES, G. W. Construction and Project Management – The Structure and its Impact on Project Participants. USA – The Experience and Trends. *International Construction Law Review*, 1993, 425; DORTER, J. B. Construction and Project Management – Australian Expectation and Experience. *International Construction Law Review*, 1993, 435.

[63] BAIRD, ANDREW, see n. 29 above, 118–119.

[64] See SWEET, JUSTIN. Judging Contracts: Some Reflections on the Third International Construction Law Conference. *International Construction Law Review*, 1994, 435–436.

While the NEC includes a number of secondary options that are not standard to other forms it is an open question whether the core clauses and secondary options provided are sufficient for the main options or modes of procurement encompassed. Notwithstanding the opportunity to supplement the clauses through the use of option Z, additional conditions, it is submitted that the NEC drafters should offer a longer list of secondary options. The reason for this is to offer *maximum* flexibility to the parties and to ensure a consistent drafting style. If it was felt inappropriate to list further secondary options in each printed contract form or book then it is recommended that a further book, headed Engineering and Construction Contract, 'additional clauses', be prepared. This book could contain sample wording for a wide variety of additional clauses that may be relevant to individual project needs. It is further submitted that the availability of such additional clauses would not detract from the NEC system as a whole and the logic of its structure which includes works information, site information, Contract Data and schedules of cost components. The secondary option clauses may be identified as follows.

- 'Performance bond' – option G.
- 'Parent company guarantee' – option H.
- 'Advanced payment to the *Contractor*' – option J.
- 'Multiple currencies' – option K.
- 'Sectional Completion' – option L.
- 'Limitation of the *Contractor's* liability for his design to reasonable skill and care' – option M.
- 'Price adjustment for inflation' – option N.
- 'Retention' – option P.
- 'Bonus for early Completion' – option Q.
- 'Delay damages' – option R.
- 'Low performance damages' – option S.
- 'Changes in the law' – option T.
- 'Construction (Design and Management) Regulations 1994' – option U.
- 'Trust Fund' – option V.
- 'Additional conditions of contract' – option Z.

No options are assigned to the letters I, O, W, X, or Y and it may be emphasized that not all of the secondary options are applicable to all main options. The secondary option clauses are discussed individually in relation to those main options and their core clauses where they are relevant. It may be noted that the drafters recommend that certain of the secondary option clauses not be used with certain main options.[65]

---

[65] See secondary options ECC: option K not with main options C, D, E and F; option N not with main options E and F; option P not with main option F; option U not to be used outside the United Kingdom.

Schedule of Cost Components

The ECC contains two schedules of cost components. The schedules are referred to as the Schedule of Cost Components (SCC) and the Shorter Schedule of Cost Components (SSCC). The SCC is part of the conditions of contract under all main options save F. The SCC contains seven headings or items for which cost components will be material: people, equipment, plant and materials, charges, manufacture and fabrication, design and insurance. The division of cost components is routine and one would not expect the term normally to be used unqualifiedly. By comparison another breakdown of cost components used in project management is as follows: direct cost, prime cost, indirect costs (overhead), fixed and variable overhead costs, labour burden, materials burden, overhead recovery, standard costs, factor costs, carriage and insurance costs.[66] The SSCC has three significant differences from the SCC:

- fewer specific cost components for people;
- the cost of equipment is based on published or agreed rates instead of a depreciation and maintenance charge; and
- all charges are allowed for by a tendered percentage for overheads for people.[67]

The drafters envisage that the SSCC would be preferable to the SCC when a large number of compensation events are anticipated, or when the compensation events will be of a low value, or on low value contracts given the higher costs involved in using the SCC. The two Schedules of Cost Components differ across main options A to E only in respect of the first introductory paragraph. The contents in these main options otherwise remain the same in the ECC. This is not the case in the SCC in the Plant Contract. The Plant Contract has only one SCC and it differs from the ECC. The Schedule of Cost Components in the Plant Contract is divided into the following seven sections: factory manufacture and fabrication; people at site; equipment used at site; brought in materials; charges; professional technical staff including design, engineering and installation services; and insurance.

The Professional Services Contract, Adjudicator's Contract, and Short Contract do not contain Schedules of Cost Components. The SCC and SSCC have two principal uses.

- They define the cost components, which are included in an assessment of changed costs arising from compensation events under all main options save F.
- They define the cost components for which a contractor and subcontractor will be directly reimbursed.[68]

---

[66] LOCK, DENNIS, see n. 26 above, pp. 55–60.
[67] Guidance notes SSCC, 101.
[68] Guidance notes SCC, 93; however the SSCC cannot be used for this purpose under main options C, D and E; Guidance notes SSCC, 101.

A materially identical SCC and SSCC are contained in the ECSC. Thus, costs are either within the SCC or SSCC and potentially directly recoverable or not. Individual items which are included as cost components in the SCC may limit certain types of restitutionary claims being made. For example, under section 6, 'Design' includes the cost of design of the works and equipment done outside the working areas. Thus omission of this cost component means the contractor has to recover the costs in the fee. Where the cost components are not within either Schedule they may still be indirectly recoverable under the fee.[69] Thus a division has been drawn in terms of where individual cost components fall and as such how they must be taken into account in bidding. With Schedules of Cost Components figures are not needed at the tender stage but are instead valued at market or competitively tendered prices. This approach differs from past approaches. A division has been set in the first instance by the drafters of the NEC; however, it is not immutable. Therefore the employer could add or delete individual cost components. Under the drafting scheme deletion would add such components' costs to the fee.[70] In theory this would, of course, impact upon the bid which the contractor would make as a result. Once again by specifying the costs in advance the risk of disagreement over the inclusion or exclusion of any individual item is lessened. The SCC should serve to reduce significantly disputes under the cost reimbursement options as this area has typically been productive of disputes. It may be noted that cost component schedules have been used successfully in other forms of contract.[71]

Cost data is available from a wide variety of sources at various levels of aggregation. In originally compiling the Schedules references were made by the drafters to a number of source documents, notably: *Target and Cost Reimbursable Construction Contracts Part C: Preparation and Contract Conditions*; *Schedule of Dayworks Carried out Incidental to Contract Works*; *Price Adjustment Formulae for Building Contracts (Series 2 revised) – Descriptions of the Indices*; *Price Adjustment Formulae for Civil Engineering Contracts; 1 Civil Engineering Works* as well as contract documents prepared by United Kingdom consultants for overseas target cost construction contracts and submissions by members of the working group, although no reference is made to these sources save the FCEC Schedule of Dayworks in the current edition of the guidance notes.[72] Published data may be based upon ranges from costs per square foot for

---

[69] The Fee is defined in clause 11.2(17) ECC.

[70] See clause 52.1 ECC.

[71] SCHNEIDER, MICHAEL E. Mastering the Interfaces – Construction Contracts Drafting for Dispute Avoidance. *International Construction Law Review*, 1993, 407 endnote 17 referring to the IChemE Reimbursable conditions and supporting guidance notes, and the UNIDO Contract, Cost Reimbursable version, Annexure XXVII.

[72] Guidance notes Consultation Document, 63 referring to PERRY, J. G. *et al. Target and Cost Reimbursable Construction Contracts Part C*; *Schedule of Dayworks Carried out Incidental to Contract Works*. FCEC, London, October 1977; *Price Adjustment Formulae for Building Contracts (Series 2 revised) – Descriptions of the Indices*. PSA, HMSO, London, 1970; *Price Adjustment Formulae for Civil Engineering Contracts; 1 Civil Engineering Works*. HMSO, NEDO, London, 1973.

certain types of buildings to detailed unit prices on individual construction components and materials. The cost data may be developed through national surveys, questionnaires, negotiated labour rates, and actual job cost data or otherwise and may vary with the source or the publishers. A critical factor in choice of cost data is currency of the information and in this regard computer databases are becoming increasingly popular.

Contract Data

The term 'Contract Data' is used in the ECC to refer to data that exists at the 'Contract Date'. Its purpose is to provide the data required under the conditions of contract peculiar to a particular contract and to define the details of the parties' agreement.[73] In general, that use of this drafting technique is seen as advantageous. Justin Sweet, for example, holds that blanks in a form contract are an 'adaptable' advantage.[74] Contract Data from both the employer and the contractor are contained in two parts. In this regard the Contract Data details reflect in part what Professor Phillip Capper, speaking generally, has called 'contract parameters'; for example, what the client has to do, what the contractor has to do, by what dates these various tasks have to be done and the pre-defined mechanisms for payment.[75] The employer's data and requirements are set out in part one and the contractor's data and proposals are set out in part two of the Contract Data of the contract respectively.[76] In comparison the FIDIC Orange Book 1st clause 1 part II contains a useful list of matters in the clause that come out of the conditions and which may be relevant to the employers requirements; as well as a definition of the Contractor's Proposal in clause 1.1.1.5 part I.

The division of subject matter between parts one and two has been assigned by the drafters but it should be noted that situations may be expected to arise in individual projects when the data may have more appropriately been provided by the *other* party. In these cases amendment to the respective parts may be called for. The Contract Data performs a similar function to the appendix to other forms of contract or their tenders.[77] Both employers and contractors are invited to use the Contract Data format and wording in the inviting, assessing and managing of contracts and are given a limited licence for this purpose by the ICE.[78]

---

[73] Guidance notes NEC, 17.

[74] SWEET, JUSTIN. Standard Construction Contracts: Some Advice to Construction Lawyers. *Construction Law Journal*, 1991, +, 14.

[75] CAPPER, PROFESSOR PHILLIP. Management of Legal Risks in Construction. A paper given to the Society of Construction Law at a meeting in Wales on 21 September 1994.

[76] See generally BARTLETT, ROBERT E, Writing Technical Proposals. *Preparing International Proposals*. Thomas Telford, London, 1997, pp. 99–159.

[77] The Consultation Document originally referred to the 'Schedule' of Contract Data. See generally for an example of such appendices: ICE 6th Appendix parts 1 and 2; DOM/1 part 1 sections A, B, and C. Section C in DOM/1 contains 15 parts. JCT 80 expressly makes the Appendix a contract document. It may also be equated with the 'Abstract of Particulars' used in GC/Works/1 3rd; and 'Time Schedule' in ACA 2.

[78] See guidance notes Appendix 5, 121.

Consistent use of terminology is as important here as in using any other form of tender in bidding. Particular instruction regarding the completion of the Contract Data is given in the guidance notes.[79]

Part one – data provided by the employer
Part one of the Contract Data consists of data provided by the employer. It will be completed by each employer under each contract to be let using the NEC. Part one comprises two sections.

- Statements given in all contracts: options chosen, description of the works, key people, where the works information and site information are found, Site boundaries, language of the contract, law of the contract, period for reply, contractor's liability for design defects, starting date, possession dates, revised programme dates, defects date, defect correction period, currency chosen, assessment interval, interest details, weather details, risks and insurance and disputes and termination.
- Optional statements which may include: arbitration procedure, completion date, take over, programme dates, payment periods, additional compensation events, additional employer risks, insurance coverage for employer plant and materials, other insurance details, method of measurement, share percentages and share ranges, actual cost forecast intervals, exchange rate references, performance bond amounts, advanced payment amounts, instalments and repayment periods, currency details, exchange rate references, completion dates, bonuses, delay damages, price adjustment factors and base dates and indices, retention amounts and percentages, bonus, delay damages, low performance damages, trustees, and additional conditions.

The marginal notes in section one correspond to the numbering of the core clauses. The optional statements in the second section reflect both additional statements and the optional clauses themselves. All optional statements are introduced or begin with the word 'if' and are in bold type. They provide guidance to users in this regard and would not be expected to be reproduced as such by the employer under part one or the contractor under part two. Thus there is a simple correspondence between part one and the conditions of contract that should facilitate use. The employer will complete part one so far as relevant to the invitation to tender. In particular the core clauses as well as the options that the employer relies upon will be inserted. The contractor's fundamental obligation under the contract will be to build or supply the works which are set out in general terms in part one and more specific terms in the works information which also appears in part one. While the ECC does not define the 'works' it is an identified term and it is elaborated upon in definitions of other terms including 'Provide the Works', and 'Works Information'. The term 'works' is also used generally in other standard

---

[79] See guidance notes NEC, 17–26.

forms.[80] Certain statements of the employer in part one are subject to change under the conditions of contract.[81]

Part two – data provided by the contractor

Part two of the Contract Data consists of data provided by the contractor in response to an invitation to tender and as part of the offer. Part two is divided into three sections.

- Statements given in all contracts: name and address of the contractor; fee percentage; areas outside the Site which are intended to be used as working areas; key people and works information for the contractor's design.
- Optional statements, which will depend upon the terms of the invitation to tender and may include, based upon the format of part two, the following: programme, completion date, activity schedule, bill of quantities, tendered total of prices and data for schedule of cost components.
- Data for Schedule of cost components.

However, there are no marginal notes and no direct correspondence to the conditions of contract. Part two is also shorter than part one and in this way underscores employer control. The data provided by the contractor will be used by the employer in the assessment of the tender and subsequently, for instance, in the assessment of compensation events.

While use of the Contract Data as a drafting tool provides additional flexibility the references themselves could be prejudicial in some cases if one is not familiar with the NEC provisions as a whole. Thus, for example, regarding timeframes, an 'assessment interval' is not to exceed five weeks. This maximum timeframe could have been included in the drafting. In this sense it is the indirectness of the language that may be misleading.[82] Some attempt has been made to mitigate the effect, by italicizing the wording and in other cases requiring the parties to insert details themselves and thus enhancing the probability that they will have to turn their minds to the detail of the provision.

---

[80] For example, GC/Works/1 3rd; and JCT 80 and often in contradistinction to the 'work'. Clause 1(1) ICE 6th defines 'Works' as meaning the Permanent Works together with the Temporary Works; and in Works Contract/2 (JCT 87 contract series works contract conditions) the 'Works' are defined with reference to the particulars in the Works Contract/1, section 1, the Invitation to Tender and may include specifications, bills of quantities, schedules of rates and otherwise. FIDIC 4th defines the 'Works' as 'the Permanent Works and the Temporary Works or either of them as appropriate'. Hence the term works is broadly used in the industry and is accorded both specific meanings in individual contexts and generically as well.

[81] For example, naming key people.

[82] DUNCAN WALLACE made the same point with reference to this practice under the RIBA and now JCT forms in *Building and Civil Engineering Standard Forms*. Sweet & Maxwell, London, 1969, p. viii.

Works information

The NEC documents exhibit a higher level of generality than is the case under most other standard forms of contract. The choice was intentional and was done to facilitate the 'flexibility' or broadest possible use of the form across traditional disciplines and sectors as well as to address the majority of options in current use. However, in making this choice the details which are essential to provide certainty in a contract cannot simply be omitted. They must still be addressed. It will be a crucial test of the form in assessing whether the level of generality that was adopted was appropriate. Andrew Baird has pointed out that the level of generality has been problematic at times in his experience with instances of both omissions from the works information as well as over-specifing occurring when moving from the use of a traditional specification.[83]

The ECC has elected to address both aspects of significant contractual detail and procedures in the 'Works Information' rather than the 'conditions of contract'.[84] There are several benefits that follow from this choice. First, it is submitted that fewer legal disputes are likely to arise over the meaning and contents of the works information than over conditions. Solicitors and the courts seem to have ceded most, although not all, of their jurisdiction in construing the meaning of specifications, schedules, rates, bills of quantities and the like to the parties to the contract and the other professionals on site. In other words, transferring details to the works information will serve to reduce the legal content of the contract from the technical content. Secondly, the removal of these details to the works information signals to the parties that the information is important but is not essential to the regulation of their legal *relationship*. This signal is reinforced by the structure of the ECC, core clauses and optional clauses. The parties are reminded that there are only nine essential issues that must be dealt with by them. The secondary option clauses structure then invites the parties to consider a further fourteen matters. It contrasts with the JCT 80 drafting which puts forward approximately forty matters as essential for the legal regulation of their relationship. Given that the parties' focus should be on the completion of the works (without denigrating the importance of defining that obligation in legal terms[85]), the simplification of contractual governance should assist in achieving their principal objective. It has been argued above that the availability of sample wording for additional conditions which may be appropriate in certain projects but which the parties are not obliged to adopt does not detract from this position. Diminishing the legal content of

---

[83] BAIRD, ANDREW, see n. 29 above, 117.

[84] Not every commentator supports this position, thus Guy Cottam, for example, says leaving the procedures to be adopted for ownership of materials off-site to the works information is 'just passing the buck': Covering all the Options. *Construction News*, 3 June 1993, 13.

[85] Barnes states that the contract contains 'only two or three traditional "legal" phrases': BARNES, DR MARTIN. The New Engineering Contract – An Update. *International Construction Law Review*, 1996, 90.

the NEC is an integral part of the strategy adopted by the drafters and also a way of shifting the emphasis in the contract away from lawyers and toward project managers and engineers. J. G. Perry, one of the NEC drafters, and D. J. Hoare[86] have set out some of the reasons behind this intention:

- the desire and need of many clients to reduce wastage of resources caused by disputes;
- the need for more efficient management of construction contracts; and
- the increasing importance of transferability of practice across national boundaries.[87]

The works information describes what the contractor is to supply or build under the contract. In this regard important procedures are brought to the attention of the parties. This is unlike other standard forms that seldom, if at all, refer to the specification itself in the general conditions. These references, tantamount to cross-references without specifics, should serve to foster integration across the contract documents. Clause 11.2(5) identifies and defines 'Works Information' in the following manner:

Works Information is information which either
- specifies and describes the *works* or
- states any constraints on how the *Contractor* Provides the Works[88] and is either
- in the documents which the Contract Data states it is in or
- in an instruction given in accordance with this contract.

Some general comments may be made. The term 'specifies' may intentionally connote 'specifications' as it might be expected that much of the employer's works information will still be given in this form although clearly the works information itself goes far beyond specifications. The 'descriptions' may be expected to comprise different types of drawings in varying degrees of detail as well as models. The description of the works itself may be expected to include their general description, arrangement and location. 'Constraints', for example, could pertain to methods of working or access. There is no requirement for the 'documents' noted to be formal contract documents. Details of where the works information is to be found are inserted in part one of the Contract Data provided by the employer. Thus part one provides: '[t]the works information is in ...'; hence emphasis is placed upon the word 'in' here. Similarly, if the contractor is to provide works information for the design, the contractor is accordingly obliged under clause 11.2(5) and part two of the Contract Data to state what the works information is *in*.

All documents comprising the works information upon acceptance by the employer should be listed in parts one and two of the Contract Data. While this requirement serves to assist in keeping track of such works

---

[86] PERRY, J. G. and HOARE, D. J., see n. 12 above, pp. 81–97.
[87] *Ibid.*, 81–82.
[88] See clause 11.2(4) ECC.

information documents not every reference in the conditions of contract to the works information necessitates a formal or corresponding entry in the Contract Data. The employer's data and requirements are set out in part one while the contractor's data and proposals are set out in part two of the Contract Data. The contractor's proposals for works information will normally centre upon design requirements.[89] The guidance notes provide details of what the works information should generally list or include.[90] Drawings should be given a broad meaning given the intent to use the NEC as a multidisciplinary form. Other forms of contract may be referred to for additional guidance; for instance FIDIC 4th which defines 'drawings' as also including calculations and technical information, samples, patterns, models, operation manuals and other technical information of a like nature.[91] The reliance on the works information has prompted one commentator[92] to suggest the use of a checklist (see Appendix 5, page 629) or standard format document to ensure the most comprehensive coverage of the details that should be addressed in the works information. Building upon this suggestion a form of sample works information could be compiled. It should be noted that this is a sample checklist for consideration of preliminary details that the conditions imply should be addressed in the works information before work begins. It does not seek to address those changes to the works information which arise after commencement of the works. The NEC form lends itself to the use of checklists and others could similarly be prepared.[93]

Site information

'Site Information' is an identified term and defined in clause 11.2(6) as information which describes the 'Site' and its surroundings and is in the contract documents which the Contract Data states it is in.[94] It can be remarked that part of this definition thus relies upon the definition of the 'Site' to give it meaning as well. The 'Site' in turn is an identified term and defined as 'the area within the *boundaries of the site* and the volumes above and below it which are affected by work included in this contract'.[95] While the definition seeks to state what site information is, it is also worthwhile noting what site information is not; that is neither information in an activity schedule,[96] nor information in a bill of quantities.[97] The definition is significant in at least two material respects.

---

[89] See Contract Data part two.

[90] See guidance notes NEC, 21–23.

[91] FIDIC 4th clause 1.1(b) (i).

[92] BAIRD, ANDREW, see n. 29 above, 114.

[93] A novel use of checklists can be seen in Pat Guthrie's text, *Cross-Check: Integrating Building Systems and Working Drawings*. McGraw-Hill, New York, 1998, setting out not only checklists but 'cross-check lists' to bring out interfaces in the work.

[94] See also discussion clause 60.2 ECC below.

[95] Clause 11.2(7) ECC. See also discussion below.

[96] Clause 54.1 ECC.

[97] Clause 55.1 ECC.

First, as site information is only referred to in part one of the Contract Data the drafters appear to have imposed the obligation for identifying where site information is to be found only upon the employer. Secondly, the employer's statement regarding the location of the site information must be given. This follows from the inclusion of the site information in section 1 of part one or the general statements for the contract rather than in the optional statements. Although site information resembles works information in that it is information that is incorporated by reference to other documents, it is also distinct from works information in certain ways. Significantly there is no express provision in the ECC to authorize changes to site information. The distinctiveness can also be used in other ways.

> The NEC is particularly well structured ... in that the Site Information and Works Information are identified as separate and different documents. It is therefore straightforward to leave a 'gap' of drawn information between the site information and the design drawings. The contractor chooses from [that] provided, detailed methods that are best suited to him to produce the performance criteria. [98]

Lastly, site information is also a factor in relation to two compensation events.[99]

In general site information may include the following:

* subsoil investigation borehole records and test results;
* reports obtained by the employer concerning physical conditions within the site[100] or its surroundings including mapping, hydrographic data and hydrological information;
* references to publicly available information about the site and its surroundings;
* information about plant, piped and other services above and below the surface of the site;
* information about buildings, structures, plant and machinery adjacent[101] to and on the site.[102]

The difficulties inherent in dealing with site conditions, including sub-soil and hydrological characteristics, are so great that only the most transparent means of dealing with them can be sanctioned. Consistent with this it is thus submitted that full disclosure of all information with regard to site conditions should be the policy that contracts adopt. It is also submitted that site information should be construed broadly and extend, where employers are so inclined, to include not only factual

[98] WILLIAMS, DAVID H, see n. 31 above, p. 24.
[99] See discussion of clauses 60.2 and 60.3 ECC below.
[100] Clause 11.2(7) ECC.
[101] Meaning lying near but not necessarily adjoining *Wellington Corporation* v. *Lower Hutt Corporation* [1904] AC 773 at 775–776, PC.
[102] Guidance notes NEC, 23.

references but also interpretative information when available as well. This would seem to be consistent with the drafters' intent.[103] The NEC marks an improvement over the ICE 6th for instance but does not go as far as the FIDIC Orange Book. Thus, under the ICE 6th, the site condition provisions are unclear in this essential respect. Under clause 4.9 of the Orange Book the employer is under an unequivocal obligation to make available to the contractor all data on hydrological and sub-surface conditions at the site and the obligation even extends to environmental impact assessments.[104] The Orange Book provision is qualified in one sense, however, in that it does not state that the tender was based upon the Site data (site information) primarily on the basis that the design role of the contractor is likely to mean the contractor will wish to pursue his or her own investigations according to the design chosen and the fact that the employer's site data may be limited in some material ways in any case. The Orange Book provision is far reaching and exceeds in scope the obligation imposed upon the employer in the ECC.[105] Clause 11(1) of the ECC only arguably 'deems' the employer to have made available site information to the contractor before tender, thus it is unclear whether the Employer is contractually bound to provide the information or not. If not, what effect will assuming that the employer has done so, by virtue of the deeming provision, have upon the contractor in the result? At a minimum the site information provisions in the NEC seek to erase some assumptions which are ambiguous in the way the ICE provision does but they do not go as far as they should. In particular they do not move as far as the commentary below suggests regarding relational duties of disclosure.

Activity schedules
The NEC uses 'activity schedules'. An activity schedule is a list of all the work the contractor intends to do to fulfil the contract. An activity list is a term that is also used in the project management literature and is a useful means of making individuals aware of their commitments and giving instructions. It is a feature of main options A and C. The list comprises various discrete activities, which are priced on a lump sum basis. In this regard the activity schedule is a pricing document. A bill of quantities is also a pricing document but one which uses unit rates according to the ECC terminology for pricing. Information in the bill of quantities is also neither works information nor site information and similarly not intended to have contractual effect. The NEC methodology with its emphasis upon activities rather than volumes necessarily could significantly change assumptions made in decision models and thus the structure of

[103] See guidance notes, 23.
[104] Similarly clause 11.1 FIDIC 4th. Clause 11.1 imposes an affirmative obligation on the employer to make available all hydrological and sub-surface conditions data to the contractor before the tender.
[105] *Guide to the Use of FIDIC Conditions of Contract for Design-Build and Turnkey, First Edition.* FIDIC, Lausanne, 1996, p. 49.

construction operations.[106] Information in the activity schedules is neither works information nor site information[107] and in this regard is intended not to have contractual effect. In the absence of provision to the contrary by the employer it is the contractor who decides how best to divide the work into discrete activities. The cardinal rule that the contractor will follow in the division of work will be to use clearly identified activities that are easily verifiable. This approach will facilitate the calculation of payments to the contractor as each activity is completed. It may be supposed that given this freedom to divide work into activities the contractor might seek to use it to require the employer to make payments to him or herself, perhaps daily if not more often. However, one may expect that an employer would not accept any such tender from a contractor. In addition there are subsequent controls which the employer may resort to. Thus, the project manager may refuse to accept the contractor's programme if such payment provisions are included as not being practical or realistic.[108] In fact, and inasmuch as any revised activity schedule which is submitted by the contractor to the project manager for acceptance may not be accepted precisely because changed prices are not reasonably distributed between the activities, it may be possible to imply a term into the contract that activity schedules should also reasonably distribute the prices as defined in the first instance. Descriptions of activities may also be expected to include other aspects of the works assigned to or assumed by the contractor; for instance, design or temporary works and may or may not be 'scheduled' as such. In general, best practice dictates that all work should be scheduled as and be based upon a logical and feasible timescale. Scheduling should preferably be derived from a network, so that activities are arranged in an achievable sequence, with the available float used as necessary to smooth the expected pattern for each different type of project resource.[109] If the employer has selected either option A or C the instructions to tenderers may ask for the submission of an activity with the tender, in which case the contractor would then submit a priced activity schedule with it. One reference the contractor may have regard to in preparing activity schedules is the *Common Arrangement of Work Sections for Building Works* (CAWS). The CAWS seeks to define an efficient and generally acceptable arrangement for specifications and bills of quantities. It could be adapted for use with works information under the NEC. Principles underlying the preparation of the CAWS are intended to reflect construction activities *and* their inputs rather than simply inputs across some 300 sections. The common work sections may be characterized either predominantly by the resources used or their output. As one moves

---

[106] See the conclusions drawn by ANGELIS, DIANA ISAZA, in 'The Effects of Activity-Based Costing on Traditional Operations Research Models (Inventory, Lot Size, Scheduling, Break Even). PhD dissertation, University of Florida, 1996.

[107] Clause 54.1 ECC.

[108] See clause 31.3 ECC.

[109] LOCK, DENNIS, see n. 26 above.

toward output the CAWS could thus be seen to be helpful in defining activities in a standard way.[110]

The requirement to submit an activity schedule with the tender should serve to reduce one area of disputes regarding the payment interface. Under traditional lump sum measured contracts the work may be divided into parts or activities.[111] The activities are valued relative to the total lump sum price of the works and paid for in the same way after measurement. This situation, in contrast to the priced activity schedule with the tender in the NEC, leads to disputes under other forms.

> The difficulty which arises ... concerns the definition and value of the activities. The matter can have considerable influence on the contractor's cash flow. Therefore, he has an interest in valuing the early activities as high as possible. The employer has the opposite interest. Disputes on the valuation, therefore, are frequent.[112]

Bills of quantities

The NEC permits the use of bills of quantities and this is a feature of main options B and D. There is no limitation on the types of bills that may be used and thus they could be either nominated or measured or specified. A bill of quantities is generally a list of all the work and materials required for completing the contract. They are typically prepared by quantity surveyors. The bill of quantities will normally fix unit rates for every item of work to be done and materials to be consumed. Under traditional lump sum contracts the bills may be used for interim valuations and valuing variations. In addition to these functions the bills may also be used under remeasurement contracts to arrive at remeasurement prices. Conversely, under main option B, while the bills will be used for interim valuations, they will not be used to value variations unless the parties agree otherwise and valuation would then proceed on the basis of actual cost. Under main option D the bills are only used for interim valuations and then again only when the parties agree. In these ways it can be observed that bills of quantities perform a more *limited* role than under either traditional lump sum or remeasurement contracts. The bill of quantities is a pricing document under the NEC and may be used to determine the contract price by combining the totals of the unit rates multiplied by their quantities.

---

[110] The CAWS forms part of the Co-ordinated Project Information which includes *Project Specification: A Code of Procedures for Building Works.* Building Project Information Committee, London, 1987; *Production Drawings: A Code of Procedure for Building Works.* Building Project Information Committee, London, 1987; *Production Drawings: A Case Study*, 3 vols. Building Project Information Committee, London, 1987–1993; *SMM 7: A Code of Procedure for Measurement of Building Works.* RICS, London, 1988; and *A Code of Procedure for Building Works.* Building Project Information Committee, London, 1987.

[111] See SENIOR, G. *Risk and Uncertainty in Lump Sum Contracts.* CIOB, Ascot, 1990, CIOB Technical Information Service 113.

[112] SCHNEIDER, MICHAEL E., see n. 71 above, 414.

Information in the bill of quantities is neither works information nor site Information. As a result the bill of quantities is intended not to have contractual effect save provision to the contrary.[113] The bill of quantities will be based upon a method of measurement that will be specified in part one of the Contract Data. In general, care must be taken in allowing for a choice of method of measurement so that the method chosen properly reflects any contractor design obligations and thus overcomes the possibility of counting any work twice.

The programme

Programming and progress monitoring are particularly important in project work today and all project sponsors should understand both the range of techniques available to them and their merits. 'It is important to appreciate that these techniques are used for forward planning with the aim of eliminating potential future problems ... Programmes which cover the whole project process ... will help the project sponsor achieve success'.[114]

The programme is an integral part of the NEC system. It is one of a series of progress planning and control techniques[115] that are well known and which include bar charts, resource tables, project administration, flow charts (flow diagrams or research planning diagrams), estimating[116] and activity loops, network techniques[117] and delta analysis.[118] Bar charts or Gantt charts are used on construction and other projects to represent pictorially work plans and delivery schedules, and dates back to the work of Henry L. Gantt during World War I. Resource tables detail planned and actual resource consumption on a given project. Flow charts, flow diagrams or research planning diagrams are pictorial models with basic elements and notations. They are more complex than bar charts and may be used to illustrate activity precedence, mutual exclusion and looping.

Delta analysis is a measure of progress in terms of time and cost. The measure is normally expressed as deviation either positive, negative or zero for both time and cost. Thus there are a total of nine different progress situations on a project at any given time with only one situation being on plan for both time and cost. Delta analysis may be portrayed either in chart or graph form. On a chart the nine different progress

---

[113] Clause 55.1 ECC.

[114] *Programming and Progress Monitoring for Works Projects*, guidance note 52. HM Treasury, Central Unit on Procurement, London.

[115] See generally DAY, D. W. J. *Project Management and Control*. Macmillan, Basingstoke, 1994.

[116] See SMITH, N. J., *Project Cost Estimating*. Thomas Telford, London, 1995, Engineering Management Series.

[117] For example, critical path methods and programme evaluation and review techniques or 'PERT'. HOUGHTON, ANTHONY. Milestones and Liquidated Damages. *Construction Law Journal*, 1992, **8**, 232.

[118] See for examples in the presentation and use of delta analysis LANIGAN, MIKE. *Engineers in Business, The Principles of Management and Product Design*. Addison-Wesley Publishing Co, Wokingham, England, 1992, pp. 259–262.

situations are shown in a three by three matrix between time deviation and cost deviation on either side of the chart. On a graph progress is measured from zero at project start to 100 on completion against plan time, plan cost, actual time and actual cost. The deviations may also be expressed formulaically. Network analysis software programs along with the growth in the use of project management has led to ideal conditions for the programme to assume a larger role in construction and more sophisticated timetabling and scheduling details.[119] The programme is clearly central to one of the NEC drafting objectives; that is, its preparation and use is intended as a stimulus to good management. However, it is now only one of many other sophisticated tools that are available.

The programme may or may not be included in the contract documents; this decision will be left to the parties.

> If a contractor's programme was found to be a contract document it would bind not only the contractor to perform to it but also the employer to facilitate performance. That is, the employer's duty to avoid prevention which in normal circumstances extends only to not obstructing the contractor in his obligation to complete on time, could be widened so that prevention could apply to programme requirements. For this reason, amongst others, most employers avoid any programme, tender or otherwise, being incorporated in the contract documents.[120]

However, as a matter of course the contractor will be expected to provide a programme with the tender or shortly thereafter. The submission of the programme in this regard is governed by clause 11.2(14), the 'Accepted Programme'. The accepted programme provisions in the ECC invest the programme with contractual status. The 'accepted programme' is either that which is identified in the optional statements in part two of the Contract Data, if the parties agree to identify the programme in the Contract Data, or the latest programme which is accepted by the project manager.[121] The programme operates at all levels of the NEC including design, construction and installation and the contract procedures assume the programme is both current and attainable. The detailed programme requirements as well as its use and effect are considered further below.

Guidance notes
The NEC contains a set of guidance notes. The Latham Report in part recommended attached guidance notes for an effective form of contract. Other forms of contract, such as the new GC/Works/1, 2, 3 and 4 (1998) and (1999) series also include a commentary as part of the new documentation; and not long ago the Electrical Contractors' Association

---

[119] HOUGHTON, ANTHONY. Milestones and Liquidated Damages. *Construction Law Journal*, 1992, **8**, 232.

[120] EGGLESTON, BRIAN. *Liquidated Damages and Extensions of Time in Construction Contracts.* Blackwell Scientific Publications, Oxford, 1992, p. 197.

[121] Clause 11.2(14) ECC.

Specialist Engineering and Construction Contract system, or 'SEACC' was released with guidance notes for each form.[122] The guidance notes are divided into eight parts: introduction, contract strategy, tender documents, explanatory notes on the core and secondary option clauses, the SCC, an introductory note to the subcontract, and seven appendices. The seven appendices are: the clause numbering system; sample form of tender; sample form of agreement; model tender assessment sheet; contract data worked example; meteorological office notice; and a sample trust deed. The purpose of the guidance notes is 'to explain the background to the ECC, the reasons for some of its provisions and to provide guidance on how to use it'.[123] The importance of guidance notes has lately been confirmed in the Latham Report and *Matthew Hall Ortech Ltd* v. *Tarmac Roadstone Ltd* which relied upon them as an aid to construction of the IChemE *Model Form of Conditions of Contract for Process Plants.*[124] However, while the guidance notes are useful to explain the background the drafters also offer this caution; they are *not* a contract document[125] and 'should not be used for legal interpretation of the meaning of the ECC or the ECSC'.[126] This is in fact the second disclaimer in the contract; the first appearing on the reverse of the cover page: 'While every care has been taken in the preparation of this document neither the Institution of Civil Engineers nor Thomas Telford Services Ltd can accept any liability for any loss or damage which may be suffered by any person or organisation as a result of its use'. The disclaimer concerns the guidance notes only. No similar clause is included in the main option merged forms of contract. The differences in drafting and operation of the NEC with other forms suggest that the guidance notes have an important role to play. If there is a conflict in or across the contract documents we may assume that well-informed drafters were aware of the conflict and that the solution in the contract is the one chosen, and, in many cases once again, we also see why the particular solution was chosen.[127] In this way the guidance notes facilitate understanding and were intended in any event to be used in training individuals in the use of the NEC.[128] The importance of training to the successful introduction of the NEC is viewed by NEC panel members as essential.[129]

---

[122] See CURTIS, PINSENT. Synopsis of the GC/Works/1, 2, 3, and 4 Contract Documentation. *International Construction Law Review*, 1997, 596. CHAPPELL, D. Contract Spreads Confusion. *Architects Journal*, 1994, **200** (20), 52–53 has suggested that conflicts between the guidance notes and the NEC Contract may lead to confusion.

[123] Guidance notes NEC, 1.

[124] Latham Report, 5.18(4), 27 and *Matthew Hall Ortech Ltd* v. *Tarmac Roadstone Ltd* (1998) 87 BLR 96.

[125] Guidance notes NEC, 1.

[126] Guidance notes NEC, 1.

[127] See SWEET, JUSTIN, n. 64 above, 433.

[128] Consultation Document guidance notes, 6.

[129] See BAIRD, ANDREW. Pioneering the NEC System of Documents. *Engineering, Construction and Architectural Management*, 1995, 2(4), 254.

In a post-*Pepper* (*Inspector of Taxes*) v. *Hart* environment more use may be made of such aids to interpretation. In the *Pepper* case it was held that the rule excluding reference to Parliamentary material as an aid to statutory interpretation should be relaxed when the legislation was ambiguous or obscure or led to an absurdity.[130]

Flow charts

The NEC contract system comprises and indeed was based upon flow charts, which set out the procedures that are to be followed by parties to the contract.[131] The importance of following contractual procedures can be seen from a major literature review carried out by Majid and McCaffer, who rank inappropriate practices and procedures as the eleventh most significant factor in causing non-excusable delay.[132] The flow charts are intended to help people using the ECC 'to see how the clauses of the various ECC options come together to produce clear and precise sequences of action for the people involved'.[133] This description of the flow charts is significant in several ways. First of all, flow charting underscores that all clauses in the ECC, and it is submitted the other interlocking NEC documents as well, are intended to work, be read and applied together. The drafters write that '[b]ecause many sequences interact, users of the flowcharts will often have to review more than one sheet in order to track the full sequence of actions in one area'.[134] Secondly, the contract, and the flow charts which depict its procedures, are designed around logical actions. As with the guidance notes the flow charts are not one of the contract documents[135] but clearly can assist in both understanding of the contract and training in its operation. The drafters, however, have not gone as far as others have occasionally called for in suggesting '[t]ime arrows and other graphics [to be] ... as legally effective as contract drawings'.[136] It may also be assumed by analogy that the drafters did not intend that the flow charts should be used for legal interpretation. The number of flow charts closely parallels the number of core and secondary option clauses in the ECC; that is, 71 flow charts in the Second Edition. Clauses 10, 11, 12,

---

130 *Pepper* (*Inspector of Taxes*) v. *Hart* [1993] AC 593, HL.
131 NEC flow charts, preface.
132 MAJID, M. Z. ABD and McCAFFER, RONALD. Factors of Non-excusable Delays That Influence Contractors' Performance. *Journal of Management in Engineering*, May/June 1998, **14** (3), 42–49, 48
133 Guidance notes Consultation Document, 3.
134 NEC flow charts, preface.
135 NEC flow charts, preface.
136 ABRAHAMSON, MAX and WINTER, JEREMY. New Contract Systems – Permanent Change or Fashion? *The Building of Construction Law*. A paper presented at the Tenth Annual Construction Conference on 19 September 1997 by the Society of Construction Law and the Centre of Construction Law and Management. King's College, London, 1997. An interesting example of the use of flow charts in a wholly different context (family law) can be seen in DICKEY QC, ANTHONY. *Family Law* with a supplement by ZUVELA, PETER. *Family Law Flowcharts*. Law Book Company, Sydney, 1997.

18, 29 and 57 as well as secondary option clauses M, U and Z do not have flow chart representations. For the most part these clauses are too general to be flow charted. Flow charts are, in numerous instances, represented over several sheets of paper or pages. It may be noted that a much larger number of clauses were not flow charted in the First Edition of the flow charts. The flow charts are represented pictorially with a defined protocol or legend and uniform abbreviations.[137] They are central to one of the key drafting objectives of the NEC; clarity and simplicity in the use and operation of the contract system.[138] The flow charts seek to achieve this end by overcoming conflicts in contract procedures and ensuring that procedures are not open-ended. Clarity, the ease with which the language of the contract can be understood, has been shown to be an important factor in reducing risk.[139] While the flow charts clearly promote this drafting objective it should also be observed that they do represent procedures entailing an administrative burden, which has been subjected to both criticism[140] and approval.[141]

In general, flow charts are pictorial models with basic elements and notations or algorithms. Glyn P. Jones:

[a]n algorithm is the word used to describe a logical procedure for the solution of any problem in a given class. An algorithmic approach to a problem uses a step by step procedure in a reasoned logical way. Flowcharts are a logical network providing a pictorial step by step representation of a process (algorithm) indicating the arrangement and action of its parts by which it produces a given result.[142]

---

[137] See the NEC flow charts for same.
[138] Guidance notes Consultation Document, 3.
[139] See BUBSHAIT, ABDULAZIZ and ALMOHAWIS, SOLIMAN A. Evaluating the General Conditions of a Construction Contract. *International Journal of Project Management*, 1994, **12**(3), 134.
[140] COX, PROFESSOR ANDREW and THOMPSON, IAN. Is the NEC Going to Succeed? – An Examination of the Engineering and Construction Contract. (Alias the NEC 2nd Edition). *International Construction Law Review*, 1996, 328 and citing in ns. 6, 7, and 8 BAIRD, ANDREW. Pioneering the NEC System of Documents, 249–270; IRELAND, P. The Influence of the Communication Flow Requirements of the NEC on the Efficiency of the Contract and Organisation Concerned. Dissertation, University of Birmingham, 1995; and BRISTOWS COOKE CARPMAEL. The NEC – Novel Enlightened Contracting? *Construction Update*, February 1995.
[141] JONES, GLYN P., writing in the preface to the second edition of his text, *A New Approach to the ICE Conditions of Contract*. The Construction Press, Lancaster, 1975, vol. 1, notes his flow charts were enthusiastically welcomed.
[142] JONES, GLYN P. *A New Approach to the International Civil Engineering Contract. A Detailed Analysis of the FIDIC International Standard Form of Civil Engineering Contract.* Construction Law Press, Lancaster, 1979. See also JONES, GLYN P. *A New Approach to the 1980 Standard Form of Building Contract.* The Construction Press, Lancaster, 1980; and POWELL-SMITH, VINCENT and CHAPPELL, DAVID. *Building Contracts Compared and Tabulated*, 2nd edn. Legal Studies and Services Publishing, London, 1990.

The provision of flow charts by commentators such as Jones fills a gap with respect to these other forms. They are more complex than bar charts and may be used to illustrate activity precedence, mutual exclusion and looping in almost any area. On the NEC flow charts the basic elements and notations appear to be taken from BS 4058.[143] In flow charting, arrows are called paths (or zero time connections); ovals are called event boxes (e.g. start, finish); rectangles are called activity boxes; diamonds are decision diamonds (yes or no); 'gates' give you 'and' and 'or'; and path branches (e.g. several arrows). The use of boxes alone as part of a contract document can also be referred to in other forms of contract. Max Abrahamson's *New Construction Contract* places boxes around conditions in the contract; similarly the RIBA/CASEC ESA/1 form uses boxes to provide alternatives or choices for the parties, as does the ACA form of building agreement 1984, 1990 edition.[144] It may be noted the SC First Edition also uses boxes to encase notes about the contract but which do not form part of it. The principal advantage of the flow charts is their explicit display of activity precedence and path uncertainty situations.

The NEC flow charts may also be thought of in terms of estimating and activity loops. Thus individual or path branches may entail uncertainty. In fact there may be no certain way of predicting the elapsed time to move from one event or activity box to the next. This may occur notwithstanding that the activity itself may be narrowly defined. The flow chart will illustrate this uncertainty with an activity loop or transit loop. The uncertainty arises because the number of loop transits before one moves to the next event or activity box is unknown. Path length, hence duration, is a common estimating problem in construction. Sophisticated tendering procedures would entail assigning probabilities to different routes along the path network. This would then permit estimates to be derived with stated levels of risk. Such an approach differs from past approaches in many instances where 'all too often risk is either ignored or dealt with in an arbitrary way: simply by adding a 10% "contingency" onto the estimated cost of a project is typical. This is virtually certain to be inadequate and cause expensive delay, [and] litigation'.[145] Some survey work has found that contractors attempted to provide for risks in normally one of four ways: as a percentage of their profit margin; as a separate percentage on all costs; as a lump sum in the preliminaries; or as a percentage in one bill where the perceived risk was in the one bill alone.[146] Overall, where the scope of

---

[143] British Standards Institution, *Specification for Data Processing Flow Chart Symbols, Rules and Conventions*. British Standards Institution, London, 1987.

[144] See ABRAHAMSON, MAX. Risk, Management, Procurement & CCS, 375–392.

[145] CAPPER, PROFESSOR PHILLIP. Management of Legal Risks in Construction. A paper given to the Society of Construction Law at a meeting in Wales on 21 September 1994, referring to and summarizing the conclusions from P. A. THOMPSON'S and J. G. PERRY'S 1992 SERC project *Engineering Construction Risks* in Annexe 1 of his paper at 11.

[146] TAH, J. H. M. *et al.* A Survey of Indirect Cost Estimating in Practice. *Construction Management and Economics*, 1994, **12** (1), 31–36.

work is not known, or risks are otherwise higher than the Contractor has the ability to bear, either a high-risk premium should be expected if the contract is to be firm price or the contract should be reimbursable.

> There is a common tendency for owners, or their advisors, to ignore this last point and believe that a low fixed price bid for a high risk contract should be accepted. Experience shows this time and again to be a mistaken view.[147]

The use of flow charts and their activities on nodes presentation has another advantage; that is it lends the NEC to other project planning and control methods such as network techniques. Research planning diagrams (RPD) can be considered a network technique. Two of the most popular of these network techniques are the critical path[148] method (CPM) and the programme evaluation and review technique (PERT) or one of their derivatives.[149] Both are used on the control of construction and engineering projects to varying degrees and their importance has been recognized with a British Standard designation. PERT uses an events-on-nodes format while research planning diagrams (RPD) use an activities-on-nodes format as do flow charts.[150]

Engineering and Construction Subcontract

The Engineering and Construction Subcontract (ECSC) is one of the forms comprising the NEC system. Designated as 'the form of subcontract for use with the New Engineering Contract'[151] it could also be used independently with other standard forms if wished. The ECSC was produced as a First Edition in 1993. As described above in relation to the drafting objectives for the NEC the ECSC is almost wholly back-to-back with the conditions of contract in the ECC. This is intended to have significant advantages and reduce the likelihood of disputes. While the provisions are said to be almost wholly back-to-back, consequential amendments are made across the forms within the NEC system.[152] The

---

[147]   MORRIS, DR PETER. Current Trends in the Organisation of Construction Projects. In *Future Trends*, see n. 7 above, p. 191. See generally NORRIS, C. *et al. Project Risk Analysis and Management.* The Association of Project Managers, London, 1991. See also CROWLEY, L. G. and HANCHER, D. E. Risk Assessment of Competitive Procurement. *Journal of Construction Engineering and Management*, 1995, **121**, 230.

[148]   Information technology has entered the field and bar chart software will now perform critical path analysis with WYSIWYG features.

[149]   The earliest published work on PERT is attributed to MALCOLM, D. G. *et al.* Application of a Technique for Research and Development Program Evaluation. *Operations Research*, 1959, **7** (5), 646–670. See generally MODER, J. J. *et al. Project Management with CPM, PERT and Precedence Diagramming.* Van Nostrand Reinhold, New York, 1993.

[150]   *Use of Network Techniques in Project Management, Parts 1 to 4* (BS 6046). British Standards Institution, London, 1984.

[151]   Cover page of the ECSC.

[152]   See generally YULE, I. R. *Back to Back Contracting.* CIOB, Ascot, 1995, Construction Paper 48.

NEC Users' Group, with respect to this back-to-back feature, has written that the 'Subcontractor therefore has the same benefits and obligations as the main Contractor. It does not allow the "large" main Contractor to browbeat the "small" Subcontractor'.[153] While there are of course many instances of subcontractors who are much larger in size than main contractors the implication here is that a level playing field is sought between the parties.[154] In this regard it may be the same implication that has motivated some of the provisions in the Housing Grants, Construction and Regeneration Act 1996.

The ECSC adopts the same overall structure as the ECC with main options, core clauses, secondary option clauses, two Schedules of Cost Components, and the Contract Data in two parts. Most of the wording in the ECSC is identical to that in the ECC save where the circumstances would otherwise require change. The nine core clauses in the ECSC use the same headings as the ECC except for clause 2 that is headed 'The *Subcontractor's* main responsibilities'. This terminological change is, of course, respected throughout the form. Apart from this change the ECSC also differs from the ECC in some other important respects. Initially, and perhaps most importantly, the sole point of contact for the subcontractor is the contractor. Thus the roles of employer, project manger, and supervisor have been *merged* and throughout the form the respective responsibilities they would have under the ECC are now borne solely by the contractor. Amendments to the ECSC thus reflect this change. To clarify and distinguish the ECSC from other aspects of the ECC the ECSC adopts the prefixes 'sub' or 'subcontract' before numerous identified and defined terms.[155]

The ECSC matches all of the ECC main options save main option F – the management contract – which is not appropriate here. The secondary option clauses are identical to those in the First Edition of the ECC save two secondary option clauses that are missing and now appear in the Second Edition of the ECC.

- 'The Construction (Design and Management) Regulations 1994' – option U
- 'Trust Fund' – option V.

Similar to the ECC, the ECSC has two Schedules of Cost Components and a Contract Data in two parts. In general, and save for changes in terminology referred to above, the ECSC corresponds to the ECC. As such, commentary on the ECC will generally apply to the ECSC

---

[153] Introductory note for Subcontractors from the NEC Users' Group, guidance notes NEC, 103.

[154] The parties to the ECSC are the '*Contractor*' and '*Subcontractor*', clause 11.2(1) and thus replace the '*Employer*' and '*Contractor*' in the the ECC, clause 11.2(1).

[155] For example, clauses 11.2(3) '**Sub**contract Date'; 11.2(4) '**Subcontract** Works' and '**subcontract** *works*'; 11.2(5) '**Subcontract** Works Information' and '**Sub**contractor'; 11.2(9) '**Sub**subcontractor' and '**subcontract** works'; 11.2(12) '**Subcontract** Completion Date' and '**subcontract** completion date' ECSC (emphasis added).

provisions, and only where changes in the wording of the subcontract merit additional explanation will they be referred to in the text.

Professional Services Contract

The Professional Services Contract (PSC) is another of the New Engineering Contract documents. The route to publication of the contract followed the NEC precedent of consultation draft, comments and then first edition. Thus, the consultation draft was released in June 1992 and the First Edition was published in September 1994 and the Second Edition in June 1998. The PSC may be used for the appointment and govern the terms of engagement of various parties; in particular, the project manager, supervisor, architect, engineer or designers could work under the PSC on a project. Anecdotal evidence suggests some solicitors are being appointed under the PSC also. The PSC is a set of conditions only with the detailed services that the consultant will provide set out in something referred to as the 'Scope'. As with all forms in the NEC the Council of the ICE has approved the PSC.

The First Edition of the PSC adopted the same format and much of the terminology in use in the ECC and NEC as a whole. As with the introduction of the NEC the PSC too has been described as 'radical'. Gillian Birkby stated that '[t]he ICE *Professional Services Contract* (PSC) ... is radically different from the traditional forms of appointment for consultants emphasizing programming to avoid delays'.[156] The parties to the form are the 'Employer', once again, and the 'Consultant'. Both the 'Employer' and 'Consultant' are identified and defined terms as understood within the NEC system.[157] It is noteworthy that the second core clause in the PSC combines 'The Parties' main responsibilities' under this heading, while other NEC forms address only *one* of the pParties' main responsibilities under the comparable clause. The adjudicator's contract is a possible exception to this but is also unique in that it deals with a third Party to the contract appointed jointly by the parties. Where the PSC is used the consultant's principal obligation is to provide the services in accordance with the 'Scope'. Under the First Edition of the PSC the term used in place of 'Scope' was 'Brief'.[158] Relying heavily upon the ECC terminology, 'Provide the Services'[159] and

---

[156] BIRKBY, GILLIAN. A New Environment for Consultants. *Proceedings of the Institution of Civil Engineers*, 1995, **108**, part 3, 141–142. See for a critique of the language in particular CHAPPELL, D. Contract Spreads Confusion. *Architects' Journal*, 24 November 1994, 52–53. See also HELPS, DOMINIC. Professional Services Contract – Back to the Drawing Board? *Construction Law*, 1995/96, **6** (5), 181–184.

[157] See clause 11.2(1) PSC.

[158] See clause 21.1 PSC.

[159] Clause 11.2(4) PSC: 'To Provide the Services means to do the work necessary to complete the *services* in accordance with this contract'. The *services* themselves are an identified term for purposes of section 1 of part one of the Contract Data.

the 'Scope'[160] may be equated with the obligation of the contractor to 'Provide the Works' in accordance with the works information in the ECC.[161] Thus, as with other forms within the NEC system, certain terms have a greater importance to the parties' responsibilities than others do. The scope, once again, is precisely this sort of term.[162] In general the employer will choose the method of procurement or main option that would be used on a project. This choice clearly influences the nature of the services that the consultant would provide under the PSC or otherwise; in particular it would influence the corresponding main options used in the PSC.

The PSC has four main options under both the First and Second Editions although the letter prefixes changed in the Second Edition and are as follows.

(1) Main option A – priced contract with activity schedule.
(2) Main option C – target contract.
(3) Main option E – time based contract.
(4) Main option G – term contract.

Each of these main options provides different payment mechanisms and risk allocation. Both of these factors are significant in choosing the appropriate main option.[163] It is noteworthy that there is no provision in the PSC for payment as a percentage of the total cost of construction. Main options A and C reflect similar risk allocations to those in the comparable main options under the ECC.[164] However, under main option G the consultant carries a disproportionate share of the risk for performance at the agreed prices.[165] This follows from the original means of pricing the work by the consultant. The consultant is originally appointed for an agreed term. Under the First Edition of the PSC the consultant only priced a task schedule provided by the employer on a lump sum basis for each activity. Under clause 11.2(18): 'A Task is a collection of items which the *Employer* selects from the *task schedule* and instructs the *Consultant* to carry out'. The task schedule is referred to in the optional statements of part two of the Contract Data if option G is used. Subsequently, when tasks were required to be carried out by the

---

[160] Clause 11.2(5) PSC: 'The Scope is information which • specifies and describes the *services* or • states any constraints on how the *Consultant* Provides the Services and is • in the documents which the Contract Data states it is in or • in an instruction given in accordance with this contract'.

[161] See clause 20.1 ECC.

[162] Cf clause 11.2(5) plant information in the PC.

[163] Some factors in relation to different payment mechanisms with emphasis upon their shortcomings are discussed by WARD, S. and CHAPMAN, C. Choosing Contractor Payment Terms. *International Journal of Project Management*, 1994, **12** (4), 216–221.

[164] See discussion of risk allocation under the main options of the ECC above. It is interesting to note that target contracts for consultants at the Millenium Experience Company were also employed to better apportion the risks for cost and time overruns: HALL, PETER. All for One and One for All. *Building*, 19 June 1998, 38.

[165] See clauses 11.2(14), 11.2(17) PSC.

consultant and instructions given, they would be carried out as originally priced. Hence there is a margin in this regard in terms of the original pricing in addition to the affects on the pricing associated with the intervening delay. There is a larger degree of risk in this wording than currently under the Second Edition. Now, with regard to the term contract main option the prices as defined may also be determined with reference to an agreed time charge for certain items. Once again this would serve to share those risks with the employer to a greater extent than before. The standard of care imposed on the consultant in carrying out these tasks is skill and care normally used by professionals providing similar services.[166] This marks a change in the wording from the First Edition of the PSC which provided: '[e]xcept where stated otherwise in the Brief, the Consultant's obligation is to Provide the Services using reasonable skill and care'. It can be seen that the familiar qualification that the exercise of the 'skill and care' be 'reasonable' has been deleted and thus arguably some subjectivity in its assessment.

The First Edition of the PSC had a shorter number of options than the ECC, numbering eight in total. The secondary option clauses that were *missing* from PSC compared to the ECC are listed below.

- 'Performance bond' – option G.
- 'Advanced payment to the Contractor' – option J.
- 'Sectional Completion' – option L.
- 'Limitation of the *Contractor's* liability for his design to reasonable skill and care' – option M.
- 'Retention' – option P.
- 'Bonus for early Completion' – option Q.
- 'Delay damages' – option R.
- 'Low performance damages' – option S.
- 'The Construction (Design and Management) Regulations 1994' – option U.
- 'Trust Fund' – option V.
- 'Additional conditions of contract' – option Z.

The First Edition of the PSC also introduced changes to the lettering of the options. This is a departure from the normal drafting principles employed in the NEC where the same clause number, letter and prefix are used consistently to facilitate ease of use. Hence, secondary option H in the ECC (parent company guarantee) is secondary option E in the PSC.[167] This detracts from overall consistency across the forms and is unexplained. Prior to the release of the Second Edition it would have been the recommendation here that the PSC revert to the original lettering of secondary options in the ECC to further the contract system's original drafting objectives and familiarity. Now with the release of the Second

---

[166] Clause 21.2 PSC.

[167] Other examples could be given, see secondary options K (ECC) but F (PSC First Edition) (multiple currencies); T (ECC) but L (PSC First Edition) (changes in the law); and Z (ECC) but M (PSC First Edition) (special/additional conditions of contract).

Edition a clean break has been made with the prefix lettering of the ECC. All secondary options begin with the prefix X and are numbered consecutively. While this has simplified the lettering it has still not addressed the absence of reinforcement that would have been achieved with lettering matching that in the ECC so far as possible.

Several new secondary options were introduced in the First Edition of the PSC.

- 'Transfer of copyright' – option G.
- 'Employer's Agent' – option H.
- 'Termination at will' – option J.
- 'Special conditions of contract' – option M.

The transfer of copyright provision permits the copyright of documents to be transferred from the consultant to the employer and thus reverse the normal situation in the conditions[168] where it would remain with the contractor. Option H permits the employer to appoint an agent expressly to act on the employer's behalf under the contract. The inclusion of the option concedes the possibility that the issues of authority or mandate might otherwise arise under the conditions. Although the PSC guidance notes refer only to a situation where a corporate body wishes to appoint an in-house or external consultant as agent there is no such limitation in the clause and almost any agency could be envisaged. The details of the agency or mandate would be defined in part one of the Contract Data. The most unusual provision is option J – termination at will. The termination provisions in the PSC are already broad and thus the employer may terminate 'if the services are no longer required'.[169] This provision alone may be tantamount to a right to terminate at will in any event. It is at least strongly arguable that is how the provision would have been construed in the absence of option J on termination at will. Now, with the addition of the option, it would seem the provision has been diluted. In general, the termination provisions in the NEC forms of contract are broader than most other forms in any case and it can be expected that they will be construed as such. Lastly, option M, the special conditions of contract, may be contrasted with option Z in the ECC regarding additional conditions of contract.

The Second Edition of the PSC added several further new secondary option clauses to those set out above with reference to the First Edition as follows.

- 'Sectional Completion' – option X5.
- 'Bonus for early Completion' – option X6.
- 'Delay damages' – option X7.
- '*Collateral warranty agreements*' – option X8.
- 'Transfer of rights' – option X9.
- 'Compliance with national legislation' – options Y.

---

[168] See clause 70 PSC First Edition.
[169] Clause 93.3 PSC First Edition.

The additional secondary option clauses that have been added to the Second Edition of the PSC give the form much more depth than the First Edition. Considerable new attention has been given to the subject of completion. This is more in keeping with the overall philosophy of the ECC and the way in which it is structured. The introduction of a provision on collateral warranties is belated recognition that they remain common in the industry. Option X9, the transfer of rights option, marks a broadening of the transfer of copyright provision that was stipulated in the First Edition and better reflects the scope of intellectual property. The final options, worded in the plural, deals with both the Construction (Design and Management) Regulations 1994 and the Housing Grants, Construction and Regeneration Act 1996 both of which are commented upon below.

Adjudicator's Contract

The NEC includes an Adjudicator's Contract (AC). While the NEC requires the appointment of an 'Adjudicator'[170] there is nothing that requires he or she be appointed under the NEC AC. The AC was one of two additional contracts published outside the original boxed set of forms along with the Professional Services Contract. Both forms were produced in consultation drafts in 1992 and released as First Editions in 1994 separately from and subsequent to the publication of the First Edition of the NEC and as Second Editions in 1998. The AC was prepared by the NEC Working Group and approved by the Council of the ICE.[171] The AC is the shortest of the NEC forms and comprises only three parts.

(1) A Form of Agreement.
(2) Conditions of Contract.
(3) Contract Data.

The form of agreement is made between the 'Parties' and the 'Adjudicator'. No limitation is placed upon the meaning of the term 'the parties' and the term is only identified unlike under all other NEC forms.[172] The parties could typically include the employer and contractor, contractor and subcontractor, purchaser and supplier, or employer and consultant. In addition, the term extends to and includes any other party (including third parties) who becomes a party to a dispute between the original parties signing the form of agreement.[173]

Agreement upon the 'Adjudicator' would be a necessary condition before the parties would be expected to formalize their relationship and certainly before the 'Contract Date'. If agreement were not reached on the appointment of the adjudicator prior to formalizing their contractual

---

[170] Part one Contract Data ECC.
[171] The Adjudicator's Contract was drafted by P. HIGGINS, ICE, F. GRIFFITHS, Chartered Institute of Purchasing and Supply, M. COLEMAN of the Association of Project Managers with assistance from Martin Barnes: acknowledgments, PSC.
[172] Cf clauses 11.2(1) ECC, 11.2(1) ECSC.
[173] Condition 1.6 AC.

relationship a potential problem would arise. A similar problem could arise even if the parties themselves were able to agree on the appointment of the adjudicator but for other reasons they were then unable to come to agreement with the adjudicator on all the essential terms of the appointment. Without a clear and express provision in the ECC on what occurs in these situations under the First Edition the parties might have to fall back upon the new provisions in the Housing Grants, Construction and Regeneration Act 1996 to assist. This contrasts with the provisions in the Second Edition of the AC which stipulates that the form of agreement applies only when the Scheme or Construction Contracts Regulations 1998 under the HGCRA 1996 applies.

The conditions of contract[174] in the First Edition of the AC are brief and comprise just five of the familiar NEC core clauses with one new addition. The headings for these conditions of contract are set out below.

- General.
- Adjudication.
- Payment.
- Title.
- Risks.
- Termination.

It can be remarked that conditions 2 and 6 can be compared to core clause 9 in the ECC on disputes and termination. In fact, some of the provisions in condition 2 repeat provisions in clause 9 of the ECC.[175] Condition 5 is another exceptional provision again compared to the core clauses in the ECC. In comparison to clause 8 in the ECC dealing with risks and insurance condition 5 of the AC is almost non-existent. The condition provides simply that 'the Parties indemnify the Adjudicator against claims, compensation and costs arising out of his work in connection with an Adjudication'. While the intent is clearly to serve as a protective mechanism for the adjudicator it is arguably too broad to achieve this and creates problems where the parties may have legitimate grounds for refusing the protection or payment of the adjudicator's fees.

The Contract Data consists of only one part with seven issues that must be addressed and the possibility of one optional statement with respect to the payment period. The statements pertain to a description of the contract, the language of the contract, the choice of law, period for retention, adjudicator's hourly fee, interest rate, and choice of currency. In comparison, the Second Edition of the AC removes the fourth condition on 'Title'. In summary the AC is exceedingly brief. In part, this brevity is addressed by reference back to the contract governing the relationship of the parties. That contract, referred to as the 'contract between the Parties'[176]

---

[174] The term 'conditions of contract' is used in the AC as a heading in contrast to and comparison with the heading 'core clauses' in the ECC, although the AC still uses the term 'clauses' to refer to the conditions in the index.

[175] See e.g. clause 91.1 ECC.

[176] See the use of the phrase in conditions 1.3, 4.1, and 6.3 AC.

will set out many of the duties of the 'Adjudicator'. Once again, some of these are expressly repeated in condition 2 of the PSC. Lastly, it may be noted that the use of this terminology does not preclude the joinder of disputes involving parties to other contracts before the same Adjudicator.[177] Further reference to the provisions of the AC for comparison will be made where relevant.

Short Contract

In February 1997 the ICE released a proposed 'Short Contract' for engineering and construction for consultation. The draft short contract was prepared originally by the NEC Panel and intended to become one of the contracts in the NEC contract system and said to have been released in response to demand from users. The contents of the draft, including the proposed name, remained open[178] until 30 July 1999 when the First Edition of the Short Contract was formally released.[179]

While there has no doubt been some pressure, including from Latham, for a short, abbreviated or minor form of contract as part of the NEC contract system, it runs contrary to some of the original views of the drafters. Thus, Martin Barnes, when asked several years ago whether such a form was being drafted, replied: 'the one that we're probably not going to act on is the demand for a minor works form. Until there is clear evidence that the NEC as it stands cannot be applied to minor works, we don't think it would be useful to extend the document in this way'.[180] Some of the rationale behind Barnes' view can be understood in terms of the proper bases upon which a particular form or procurement method is selected. In many instances, although value is stated to be a relevant factor, it may, in fact, be unimportant beside many of the others that should be properly considered instead of or at least before focusing upon it. As such, value of the works should *not* be determinative in selection of a minor works form[181] but rather the characteristics of the works

---

[177] See clauses 91.3 ECSC and 91.3 PSC First Edition.

[178] PETER HIGGINS, Chairman NEC Panel, in a letter to consultees, 20 February 1997, asked for comments on a number of specific topics including the name of the contract.

[179] Original announcement by the President of the Institution of Civil Engineers at their offices in London. The drafters on the Panel included Dr Martin Barnes, Tom Nicholson, Nigel Shaw, Andrew Baird, Peter Higgins, Professor Phillip Capper and David Maidment. The guidance notes and flow charts were released in September 1999.

[180] ALLEN, JOHN D. NEC – is it the Answer to Latham's Prayers? *Construction News*, 23 February 1995, 12 quoting Dr Martin Barnes. Dr Barnes is also quoted as elaborating on this as follows: '[I]f you use the NEC with the right choice of main options, and with none of the secondary options, you end up with an extremely simple contract which is perfectly usable on minor works': 12.

[181] See guidance notes on minor works forms; e.g. ICE MW Form 2nd, clause 1 lists six factors which are relevant to selection of the form only one of which is *value*: 1(f). See generally COTTAM, G. and HAWKER, G. *ICE Conditions of Contract for Minor Works: A User's Guide and Commentary*. Thomas Telford, London, 1991.

themselves[182] along with the employer's objectives and preferences in terms of risk allocation. Ultimately, the selection of a 'minor' or 'short' works contract may even have less to do with value than simply whether lawyers are involved or not.[183] According to Professor Justin Sweet, it is pressure from contracting parties who are looking for less 'legalistic' documents more than any other factor that gives rise to the use and selection of minor or abbreviated forms. One issue in particular stands out in documents that are too legalistic. 'A problem for the non-lawyer is that legal terminology provides little assistance in pointing to the consequences of breach'.[184] Paradoxically, and once again according to Sweet, once lawyers are involved, full contract forms should be preferred over minor forms.[185]

The NEC Short Contract (SC) is a multidisciplinary form like the ECC and intended to be used for both building and engineering contracts. The drafters have recognized it is fallacious, for some of the reasons discussed above, to choose a contract solely on the basis of value. Thus, the SC does not set any threshold value for use or not for use. Instead, the emphasis is upon the relative degree of sophistication of the management techniques that will be employed and the desired level of risk. These should be the deciding factors in the selection of the SC or not.

The SC is released as a complete package. Thus it contains the Contract Data, 'The *Contractor's* Offer', and 'The *Employer's* Acceptance'. It also contains the 'conditions of contract',[186] and several pre-printed forms. The pre-printed forms include the 'Price List', 'Works Information', and 'Site Information'. The SC differs from the ECC in this respect, and clearly is intended to and will facilitate use. Together these documents comprise the contract documents, along with the plans and drawings and any other information both referred to in the site information or works information and incorporated as such. For the first time in the NEC the forms are being released on compact disc. This should facilitate completion, storage, and even delivery or transmission to other parties. It will be recommended below that this innovation be extended as a whole to all the forms in the contract system.

Overall, the SC adopts the same drafting style and objectives as the ECC Second Edition. The headings for all the conditions of contract correspond quite closely to those in the ECC Second Edition save clause 4 which is abbreviated to 'Defects' alone, and condition 8 which is

---

[182] GRIFFITH, A. and HEADLEY, J. D. Using a Weighted Score Model as an Aid to Selecting Procurement Methods for Small Building Works. *Construction Management and Economics*, 1997, **15** (4), 341–348.

[183] SWEET, JUSTIN, see n. 74 above, 13–14. In the United States the practice is to abbreviate forms also, e.g. B 151, a shorter version of B 142, and A 107, a shortened combined version of A 101 and A 201.

[184] EGGLESTON, BRIAN. *Liquidated Damages and Extensions of Time in Construction Contracts.* Blackwell Scientific Publications, Oxford, 1992, p. 12.

[185] SWEET, JUSTIN, see n. 74 above.

[186] In contrast to 'core clauses' in the ECC.

expanded to 'Limitation of liability, indemnities and insurance'.[187] The single most distinguishing feature in the contract is its abbreviated length and the omission of many clauses and subclauses in comparison to the ECC. Thus, for example, condition 11.2 has only 13 subconditions and not the minimum 20 subclauses that it has in either main option A or B of the ECC. Once again, comparable reductions in the number of conditions and subconditions could be referred to throughout the SC. The SC is also shortened by not providing for any secondary options as well as restarting each new condition immediately following the preceding condition without a page break. The absence of secondary options suggests that if the employer or the parties are interested in even one of the secondary option clauses in the ECC that they should use the ECC for this reason. It is an open question whether the drafters would condone the addition of any such secondary option clauses to the SC rather than selecting the ECC at the outset. Presumably, it would come down to the two factors most important in the choice of the SC overall; the complexity of the management involved and the degree of risk to be borne. Some research demonstrates that there is a relationship between project complexity and project management structure that should be taken into account to achieve the highest satisfactory project performance.[188] The SC was drafted to comply with the Housing Grants, Construction and Regeneration Act 1996 from the outset; however, in the First Edition, unlike the consultation draft, three separate clauses are included and should be substituted for others if the HGCRA 1996 applies.[189]

Partnering Agreement

The NEC panel has recently released a Partnering Agreement (PA) for consultation. The PA is intended to be used by parties contracting under one or more of the main options in the NEC system. The PA adopts the traditional NEC clause structure along with contract data, although it omits options. A variety of common objectives may be adopted by the parties which may be measured against key performance indicators. It borrows some content from the Construction Industry Council Guide to Project Team Partnering and extends it by dealing with multi-project or serial partnering as well. A new feature is the inclusion of a partnering information section which permits project-specific requirements to be included for value engineering and value management, risk management, joint design, participation in partnering workshops, office sharing, or common information systems. It thus builds upon very recent trends in industry. The PA is multi-party and is intended to include all members of

---

[187] A change was also made to the heading of core clause 8 in the PSC Second Edition which is now 'Indemnity, insurance and liability'.

[188] See KOPECKY, JOHN JOSEPH. Organizational Response to the Management of Complexity. PhD dissertation, The George Washington University, 1994 and GIDADO, K. I. 'Project Complexity: The Focal Point of Construction Production Planning. *Construction Management and Economics*, 1996, **14** (3), 213–225.

[189] Clauses 93UK to 95UK for clauses 93 to 95.

the project team. It may be given legal effect by inserting an optional additional clause in any of the other NEC main option contracts. To reflect the fact that members of the project team may change, the PA is undated and employs an identifying number in place of a date.

The release of the PA by the NEC panel at this time is progressive and accords with greater recognition of and protection for collaborative working relationships. Cox and Thompson, have focused upon the importance of collaboration, ideally pre-contractual collaborative relationships.[190] The commentators have observed that most standard forms of contract encourage non-collaborative behaviour and thus operate to drive a wedge between the parties. However, in a survey of leading forms the authors concluded that the NEC still offered the *greatest* number of features providing support for collaboration.[191] Sally Roe noted several years ago that many features of the NEC either lend themselves directly or are similar to partnering.[192] The features Roe refers to, namely the commitment to co-operation, early warning, and the pre-pricing of variations, all *suggest* partnering. Experience under the form has confirmed that the NEC is being used for work under partnering agreements usually under the target contract options.[193] Others too have singled out or favoured the NEC as an appropriate vehicle for partnering.[194] Clause 10.1 anticipates the notion of partnering and it may be observed that the Latham Report referred to contract conditions which supported partnering and the work of Baden Hellard emphasizing teamwork and co-operation over confrontation and conflict.[195] Success in partnering suggests that it is more likely to be achieved when the contract is non-adversarial as well as framed in simplified contract language as in the case of the NEC.[196] The PA adds a unique dimension to the contract system.

Plant Contract

The ICE released a proposed 'Plant Contract' for procuring plant or other items for consultation in July 1996. The Plant Contract (PC) is intended to form one of the forms in the NEC system. The PC was released, as in the

---

[190]   COX, ANDREW and THOMPSON, IAN. *Contracting for Business Success*. Thomas Telford, London, 1998, pp. 171–172.

[191]   COX, ANDREW *et al.* Contracting Strategies in the Project Environment. *European Journal of Purchasing & Supply Management*, March 1998, **4**, special issue.

[192]   See ROE, SALLY. Partnering in Construction. A paper given to the Society of Construction Law in London in November 1995, 15.

[193]   NICHOLSON, TOM. NEC – an Update. *Proceedings of the Institution of Civil Engineers*, November 1997, **120**, 186–187.

[194]   See National Economic Development Council. *Partnering in the Public Sector.* NEDC, London, 1992, which favoured the NEC.

[195]   See generally HELLARD, RON BADEN. *Project Partnering: Principle and Practice.* Thomas Telford, London, 1995.

[196]   See the CRINE report, *Cost Reduction for the New Era.* Institute of Petroleum, London, 1994; and also on the link between good faith and partnering, HEAL, ANDREW J. Construction Partnering: Good Faith in Theory and Practice. *Construction Law Journal*, 1999, **15**, 167.

case of the Short Contract, in response to a demand for a version of the NEC form specifically for procuring plant and other items from suppliers. Once again, there was reluctance on the part of the NEC Panel to accede to the demand, given the view that the ECC is suitable for such procurement. However, in response to the suggested demand, and several other reasons that were felt to be important, the draft was prepared and released in any event. Some of these reasons may be summarized as follows:

- to address the perception of some users that the terminology in the ECC was too construction based for plant procurement;
- to overcome any inappropriateness in the ECC as a result of its emphasis upon site work;
- to cater for new options and secondary options;
- to allow a wider spectrum of industry to benefit from the NEC.[197]

The PC was drafted by a Task Group of the NEC Panel.[198] The form principally addresses the situation where the primary activity occurs at the suppliers' or manufacturers' place of business and where little or no work (save installations) occurs on site. The PC is intended to be used for supplying all types of plant. The emphasis is upon supply or supply and delivery. It not intended for supply and install situations. The drafting objectives of the form address time, cost and quality across the conditions. The PC retains other principal features of the ECC Second Edition.

The Parties to the contract are the 'Purchaser' and the 'Supplier'. The contract retains essentially the same nine core clauses as the ECC save clauses 2 and 8 that become the supplier's main responsibilities and indemnities and insurance respectively. The six main options in the ECC are reduced to four in the PC.

(1) Main option A – priced contract with activity schedule.
(2) Main option B – target contract with activity schedule.
(3) Main option C – cost reimbursable contract.
(4) Main option D – term contract with price list.

It can be seen that the bills of quantities main options, B and D in the ECC have been deleted. In addition, main option F, the management contract, has been replaced with the 'term contract with price list'. The term can be agreed by the parties and will operate in an umbrella or framework sense. The purchaser may place 'Batch Orders' according to requirements. 'Batch Orders' is a defined term in clause 11.2(28) and defined as follows: 'an instruction given by the *Project Manager* to the *Supplier* to provide the *plant* and carry out the activities selected from the *price list*'. Each batch order includes: a list of plant items and activities from the price list; the place of delivery; the access date; the completion date; the

---

[197] PETER HIGGINS, Chairman NEC Panel, in a letter to consultees, 29 July 1996.
[198] The NEC Panel members are set out in Chapter 3 above. The members of the Task Group were P. A. BAIRD, N. C. SHAW, and A. R. WESTBROOK. A. R. WESTBROOK was the only Task Group member who was not also a member of the NEC Panel. Mr Westbrook, FRICS, O'Brien-Kreitzburg, was formerly with BAA Plc.

name of the supervisor and an assessment of the lump sum price for the batch order using the prices in the price list.[199] A quotation procedure operates for each batch in the same way as under the ECC main options.[200] Each batch order operates within the main contract and carries its own completion, access and 'defects date'.[201] An instruction changing a batch order is a compensation event.[202]

The secondary option clauses have been modified for plant procurement. In addition, three new secondary option clauses have been added as follows.

- 'Country limitation of compensation event assessment' – option M.
- 'Extending the *defects* date' – option W.
- 'Spare parts' – option X.

Option M permits the risk of choosing a particular country as the source of supply to be placed upon the supplier. Hence, in the event of failure to supply from that country for reasons that might otherwise excuse non-performance, no change is made either to the completion date or to the prices. Under option W, after completion but before the defects date, if the whole of the plant cannot be used due to a defect the defects date is delayed by the same period.[203] Similarly, if a part of the plant is replaced due to a defect, the defects date for that part of the plant is delayed for the same period.[204] Option X addresses the question of spare parts provision during the operating life of the plant. Individual clauses of the PC will be returned to throughout where relevant.

Survey and Investigation Contract

The NEC drafters also intend to add a survey and investigation contract to the NEC system. The survey and investigation contract is intended to be used for site investigation, marine and estuarial surveys, land surveys, and traffic surveys. In effect, the contract, once available, should be capable of use in any project involving the collection and analysis of data either with or without testing.[205]

Sample Form of Agreement

The NEC contains a Sample Form of Agreement although it is not one of the agreed contract documents.[206] The NEC stands in marked contrast

---

[199] Clause 55.1 PC.

[200] Clause 55 PC.

[201] Clauses 11.2(28), 11.2(29), 11.2(31), 12.3 PC.

[202] Clause 60.1(20) PC.

[203] Clause W1.1(1) PC.

[204] Clause W1.1(2) PC.

[205] See BARNES, MARTIN. The New Engineering Contract: A Promising Start. *Proceedings of the Institution of Civil Engineers*, August, 1994, **102**, part 1, 94–95.

[206] An 'agreement' signifies a mutual contract on consideration between two or more parties, and is not understood to be synonymous to promise or undertaking: see *Wain* v. *Walters* (1804) 5 East 10 at 16 per Lord Ellenborough CJ, and see also *Goldsack* v. *Shore* [1950] 1 KB 708.

with many other standard forms in this respect, which include forms of agreement or articles of agreement in the package documentation.[207] The drafters give the same reason for not including a form of agreement as one of the contract documents as for not including a form of tender;[208] no form was included in the ECC because many employers have standard forms containing their own requirements.[209] Various reasons may be noted in favour of including a form of or articles of agreement but in general it is simply that the articles are the best evidence available that a contract has been formed between the parties.

The NEC Sample Form of Agreement begins with the insertion of a date stating that the agreement is made on a certain date. In practice it is recommended that the date the contract is signed be the date of the agreement. The parties are described as the employer and the contractor in the familiar italicized type, which is used throughout the conditions of contract, although oddly not in the remainder of the Sample Form itself. The drafters would presumably endorse the statement that any form of agreement that the parties enter into adopts both the formats and wording of the ECC. In fact this recommendation is made by the drafters with respect to completion of the Contract Data.[210] The form contains only one recital; 'whereas the Employer wishes to have provided the following works'.[211] The substance of the agreement is set out in three numbered paragraphs.

(1) The Contractor will provide the works in accordance with the conditions of contract
(2) The Employer will pay the Contractor the amount due in accordance with the conditions of contract
(3) The documents forming part of this agreement are the:
   • Contractor's tender
   • Employer's letter of acceptance
   • Contract Data part one
   • Contract Data part two, and the following documents.[212]

The form of wording differs from and is inconsistent both with the wording of the Sample Form of Tender and itself. Thus the terms 'employer' and 'contractor' are both italicized and non-italicized and 'provide the works' is not capitalized. Consistent use of terminology would suggest that this should not occur. The contractor also agrees to provide the works in accordance with parts one and two of the Contract Data in the tender but in accordance with the conditions of contract in the

---

[207] See e.g. JCT 80, JCT MW, IFC 84, JCT 81, FIDIC 4th, ICE 6th, NSC/A, and DOM/1.
[208] See guidance notes NEC, 26.
[209] Guidance notes NEC, 17.
[210] Guidance notes NEC, 17.
[211] See discussion below. Examples of other forms with recitals include: DOM/1 and JCT NSC/A.
[212] Cf the ICE MW 2nd form which includes a contract schedule that lists contract documents including letters.

agreement. As parts one and two of the Contract Data are not synonymous with and exclusive to the conditions of contract a different agreement is reached depending upon whether the form of agreement or form of tender governs.[213] It may be noted that whether the consideration due to the contractor is the 'sum' or the 'amount' due, is still prospective in both cases and to be arrived at in accordance with the conditions of contract. Thus it is not a determined but *determinable* sum only upon formation of the agreement. There is another unusual aspect to this feature. That is, if no form of agreement is used the conditions of contract in the ECC do not impose a clear obligation upon the employer to pay the contractor. Once again the obligation to pay rather arises from construing the contract as a whole, and in particular clauses 51.1 and 51.4.[214] It is unlike the clear mutuality that is evident in the form of agreement with only two articles setting out the exchange of the provision of the works for payment. To reiterate, it is not that the employer does not have a defined obligation to make payment under the ECC, rather it is not framed as starkly as under other standard forms. However, the converse may also be argued if one prefers to emphasize instead the fifth core clause headed payment and the provisions which follow on both assessment – determinability itself – and then payment.

A list of contract documents is given which includes the option to add further contract documents. It is suggested that best practice in the use of the form would be to include all secondary options that will be relied upon and constitute separate agreements. Thus, any performance bond, parent company guarantee, trust fund documentation, schedules of cost components and arguably core clause 9 itself may appropriately be included in the list.[215] This overcomes the necessity to incorporate these documents by reference into the contract documents. Parts one and two of the Contract Data also refer to many additional documents which are intended to form part of the contract. The assumption here is that express listing of parts one and two in the list should ensure that parts one and two at a minimum become contract documents. However, the additional documents referred to in the Contract Data would only have the status of contract documents if they were expressly or impliedly incorporated into the contract by reference upon the proper interpretation of parts one or two.

The incorporation of documents by reference into the contract documents is not unusual in construction contracts but always carries a risk of uncertainty. In the case of the NEC in particular, with no required

---

[213] In the list of documents forming part of the agreement in section 3 the contractor's tender is specifically included.

[214] Clause 51.1 unamended and amended 2nd ECC imposes first a certification obligation and second a payment obligation on the project manager as the employer's agent and which, when read with a liability to pay interest when there has been a failure to certify, reinforces the payment obligation.

[215] The subject of incorporation of arbitration clauses by reference is discussed separately below.

form of tender, form of agreement, articles of agreement or recitals, the risk of uncertainty over which documents do in fact comprise the contract is great. To alleviate this risk the parties should clearly indicate, in either the Sample Form of Agreement or a letter of acceptance, which documents these are. Any risk would also be exaggerated when subcontracts are involved as uncertainty surrounding the main contract documents is passed along to subcontractors who may seek to rely upon their terms as well. As Phillip Capper has stated, 'the essential reason for having a *contract* at all is this: to try, so far as legal provisions reasonably can, to render more certain the practical and financial consequences of matters which are physically and factually uncertain at the time of entering into the contract'.[216]

Contract strategy and tendering
Contract strategy

The choice of the proper method of procurement is the most important decision that an employer will make. It is critical that sufficient time and resources are devoted at the outset of a project to this decision if the best chance of a successful outcome is to be realized. The method of procurement that the employer chooses should fully satisfy the objectives for the particular project. Those objectives should also be fulfilled in the compilation of the contract documents, the tender, negotiation and subsequent award of the contract. Time and again it has been stated that if only a portion of the time that is typically devoted to technical details were invested instead in the preparation of a full brief and matching contract documentation projects would prove to be less dispute prone and more successful.[217] After all, '[c]ontractual documents are tools for managing risks. Their purpose is to determine the consequences of particular risks which you must previously have identified'.[218]

Tendering

The NEC documentation differs from traditional contracts in at least three significant ways. It includes a Contract Data section in two parts, the works information and the site information. As a result of these differences the amount of time and effort required to tender under the NEC is greater than under traditional forms of contract with research showing factors varying from 10% to 75%.[219] While these increases in time have been noted the same research has shown that many contractors

---

[216] CAPPER, PROFESSOR PHILLIP, see n. 75 above.
[217] See LOOTS, P. C. *Engineering and Construction Law with Illustrations and Cases.* Juta & Co Ltd, Cape Town, 1985, p. 3.
[218] CAPPER, PROFESSOR PHILLIP, see n. 75 above.
[219] BROOME, JON C. and PERRY, JOHN G. Experiences of the Use of the New Engineering Contract. *Engineering, Construction and Architectural Management*, 1995, **2**(4), 275.

have felt that the extra time involved in tender preparation has produced benefits that have outweighed the work involved.[220]

The formation of a contract under the NEC may arise through negotiation or open tendering. The general law of contract will apply if the contracts are negotiated; hence the rules regarding offer and acceptance. An offer may come from the contractor in the form of an estimate.[221] Acceptance on the part of the employer must pertain to all essential terms. Lord Justice Lloyd has summarized the principles applicable to whether the parties have entered a binding contract in *Pagnan SpA* v. *Feed Products Ltd*[222] and they have been considered recently in *Hall and Tawse South Ltd* v. *Ivory Gate Ltd* and *Mitsui Babcock Energy Ltd* v. *John Brown Engineering Ltd*.[223] A contract will not arise in circumstances of an 'agreement to agree'.[224] Thus acceptance cannot be conditional or ambiguous.[225] A counter-offer rather than acceptance arises if the employer amends the offer before purported acceptance. Any amendment would operate as refusal of the original offer.[226]

Another question has lately arisen with regard to the formation of contracts – can agreements that seek to regulate the course of the negotiations themselves be enforced? Two arguably contrasting approaches have emerged from the most recent English case law. In the older case of *Walford* v. *Miles*[227] the House of Lords ruled that a contract to negotiate was not binding in English law. Lord Ackner stated that a:

> duty to negotiate in good faith is unworkable in practice as it is inherently inconsinent with the position of a negotiating party [and that during negotiations] . . . either party is entitled to withdraw from those negotiations, at any time and for any reason.[228]

The decision was overwhelmingly criticized[229] and it is perhaps not surprising that when a second opportunity came up to consider roughly

---

[220] *Ibid.*

[221] *Croshaw* v. *Pritchard and Renwick* (1899) 16 TLR 45.

[222] *Pagnan SpA* v. *Feed Products Ltd* [1987] 2 Lloyd's Rep 601, 619, CA.

[223] *Hall and Tawse South Ltd* v. *Ivory Gate Ltd* (1999) Con LR 117; *Mitsui Babcock Energy Ltd* v. *John Brown Engineering Ltd* (1997) 14 CLD-05-17.

[224] *Courtney & Fairbairn Ltd* v. *Tolaini Bros (Hotels) Ltd* [1975] 1 All ER 716, CA.

[225] *Peter Lind & Co Ltd* v. *Mersey Docks and Harbour Board* [1972] 2 Lloyd's Rep 234.

[226] *Trollope & Colls Ltd and Holland, Hannen & Cubitts Ltd* v. *Atomic Power Constructions Ltd* [1962] 3 All ER 1035.

[227] *Walford* v. *Miles* [1992] 2 AC 128, [1992] 1 All ER 453, HL.

[228] *Walford* v. *Miles* [1992] 2 AC 128, 138, [1992] 1 All ER 453, 461.

[229] See BUCKLEY, R. P. *Walford* v *Miles*: False Certainty about Uncertainty – An Australian Perspective. *Journal Contract Law*, 1993, **6**, 58; JAMIESON, B. Lock-Out Agreement is Unenforceable. *Lloyds Maritime and Commercial Law Quarterly*, 1992, 16; JAMIESON, B. When Lock-Out Agreement Enforceable. *Lloyds Maritime and Commercial Law Quarterly*, 1992, 186; DAVENPORT, B. J. Lock-Out Agreements. *Law Quarterly Review*, 1991, **107**, 366; and NEILL, P. A Key to Lock-Out Agreements? *Law Quarterly Review*, 1992, **108**, 405.

similar facts the Court of Appeal distinguished *Walford* and held in *Lambert* v. *HTV Cymru (Wales) Ltd* that a clause to 'use all reasonable endeavours' was enforceable.[230] Lord Steyn has also remarked privately: '[i]f the issue were to arise again, with the benefit of fuller argument, I would hope that the concept of good faith would not be rejected out of hand. There is no need for hostility to the concept: it is entirely practical and workable'.[231] In the construction law context, while some parallels may be drawn to letters of intent, they have been more favourably received[232] than contracts to negotiate. The shift in approach toward this recognition moves the courts closer to what would be relational analysis of the issue.

In general, a building or engineering contract requires no set formalities and it may be entered into in writing, orally, in part orally and in writing, by deed or by conduct. The NEC departs from the lack of these formalities. The contract is executed in and all communications under the contract are effected in writing.[233] The ECC need not be executed as a deed. However, certain secondary option clauses may be; for instance, the performance bond, parent company guarantee or trust deed. The execution of these secondary option clauses does not require a seal to be affixed at the time.[234] Thus consideration is a formal requirement for the obligations to be enforceable if they have been incurred under the secondary option clauses. This view is premised upon the applicability of *Stilk* v. *Myrick*.[235] It is arguable, however, that the *Stilk* case has been overturned by *Williams* v. *Roffey Bros and Nicholls (Contractors) Ltd*[236] which supports the enforcement of promises given for the same work which constitutes a practical benefit. The *Roffey* case itself has been said to herald a new approach by the courts in determining

---

[230] *Lambert* v. *HTV Cymru (Wales) Ltd, Construction Law Letter* (1998): 12.

[231] Lord Steyn. Contract Law: Fulfilling the Reasonable Expectations of Honest Men. *Law Quarterly Review*, 1997, **113**, 439.

[232] *British Steel Corporation* v. *Cleveland Bridge and Engineering Co Ltd* [1984] 1 All ER 504; and *Hall and Tawse South Ltd* v. *Ivory Gate Ltd* (1999) 62 Con LR 117; however, recovery proceeds rather on the basis of restitutionary principles: see BALL, S. N. Work Carried our in Pursuance of Letters of Intent – Contract or Restitution. *Law Quarterly Review*, 1983, **99**, 572; but see *Kleinwort Benson Ltd* v. *Malaysia Mining Corporation Berhad* [1989] 1 All ER 785, [1989] 1 WLR 379, CA, commented on by PHANG, PROFESSOR ANDREW. Positivism in the English Law of Contract. *Modern Law Review*, 1992, 55, 102; and see generally FURMSTON, MICHAEL. *Contract Formation and Letters of Intent*. John Wiley & Sons, New York, 1998.

[233] Clause 13.1 ECC. Writing requirements may also arise by statute; for instance, in the United Kindom the Law of Property (Miscellaneous Provisions) Act 1989, section 2 requires agreements involving the sale or transfer of an interest in land to be in writing.

[234] For example, in the United Kingdom under the Law of Property (Miscellaneous Provisions) Act 1989, section 1(1)(b) for individuals and the Companies Act 1985, section 36A for companies.

[235] *Stilk* v. *Myrick* (1809) 2 Camp 317; *Sharpe* v. *San Paulo Rly Co* (1873) 8 Ch App 597.

[236] *Williams* v. *Roffey Bros and Nicholls (Contractors) Ltd* [1991] 1 QB 1, [1990] 1 All ER 512, CA.

the enforceability of promises, one where the courts are 'guided less by technical questions of consideration than by questions of fairness, reasonableness and commercial utility'.[237]

Actions for breach of the ECC will be subject to a six-year limitation period in the ordinary course.[238] However, if secondary option clauses are separately executed as deeds; e.g. options G, H or T, the limitation period in respect of these separate agreements is twelve years from the date of the agreement. The formation of the contract through the process of tendering may conveniently be divided into three stages: the invitation to tender or instructions to tenderers, the form of tender itself, and the acceptance of the tender by the Employer.

Invitation to tender or instructions to tenderers

The NEC contains neither a form of instructions to tenderers nor a form of invitation to tender on behalf of the employer, despite the suggestion to the contrary in the Latham Report.[239] In the United Kingdom tendering may be subject to requirements at the department, local authority or government level. At common law an invitation to tender has been construed as an 'invitation to treat' and not a formal offer; as such the employer is under no obligation to accept either the lowest of any tenders submitted or any tender at all.[240] The NEC contains a form of tender in the guidance notes but these do not expressly refer to this general freedom of choice of the employer. Bidding in the European Union itself has become heavily regulated. Public procurement rules in the EEC (later EU) began with the Public Works Directive[241] which was later amended by subsequent EEC Directives and supplemented by other important public services and compliance directives.[242] The Public Works Directive has been construed in recent cases including *R* v. *Portsmouth City Council, ex*

---

[237] ADAMS, J. and BROWNSWORD, R. Contracts, Consideration and the Critical Path. *Modern Law Review*, 1990, 53, 536, 537. See also *Re Selectmove Ltd* [1995] 2 All ER 531, [1995] 1 WLR 474, CA. See generally CHEN-WISHART, MINDY. Consideration, Practical Benefit and the Emperor's New Clothes. In *Good Faith and Fault in Contract Law* (eds Jack Beatson and Daniel Friedmann). Clarendon Press, Oxford, 1995, pp. 123ff for a detailed look at the effect of *Williams* v. *Roffey Bros and Nicholls (Contractors) Ltd* [1991] 1 QB 1, [1990] 1 All ER 512, CA, the meaning of 'practical benefit' and the doctrine of consideration.

[238] Limitation Act 1980, section 5.

[239] See the Latham Report paragraph 5.20(6), 40.

[240] *Spencer* v. *Harding* (1870) LR 5 CP 561.

[241] Public Works Directive 71/305/EEC (OJ L 185, 25 August 1971) as later amended by subsequent EEC Directives 72/277/EEC (OJ L 176, 3 August 1972), 78/669/EEC (OJ L 225, 16 August 1978), 89/440/EEC (OJ L 210, 21 July 1989), and 93/37/EEC (OJ L 199, 9 August 1993).

[242] (1) Public Services Directive 77/62/EEC (OJ L 13, 15 January 1977) as later amended by 80/767/EEC (OJ L 215, 18 August 1980), 88/295/EEC (OJ L 127, 20 May 1988), and 93/36/EEC (OJ L 199, 9 August 1993); (2) Public Services Directive 92/50/EEC (OJ L 209, 24 July 1992); and (3) Compliance Directive 89/665/EEC (OJ L 395, 30 December 1989).

parte Peter Coles, Colwick Builders Ltd and George Austin Ltd and *Ballast Nedam Groep NV* v. *Belgian State.*[243] An enforcement scheme has been implemented in the United Kingdom primarily under the Public Works Contracts Regulations 1991, the Public Services Contracts Regulations 1993, and the Public Supply Contracts Regulations 1995.

Lately, courts in the United Kingdom and elsewhere have been moving toward stricter interpretations of what constitutes an invitation to tender. Undertakings have been found to have been given by employers to accept tenders conforming to the conditions of tender;[244] and implied duties have been imposed on employers to consider all tenders conforming to the instructions to tenderers or conditions of tender.[245]

National law may dictate additional procedures or criteria, which are also relevant to the award of the contract; particularly in the case of public works contracts.[246] Under the NEC one would expect that any invitation or instructions to tenderers would also include part one of the Contract Data, the works onformation, site information and bill of quantities. The works information itself could comprise a description of the works, plans, drawings, details and designs, specifications and other relevant material. Where the works information is comprehensive and replaces the specification difficulties have arisen in practice in some early use of the form through either omissions or over-specifying.[247]

---

[243] *R* v. *Portsmouth City Council, ex parte Peter Coles, Colwick Builders Ltd and George Austin Ltd* (1997) 81 BLR 1 (CA); and *Ballast Nedam Groep NV* v. *Belgian State* (Case C-5/97) (1998) 88 BLR 32 (ECJ). See generally MEDHURST, DAVID. *EU Public Procurement Law.* Blackwell Science, Oxford, 1997. See lately His Honour Judge GEDDES, A. Enforcing EC Public Procurement Rules. A paper given to the Society of Construction Law at a meeting in London on 7 April 1998.

[244] See *Harvela Investments Ltd* v. *Royal Trust Co of Canada (Channel Islands) Ltd* [1986] AC 207, [1985] 2 All ER 966, HL; cf *Spencer* v. *Harding* (1870) LR 5 CP 561 at 563 per Willes J.

[245] *Blackpool and Fylde Aero Club Ltd* v. *Blackpool Borough Council* [1990] 3 All ER 25, [1990] 1 WLR 1195, CA; *Fairclough Building Ltd* v. *Port Talbot Borough Council* (1992) 62 BLR 82, CA.

[246] See e.g. Council Directive 71/305/EEC (OJ L 185, 16 August 1971) as amended by Council Directive 89/440/EEC (OJ L 210, 21 July 1989) and Council Directive (EC) 90/531 concerning public works; and Council Directive 77/62/EEC (OJ L 013, 15 January 1977) as amended by Council Directive 88/295/EEC (OJ L 127, 20 May 1988) and Council Directive 90/531/EEC (OJ L 297, 29 October 1990) concerning public supply contracts. See generally *Public Procurement: Global Revolution*, ARROWSMITH, SUE and DAVIES, ARWEL (eds). Kluwer Law International, London, 1998; GEDDES, A. *Public and Utility Procurement: A Practical Guide to the UK Regulations and Associated Community Rules*, 2nd edn. Sweet and Maxwell, London, 1997; BRIGHT, CHRISTOPHER. *Public Procurement Handbook.* Wiley Chancery, London, 1994; WEISS, FRIEDL. *Public Procurement in European Community Law.* The Athlone Press, London, 1993 and TURPIN, COLIN C. *Government Procurement and Contracts.* Longman, Harlow, 1989.

[247] BAIRD, ANDREW, see n. 29 above, 117.

Sample form of tender

The NEC contains a Sample Form of Tender in the guidance notes. It is expressly described as a 'sample' and may be contrasted with other standard forms in this regard which prescribe a form of tender that is typically a contract document.[248]

The Sample Form first leaves space for insertion of the 'works' as the contractor describes them. As the works are italicized the intention is for the works, as the contractor describes them, to correspond with their description according to the same term in part one of the Contract Data. Martin Cutts, author of *The Plain English Guide*,[249] is in favour of italicization when first used in a text as it brings the italicized word to the reader's attention.

The form of tender also shortly sets out to whom the tender is submitted or addressed. Significantly the form contains an offer to 'Provide the Works in accordance with Contract Data part one and the attached Contract Data part two for a sum to be determined in accordance with the conditions of contract'. Contractors or tenderers complete the tender by inserting their name, position, the name and address of their company and date. No provision is made for the formalities of witnesses or attestation under seal. It is the tender itself and written acceptance of it by the employer that constitutes a contract between the parties. No representation is made that the contractor has not colluded with any other contractor in the preparation of the tender as common law and statute law govern the matter.

At common law collusive tendering is not *per se* invalid or unenforceable between or among parties;[250] however, such agreements are routinely subject to statutory limitations or prohibitions.[251] The offer remains open for acceptance for a stated period of time, which may be inserted in the Sample Form.

To return to the formal offer to provide the works as set out above several points should be made. First, the form clearly indicates that the offer is coming from the tenderer. This reinforces the status of the invitation or instructions to tenderers as mere invitations to treat as discussed above. Secondly, the description clearly incorporates by reference parts one and two of the Contract Data into the offer. This should overcome any ambiguity surrounding this point. Thirdly, the capitalization of 'Provide the Works' and the status of that phrase as a defined term in the ECC also have significance. It is arguable that the content of contractor's obligation will thus be informed by the definition of that phrase. Lastly, there is no lump sum contract price and rather the offer is made in consideration for a sum to be determined in accordance with the conditions of contract.

---

[248] See e.g. FIDIC 4th, ICE 6th, NSC/T, NAM/T, JCT 80.

[249] CUTTS, MARTIN. *The Plain English Guide.* Oxford University Press, Oxford, 1995, p. 59.

[250] *Metcalf* v. *Bouck* (1871) 25 LT 539; *Jones* v. *North* (1875) LR 19 Eq 426.

[251] See e.g. the Restrictive Trade Practices Act 1976, sections 6–11; and the Treaty of Rome, arts 85 and 85.

A question arises as to why the NEC does not include a form of tender in the contract documents rather than the 'sample' Form of Agreement in appendix 2 of the guidance notes?[252] The drafters state that no standard form of tender was included in the ECC because many employers have standard forms containing their own requirements.[253] However, this seems to be an omission for two important reasons. First, it is illogical not to issue a form of tender for a reason that equally applies to the other contracts in the package. In all likelihood, where employers have their own tender forms they will also often have their own contract documents. Secondly, as the NEC is intended to be complete, and with completeness also arguably defined by reference to packages under other standard forms, the absence of the form of tender detracts from the drafters' intent. These reasons stand apart from others that support not only a form of agreement but fuller expression within the articles themselves. It can be contended that the articles of agreement are important to reinforce guiding principles; for instance the spirit of mutual trust and co-operation in the ECC. By comparison article 4 in the JCT/NSC/A form underscores arbitration as the chosen mode of dispute resolution.

A further question arises as to why the NEC did not include further sample forms. An excellent counterpoint to the NEC in this regard is one new volume introduced in the second edition of the ENAA Model Form of Contract for Process Plant 1992. Volume 4, 'Work Procedures', comprises ten works procedures in total. The model form of contract is published by the Engineering Advancement Association of Japan.[254] The procedures are wide ranging and include sample formats, tables, charts and even letters as well as other documents. A very significant role has been attributed to them by the former chairman[255] of the ENAA's Special Committee on Legal Issues, who called them 'indispensable for the smooth execution of the project'.[256]

The Sample Form of Agreement provides that a party to the ECC may sign either under hand or seal in accordance with usual practice.[257] There

[252] Although the term 'agreement' used in the sample form is replaced by the term 'contract' in the conditions, it is submitted nothing turns on this fact and other standard forms follow both the same, e.g. JCT 80, and different practices, e.g. ACA 2.

[253] Guidance notes NEC, 17.

[254] The ENAA has also more recently released a Model Form of Contract for Power Plant Construction 1996. The 1996 model form comprises three volumes with no Work Procedures as does the 1992 form. It is intended, however, that the Works Procedures would be substantially applicable to the 1996 contract and could be used with some amendments, see HOSHI, HIROMI. ENAA Model Form of Contract for Power Plant Construction. *International Construction Law Review*, 1997, 63.

[255] FURUYA, KUNIHIKO. ENAA Revised Model Form of Contract. *International Construction Law Review*, 1993, 9.

[256] *Ibid.* JAYNES, GORDON L. Turnkey Contracts: Japan's Model Forms. *International Construction Law Review*, 1993, 251 called the Work Procedures '...virtually a do-it-yourself kit for on-the-job use of the Model Forms'.

[257] See e.g. the United Kingdom Companies Act, 1985 section 36A.

is no provision for witness attestation unlike some other forms.[258] A formal agreement is a normal safeguard to overcome uncertainty surrounding the meaning and relationship of documents or communications that make up the contract.

There is a precedent for the ENAA Works Procedures: that is, the procedures set out in the *Manual of the BPF System: The British Property Federation System for Building Design and Construction.*[259] The systems approach, in forms like the BPF and the NEC system, has lately been argued to be the best approach to contract planning and an approach which would appear to lead to a better understanding of party objectives than under traditional non-systems or discrete forms of contract.[260] It has been said that the BPF system is 'evidence of a profound dissatisfaction with the traditional building system, and a determined attempt to put something better in its place'.[261] The BPF Manual divides the project into five stages: concept, preparing the brief, design development, tender documents and tendering, and construction and sets out the recommended procedures to be followed in respect of each. It is similar in this respect to other systems which divide projects or developments into different stages; for example, the RIBA Plan of Work which utilizes work stages in terms of activities and actions as well.[262] It also contains three appendices: schedules of responsibilities and duties, checklists, and BPF system forms. In the result the BPF model presents a truly complete picture of the best practice administration of a project and one which compares very favourably with the ENAA Work Procedures. Volume 4 Work Procedure 2, Payment Application Procedure sets out sample documents for all payment and invoice applications including those for advance payments, progress payments, payment on shipping and release of retention. It is submitted that in these two models there is still more upon which future editions of the NEC should draw.[263]

---

[258] For example, IFC 84, JCT 87.

[259] *Manual of the BPF System The British Property Federation System for Building Design and Construction.* British Property Federation, London, 1983.

[260] CHEUNG, SAI ON and LENARD, D. Construction Contracts: A Systems Review. *Australian Institute of Quantity Surveyors*, 1997, **1** (1), 46–51.

[261] According to McGRAW, MARK C. Adjudicators, Experts and Keeping Out of Court. *Construction Law Journal*, 1992, **8**, 337, n. 21. See generally PENNINGTON, I. *A Guide to the BPF System and Contract.* Chartered Institute of Building, Ascot, 1985.

[262] See COX, STANLEY and HAMILTON, ALAINE. *Architect's Job Book*, 6th edn. RIBA Publications, London, 1995.

[263] See for additional background on process plant forms SASAKI, T. ENAA Model Form of Contract, *International Construction Law Review*, 1987, 94; WESTRING, GOSTA. Turnkey Heavy Plant Contracts from the Owner's Point of View. *International Construction Law Review*, 1990, 234; and GOULD, NICHOLAS. Comments on the ENAA Model Form International Contract of Plant Construction. *International Construction Law Review*, 1994, 498.

Acceptance of tender
Acceptance of the Sample Form of Tender by the employer constitutes a formal contract. The formal contract documents are determined at the time of tender. Under the NEC the tenderer would also be expected to submit part two of the Contract Data and the works information. In the ordinary course the contents of the tender may also include the contractor's activities schedules, bills of quantities and programme. The type of contract or method of procurement agreed will correspond to one of the main options. Unsuccessful tenderers are not, as a rule, entitled to recover the costs of their unsuccessful bid save in exceptional cases such as those involving fraud and one could expect this rule to apply here.[264]

---

[264] *William Lacey (Hounslow) Ltd* v. *Davis* [1957] 2 All ER 712, [1957] 1 WLR 132.

5. Roles and responsibilities

Civil Engineering will always be the art of implementing appropriate solutions to practical problems. The combined activities of design and project management represent the core of this process. For successful Civil Engineering, the two must be interwoven to form a continuous process, with iteration between technical and external aspects leading to optimum solutions.

The Institution of Civil Engineers.
Whither Civil Engineering?

General

The ECC casts the roles and responsibilities of those involved in contracting and construction in new terms. There are familiar and unfamiliar roles as well as significant omissions. One omission, the *engineer*, is all the more significant when it is recalled that the ECC is the product of the Institution of Civil Engineers whose coat of arms is emblazoned on the back cover of the contracts. Of the new roles three may be noted: the 'Project Manager', 'Supervisor' and 'Adjudicator'. It is not entirely accurate to say that they are new for they have been used in other standard forms; however, their presence in a multi-purpose form rather than one dedicated to a particular mode of procurement is new. The central change the ECC introduces in the roles is their division and reassignment. Thus the ECC divides the roles and the responsibilities of the engineer in engineering contracts, and the architect in building contracts,[1] into at least four others.[2] Architects and engineers have been replaced from a drafting point of view by project managers, supervisors, and adjudicators. The fourth role that may be added

1   See SLVID, R. How the Construction Industry Sees the Architect's Role. *The Architects Journal*, May 1993, **197** (20) 23.
2   Under GC/Works/1 3rd the 'Superintending Officer' may be either an architect or an engineer in practice, while ACA 2 and IFC 84 and the JCT Local Authorities editions use the term 'Supervising Officer'. The FIDIC Orange Book 1st uses the term 'Employer's Representative' in cl. 3l. In these ways the statutory protection afforded the use of the term 'architect' or 'engineer' is also overcome and cross-disciplinariness is enhanced. See with regard to the Orange Book, MATHEOU, M. and THOMAS, G. FIDIC Design-Build Conditions – The Demise of the Engineer. *Construction Law*, 1995, 5 February/March 1995, 208–211.

is that of the employer's designer. Although the form assumes this role it is not expressly mentioned. Notwithstanding this division, it was not intended that individuals with other professional designations would replace either architects or engineers in these roles. It was more likely intended that recognition should be given to the different aspects inherent in each role and the necessity for the involvement of additional personnel.[3] The separation of the roles of the contract administrator, project or lead manager and Adjudicator were endorsed in the Latham Report as well as the clear definition of the project or lead manager's role as client's representative.[4] It was the JCT Management Contract which introduced the term 'Contract Administrator' for the person appointed to issue instructions and certificates under the contract who was not an architect. This designation was intended to eventually replace 'Supervising Officer' in other JCT forms and because use of the title 'Architect' was restricted to those registered under the Architects (Registration) Act 1931 and Architects Registration Act 1934. Since that time these earlier acts have been consolidated in the Architects Act 1997. The term 'Supervising Officer' was first introduced into the Local Authorities versions of the JCT form for use where the Chief Officer of the Local Authority was, for example, an engineer. It was later used in the JCT MW form and in the JCT IFC to extend to cases where the person concerned was not an architect. 'Contract Administrator' has now become a more appropriate description than 'Supervising Officer' in JCT forms.[5]

The changes to the role of engineer have been made despite the views of some that the concept of the 'independent' engineer (or architect) is preferable. It is noteworthy that there was even some division of opinion among even members of the Legal Affairs Committee of the ICE when this issue was discussed and not every member favoured a full rationalization of the engineer's roles.[6] Despite this view drafting organizations have been moving towards the conclusion that the engineer as defined had to be changed for numerous reasons.[7]

---

[3] Perhaps reflecting a mid-way stage in the evolution in terminology is the use of 'the Architect/the Contract Administrator' as the 'Contract Administrator' in both the IFC 84 and JCT MW forms.

[4] Latham Report, paragraph 5.18(5), 37.

[5] JCT forms: *JCT Newsletter*, May 1987, **1**, 2, RIBA Publications, London, 1987.

[6] See BARNES, DR MARTIN. *Specification and Partial Draft for A New Style Conditions of Contract: Comments Received from the Members of the Legal Affairs Committee.* Martin Barnes Project Management, London, February 1987, p. 2.

[7] It is not only drafting organizations but academics and others who have increasingly focused attention on the role of the engineer, see e.g COTTAM, GUY. The Powers of the Engineer. *International Construction Law Review*, 1986, 149; WESTRING, GOSTA. Balance of Power in the FIDIC Contract with Special Emphasis on the Powers of the Engineer. *International Construction Law Review*, 1984, 117; MORTIMER-HAWKINS, MICHAEL. FIDIC – An Engineer's View of the Engineer's Role.' *International Construction Law Review*, 1984, 4; KRISTENSEN, HANS. FIDIC – Another Engineer's View of the Engineer's Role. *International Construction Law Review*, 1985, 51; LUDLOW, MICHAEL R and GORDON REES, J. Engineer's Role under FIDIC Standard Conditions of Contract. *International Business Lawyer*, 1992, 525; and HOCHULI, U. Role of the Engineer under FIDIC. *International Business Lawyer*, 1992, 242.

FIDIC,[8] in particular, in reconsidering the 4th Edition, has noted the perception of bias in developed countries which is accentuated in developing countries.[9] Edward Corbett has written: '[t]o many people, the idea of an independent engineer is a quaint English notion out of touch with everyday reality. Many in continental Europe and elsewhere are far happier with an engineer planted firmly in the client's camp'.[10] It may be noted that it is only a *perception* of bias that is referred to here and not the current tests which the English courts apply when a decision is impugned on grounds of apparent bias, that is, whether there was a real danger of bias on the part of the decision maker, and whether a reasonable person might reasonably suspect bias on the decision maker's part.[11] Other drafting organizations became concerned over the independence issue even earlier than FIDIC. As early as 1977 the difficulties inherent in the engineer's dual role were the subject of a review by the Conditions of Contract Standing Joint Committee of the ICE.[12] The perception of bias is worsened when coupled with other factors such as payment of the engineer by the employer or when the engineer is an in-house employee of the employer.[13] The withholding of powers from the engineer coupled with the need for more and more employer approvals have weakened the engineer's independence in any case and greater use of design and build forms has further complicated the engineer's role in relation to supervision of the contractor client.[14] Lastly, closer judicial scrutiny of the engineer in the performance of these functions too has fostered the drift towards eventual separation of the roles. Clearly, there are also those who have identified these factors and championed this change in the role of the engineer as a result.

The controversy is over whether or not to preserve the consulting engineer's traditional capacity to resolve disputes between owners and contractors. The FIDIC is conducting an in-depth inquiry into

---

[8] BOWCOCK, JOHN. The FIDIC Contract Forms: The Present and Future. *The Patrick McCreight Memorial Lecture.* A paper given in London on 7 November 1995 by the Society of Construction Law. Society of Construction Law, London, 1995, p. 10.

[9] Others have noted this point in a wider context; see NICKLISCH, FRITZ. The Role of the Engineer as Contract Administrator and Quasi-Arbitrator in International Construction and Civil Engineering Projects. *International Construction Law Review*, 1990, 322–23.

[10] CORBETT, EDWARD. FIDIC 5th or a New Style Red Book. *International Construction Law Review*, 1993, 290.

[11] See *R* v. *Gough* [1993] AC 646 at 669–670, [1993] 2 All ER 724 at 737–738 per Lord Goff, and Lord Woolf at 671, 738 respectively.

[12] CCSJC/GN 2AB September 1977, ICE, ACE and FCEC. GILBERT, JOHN. The ICE 6th Edition – Some Initial Thoughts. *Construction Law Journal*, 1991, 7, 201 sets out several clauses in the ICT 6th form which detract from the engineer's independence.

[13] BOWCOCK, JOHN, see n. 8 above, p. 10.

[14] See generally FRANKS, J. *Design and Build Approach to Procurement.* CIOB, Ascot, Construction Paper 27, 1993.

this issue as it prepares the FIDIC 5th ... [t]his Note ... concludes that FIDIC should, and most likely will, modernize the Red Book in its next edition by severely limiting the role of the consulting engineer as an adjudicator'.[15]

Although there is no express reference to surveyors in the ECC they will almost certainly be involved. In particular, quantity surveyors could well be expected under several of the main options. The employer normally appoints the quantity surveyor either directly or indirectly. The key role of a quantity surveyor is the measurement of inputs to the construction process upon which payments may be made. In an early case, *Taylor* v. *Hall* a quantity surveyor was held to be a person whose 'business consists in taking out in detail the measurements and quantities, from physical plans prepared by an architect, for the purpose of enabling builders to calculate the amounts for which they would execute the plans'.[16] This measurement role extends to valuations and in the ECC may include assessments if properly assigned. The proper assigning of responsibility to a quantity surveyor is central to any finding that the surveyor has jurisdiction or authority to waive the benefit of any contractual provisions,[17] or determine whether work has been executed in accordance with the contract.[18] While quantity surveyors can be expected to play a measurement role, the forward nature of the work done under the NEC suggests that an 'estimator' may often be more suitable.

The functions, duties, responsibilities and powers of the consultants under the NEC turn upon the wording of the relevant main option and any relevant terms of engagement. *Chesham Properties Ltd* v. *Bucknall Austin Project Management Services Ltd and others* has also looked at the functions, duties, responsibilities and powers of consultants *vis-à-vis* each other and considered in particular when they might owe duties to report on each others deficiencies in performance of their roles under different wordings.[19] The ECC makes a departure from other standard forms by overcoming the division of roles which consultants have had to assume; that is agent and independent actor. By providing for an adjudicator the project manager may act on behalf of and solely in the best interests of the employer. The project manager need not act impartially – he or she manages on behalf of the employer and in this sense may be partial. On this basis it has been remarked that the project manager need not act

---

[15] LYONS, M. BETH. The Role of the Consulting Engineer in Developing Country Construction Under the FIDIC Form of Contract. *Law and Policy in International Business*, 1994, **26**, 274.

[16] *Taylor* v. *Hall* (1870) IR 4 CL 467 at 476 per Morris J.

[17] *Sutcliffe* v. *Chippendale & Edmondson* (1971) 18 BLR 149.

[18] See *John Laing Construction Ltd* v. *County and District Properties* (1982) 23 BLR 1; see also *Rosehaugh Stanhope Properties (Broadgate Phase 6) plc and Rosehaugh Stanhope (Broadgate Phase 7) plc* v. *Redpath Dorman Long Ltd* (1990) 50 BLR 69; (1990) 29 Con LR 80, CA.

[19] *Chesham Properties Ltd* v. *Bucknall Austin Project Management Services Ltd and others* (1997) 82 BLR 92.

fairly. Professor Andrew Cox and Ian Thompson write: 'The project manager is the client's representative ... [t]herefore he does not have an obligation to act fairly or impartially'.[20] However, this view would seem to contradict the obligation imposed on the project manager in clause 10.1 to act in a spirit of mutual trust and co-operation. It would also seem to run contrary to some trends suggesting fairness in decision making, for example, the Construction Round Table's *Declaration of Commitment to Fair Construction Contracts* requiring members to declare their intention to give effect to certain principles in the conduct of their projects and which include: 'to deal fairly with those whom we contract and with those who are contracted to them in an atmosphere of mutual co-operation'. Members sign the Declaration and then deposit it with the Chartered Institute of Purchasing and Supply. Similarly the Construction Clients' Forum has released a policy document entitled *Constructing Improvement* which suggests a pact between clients and industry and commits Forum members to a series of specific steps including fairness.[21] The contractor is free to negotiate with the project manager fully aware of this role. The contributor need not expect impartiality from the project manager but if the actions of the project manager infringe any of the contractor's rights under the contract the independent adjudicator or the arbitrator may be looked to for potential redress. Duties of impartiality are not always express in the forms of contract and thus, when sought, may have to be established on the basis of an implied term.[22]

Employer

The 'Employer' plays an important role in the NEC. At the outset, pursuant to clause 10.1, the employer is placed under a mandatory obligation to act as stated in the contract and in a spirit of mutual trust and co-operation. The employer is one of the parties to the contract under the ECC,[23] Short Contract,[24] Professional Services Contract,[25] and Adjudicator's Contract.[26] Under the Plant Contract the 'Employer' becomes the 'Purchaser', and the 'Contractor' becomes the 'Supplier' as a matter of comparison, although many of the actions of the purchaser under the Plant Contract remain the same as those of the employer under the ECC.[27] Thus,

---

[20] COX, PROFESSOR ANDREW and THOMPSON, IAN. Is the NEC Going to Succeed? – An Examination of the Engineering and Construction Contrct. (Alias the NEC 2nd Edition). *International Construction Law Review*, 1996, 330.

[21] *Construction Industry Law Letter*, 1995, 1104. See also REDMOND, JOHN. Give and Take: the Pact. *Building*, 8 May 1998, 40.

[22] See e.g. ICE MW 2nd.

[23] Clause 11.2(1) ECC.

[24] Clause 11.2(1) SC.

[25] Clause 11.2(1) PSC.

[26] See Form of Agreement and clause 1.1 AC.

[27] For example, under the PC the employer is also given rights to use the supplier's design (clause 22.4), take over the site (clause 35), acquire title to plant and materials (clause 70), insure (clause 83), refer disputes to adjudication and terminate the supplier (clauses 90, 94).

for example, the employer has the authority to replace the project manager or the supervisor.[28] The employer is also given rights to use the contractor's design,[29] take over the site,[30] acquire title to plant and materials,[31] insure,[32] refer disputes to adjudication[33] and terminate the contractor.[34] These are important rights and exist independently of those that the employer exercises through the project manager. The effect is that the employer plays a significant role in the operation of the contract.[35]

The employer will normally be represented toward the contractor during the works by one or more consultants described above or by the employer's own employees. Under the PSC itself the employer may even expressly confirm the appointment of an agent toward the consultant.[36] By analogy to cases which have held the employer to be under an implied obligation that the architect/engineer or contract administrator will perform their duties with reasonable skill and care,[37] the Employer will be under a like obligation with respect to the project manager. It follows that the employer will be liable toward the contractor in negligence for breach of contract by the project manager. It also seems reasonable to consider the employer act toward the adjudicator as toward the architect or engineer when either of them are exercising an independent or impartial function. Impartiality as a duty itself is prescribed in certain forms, for example, clause 2.6 of FIDIC 4th, but must be understood as still being limited by the agent's role which an engineer would play under these conditions as well. Under clause 2(8) of the ICE 6th form the engineer is exempted from acting impartially in matters requiring specific approval of the employer; however, the duty would continue to operate at all other times and whether the engineer was acting as agent, certifier or arbiter. Thus an amployer who interfered with the exercise of discretion by an adjudicator could similarly be seen to commit a breach of contract[38] on this view. The failure of an employer to act to appoint a substitute project manager who is failing to apply properly the contract may also constitute a breach of the employer's obligations. The outcome in this situation will turn in part upon what

---

[28] Clause 14.4 ECC.

[29] Clause 22.1 ECC.

[30] Clause 35 ECC.

[31] Clause 70 ECC.

[32] Clause 87 ECC.

[33] Clause Y2.5/90.5 ECC unamended Second Edition.

[34] Clause 94.2 ECC

[35] See generally on the duties of the employer *Construction Management Forum Report and Guidance.* University of Reading, Reading, 1989, section 2.0, pp. 12–13; and the *Manual of the BPF System*, particularly stage 1 and 2, pp. 17–30; and *Briefing the Team. A Guide to Better Briefing for Clients.*

[36] See secondary option clause H, PSC First Edition and secondary option clause X10, PSC Second Edition.

[37] See *London Borough of Merton* v. *Stanley Hugh Leach Ltd* (1985) 32 BLR 51.

[38] See *London Borough of Merton* v. *Stanley Hugh Leach Ltd* (1985) 32 BLR 51.

effect the court gives to first the adjudicator's and second the arbitrator's powers to correct failures on the part of the project manager in the administration of the contract.[39]

Project Manager
General
The 'Project Manager' is responsible for management of the project on behalf of the employer and fulfils an exceedingly important role in the NEC, discharging some 110 or so duties.[40] One reason behind this number of duties is the number of roles that the project manager effectively fulfils unlike the case of his or her counterparts under other forms. The project manager may assume functions exercised under other forms by the employer, the engineer's representative, assistants, the quantity surveyor and, of course, the architect and engineer among others. In this role a good project manager should also be expected to have some business acumen. On many occasions commercial judgment in assessing risk will be necessary, valuing compensation events and accepting quotations. These skills would not be expected to the same degree for architects or engineers under traditional forms. Both architects and engineers as professional bodies have become increasingly aware of this fact and been revising both tertiary and professional curricula with a view to improving business and management skills for their respective professions.[41] The ability of the project manager to exercise these skills follows in part from the increasing extension of project management into

---

[39] See generally *Panamena Europea Navigacion (Cia Lda)* v. *Frederick Leyland & Co Ltd* [1947] AC 428, HL; *Perini Corpn* v. *Commonwealth of Australia* (1969) 12 BLR 62; and *Lubenham Fidelities and Investment Co Ltd* v. *South Pembrokeshire District Council* (1986) 33 BLR 39, CA.

[40] Cf the suggested list of project manager's duties in table 1: *Code of Practice for Project Management for Construction and Development*, 5; and the typical job specification for a project manager in appendix 1 of the same *Code of Practice*, 85–91; the specimen job description for a project manager in *Managing Construction Projects A Guide to Processes and Procedures* (eds AUSTEN, A. D. and NEALE, R. H.), appendix B. International Labour Office, Geneva, 1984, section 4.2, pp. 143–144; University of Reading. The Construction Manager: Schedule of Duties. *Construction Management Forum Report and Guidance.* University of Reading, Reading, 1989, pp. 21–22; Appendix 1: Schedule of Responsibilities and Duties. *Manual of the BPF System*, pp. 63–64.

[41] This can be seen for example in the recent report *Educating the Professional Team.* See also BURTON, R. *Steering Group on Architectural Education – Report and Recommendations.* RIBA, London, 1992; Engineering Council. *Competence and Commitment.* Engineering Council, London, 1995; Royal Academy of Engineering. *The Education of Young People* (Royal Academy of Engineering, London, 1995. SCOTT, NEIL *et al.* A Window on Management Training within the Construction Industry. *Industrial & Commercial Training*, 1997, **29** (5), 148–152 survey the attitudes of civil engineers and their companies and conclude that moves toward modern management practices are being made.

other fields.[42] The importance of learning and applying these types of skills to achieve the successful introduction and the use of the NEC contract system in projects has been made clear.[43] A link has also been suggested between sound project management and the fostering of co-operation on sites.[44]

The duties that the project manager assumes may also usefully be considered in relation to those to be performed if he or she were appointed under the NEC Professional Services Contract. The employer solely appoints the project manager. The form leaves open whether the project manager may be a company and this view is supported by the absence of any reference to 'key people' with respect to the project manager. One may expect in many instances the appointment will be made pursuant to the PSC. There is no limitation in the contract on the appointment of an individual from the employer's staff to serve in this capacity or as supervisor for that matter; notwithstanding that the project manager or supervisor also fulfil certification roles.[45] However, if either or both of these roles is fulfilled by an employee the terms of the employment contract between the parties should be tested against the PSC to avoid any conflicts in their provisions. For instance the unilateral right of the employer to replace the project manager or supervisor (clause 14.4) should not be qualified in a non-conforming employment contract between the employer and either of these parties.[46] If the project manager were appointed under the PSC First Edition the contract between these parties is likely to consist of numerous documents.

- A letter or form of offer.
- Part one of the Contract Data of the PSC.
- Part two of the Contract Data of the PSC.
- An 'activity schedule' if main options A or C PSC First Edition are used.
- A 'task schedule' if main option D PSC First Edition is used.

---

[42] See ALLINSON, K. *The Wild Card of Design: A Perspective on Architecture in a Project Management Environment.* Butterworths Architecture, Oxford, 1993. See generally for a suggested model list of skills for project managers: Construction Industry Council. *Project Management Skills.* Construction Industry Council, London, 1996; and BAIRD, ANDREW. Pioneering the NEC System of Documents. *Engineering, Construction and Architectural Management,* 1995, **2** (4), 249.

[43] BROOME, JON C. and PERRY, JOHN G. Experiences of the Use of the New Engineering Contract. *Engineering, Construction and Architectural Management,* 1995, **2** (4), 275.

[44] MOSHINI, R. A. and DAVIDSON, C. H. Determinants of Performance in the Traditional Building Process. *Construction Management and Economics,* 1990, **10**, 343–359.

[45] See generally *Ranger* v. *Great Western Rly Co* (1854) 5 HL Cas 72, HL; *Panamena Europea Navigacion (Cia Lda)* v. *Frederick Leyland & Co Ltd* [1947] AC 428, HL.

[46] Cf the absence of any right of the employer to replace the engineer under the FIDIC 4th condition.

- A brief – yet if the PSC Second Edition is used the brief would be replaced with the scope.
- A letter of acceptance from the employer.[47]

While all of these documents are relevant to the duties of the project manager the brief may be singled out as one of the most important overall. In particular, the brief specifies and describes the services of the project manager.[48] Thus the brief will set out in detail not only the services of the project manger and the employer's objectives but effectively their relationship as a result of the two. Numerous references are made in the conditions of the First Edition of the PSC to the brief, and in the Second Edition of the PSC to the scope, which replaces the brief, and thus where and how these conditions will be elaborated upon. The Guidance Notes in the PSC First Edition contain a table setting out individual clause numbers for the PSC, the relevant item and the effect.[49]

The project manager is given far-reaching powers[50] over the conduct of the 'works' under the ECC. The project manager may or may not seek the views of the employer in fulfilling the majority of these powers. The employer's designers may also be expected to be managed in many instances. If not every power can be delegated to the project manager it has been suggested[51] that a special condition[52] be added to put the contractor on notice of what situations the employer alone will decide. This over-arching power of delegation distinguishes the project manager from others, such as the engineer, under the ICE 6th.[53]

The ECC sets out in its various clauses the actions[54] (*viz.* instructions, submissions, proposals, records, acceptances, notifications and replies) that the project manager will take. These actions give the project manager powers to change the 'Works Information', vary the manner in which the contractor carries out the works, accelerate the works and generally impose judgment on the contractor in many details. Conversely, the project manager appointed under the PSC is under an obligation to comply with instructions of the employer where practicable which change the brief.[55] Limitations are placed upon carrying out these actions in

---

[47] Guidance notes PSC First Edition, 6.

[48] See clause 11.2(5) PSC First Edition.

[49] Guidance notes PSC First Edition, 8.

[50] CORBIN, A. L. gives a definition of power which will suffice here: '[t]he legal relation of A to B when A's own voluntary act will cause new legal relations either between B and A or between B and a third person': 'Legal Analysis and Terminology. *Yale Law Journal*, 1919–20, **29**, 168.

[51] BAIRD, ANDREW. The New Engineering Contract – A Management Summary for Plant Industry Users. *International Construction Law Review*, 1994, 114.

[52] For example, an additional condition of contract under option Z.

[53] Some eight matters are detailed in the ICE 6th that cannot be delegated by the engineer.

[54] See also clause 10.1 of the PSC First Edition where actions refer to the requirement that the consultant act as stated in the PSC.

[55] Clause 21.3 PSC First Edition.

certain cases through the procedures that are required. Thus, for instance, in certifying a payment due to the contractor, time frames are imposed and interest may have to be paid.[56] Guidance is also given in limited instances when an action is negative. The guidance is most often given in the form of legitimate reasons for refusing an action put forward or sought by the contractor.[57] While the project manager thus has a broad jurisdiction the clearer allocation of risk should serve to alleviate some of the concern that the contractor may feel as a result of this. For example, the compensation event procedure serves as a check or limitation upon the actions of the project manager.

It is submitted that the appointment of the project manager will normally be a condition precedent to the contractor's obligation to commence the works.[58] Indeed it would appear that the earlier the appointment of the project manager is made the more likely that better construction performance will be achieved.[59] The employer is also likely to be under an implied obligation to appoint a replacement project manager if the original appointee becomes unable to act for any reason.[60]

Authority

The project manager's actions will normally serve to bind the employer. The fact that the project manager's actions may bind the employer and yet this can occur without having obtained express permission from the employer underscores the breadth of his or her role and authority.[61] Similarly, the employer may also be bound if any of the actions the project manager takes fall within the employer's apparent or ostensible authority to act. Conversely if the project manager's actions fall outside the employer's authority, the Employer could be liable for breach or want of authority.

In general, in the absence of express authority to the contrary, courts have construed the implied authority of architects and engineers to be exceedingly limited. It is submitted that these precedents are apposite in the case of the project manager. The project manager would not have implied authority to order a change to the works information that is already included in the contract;[62] to waive the terms of the contract;[63] or

---

[56] Clause 51 unamended and amended 2nd ECC.

[57] See e.g. clauses 15.1, 21.2, 23.1, 24.1, 26.2, 26.3, 31.3 etc. ECC.

[58] See *Coombe* v. *Green* (1843) 11 M & W 480.

[59] For example, in relation to time performance, WALKER, D. H. T. Construction Time Performance and Traditional versus Non-Traditional Procurement Methods. *Journal of Construction Procurement*, 1997, **3** (1), 42–55.

[60] See *Kellett* v. *Stockport Corpn* (1906) 70 JP 154; *Croudace Ltd* v. *London Borough of Lambeth* (1986) 33 BLR 20, CA.

[61] See e.g. clause 36 on acceleration or clause 62.3 on accepting quotations on compensation events. See generally THOMPSON, P. The Client's Role in the Project Management. *Project Management*, May 1992, **9** (2), 90–92.

[62] *Sharpe* v. *San Paulo Rly Co* (1873) LR 8 Ch App 597; *Tharsis Sulphur and Copper Co* v. *McElroy & Sons* (1878) 3 App Cas 1040, H.

[63] *R* v. *Peto* (1826) 1 Y & J 37; *Cooper* v. *Langdon* (1841) 9 M & W 60.

to enter into subcontracts on behalf of the employer.[64] Terms can be implied in law or in fact. Terms implied in fact often give effect to the presumed but unexpressed intention of the parties.[65] Terms may be implied in law as a result of the parties' legal relationship or as result of operation of law as under a particular statute.[66] The significance of the implication of a term at law is that it constitutes a condition of the contract the breach of which gives the aggrieved party the right to repudiate the contract. Professor Michael Furmston notes many standard forms are 'incomplete' leaving the courts to solve problems by implication of terms.[67] This topic is sometimes discussed in US doctrine in terms of 'default rules'. In general, default rules apply when the parties to a contract which is otherwise enforceable have failed to provide for a particular event or contingency.[68] There are ways in which traditional contract law has addressed these situations including interpretation, the doctrine of mistake and once again through implied terms. Ian Ayres and Robert Gertner suggest the principle that default rules should ideally reflect whatever allocation of risk that the majority of contracting parties themselves would choose. One rationale for this allocation is that it saves these parties the cost of transacting around the default rule.[69]

In the normal course, the contractor will assume that the project manager has complete authority to make decisions, take actions and bind the employer under the contract. Likewise the contractor will assume that the project manager will confer with the employer when necessary to validate his or her authority. The NEC regards the question of authority delegated by the employer to the project manager in so far as the contractor is concerned as given. Whatever recourse the project manager must have to the employer with respect to decisions is principally a matter for those parties pursuant to their terms of engagement. From the contractor's point of view the project manager's authority need not be restated as a matter of course in every instance in the ECC. In practical terms best practice would see the project manager not only informing the Employer of decisions on a routine basis but conferring on the more important questions to be decided on the employer's behalf. A project

[64] *A Vigers Sons & Co Ltd* v. *Swindell* [1939] 3 All ER 590; but see *Wallis* v. *Robinson* (1862) 3 F & F 307.

[65] See e.g. *Trollope & Colls* v. *NW Metropolitan Regional Hospital Board* [1973] 1 WLR 601 (1973) 9 BLR 60.

[66] See on legal relationship *Liverpool City Council* v. *Irwin* [1976] AC 239, [1976] 2 All ER 39, HL; and on particular statutes the Sale of Goods Act 1979; and the Supply of Goods and Services Act 1982 as amended by the Sale and Supply of Goods Act 1994.

[67] FURMSTON, PROFESSOR MICHAEL. The Liability of Contractors: Principles of Liability in Contract and Tort. *The Liability of Contractors* (ed. LLOYD, HUMPHREY). Centre for Commercial Law Studies, Queen Mary College. Longman, London, 1986, p. 13.

[68] See CRASWELL, RICHARD. Efficiency and Rational Bargaining in Contractual Settings. *Harvard Journal of Law & Public Policy*, 1992, **15**, 805.

[69] AYRES, IAN and GERTNER, ROBERT. Filling Gaps in Incomplete Contracts: An Economic Theory of Default Rules, *Yale Law Journal*, 1989, **9**.

manager may have limited implied authority to employ a quantity surveyor to prepare tender documents[70] or measure and value changes to the works information[71] although perhaps not to undertake other work.

Only the project manager may vary the contents of the works information by giving instructions to the contractor under clause 14.3. No other explicit authority is given under the contract to the employer, supervisor or adjudicator to effect a change to the works information.[72] As a general rule such a change would amount to a compensation event; however, there are some exceptions to this. The exceptions include giving an instruction to accept a defect; giving an instruction to change works information provided by the contractor for his or her design at the contractor's request or in complying with other works information provided by the employer.[73] While the project manager has the power to issue such instructions, their true effectiveness will ultimately depend upon whether there is any adequate means of measuring their implementation. This is because 'for every instruction which is sent out a resulting feedback signal must be generated, otherwise there will be no means of knowing when corrective actions are required'. One such feedback signal is the progress return form.[74]

There is no limitation on the project manager also serving as the designer or the supervisor on the project or, for that matter, serving in all three roles.

Duties

At common law a project manager would owe duties of care and skill toward the employer as well as supervision, monitoring and inspection.[75] The general duty of care and skill today is owed concurrently in tort and contract.[76] The duty will extend to a wide variety of the project manager's functions under the contract. For instance, it may extend to the securing of competitive tenders;[77] the acceptance of proposed Contract Data for subcontractors;[78] and the giving of instructions in general.[79]

---

[70] See *Moon* v. *Witney Union Guardians* (1837) 3 Bing NC 814; *Waghorn* v. *Wimbledon Local Board* (1877) 2 *Hudson's BC*, 4th edn 52; *Young* v. *Smith* (1879) 2 *Hudson's BC*, 4th edn 70.

[71] See *Birdseye* v. *Dover Harbour Comrs* (1881) 2 *Hudson's BC*, 4th edn 76; *Beattie* v. *Gilroy* (1882) 10 R 226 (Ct of Sess).

[72] But see discussion clause 14.3 below.

[73] Clause 60.1(1) ECC.

[74] LOCK, DENNIS. *Project Management*, 4th edn. Gower, Aldershot, 1988, p. 220. There is an extensive social science literature on the relationship between feedback and behaviour going back almost 100 years, see BAKER, DIANE F. and BUCKLEY, M. RONALD. A Historical Perspective on the Impact of Feedback on Behaviour. *Journal of Management History*, 1996, **2** (4), 21–33.

[75] See *Sutcliffe* v. *Chippendale & Edmonson* (1971) 18 BLR 149 at 162.

[76] *Henderson* v. *Merrett Syndicates Ltd* [1994] 3 WLR 761, [1994] 3 All ER 506, HL; but see *Bagot* v. *Stevens, Scanlon & Co Ltd* [1966] 1 QB 197, [1964] 3 All ER 577.

[77] See *Hutchinson* v. *Harris* (1978) 10 BLR 19, CA.

[78] See clause 26.3 ECC and *Pratt* v. *George J Hill Associates* (1987) 38 BLR 25, CA.

[79] Clause 14.4 ECC.

The project manager will supervise, monitor and inspect the works with the assistance of the supervisor.[80] As the term 'supervision' is not used in the clauses the amount of supervision required will be determined as a question of fact in each case. The subject of supervision in general, notably for architects, is not free from debate. Professor Anthony Lavers[81] has suggested the reasons in part are historical and he argues convincingly that supervision at least for architects today acting under standard terms of engagement should not be assumed. Lavers notes how early terms of engagement for architects from 1872 imposed a duty of supervision. However, even though there was also a duty of 'inspection' in the terms of engagment, little attention was given to it until the reference to 'supervision' was removed from the terms in the 1970s and from which time 'inspection' became the key obligation for architects under the standard terms. Despite this change and which was carried through with the 1992 revision of the RIBA *Standard Form of Agreement for the Appointment of an Architect*, SFA/92, Lavers notes: 'the construction industry ... have continued to operate as though supervision was an unquestioned part of the normal services offered by architects' and criticizes this situation and the cases, e.g. *Alexander Corfield* v. *David Grant*,[82] which perpetuate a duty of supervision. One consequence of this perpetuation is the implication of a duty to supervise which may not accord with the parties' expectations. However, the cases on supervision and even some of the later inspection cases remain good law where clear duties of supervision, e.g. with a clerk of works, are imposed. Thus, in the case of the ECC the issue is whether and to what extent these cases would be applicable. It would seem that a stronger case could be made out for a duty of supervision on the part of the supervisor than the project manager. The project manager's terms of engagement will also be relevant to this question. The standard imposed upon the project manager is not absolute[83] and liability will not attach in every case of a breach of duty to discover a defect.[84] In fact, the structure of the ECC and the joint obligations imposed upon the contractor in the early warning procedures and correcting of defects[85] should militate further against any finding of a breach of duty for an undetected minor defect. If the analogy of the supervisor to a clerk of works[86] or resident engineer is correct then the

---

[80] For example, pursuant to clauses 21, 23, 31, 40.

[81] LAVERS, PROFESSOR ANTHONY. The Architect's Responsibility for Inspection or Supervision. A paper given to the Society of Construction Law at a meeting in Manchester on 22 February 1994. See also GOODALL, FRANCIS. Supervision: An Architect's View. A paper given to the Society of Construction Law at a meeting in London on 5 April 1988, 14–15.

[82] *Alexander Corfield* v. *David Grant* (1992) 59 BLR 102.

[83] *Clemence* v. *Clarke* (1880) 2 *Hudson's BC*, 4th edn 54 at 58.

[84] *East Ham Borough Council* v. *Bernard Sunley & Sons Ltd* [1966] AC 406 at 428, [1965] 3 All ER 619 at 626, HL, per Viscount Dilhorne; *Gray* v. *T P Bennett & Son* (1987) 43 BLR 63.

[85] Clauses 16 and 43 ECC respectively.

[86] See generally COX, STANLEY and HAMILTON, ALAINE. *Clerk of Works Manual*, 3rd edn. RIBA Publications, London, 1994, setting out the responsibilities and duties of a clerk of works.

project manager may not be held responsible for negligence on the supervisor's part in dealing with matters of detail left to his or her authority.[87] A check upon this is that the project manager is limited in what can be delegated to the supervisor. *Saunders and Collard* v. *Broadstairs Local Board* recognizes a similar limitation on the delegation of responsibility for important matters to the clerk of the works. By comparison, limitations are also imposed on the delegation of important functions by the engineer to the engineer's representative under clause 2(3) of ICE 6th.[88] The general duties of the project manager pertain mainly to and arise as incidents of the agency relationship with the employer.[89] Lately it has been held that it is normally the duty of the project manager to see that all insurances required of the contractor have been put in place.[90]

The project manager may submit any dispute arising under or in connection with the contract to the Adjudicator.[91]

Certification[92]

Certification is an important function under standard forms and is no exception under the ECC. Certification is also a controversial function and the alleged wrongful issue of certificates is a significant basis for instituting claims.[93] The project manager or the supervisor may perform the certification role under the ECC. There is no impediment to either of them fulfilling this role concurrently with their duties to monitor the construction of the 'works'.[94] In general the project manager issues certificates to the employer and the contractor while the supervisor issues certificates to the project manager and the contractor.[95] For this to be valid the correct person must issue the certificate to the correct recipients[96] although the ECC recognizes a power of delegation of actions, which would include the certifying role, by either the project

---

[87] *Leicester Board of Guardians* v. *Trollope* (1911) 75 JP 197; *Gray* v. *T P Bennett & Son* (1987) 43 BLR 63.

[88] *Saunders and Collard* v. *Broadstairs Local Board* (1890) 2 *Hudson's BC*, 4th edn 164, DC. See generally *The Clerk of Works and the Site Management Team.* CIOB, Ascot, 1975, CIOB Site Management Information Service 63.

[89] See generally REYNOLDS, PROFESSOR FRANCIS M. B. *Bowstead & Reynolds on Agency.* Sweet & Maxwell, London, 1995; and FRIDMAN, G. H. L. *Fridman's Law of Agency*, 7th edn. Butterworths, London, 1996.

[90] *Pozzolanic Lytag* v. *Bryan Hobson Associates* (1999) 63 Con LR 81.

[91] Clause 90.1 unamended 2nd ECC.

[92] See also 'Payment' below.

[93] Feedback from Claims RIBAir Update 1985/94. In *Architects' Liability.* RIBA Indemnity Research and RIBA Insurance Agency, London, March 1994, 4. See generally HIBBERD, P. R., 'Certification. CIOB, Ascot, 1991, Technical Information Service, 126.

[94] See *Sutcliffe* v. *Thackrah* [1974] AC 727, [1974] 1 All ER 859, HL.

[95] Clause 13.6 ECC.

[96] *Ess* v. *Truscott* (1837) 2 M & W 385; *Lamprell* v. *Billericay Union* (1849) 18 LJ Ex 282; *A-G* v. *Briggs* (1855) 1 Jur NS 1084; cf *Re De Morgan Snell & Co and Rio de Janeiro Flour Mills and Granaries Ltd* (1892) 8 TLR 292, CA.

manager or supervisor to others.[97] However, before any certificate issued by a delegate would be upheld in this respect proper notification to the contractor in advance of the action should have been made.[98] Case law also recognizes powers of delegation although usually not of the certifying function itself but rather measurements and valuations leading up to certification.[99] The ECC grants the employer a unilateral right to replace either the project manager or supervisor as certifier or for all purposes after proper notification to the contractor of the name of the replacement.[100] This reverses the normal rule that the appointment of the certifier is irrevocable: *Mills* v. *Bayley*.[101] In general the appointment of a contract administrator should last until completion in the absence of a contrary provision: *Thomas* v. *Hammersmith Borough Council CA* and *Edwin Hill & Partners* v. *Leakcliffe Properties Ltd.*[102]

Hudson's has defined certificates thus:

> As generally understood in building contracts, a certificate is the expression in a definite form of the exercise of the judgment, opinion or skill of the engineer, architect or surveyor in relation to some matter provided for by the terms of the contract.[103]

The certificate should be in writing.[104] Under the ECC various types of certificate may be issued relative to important aspects of the works including a defects certificate,[105] payment certificate,[106] taking over certificate,[107] completion certificate,[108] and termination certificate.[109] Only the 'defects certificate' is a defined term: 'The Defects Certificate is either a list of Defects that the Supervisor has notified before the defects date which the Contractor has not corrected or, if there are no such Defects, a statement that there are none'.[110]

It may be reasoned that any certificate issued under the ECC must comply with the relevant time limits to be valid.[111] It must also comply

[97] Clause 14.2 ECC.

[98] Clause 14.2 ECC.

[99] See *Clemence* v. *Clarke* (1880) 2 *Hudson's BC*, 4th edn 54, CA.

[100] Clause 14.4 ECC.

[101] *Mills* v. *Bayley* (1863) 2 H & C 36. See generally on replacement of the certifier: *Ranger* v. *Great Western Rly Co* (1854) 5 HL Cas 72, HL.

[102] *Thomas* v. *Hammersmith Borough Council* [1938] 3 All ER 203, CA; *Edwin Hill & Partners* v. *Leakcliffe Properties Ltd* (1984) 29 BLR 43.

[103] *Hudson's Building and Engineering Contracts*, 11th edn, (ed. I. N. Duncan Wallace) Sweet & Maxwell, London, 1994, vol. 1, p. 829. See McINNIS, J. A. *Certificates. Hong Kong Construction Law.* Butterworths, Singapore, 1995, Div VII.

[104] Clause 13.1 ECC.

[105] Clauses 11.2(16) and 43.1 ECC.

[106] Clause 50.5 ECC uses the term 'payment certificate' although the term is not otherwise used in the core payment clause.

[107] Clause 35.4 ECC although the term 'taking over certificate' is not used.

[108] Clause 30.2 ECC although the term 'completion certificate' is not used.

[109] Clauses 94.1, 94.3, 94.5 ECC the term 'termination certificate'.

[110] Clauses 11.2(16) and 43.1 ECC.

[111] *ECC Quarries Ltd* v. *Merriman Ltd* (1988) 45 BLR 90.

with the other formal requirements in the contract; for instance writing.[112] The explicit reference to 'certificate', indeed the italicized reference to 'writing' as the 'language of this contract', in clause 13.1 makes it unlikely that any oral communication would be construed as a certificate as this seems to be clear provision to the contrary.[113]

Notwithstanding the clear minimal criteria for formal validity for a certificate under the ECC there will be communications which raise the issue whether any given communication was to operate as a certificate. This issue will likely be answered objectively by the court on the facts and whether or not the communication was intended to operate as a certificate.[114]

Clause 13.2 stipulates that a certificate has effect when it is received at the last address notified by the recipient for receiving communications or, if none is notified, at the address of the recipient stated in the Contract Data. As certificates normally require issuance or delivery[115] – in the language of the ECC 'receipt' – for validity, the certificate will not be valid until it reaches the prescribed address. Contractors may wish to stipulate an address on site to avoid any delay associated with normal means of delivery and apart from the option of electronic means to effect it.

The role of the project manager and supervisor as certifiers is critical to the successful carrying out of the contract. As a result of their pivotal role in carrying out the contract in this respect a court may well imply certain obligations which have been found to pertain to the certifying function when carried out by architects or engineers. Thus, for example, if this assumption is correct either the project manager or supervisor could be obliged to hear submissions from the contractor before certifying.[116] As to limits at the outside of the certifier's functions it could be expected that collusion with the employer amounting to fraud on the part of the project manager or supervisor will disqualify them.[117] Certifiers have been held liable for negligence in certifying when it has caused irrecoverable loss to the employer[118] and negligence may disentitle a certifier to the payment of any fees.[119]

---

[112] See *Crestar Ltd* v. *Carr* (1987) 37 BLR 113, CA.

[113] *Coken* v. *Young* (1860) 2 F & F 98; *Roberts* v. *Watkins* (1863) 14 CBNS 592; *Elmes* v. *Burgh Market Co* (1891) 2 *Hudson's BC*, 4th edn 170. The italicization indicates that the phrase is identified in the Contract Data.

[114] *Minster Trust Ltd* v. *Traps Tractors Ltd* [1954] 3 All ER 136 at 145 per Devlin J; *Token Construction Co Ltd* v. *Charlton Estates* (1973) 1 BLR 48, CA. Cf *Costain International* v. *A-G of Hong Kong* (1983) 23 BLR 54.

[115] *London Borough of Camden* v. *McInerney Construction Law Journal* 2 (1986): 293; *Anglian Water Authority* v. *RDL Contracting Ltd* (1988) 43 BLR 98.

[116] See *Page* v. *Llandaff and Dinas Powis RDC* (1901) 2 *Hudson's BC*, 4th edn 316; *Re Fuerst Bros & Co Ltd and R S Stephenson* [1951] 1 Lloyd's Rep 429.

[117] See *South Easter Rly* v. *Warton* (1861) 2 F & F 457; *Batterbury* v. *Vyse* (1863) 32 LJ Ex 177.

[118] *Sutcliffe* v. *Thackrah* [1974] AC 727, [1974] 1 All ER 859, HL.

[119] *Money penny* v. *Hartland* (1826) 2 C & P 378; *Nye Saunders & Partners* v. *Brisow* (1987) 37 BLR 92, CA; cf *Hutchison* v. *Harris* (1978) 10 BLR 19, CA.

Supervisor

The ECC adopts the role of the 'Supervisor' for certain functions. The BPF system introduced the supervisor as the person or firm responsible for monitoring the construction of the works in accordance with the contract documents. The employer appoints the supervisor and no limitations are imposed upon the supervisor's qualifications from a specialist point of view. Thus the supervisor may be an architect, engineer, quantity surveyor or otherwise. In most cases it may be expected that the supervisor will be appointed pursuant to the PSC. The supervisor's principal function is to monitor the contractor's performance; in particular as against the works information. It will entail testing materials and workmanship independently and observing similar tests by the contractor.[120] It will also entail the identification of and assured correction of defects.[121] The supervisor, under clause 41 of the PSC First Edition, is under an obligation to correct his or her own defects as well. As early as 1982 the United Kingdom Government set out a series of proposals seeking to enhance the status of standards and quality assurance in order to increase efficiency and promote international competitiveness. These proposals underscored the importance of quality assurance systems.[122] Under the PSC the obligation is framed in terms of the operation of a quality management system.[123]

The presence of a person in a support role for the principal contract administrator, here the project manager, is common in many forms of contract. A clerk of the works, resident engineer or engineer's representative may also fulfil it. The supervisor under the NEC can be equated with any of these roles as the circumstances dictate. Thus guidance may be taken from decided cases considering both their roles and the extent of their liabilities[124] in arguing either for or against obligations of the supervisor although in each case it will be a matter of interpretation.

The supervisor is appointed by and acts solely on behalf of the employer. The supervisor's actions are independent of the employer and vice versa. The significance of the appointment of the supervisor by the employer is that negligence on the supervisor's part may then be attributable to the employer. In this way any finding of negligence on the supervisor's part could also serve to reduce the liability of the project

---

[120] See clause 40 ECC.

[121] See clauses 42 and 43 ECC.

[122] See Department of Trade. *Standards, Quality and International Competitiveness.* Department of Trade, London, HMSO, 1982.

[123] See clause 40 PSC First Edition.

[124] See e.g. on the role of a clerk of works as an inspector – inspections are carried out under clause 40 ECC by the supervisor – *Kensington and Chelsea and Westminster Area Health Authority* v. *Wettern Composites* (1984) 31 BLR 57, H. H. Smout QC; and the role of the engineer's representative (or engineer's representative assistant(s)) clause 2(3) and (5) ICE 6th. It may be noted that while the clerk of works under clause 12 of the JCT 80 form is to act solely as inspector, the engineer's representative under clause 2(3) of ICE 6th is fully empowered to assume any delegation for the engineer.

manager.[125] As the supervisor is acting solely as the employer's agent the employer might be under an implied obligation to act with reasonable skill and care in carrying out functions. It follows that negligence on the part of the supervisor would render the employer liable for breach of contract.[126]

The extent of the power to delegate authority, in this case involving the project manager, would be a question of interpretation.[127]

It is submitted that the appointment of the supervisor, unlike the project manager, is not a condition precedent to the commencement of the works as the role may be fulfilled later or allowed for by the project manager in some other way.[128]

Designers

The NEC makes no express reference to designers as such. However, the employer may appoint one or more designers under the PSC or otherwise. The design role may or may not exist independently from that of the project manager, supervisor or contractor. An employee of the employer may also fulfil the designer role. The majority of appointments of designers will come from the architectural and engineering professions and may or may not be from different disciplines.[129] One or more lead designers may be appointed depending upon the nature, size and complexity of the project.

Designers will become involved in the project at an early stage. Typically the designers will play a role in advance of the contractor and so as to assist in the preparation of the tender documentation. The exception to involvement in this regard is when a design and construct method of procurement is envisaged. The role of the designer in such cases could be limited to setting out the employer's requirements for the works information, performance specifications[130] and defining the relevant standards.

---

[125] See *Kensington and Chelsea and Westminster Area Health Authoriy* v. *Wettern Composites* (1984) 31 BLR 57, cf *Leicester Guardians* v. *Trollope* (1911) 75 JP 197. The topic of contribution has lately been canvassed in *Oxford University Fixed Assets Ltd* v. *Architects Design Partnership (a firm)* (1999) 64 Con LR 13, and *Plant Construction plc* v. *Clive Adam Associates (a firm)* (1997) 55 Con LR 41.

[126] See *London Borough of Merton* v. *Stanley Hugh Leach Ltd* (1985) 32 BLR 51.

[127] See discussion above and cf *Saunders and Collard* v. *Broadstairs Local Board* (1890) 2 *Hudson's BC*, 4th edn 164, DC above.

[128] See *Jones* v. *Cannock* (1850) 5 Ex 713.

[129] For example, civil, electrical or mechanical engineering, or architectural disciplines.

[130] On the effects and use that performance specifications have on the legal obligations of the parties to a construction contract, see LUPTON, S. and STELLAKIS, E. A. S. *Performance Specification: An Analysis of Trends and Development of a Conceptual Framework: Report to the Joint Contracts Tribunal.* London, 1994; see also HARRISON, H. W. and KEEBLE, E. J. *Performance Specifications for Whole Buildings: Report on BRE Studies 1974–1982* Building Research Establishment, Garston, Watford, 1983; British Standards Institution. *Guide to the Preparation of Specifications* BS 7373. British Standards Institution, London, 1991.

The NEC contemplates a portion of design responsibility vesting in the contractor and the relevant division of that responsibility according to the works information.[131] It is for this reason that the employer's designer is not specifically referred to in the conditions of contract. The responsibility for supervision of that portion of the employer's design allocated to the employer under the works information rests with the project manager.[132]

Contractor

The 'Contractor' is one of two parties to the ECC[133] along with the 'Employer'. The contractor's main responsibilities are set out under the second core clause. The obligations are extensive. In particular, clause 2 governs provision of the works, contractor's design of the works, contractor's design of equipment, people, co-operation, Subcontracting, approval, access and instructions. These are the *main* responsibilities of the contractor. It is noteworthy that these obligations are set out in a *separate* core clause. This contrasts with the project manager's, supervisor's and employer's responsibilities, which are set out across the form. In summary, the contractor assumes numerous obligations under the contract with specific obligations somewhat dependent upon the main option chosen.

The contractor plays an important design role under the NEC and contractor design is one of the drafting principles underlying the form. Clause 21, setting out one of the main responsibilities of the contractor, thus assumes that the contractor will play a role in design of the works. Clause 23 addresses the design of equipment separately from the contractor's design in clause 21 although the two clauses share certain features. The contractor is under a duty to act as stated in the contract and in a spirit of mutual trust and co-operation[134] and this too would include fulfilling the design role.

The principle of co-operation that should govern relations between the Employer, contractor, project manager and supervisor[135] also finds expression in terms of the contractor's relations with 'Others'.[136] 'Others' is a defined term and refers to people or organizations who are *not* the employer, the project manager, the supervisor, adjudicator, the contractor or any employee, subcontractor or supplier of the contractor.[137] This duty in relation to the contractor and as part of an overall theoretical foundation for the NEC are discussed elsewhere in this book.[138]

---

[131] Clause 21.1 ECC.
[132] Clause 21.2 ECC.
[133] Clause 11.2(1) ECC.
[134] Clause 10.1 ECC.
[135] Clause 10.1 ECC.
[136] Clause 25.1 ECC.
[137] Clause 11.2(2) ECC.
[138] See discussion Chapter 6 below.

Subcontractors and suppliers

'Subcontractors' and 'suppliers' are important roles in the NEC contract system. In principle, the NEC assumes that subcontractors may be used in the completion of the works. More than other forms of traditional general contracting the NEC has elevated the subcontractor to a place of central importance in the procurement of the works. It has done so explicitly through the drafting objectives it has pursued and the release of an almost fully *back-to-back* form of subcontract for use with the ECC. It may be noted, however, that while the NEC has moved a considerable distance in this regard, and compared to other forms of contract, the drafters have still not moved as far as Latham originally recommended. If Latham's recommendations regarding subcontracting and the NEC had been fully subscribed the options available to the parties would have been far more limited. For instance, Latham called for identical secondary options to be used in both main contract and subcontract forms. If this were adopted it would once again significantly reduce the choice available. The term 'Subcontractor' is defined in a limitative way as 'a person or corporate body who has a contract with the Contractor to provide part of the *works* or to supply Plant and Materials[139] that he or she has wholly or partly designed specifically for the *works*'.[140] Thus either a natural or legal person falls within the definition. The definition in this way also embraces the supply role in contracting. The requirement of a contract serves to reinforce the provisions regarding approval over proposed subcontractors or their conditions of subcontract.[141] The NEC, as a series of interlocking agreements, seeks to protect the integrity of the system in those instances when it does not have control. If it does not have control the subject matter is moved outside the system. Similarly the requirement that plant and materials have to have been both 'designed' and 'designed specifically for the works' serves to take many routine suppliers outside the definition of subcontractor. The intention in excluding suppliers in this way is likely to be an attempt once again to preserve the overall integrity of the contract system.[142] Suppliers subcontracting to the contractor who are outside the approvals are not defined as subcontractors for ECC purposes. Conversely the operation of the definition seeks to ensure that those suppliers who do supply plant and materials which have been wholly or partly designed specifically for the work are regarded as subcontractors and thus that the procedures inherent in this classification apply to them.

The role of subcontractor must also be considered with that of suppliers under the Plant Contract. Thus the '*Supplier*' has assumed for the most part the role, and many of the responsibilities, of what would be the contractor under the ECC and the subcontractor under the ECSC. Pursuant to clause

---

[139]   Clause 11.2(10) ECC.
[140]   Clause 11.2(9) ECC. See also clause 11.2(9) ECSC similarly defining subsubcontractor.
[141]   Clause 26 ECC.
[142]   See clause 23.1 regarding approval of the contractor's design of items of equipment illustrating control.

20 of the PC the supplier's main responsibility is to 'provide the plant'; unless otherwise stated in the PC the supplier must deliver plant to site, offload plant at the site, and install the plant at the site.[143] Some of other responsibilities under the Plant Contract are returned to below.

Adjudicator

The 'Adjudicator' is normally appointed jointly by the employer and the contractor or jointly by the contractor and the subcontractor or subcontractors. The terms of appointment should be pursuant to the NEC (AC). Various options exist for reaching agreement on the person who is to serve as the adjudicator. A name or names may be put forward by the employer in the tender information with a possible option given to the contractor to approve one. Alternatively notice of a person proposed to act by the employer in part one of the Contract Data may name the adjudicator. Any disagreement with the person proposed could be the subject of discussion between the employer and the contractor at any time up to the arrival of the 'Contract Date'. If the parties themselves could not reach agreement a third party named in the Contract Data could make the appointment.[144]

The types of procedure on adjudication now depend on whether one is working under the amended or unamended Second Edition of the ECC. Under the unamended Second Edition disputes arising under or in connection with the contract are submitted to and settled by the adjudicator.[145] The types of dispute that the Adjudicator may hear, who may refer the disputes, and the time frame in which disputes must be decided are all set out in clause 9 in an adjudication table. In the amended Second Edition, if the contractor is dissatisfied with an action or a failure to take action, or with any other matter, the meeting procedure under clause 9 may be invoked and following that the adjudication procedure.[146] The procedures to be followed by the adjudicator and what recourse the parties have if either one is dissatisfied with a decision of or settlement by the adjudicator are also set out in core clause 9.

Others

The ECC includes provisions that regulate the parties' dealings with third parties. These third parties are referred to as 'Others' in the contract and the term is defined in clause 11.2(2). 'Others are people or organizations who are not the *Employer*, the *Project Manager*, the *Supervisor*, the *Adjudicator*, the *Contractor*,[147] or any employee,

---

[143] Clause 20.1 PC. Certain of the other responsibilities of the supplier are referred to here throughout where relevant.

[144] Section 9 part one Contract Data.

[145] Clause 90.1 unamended 2nd ECC.

[146] Clauses 90.2 and 90.3 amended 2nd ECC.

[147] The 'Contractor' is only identified and not defined in clause 11.2(1) and is rather part of the definition of the term the 'Parties' in clause 11.2(1), although quasi-defined in the Contract Data.

Subcontractor[148] or supplier of the *Contractor*.' Neither the terms 'project manager', 'supervisor' nor 'adjudicator' are defined in clause 11.2 of the ECC although they are quasi- or effectively defined by virtue of their inclusion and assigned descriptions in the Contract Data.

There are a number of observations that may be made regarding the definition. Initially, the definition purports to operate exclusively; that is, save for those named or excluded from the meaning of 'Others', anyone else may still come within the meaning. Thus others may be people, presumably legal or natural,[149] as well as organizations. Of all those named in the definition only the subcontractor is formally defined.[150] The others named in the definition, save employee or supplier, are merely identified terms, although the others identified are quasi-defined in the Contract Data. The clause raises a difficult point of interpretation concerning which of two competing rules of interpretation might govern.[151] According to the *expressio unius* rule it could be inferred that the *exclusion* of employees, subcontractors and suppliers of the contractor means that employees, subcontractors and suppliers of the Employer, project manager, supervisor do not fall within the meaning of the term others. In contrast, according to the *ejusdem generis* rule, if those excluded from the meaning of the term others constitute a genus then one may still arguably be able to bring employees, subcontractors and suppliers of the employer, project manager, supervisor within the meaning of 'others' as well. Clause 11.2(2), of course, only defines who others are under the contract. It is submitted that the true meaning of the clause will only be found when read with the other contractual provisions that address the contractor's interactions with others on site and a broad purposive or commercial interpretation is given to it.[152] Thus the contractor must co-operate with 'Others' in obtaining and providing information;[153] share the working areas with 'Others';[154] obtain 'Others'' design approvals;[155] provide 'Others' access;[156] show 'Others' work on the programme;[157] and not hinder 'Others'.[158] The contract not only imposes affirmative obligations on the contractor in these respects but

---

[148] Clause 11.2(9) ECC.
[149] Cf the use of 'person' or 'corporate body' in clause 11.2(9) in the definition of subcontractor.
[150] Clause 11.2(9) ECC.
[151] The two rules may be stated as follows: *expressio unius est exclusio alterius*: 'expression of one thing is the exclusion of another': Co Littleton 210a; and *ejusdem generis*: 'of the same kind, class or nature': *Black's Law Dictionary* rev, 4th edn. West Publishing Co., St Paul, 1968, p. 608.
[152] See Steyn LJ in *Mannai* v. *Eagle Star* [1997] AC 749, 770.
[153] Clause 25.1 ECC.
[154] Clause 25.1 ECC.
[155] Clause 27.1 ECC.
[156] Clause 28.1 ECC.
[157] Clause 31.2 ECC.
[158] Clause 95.3 ECC.

also bestows certain rights upon the contractor as a result of the anticipated interactions. In addition, the failure of 'Others' to work according to agreed times or conditions is a compensation event.[159] Lastly, and once again, it is the fundamental principle of co-operation that governs the Contractor's relations with 'Others'.[160]

---

[159]   Clause 60.1 ECC.
[160]   Clauses 10.1 and 25.1 ECC.

6. General

The management of projects has become a science with its own set of rules, techniques and words which are not even mentioned in the existing standard forms. If the conditions of contract were redraughted from first principles, having regard to modern management methods, a much more purposeful document could be produced.

Dr Martin Barnes, Towards Simpler Contracts.
Proceedings of the Institution of Civil Engineers

Introduction

The first group of the core clauses in the ECC are under the heading 'General'. There are a total of ten clauses under this heading and all apply generally under the contract and the conditions of contract save provision to the contrary. Clause 10 styled 'Actions' sets out standards of conduct for the 'Employer', 'Contractor', 'Project Manager', 'Supervisor' and 'Adjudicator'. Clause 11 describes what are referred to as 'identified and defined terms' and is the only comprehensive definition section in the form. However, other clauses in the form act as *de facto* definition sections, for instance, clause 31.2 of the ECC. Other clauses address interpretation,[1] communications,[2] the project manager and the supervisor,[3] adding to the working areas,[4] early warning,[5] ambiguities and inconsistencies,[6] health and safety,[7] and illegal and impossible requirements.[8] With regard to interpretation Martin Barnes has noted, '[a]lthough uncertainty of events was inherent in engineering contracts, claims resulted more from uncertainty in the interpretation of the words of the contract'.[9] All of these clauses are discussed below.

[1] Clause 12 ECC.
[2] Clause 13 ECC.
[3] Clause 14 ECC.
[4] Clause 15 ECC.
[5] Clause 16 ECC.
[6] Clause 17 ECC.
[7] Clause 18 ECC.
[8] Clause 19 ECC.
[9] BARNES, DR MARTIN *et al.* Towards Simpler Contracts. BARNES *et al.* introducers. Reported by BARBER, J. N. In *Proceedings of the Institution of Civil*

While the general provisions to a contract may vary considerably it is interesting to note that the Latham Report recommended further additions including that '[c]ore Clause 1 in both main and subcontract documents should contain an express provision that none of the Core Clauses will be amended by either party to the contract'.[10] In response to the recommendation, Martin Barnes has replied:

> [t]his proved impossible to implement if for no other reason than that it could be circumvented easily by clients using contracts which were amended versions of the NEC but were not claimed to be. Instead, the text of the Contract Data has been tightened so that amendment is more firmly discouraged and made more apparent.[11]

The issue raised more generally by these comments, that is, whether standard forms themselves should be capable of amendment by the parties, is more contentious and is returned to below. While definitions seek to facilitate understanding and ease of interpretation, in general if a defined expression is used in a context in which the definition will not fit, it may still be interpreted according to its ordinary meaning under early cases like *Strathern* v. *Padden*.[12] Lately the trend in interpretation has been toward more common sense meanings, for instance, the comments of Lord Hoffman in *Investors Compensation Scheme Ltd* v. *West Bromwich Building Society* noting

> [t]he 'rule' that words should be given their 'natural and ordinary meaning' reflects the common sense proposition that we do not easily accept that people have made linguistic mistakes, particularly in formal documents. On the other hand, if one would nevertheless conclude from the background that something must have gone wrong with the language, the law does not require judges to attribute to the parties an intention which they plainly could not have had.[13]

It may be briefly noted that new schools of thought on approaches to legal interpretation are developing and when one refers to 'context', on some views that may be seen as distinct from either a common sense or commercial interpretation, or for that matter an objective interpretation. The approaches of these various schools toward legal interpretation can

---

Engineers. June 1986, **80**, part 1, 818. See subsequently BARNES, MARTIN. The New Engineering Contract. *International Construction Law Review*, 1991, 247. See generally, CARRICK, D. NEC Suite of Contracts Part 3: A Review of Core Clauses. *Civil Engineering Surveyor*, December 1997/January 1998, 23.

[10] Latham Report, paragraph 5.20(5), 39.

[11] BARNES, MARTIN. The New Engineering Contract – An Update, see n. 9 above, 92–94.

[12] *Strathern* v. *Padden* 1926 SC (J) 9 at 13; but compare *Midland Rly Co* v. *Ambergate, Nottingham and Boston and Eastern Junction Rly Co* (1853) 10 Hare 359, 1 WR 162.

[13] Lord Hoffman in *Investors Compensation Scheme Ltd* v. *West Bromwich Building Society* [1998] 1 WLR 896 at 912–913.

be seen in a series of recent House of Lords decisions.[14] While it may be sometime before the full effect of these decisions is known they will eventually impact the interpretation of construction contracts.

Actions

The NEC is designed around a series of actions that are intended to be logical and to reduce the number of disputes. The principles behind this structure are derived from both project management and engineering theory. Project management techniques are goal oriented. The techniques focus on objectives. The reference by the NEC drafters to the three principal *objectives* in the design of the NEC is thus not coincidental. Project management theory also divides along two general lines; the organization and behaviour of the people involved, and the methodology that they will employ.[15] Thus in the NEC there are the employer, contractor, project manager etc. employing programmes, activity schedules etc. To a certain extent these two general lines may also be discerned in other standard forms. However, the NEC differs from them in that it is one of the first forms to make this explicit and to state that it was pursued intentionally in drafting the contract from the outset.

A definition for project management may be given: 'project management can be defined as planning, directing, and controlling resources (people, equipment, materials) to meet the technical, cost and time restraints of the project'.[16] Projects themselves are often defined in terms of the sequence or series of related tasks directed to a particular output to be performed over time. Poor planning has been ranked, based on a major literature review by Majid and McCaffer, as the third most significant factor in causing non-excusable delay.[17] Every aspect of this definition finds expression in and could be referable to features of the ECC conditions of contract. In project management theory a typical project is reducible to a series of steps that proceed from the general to the specific. Thus one may begin with a statement of work which is a short written description of the objective(s) to be achieved. It may specify the starting

---

[14] *Deutsche Genossenschaftsbank* v. *Burnhope* [1995] 1 WLR 1580; *Mannai Investment Co Ltd* v. *Eagle Star Life Assurance Co Ltd* [1997] AC 749; and *Investors Compensation Scheme Ltd* v. *West Bromwich Building Society* [1998] 1 WLR 896.

[15] See generally NEWCOMBE, R., *Construction Management 1: Organisation Systems.* Mitchell, London; CIOB, Ascot, 1990; LANGFORD, D.A. and MALE, S.P., *Strategic Management in Construction.* Gower, Aldershot, 1991.

[16] CHASE, RICHARD B. and AQUILANO, NICHOLAS J. *Production & Operations Management A Life Cycle Approach*, 6th edn. Irwin, Homewood, 1992, 542. See also AHUHA, H.N. *et al. Project Management; Techniques in Planning and Controlling Construction Projects*, 2nd edn. John Wiley, New York, 1994.

[17] ABD MAJID M.Z. and McCAFFER, RONALD. Factors of Non-excusable Delays that Influence Contractors' Performance. *Journal of Management in Engineering*, May/June 1998, **14**(3), 48. See generally GORDON, J. and TULIP, A. Resource Scheduling. *International Journal of Project Management*, 1997, **15**(6), 359–370; and NEALE, RICHARD H. and NEALE, DAVID E. *Construction Planning.* Thomas Telford, London, 1989.

date and/or the completion date. To this point the statement of work resembles part one of the Contract Data. As the size of the project or its complexity increase the statement of work for the project may be referred to as a programme. It is interesting to note that the terms 'programme' and 'project' are often used synonymously in project management literature.[18]

Projects themselves are capable of further subdivision. One or more of the parties or indeed other organizations may perform the tasks.[19] Tasks further break down into subtasks. This language, although not adopted in the ECC, does form part of the NEC terminology and is used in the PSC. In particular the contract documents between the employer and the consultant under main option D in the First Edition – the term contract – include a 'task schedule'. The 'task schedule' is an identified term and refers to an optional statement in part two of the Contract Data, PSC. It will normally be prepared by the employer and will set out what tasks are expected of the consultant. Tasks themselves are a defined term in the contract and described as 'a collection of activities selected from the *task schedule* by the *Employer*'. With the benefit of the task schedule the consultant is then able to price the activities which are set out. It follows that the prices and the price for services provided to date (PSPD), are all defined with reference to the tasks and task schedule.[20]

To provide an example, the engineering department of the port authority of New York and New Jersey has introduced *task cards* to outline projects. The cards outline tasks, associated resources, budgets and schedules and interdependencies. Individual task cards may be rolled into a summary task card. The advantage of the use of the task cards is in the *integration* they afford furthering project planning and delivery.[21]

The further subdivision of the project could be expected to continue in practice with subtasks breaking down into work packages. In project management terms the work package is made up of and referred to as being composed of a group of activities which are combined and capable of assignment; that is to the contractor, subcontractor or otherwise. The division of a structure in this way is referred to as the 'work breakdown structure'.[22] The use of these terms to describe the subdivision of a project admits of some small variation but the theory of a project as a series of activities is constant. Further refinement of the theory is seen once the precedence relationships between the activities is added.[23] The choice of

---

[18] CHASE, RICHARD B. and QUILANO, NICHOLAS A. See n. 16 above, p. 543.

[19] See clauses 25, 26 and 27 ECC.

[20] See clause 11.2(14) and 11.2(17) PSC First Edition. Detailed procedures are also set out for the assessment of tasks in clauses 55.1 to 55.4 PSC First Edition.

[21] See ZIPF, PETER J. An Integrated Project Management System. *Journal of Management in Engineering*, May/June 1998, **14**(3), 38–41. See for anecdotal evidence of the importance of integration in improving cost and time performance LEITCH, JOHN. BAA Gets Capital Rewards. *Contract Journal*, 17 June 1998, 3.

[22] See n. 16 above, p. 543.

[23] See KRAJEWSKI, LEE J. and RITZMAN, LARRY P. *Operations Management Strategy and Analysis*, 3rd edn. Addison Wesley, Wokingham, 1993, p. 642.

the term 'activity' once again, as in the case of main options A and C, is intentional and thus reflects the terminology in use in both the project management and engineering literature. This is developed below. Activity schedules also form the basis of two of the four main options utilized under the PSC, namely main options A and C in the priced contract with activity schedule, and target contract respectively of the First Edition.

Actions are the most discrete form of activity. Actions are stipulated in the following manner in clause 10.1: 'The *Employer*, the *Contractor*, the *Project Manager* and the *Supervisor* shall act as stated in this contract in a spirit of mutual trust and co-operation. The *Adjudicator* shall act as stated in this contract and in a spirit of independence'. The mandatory expression of the obligation stated also in the future tense contrasts markedly with NEC drafting style in the present tense. The clause requires some elaboration at the outset. In the first instance it is appropriate that the clause imposes obligations regarding how to act – it is listed opposite the heading 'Actions' in the contract. Thus depending upon those named the required acts are set out. Both of the named groups that are identifiable on the works must or shall act as stated in the contract. It is arguable that it imposes one solitary affirmative obligation. The second affirmative obligation is dependent upon the group identified: thus the first group acts 'in a spirit of mutual trust and co-operation', while the adjudicator acts 'in a spirit of independence'. The obligations thus contrast sharply and clearly seek to underscore the essential qualities of these roles as well as distinguish them from the actions of those acting in traditional roles; namely architects and engineers. It is also arguable either way that the requirement to act in a spirit of mutual trust and co-operation imposes one or two obligations although the duty of co-operation as discussed below appears to have an independent content. In general conjunctive words should be read as conjunctive unless in a rare case the context shows that the necessary meaning is disjunctive.[24] In fact, the 'mutuality' in clause 10.1 may be almost as important as co-operation. This stems from the conclusion that mutuality, or what is also termed 'reciprocity' is an extremely important variable for project success. In fact, Robert E. Scott has developed an argument that, in the absence of mutuality, there is a greater likelihood that co-operation can be exploited.[25] Others, such as David Cornes,[26] have even questioned legally whether one can act 'in a spirit' of mutual trust; however, the rejoinder of Andrew Cox and Ian Thompson[27] might be to say that the

---

[24] For example, as in *Golden Horseshoe Estates Co Ltd* v. *R* [1911] AC 480, 80 LJPC 135, PC.

[25] SCOTT, ROBERT E. Risk Distribution and Adjustment in Long-Term Contracts. *The Complex Long-Term Contract Structures and International Arbitration* (ed. NICHLISCH, FRITZ). C.F. Muller Juristischer Verlag, Heidelberg, 1987, pp. 72–74.

[26] CORNES, DAVID. The Second Edition of the New Engineering Contract. *International Construction Law Review*, 1996, 97.

[27] COX, PROFESSOR ANDREW and THOMPSON, IAN. Is the NEC Going to Succeed? – An Examination of the Engineering and Construction Contract. (Alias the

point has been missed as it is rather the intention of the drafters to avoid the courts.

P. W. G. Morris and G. H. Hough have identified some 80 factors that are important to the success of a major project and which in turn may be broken down into 10 categories grouped in relation to project definition; planning, design and technology management; politics; schedule duration/urgency; finance; insurance; legal agreements; contractual matters; project implementation; and human factors.[28] Morris and Hough have surveyed clients and consultants and ranked the 10 categories in order of importance with the category of legal agreement ranking fifth. Legal agreement in this regard is understood as referring to the client's commitment to making the contract work. These survey results reinforce the importance of positive and co-operative attitudes, almost in a relational sense, in project success. Others have reached similar conclusions[29] and it may be noted that many of these factors have counterparts in manufacturing environments.[30]

With regard to the NEC, preliminary research by Broome based upon questionnaire surveys and interviews has also confirmed that under the NEC there is a 'greater degree of cooperation and openness compared with normal contracts [and that] this lack of conflict and dispute is reflected in the relatively fast settlement of the final account and few referrals to the adjudicator' and that this too is seen as a success factor.[31]

The wording of clause 10.1 contrasts sharply with that in the Consultation Document which was headed: 'Duties and procedures' and simply stated that the same parties mentioned 'shall carry out the duties and procedures stated in the Contract'. By changing the wording attention is focused upon the actions of the named individuals rather than upon whether the contract wording imposed a duty which is enforceable. The change in wording from that in the Consultation Document to that in the Second Edition is attributable to a recommendation in the Latham Report. 'A specific duty for all parties to deal fairly with each, and with their subcontractors, specialists and suppliers, in an atmosphere of mutual co-operation' and 'A statement should be written into Core Clause 1 that the employer and the contractor affirm that they both intend to establish a fair and reasonable agreement with each other to undertake the project in a spirit of mutual trust and co-operation, and to trade fairly with each other

NEC 2nd Edition). *International Construction Law Review*, 1996, 332. See also CORNES, D. and BARNES, M. NEC Controversial Contract. *New Builder*, 31 January 1991, 20–21 briefly arguing over the merits of the NEC.

[28] MORRIS, P.W.G. and HOUGH, G.H. *Preconditions of Success and Failure in Major Projects*. Major Projects Association, Oxford, 1986, Technical Paper 3.

[29] KOMETA, SIMON T. *et al*. An Evaluation of Clients' Needs and Responsibilities in the Construction Process. *Construction Management and Economics* 1, 1995, 57–76.

[30] See MILLER JR., KENNETH LEE. Critical Success Factors for Engineering and Managing Strategic Projects in a Manufacturing Environment. PhD dissertation, Case Western University, 1996.

[31] BROOME, J.C. Best Practice with the New Engineering Contract. *Proceedings of the Institution of Civil Engineers*, May 1997, **120**, 74–81.

and with their subcontractors and suppliers …'.[32] The drafters adopted the recommendation with a twist – and added a requirement of *mutual trust*[33] to the general duty of co-operation that was always expressed in the contract.[34]

It is an open question whether this wording will be construed to impose *one* or *two* separate and identifiable obligations. David L. Cornes states: '[t]hese additional words in the NEC may have some legal effect but it is difficult to see with precision what it might be. Perhaps it is merely an exhortation to the parties to behave properly, with little or no legal consequences beyond those which arise in the ordinary course of events'.[35] By comparison, Dr Martin Barnes sets out a minimalist view that 'it at least constitutes an effective declaration of intent which should help mould the behaviour of the parties'.[36] Barnes' position in this regard is the most cautious view that could be taken. It accords with the common law view that declarations of intent without more are non-binding.[37] Declarations of intent are increasingly common in partnering charters and are consistent with a theoretical framework developed for the NEC based upon co-operation and relational contracting. Another interesting example of just such a declaration can be seen in the Construction Round Table's *Declaration of Commitment of this Organisation to Fair Construction Contracts* comprising a number of principles that signatories may agree to uphold including one very similar to clause 10: 'To deal fairly with those whom we contact and with those who are contracted to them in an atmosphere of mutual co-operation'.

The wording of the ECC is at its broadest in clause 10.1. It seeks to set not only the 'tone' of the relationship among the parties but also the nature of the general obligations that are being imposed; obligations which are exceedingly general. Telser[38] writes of how certain contracts can be 'self-enforcing' when adherence to the terms of the contract is simply more advantageous than breaching it. There are once again many possible explanations for this including the costs of third party intervention. Robert E. Scott writes:

> a party may be induced by a self-enforcing penalty or pledge agreement to commit to a strategy of conditional cooperation. Thereafter, the security interest or penalty bond functions as a credible commitment, binding the promisor to the predictable pattern of future behaviour.[39]

---

[32]   Latham Report, paragraph 5.18(1), 37; and paragraph 5.20(4), 39 respectively.
[33]   Clause 10.1 ECC.
[34]   Consultation Document NEC, clause 25.1.
[35]   CORNES, see n. 26 above, 102.
[36]   BARNES, DR MARTIN. The New Engineering Contract – An Update, see n. 9 above, 93.
[37]   *Harris* v. *Nickerson* (1873) LR 8 QB 286.
[38]   TELSER, L.G. A Theory of Self-Enforcing Agreements. *Journal of Business*, 1980, **53**, 27–44.
[39]   SCOTT, ROBERT E., see n. 25 above, p. 79.

The general obligations in clause 10.1 are framed in affirmative terms using mandatory language; that is the word 'shall' is used with respect to how those named are required to act. Courts will construe the obligations in this sense and as distinct from obligations which are framed in permissive terms or drafted utilizing the term 'may'.[40] This interpretation could differ from that intended by the drafters. The drafters' intention was to use the term 'shall' in the clause to express the future tense or futurity but all other tenses in the NEC were expressed in the present tense, 'for simplicity'.[41] While the use of 'shall', in this way, accords with grammatical usage,[42] it differs from the way it is normally construed as either directory or mandatory.

The clause imposes the obligation to 'act' as stated in the contract. It is submitted this underscores the necessity for action with regard to every single obligation that is imposed upon those named. Thus whether the obligation is described in the present particle drafting style of the NEC as to: act,[43] submit[44] or resubmit,[45] give,[46] accept,[47] assess,[48] notify,[49] provide,[50] pay,[51] repay,[52] employ,[53] indemnify,[54] comply,[55] put,[56] make,[57] proceed[58] communicate,[59] reply,[60] issue,[61] remove,[62] co-

[40] See guidance notes NEC on clause 10.1 ECC, 27.
[41] Guidance notes NEC on clause 10.1 ECC, 27.
[42] Guidance notes NEC on clause 10.1 ECC, 27. 'Shall' is used to express futurity or the future tense: ROBERTS, P.D. *Plain English: A User's Guide*. Penguin, London, 1988, p. 114.
[43] Clauses 10.1, 18.1 ECC.
[44] Clauses 21.2, 23.1, 24.1, 26.2, 26.3, 26.4, 31.1, 32.2, 36.2, 36.5, 54.2, 61.4, 62.1, 62.2, 62.3, 62.4, 85.1, 87.1 ECC.
[45] Clause 13.4 ECC.
[46] Clauses 16.1, 16.4, 17.1, 19.1, 33.2, 42.1, 50.4, G1.1, H1.1 ECC.
[47] Clauses 21.2, 23.1, 24.1, 26.2, 26.3, 26.4, 31.3, 32.2, 36.3, 36.5, 54.2, 85.1, 87.1, G1.1, J1.2 ECC.
[48] Clauses 33.2, 40.6, 45.1, 50.1, 53.1, 53.3, 53.4, 63.11, 64.1, 64.2, 97.4 ECC.
[49] Clauses 13.5, 31.3, 40.3, 42.2, 61.1, 61.4, 61.6, 62.5, 64.3, 73.1, (91.1 unamended 2nd ECC), 93.1, 94.1 ECC.
[50] Clauses 20.1, 28.1, 33.2, 40.2, 84.1, (91.1 unamended 2nd ECC) ECC.
[51] Clauses 33.2, 40.6, 45.1, 51.1, 51.2, 51.3, 51.4, 53.2, 86.1, 87.3, R1.1, S1.1, V3.1(6) ECC. The operative action may be either to pay or make under certain clauses, e.g. clause 51.1 ECC.
[52] Clauses J1.3, R1.2 ECC.
[53] Clause 24.1 ECC.
[54] Clauses 21.4, 83.1 ECC.
[55] Clause 85.3 ECC.
[56] Clause 61.1 ECC.
[57] Clause 92.1 ECC.
[58] Clause 90.2 unamended 2nd ECC.
[59] Clauses 13.1, 13.7, 92.1 ECC.
[60] Clauses 13.3, 13.4, 62.3 ECC.
[61] Clauses 13.6, 43.2, 94.1 ECC.
[62] Clauses 24.2, 72.1 ECC.

operate,[63] share,[64] obtain,[65] obey,[66] show,[67] state,[68] record,[69] decide,[70] certify,[71] keep,[72] prepare,[73] extend,[74] prepare,[75] take over,[76] appoint,[77] change,[78] consider,[79] instruct,[80] implement,[81] advise,[82] include,[83] choose,[84] do,[85] allow,[86] mark,[87] use,[88] manage,[89] maintain,[90] subcontract,[91] design,[92] replace,[93] arrange,[94] inform,[95] correct,[96] advise,[97] carry,[98] carry out,[99] bear,[100] leave,[101] or settle[102] the actions must be carried out and be carried out either in a spirit of mutual trust and co-operation or a spirit of independence.

[63]   Clauses 16.3, 25.1 ECC.
[64]   Clause 25.1 ECC.
[65]   Clause 27.1 ECC.
[66]   Clause 29.1 ECC.
[67]   Clauses 31.2, 31.4, 32.1 ECC.
[68]   Clauses 13.4, 61.6 ECC.
[69]   Clause 16.4 ECC.
[70]   Clauses 30.2, 50.1, 61.4, 61.5 ECC.
[71]   Clauses 30.2, 35.4, 51.1, 94.4 ECC.
[72]   Clause 52.2 ECC.
[73]   Clause 20.4 ECC.
[74]   Clauses 43.3, 62.5 ECC.
[75]   Clause 20.4 ECC.
[76]   Clauses 35.2, 35.3 ECC
[77]   Clause 92.2 ECC.
[78]   Clauses 36.3, 36.4, 44.2 ECC.
[79]   Clause 50.4 ECC.
[80]   Clauses 61.1, 61.4, 62.4, 73.1 ECC.
[81]   Clause 65.1 ECC.
[82]   Clause 20.3 ECC.
[83]   Clauses 62.2, 65.3, 65.4, (91.1 unamended 2nd) ECC.
[84]   Clause 92.2 ECC.
[85]   Clauses 20.2, 30.1, 40.5 ECC.
[86]   Clause 52.3 ECC.
[87]   Clause 71.1 ECC.
[88]   Clause 97.4 ECC.
[89]   Clause 20.2 ECC.
[90]   Clause V3.1(4) ECC.
[91]   Clause 20.2 ECC.
[92]   Clause 21.1 ECC.
[93]   Clause 82.1 ECC.
[94]   Clauses 24.2, 43.3, V2.3 ECC.
[95]   Clause V2.3 ECC.
[96]   Clauses 40.4, 43.1, 60.6, 61.6 ECC.
[97]   Clause 20.3 ECC.
[98]   Clause 81.1 ECC.
[99]   Clause 42.1 ECC.
[100] Clause 85.4 ECC.
[101] Clause 96.2 ECC.
[102] Clauses 90.2, 91.2, 92.1 unamended 2nd ECC. The obligation to 'settle' is also imposed on the tribunal, clause 93.2 ECC. This wording has changed in the amended Second Edition of the ECC as a result of secondary option Y (UK) 2.

It is submitted that the proper meaning to be given to 'action' encompasses at least all of these obligations and that it was precisely due to the large number of obligations that the term 'actions' was left undefined. In addition, under clause 10 it clearly states that those named must act as 'stated' in the contract and thus the above terms frame the statements to which clause 10 is referable. As some of these terms do not possess a defined legal content there may be initial difficulties posed in interpretation. Writing of some similar terms in the context of the JCT Management Contract Tony Blackler and others have noted:

> [m]any of the Management Contractors' obligations are nebulous and will be difficult for a court to interpret and thus to enforce. Words such as preparing, advising, assisting, co-operating, organising, collaborating, co-ordinating, liaising and arranging, which abound in the Third Schedule, may prove to have little real substance if tested in proceedings.[103]

Thus, it will be for the parties in the first instance and the courts if need be to fill in the content in a pragmatic and realistic way.

The above actions are imposed as duties or obligations on either the project manager, supervisor, contractor or adjudicator. The actions arise under both main and secondary option clauses. The majority of the obligations are imposed roughly equally on the project manager and the contractor alike with a smaller number of obligations imposed on the supervisor – approximately 85 apiece on the project manager and contractor and 10 on the supervisor. While all of the obligations referred to are affirmative in nature there are also a number of negative obligations which are also imposed principally upon the contractor; thus in certain circumstances the contractor must *not* proceed,[104] appoint,[105] start work,[106] bring,[107] put,[108] notify,[109] or implement[110] certain actions save as otherwise provided for.

The attempt to inculcate shared goals and common values in a construction project in modern standard forms is unusual but not without precedent. The National Contractors Group in its report *Building Toward 2001* has suggested there is a need for a new form of contract that arranges the resource groups on a construction project so that they all have identical goals which in their view are to produce a timely, economical, profitable and high quality product.[111] Perhaps the best recent example of promoting these ends is found in the JCT Management

---

[103] *Rowe & Maw, JCT Management Contract*, 10.
[104] Clause 21.2 ECC.
[105] Clauses 26.2, 26.3 ECC.
[106] Clause 30.1 ECC.
[107] Clause 41.1 ECC.
[108] Clause 61.2 ECC.
[109] Clause 61.7 ECC.
[110] Clause 65.5 ECC.
[111] *Building Toward 2001*. National Contractors Group, London, 1990.

Contract (JCT 87). Reference to the management contractor's duty to co-operate can be found in the recitals, the articles of agreement and the conditions of contract. The third recital, for example, provides in part:

> the Employer and the Management Contractor have agreed that the Management Contractor will ... co-operate with the Professional Team during the design stages and in the planning, programming and cost estimating for the Project, and will secure the carrying out and completion of the Project ...[112]

Recitals may be taken as an aid to interpretation. Lord Esher, MR in *Ex p Dawes, Re Moon* states:

> [n]ow there are three rules applicable to the construction of such an instrument. If the recitals are clear and the operative part is ambiguous, the recitals govern the construction. If the recitals are ambiguous, and the operative part is clear, the operative part must prevail. If both the recitals and the operative part are clear, but they are inconsistent with each other, the operative part is to be preferred.[113]

However, the meaning of the recital will depend upon whether the words in the operative part of the contract are clear, unclear or inconsistent with the recital.[114] However, in certain cases, if the court views the recital as manifesting a clear intention to act in a prescribed way it may infer a covenant to so act. Lord Denman CJ in *Aspdin* v. *Austin* states: 'where words of recital or reference manifested a clear intention the parties should do certain acts, the courts have from these inferred a covenant to do such acts'.[115] Thus, the cases provide an argument in favour of enforcing the agreement to co-operate in the recital and as an obligation of the parties. It may be added that the first recital also refers to the professional advisers as 'the Professional Team'. Team building is a well-known management technique to foster shared goals.

The duty to co-operate also appears in the first article of JCT 87 stating in part: 'the Management Contractor will (1) subject to the Conditions co-operate with the Professional Team during the design stages and in the planning, programming and cost estimating for, and in securing the carrying out and completion of the Project ...'. Lastly, in the actual conditions of contract: '[t]he Management Contractor shall upon and subject to the Conditions co-operate with the Professional Team as stated in Article 1'.[116] It has been said:

> [t]he JCT Management Contract is in legal terms an attempt to solve a fundamental structural problem, which has increasingly bedevilled conventional 'lump sum' contracting as practised in the United

---

[112] See on the function or nature of recitals as narratives or general statements of intention: *IRC* v. *Raphael* [1935] AC 96, HL.

[113] *Orr* v. *Mitchell* [1893] AC 238, HL.

[114] Lord Esher, MR in *Ex p Dawes, Re Moon* (1886) 17 QBD 275 at 286, CA.

[115] Lord Denman CJ in *Aspdin* v. *Austin* (1844) 1 QB 671 at 683.

[116] Clause 1.4 JCT 87.

Kingdom. One of the perceived results of the traditional system was that, rather than maximising the collective energy and resources of a contractor and professionals towards the common goal of project completion, it tended to set the two teams against each other. The resultant tension was frequently fuelled by the astute contractor's ability to exploit the fiction that a building would be fully designed at the outset of the conventional system.[117]

The duty of the management contractor to co-operate is qualified. However, it is not a narrow duty either. The expression given to the duty comprises both words of limitation (e.g. 'subject to the conditions'), and words of general application (e.g. 'co-operate … in securing the carrying out and completion of the work'). It is uncertain how these two phrases would be construed together or whether the latter phrase could even operate to impose liability on the management contractor for matters beyond the specific remit, for instance design liability.

The express reference to a 'spirit' of mutual trust and co-operation presumably articulates the preference of the drafters in any contest with the 'letter' of provisions.[118] The importance of both general obligations is underscored by their placement in the contract; that is as the first core clause under the heading 'General'. The open wording is closer to that found in civilian codes than wordings in traditional building or engineering contracts.

Jurisprudence can be cited in support of the proposition that where the performance of a party's obligations requires the co-operation of the other party a term will be implied into their contract that co-operation will be given.[119] The actual instances, however, of co-operation in the cases seem narrow.[120] The number of instances are limited no doubt by either one of the two principal tests which must be satisfied before the implication of any term, both of which focus upon the fact that the term must be necessary before it will be implied. The combined effect of a strict judicial philosophy toward the criteria for implying a term[121] and the comprehensive nature of standard forms thus not only militates against the implication of terms but serves to narrow the scope of any terms which are implied.

---

[117] *Rowe & Maw, JCT Management Contract,* 6.

[118] Justice William O Douglas said 'the choice between the "letter" and the "spirit" is an ancient one even in the law': *Davies Warehouse Co* v. *Bowles,* 321 US 144, 158, 1944.

[119] *Mackay* v. *Dick* (1881) 6 App Cas 251 at 263, HL; *Luxor (Eastbourne) Ltd* v. *Cooper* [1941] AC 108 at 118, HL; *London Borough of Merton* v. *Stanley Hugh Leach Ltd* (1985) 32 BLR 51 at 80.

[120] For example, with regard to the timing and possession of the site: *Freeman* v. *Hensler* (1900) 2 *Hudson's BC* 4th edn 292 CA; planning permissions *Ellis-Don Ltd* v. *Parking Authority of Toronto* (1978) 28 BLR 98 (Ont HC) among others.

[121] See e.g. the passage in the speech of Lord Pearson beginning with the phrase: '… the court does not make a contract for the parties' in *Trollope & Colls Ltd* v. *North West Metropolitan Regional Hospital Board* [1973] 2 All ER 260 at 267, [1973] 1 WLR 601 at 609, HL.

There are two further aspects of the implied duty of co-operation that merit attention:

- the disproportionate number of cases that concern architects in some way; and
- the negative reformulation of the duty.

The implied duty of co-operation is often cast in the context of the employer's relationship with the architect. Thus, for example, if an architect is failing to give effect to the terms of the contract, and in the absence of a relevant arbitration clause, the employer's implied duty of co-operation will necessitate intervention to rectify the situation.[122]

A significant case, which has taken the implied duty of co-operation to its present boundaries, but which still concerned the relationship of the employer to the architect; although not the employer to the contractor *per se*, is *London Borough of Merton* v. *Stanley Hugh Leach Ltd.*[123] Mr Justice Vinelott held in that case that the implied duty of co-operation extended to matters which the architect must do to enable the contractor to carry out his or her work. The failure on the part of the architect to fulfil these responsibilities gives rise to the liability of the employer. The clearest examples concern the failure of the architect to issue instructions either at all or in a timely way.[124]

The second point, the negative reformulation of the duty, can be put in this sense: the employer is under an implied duty not to hinder or prevent the contractor from carrying out obligations under the contract. A leading and forcefully articulated authority for this proposition is once again the *London Borough of Merton* case,[125] which sets some boundaries on the implied duty of co-operation. Given this, the case for not only the recognition and inclusion of an express duty of co-operation in standard forms is warranted but also the elevation of that express duty to the status of a fundamental principle seems fully justified.

The refusal to agree to the duty to act in a spirit of mutual trust and co-operation is also a ground for not accepting a proposed subcontractor.[126]

---

[122] *Frederick Leyland & Co Ltd* v. *Compania Panamena Europea Navigacion Limitda* (1943) 76 Ll L Rep 113, CA (Eng); affirmed sub nom *Panamena Europea Navigacion (Compania Limitda)* v. *Frederick Leyland & Co Ltd (J Russell & Co)* [1947] AC 428, HL; see also *Perini Corpn* v. *Commonwealth of Australia* (1969) 12 BLR 82 and on the necessity for the absence of an arbitration clause: *Lubenham Fidelities Investment Co Ltd* v. *South Pembrokeshire District Council* (1986) 33 BLR 39, CA.

[123] (1985) 32 BLR 51.

[124] See e.g. *Holland Hannen and Cubitts (Northern) Ltd* v. *Welsh Health Technical Services Organisation* (1985) 35 BLR 1, (1985) 7 Con LR 14, CA.

[125] (1985) 32 BLR 51 but see also *Barque Quilpué Ltd* v. *Brown* [1904] 2 KB 264 at 274, CA; *Cory Ltd* v. *City of London Corpn* [1951] 2 KB 476 at 484, CA; *Glenlion Construction* v. *The Guinness Trust* (1987) 39 BLR 89 at 103; *Jardine Engineering Corpn Ltd* v. *Shimizu Corpn* (1992) 63 BLR 96 at 117; and *J & J Fee Ltd* v. *Express Lift Co Ltd* (1993) 34 Con LR 147 at 157.

[126] Clause 26.3 ECC.

Clauses 10 and 26.3 together are indeed important and are carried through subcontractual arrangements under essentially identical clauses. Thus, '[t]he NEC Subcontract places a similar obligation on all parties along the supply chain. This requirement is perhaps the single-most important feature of the NEC, for without it much of the contractual mechanism would break down'.[127] While important, it may be somewhat of an overstatement to suggest that the contractual mechanism would break down, rather one would lose the back-to-back quality which the family of forms currently possess. In general, the absence of 'team spirit' among the project participants has been shown to be a common cause of disputes.[128]

Key identified and defined terms

Clause 11 sets out certain 'identified and defined' terms in the 'conditions of contract'. The terms are literally 'set out' without any conventional introduction to them such as the 'terms have the following meanings...' etc. Pursuant to section 1 of part one of the Contract Data the 'conditions of contract' are the core clauses and the clauses for the options agreed. Two drafting conventions are used in clause 11 and noted in 11.1: 'In these conditions of contract, terms identified in the Contract Data are in italics and defined terms have capital initials'. It may be noted that in the opening words of clause 11.1 the term 'conditions of contract' is unitalicized although it is not clear why. It cannot be because the term is unidentified in the Contract Data as it appears in the optional statements regarding option Z. It is also italicized in secondary option clause L1.1; perhaps it is because the actual identification of the term does not occur in clause 11 itself. If this is the reason it is a weak one and it is submitted that consistency dictates it should be italicized. To reiterate, clause 11 is both for identification and definition purposes. Identification is a means of alerting the reader to the fact that further information is contained in the Contract Data on each of the italicized terms. However, it should be noted that not all identified terms in the conditions appear in clause 11.2; only a small number do. Other identified terms appear subsequently and for the first time throughout the conditions.[129]

---

[127] COX, PROFESSOR ANDREW and THOMPSON, IAN, see n. 27 above, 332.

[128] SMITH, G.A. Beyond ADR – Dispute Resolution in the Construction Industry through Realistic Contract Risk Allocation. *The Organization of Management of Construction: Shaping Theory and Practice* (eds LANGFORD, D.A. and RETICK, A.), vol. 2, pp. 881–890 n. 1 references omitted listing survey results of specific causes of construction disputes.

[129] For example, *'law of the contract'*, clause 12.2; *'language of this contract'*, clause 13.1; and *'period for reply'*, clause 13.3 ECC. In this title identified or defined terms are occasionally capitalized or italicized for emphasis and placed in italics to indicate this. This commentary has not adopted capitalization and italicization as it used in the NEC throughout except in quotations. VALENTINE, D.G. The New Engineering Contract: Part 1 – a New Language – Construction Law Journal, 1991, **12**, 307 n. 11 has criticized clause 11 as not being in alphabetical or any other apparent order.

Identified terms are, for the most part, ones that invite greater detail. For instance; *'boundaries of the site'*,[130] or *'working areas'*.[131] The parties to the Contract – the *'Employer'* and the *'Contractor'*[132] – as well as the *'Project Manager'*, the *'Supervisor'*, and the *'Adjudicator'*[133] are all italicized terms. They also all have capital first letters, referred to as 'capital initials' and as such should be defined but no formal definitions are given in clause 11.2.

The intention of the drafters may have been to treat the descriptions of these individuals or parties *as* definitions. Alternatively it may have been an oversight. In either case it could easily be clarified. To summarize again, terms in the contract may be either identified *or* defined or identified *and* defined. Their identification 'and/or' defining is primarily in clause 11.2. However, it may be noted that the drafting style in the contract itself suggests many more definitions. As mentioned the terms 'Employer', 'Project Manager', 'Supervisor', 'Adjudicator' and 'Contractor' are effectively defined in the Contract Data. This follows from the declarative style: 'The *Employer* is ...'.

The same style prevails in the describing of many other important elements in the contract: the: *'works* are'; *'boundaries of the site* are'; *'language of this contract* is' etc. There are many examples of this. The same declarative style is also used in the conditions of contract. The two most significant illustrations are in clauses 60.1: '[t]he following are compensation events', and 80.1 '[t]he *Employer's* risks are'. The two declarative clauses end differently: clause 60.1 with a full stop, clause 80.1 without punctuation at all. The argument that the clauses are effectively definitions would be further supported if both statements ended or introduced the subclauses that follow with a full colon. The effect of construing these clauses as definitions would strengthen them in their operation.

The definitions are exceedingly brief at times; for instance, the 'Parties' are defined as simply the *'Employer* and the *Contractor'*.[134] The choice of these terms is clearly intended to be representative only and users of the NEC may or may not fall strictly within their compass in any actual case. This is acceptable if is sufficient to identify them.[135] The ECC also uses the singular 'Party' in the conditions, e.g. clauses 83.1, 83.1 and even though this term is undefined, clause 12.1 provides words in the singular also mean in the plural and the other way around; hence one could state this rule is also applied to defined terms. Similarly, the generic references to the 'Project Manager', 'Supervisor', and 'Adjudicator' are also acceptable provided not more than one at a time act pursuant to the contract or ambiguity would be introduced. It may be

---

[130]   Clause 11.2(7) ECC.
[131]   Clause 11.2(8) ECC.
[132]   Clause 11.2(1) ECC.
[133]   Clause 11.2(2) ECC.
[134]   Clause 11.2(1) ECC.
[135]   *Simmons* v. *Woodward* [1892] AC 100, HL.

noted that these terms for key people, given their capitalization in the ECC, should mean that they are defined terms but they are not. The importance of key people and the management relationships they have with the employer, sponsor and others in the project team has been explained elsewhere.[136]

The ECC has no cross-references as one means of simplifying the drafting. Some commentators are in favour of cross-references[137] in a standard form while others are opposed.[138] Most standard forms do use cross-references where one clause normally refers to another clause in the same form. However, there are exceptions. Thus under JCT NSC/C cross-references are made to definitions in JCT 80 for certain terms and in so doing occasional ambiguity, which is a source of disputes,[139] is introduced.[140]

In contrast, the NEC uses a measure of parallel drafting to reinforce meaning and understanding.[141] Martin Barnes outlines three ways to simplify standard forms:

(a) express the responsibilities of the parties more simply, perhaps with some rearrangement of the allocation of risk and responsibility
(b) incorporate management procedures into the contract, so that it is more clearly management-based (c) avoid legalistic words, style and layout.[142]

These suggestions have been carried through in the drafting of the NEC. The importance of these drafting measures is supported by research which indicates with few exceptions, that employers, contractors, and consultants interpret contract clauses differently, and within any one contracting party group, individuals interpret contract clauses across a

---

[136] See generally KLIEM, R.M. and LUDIN, I.S. *The People Side of Project Management*. Gower, Aldershot, 1992.

[137] For example, CORNES, n. 26 above, 98: '[t]he omission of cross-references, as a drafting policy decision may prove to lead to danger in the context of legal certainty, rather than simplicity'; and ROYCE, NORMAN. The Bill Tompkins Memorial Lecture. 'How Fair Are We in Dispute Resolution in the Construction Industry?'. *Arbitration*, 1991, 106.

[138] See e.g. POWELL-SMITH, VINCENT. The New Form – An Overview. *The ICE Conditions of Contract for Minor Works 1988*. Proceedings of a conference in London on 7 October 1988 by IBC. IBC, London, 1988, 1.

[139] SMITH, G.A., see n. 128 above, n. 1 references omitted listing survey results of specific causes of construction disputes and which include ambiguous contract provisions. See also BUBSHAIT, ABDULAZIZ A. and ALMOHAWIS, SOLIMAN A. Evaluating the General Conditions of a Construction Contract. *International Journal of Project Management*, 1994, **12**(3), 134 who consider internal consistency to be an important factor in reducing risk associated with the conditions.

[140] Thus, e.g. 'Completion Date' in clause 1.3 JCT 80 may easily be confused with 'Date for Completion' in clause 1.4 JCT NSC/C.

[141] For example, '*completion date*' is used in clause 11.2(12) ECC but '*subcontract completion date*' is used in clause 11.2(12) of the ECSC.

[142] BARNES, DR MARTIN *et al*. Towards Simpler Contracts, see n. 9 above, 818–821,

range of risk apportionment possibilities. The research was based upon an investigation into the interpretation of 18 clauses in the Canadian standard form lump sum contract CCDC2-1982[143] and then followed up with a further seven revised contract clauses in CCDC2-1994.[144]

Notwithstanding the absence of cross-references some clauses still approximate them. For example, clause 11 comes very close to a cross-reference in certain cases and given the brevity of the definitions. Hence, 'The Working Areas are the *working areas...*'.[145] The brevity of this definition is accentuated when one observes that the contractor may propose additional working areas for acceptance by the project manager.[146] At times slight ambiguity is introduced over the positioning of defined terms. For example, 'Others' which is a defined term, as such, should start with a capital letter or initial. However, as it also begins the sentence in which it is introduced it would be capitalized in any event. The result is that one can only confirm the term is a defined term because of the structure of the phrase and its later capitalization in the contract.[147] In a quantitative and qualitative study of projects in Hong Kong 'ambiguities in contract documents' ranked as fifth overall in the top ten common categories underlying construction claims.[148]

The identification of terms is not always consistent.

Works Information is information which either • specifies and describes the *works* or • states any constraints on how the *Contractor* Provides the Works and is either • in the documents which the Contract Data states it is in or[149] • in an instruction given in accordance with this contract.

Site Information is information which

- describes the Site and its surroundings and
- is in the documents which the Contract Data states it is in.

[143] HARTMAN, FRANCIS and SNELGROVE, PATRICK. Risk Allocation in Lump-sum Contracts – Concept of Latent Dispute. *Journal of Construction Engineering and Management*, 1996, **122**, 291–296. HARTMAN, FRANCIS *et al.* Effective Wording to Improve Risk Allocation in Lump Sum Contracts. *Journal of Construction Engineering and Management*, 1997, **123**, 379–387.

[144] HARTMAN, FRANCIS *et al.* Effective Wording, *ibid.*, 379–387.

[145] Clause 11.2(8) ECC.

[146] Clause 15 ECC.

[147] See clause 27.1 ECC. Cf the use of 'other people' in clause 16.2 which is used distinctly from 'Others': guidance notes NEC on clause 11.2 ECC, 27.

[148] KUMARASWAMY, MOHAN M. Common Categories and Causes of Construction Claims. *Construction Law Journal*, 1997, **13**.

[149] In general disjunctive words, such as 'or' in this definition should be read as disjunctive unless the context exceptionally shows that the necessary meaning is conjunctive as in *A-G* v. *Chiu Man-lun* [1989] 1 HKLR 99 (HKCA). See also *Mersey Docks and Harbour Board* v. *Henderson Brothers* (1888) 13 App Cas 595 at 603, 58 LJQB 152, HL, per Lord Halsbury LC; *Walker* v. *York Corpn* [1906] 1 KB 724, 75 LJKB 413; *Green* v. *Premier Glynrhonwy Slate Co* [1928] 1 KB 561, 97 LJKB 32, CA.

Thus, 'Works Information' and 'Site Information', which are both given dedicated sections in the Contract Data as well as being defined, should also be identified terms although they are not. The only basis for a distinction from the other italicized terms here is that these two terms refer to their description elsewhere. However, the principal reason for italicization, drawing attention to the further information contained in the Contract Data, remains and also suggests italicization. A stronger argument may be made in this regard with respect to the term 'programme' which also appears in part two of the Contract Data.

The NEC employs a flexible but complex system of dating.[150] Thus dates are distinguished by or qualified with reference to whether they are the 'Contract Date', 'possession dates', 'starting date', 'completion date', 'defects date' or 'base date'. The dates as qualified serve various purposes. The 'Contract Date' is defined as 'the date when this contract came into existence'.[151] Subject to what is said below regarding formation of the contract, if the parties date their agreement that *prima facie* will be taken to be the date when they executed their agreement and evidence will be admissible to prove that date.[152]

The definition serves at least three purposes:

- it acknowledges that the time leading up to the formation of the contract may take place over an indefinite period;
- it sets a date which may be relevant to the calculation of certain limitation or prescription periods under the general law; and
- it serves as a reference point for establishing knowledge of the parties,[153] setting certain base measurements,[154] taking actions under the contract,[155] determining the substance of the governing law,[156] and setting the total of the prices to be used in calculating the initial value of the trust fund.[157]

The 'possession date' is undefined but is an identified term. There may be one possession date or several possession dates if parts of the site are given to the contractor consecutively. The possession date is relevant to giving possession of the whole site or a part of the site.[158] The ECC envisages the giving of possession of parts of the site only as the general

---

[150] Additional aspects of this system of *dating* are also discussed in other sections of this commentary.

[151] Clause 11.2(3) ECC.

[152] *Hunt* v. *Massey* (1834) 5 B & Ad 902; *Anderson* v. *Weston* (1840) 6 Bing NC 296. See on rebuttal of the presumption *Hall* v. *Cazenove* (1804) 4 East 477.

[153] Knowledge of the contractor in relation to the physical conditions on site is determined as at the 'Contract Date' under clause 60.1(12) ECC.

[154] For example, in the bill of quantities under clauses 60.4, 60.5 ECC.

[155] For example, providing a performance bond under clause G1.1, a parent company guarantee under clause H1.1, making an advanced paymet under clause J1.1 ECC.

[156] Under clause T1.1 ECC.

[157] Under clauses V2.1 and V1.1(3) ECC.

[158] Under clause V1.1(3) ECC.

rule.[159] In the case of partial possession, possession dates are inserted in part one of the Contract Data, section 3 and pertain to the individual parts of the site. Where the site, however, is not divided into parts a potential problem arises. Thus, according to clause 30.1, the contractor is not to start work until the first possession date but as there are no parts of the site there are no possession dates and thus there is no first possession date.[160] While this interpretation is possible on the wording it is suggested that a better interpretation would be rather to regard the time for possession of the site to be given as being the 'starting date' as inserted in section 3 of part one of the Contract Data. The 'Site' itself is defined as the area within the boundaries of the site and the volumes above and below it which are affected by work in the contract.[161]

The employer must give the contractor possession of the site in accordance with clause 33 ECC. This provision may reflect the NEC's electrical and mechanical plant contract heritage where possession of the site may be not be required for much of the contract period where offsite design and fabrication is done after a starting date but prior to a first possession date. The taking of only partial possession of the site under the ECC also parallels other engineering forms.[162] The possession date is relevant to starting and the contractor is not to start work on the site until the possession date.[163] Failure by the employer to deliver possession of a part of the site by the possession date in the first instance[164] is a compensation event.

Part one of the contract uses the 'starting date' as an identified term in the quasi-defined sense that other terms have been referred to here regarding their use in the Contract Data. The Employer inserts the actual starting date. In contrast to the defects date the starting date will be inserted as a date certain. Although the starting date is less significant than either the completion date or the defects date it is still relevant to numerous matters under the contract. Thus, the starting date:

- sets the beginning of the period from which forecasts of the total actual cost for the whole of the works are prepared;[165]
- must be shown on each programme which the contractor submits for acceptance;[166]
- begins the interval from which revised programmes must be submitted;[167]

---

[159] Clause 33.1 ECC.

[160] VALENTINE, D.G. The New Engineering Contract: Part 2 – Claims for Extensions of Time. *Construction Law Journal*, 1991, **12**, 322.

[161] Clause 11.2(7) ECC.

[162] For example, clauses 42.2 FIDIC 4th and 42(1), (2) ICE 6th.

[163] See discussion below under clause 8 ECC.

[164] See the discussion of this requirement below under clauses 33.1 and 60.1(2) ECC.

[165] Clause 20.4 ECC under all main options save A and B.

[166] Clause 31.2 ECC.

[167] Clause 32.2 ECC.

- begins in the first instance the period from which the first 'assessment interval' is determined;[168]
- begins the period and defines the coverage and parties for insurance for stipulated contractor's risks[169] as well as limits the timing of their submission by the contractor to the project manager in respect of the contractor's risks[170] and the project manager to the contractor in respect of employer's risks.[171]

The start of a project also has symbolic importance and can significantly influence progress.[172]

The 'completion date' is defined simply as 'the *completion date* unless later changed in accordance with this contract'.[173] If this were the only definition it would be unhelpful for it is a cardinal rule of drafting that one does not define a term by reference to itself. However, more detail is provided in clause 11.2(13). Thus, 'Completion is when the *Contractor* has done all the work which the Works Information[174] states he is to do by the Completion Date[175] and corrected notified Defects[176] which would have prevented the *Employer* from using the *works*'. It is the project manager who will decide the actual date of completion which must then be certified within one week of completion.[177] It should be noted that the determination of completion and the completion date must also be considered in relation to the secondary option clauses. Thus if option L applies the references to these two terms in the conditions of contract may refer either to the whole of the works or any section of the works.[178]

It can be seen from clause 11.2(12) that the 'Completion Date' is both a defined and an identified term, both capitalized and italicized respectively. The use of these two drafting techniques underscores the importance of drawing the parties' attention to the phrase. It has been argued above that by setting out terms in the Contract Data the drafters have in effect defined those terms. The completion date was given this treatment. As such there must have been another intention in including subclause (12) in clause 11.2.

The wording of the subclause gives an indication of the possible intention. That is, by referring to the mutability of the completion date; i.e. it is the completion date only insofar as not *later* changed in

---

[168] Clause 50.1 ECC.
[169] Clauses 81.1 and 84.2 ECC.
[170] Clause 85.1 ECC.
[171] Clause 87.1 ECC.
[172] Project Kick-off; Getting the Project off on the Right Foot. *Project Management Institute*, 1992, **10**(2), 115–122.
[173] Clause 11.2(12) ECC. See generally BREWER, G. *Problems of Practical Completion.* RICS, London, 1995.
[174] Clause 11.2(5) ECC.
[175] Clause 11.2(12) ECC.
[176] Clause 11.2(15) ECC.
[177] Clause 30.2 ECC.
[178] Clause L 1.1 ECC.

accordance with the contract, some of the mystique surrounding completion is erased. The changes in accordance with the contract will predominantly occur under the compensation event procedure and as a result of which the completion date originally inserted in the Contract Data will be *later* changed. Henceforth, completion becomes not so much a finite end, one agreed in advance and subject to change only after protracted debate, but an objective that both parties must work toward. Pursuant to clause 11.2(12) not only may time for completion be extended but one must expect that it is *likely* to be extended, but, of course, under the mechanism providing for it in the contract. If at times in practice the perceived immutability of the completion date has resulted in unfairness to either of the parties the NEC would appear to be seeking to break with old attitudes.

The flexibility inherent in the description of the completion date also finds expression in the description of the defects date. The term is neither formally identified nor defined but once again appears only in the Contract Data.[179] It is inserted by the employer and serves initially to specify the number of weeks that must pass before the agreed defects date is reached. The drafting is unusual in the manner this is expressed. Thus the 'defects date' is not inserted as a date *per se* but as an agreed number of weeks after 'Completion of the whole of the *works*'.[180] The date itself is simply determinable by reference to the exact number of those weeks.

The defects date is significant in determining the time period during which certain contractual obligations run including:

- in the first instance one of two possible due dates for making conditional payments to the contractor following tests and inspection;[181]
- for giving mutual notifications between the contractor and supervisor of defects which either finds;[182]
- correcting defects;[183]
- in the first instance one of two possible dates for issuing the defects certificate by the supervisor;[184] and
- notifying compensation events.[185]

Baird[186] equates the '*defects date*' with the 'maintenance/warranty phase' under other forms. It leaves the contractor with the risk of performance of the works to the very end of the contract rather than leaving the impression that it ceases with take over or completion. It is an open

---

[179]   Section 4 part one.
[180]   The phrase is used in numerous clauses of the ECC including 20.4, 32.2, 50.1, 53.3, 97.1 and 97.2.
[181]   Clause 40.5 ECC.
[182]   Clause 42.2 ECC.
[183]   See clauses 42.1 and 42.2 ECC.
[184]   Clause 43.2 ECC.
[185]   Clause 61.7 ECC.
[186]   BAIRD, ANDREW. The New Engineering Contract – A Management Summary for Plant Industry Users. *International Construction Law Review*, 1994, 122.

question whether future maintenance obligations under the NEC will be tested against durability as one of the attributes of 'satisfactory quality' under the amended Sale and Supply of Goods Act 1994.[187] Previously the term used referred to 'merchantable quality'. A number of specific qualities which may be considered in determining satisfactory quality are now contained in the legislation. The list of qualities is not exhaustive. An article will be found to be of satisfactory quality if it is suitable for at least one of its normal uses. Thus it need not be suitable for all possible uses to satisfy the legislation. The warranty of satisfactory quality may operate independently from that of fitness for purpose under section 14(3) of the Sale of Goods Act 1979 when non-standard goods are involved and this fact has been made known to the seller.

Turning to the final way in which dates are used according to secondary option N the parties may choose a '*base date*' against which to assess price adjustments for inflation. In practice the base date is likely to be earlier than either the possession date or starting date to reflect the fact that the contractor's bid will normally be submitted for consideration before either of these other two dates is reached. In this way the contractor may have the benefit of the price adjustment for inflation from the earliest possible opportunity, i.e. the base date. The use of a base date has also been adopted in the new FIDIC Orange Book.[188]

It may be noted that clause 11.2(12) of the ECSC similarly defines the subcontract completion date as 'the *subcontract completion* date unless later changed in accordance with this subcontract'. The back-to-back nature of this drafting overcomes unnecessary complexity under other subcontract forms; e.g. under NAM/SC in the absence of a definition of 'practical completion' in the subcontract and presumably agreement of the parties on the date, a series of default provisions become operative including notice by the subcontractor under clause 15.1, possible dissent by the contractor resulting in a deemed date or one determined by an arbitrator under clause 15.2, or, in the absence of either of these, a second deemed date the same as the certified practical completion under the main contract, again under clause 15.2 NAM/SC. This contrasts with the unusual provision in clause 4.5 of the ICE MW 2nd form providing a definition of practical completion as: 'when the Works reach a state when notwithstanding any defect or outstanding items therein they are taken or are fit to be taken into use or possession by the Employer'.

Other remaining identified and defined terms are discussed in the context in which they arise below.

---

[187] 'Satisfactory quality' is defined in section 14 of the Sale of Goods Act 1979 as amended by the Sale and Supply of Goods Act 1994.

[188] The Orange Book 1st contains a similarly complex system of dating with defined terms for the 'base date' – clause 1.1.3.1 the date 28 days prior to the latest date for submission of the tender for acceptance by the employer; the 'effective date' – clause 1.1.3.2 the date on which the contract enters into legal force and effect; and the 'commencement date' – clause 1.1.3.3 the date on which the contractor receives notice to commence from the employer's representative.

Interpretation and the law

The contract has only very brief provisions regarding interpretation and the law. The drafters use the term 'interpretation' here in preference to 'construction' but nothing turns on the distinction between the two which are used interchangeably in case law. In the contract, except where the context shows otherwise, words in the singular also mean the words in the plural and the other way round and words in the masculine also mean in the feminine and neuter.[189] The drafters of the ECC may be forgiven for this inclusion but it adds very little to assist in interpretation. They have consistently adopted the masculine third person throughout and no ambiguity arises. The reference to the feminine and neuter genders may be appropriate in other translations, e.g. French and German respectively but do not arise as issues here. In a similar respect, the words 'except where the context shows otherwise' would be implied in any case[190] and thus add little to the interpretation of the provisions. In an unusual change from the Consultation Document the 'other way round' also replaces the word 'reverse'.[191]

The second rule of interpretation, more precisely a choice of law or conflict of laws provision, is that '[t]his contract is governed by the *law of the contract*'.[192] The law of the contract as an italicized term is referred to in the Contract Data.[193] The reference to 'this contract' it is submitted refers to the contract between the employer and the contractor.[194]

Communications

The current construction culture is perceived by some as suffering from entrenched attitudes, poor communications, lack of trust and generally adversarial relationships at all levels.[195]

Culture may be thought of as the set of attitudes that people at work share with each other and which affect how they do things on a daily basis. In management terminology *culture* is 'the way in which a group of people solve problems'.[196] Culture, as it can be understood within one organization, is influenced by a host of variables ranging from mission, and technology, systems and procedures to core values and personnel

---

[189]   Clause 12.1 ECC.

[190]   See *Meux* v. *Jacobs* (1875) LR 7 HL 481 at 493, 44 LJ Ch 481.

[191]   Consultation Document ECC, 14; the term the 'converse' may have been the most accurate.

[192]   Clause 12.2 ECC. See generally *Dicey & Morris on the Conflict of Laws* (ed. COLLINS, LAWRENCE), 12th edn. Sweet & Maxwell, London, 1993, 1997 Supp.

[193]   Part one, section 1.

[194]   See Consultation Document ECC, 13 clause 11.1(1): '*the Contract* is this contract between the *Employer* and the *Contractor*'.

[195]   European Construction Institute. *Implementing TQ in the Construction Industry A Practical Guide*. Thomas Telford, London, 1996, p. 69.

[196]   DINGLE, JOHN. *Project Management Orientation for Decision Makers*. Arnold, London, 1997, p. 239 quoting HOFSTEDE, G. *Culture's Consequences – International Differences in Work-Related Values*. Sage Publications, London, 1984.

training. It can equally be influenced by subjective variables.[197] The same influences today determine the wider culture within the construction industry as a whole. It is for this reason that many of the recent initiatives being undertaken with regard to improving the industry, or changing its culture, address the same variables.[198] Many of the changes, which are sought to be introduced into industry, seek to improve efficiency and reduce costs and Latham, for example, held out improvements of as much as 30% overall.[199]

The prevalence of poor communications and lack of trust inhibit success of projects and can impact upon costs. Thus, for example, mistrust among individuals entering a project is more likely than not to worsen and then, as the project proceeds, diminishes the chances of a successful outcome.[200] In a recent European Construction Institute survey of the construction industry a wide range of specific problems and potential barriers to changing the culture of the industry were identified. *Implementing TQ in the Construction Industry A Practical Guide* lists them as internal communication, blame culture, functional bureaucracy, long standing practices, organizational structure, convincing staff of its worth, use of agency staff, short termism, and project culture.[201] It has been noted that the problems are generic and thus susceptible to solutions adopted from other sectors. In this regard improved leadership, communications and teamwork have been held out as furthering culture change. Change is also said to be facilitated through new collaborative forms of working that stress goals such as co-operation, mutual interest, and non-adversariality.[202] The point is that culture can be changed if these aspects of it are addressed. However, for the changes to be meaningful they must be systematic or coherent. This in part is one of the reasons why some changes have been underpinned by legislation such as the HGCRA.

The subject of the exchange of information among the employer, project manager, supervisor and contractor is dealt with in general under the marginal note headed 'communications'. The provisions overall are intended to facilitate the exchange of information in the administration of the contract[203] – like a *document distribution matrix* in organizing internal

---

[197] See e.g. LIGHTBURN, EDWARD writing 'Maschismo in the Construction Industry. In *Commercial Dispute Resolution*, (eds ODAMS, MARTIN and HIGGENS, JOANNA). Construction Law Press, London, 1996, p. 17.

[198] See e.g. *Training the Team*, and *Educating the Professional Team*.

[199] See generally *Towards a 30% Productivity Improvement in Construction*, and for additional background on structural change in the construction industry BEDELIAN, H.M. Successful Major Projects in a Changing Environment. *Proceedings of the Institution of Civil Engineers*, August 1986, **114**, 117–123.

[200] MUNNS, A.K. Potential Influence of Trust on the Success for Completion of a Project. *International Journal of Project Management*, 1995, **13**(1), 19–24.

[201] European Construction Institute. *Implementing TQ*, 74.

[202] *Ibid.*

[203] See for an interesting approach to integrating different types of construction information BRANDON, PETER and BETTS, MARTIN. *Integrated Construction Information*. E & FN Spon, London, 1995. See also KWAKYE, A.A. Project Risks

contract and project communications – and to reduce disputes. Poor communications between and among the parties involved in a project is often a cause of disputes.[204] Majid and McCaffer,[205] for example, rank *inefficient communication* as an individual factor, based on a major literature review, as the seventeenth most significant factor in causing non-excusable delay. With regard to the ECC provisions, notwithstanding the intentions behind them, the provisions give rise to more ambiguities than most other provisions in the contract. One of the reasons for this may be the necessity for the clause to apply to all situations addressed in the contract. Thus, it appears that in attempting to address not only individual but general cases which arise some ambiguity has unintentionally resulted. Whatever the reasons behind the drafting choices which were made some of the confusion that may ensue can perhaps be addressed at this stage. Clause 13.1 provides as follows:

> Each instruction, certificate, submission, proposal, record, acceptance, notification and reply which this contract requires is communicated in a form which can be read, copied and recorded. Writing is the *language of this contract*.[206]

At the outset it may be observed that the phrase 'writing is the *language of this contract*', does not add any meaning to the clause. The italicization highlights the fact that it is an identified term that appears in part one of the Contract Data, section 1. However, if writing were literally the language of the contract then one would presumably have to insert that fact in part one; as such the relevant part of section 1 would read: 'The *language of this contract* is *writing*'. This cannot have been the intention but does serve to demonstrate this obscure point. It is more likely that the phrase was intended only to underscore the importance of writing in communications.[207] The ECC adopts an open-ended approach to the subject of the exchange of information or 'communications'. The term 'communications' is not defined, nor does it state in the clause that the term itself encompasses all of the various eight modes of exchanging information that are listed.[208] In contrast, clause 13.1 of the PSC First Edition lists only seven modes of communication and omits 'reply'. It

---

and Information Management. *Construction Project Administration in Practice.* Addison Wesley Longman, Harlow; CIOB, Ascot, 1997, pp. 41–55.

[204] SMITH, G.A. See n. 128 above, n. 1 references omitted.

[205] ABD MAJID, M.Z. and McCAFFER, RONALD. Factors of Non-excusable Delays that Influence Contractors' Performance. *Journal of Management in Engineering*, May/June 1988, **14**(3), 48.

[206] Clause 13.1 ECC. Subsequent references to the necessity to comply with this clause in the text below will simply be abbreviated to 'writing'.

[207] Cf FIDIC 4th which uses 'language/s' as referring to the language or languages in which the contract documents are drawn, and provision for paramountcy in the event of a conflict, the 'Ruling Language', clause 5.1.

[208] Cf FIDIC 4th clause 1.5 which also uses the term 'communication' and is similarly undefined.

would appear that this omission is unintentional as reply is dealt with specifically in clause 13.3 and where 'period for reply' is also an identified term. Research indicates that different organizational forms impact on the use and types of both information and communications.[209] However, it is submitted that subsequent provisions in the clause do clarify this is how the term 'communications' is to be used.[210] If this interpretation is accepted, a valid communication may be effected by any of these modes provided the other requirements for validity are satisfied. Following the procedure laid down for giving notices in general under standard forms is clearly important to preserve their effect and validity. This leaves open, however, whether something other than one of the eight modes *must* satisfy clause 13.1 and whether it constitutes a communication in any event.[211] The drafters do not assist on this point although there is some evidence of a broad meaning being given to the term 'communications' in Flow Chart 13. Flow Chart 13 indicates that 'communications required by the contract "include" those listed'. Thus it supports an even broader meaning for communication than the eight listed modes as it leaves open the possibility of other modes. Further Flow Chart 13 indicates that notwithstanding one of the eight modes of communication is not used the mode nevertheless still has effect when it is received in accordance with clause 13.2; that is, when 'received at the last address notified by the recipient for receiving communications or, if none is notified, at the address of the recipient stated in the Contract Data'.[212] While this may have been the intent it is submitted that the references to 'a communication' contradicts this assertion. The actual intent should be clarified with an amendment to the clause.

The requirements for formal validity of a communication will depend upon the nature of the communication. There is only one requirement that applies to every form of communication: all modes of communication must be 'in a form that can be read, copied and recorded'. The requirement for the form to be capable of being read, copied and recorded serves to reduce the scope for constructive notices.[213] Therefore each instruction, certificate, submission, proposal, record, acceptance, notification and reply referred to in clause 13.1 must satisfy this

---

[209] See PIETROFORTE, R. Communication and Governance in the Building Process. *Construction Management and Economics*, 1997, **15**(1), 71–82.

[210] For example, clauses 13.2, 13.3 and 13.4 all referring to 'a communication'.

[211] By comparison in the FIDIC Orange Book 1st part I the parties may agree to any 'system of electronic communication stated in the Appendix to Tender': clause 1.8.

[212] As a general rule an address that a person concerned is known to have left is not a proper address for service (*White* v. *Weston* [1968] 2 QB 647, [1968] 2 All ER 842, CA); this position could be otherwise where the use of the last address is expressly authorized (see *Re Follick, ex p Trustee* (1907) 97 LT 645). For other relevant cases, see *Hanrott's Trustees* v. *Evans* (1887) 4 TLR 128; *R* v. *Farmer* [1892] 1 QB 637, [1891–94] All ER Rep 921, CA; see also *Re Webb* [1896] 1 QB 487; and *Berry* v. *Farrow* [1914] 1 KB 632.

[213] Cf GC/Works/1 3rd clause 1(6) requiring notices to be in writing, typescript or printed.

requirement for validity. The fact that one may prove a communication is an instruction, certificate etc. is insufficient for formal validity if it cannot be 'read, copied and recorded'. The Consultation Document originally qualified this requirement stipulating that it had to be done 'conveniently' as well but this has wisely been deleted. The subject of convenience is too vague and transitory to be of much assistance. The language is broad enough to extend to electronic forms of communication such as e-mails and EDI although survey evidence suggests this is rare in main stream construction processes.[214]

There are procedures for dealing with communications as defined. Thus to operate, a communication must be given within any applicable time limit or 'period for reply'.[215] Clause 13.3 stipulates either the project manager, supervisor or contractor reply to a communication, if the contract requires, within the 'period for reply'. The exact wording of the clause, which bears repeating, is as follows: 'If this contract requires the *Project Manager*, the *Supervisor* or the *Contractor* to reply to a communication, unless otherwise stated in this contract, he or she replies within the *period for reply*'. The 'period for reply' is an identified term and thus appears in the Contract Data.[216]

The contract is not clear on whether the stipulation is a matter of formal validity for the communication or merely serves to prevent the communication being received. The fact that the project manager, from a jurisdictional point of view, may only extend a period for reply either by agreement or prior to the expiry of the period for reply itself, however, suggests time limits are substantive. The extension of the time limit alone is subject to a 'double agreement' requirement. Thus not only must the project manager and the contractor agree to extend the time limit for the period to reply but the project manager must also notify the contractor of their agreement as well. The clear intention is to lessen the risk of misunderstanding in reaching agreement as to the extension. It would also seem to seek to avoid any uncertainty over who has the ultimate authority to grant the extension and hence the necessity for doing so explicitly.

In those instances where a time limit is given for a reply in the contract this time limit will prevail over the 'period for reply' which is agreed and inserted in the Contract Data. Thus the Contract Data period for reply should be regarded as supplementary only to any time limits set out in the conditions of contract. This interpretation, it is submitted, should be given to any clause capable of giving rise to a time limit for reply whether made explicitly or not. In fact, very few of the ECC clauses explicitly give a

---

[214] O'BRIEN, M.J. and AL-SOUFI, A. A Survey of Data Communication in the UK Construction Industry. *Construction Management and Economics*, 1994, **12**(5), 457–465.

[215] Clause 13.3 ECC. The '*period for reply*' is an identified term in section 1 part one of the Contract Data, given as an agreed number of weeks, and in respect of a communication. In general, a 'period' means a time that runs continuously, see *Tyler* v. *London & India Docks Joint Committee* (1892) 9 TLR 11.

[216] Section 1 of part one of the Contract Data ECC.

period for reply. Most create a period of reply by reference to defined dates, e.g. 'Completion Date', 'defects date' etc. However, there are also numerous clauses which implicitly give rise to a period for reply, e.g. clause 19.1, 23.1 etc. In these cases the general period for reply stated in the Contract Data governs. In general, the common law approach to time stipulations, as distinct from that in equity originally, is strict.[217] The modern approach of the courts to time provisions in contracts today has softened. In general time provisions will not be regarded strictly unless the contract expressly stipulates time is an essential term or a condition of performance; the nature of the contract is such that time should be considered to be of the essence; or a party to the contract subsequently stipulates time to be of the essence where the other party is guilty of inordinate delay.[218]

The ability to agree to an extension of time is limited by the period of reply itself. Thus it could not be agreed to extend the period for reply once it has lapsed by effluxion of time. The extension of time provision should be read with its counterpart in the ECSC.[219] Therefore if an extension of time is going to be given by the contractor to the subcontractor under the subcontract, and if it is relevant to a time frame under the main contract, the extension of time for the subcontractor would prove nugatory if the contractor were unable to obtain a corresponding extension of time from the project manager under the main contract.

The provisions regarding the period for reply seem to raise an anomaly. That is, the contract requires the project manager to reply within the period for reply, unless otherwise stated in the contract. A reply is also one of the eight modes of exchanging information which qualifies as a communication. In this regard the reply itself must satisfy the general requirements for communications including replying within the period for reply when applicable. However, there is no time frame for issuing any form of communication in the first instance when the contract is silent on the matter. Thus, in the case of the issuance of a record by the project manager pursuant to clause 16.4, no time frame is given and the period for reply is not applicable. In this example the record itself may oblige the contractor to reply to the record (or even the proposals which the record will contain under clause 16.4) within the period for reply but once again no time frame is given in the first instance regarding issuance.

---

[217] See *Parkin* v. *Thorvold* (1852) 16 Beav 59 at 65 per Sir John Romilly MR, and *Raineri* v. *Miles* [1981] AC 1050 at 1081, HL, per Lord Edmund-Davies.

[218] MORTON, CATHERINE. Time Bars and Conditions Precedent. *Building and Construction Law*, 1995, **11**, 303 citing among others *United Scientific Holdings Ltd* v. *Burnley Borough Council* [1978] AC 904 at 939–940, [1977] 2 All ER 62 at 80 per Viscount Dilhorne, Lord Simon at 83; *Halsbury's Laws of England*, 4th edn., vol. 9 paragraph 481; *Chitty on Contracts* (ed. GUEST, PROFESSOR A.G.), 27th edn., Sweet & Maxwell, London, 1994, paragraphs 21–012 to 21–015; and LINDGREN, K.E. *Time in the Performance of Contracts*, 2nd edn. Butterworths, Sydney, 1982, paragraphs 244 to 245.

[219] Clause 13.5 ECSC.

It may be observed that while examples such as this in clause 16.4 will arise only exceptionally, as most communications will have to be given within finite time frames under the contract, they may still result in delays. It is submitted that where an obligation is imposed by the contract for taking a certain action the court will incline to implying a *reasonable time* for its performance as a general rule.[220] The period for reply is relevant to an allegation by the contractor that a compensation event has occurred. Thus when the project manager or supervisor does not reply to a communication from the contractor within the period required by the contract a compensation event occurs. The early warning procedure may be relevant in this regard.[221] The period for reply may be either that stated in the Contract Data or the time limit given in the conditions of contract. It is submitted that the interpretation that should govern if an express time limit is given in the conditions, e.g. two weeks,[222] and the period for reply in the Contract Data is less than two weeks, is that no compensation event will occur until the longer time limit has been exceeded.

In certain instances the ECC provides for the project manager to reject the contents of a communication from the contractor and later reconsider a further communication addressing the same issue, for instance, revisions to a programme[223] or a quotation for a compensation event.[224] In these cases, although the project manager must reply to the resubmitted communication[225] no time frame is expressly given in the relevant clause. It is submitted in this case that, depending upon the nature of the communication, either another time limit will govern or the normal period for reply will govern. For instance, other time limits are expressly given in relation to the project manager's reply to submission of a quotation; namely two weeks.[226] If the project manager's reply is 'not acceptance', the reasons must be stated for the non-acceptance and where the contractor remains under an obligation to resubmit a communication on the issue then this must be done within the period for reply.[227] The contractor's resubmission must substantively seek to address the reasons for non-acceptance by the project manager. Clause 13.4 of the ECC states the Contractor's resubmission must 'tak[e] account of these [the project manager's reasons for nonacceptance] reasons'. If one reads the clause as giving rise to obligations on both the project manager's and contractor's parts to reply then in such cases resubmissions should be sufficient to overcome any arguments suggesting otherwise.

---

[220]   See e.g. *Allridge (Builders) Ltd* v. *Grand Actual Ltd* (1997) 55 Con LR 91.
[221]   Clause 60.1(6).
[222]   Clause 31.3 ECC.
[223]   Clause 32.2 ECC.
[224]   Clause 62 ECC. Quotations comprise proposals from the contractor regarding changes to the prices and the completion date as defined: see clause 62.2 ECC.
[225]   Clause 13.4 ECC.
[226]   Clause 62.3 ECC.
[227]   See clause 13.4 ECC.

There are other instances of where the communications provisions could yet be improved. For instance, the meaning of clause 13.5 could be clarified if the relationship to some other clauses was expressed. This follows from the fact that the contract clearly imposes obligations on the parties to reply in numerous cases.[228] Quite apart from simple changes in wording a more fundamental means of improving the communications procedures would be if, for example, sample communications procedures were included with the forms. In this regard the ENAA Model Form provides a favourable precedent for comparison.[229] In the case of a communication in the mode of a 'certificate' alone it must be issued to the proper persons. Thus, for a certificate to be effective, a project manager must issue the certificate to the employer and the contractor while the supervisor must issue the certificate to the project manager and the contractor.[230]

The contract requires a communication, which is a 'notification,' to be communicated separately from other communications.[231] The choice of the term 'notification' is ambiguous. A notification is but one of the eight modes of communication which is referred to in clause 13. The question this single reference raises is whether the other seven modes of communication must similarly be communicated separately. The contractor or the project manager 'notifies' the other pursuant to the conditions of contract in a large number of cases.[232] The term 'notification' itself is used expressly in the conditions.[233] It is submitted, at a minimum, that any clause expressly using either the term 'notifies' or 'notification' comes within the meaning of clause 13.7 and that the contents of this mode of communication be given separately from other communications. Further, it is submitted that the intention of the drafters was likely to impose this requirement on all forms of communication, which have been referred to at least once by them collectively as 'information'.[234] However, the drafters were seeking to avoid the situation where a document which is intended for one purpose is construed also to satisfy another purpose, e.g. notice. This has been the case particularly regarding programmes; however, it seems just as likely, if not more so in fact, that a communication would be missed because it is included with a series of other documents all of which serve other legitimate purposes.

---

[228] For example, clauses 31.3, 61.4, 62.3.

[229] For example, Works Procedure 1, Correspondence Procedure, vol. 4 of the ENAA Model Form of Contract, 1992 which sets out a uniform procedure to be followed for the exchange of correspondence between the owner, contractor and project personnel as well as sample documents illustrating: the numbering of correspondence; blank forms for correspondence; description of meetings; distribution of correspondence; and a communication log.

[230] Clause 13.6 ECC.

[231] Clause 13.7.

[232] See e.g. clauses 14.2, 14.4, 16.1, 17.1, 19.1, and 31.3.

[233] For example, clause 90.1 unamended 2nd ECC in the Adjudication Table.

[234] Guidance notes NEC on clause 13.7 ECC, 29.

A similar ambiguity is raised in clause 13 with regard to the meaning of 'submission' as that concerning 'notification'. The term 'submission' is used as one of the eight modes of communication but as the sole mode with respect to which the project manager may *withhold* acceptance. Thus the '*Project Manager* may withhold acceptance of a submission by the *Contractor*'.[235] Therefore the question which this raises is whether the project manager may withhold acceptance *only* in respect of a 'submission' or may also withhold acceptance in respect of the other seven modes of communication. The answer is unclear; however, a large and liberal interpretation of the clause, it is submitted, would extend the right of the project manager to withhold acceptance in respect of any mode of communication. There is some arguable support that may be put forward in favour of this interpretation.

First, the use of the term 'submission' in the conditions is very broad:[236] the contractor may *submit* proposals, forecasts,[237] proposed subContract Data,[238] quotations,[239] programmes,[240] policies and certificates[241] and disputes.[242] Proposals may be given under several clauses with respect to adding to the working areas, dealing with early warning events, accelerating the work and adding to the working areas.[243] Secondly, there is duplication in the use of 'submit' with certain of the prescribed modes of communication, e.g. the submission of policies and certificates.[244] Thirdly, there is repetition in the use of the modes, e.g. the project manager 'records the proposals ... and gives a copy of his record to the *Contractor*'.[245] In summary, the varying use of not only the terms 'submit' and 'submission' but the apparent substitution of one mode for another in certain clauses in the conditions supports the view that they be given a large and liberal interpretation. As such a project manager could withhold acceptance of any mode of communication, which is referred to as or amounts to a submission in the relevant clause.

A separate but equally important question also arises in relation to 'submissions' and the withholding of acceptances regarding compensation events. That is, if the project manager withholds acceptance for a reason stated in the contract, will it not be a compensation

---

[235]   Clause 13.8 ECC. This clause was omitted from the First Edition and was amended in the Second Edition when the words 'for any reason' were deleted.

[236]   For example, clauses 15, 20.4, 26.4, 36.1, 50.3, 54.2, 62.3, 62.5, 85.1, (90.1 amended 2nd) ECC.

[237]   Clause 20.4 ECC. Forecasts arise in relation to quotation events, actual cost, assessing the contractor's share, and removal of equipment on termination.

[238]   Clause 26.4 ECC.

[239]   Clause 36.1 ECC.

[240]   Clause 50.3 ECC.

[241]   Clause 85.1 ECC.

[242]   Clause 90.1 unamended 2nd ECC.

[243]   Clause 15 ECC. As to the meaning of 'propose', see *Re Trustees of Magdalen Charity, Hastings* v. *Shelower* (1968) 19 P & CR 389.

[244]   Clause 85.1 ECC.

[245]   Clause 16.4 ECC.

event?[246] As discussed above there is a wide variety of instances where the contractor will make a 'submission' to the project manager. In these cases the project manager is given the power to withhold acceptance of the 'submission' from the contractor. An explanation for the withholding of acceptance not being a compensation event has to do with the allocation of risk. Under the principles for the allocation of risk in the ECC all risks carried by the employer are treated in the same way. Thus if the contractor is outside of clause 60, e.g. in cases when acceptances are withheld for reasons stated in other clauses of the contract, then the contractor is also outside the logic of the allocation of risk in the form.

The issue may be examined from another perspective. The events that are at the employer's risk are set out in the conditions.[247] In certain cases when an employer's risk event occurs a procedure may be outlined which entails the contractor making a submission to the project manager on how it should be dealt with. The project manager may accept or withhold this acceptance with respect to any of these submissions.[248] However, he may not do so 'for any reason'. This implication clearly follows from the deletion of this phrase in clause 13.8 from the November version of the ECC.[249] The project manager's reasons for withholding acceptance may be foreseeable or not foreseeable.

Thus, clause 13.8 addresses foreseeability indirectly. By providing, in effect, that when the project manager withholds acceptance for a reason that is stated in the contract it is not a compensation event, the drafting is saying that the risk was foreseeable. By classifying the risk as foreseeable the burden of carrying it shifts from the employer to the contractor. Accordingly, once again the contractor cannot claim it amounts to a compensation event. This, of course, contrasts with the withholding of acceptance by the project manager for a reason that is *not* stated in the contract and which would be a compensation event.[250] While there is no general common law duty to provide reasons for a decision a very strong case can be made for them on the basis of attaining instrumental and non-instrumental objectives underlying process rights[251] and quite apart from their overall importance under the ECC. Case law has created several

---

[246]   Clause 13.8 ECC.

[247]   See generally clause 81.1 ECC stating that from the starting date until the defects certificate has been issued the risks which are not carried by the employer are carried by the contractor.

[248]   Clause 13.8 ECC. See also discussion of clause 60.1(9) below.

[249]   One document in the NEC, that is the ECC itself, was released early in July 1995 prior to the simultaneous release of all contract documents in November 1995. The November Second Edition, also referred to here as the amended Second Edition is thus a new version of the ECC which made a small number of changes and corrections to the unamended Second Edition. Further Second Editions of the PSC and AC followed in June 1998 along with the First Edition of the SC in July 1999.

[250]   Clause 60.1(9).

[251]   See lately CRAIG, P.P. The Common Law, Reasons and Adminstrative Justice. *Cambridge Law Journal*, 1994, **53**, 282.

exceptions to the general rule when reasons may be required in the individual circumstances and which may be relevant here.[252]

There are two exceptions to when the withholding of acceptance by the project manager for a reason *not* stated in the contract will still not be treated as a compensation event. They are, if the project manager withholds an acceptance of a quotation for an acceleration or a quotation for not correcting a defect. In these two cases it is still not a compensation event even though no reason is given nor required to be given for the project manager so doing. There is no explanation given as to why these two cases are treated as exceptions although a possible explanation can be put forward. First of all, in the case of the acceptance of a quotation for acceleration it would appear to follow from the fact that acceleration must be by agreement. Secondly, in the case of a quotation for not accepting a defect, it would appear to follow as no reason need be given by the project manager for taking this action. In fact, in both exceptions, no reason need be given by the project manager for not accepting a quotation, and in both cases no further action is necessary.[253]

The wording in clauses 60.1(9) and 13.8 may be contrasted. In the former case withholding acceptance is phrased negatively: an acceptance is withheld 'for a reason not stated in this contract'. In the latter case withholding acceptance is phrased affirmatively: 'for a reason stated in this contract'. The affirmative and negative formulations of the same rule serve to overcome any *a contrario* argument that may have otherwise been put forward. In the case of communications in general one reason is given expressly entitling the project manager to withhold acceptance; more information is needed to assess the contractor's submission fully.[254]

It is unclear whether the withholding of an acceptance for a reason stated in the contract to avoid being treated as a compensation event, save where more information is needed, must pertain to a reason in the relevant clause or whether any reason within the conditions will suffice. For instance, could a project manager withhold acceptance of the contractor's design not for the reasons stated in clause 21.2[255] but for reasons stated in clause 31.3?[256] It would seem that as the basis for the allocation of the risk to the contractor was its foreseeability it would be unfair to attribute foresight to the contractor in respect of matters that may not be directly related to the risk. It is on this basis that references in clauses 13.8 and 60.1(9) to reasons stated in '*this* contract' should be limited to reasons stated in the relevant clause in question in the contract.

---

[252] See generally RICHARDSON, G. The Duty to Give Reasons. *Public Law*, 1986, p. 437; AKEHURST, MICHAEL. Statements of Reasons for Judicial and Administrative Decisions. *Modern Law Review*, 1970, **33**, 154.

[253] Clause 36 ECC regarding acceleration and clause 44 ECC regarding not accepting a quotation for accepting a defect.

[254] Clause 13.4 ECC.

[255] For example, it does not comply with the works information or it does not comply with the applicable law.

[256] For example, it does not represent the contractor's plans realistically.

Foreseeability has been put forward as a guiding principle for the allocation of risk:[257] 'If a risk is reasonably foreseeable to an experienced designer/contractor then it is acceptable ... to allocate risk to the contractor but not otherwise'.[258] This formulation is strikingly similar to that expected of the contractor with regard to the contractor's early warning obligation.[259] It is also consistent with the suggestion by Jones as to how a philosophy of risk allocation according to foreseeability would be expressed.[260] It is interesting to note that a similarly worded test has been introduced in the ECC notwithstanding Max Abrahamson's[261] rules for risk allocation[262] and which are held out as an alternative to foreseeablility by Jones.[263] Abrahamson was once again the legal adviser to the NEC drafters and played a significant role in developing the contract system.[264] Notwithstanding tests for risk allocation, such as those discussed here, all too often the risks are still simply allocated subjectively in contracts and despite the availability of more sophisticated models for addressing them.[265]

One may turn to a further question of interpretation that also arises on the proper meaning of withholding an acceptance by the project manager. How does one communicate the withholding of an acceptance when no reason need be given[266] yet still satisfy clause 13.1 requiring 'acceptances' to be communicated in a form that can be read, copied and recorded? If this formal aspect of the acceptance pertains then it would indeed seem the withholding of the acceptance must be communicated to the contractor even though no express requirement for this is stipulated in the clauses on acceleration and accepting defects themselves. The answer to this is that the acceptance must be communicated when 'this contract requires'. It can be argued that as neither clause 36 nor 44 *requires* the communication of the acceptance there is no obligation to comply with clause 13.1.[267]

The project manager is given a general power to withhold acceptance if more information is needed in order to assess the contractor's

---

[257]   JONES, D.S. Philosophies of Risk Allocation – The Case for Foreseeability. *International Construction Law Review*, 1996, 570 referring to one of the principles held out by the organizers of the World Conference on Construction Risk III in Paris, April 1996.

[258]   *Ibid.*

[259]   See clauses 16.1 and 61.5 ECC.

[260]   JONES, D.S., see n. 257 above, 578.

[261]   Professor Abrahamson was legal adviser to the working group.

[262]   See ABRAHAMSON, MAX. Risk Management *International Construction Law Review*, 1984, 241.

[263]   JONES, D.S., see n. 257 above, 575–576.

[264]   *Foreseeability* is a criterion used in many standard forms, see e.g. clause 12.1 FIDIC 4th, clause 13 ICE 6th but cf 'reasonably apparent' in clause 26.1.1 JCT 98.

[265]   AL-BAHAR, JAMAL F. and CRANDALL, KEITH C. Systematic Risk Management Approach for Construction Contract Projects. *Journal of Construction Engineering and Management*, 1990, **119**, 743–756.

[266]   For example, in the case of quotations for acceleration and the accepting of defects.

[267]   See also clause 13.2 ECC on when a communication has effect.

submission fully.[268] The term 'submission' is used in the clause but communications within the meaning of clause 13 also include an instruction, certificate, proposal, record, acceptance, notification and reply. To read the power of the project manager to withhold acceptance as being limited to *only* submissions and not the other forms of communication seems unduly narrow but is nevertheless an interpretation of clause 13 which could be put forward. A court would be likely to impose a requirement that the project manager exercise this power only for the reason given and would not construe it as a general power to withhold acceptance in any case in which he or she could make up their mind or had other reasons for not accepting the proposal. This provision too overlaps with clause 13.8; where the project manager may withhold acceptance of a submission by the contractor.

The drafting of clauses 13.4 and 13.8 differs in this regard from drafting conventions used in other clauses. The drafting convention normally used when a submission from the contractor may not be accepted by the project manager is to state a reason or reasons for the non-acceptance *without* a general power of non-acceptance prefacing the reason.[269] One question this raises is thus what effect, if any, should be attributed to the difference. From the contractor's view in turn, if it is believed that the project manager has withheld acceptance for an invalid reason, the contractor may contend that the acceptance has been withheld within the meaning of clause 60.1(9). It could also be that the contractor instead agreed with the reason(s) of the project manager for withholding the acceptance and thus decides to act on it or take it into account and resubmit his communication within the normal period for reply. In this latter case the same considerations would pertain as in any earlier extension of the period for reply itself.[270] In theory, there is no limit on the number of resubmissions that could be made in this way although clearly there would be in practice. If ultimately the project manager were to decide not to consider any further resubmissions he or she would then be likely to consider either the giving of an early warning[271] or the issuing of an appropriate instruction.[272] Acceptance, on the other hand, if that course were taken, would proceed in accordance with clause 14 of the ECC.

The above illustration once again shows the real importance of communications generally to the successful implementation of the NEC. Building projects are more likely to be successfully completed where open communications are facilitated among the parties. Projects on the whole do benefit from the promotion of federative mechanisms such as informal co-operation that circumvent rigid or closed communications and hierarchical provisions in traditional standard forms.[273] The express

---

[268]   Clause 13.4 ECC.
[269]   See eg clauses 15.1, 23.1.
[270]   See discussion clause 13.5 ECC above.
[271]   See clause 16 ECC.
[272]   For example, under clause 14.3 ECC.
[273]   PIETROFORTE, ROBERTO, n. 209 above, 71–82.

communication provisions in the NEC would seem to improve on those in traditional standard forms through their more open exchange of information. However, notwithstanding this general comparison, the NEC provisions still admit of considerable complexity in their precise operation.

Project Manager and Supervisor

Clause 14 headed the 'Project Manager'[274] and the 'Supervisor'[275] is a sort of omnibus provision that deals with four separate topics under the one heading. Each topic dealt with in the clause has posed problems on its own in practice and cases have arisen as a result of these problems that have been heard in the courts. The answers, which the courts have given have not always been clear or consistent and the attempt by the drafters to address some of the inconsistencies is thus not surprising. The fact that the clause follows immediately after the provisions governing communications under the contract is also telling, as many of the problems surrounding the topics themselves seem to have been rooted in misunderstandings over the meaning of given actions or the effects of pieces of information.

Clause 14.1 addresses the first topic: what effect if any should be given to the 'acceptance' by the project manager or the supervisor of either a communication from the contractor or his work. At the outset it will be assumed that no issue arises over whether an acceptance has taken place as a matter of fact. In general, it is a question in all of the circumstances whether acceptance has occurred. Acceptance will be governed by clause 13 and the general law. One consequence of acceptance at law can be the implying of a promise to pay a reasonable sum for work done notwithstanding non-completion.[276] Thus it is open to the contractor to contend that acceptance on the part of the employer has given rise to a new contract to pay for the work that has been done.[277] The issue in building contracts has often turned upon acceptance[278] although it is assumed for purposes of this discussion. Thus, if we have acceptance of the contractor's work by the project manager under clause 14.1 only, this issue could arise. Why it should not arise, however, is precisely because the drafters have stated that acceptance 'does not change the *Contractor's*

---

[274] See discussion of the project manager in Chapter 5 above.

[275] See discussion of the supervisor in Chapter 5 above.

[276] The knowledge of the incompletion is a critical factor: *Munro* v. *Butt* (1858) 8 E & B 738; *Appleby* v. *Myers* (1867) LR 2 CP 651.

[277] *Hoenig* v. *Isaacs* [1952] 2 All ER 176 at 181, CA; *Holland Hannen and Cubitts (Northern) Ltd* v. *Welsh Health Technical and Services Organisation* (1981) 18 BLR 80.

[278] For example, *Sumpter* v. *Hedges* [1898] 1 QB 673, CA. The case also illustrates the issue acceptance gives rise to in relation to rescission for failure to perform and the voluntary acceptance of a benefit under the contract, see TREITEL, G. *The Law of Contract*, 8th edn. Sweet & Maxwell, London, 1995, pp. 732–736. See also the discussion below in the context of clause 21 ECC.

responsibility to Provide the Works ...'.[279] This must be taken to be express provision to the contrary with regard to the effect of acceptance. It will not operate to change the contractor's responsibility to provide the works or liability for design.[280] The issue is dealt with also under both other forms of contract[281] and judicial doctrines.[282]

In summary approvals are often features of standard forms and vary in detail as to whether they are required over materials, workmanship or procedures. The approving authority too may vary from the employer to any agent employed by the employer or statutory bodies. It is not uncommon to require approval to be subjective and be expressed as being to one's 'satisfaction'.[283] This formulation is avoided in the ECC as a result of the subjective connotation. In addition to the use of this formulation in other forms of contract, statutory powers are often conferred in similarly subjective terms entitling the designated body to act when a prescribed state of affairs exists. There are significant issues surrounding approvals including the authority to approve, in what form approval is communicated (e.g. certificate), the effect of approval on liability for the work and subsequent responsibility for corrections or defective work. The failure of the project manager to give approval could also be a breach of clause 10.1.

Both the project manager and the supervisor may delegate any of their actions and may cancel any delegation.[284] It is a condition of the validity of the delegation that the contractor is notified of the delegation.[285] To be meaningful the notification should provide clear details of the nature of the delegation, to whom the delegation has been made and for what period of time. The conditions of contract do not address the status of an action

---

[279] Clause 14.1 ECC.

[280] Clause 14.1 ECC.

[281] Cf FIDIC 4th clause 8.2 which provides in part: 'Where the Contract expressly provides that part of the Permanent Works shall be designed by the Contractor, he shall be fully responsible for that part of such Works, notwithstanding any approval by the Engineer'.

[282] See e.g. on the effect of approval by the engineer under the ICE conditions of designs by the contractor *Holland Hannen and Cubitts (Northern) Ltd* v. *Welsh Health Technical and Services Organisation* (1985) 7 Con LR 14, (1985) 35 BLR 1, CA; lately on the difference between 'comment' and 'approval' *J Sainsbury plc* v. *Broadway Malyan (a firm)* (1999) 61 Con LR 31; and even the 'Spearin Doctrine' from *United States* v. *Spearin* 248 US 132 (1918), *viz.* the implied warranty of the employer/owner that the designs are adequate.

[283] See for cases on the general evidential standard required before a person can be 'satisfied' of a state of affairs or certain criteria: *Everett* v. *Griffiths* [1920] 3 KB 163; and *Fletcher* v. *Ilkeston Corpn* (1931) 96 JP 7.

[284] Clause 14.2 ECC: 'A reference to an action of the *Project Manager* or the *Supervisor* in this contract includes an action by his delegate'.

[285] *Quaere* whether the employer must also be informed of or consent to the delegation pursuant to the maxim *delegatus non potest delegare*; Broom, Max 840. Best practice would dictate that all persons concerned with the delegation should be informed. Notification must comply with clause 13 ECC requirements.

that is taken pursuant to a valid delegation that is subsequently cancelled. Thus it is an open question whether the decision is void or merely voidable. Perhaps this classification is less important than full compensation in any event.

Recognition of the authority of either or both the project manager and supervisor to delegate actions that they must take under the contract follows from the size and number of people involved on construction projects today. It is inevitable that the two individuals fulfilling these roles will at times have to rely upon others to assist them in the performance of their functions. This provision gives formal recognition to this practice. Delegation may or may not be made to employees of either the employer or the project manager or supervisor, but there is no restriction on such delegations in the conditions. Similarly delegations may be made by either the project manager to the supervisor or vice versa although this is not recommended save but on the smallest of contracts and where it occurs for otherwise unavoidable reasons.[286] From the point of view of interpretation, a reference in the conditions of contract to an action by the project manager or the supervisor includes an action by a delegate[287] so far as applicable.

The project manager may give an instruction to the contractor that changes the works information.[288] The instruction may be authorized under a number of clauses including 14.3, 19.1 and 44.2. When an instruction is given that changes the works information for these reasons it may also fall within clause 60.1(1) as a compensation event. As an instruction the contractor is under an express obligation to obey it if it is given in accordance with the contract.[289] This important provision is the equivalent under other standard forms of the authority of the contract administrator to make changes to or effect 'variations'.[290] to the works. Peter R. Hibberd writes that: 'variations in construction projects create a considerable number of managerial and legal problems' and therefore variation clauses are material.[291] The authority given to the project manager alone under clause 14.3 is not expressly contradicted anywhere else in the conditions of contract. However, pursuant to clause 92.1 the adjudicator's powers include the power to review and revise any action or inaction of the project manager. Although this power of the adjudicator so to act is not put forward by the drafters as illustrative of the

---

[286]   See guidance notes on clause 14.2 ECC clause 14.2, 30.

[287]   Clause 14.2 ECC.

[288]   Clause 14.3 ECC.

[289]   See clause 29.1 ECC.

[290]   A lengthy definition of variations is given in the JCT Practice Note 14: variations and provisional sum work. See lately on the meaning of 'variation' under clause 27.1 MF/1 *Strachan & Henshaw Ltd* v. *Stein Industrie (UK) and GEC Alsthom Ltd* (1998) 87 BLR 52 (CA), and 'authorised variations' under an amended clause 8 of the Blue Form, *Costain Civil Engineering and anor* v. *Zanen Dredging and Contracting Company Ltd* (1997) 85 BLR 77 QB.

[291]   HIBBERD, PETER R. *Variations in the Construction Industry*. Collins, London, 1986, p. vii.

adjudicator's power to change the works information,[292] it is submitted that this is precisely how it will be interpreted given the broad legal meaning normally attributed to the power to review and revise.[293]

This interpretation follows from the fact that, in certain cases, the normal consequences of a decision taken or settlement by the adjudicator, *viz.* time and cost consequences, will not be appropriate to the nature of the dispute, for example, if the contractor becomes aware that the works information requires an illegal action but the project manager refuses to issue an instruction changing the works information. In this case the contractor may submit the dispute to the adjudicator. If the adjudicator agrees with the contractor, the adjudicator may review and revise the disputed inaction of the project manager and, it would seem in so doing, effect a change to the works information. The effect of the adjudicator's decision must be to change the works information, as the contractor cannot be compensated for the time and costs consequences of performing an illegal act.[294] The contractor is either relieved of the obligation to perform the contract or a change to the works information is effected which removes the cause of the illegality. If there were any further instructions which followed as a result of this decision by the adjudicator then presumably those would be issued by the project manager as changes to the works information once again under clause 14.3. The NEC choice to compensate for both cost and time is borne out ultimately with almost all provisions in a construction contract being reducible to cost, time or quality.[295]

The last topic in clause 14 sets out the right of the employer to replace the project manager or the supervisor. Notwithstanding the naming of personnel under 'key people' in part one of the Contract Data, the employer is given an unfettered right to replace them upon notice in advance to the contractor of their names.[296] When working under a target contract, such as main options C or D, J. G. Perry and P. A. Thompson would recommend possibly extending the target system to include site personnel as a necessary positive motivator.[297]

Adding to the working areas

The delineation of boundaries on a project is a matter of particular importance for both the contractor and the employer. Occupation and use

---

[292] See guidance notes NEC on clause 92.1 ECC, 78.

[293] Particularly in view of the decision of *Beaufort Developments (NI) Ltd* v. *Gilbert-Ash (NI) Ltd and ors* (1998) 88 BLR 1 (HL).

[294] This interpretation is contrary to that placed on the adjudicator's authority by the drafters: see guidance notes NEC on clause 14.3 ECC, 30.

[295] JONES, D.S., see n. 257 above, 570.

[296] See clause 14.4 ECC. See also the discussion of clause 24 ECC below. Notification must satisfy clause 13 ECC requirements..

[297] PERRY, J.G. and THOMPSON, P.A. *Target and Cost Reimbursable Construction Contracts Part A: A Study of their Use and Implications*. CIRIA, London, 1982, CIRIA Report 85, Part A (formerly CIRIA Report 56), p. 15.

as well as the ultimate availability of the entire site can be taken as minimum obligations that the employer assumes toward the contractor, notwithstanding contractual provisions which may impinge on the same such as clause 25.1 regarding sharing of the working areas by the contractor. However, the site itself may be far less than adequate for the completion of the contract. Stores and compounds, laboratories, workshops, labour camps and the like may have to be accommodated, and working areas in addition to the Site may be needed for this purpose.[298] The prospect that the space allocated for these matters is insufficient is very real and for this reason the contractor is given a right to propose that the working areas be added to.[299] The working areas are stated in part two of the Contract Data and include the site. Their descriptions in the Contract Data should be sufficient to identify them clearly. The right of the contractor in this regard is also implicitly recognized in the definition of the working areas, which concedes they may be changed under the contract.[300]

In response to the contractor's proposal, the project manager is given the choice either to accept it or not. Two reasons given for the project manager not accepting the proposal are that the proposed addition is not necessary for providing the works or the proposed area will be used for work not in the contract.[301] Reliance by the project manager upon either of these reasons to support the non-acceptance of the contractor's proposal precludes a compensation event arising.[302] The notion of reliance is, of course, important generally in contract theory.[303] The drafting convention or phrase 'not accepting' is used throughout the ECC and suggests a more passive action on the part of the project manager than refusal.[304]

The 'Working Areas' are defined as the 'working areas' unless later changed in accordance with the contract.[305] They are italicized indicating that the working areas are identified for Contract Data purposes. A change made pursuant to clause 15.1 would be a change made in accordance with the contract. However, the power of the project manager to effect a change to the working areas is not limited to clause 15.1. The contractor may also propose additional works areas in part two of the

---

[298] See section 44 SCC for additional examples.
[299] Clause 15.1 ECC.
[300] See clause 11.2(28) ECC.
[301] Clause 15.1 ECC. Under the First Edition the two reasons were joined conjunctively with the word 'and'. It is submitted that the use of two bullet points in the First Edition suggested that either reason could still operate independently of the other.
[302] Clause 13.8 ECC.
[303] Contract doctrine has paid particular attention to the importance of *reliance* in liability and damages especially following articles by Lon Fuller: see FULLER, L.L. and PERDUE JR. W.R. The Reliance Interest in Contract Damages. *Yale Law Journal*, 1936–37, **46**, 52; and FULLER, L.L. Consideration and Form. *Columbia Law Review*, 1941, **41**, 799; and more recently in work by Randy Barnett, see BARNETT, R.E. A Consent Theory of Contract. *Columbia Law Review*, 1986, **86**, 269.
[304] Refusal implies a conscious act of volition: see *Re Quintin Dick* [1926] 1 Ch 992.
[305] Clause 11.2(8) ECC.

Contract Data for temporary use for the purposes of the contract. The project manager may accept these additions to the working areas as well. It may be noted that the additions would remain subject to the obligation of the contractor to continue to co-operate with any others sharing the working areas.[306]

The identification of an area as a 'working area' has consequences with regard to title to equipment, plant and materials[307] and the schedules of cost components. With regard to the schedules of cost components, whether or not an input is included in the schedules in many instances is determined with reference to whether the input was employed directly or expended in the working areas and for what proportion of time. Thus, for example, people who are directly employed by the contractor and whose normal place of working is within the working areas, and people who are directly employed by the contractor and whose normal place of working is not within the working areas but who are nevertheless within them for a period not less than one week, are considered cost components.[308] A series of other cost components are also determined with reference to the working areas; for example, under the SCC for certain travel payments (section 1); the cost of equipment used within the working areas (section 2); certain transportation costs (section 2); certain delivery and removal costs for plant and materials (section 3); payments to utilities for provision and use in the working areas (section 4); certain rent, access charges and facilities payments (section 4); a charge for overhead costs incurred within the working areas (section 4); certain manufacture and fabrication costs (section 5); and certain design costs although done outside the working areas (section 6).

Early warning

The NEC introduces a system of early warning that requires the contractor to give notice of events that may increase the cost of or time for the work.[309] '[T]he procedure is designed to motivate the parties to ensure, so far as possible, collaborative problem-solving.'[310] Loosemore has written that the early warning system 'is an improvement on JCT 80 which allocates specific monitoring responsibilities, since it encourages project members to help each other by encouraging a recognition of the interdependency of risks'.[311] Although the terminology is new the

---

[306]   See clause 25.1 ECC.

[307]   See clauses 70 and 71 ECC.

[308]   SCC and SSCC ECC, section 1.

[309]   Cf the early warning obligation imposed on the employer under clause 16.1 of the PSC First Edition although only with regard to matters which could change the prices or accepted programme as defined.

[310]   PERRY, JOHN G. The New Engineering Contract: Principles of Design and Risk Allocation. *Engineering, Construction and Architectural Management*, 1995, **2**(3), 201.

[311]   See LOOSEMORE, MARTIN. Dealing with Unexpected Problems – Do Contracts Help? A Comparison of the NEC and JCT 80 Forms. *Engineering, Construction and Architectural Management*, 1994, **1**(2), 130.

concept of early notice of potential problems is not new in standard forms;[312] nor, for that matter, is the inclusion of a sanction.[313] The absence of a similar obligation upon consultants acting under the JCT forms has been the subject of criticism.[314] Where the NEC differs from these other forms is in so clearly, closely and unequivocally relating these concepts. As such, it may also more effectively serve to reduce disputes, the single provision serving to reinforce the contractor's obligation and understanding of it.

> Many contracts provide that the contractor must give notice of claims when the incident arises. The clause on early warning in the New Engineering Contract deserves particular mention. In the context of variation orders, it allows the employer to reconsider such an order if the consequences of which the contractor gives warning are out of proportion with the expected advantages of the variation. At that stage, when the variation order is made, it is often still possible to avoid or clearly circumscribe a dispute which, if it arises later, may be bitter and costly.[315]

The context for the early warning system can be best understood against the original early warning provisions in the Consultation Document. In that Document, while the early warning system was still separate it was also reinforced by a system of 'Management Meetings'.[316] As with early warning meetings in the ECC, either the project manager or the contractor could require the other to attend one of these management meetings.[317] The 'business' or agenda of the management meeting expressly included dealing with early warnings and reviewing plans for the remaining work.[318] The effect of early warnings being considered both separately from, as well as a necessary component of, the management meeting served to underscore their centrality and importance within the NEC. Although clause 16 in the Second Edition of the ECC reproduces some of the content of the original management meeting clause, the removal of the *dual* context in which early warnings were set lessens the management stimulus that would have been achieved overall. While no reasons are given for this change it may have been felt by the drafters that the reference to a 'management meeting' had connotations that were best left out of subsequent editions of the form. This is despite the fact that the

---

[312] Cf clause 12 ICE 6th and clauses 25 and 26 JCT 80.

[313] Cf clause 14(8) ICE 6th which could result in additional delays and costs being found to have not been unavoidably incurred.

[314] See LOOSEMORE, MARTIN, n. 311 above, 123–124.

[315] SCHNEIDER, MICHAEL E. Mastering the Interfaces – Construction Contracts Drafting for Dispute Avoidance. *International Construction Law Review*, 1993, 410 (ns. omitted).

[316] See clause 15.1 Consultation Document, 14.

[317] Clause 15.1 Consultation Document, 14.

[318] Clause 15.2 Consultation Document, 14; remaining work included appointments of subcontractors and work by the employer and other people.

project manager or the contractor retained the right to summon the other for an 'early warning meeting'.[319] It would seem that, with stimulus to good management an express objective of the NEC and general agreement that 'good' management practices today include regular meetings where early warnings would most certainly play a part, removal was premature.

> The meeting structure will depend upon the nature and complexity of the project as well as who will be chairman, who will attend, their duration, style and frequency. All meetings should have a mission, a standard agenda, a checklist and an attendee list. In addition '[r]egular project progress meetings ... provide a suitable forum where essential two-way communication can take place between planners and participants. The main purposes of the progress meetings emerge as a means of keeping periodic check on the project progress, and the making of any consequential decisions to implement corrective action if programme slippages occur or appear likely.[320]

The purpose of the early warning procedure as currently framed is clear from clause 16.1 of the ECC. That is, to impose an obligation upon *both* the contractor and the project manager to give an early warning by notifying the other as soon as either one becomes aware of any matter which could either increase the total of the prices, delay completion, or impair the performance of the works in use.[321] The true importance of mutuality has been emphasized by Martin Loosemore:

> Thus clause 16.1 gives much wider responsibility for monitoring to both the project manager and the contractor, than JCT 80 does. Rather than highlighting specific events the responsibility is expanded to any event that could affect performance. The use of the word 'could' is important since it emphasizes the need to look out for potential problems ... The lack of distinction made between the contractor's monitoring responsibilities and those of the manager of the project represents one of the major differences and advances over the JCT 80 provisions.[322]

It can be seen from this that three subjects are material and pertain respectively to *cost, timing of completion* and *quality of the works in use*. It has been noted in the early use of the NEC that contractors often invoked the early warning procedures unnecessarily; however, more recent experience would suggest the procedures are increasingly being used more in accordance with the drafters' original intentions.[323]

---

[319]   Under clause 16.2 ECC.

[320]   LOCK, DENNIS. Resource Scheduling. In *Gower Handbook of Project Management*, 2nd edn. Gower, Aldershot, 1994, p. 223.

[321]   Clause 16.1 ECC.

[322]   LOOSEMORE, MARTIN, see n. 311 above, 130.

[323]   That is, in the three situations pertaining to time, cost and quality: an estimate made by Ernest J. Bayton.

One interesting aspect of the early warning procedures is that they actually operate on twin tracks. Thus, it creates a mandatory obligation on both the project manager's and contractor's parts to give an early warning by notifying the other in the designated cases. The notification itself would have to comply with clause 13 requirements. In addition to this mandatory track there is a second or twin track which operates permissively. According to the twin track either the project manager or the contractor may instruct[324] other people[325] to attend an early warning meeting.[326]

Thus there are two potential sets of instructions that may be issued, one mandatory with respect to designated events, and one permissive insofar as who else may be instructed to attend. The first instruction is also mandatory in terms of the obligation of the contractor to obey it if given in accordance with the contract.[327] The second instruction remains permissive in the sense of the instructing party being required to obtain the consent[328] of the other to the attendance of the other people.[329] It should be added that, if the result of any such early warning meeting is that a compensation event has either happened or is expected to happen, then formal notification under clause 61 should be given.

Disincentives are employed to ensure that the early warning procedure is respected; in particular, regarding the first of the twin track procedures. Thus, if the project manager decides that the contractor did not give an early warning of an event which an experienced contractor could have given[330] it will be taken into account in the assessment of any relevant cost and time risk allowances.[331] The assumption underlying the disincentives is that the early warning might have allowed actions to be taken which would have reduced the effects of the event in terms of cost and time or end quality of the works in use.

It is incumbent upon the project manager to notify the contractor, if the project manager decides that the contractor did not submit an early warning, when instructions are given regarding submitting quotations for dealing with the event.[332] If this notification is given the project manager can deal with the assessment of the event *as if* the contractor had given an early warning.[333] The effect of this is to reallocate time and cost risks to

---

[324] The language of 'instruction' is not usually seen in relation to actions of the contractor; it is also used in clause 87.1 ECC.

[325] 'Other people' is used intentionally to distinguish it from 'others' as defined in clause 11.2(2) ECC: guidance notes NEC on clause 11.2(2) ECC, 27.

[326] Clause 16.2 ECC.

[327] Clause 29.1 ECC.

[328] Consent itself is a relative term: see BRILMAYER, L. Consent, Contract and Territory. *Minnesota Law Review*, 1989, **74**, 1.

[329] Clause 16.2 ECC.

[330] Clause 61.5 ECC.

[331] Clause 63.4 ECC.

[332] Clause 61.5 ECC.

[333] Clause 63.4 ECC.

the contractor earlier than may have otherwise been the case. Thus, the contractor will receive potentially less compensation than if an early warning had been given. The disincentive for the project manager in failing to give an early warning is not expressed in the same way as for the contractor. However, it can be assumed that the project manager will wish to act in the best interests of the employer by seeking to address any events which may impact upon the designated matters as soon as such events are noticed. If this disincentive is not viewed as a sufficient deterrent, another interpretation could treat it as a breach of contract for which the employer would be liable.[334] Overall the quotation procedure should not simply provide an incentive for opportunistic behaviour. In literature on the adaptation of contractual obligations it has been observed that 'allowing recontracting may facilitate the reallocation of initially efficiently assigned risks. This leads to moral hazard problems that may attenuate incentives for efficient risk minimization ... by the party who subsequently seeks modification'.[335]

At any early warning meeting all those who attend are under an express duty of co-operation,[336] although the duty cannot necessarily be enforced contractually with regard to the 'other people' (clause 16.2), who may be instructed to attend by either the contractor or project manager and who are not privy to an NEC contract. The attendees are obliged to co-operate in three respects:

- making and considering proposals for how the effect of each matter which has been notified as an early warning can be avoided or reduced;
- seeking solutions that will bring advantage to all those who will be affected; and
- deciding upon actions to be taken, and who, in accordance with the contract, will take them.[337]

The structure of the clause is logical. The obligees are first asked to make and consider proposals which seek to avoid or reduce the adverse consequences of events from the cost, time of completion or quality in the use of the works regards. In the second instance the obligees are encouraged to seek 'win-win'[338] proposals put forward, while in the third

---

[334]   O'REILLY, MICHAEL. *Civil Engineering Construction Contracts*. Thomas Telford, London, 1996, p. 317. O'Reilly suggests it may reverse the position at common law under both *East Ham Borough Council* v. *Bernard Sunley & Sons Ltd* [1966] AC 406, [1965] 3 All ER 559, HL, and *AMF International Ltd* v. *Magnet Bowling Ltd* [1968] 2 All ER 789, [1968] 1 WLR 1028: O'Reilly above, p. 317, n. 19.

[335]   AIVAZIAN, V.A. The Law of Contract Modifications: The Uncertain Quest for a Benchmark of Enforceability. *Osgoode Hall Law Journal*, 1984, **22**, 175.

[336]   Clause 16.3 ECC.

[337]   Clause 16.3 ECC.

[338]   The Latham Report paragraph 5.18(2), 37 provided: '[f]irm duties of teamwork, with shared financial motivation to pursue those objectives. These should involve a general presumption to achieve "win-win" solutions to problems which may arise during the course of the project'; and paragraph 5.20(4): 'Core Clause 16.3 should be strengthened to make it clear that "win-win" solutions to problems will be devised

instance the obligees are asked to set clear lines of responsibility for carrying out any of the proposals. Given that the issue of responsibility for taking an action must be determined in accordance with the contract[339] those present at an early warning meeting may be unable to reallocate the responsibilities save on the basis of mutual consent.

The project manager will act as the secretary at the early warning meeting.[340] The proposals that are considered at the meeting and any decisions which are taken must be recorded by the project manager and a copy of the record provided for the contractor.[341] Although no express affirmative obligation is imposed upon the project manager to provide the record to the contractor contemporaneously with the meeting clearly it would have to be given soon enough after the meeting to be meaningful. A record is one of the eight designated modes of exchanging information under the contract and qualifies as a communication within clause 13 of the ECC. Paradoxically, the record as referred to in clause 16.4 will contain 'decisions' which also fall within clause 13 as a communication. It is suggested that the period for reply in the contract[342] would be a reasonable guide to decide the time frame for the project manager to provide a copy of the record to the contractor, even though it is not directly applicable to this situation. Quite apart from the role of the record in this regard it may be important in other respects as well, for instance, in dealing with the 'open texture in language and approximation involved in legal methods' which Phillip Capper has referred to as 'shortcomings'.[343] Thus the 'identification, collection and maintenance of records [afford g]ood and cogent evidence of pertinent data [that] will reduce levels of uncertainty in the contractual risk assessment'.[344] In general a survey of arbitrators has concluded that the party keeping the most detailed *records* holds a decided advantage in any later dispute resolution proceedings.[345]

The early warning procedures and the duties imposed as a result thereof raise parallels with the duty of a person to warn in general under certain circumstances. Thus, for instance, duties have been imposed upon contractors to warn of defective designs. There is jurisprudence that considers the issue or the duty of a contractor to warn the employer in certain circumstances normally associated with unsuitable or defective

in a spirit of partnership'. Martin Barnes holds out that this was always the intention of the early warning procedure although in the Second Edition the obligation was made more explicit: The New Engineering Contract – An Update, n. 9 above, 93.

[339] Clause 16.3 ECC.

[340] Clause 16.4 ECC.

[341] Clause 16.4 ECC. Cf the requirement for monthly progress reports in clause 4.15 FIDIC Orange Book 1st part I.

[342] Clauses 13.3, 13.4 and 13.5 ECC.

[343] CAPPER, PROFESSOR PHILLIP. Management of Legal Risks in Construction. A paper given to the Society of Construction Law at a meeting in Wales on 21 September 1994.

[344] *Ibid.*

[345] KANGARI, R. Risk Management Perceptions and Trends of US Construction. *Journal of Construction Engineering and Management*, 1995, **121**, 422–429.

designs.[346] Although there is not a consistent body of case law supporting the duty to warn[347] it should be expected that arguments based on this case law will eventually be put forward concerning failures to give early warnings. It could also be argued that the imposition of a duty to warn upon a contractor working under the NEC is more warranted than when working under traditional forms of contract that continue to perpetuate a dichotomy between design and construction. The argument is that under the traditional forms a duty to warn should not be implied at least upon the basis of necessity under *The Moorcock* because it cannot be said to be necessary to make the contract work.[348] Further, that the duty of co-operation under clause 10 also arguably provides a stronger basis for imposing a duty to warn than under other forms. *Hudson's*, for example, raises both the duty of co-operation in general as well as the workmanship obligation as possible rationales for a duty to warn.[349] Therefore, taking these points together, it can readily be argued that the NEC contractor is under a duty to warn (at least) in those cases of design defects which there is reason to believe exist.

Ambiguities and inconsistencies

Pursuant to clause 17.1, either the project manager or the contractor must notify the other as soon as there is awareness of an ambiguity or inconsistency in or between the contract documents.[350] Thus, when an ambiguity or inconsistency is noticed in this regard the project manager has the responsibility to issue an instruction to resolve it.[351] Similar provision is made in other forms.[352] From that time the contractor is under an obligation to obey the instruction if it has been given in accordance with the contract.[353] If the instruction involves a change to the works information it may entail a compensation event.[354] It is submitted that unintentional additions or omissions from the contract documents could entail ambiguities or inconsistencies as these terms are

[346]   See notably *Equitable Debenture Assets Corpn Ltd* v. *William Moss & Ors.* Construction Law Journal, 1984, **1**, 131; *Victoria University of Manchester* v. *Hugh Wilson & Lewis Wormersley (A firm)*. Construction Law Journal, 1984, **1**, 162.

[347]   See e.g. *University Court of the University of Glasgow* v. *William Whitfield and John Laing (Construction) Ltd (Third party)* (1988) 42 BLR 66; *Oxford University Press* v. *John Stedman Design Group & Ors* (1990) 34 Con LR 1; and *Chesham Properties Ltd* v. *Bucknall Austin Project Management Services Ltd and Ors* (1997) 82 BLR 92. See generally WILSON, S. and RUTHERFORD, L. Design Defects in Building Contracts: A Contractor's Duty to Warn? *Construction Law Journal*, 1994, **10**, p. 90.

[348]   See *Hudson's*, vol. 1, p. 546.

[349]   *Ibid.*

[350]   Notification must satisfy clause 13 ECC requirements.

[351]   Clause 17.1 ECC. Similar provision is made in other forms, see e.g. clauses 1.5 ACA/ BPF, 13 ICE 6th, 5.3 FIDIC 4th, 2.3 JCT 89 and 2 GC/Works/1 3rd.

[352]   See e.g. clauses 1.5 ACA/BPF, 13 ICE 6th, 5.3 FIDIC 4th, 2.3 JCT 89 and 2 GC/ Works/1 3rd.

[353]   See clause 29.1 ECC.

[354]   Clause 60.1(1), see also clause 63.7 on assessment.

understood and thus could be corrected using the same instruction procedure.

Ambiguities and inconsistencies among provisions in various contract documents pose a significant source of disputes. One manner of seeking to avoid these problems has been through priority of document clauses, or precedence of documents clauses in US terminology. Clause 2.2.1 of the JCT 1980 form is a good example of such a priority of documents clause and provides that the articles, conditions and appendix take priority over the contract bills.[355] The JCT provision, however, is incomplete in that questions surrounding other contract documents are left unaddressed.[356] The ICE 6th form has taken a different approach, preferring to state in clause 5 that 'the documents forming the Contract are to be taken as mutually explanatory of one another. . .'.[357] This approach is closer to the ECC's and thus the clause does not outline a strict hierarchy or priority for the contract documents.

By way of comparison FIDIC 4th adopts a hybrid approach to document priority. Thus, in one respect, no priority is indicated given the wording in clause 5.2 that the 'several documents forming the Contract are to be taken as mutually explanatory of one another'. However, on the other hand, once any ambiguities or discrepancies have arisen then a strict priority scheme is enumerated. In this way FIDIC 4th is unusual in listing a scheme of priority for all relevant documents.[358] The FIDIC preordained system of priority is subject to amendment or deletion according to the parties' wishes in the form's particular conditions.[359] The ECC, ICE 6th and FIDIC 4th all use the term 'ambiguities',[360] with the latter two forms also coupling that term with 'discrepancies', which arguably, has a narrower meaning than 'ambiguities'.[361] The ECC couples the term 'ambiguities' instead with 'inconsistencies'. A comparison of dictionary definitions for these terms arguably only places their differences no higher than semantic. The JCT and ECC clauses make clear that ambiguities or

---

[355] See e.g. *English Industrial Estates Corpn* v. *George Wimpey & Co Ltd* [1973] 1 Lloyd's Rep 118, CA; *Gold* v. *Patman and Fotheringham Ltd* [1958] 2 All ER 497, [1958] 1 WLR 697, CA; and *North West Metropolitan Regional Hospital Board* v. *T A Bickerton & Son Ltd* [1970] 1 All ER 1039, [1970] 1 WLR 607. JCT 80 addresses discrepancies in or divergences between documents in clause 2.3.

[356] Vincent Powell-Smith called for the elimination of clause 2.2.1 JCT 80 because it contradicts the normal rule of interpretation that specially prepared conditions take precedence over printed conditions in the event of a conflict: Blight within JCT 80. *Contract Journal*, 26 June 1994, 14.

[357] FIDIC 4th uses similar language but does adopt priority of documents.

[358] Clause 5.2: '(1) the Contract Agreement (if completed); (2) The Letter of Acceptance; (3) The Tender; (4) Part II of these Conditions; (5) Part I of these Conditions; and (6) Any other document forming part of the Contract'.

[359] See clause 5.2 FIDIC 4th. An example is also given in the particular conditions as to the wording that may be adopted when no order of preference is intended.

[360] ACA 2 clause 1.5 also uses the term 'ambiguities'.

[361] Under clause 1.8 JCT NSC/C the subcontractor is obliged to notify the contractor of discrepancies in or divergences between any two or more documents.

inconsistencies may arise not just 'between' documents, but 'in' any one document as well.[362] As such, the ECC wording appears to extend beyond the issue of priority of documents which clauses of this type are typically limited to.

The intention of the ECC clause appears to be to ensure that action is taken to address ambiguities or inconsistencies as soon as the project manager or contractor becomes aware[363] of them. The ambiguities or discrepancies are addressed through instructions of the project manager rather than through attempts to ascertain what the mutual intentions of the parties were at the time of contracting or the artificial listing of a notional priority. Additional conditions included under secondary option Z would be in a no different or higher priority position by virtue of being *additional* conditions. Once an ambiguity or inconsistency is noticed in the contract documents, if the project manager issues an instruction to resolve it by changing the works information, the matter is treated as a compensation event[364] and assessed depending upon whether the works information was originally provided by the employer or the contractor. If the works information was provided by the employer and is changed, the effect of the compensation event is assessed as if the prices and the completion date were for the interpretation most favourable to the contractor.[365] If the works information was provided by the contractor and is changed, the effect of the compensation event is assessed as if the prices and the completion date were for the interpretation most favourable to the employer.[366] The effect of these rules of interpretation and assessment is that only in the first case, where the works information was provided by the employer, is the project manager's instruction resolving the ambiguity or inconsistency likely to be treated as a compensation event.[367] This approach is tantamount to prioritizing the employer's

---

[362] Clause 2.3 JCT 1980, and clause 17.1 ECC. See also clause 1.8 JCT NSC/C imposing a like obligation on the subcontractor to notify the contractor in such cases. It may be noted that JCT 80 also uses the term 'divergences' in clauses 2.3 and 6.1 particularly regarding statutory requirements. Lately, in *Copthorne Hotel (Newcastle) Ltd* v. *Arup Associates* (1998) 85 BLR 22 the Court at first instance and the Court of Appeal subsequently dealt with ambiguity arising between two provisions of JCT 87: clauses 1.7 and 3.21. In a detailed analysis by Judge Hicks, endorsed broadly by the Court of Appeal, general principles of construction were employed to resolve the ambiguity.

[363] In contrast to the ECC wording JCT 80 qualifies the necessity to take action by introducing the clause with the word 'if' and which has led to a measure of ambiguity over whether the contractor must find them or not.

[364] Clause 60.1 ECC.

[365] Clause 63.7 ECC. This is an application of the *contra proferentem* rule of interpretation. The employer may provide works information in part one of the Contract Data, section 1. See generally on the operation of the rule, LAWSON, RICHARD. *Exclusion Clauses and Unfair Contract Terms*, 4th edn. FT Law and Tax, London, 1995, pp. 26–43.

[366] Clause 63.7 ECC. The contractor may provide works information in part two of the Contract Data.

[367] See guidance notes NEC on clause 17.1 ECC, 31.

works information (part one of the Contract Data) ahead of the contractor's works information (part two of the Contract Data). The effect of this choice is also seen in the operation of the contractor's share provisions.

One aspect of the ECC provisions which has not been addressed is how to deal with ambiguities or inconsistencies in or between instructions themselves. The instructions are seen as the tool to address these issues without conceding that they may too be creative of the issues. One form that has sought to address this is the JCT/MT form. Under JCT/MT a system of priority coding for orders, which would include instructions,[368] issued under the contract has been adopted. Pursuant to clause 2.2 all orders must state a commencement date and a reasonable date for completion unless subject to any priority coding. It can be seen that the intent is to address priority issues in the limited sense of timing. However, it is submitted that the provision is a model in two respects. First, it recognizes that priority issues arise in relation to orders or instructions. Secondly, the system of priority coding could usefully have broader applications than timing alone. A similar reciprocal obligation is imposed on the employer and consultant under the PSC and the model would appear to warrant extension to other NEC contract system documents. In this case the obligation then falls upon the employer to give an instruction to resolve the ambiguity or inconsistency (clause 16.1 of the PSC, First Edition).

Health and safety

An obligation to comply with health and safety requirements that are agreed and set out in the works information is expressly imposed upon the contractor in clause 18.1.[369] The clause thus expressly imposes responsibility upon the contractor in both these regards, and indirectly underscores the contractor's statutory obligations.[370] However, it should be noted that this is not a compliance with laws clause as that term is generally understood. This is because clause 18 only imposes an obligation with those health and safety requirements stated in the works information. In practice the employer may decide to incorporate a full compliance with laws clause in the works information to address this.

---

[368] The JCT/MT form uses the term 'order' both in place of and in addition to 'variation' also: see clauses 1.1, 2.1, 2.2, and 3.6.

[369] Cf Works Contract/1 section 2: tender requiring the works contractor to attach a health and safety policy as well as give notice of any potential hazards in carrying out the works and the precautions to be taken against such hazards; and FIDIC 4th clause 19.1 imposing not only a safety obligation on the contractor regarding all persons on site but to protect the environment as well.

[370] For example, the Health and Safety at Work etc. Act 1974. The Act imposes duties on employers to ensure the health, safety and welfare of their employees so far as reasonably practical: section 2. See generally *Halsbury's Statutes*, 4th edn. vol. 19, Health and Safety etc. at Work; *Halsbury's Laws of England*, 4th edn. reissue, vol. 20, paragraphs 401ff.

Both are consistent with the contractor having possession of the site.[371] It is also consistent with the contractor's responsibility to insure for liability for death or bodily injury to employees arising out of and in the course of their employment in connection with the contract.[372] In this way it makes a small departure from English statutory obligations which also impose responsibilities upon consultants on site.[373]

There are several important changes in the provision from the Consultation Document. First, the clause now addresses 'Health' and safety. Formerly, only safety was expressly referred to both in the heading or marginal note and in the text of the clause. This indicates the contractors' responsibilities have been added to and that the health and safety obligations should not be viewed synonymously. Secondly, there has been a deletion of clause 18.2. This clause provided that the employer, project manger, contractor or supervisor could instruct a change to the conduct of the work when any one of them decided that there was a risk of injury to people or damage to the works or other property. This language is clearly evocative of tort concepts and it may have been deleted as superfluous. Concise conditions are preferred over superfluous interpretations and serve as an important factor in the reduction of risk.[374]

There are other reasons why clause 18.2 may have been deleted. Perhaps it came too close to imposing an affirmative duty to warn; a duty that appeared to be imposed problematically upon all those involved, and notwithstanding their different degrees of involvement. It is one of the very few instances when a contractor could purport to instruct a change (although the contractor is able to 'instruct' the project manager to attend an early warning meeting). The change itself was to be as to the conduct against the method of the work. The significance in the use of this different wording is also unclear. Thus for these and perhaps other reasons the clause may have been simply too problematic to remain in the subsequent editions of the ECC. It is suggested that, if a clear intention can be discerned from clause 18.2 to reduce the risk of injury in carrying out the work, then it would have been prudent to have also included a short clause to that effect in the early warning procedures in clause 16.

Notwithstanding the deletion of clause 18.2, all employers still owe duties of care toward their employees to ensure the employee's safety.[375] Although distinctions are made between employees and truly independent contractors the duty has been extended beyond the bounds of direct contractual relationships. Thus contractors have been found to owe duties of care toward and with regard to the safety of subcontractors'

---

[371] Clause 33 ECC.
[372] Clause 84.2 and insurance table ECC.
[373] See the Health and Safety at Work etc. Act 1974, sections 2 and 3.
[374] See BUBSHAIT, ABDULAZIZ A. and ALMOHAWIS, SOLIMAN A. Evaluating the General Conditions of a Construction Contract. *International Journal of Project Management*, 1994, **12**(3), 134.
[375] *Wilsons and Clyde Coal Co Ltd* v. *English* [1938] AC 57, [1937] 3 All ER 628, HL.

employees.[376] At common law duties have been imposed with respect to the effectiveness of supervision,[377] the adequacy of materials[378] and the competency of staff.[379] In all cases the duty is that of reasonable care. Clause 18.1 does not purport to regulate liability for breach of statutory duties, which remain subject to criminal or quasi-criminal prosecutions as well as civil actions. In practice many of the details regarding the health and safety requirements of the employer will be specifically set out in the works information, e.g. safety officers, safety plans, safety training, safety policies etc.[380]

Additional health and safety requirements are imposed for United Kingdom contracts that are now subject to the Construction (Design and Management) Regulations 1994 (CDM Regulations).[381] The CDM Regulations created a new role player in construction: the 'planning supervisor'. The planning supervisor is responsible for ensuring that projects are designed safely. The NEC takes the regulations into account without putting the planning supervisor on the team. Given the fact that this role also significantly entails improving communications between other members of the team, it would seem that recognition of the planning supervisor's role and responsibility should be express in any new edition of the contract and perhaps notwithstanding it is an international form.

The timing of the introduction of the CDM Regulations being roughly when the Second Edition of the NEC was being released has perhaps given rise to a small problem of application. The CDM Regulations apply to eligible contracts in the United Kingdom; however, they are included and referred to only as a secondary option clause in the ECC. In fact, the heading for option U seems to suggest it must be used as it provides 'to be used for contracts in the UK'. The guidance notes confirm this view and provide 'this option should be used wherever the regulations apply'. This provision, however, is contrary to the intent of the drafters that the use of any of the secondary options is indeed optional. The ECC itself provides

---

[376] *McArdle* v. *Andmac Roofing Co* [1967] 1 All ER 583, [1967] 1 WLR 356, CA.

[377] See *Bett* v. *Dalmeny Oil Co* (1907) 7 F 787 at 790, Ct of Sess, per Lord McLaren; *Wilsons and Clyde Coal Co Ltd* v. *English* [1938] AC 57 at 78, [1937] 3 All ER 628 at 640, HL, per Lord Wright.

[378] See *Wilsons and Clyde Coal Co Ltd* v. *English* [1938] AC 57 at 78, [1937] 3 All ER 628 at 640, HL, per Lord Wright; *Knowles* v. *Liverpool City Council* [1993] 4 All ER 321 at 324, [1993] 1 WLR 1428 at 1431, HL, per Lord Jauncey of Tullichettle.

[379] See *Hudson* v. *Ridge Manufacturing Co Ltd* [1957] 2 QB 348, [1957] 2 All ER 229.

[380] Cf the use of '*health and safety requirements*' as an identified term in clause 17.1 PSC First Edition and specifically referring to section 1 part one of the Contract Data in the PSC.

[381] The CDM Regulations implement the Temporary or Mobile Construction Sites Directive, 92/57/EEC (OJ L245, 25 August 1992) as amended. The CDM Regulations and an Approved Code of Practice came into force on 31 March 1995. The Health and Safety Executive has also approved a Code of Practice for use with the CDM Regulations which came into effect on the same date. See generally HENDERSON, DAVID and PARRY, GARETH. *Construction (Design & Management) Regulations 1994.* Sweet & Maxwell, London, 1996.

on page 1 under the heading 'Schedule of Options': 'The following secondary options should then be considered. It is not necessary to use any of them. Any combination other than those stated may be used'. If this is the case what possible explanations could be given for the situation? Two explanations may be suggested:

- it is likely that the drafters intended to keep the form as 'international' as possible and thus removed clauses peculiar to the United Kingdom to the secondary option clauses for this reason; or
- the drafters intended the subject matter of option U – when a compensation event arises as a result of the CDM Regulations – to be mandatory.

The first explanation is similar to the difficulties in allowing for changes to several clauses in the Second Edition as well as a result of the Housing Grants, Construction and Regeneration Act 1996. In the case of this legislation the changes have similarly been dealt with as a secondary option clause.[382] Despite these possible explanations the secondary option clause still seems out of place with other peculiar and applicable United Kingdom health and safety legislation for which no express reference or allowance has been made in the form.[383]

The CDM secondary option clause also raises other issues. According to clause U1.1, a delay to the work or additional or changed work caused as a result of the application of the CDM Regulations is a compensation event if an experienced contractor could not reasonably be expected to have foreseen it. This is a novel provision and it has been suggested that it may restrict contractors' entitlements rather than enlarge them because of the imposition of a foreseeability requirement.[384] It is a fair criticism of the clause that its subject matter is already rationally dealt with under the main compensation events. Hence the clause may be either limiting or

---

[382] It may be that a United Kindom version of the form should be separately issued to cater for either option U and/or option Y.

[383] Notably the Health and Safety at Work etc. Act 1974, the Management of Health and Safety at Work Regulations 1992, SI 1992/2051, and its approved Code of Practice, and the Provision and Use of Work Equipment Regulations 1992, SI 1992/2932. This point may be further underscored with more recent legislation, notably the Construction (Health, Safety and Welfare) Regulations 1996, SI 1996/1592, which were made under the Health and Safety at Work etc. Act 1974 and implement another part of the Council Directive 92/57 (OJ L245, 25 August 1992) imposing further requirements with respect to the subject in addition to the CDM Regulations. The Management of Health and Safety at Work Regulations 1992 primarily implemented the EEC Framework Directive, 89/391/EEC (OJ L183, 29 June 1989) regarding the introduction of measures to encourage improvements in the health and safety of workers at work. A series of other directives, sometimes referred to as 'daughter directives' has also been developed under the Framework Directive which may be directly relevant to construction law: see *Redgrave, Fife & Machin: Health and Safety* (eds HENDY, JOHN *et al.*) 2nd edn. Butterworths, London, 1993, pp. lviii–lxiii.

[384] EGGLESTON. *The New Engineering Contract, A Commentary*, Blackwell Science, London, 1996, referring to unquoted sources at 45.

superfluous on these interpretations. The CDM Regulations should not as a whole, however, detract from contractors' entitlements under the ECC.[385]

Under the PSC both the employer and the consultant are required to act in accordance with health and safety requirements.[386] In this regard the CDM Regulations stipulate both a health and safety plan and health and safety file. The health and safety plan serves important purposes both before and during construction. In the pre-construction phase it serves to bring together relevant information from a variety of sources. During the construction phase it will integrate health and safety policies and assessments, details in administration, and management of the related risks. The health and safety file is developed over the course of construction and intended to be used post-construction during the project's remaining life. It becomes a record that subsequently informs the user on all aspects of the project relating to health and safety.[387] The position here is that both the plan and file are tailor-made for and easily accommodated within the NEC framework.[388] This appears to be unlike some other forms of contract which have had to amend or supplement their current documentation as a result of the changes. The JCT originally addressed the CDM Regulations by Amendment 17 together with Practice Note 27 envisaging the contractor taking on the role of 'principal contractor' under the regulations and the architect assuming the role of 'planning supervisor'. The amending clause adds a new relevant event to the form which would appear to entitle the contractor to additional time and money under the contract with respect to actions of the architect as planning supervisor. If this interpretation is correct it would be similar to the effect of secondary option U of the ECC.[389] Lastly, the CDM Regulations also promote information technology in construction in the same way as project management does with both increasingly relying upon software[390] for their administration. In this

[385] *CDM Regulations – Case Study Guidance for Designers: An Interim Report*. CIRIA, London, March 1995, CIRIA Report 145, 3.

[386] Clause 17.1 PSC First Edition.

[387] For examples of how the health and safety plan and health and safety file may be developed see *The CDM Design Regulations: A Design Risk Assessment* (eds WILLIAMS, BRENIG and TUBBS, DAVE). Blackwell Science, Oxford, 1996.

[388] See *Managing Construction for Health and Safety: Construction (Design and Management) Regulations 1994 Approved Code of Practice L54*. HSE Books, HMSO, London, 1995; and see also on the health and safety plan and health and safety file, *A Guide to Managing Health and Safety in Construction*. HSE Books, HMSO, London, 1995, Appendices 2 and 4.

[389] RIBA has produced a new form of appointment: *Conditions of Engagement for the Appointment of an Architect*, CE/95; see also *Engaging an Architect: Guidance for Clients on Health and Safety: the CDM Regulations 1994*; *Form of Application as Planning Supervisor*, PS/95; and the CDM Supplement, SFA/92.

[390] For example, *Planning Supervisor*, one of four programs released by WMB Building Software Solutions, in association with Lewis & Hickey Project Management. See DAVIDSON, MALCOLM. Safety Net. *Building*, January 1996, **12**, 36 for a favourable review of the Planning Supervisor software.

sense too the impact of the CDM Regulations on the NEC should be self-reinforcing.

Illegality and impossibility

The ECC addresses both illegality and impossibility expressly in one provision that divides into two parts.[391] The traditional rule in English law with regard to the effects of illegality in a contract is one of non-recovery under *Holman* v. *Johnson* and *Vandyck* v. *Hewitt*.[392] The rule is also expressed by the Latin maxim *in pari delicto potior est conditio possidentis defendentis*.[393] While this represents the current law it remains subject to a very large exception; a claim may stand notwithstanding the illegality provided it is *not* the basis for the recovery.[394] The consequence of so large an exception has left the English law, in the view of one senior judge, to be in a 'confused and unsatisfactory state'.[395] The clear contradiction has lately prompted a call by Lord Goff in *Tinsley* v. *Milligan*[396] for legislative reform with a view to the New Zealand experience and that jurisdiction's passage of an Illegal Contracts Act in 1970.[397] It is against this background that the ECC provision will be construed.

Pursuant to the first part of clause 19.1 the contractor is under an obligation to notify the project manager as soon as he or she becomes aware that the works information requires an act which is illegal or impossible. A similar obligation is imposed on the consultant under clause 18.1 of the PSC, First Edition, in which case, if the employer agrees, the consultant will issue an instruction to change the brief accordingly. Both the notification of the contractor and any reply of the project manager must satisfy clause 13 of the ECC requirements. Under the second part of clause 19.1, if the project manager agrees with the contractor, then the project manager must give an instruction to change appropriately the works information. It follows that if the contractor has satisfied the clause requirements and the project manager issues the appropriate instruction changing the works information that the compensation procedures would be applicable.[398] However, before this

---

[391] Cf the unusual provision in JCT MW clause 5 excusing the contractor from liability for non-compliance with statutory requirements where it results from carrying out the work in accordance with the contract or any instruction of the architect/contract administrator.

[392] *Holman* v. *Johnson* (1775) 1 Cowp 341; and *Vandyck* v. *Hewitt* (1800) 1 East 96.

[393] Broom, Max 290, 729.

[394] *Bowmakers Ltd* v. *Barnet Instruments Ltd* [1945] KB 65, [1944] 2 All ER 579, CA.

[395] *Bedford Insurance Co* v. *Instituto de Resseguros do Brasil* [1985] QB 966 at 983, [1984] 3 All ER 766 at 773 per Parker J.

[396] *Tinsley* v. *Milligan* [1993] 3 All ER 65 at 80, HL.

[397] See generally SUTTON, R.J. Illegal Contracts Act 1970. *Recent Law Review*, 1972, 28; and COOTE, B. The Contracts and Commercial Law Reform Committee and the Contract Statutes. *New Zealand University Law Review*, 1988, **13**, 160.

[398] See clause 60.1(1) and the notification procedures in clause 61 ECC.

result would pertain, two important limitations in the clause would have to be overcome.

First, the express reference to the works information operates as a limitation on the applicability of clause 19.1. Thus, to invoke the clause and the exception that it affords, the contractor must demonstrate the contention of illegality or impossibility *with reference to* the works information. A contention of illegality or impossibility at large would be irrelevant and specifics must be given if the contractor is to succeed on this ground. Secondly, the necessity for the project manager actually to agree to the contention *prior* to issuing any instruction dealing with this ground is a further limitation on the scope of the provision. It would not be surprising in practice if a contention that something is impossible, for instance, is met with a denial. A. A. Kwakye makes the same point: '[t]he NEC standard form of contract is silent on some important points such as ... should a project manager decline to consent to the issue of instructions to change illegal or impossible work'.[399] This is in fact much closer to the common law position and the one that implicitly supports the employer's position.[400] It is more likely that the works information would have ended up imposing financially impossible demands which, unfortunately for the contractor, would fall outside the provision. Lastly, assuming that the two limitations referred to can be overcome by the contractor, the end result is not the remedy that normally would necessarily accompany a finding of illegality or impossibility. Instead, by establishing one or the other of the grounds the contractor only becomes entitled to a change to the works information. In this way clause 19.1 differs significantly from both the common law and the provisions of certain other standard forms.

At common law contractual obligations are routinely viewed as absolute and a party is not excused from performance simply because the performance has become more expensive, impracticable[401] or even impossible.[402] A small number of commentators argue, however, that the historical precedents have been misunderstood and that contractual obligations may be excused on both impossibility and impracticability. John D. Wladis, for example, argues that the leading case of *Paradine* v. *Jane*[403] does not stand for the proposition that contractual obligations are absolute and must be performed despite their seeming impossibility.[404] Similarly, another series of cases would seem to refute *Davis Contractors Ltd* v. *Fareham UDC*[405] and its proposition that performance of a contract

---

[399] KWAKYE, A.A. *Construction Project Administration in Practice*. Addison Wesley Longman, Harlow; CIOB, Ascot, 1997, p. 106.

[400] The common law position is returned to below.

[401] *Davis Contractors Ltd* v. *Fareham UDC* [1956] AC 696, [1956] 2 All ER 145, HL.

[402] *Paradine* v. *Jane* (1647) Aleyn 26, 82 ER 897, Style 47, 82 ER 519.

[403] *Paradine* v. *Jane* (1647) Aleyn 26, 82 ER 897, Style 47, 82 ER 519.

[404] WLADIS, JOHN D. Common Law and Uncommon Events. The Development of the Doctrine of Impossibility of Performance in English Contract Law. *Georgetown Law Journal*, 1987, **75**, 1575.

[405] *Davis Contractors Ltd* v. *Fareham UDC* [1956] AC 696, [1956] 2 All ER 145, HL.

may not be excused by frustration on the ground of impracticability.[406] Clause 19.1 is consistent with the views of these commentators in two respects. First of all, clause 19.1 implicitly affirms that there is no obligation upon the contractor to perform an impossible obligation. Secondly, and consequent upon this affirmation, it also implicitly endorses that the contract must be adjusted, and that the adjustment is compensable (clause 60.1(1) of the ECC). This interpretation assumes that other circumstances, such as fault on the part of the contractor in providing the design under clause 61.4 of the ECC, would not preclude compensation. Once again, a re-evaluation of traditional views of frustration, excuse and the potential role of the courts in adjusting contractual obligations has been argued for.[407] In these choices the ECC moves forward from more traditional ways of addressing impossibility through *force majeure* or frustration alone. The provisions on illegality and impossibility in clause 19.1 must be read with clause 95.5 and R17 and R18.

The ECC provisions on illegality and impossibility resemble those in other civil engineering forms. Thus, just as the ECC has not expressly used the term '*force majeure*', unlike, for instance, JCT 80,[408] neither has ICE 6th or FIDIC 4th. Instead, these latter forms refer to adverse physical obstructions or conditions that would impact upon performance.[409] Both the ICE and FIDIC forms exclude from their ambit weather or climatic conditions as well as events that could reasonably have been foreseen.[410] However, this language is qualified by references, again in both forms, to 'physical or legal impossibility'. Here again the terminology resembles clause 19.1 of the ECC. The language of these forms has been considered on several occasions and it may serve in a qualified sense as providing some assistance in construing clause 19.1.[411] Even if found not to be applicable to clause 19.1 these cases may assist in answering the more important question of whether the language invokes the general doctrine of frustration. It has been suggested, at least with respect to the FIDIC

---

[406] McINNIS, J.A. Frustration and Force Majeure in Building Contracts. *Force Majeure and Frustration of Contract* (ed. MCKENDRICK, EWAN), 2nd edn. Lloyd's of London Press, London, 1995, pp. 196–206.

[407] *Ibid.*, pp. 210–213.

[408] Clauses 25.4.1 and 28.1.3.1 JCT 80.

[409] Clause 12(1) ICE 6th and clause 12.1 FIDIC 4th. The FIDIC 4th form also contains a *force majeure* provision in clause 66.1 excusing non-performance which becomes impossible or unlawful due to any circumstance outside a party's control. See also clause 13.1 FIDIC 4th excusing non-performance on the part of the contractor alone when it has become legally or physically impossible; cf the narrower frustration provision in clause 64 ICE 6th.

[410] Clause 12(1) ICE 6th and clause 12.1 FIDIC 4th. GC/Works/1 3rd, clause 36, actually excludes weather as a ground for extension of time altogether and no reimbursement of cost is given.

[411] See notably *Hollard Dredging (UK) Ltd* v. *The Dredging and Construction Co Ltd* (1987) 37 BLR 1; *Yorkshire Water Authority* v. *Sir Alfred McAlpine & Son (Northern) Ltd* (1986) 32 BLR 114; and *A E Farr Ltd* v. *Ministry of Transport* [1960] 3 All ER 88.

conditions, that it does.[412] Focusing on the ECC provisions the enumeration of war and radioactive contamination as described should remove them from the general operation of clause 19.1 and by extension the doctrine of frustration if found to be applicable. This follows from the fact that the doctrine is generally held to be inapplicable to cases or events that the parties have expressly provided for.[413] In other cases recognized at law, save illegality or impossibility, the parties may be excused or released from further performance. Hence, once again, a balance has been struck between rights excusing performance at common law and the desirability of maintaining ongoing contractual relations. In the past, the doctrine of frustration has been firmly tied to notions of impossibility. The ECC provisions mark a small departure from the historical position. Hence, while conceding excuse at common law in general cases, impossibility (indeed impracticability here as put forward) has been dealt with exceptionally. The ECC has moved from requiring the performance of impossible obligations without more to an expanded equitable and co-operative solution based upon excuse, adjustment and compensation. In these ways the ECC has moved closer toward a rapprochement between impossibility of performance at common law and the doctrine of frustration.

---

[412] WALLACE, I.N. DUNCAN. 'It is tentatively suggested that ... what is aimed at ... is a state of affairs affecting the works as a whole which would give rise to frustration under English law': *The International Civil Engineering Contract. A Commentary on the FIDIC International Standard Form of Civil Engineering and Building Contract.* Sweet & Maxwell, London, 1974, p. 45.

[413] *Ocean Tramp Tankers Corpn v. V/O Sovfracht, The Eugenia* [1964] 2 QB 226 at 239, [1964] 1 All ER 161 at 166, CA, per Lord Denning MR.

7. The contractor's main responsibilities

Once upon a time, or so the story goes, a contractor did not lose any payment for works that fell down the day after completion due to their design, because that was none of his business ... Law recognised the specialisation of the engineer and architect in design and supervision and of contractors in construction, which was a glory of the UK construction industry and a valuable export.

Max W. Abrahamson,
Contractor's Rights-over against Architects, Engineers and Surveyors in Respect of Liabilities Incurred to the Employer.
The Liability of Contractors

General

The contractor's main responsibilities are set out under the second core clause. Specifically the core clause addresses provision of the works, design, people, co-operation, subcontracting, approval, access and instructions. These matters may be regarded as the 'main' responsibilities of the contractor.[1] In this sense they stand apart from other responsibilities of the contractor according to the terms of the contract. No specific distinction is drawn, however, between breach of 'main' as opposed to other responsibilities in general. The separate designation of the contractor's responsibilities, when the project manager's responsibilities are not similarly isolated, may be contrasted with the grouping of the employer's and consultant's responsibilities together in the PSC.[2]

Providing the works

'Providing the Works' may be viewed as the ECC equivalent to what has traditionally been the principal obligation of a contractor to 'complete the

---

[1] Cf the Consultation Document, which made no reference to 'main' in the heading.

[2] See core clause 2 'The Parties' main responsibilities' in the PSC First and Second Editions. This follows in the PSC from the separate obligations accorded both the employer and the consultant in the PSC (see clauses 20 and 21 in the PSC) and once again unlike core clause 2 in the ECC. Cf the 'Obligations of the Consultant' and 'Obligations of the Client' in clauses 3–6 and 7–12 respectively of the FIDIC Client/ Consultant Model Services Agreement or White Book.

works'. The obligation to provide the works is assumed unusually by implication by the contractor under each main option. The contractual contents of the obligation to provide the works differ somewhat according to the main option chosen. In main options A and B, the price based contracts, the obligation is framed starkly: to provide the works in accordance with the works information. In addition, in the case of main options C, D, E and F, the contractor assumes further obligations. These obligations are discussed in relation to and as part of the principal obligation to provide the works by virtue of their inclusion in clause 20. There are, of course, other obligations which are imposed on the contractor under other clauses but which are different for this reason. In the case of main options C, D, E and F the contractor agrees to give advice[3] on design and subcontracting[4] and prepare certain cost forecasts.[5] Finally, in the case of main option F alone the contractor assumes the additional obligation to manage the design, construction and installation of the works. It may be underscored that this obligation in main option F – the management contract – is not in substitution for the principal obligation to provide the works, but, once again, in addition to it. It is unusual to frame the contractor's principal obligation in this way. One exception, is the NSC/C which provides an arguably broader completion obligation on the subcontractor, who must not only carry out and complete the subcontract works but do so in accordance with programme details and in accordance with the progress of the works as a whole among other matters. In summary, the contractor assumes one or more obligations in terms of providing the works depending upon the main option chosen and while all of the obligations are important it is the provision of the works which remains the most fundamental commitment of the contractor toward the employer.[6] The commitment is, of course, expressed as a legal obligation.

The completion obligation, as it is sometimes referred to,[7] has been construed strictly in the past and held to extend to all work that is indispensably necessary under the contract.[8] It extends to work implied to be necessary under the contract,[9] arising as a result of inaccurate

---

[3] Cf clause 4 FIDIC Orange Book 1st part II imposing an obligation on the contractor to 'check the design criteria and calculations (if any) included in the Employer's Requirements'. A definition of 'Employer's Requirements' is contained in clause 1.1.1.2 part I.

[4] Clause 20.3 ECC.

[5] Clause 20.4 ECC.

[6] Cf the obligation of the consultant under the PSC to 'Provide the Services in accordance with the Scope': clause 21.1 PSC Second Edition.

[7] The definition of the term 'completion' in the PSC Second Edition may be contrasted with clause 11.2(8) providing 'Completion is when the Consultant has • done all the work which the Scope states he is to do by the Completion Date and • corrected Defects which would have prevented the *Employer* from using the *services*'.

[8] *Williams* v. *Fitzmaurice* (1858) 3 H & N 844; *Sharpe* v. *San Paulo Rly Co* (1873) 8 Ch App 597.

[9] *Williams* v. *Fitzmaurice* (1858) 3 H & N 844.

specifications[10] or unforeseen ground conditions,[11] and lately even the liability for payment of damages for breach of a primary obligation.[12] Aspects of the work not falling within the completion obligation fall to be ordered as extras, variations[13] or changes[14] to the contract and paid for pursuant to the applicable clauses.[15]

The ECC imposes no limitations on the meaning of the word 'change' and the drafters have equated it with 'variation' as used in other standard forms. As such, a change minimally includes additions to and deletions from the works information as well as alterations to the works information.[16]

In summary, at common law the content of the completion obligation has been somewhat vaguely defined. Although the precise wording of the obligation is 'Provides the Works', the reference to 'Completion' in clause 30.2 underscores the relationship between the two notions. It has existed more as a notion than a precise obligation with a defined or certain content. The ECC seeks to clarify the completion obligation by defining it with reference not only to the works information in clause 20.1 but also to the contract itself in clause 11.2(4). The theory is that the more precise the contents of the works information the more precise the contents of the contractor's responsibility in this regard.

Clause 11.2(4) states:

> To Provide the Works means to do the work necessary to complete the *works* in accordance with this contract and all incidental work, services and actions which this contract requires.[17]

Some points may be made. The ECC also uses the term 'Provides the Works' apparently synonymously with 'Provide the "Works"' (e.g. clause 11.2((5)), and it is arguable that the plural usage is acceptable under clause 12.1, the interpretation clause, which equates singular and plural usage except where the context shows otherwise, although the use of 'Providing the Works' in clause15.1 is more questionable. The term '*works*' is an identified term set out in section 1 of part one of the Contract Data. The term 'services' is unidentified and undefined,

---

[10] *Sharpe* v. *San Paulo Rly Co* (1873) 8 Ch App 597.

[11] *Jackson* v. *Eastbourne Local Board* (1885) 2 *Hudson's BC*, 4th edn. 81, HL.

[12] *Babcock Energy Ltd* v. *Lodge Sturtevant Ltd* (1994) 41 Con LR 45.

[13] See e.g. clauses 13.1 JCT 1980; 51.1 FIDIC 4th; and 51 ICE 6th.

[14] See e.g. clause 12 JCT 81.

[15] In the ECC that is the compensation event clause 60.

[16] Guidance notes NEC on clause 14.3 ECC, 30. Cf clause 51.1 FIDIC 4th which uses 'change' and 'variation' synonymously as well. The word 'change(s)' itself is also used in a number of respects including with regard to change of decision; change of works information; changes in the law; and change of prices and completion date.

[17] 'Require' means to 'ask for' or 'request' and not, 'have need of': see *Metropolitan Water Board* v. *Johnson* [1913] 2 KB 900. Alternatively, 'require' means 'demand as of right' and does not mean 'compel': see *Church of Scotland* v. *Watson* 42 SLR 299. 'Required' does not mean 'ordered' or 'instructed': *see British Transport Commission* v. *Inverness-shire Assessor* 1952 SLT 298.

although clause 33.2 of the ECC contemplates that the services will be those as described in the works information. The language in the clause is reminiscent of the tests used in the past defining the contractor's obligation in terms of what work was 'necessary' to 'complete' the contract. Counsel may seek to rely upon cases construing these aspects of the definition given the use of this language. The contractor's obligation under the ECC may even be stricter than under the past tests given not only these express references but also the apparently additional obligations to do 'all incidental work, services and actions that the contract requires'.[18] Whether a matter is 'incidental' or not is inherently problematic. It is submitted that the intention was likely to address omissions from the works information. It will operate in the employer's favour and not amount to a compensation event if it can be brought within the second exception in clause 60.1(1); that is, an instruction given by the project manager changing the works information to comply with other works information, *viz.* said to be incidental to it and provided by the employer. The import of the addition of the phrase 'which this contract requires' is also an open question. The Consultation Document omitted the phrase from the original clause. When read with the requirement already stipulated in the clause to complete the works 'in accordance with this contract' it is arguable that incidental matters need only be completed if stipulated in the contract. The addition of the phrase may too have implications for quality or workmanship and materials. Thus, for instance, in contrast to the wording in JCT 80, workmanship, an inseparable aspect of the works, must be only to the standards described in the contract bills in the first instance.[19] As such, under the JCT form, the effect of standards that one would seek to argue for on the strength of the wording in other contract documents do not have an express basis. However, under the ICE 6th, workmanship must be as described in the entire contract documents.[20] It would seem therefore that the ECC provision combines elements of both approaches: the specificity of the JCT form and the generality of the ICE form. When the ECC provisions are then read with the absence of a precedence of documents clause the large measure of authority, which the project manager holds, is evident. In one respect, if there is always a contractual reference point against which the works or their workmanship can be measured, unlike the other two forms described, it reduces the potential or likelihood of terms being used in this respect. Lastly, the reference to 'actions' itself which is introduced and mandated under clause 10 suggests a very wide scope indeed for the clause. A narrower meaning for actions in this context may seek to limit it to those instances when the phrase 'Provide the Works' is actually used.[21] Before leaving the definition, a troubling aspect of the wording must be

[18] Cf clause 8.1 FIDIC 4th.
[19] Clause 8.1.2 JCT 80.
[20] Clause 36(1) ICE 6th.
[21] That is: clauses 11.2(4), (5), (11), (30), 14.1, 15.1, 20.1, 20.2, 23.1, 26.2, 26.3, 26.4, 31.2, V1.1(6) ECC.

noted, that is, determining what effect, if any, should be given to variable usage of the term 'work'. Thus, in the definition the term 'work' or the plural 'works' is used four separate times in the clause, quite apart from its use in numerous other definition clauses.[22] It seems that the definition could be simplified by dropping one of the references to work and so the definition then reads: 'Provide the Works means to complete the *works* in accordance with this contract, and all incidental work, services and actions which this contract requires'. The necessity to impose a duty on the contractor to complete in accordance with the contract is still necessary because the definition of 'completion', which would be expected to be achieved before provision of the works, only requires the contractor to do all the work which the works information states, and not what the contract states he or she must do. Therefore, the obligation of the contractor to provide the works encompasses:

- fulfilling the works information;
- completing the 'works' as described in the Contract Data;
- incidental work, services and actions which the contract requires; and
- corrected notified defects which would prevent the employer from using the works.

Reference to the notion of completion has generally been avoided in the ECC in delineating the contractor's principal obligation to avoid some of the problems over its meaning that have arisen, in particular regarding the meaning of practical and substantial completion.[23] However, the definition of the term 'completion' in clause 11.2(13) may still give rise to the same issues.[24] The definition is as follows:

Completion is when the Contractor has
  - done all the work which the Works Information[25] states he is to do by the Completion Date[26] and
  - corrected notified Defects[27] which would have prevented the Employer from using the *works*.

The definition of 'completion' thus requires satisfaction of two criteria as defined. With regard to the first criterion the obligation is imposed in affirmative inclusive terms; however, it is also both possible and acceptable for the works information to state the obligation in negative

---

[22] Clauses 11.2(5), (9), (10), (11), (13), (15), (23), (24), (27) and (30) ECC.

[23] See e.g. *H W Nevill (Sunblest) Ltd* v. *William Press & Son Ltd* (1981) 20 BLR 78; *Westminster City Council* v. *J Jarvis & Sons* [1970] 1 All ER 943, HL; and *Emson Eastern Ltd (in receivership)* v. *EME Developments Ltd* (1991) 55 BLR 114.

[24] For example, Guy Cottam thinks clause 11.2(13) likely means 'substantial' or 'practical' completion rather than absolute completion: Contract to Suit All Occasions? *Construction News*, 27 May 1993, 14. Cf the term 'substantial completion' that is used unqualifiedly in clause 13(1) FCEC.

[25] Clause 11.2(5) ECC.

[26] Clause 11.2(12) ECC.

[27] Clause 11.2(15) ECC.

exclusive terms. This is recognized in the guidance notes and could even extend to listing which work could remain undone on the completion date.[28] Thus the parties could agree that the contractor do all work in the works information save that listed. The exclusive approach may work where the contractor has a large or comprehensive design role although it is unlikely to be used as often as specifying obligations in the works information in affirmative inclusive terms.

The second criterion is the more problematic of the two given in the definition. In practice, it will mean that any *use* of the works by the employer will detract from any argument that the works were not complete. It is also submitted that in keeping with the NEC present tense drafting style the second criterion should also be restated 'which prevent the *Employer* from using the *works*'. These two aspects of completion seem to borrow[29] from both building and engineering precedents. For instance, under JCT 80 the contractor completes the works when that which is specified in the contract bills is done,[30] yet under FIDIC 4th, the contractor must do everything that is in effect necessary to complete the works.[31]

The term 'completion' is used sparingly in the contract. Pursuant to clause 30.1 the contractor is to do the work so that completion is on or before the completion date. It is an unqualified completion that is referred to, however, unencumbered by terms such as 'practical' or 'substantial' in other forms.[32] Notwithstanding the definition given to 'completion' in clause 11.2(13) the project manager is still central to the issue and must in fact decide and certify the date of completion itself within one week of it taking place.[33] Hence there are two important actions here; they are the *acts* of deciding and certifying. The obligation to make the decision in the first instance is imposed upon the project manager without any contribution from the contractor. The decision making is self-limiting and thus, appears to be a potentially open-ended freedom of decision. However, in effect, certification must occur within one week of completion. This short time frame thus serves as a limitation on the

---

[28] Guidance notes, NEC 22.

[29] See for some interesting observations on this drafting practice generally GROSHEIDE, F.W. Legal Borrowing and Drafting International Commercial Contracts – Some Methodological Reflections. In *Comparability and Evaluation: Essays on Comparative Law, Private International Law and International Commercial Arbitration in Honour of Dimitra Kokkini-Iatridou* (eds BOELE-WOELKI, K. *et al.*). Martinus Nijhoff Publishers/ TMC Asser Institute, The Hague, 1995.

[30] Clause 2.1 ECC.

[31] For example, remedy defects, clause 8.1, complete to the satisfaction of the engineer and comply with all instructions touching on or concerning the works, clause 13.1 FIDIC 4th. Cf article 1.2 DOM/1 whereby the subcontractor must 'carry out and complete the Sub-Contract Works'.

[32] See e.g. clause 17.1 of JCT 80 and clauses 48 of ICE 6th and 48.2 of FIDIC 4th respectively, 'practical completion' and 'substantial completion'.

[33] Clause 30.2 ECC. The completion date itself may be changed by the project manager in certain cases, e.g. acceleration (cl 36 ECC).

freedom of action, which the project manager is given, in the first instance. In the event it were unacceptable to the contractor it would of course be referable to the adjudicator as a disputed action. The adjudicator's powers would then include the power to review and revise the action – certification – in settling the dispute. With regard to the actual contents of the ECC certificate by the project manager it may well be viewed in the same way others have viewed such contents under different standard forms; namely as expressions of opinion that all required work has been completed.[34] If so, the presence of patent, although not necessarily latent, defects becomes problematic. Thus, patent defects could preclude the issue of a certificate of completion[35] save where the defects were minimal or trifling;[36] conversely latent defects discovered subsequent to completion would not detract from completion being certified.[37] Once again, these decisions would only potentially be applicable if the courts were inclined first to equate ECC certificates with those issued under other standard forms[38] and secondly, decide the case law was apposite. One solution recently put forward to deal with defects was that of the then Department of the Environment and contained in its consultation paper *Latent Defects Liability and 'Build' Insurance.*[39] The paper proposes the creation of a statutory right, such as that in section 1 of the Defective Premises Act 1972, for successive owners and tenants, to benefit from original contractual rights to recover for losses incurred in repairing and reinstating work as a result of a breach of contract by the original contractors or consultants. However, unlike section 1, the proposed right was to be subject to the terms of the original contract and thus could even be wholly excluded. In addition, once again unlike section 1, the proposed right excludes all losses other than repair and reinstatement.

Some important consequences either follow directly as a result of or are relevant in relation to completion including the following:

---

[34] *Westminster City Council* v. *J Jarvis & Sons Ltd* [1970] 1 All ER 943 at 948, HL, per Viscount Dilhorne.

[35] *Westminster City Council* v. *J Jarvis & Sons Ltd* [1970] 1 All ER 943 at 949, HL, per Viscount Dilhorne.

[36] *H W Nevill (Sunblest) Ltd* v. *William Press & Son Ltd* (1981) 20 BLR 78 at 87 per Judge Newey QC; and *Emson Eastern Ltd (in receivership)* v. *EME Developments Ltd* (1991) 55 BLR 114 at 122 per Judge Newey QC. Such defects are often said to fall within the maxim *de minimus non curat lex*, the law does not concern itself with trifles: Broom, Max 142.

[37] *Westminster City Council* v. *J Jarvis & Sons Ltd* [1970] 1 All ER 943 at 949, HL, per Viscount Dilhorne.

[38] See lately on the effect of certificates *Oxford University Fixed Assets Ltd* v. *Architects Design Partnership*, (1999) 64 Con LR 12; and *Matthew Hall Ortech* v. *Tarmac Roadstone* (1998) 87 BLR 96.

[39] *Latent Defects Liability and 'Build' Insurance*. Department of the Environment, HMSO, London, April 1995. See also Latham Report, 101–106.

- taking over the works;[40]
- making certain assessments[41] due in respect of the whole of the works;[42]
- timing and taking certain weather measurements;[43]
- assessing certain compensation events;[44]
- releasing a portion of retention moneys;[45]
- calculating any bonus;[46]
- calculating any delay damages;[47]
- stipulating sectional completion;[48]
- assessing the cost of correcting defects;[49] and
- revising prices following acceleration.[50]

The principal obligation of the contractor as noted is to provide the works. However, this obligation is not without qualification. In short, it will be measured against the contents of the works information.[51] The obligation to provide the works in accordance with the works information stands in contrast to JCT 80 in another respect. Thus pursuant to clause 8.1 in JCT 80 all materials and goods shall, 'so far as procurable', be of the kinds and standards described ...[52] The JCT wording admits of a qualification to the contractor's obligations insofar as the kinds and standards of materials and goods are concerned; they need only comply with these 'so far as [they are] procurable'. This seems to excuse contractors who have failed to make inquiries regarding the availability of certain materials and goods. The ECC makes no similar allowance and indeed nor would a court according to ordinary principles regarding the award of damages for breach of a contract to supply goods. The ECC in this way is also closer to other contractual precedents.[53] While these have been the drafting choices it is submitted a better course would be to make the inquiries in the first instance and if it is foreseeable

---

[40] Clause 35.2 ECC.
[41] Cf use of the term 'ascertain' in clause 26.1 JCT 80, clause 4.2 IFC 84 and clause 9 GC/Works/1 3rd.
[42] Clause 50.1.
[43] See clause 60.1(13) ECC.
[44] See clause 63 ECC.
[45] Option P, clause P1.1 and clause P1.2 ECC.
[46] Option Q, clause Q1.1 ECC.
[47] Option R, clause R1.1 and clause R1.2 ECC.
[48] Option L, clause L1.1 ECC.
[49] See e.g. options C, D and E, clause 11.2(30).
[50] See e.g. options A, B, C, D, E and F, clause 36(4).
[51] Clause 20.1 ECC. 'Works Information is information which either • specifies and describes the works or • states any constraints on how the *Contractor* Provides the Works and is either • in the documents which the Contract Data states it is in or • in an instruction given in accordance with this contract': clause 11.2(25).
[52] The same phrase, 'so far as procurable' is used in clause 1.9.2 JCT NSC/C regarding the execution of the subcontract works and thus serves to limit the contractor's obligations in terms of procuring materials and goods.
[53] For example, ICE 6th, IFC 84.

that there may be difficulties in procuring certain materials and goods to make an allowance for them at that time.

The provision of the works entails additional obligations depending upon the main option chosen. Thus, under main options C, D and E two obligations are added while under main option F three are added. Hence in respect of these four main options the contractor will advise the project manager on the practical implications of the design of the works and on subcontracting arrangements.[54] It amounts to an express obligation being imposed on the contractor to inform the project manager how the works will be provided, what portions of the works will be carried out by the contractor and those portions which will be subcontracted.

The second additional obligation imposed on the contractor in main options C, D, E and F is to prepare forecasts of the actual cost for the whole of the works in consultation with the project manager and then the submission of the forecasts.[55] The obligation, it may be noted, is not only to prepare and submit the forecasts, but also to do so 'in consultation with' the project manager. Whether or not an obligation is imposed upon the contractor in this regard, the preparation of forecasts or predicting future outcomes should be an essential part of any successful contractor's planning processes.[56] The forecasts will be prepared according to intervals stated in the Contract Data and which run from the starting date until 'Completion of the whole of the *works*'.[57] The contractor must also submit with each forecast an explanation of the changes made since the previous forecast.[58]

The ECC management contract, or main option F, adds one final clause or additional obligation in terms of providing the works. Clause 20.2 sets out the essence of the management contracting relationship in ECC terms; that the contractor agrees to manage the design and the construction and installation of the works. However, this obligation is qualified with respect to subcontracting.[59] The contractor will subcontract the design, construction and installation of the works and other work, so far as it is stated in the works information that this must be done,[60] although other work may be done or subcontracted by the contrator which is not stated to be subcontracted in the works information.[61] Hence while the obligation to manage remains central under the core clause the parties by agreement may attenuate the management contractor's role in terms of what else he need do and may do pursuant to the works information. Once again any of

[54] Clause 20.3 ECC.

[55] Clause 20.4 ECC.

[56] See FARROW, J.J. and RUTTER, D.K. *Performance Settting and Monitoring on Building Projects for Contractors* (ed. HARLOW, PETER), CIOB, Ascot, 1996, Construction Papers 67.

[57] Clause 20.4 ECC.

[58] Clause 20.4 ECC.

[59] See again clause 20.3 ECC.

[60] Clause 20.2 ECC.

[61] Clause 20.2 ECC.

the work the contractor need not do may expectedly be performed through subcontractors on site. One consequence of the allocation of the work according to what the contractor must not, may, and must subcontract concerns how fees will be paid. Thus the work that must not and may be subcontracted will be covered by the fee. In contrast the work that must be subcontracted will be included in the actual cost.[62]

The management contractor's obligations under the ECC may be contrasted with those under the JCT Management Contract, JCT 87. Pursuant to its terms the contract is divided into two distinct periods, one pre-construction and one post-pre-construction. The two periods are factually divided by an employer's notice requiring the management contractor to proceed or there is deemed determination.[63] The management contractor's obligations are set out in the conditions of contract.[64] Importantly a general obligation is imposed upon the management contractor to co-operate with the professional team;[65] hence a similar provision to that imposed on the management contractor under clauses 10.1 and 25.1 of the ECC. Specific obligations are imposed upon the management contractor as well.[66] In addition, a very detailed series of 'services' to be provided by the management contractor are described as 'specific obligations' to be carried out by the management contractor. The services are contained in the Third Schedule to the form and divided between the two periods of the contract: pre-construction and post-pre-construction. The post-pre-construction services fall under seven separate headings: planning and programming; works contracts; monitoring works contractor's off-site preparation and work in association with site staff; instituting effective cost control and payment discipline; establishing good labour relations; site management and quality control; and controlling and reporting on performance.[67] Under the JCT form the management contractor assumes no responsibility for design of the works.

Contractor's design
The issue of contractor design is complex and complicated in part by the fact that the term 'design' has no precise meaning.[68] The contractor's design obligation arises in part from the obligation to provide the works and duty to comply with the project manager's instructions.[69] This wording contrasts with clause 21.1 of the NEC First Edition where the

---

[62] See guidance notes NEC table clause 20.2 ECC, 37.
[63] Clauses 2.1 and 2.2 JCT 87.
[64] Clauses 1.4 to 1.8 JCT 87.
[65] Clause 1.4 JCT 87.
[66] For example, prepare all necessary programmes, enter into the works contracts, provide continual supervision etc.: clause 1.5 JCT 87.
[67] Clause 1.6 JCT 87.
[68] See LLOYD, H. Problems of Fitness of the Product. *Building and Construction Law*, 1990, **6**, 11–12.
[69] Clause 29.1 ECC.

words 'complies with the Works Information' have been removed. The removal of these words may be to overcome the argument that a contractor could have made when seeking to preclude the employer from raising any argument of non-compliance between the design and works information and notwithstanding clause 10.1. The contractor's design responsibility is thus a function of the terms of the contract both express and implied, but also a function of any potential reliance on the skill and judgment of the contractor by the employer. The question of reliance can be illustrated most sharply by cases concerning nominated subcontractors. Thus in the presence of a nominated subcontractor fulfilling a design role, in the absence a contractual provision to the contrary, no reliance upon the contractor by the employer will be found to exist.[70] The standard imposed upon the contractor with regard to design is usually either that of fitness for purpose or the lower standard of the exercise of reasonable skill and care. In general, when a contractor assumes a design obligation, the higher standard is held to. This contrasts with the professional designer, architect or engineer for instance, who is normally only subject to the lesser standard. Therefore, at common law if a contractor has assumed a design obligation a term will be implied that the works will be fit for their purpose[71] unless there has been no reliance on the contractor's skill and judgment or the contract has excluded the obligation.[72] The fitness for purpose obligation is more onerous than the use of 'reasonable skill and care' in carrying out the design and, as a result, standard forms have often expressly adopted this lesser standard. It has also been argued to be an uninsurable obligation. As recently as 1994 Martin Lenihan wrote:

> [i]t seems to me that the most convincing argument for not imposing fitness for purpose obligations upon either Contractor or Consultant is quite simply that the Contractor/Consultant's Professional Indemnity Insurance Policies ... do not protect them against claims/liability arising out of a fitness for purpose obligation. This risk is uninsurable. To the best of my knowledge (and upon recent enquiry), there is (still) no insurance protection available in the insurance market to protect a Contractor/Consultant from this risk.[73]

---

[70] *Norta Wallpapers (Ireland) Ltd* v. *John Sisk & Sons (Dublin) Ltd* (1977) 14 BLR 49. The ECC makes no provision for nominated subcontractors.

[71] *Viking Grain Storage* v. *T H White Installations Ltd* (1985) 33 BLR 103; *Basildon District Council* v. *J E Lesser (Properties) Ltd* [1985] QB 839, [1985] 1 All ER 20; *Test Valley Borough Council* v. *Greater London Council* (1979) 13 BLR 63, CA. See lately FLEMING, H. Fitness for Purpose: The Implied Obligation in Construction Contracts. *Construction Law Journal*, 1997, **13**, 227.

[72] See *Lynch* v. *Thorne* [1956] 1 All ER 744, [1956] 1 WLR 303, CA.

[73] LENIHAN, MARTIN (original emphasis): To 'B' or 'D & B'? Design and Build in the 90s. A joint paper (with John Redmond) given to the Society of Construction Law in London on 8 March 1994, 5–6.

The issue is dichotomous and has been observed to be so by the courts. Thus, it was held in *Independent Broadcasting Authority* v. *EMI Electronics and BICC Construction* and *Storey* v. *Charles Church Developments Ltd* that a design and build contractor's duties were concurrent in tort and contract; in *Alfred McAlpine Construction Ltd* v. *Panatown* that the clients of a design and build contractor could recover substantial damages for breaches of contract notwithstanding the building was owned by another company; and in *George Fischer Holding Ltd (formerly George Fischer (GB) Ltd)* v. *Multi Design Consultants Ltd* that liability could be imposed on designers engaged under a design and build contract for breach of a collateral warranty.[74]

The ECC wording may be contrasted with the JCT Standard Form of Building Contract with Contractor's Design, 1981; clause 2.5.1 providing in part:

> the Contractor shall have in respect of any defect or insufficiency in such design the like liability to the Employer, whether under statute or otherwise, as would an architect or, as the case may be, other appropriate professional designer holding himself out as competent to take on work for such design ...

This wording imposes a 'reasonable skill and care' standard on the contractor that contrasts markedly with the more clearly worded option M in the ECC. M1.1 states: 'The *Contractor* is not liable for Defects in the *works* due to his design so far as he proves that he used reasonable skill and care to ensure that it complied with the Works Information'.

The ECC drafters have opted for the higher standard as the general rule and provided that the lesser standard must be expressly adopted as an option if that is the intention of the parties. No reasons are given for this preference. However, several factors, which may have been relevant to their choice, may be put forward as follows.

- A 'product orientation' more representative of engineering than building contracts.
- A low performance damages option that may serve to mitigate some of the harshness associated with the higher standard.
- The limitation of the responsibility for defects due to the design, rather than liability for design itself. With regard to this, the necessity for the design fault to translate into a defect[75] further distances the contractor from the prospect of liability and thus in turn, if the fault does eventuate in a defect, arguably supports the imposition of the higher standard.

---

[74] *Independent Broadcasting Authority* v. *EMI Electronics and BICC Construction* (1980) 14 BLR 1 at 47, HL; *Storey* v. *Charles Church Developments Ltd* (1996) 12 Const LJ 206; *Alfred McAlpine Construction Ltd* v. *Panatown* (1998) 88 BLR 67; *George Fischer Holding Ltd (formerly George Fischer (GB) Ltd)* v. *Multi Design Consultants Ltd* (1999) 61 Con LR 85.

[75] The necessity for the design fault to translate into a defect as defined in clause 11.2(15) itself is a further limitation on the contractor's responsibility.

Regarding the second point, A.A. Kwakye sees this as an advantage of the form: '[t]he client will be able to recover damages from the contractor if any installed equipment fails to function in accordance with a specified performance level'.[76] The higher standard of care, which is imposed upon the contractor under the ECC as a result of the design role, is supportable for other reasons. It is also the standard imposed for end products, e.g. houses. It recognizes that a line has to be drawn between the theoretical design component and construction components of a product and that by simply expressly recognizing the contractor's design role should not lessen responsibility.[77] Policy arguments may be inveighed in this way. An independent designer may have less reason to compromise on standards than would a contractor who may increase profits as a result.

In other circumstances the wholesale subcontracting of the design obligation by the contractor might relieve the contractor of the obligation to provide works which are fit for their purpose on the basis of there having been no reliance; but the express terms of the ECC would seem to preclude this.[78] In effect the higher standard upon the contractor is also tantamount to a reverse onus. Option M provides that the contractor is not liable so far as it is proven that reasonable skill and care has been taken. It can be observed that the two standards read together (given this fact) are arguably not too different from each other. Under the fitness for purpose test the higher standard is imposed directly upon the contractor but it is then incumbent upon anyone alleging a breach thereof to establish this standard. Conversely, under the reasonable skill and care standard, ostensibly the lower standard to satisfy, it is the contractor who carries the burden of proof; in this case namely to show that reasonable skill and care has been taken. Therefore, in any given case depending upon the circumstances, the substance of the obligation could be said to be very close under either standard. John Scriven regards the design liability under the core clause as 'absolute'.[79] In Scriven's view secondary option clause M does not specify the nature of the duty of skill and care. Thus he concludes that in the absence of an express exclusion of the fitness for purpose obligation, or again what he refers to as an absolute duty, it may still be implied as a term of the contract when using the secondary option clause M.[80]

---

[76] KWAKYE, A.A. *Construction Project Administration in Practice*. Addison Wesley Longman, Harlow; CIOB, Ascot, 1997, p. 105.

[77] LLOYD, QC, HUMPHREY. Contractor's Liability For Design: An English Point of View. In *The Liability of Contractors*, (ed. LLOYD), pp. 139–148 quoting Sir Hugh Casson, a former president of the Royal Academy who may have put it best when he said: 'to design is to decide', p. 139.

[78] Cf *Norta Wallpapers (Ireland)* v. *John Sisk & Sons (Dublin) Ltd* (1976) 14 BLR 49; and see generally *John Mowlem & Co Ltd* v. *British Insulated Callenders Pension Trust Ltd* (1977) 3 Con LR 64.

[79] SCRIVEN, JOHN. Design Risk and Liability under Design and Build Contracts. *Construction Law Journal* 12 (1996): 226, 230.

[80] *Ibid.*

Responsibility for design by the contractor may entail other responsibilities as well. For instance, the timely provision of design plans, drawings or information at common law;[81] however, under the ECC there is no express time frame for submission of designs to the project manager even though the project manager must reply to the submission within a set time frame.[82] This contrasts with the FIDIC Orange Book, which imposes an obligation on the contractor to provide a complete set of up-to-date 'as-built' drawings as the work proceeds.[83]

Apart from the implication of a term imposing responsibility on a contractor for design, an implied obligation may also arise on the part of the contractor to warn the employer of any defects in the design of which he or she has knowledge.[84]

Traditionally the role of contractors in design has been viewed as limited as a result of an artificial division between design and construction. Responsibility for design has been seen as belonging to the employer or those designing the works on the employer's behalf. The contractor's obligation has been limited to construction of the works. Notable exceptions to this division of responsibility have again come in the form of design and build contracts.[85] Considerable variation has emerged in design and build forms of procurement. Thus new terms include 'design and construct', 'develop and construct' and 'design and manage'.[86] The ECC also allows for a design and manage method of procurement if option F is utilized. As the ECC also contemplates supply and industrial plant projects the variations on the contractor's contribution to design are vast. In addition, as architects seek to define new roles for themselves and with the loss of traditional responsibilities, other forms including 'architect design and build' and 'total procurement' have also

---

[81] See *Neodex Ltd* v. *Swinton and Pendlebury Borough Council* (1958) 5 BLR 34; *Holland Hannen and Cubitts (Northern) Ltd* v. *Welsh Health Technical and Services Organisation* (1981) 18 BLR 80; and *H Fairweather & Co Ltd v London Borough of Wandsworth* (1987) 39 BLR 106.

[82] Clauses 13.3, 13.4 ECC.

[83] Clause 5.6 FIDIC Orange Book 1st part I.

[84] *Brunswick Construction Ltd* v. *Nowlan* (1974) 21 BLR 27 (Can SC); *Equitable Debenture Assets Corpn Ltd* v. *William Moss Group Ltd* (1984) 2 Con LR 1; *Victoria University of Manchester* v. *Hugh Wilson & Lewis Womersley (a firm)* (1984) 2 Con LR 43; *University Court of Glasgow* v. *William Whitfield and John Lang (Construction) Ltd* (1988) 42 BLR 66; *Lindenberg* v. *Canning* (1992) 62 BLR 147. See generally NISSEN, A. Duty to Review a Design – Is it Real or Artificial? *Construction Law Journal*, 1997, **13**, 221; WINTER, JEREMY. Duty to Warn: A Comparative Approach. In *Legal Obligations in Construction*, (eds UFF and LAVERS), p. 399; and lately *Tesco Stores* v. *Norman Hiscox Partnership* (1998) 56 Con LR 42.

[85] For example, JCT 81, ICE Design and Construct, and FIDIC Orange Book. See generally TURNER, D.F. *Design and Build Contract Practice*, 2nd edn. Longman, London, 1995.

[86] CHEVIN, D. Design and Build: Client Survey. *Building*, Building Design Build Supplement, 30 July 1993, 17.

emerged. These latter configurations seek to confer a larger role safeguarding quality on the project.[87]

In building contracts the design is often done by professional architects and in civil engineering contracts by professional engineers. One prominent exception to this in the engineering sector has been electrical and mechanical plant contracts that have been designed and built by contractors. In this latter case the contractors would normally design and construct the plants according to the employer's performance requirements rather than the original design.[88] The traditional standard forms of contract, which perpetuated the dichotomy, reinforced the separation of design and construction in this way. Ann Minogue, referring to the fiction of separating design from construction in clause 5.4 of the JCT 80 has written:

> it must be time that the JCT looked again at clause 5.4 to acknowledge the reality of today's projects, where virtually every element requires some design input from the contractor or subcontractor. It cannot be right to continue with a provision in a standard form that departs so far from normal practice.[89]

Even the BPF system, which conceded design responsibility could reside with the contractor, still maintained overall control in the employer's hands through a design leader. In the BPF system the design leader 'sanctions' or effectively approves the contractor's design to ensure compliance with the contract. This reluctance, however, fails to acknowledge the contractor's real contribution to design which contractors make indirectly as a result of their choices in methods and procedures. Recognition of the contractor's contribution in these and other small but important ways has grown in recent years to the point where it has now been formally endorsed through first the development and second the use of design and build methods of procurement. It has also been recognized by the drafting organizations themselves. Edward Corbett states:

> [t]he loyalty of the Red Book to the traditional format of re-measurement and client design begins to look dogmatic at a time when procurers world-wide have been amending the Red Book to create lump-sum fixed price contracts and to pass to the contractor some or all of the responsibility for design.[90]

---

[87] See AKINTOYE, AKINTOLA and FITZGERALD, EMON. Design and Build: A Survey of Architects' Views. *Engineering, Construction and Architectural Management*, 1995, **2**(1), 27–44.

[88] The role of architects still remains significant with over 30% of clients approaching an architect before a contractor: Gallup, 27.

[89] MINOGUE, ANN. 'Drawing Hidden Meaning. *Building*, 8 September 1995, 40.

[90] CORBETT, EDWARD. 'FIDIC 5th or a New Style Red Book? *International Construction Law Review*, 1993, 291.

Regarding the traditional measure and value payment mechanism David Greenwood and Rudi Klein also write: '[p]ressures upon the certifier, the potential for manipulation by the applicant and the lack of procedural transparency further down the contractual chain, mean that this has become a less than perfect system'.[91] These issues have now been addressed in part with the release of the supplement to the Red Book that was published in October 1996. The supplement comprises three sections: providing for adjudication as an alternative to the traditional engineer's role; payment on a lump sum basis rather than the measure and value basis referred to here; and alternative wording to assure the contractor that there will be no penalty due to late certification by the engineer.

The ECC has taken the evolution of contracts forward by embracing contractor design as the norm and focusing attention on the design construction interface; notably by requiring particulars of the contractor's design to be inserted in the works information. The design construction interface is one of the most problematic in industry. In general, the term 'interface' refers to an area where parties' responsibilities and activities overlap, e.g. the employer's contributions in terms of materials, payment mechanisms, access to the site, and of course design and construction.[92] Clause 21 assumes that the contractor will play a role in design of the works. Although the ECC is also suitable for works which entail no formal design responsibility on the part of the contractor, that is, no inclusions are made in the works information in this regard, it is submitted that this practice will increasingly become the exception in the use of the form. The contribution that the ECC makes on this issue is to accord full and proper recognition to the contractor's design role in the construction of the works.

There are benefits that will flow from the recognition of this role and the identification in the works information of the precise content of the contractor's design obligation. That is, clearer lines of responsibility in terms of liability for design and defects in design and construction. The assigning of an equivalent standard of care for design and construction as well may serve to address some of the uncertainty which follows in practice regarding who are the appropriate parties to name in a civil action involving questions of liability for design and defects in design and construction. The proper use of the ECC where design responsibility can clearly be allocated and the avoidance of incomplete elements of work being unnaturally divided between designers and contractors working independently further reinforces this point. Under clause 21.3 of the ECC

---

[91] GREENWOOD, DAVID and KLEIN, RUDI. Security of Payment in the light of the Latham Report: An Opportunity to Remove Unacceptable Risks? *Construction Law Journal*, 1995, **11**, 260. See BOWCOCK, JOHN. The New Supplement to the FIDIC Red Book. *International Construction Law Review*, 1997, 49.

[92] See generally SCHNEIDER, MICHAEL E. Mastering the Interfaces – Construction Contracts Drafting for Dispute Avoidance. *International Construction Law Review*, 1993, 404. See also lately where responsibility for design is divided *E H Cardy & Son Ltd* v. *Taylor and Paul Roberts & Associates* (*Third party*) (1994) 38 Con LR 79.

the contractor may also submit a design for acceptance in parts only if the design of each can be assessed fully. This practice may be expected to be followed in fast track projects. Incomplete documentation is, after all, a major cause of cost overruns on projects.[93] This was understood by the drafters and in 'The Need For and Features of the NEC', it was noted that '[e]ver since mechanisms were introduced into contracts making it possible to invite tenders without making a complete statement of what the contractor was required to do, their misuse has grown'.[94]

The ECC is adaptable insofar as the scope of the design role of the contractor is concerned. As noted it may, theoretically, be nil or 100%. Between these poles any percentage contribution is possible. In this regard the ECC resembles JCT 81 with one significant difference. The JCT 81 form is the only contract in the JCT family of forms that imposes *dual* responsibility for design and construction of the works.[95] While other JCT forms are occasionally amended in practice to accommodate a design and build mode of procurement the risks in so doing are manifest. Professor I.N. Duncan Wallace QC, many years ago, referred to consequences of such practices as 'utterly disastrous' and went on to say in the introduction to his text *Building and Civil Engineering Standard Forms* that:

> [i]t cannot be too strongly emphasized that the consequences of this [using a traditional form and amending for a 'package-deal'] will usually be utterly disastrous should any dispute caused by defective work or design, or by delay in completion, arise in such cases. Both parties need completely different contractual protection, particularly in regard to the very necessary power of *each* party to vary the work. In addition, the employer needs a long-term protection in regard to design and sound construction, and different financial arrangements in regard to interim payment are also likely to be required, which the standard forms are simply not designed to provide. In fact there is hardly a provision in the standard forms which does not need to be thought out afresh and radically revised in these quite different situations. The serious potential consequences, for the employer in particular, if these forms, however much amended, are used, cannot be over-emphasised, and advisers allowing this to happen will bear a heavy responsibility for doing so.[96]

The wording of clause 2.1 which imposes the dual responsibility indicates that the contractor's contribution for design may similarly range from nil to 100%; although in practical terms the rationale for a JCT 81

---

[93] HODGETTS, M.F. Risk Management and Cost Control. *Building Economist*, 1987, **26**(3), 17–20.

[94] The Need For and Features of the NEC, Consultation Document 8.

[95] The use of the Contractor's Designed Portion Supplement for use with certain other JCT forms is put in a different category here.

[96] WALLACE, I.N. DUNCAN. *Building and Civil Engineering Standard Forms*. Sweet & Maxwell, London, 1969, p. v.

contract strategy is largely defeated if there is not a significant contractor design allocation. Clause 2.1 of the JCT 81 provides in part: '[t]he Contractor shall upon and subject to the Conditions carry out and complete the Works referred to in the Employer's Requirements ...' etc. The wording of this clause is sometimes amended in practice to clarify or qualify the assumption of responsibility by the contractor for designs prepared either by or on behalf of the employer and which are part of the contract documents. The significant difference is that the ECC is clear on the point that the contractor does not assume any responsibility for the employer's design. If it is intended that the contractor should assume design responsibility for a design done by or on behalf of the employer this would or should normally be made clear to tenderers at the outset. If the contractor did agree to assume responsibility for the employer's design then it should properly become part of the works information. The importance of a clear division of responsibility is underscored by the assigning of fault in employer design to the employer as an employer risk.[97] The ECC thus parallels other standard forms that seek to clarify both the division of as well as the responsibility for design.[98] By comparison, under both JCT 81 and ICE Design and Construct the contractor assumes design responsibility even for designs prepared by the employer. This design responsibility appears in these forms primarily in the employer's requirements and conditions of contract whereas in the ECC it appears in the works information and conditions.

The division of design responsibility and the freedom of action in this regard, which the NEC affords, are seen as problematic by at least one commentator. In Brian Eggleston's view the NEC should have made an assumption about design responsibility at the outset. Eggleston sees NEC drafting, which neither assumes essentially employer design nor contractor design as troublesome. In short, in his view, it is not possible for the various provisions of the form to operate equally well in any situation.[99] He questions both individual aspects of this approach[100] as well as the more general issue whether a contract can satisfactorily be wholly flexible on design at all.[101] In response to this criticism it would seem that it is not the assumptions themselves which are problematic but the additional attention that must be given to preparing the works information if it is to be successful. In practice existing standard forms do admit of a considerable amount of contractor design at present and it is arguably less the portion of either contractor or employer design that causes problems than the unintended overlap between the two.

---

[97] Clause 80.1 ECC.

[98] See generally MURDOCH, JOHN and HUGHES, WILL. *Construction Contracts: Law and Management*, 2nd edn. E & FN Spon, London, 1996, pp. 180–192.

[99] EGGLESTON, *A Commentary*. See for reviews of the text JONES, DAVID. *Construction Law Journal*, 1997, **13**, 139; and LLOYD, HUMPHREY. *International Construction Law Review*, 1996, 599.

[100] EGGLESTON. *The New Engineering Contract, A Commentary*. Blackwell, London, 1996, p. 110 regarding clause 60.3.

[101] *Ibid.* p. 111.

The participation of the contractor in the design of the works is straightforwardly the design of those parts of the works that the works information states that he or she is to design.[102] The design obligations may be specified in a variety of ways including exclusively; hence the contractor may be required to design all works save for those portions of the works listed. Precise formulation of the design obligation will be a matter for the employer and advisers. Various approaches may be employed to determine not only who has the design responsibility but also which design will be acceptable to the project manager: for instance using a 'generate-test' cycle to inform decision making through a process of generated alternatives which are tested against project requirements[103] and cost restraints.[104] It is submitted that this clause and its express limitation of the contractor's design responsibility to what is stated in the works information may serve to restrict the contractor's liability for selection of materials and perhaps overcome some of the complexity seen in recent case law.[105] Thus the reasoning in the case of *Rotherham Metropolitan Borough Council* v. *Frank Haslam Milan & Co Ltd and M J Gleeson (Northern) Ltd* may be inapplicable insofar as it touches on this clause.[106] The form of the statement of the contractor's design will depend upon the extent of design responsibility. It was an NEC drafting principle that the employer be able to determine the design boundary between the employer and the contractor.[107] It is recommended that where the contractor has only a small design responsibility a list of those parts of the works should be included in the works information.[108] Conversely, where the contractor has a larger design role, up to a full design and build role, a list of what the employer will design should be included in the works information with all remaining design responsibility being assigned to the contractor. Details of the design may be given in any acceptable form including specific prescription, general briefs and performance specifications.[109] The

---

[102] Clause 21.1 ECC.

[103] JOHNSON, ROBERT E. *The Economics of Building, A Practical Guide for the Design Professional*. John Wiley & Sons Inc, New York, 1990, p. 11.

[104] *Ibid.* 29.

[105] See generally McINNIS, J.A. Recent Developments in Construction and Arbitration. *Law Lectures for Practitioners*. Hong Kong Law Journal, Hong Kong, 1997, 99–102.

[106] *Rotherham Metropolitan Borough Council* v. *Frank Haslam Milan & Co Ltd and M J Gleeson (Northern) Ltd* (1996) 78 BLR 1, CA.

[107] PERRY, JOHN G. The New Engineering Contract: Principles of Design and Risk Allocation. *Engineering, Construction and Architectural Management*, 1995, **2**(3), 197–208.

[108] Guidance notes NEC, 21.

[109] The importance of performance specifications themselves and the influence they may exert over conditions of contract has been referred to lately by Sarah Lupton: see 'Performance Specification: The Legal Implications. *International Construction Law Review*, 1996, 28. It is interesting to note that the concept of performance-based building regulations is not new and they were first promoted by the Building Research Establishment in the 1930s: *Building Regulations in ECE Countries*, 2nd Report. United Nations, UN Publication sales no E.85.11.E.14, New York, April 1985, p. 12.

guidance notes recommend that details of the contractor's design include size or space limitation; design standards and codes of practice; materials and workmanship specifications inclusive of applicable standards; loading and capacity requirements; and operational performance requirements and design life.[110] The works information should also set out any procedures which either the contractor intends to follow or which the employer expects the contractor to follow. The procedures should include particulars of design, which the contractor will submit to the project manager.[111] If the works information does not stipulate that the contractor's design has to be accepted by the project manager then the obligation is to provide the works in accordance with clause 20.[112] Conversely if the 'acceptance'[113] of the project manager is required under the works information then the contractor must not proceed with the relevant work until the project manager has accepted it. The wording of the clause in the Second Edition differs somewhat from that in the First Edition and arguably serves to reinforce the contractor's own responsibility for those parts of the works which he or she designs. In comparison, the First Edition required the contractor's design to comply with the works information and thus arguably left the employer with some partial responsibility for the basis of that design.

One question that arises is whether the 'acceptance' by the project manager should be equated with 'approval', as it is understood under other standard forms. The pertinency of this comparison is reinforced given that the Consultation Document originally used the term 'approval' in place of 'acceptance' in the Second Edition. This interpretation accords with the very narrow meaning given to 'acceptance' by the drafters, namely 'to prevent abortive work which would result if the *Contractor* began to manufacture or construct a design which had not been accepted'.[114] In general, approvals may be an express requirement under the conditions,[115] the contract bills or the specification and may pertain to methods, workmanship or materials. The approval may be stated to derive from a contract administrator, independently or on behalf of the employer;[116] or a statutory authority. The issue of approval often arises in the context of certification which may require the certifier's 'approval' of the method, workmanship or materials. To some commentators such approvals are likely to be objectionable on the basis of their suggestions that all certification functions should be assigned to a neutral third party

---

[110] Guidance notes NEC. 21.

[111] Clause 21.3 ECC and see guidance notes NEC, 22.

[112] See discussion above.

[113] Clause 21.2 ECC. The submission for acceptance must meet clause 13 ECC requirements.

[114] Guidance notes NEC on clause 21.2 ECC, 34.

[115] See e.g. clause 2.1 JCT 80 using the term 'approval'. The concept may also be referred to in different terms, e.g. clause 8.1 JCT 80 'reasonable satisfaction'.

[116] See *Lord Bateman* v. *Thompson* (1875) 2 *Hudson's BC* 4th edn. 36, CA.

figure.[117] At times approvals are discouraged because of the responsibility they may entail. In *Risk Management for Architects* Ray Cecil has written regarding approval of drawings.

> Many kinds of drawings are submitted to the architect 'for approval'. If you 'approve' a drawing, it might be inferred that you checked it for content and that it is in accordance with your requirements. You will know very well that this is not what you intended, so do not write or rubber stamp 'APPROVED' on your consultants', sub-contractors' or suppliers' drawings.[118]

However, in standard forms there are routinely other provisions that also address these aspects of the works or the contractor's performance. Hence the question that has arisen is whether the other provisions also remain in effect and enforceable despite certificated 'approval'.

In the ECC context the counterpart of this question is whether provisions such as those in section 4 regarding tests and inspections remain enforceable notwithstanding 'acceptance' by the project manager. This distinction was clearly set out by Devlin J in *Minster Trust Ltd* v. *Traps Tractors Ltd*:

> If work under a contract is to be completed to the satisfaction of a certifier, it may mean that his duty is merely to see that the requirements of the contract are met, or it may mean that he is entitled to impose a standard of his own. It may be that his standard is that to which the parties submit and that it constitutes the only provision in the contract about quality; or it may be that his standard is an added protection, so that performance under the contract must satisfy both the contract requirement and the certifier.[119]

Therefore, where a contract provides for certificated approval, it is a question of construction whether the issue of the certificate discharges the contractual obligation to perform, which is an additional obligation. In general the clauses amount to added obligations and do not detract from other contractual provisions. The approval clauses themselves are normally given a reasonable interpretation and are construed against the drafter.[120] In addition, the employer's promise to pay is often held to be

---

117   HOLTZMAN, HOWARD. Use of Impartial Technical Experts to Resolve Engineering and Other Technological Disputes before Arbitration. In *Commercial Arbitration, Essays in Memoriam Eugenio Minoli*, Turin, 1974, p. 233. Cf DAVIS, BENJAMIN J. The ICC Pre-Arbitral Referee Procedure in Context with Technical Expertise, Conciliation and Arbitration. *International Construction Law Review*, 1992, 218; ARNALDEZ, JEAN-JACQUES and SCHAFER, ERIK. Le Réglement de Reféré Pré-Arbitral de la Chambre de Commerce Internationale. *Revue de L'Arbitrage*, 1990, 835.

118   In CECIL, RAY. *Risk Management for Architects*. RIBA Indemnity Research, London, 1992, p. 22.

119   Devlin J in *Minster Trust Ltd* v. *Traps Tractors Ltd* [1954] 3 All ER 136 at 145, [1954] 1 WLR 963 at 974.

120   *Dallman* v. *King* (1837) 7 LJCP 6; *Stadhard* v. *Lee* (1863) 32 LJQB 75.

independent of the approval requirement.[121] Hence, acceptance by the project manager may be construed only as a term of the contract and not as a condition. The effect of this is that the employer could not refuse to honour the obligation to make payment notwithstanding failure of the contractor to obtain an acceptance from the project manager. However, the employer would not be without recourse under the contract and would retain remedies to set-off[122] payments to the contractor or otherwise to the extent that the value of the works was diminished. It must be noted, once again, this assumes that acceptance may be equated with approval.

The drafters of the ECC have purported to address this issue expressly. Thus, acceptance by either the project manager or the supervisor of the contractor's work is stated not to detract from the contractor's responsibility to provide the works or from liability for the design.[123] While acceptance of the contractor's design by the project manager is a requirement for the contractor to proceed with the works,[124] it contrasts with the ability of the contractor to proceed notwithstanding the non-acceptance by the project manager of the contractor's design of equipment.[125] Presumably, given the right of the project manager to not accept the contractor's design of equipment under clause 23.1, clause 13.1 would then govern the situation and the contractor would have to resubmit the particulars of the design of the item of equipment. Acceptance by the project manager also stands in contrast to the requirement of the contractor to obtain 'approval' from others where necessary under clause 27.1. John Scriven has put it in these terms:

> [b]ecause the design has to be 'accepted' by the project manager, it is not as clear as it could be that, once the design is accepted, the contractor remains liable for defective design, although this is implied by a provision limiting the contractor's liability for design after completion of the works.[126]

John Scriven regards the design liability under the clause as 'absolute'. In his view secondary option clause M does not specify the nature of the duty of skill and care. Thus he concludes that, in the absence of an express exclusion of the fitness for purpose obligation, or again what he refers to as an absolute duty, it may still be implied as a term of the contract when using the secondary option clause M.[127]

---

[121] *Dallman* v. *King* (1837) 7 LJCP 6, 9.

[122] See generally on the subject of set-off and cross-claims *Halsbury's Laws of England*, 4th edn. reissue, vol. 6 paragraph 64 and for cases on the subject see 8(2) Digest 2nd reissue 60–66, 470–506.

[123] Clause 14.1 ECC.

[124] Clause 21.2 ECC.

[125] Clause 23.1 ECC.

[126] SCRIVEN, JOHN. Design Risk and Liability under Design and Build Contracts. *Construction Law Journal*, 1996, **12**, 229.

[127] *Ibid.*

In conclusion the term 'acceptance' should be given its ordinary legal meaning here as the converse of agreeing to the offer of the contractor. Whether or not the term is viewed as distinct from the concept of 'approval' under various standard forms, and which may connote responsibility for the design, express negating of this interpretation in the ECC and the relative quality of acceptance suggest that it be construed narrowly, as an additional obligation and one which neither shifts the risk for design on to the employer nor derogates from the other provisions with respect to otherwise providing the works in accordance with the works information.

The acceptance of the project manager may be given with respect to parts of the contractor's design when each part is capable of full assessment.[128] A full assessment is not possible if the nature of that part of the design necessitates additional information on another part of the design, which is interlocking and not presently available. This may operate as a limitation in fast track projects where information relevant to the design but effectively part of a later design package is not available at the time of submission by the contractor.[129] The project manager's acceptance must be in a form that can be read, copied and recorded,[130] and within the '*period for reply*' to communications.[131] Failure of the project manager to reply within the period for reply is a compensation event.[132] The procedures outlined of full or partial design, submission, acceptance within time, and proceeding with the relevant work accords with ECC management principles, will encourage timely action by the parties and serve to reduce delays.

Management is a critical factor in construction duration. Research by Derek Walker[133] indicates that four factors affect construction time performance: construction management effectiveness, the sophistication of the client and the client's representative in terms of creating and maintaining positive project team relationships with the construction management and design team, design team effectiveness in communicating with construction management and client's representative teams,[134] and a small number of factors describing project scope and complexity. The latter factors, regarding project scope and models in relation to construction time duration, were developed initially by Bromilow and Henderson.[135]

---

[128]   Clause 21.3 ECC.
[129]   See generally KWAKYE, A.A. *Fast Track Construction*. CIOB, Ascot, 1991, CIOB Occasional Papers 46.
[130]   Clause 13.1 ECC.
[131]   Clause 13.1 ECC and as inserted under 1 in part one of the Contract.
[132]   Clause 60.1(6) ECC.
[133]   WALKER, DEREK H.T. An Investigation into Construction Time Performance. *Construction Management and Economics*, 1995, **13**, 262–274.
[134]   Teams are looked at from an organizational perspective in BRINER, W. *et al. Project Leadership*, 2nd edn. Gower, Aldershot, 1996.
[135]   See BROMILOW, F.J. and HENDERSON, J.A. *Procedures For Reckoning and Valuing the Performance of Building Contracts*, Division of Building Research

The degree to which the conditions of contract promote the completion of the project on time or on schedule can be an important factor in the evaluation of risk under the conditions.[136] The central features of project duration are thus scope, complexity and managerial effectiveness. Much of Walker's research is and many of his conclusions are supported by, graduate work.[137] S.G. Naoum, in *Procurement and Project Performance – A Comparison of Management Contracting and Traditional Contracting*, views the procurement method as well as the experience of the designer as the two most important factors affecting time and cost overruns.[138]

A number of researchers, including Bromilow[139] as well as others working under the auspices of NEDO,[140] have examined different variables to determine what affects performance. While it should be noted that there is some variance over the significance of a wide variety of these variables there is considerable agreement on the significance of two issues of particular relevance to our assessment of the NEC: that is the role of management[141] and the form of procurement,[142] although it can be argued it is an open question, which of these two play a greater role in terms of performance.[143]

Two reasons are given for the project manager not accepting the contractor's design: it does not comply with the works information, or it does not comply with the applicable law.[144] Under the First Edition the two reasons were joined conjunctively with the word 'and' and were not

Special Report, 2nd edn. Commonwealth Science and Industry Research Organisation (CSIRO), Melbourne, 1976; and BROMILOW, F.J. *et al.* AIQS Survey of Building Contract Time Performance. *Building Economist*, 1980, **19**, 79–82.

[136] See BUBSHAIT, ABDULAZIZ A. and ALMOHAWIS, SOLIMAN A. Evaluating the General Conditions of a Construction Contract. *International Journal of Project Management*, 1994, **12**(3) 134.

[137] Data compiled by IRELAND, V. The Role of Managerial Actions in the Cost, Time and Quality Performance of High Rise Commercial Building Projects. PhD dissertation, University of Sydney, Australia, 1983; and SIDWELL, A.C. A Critical Study of Project Team Organisational Forms within the Building Process. PhD dissertation, University of Aston, Birmingham, Department of Commerce and Environmental Health, 1982.

[138] NAOUM, S.G. Occasional Paper 45. CIBO, Ascot, 1991.

[139] BROMILOW, F.J. Measurement and Scheduling of Construction Time and Cost Performance in the Building Industry. *The Chartered Builder*, June/July 1974, 10.

[140] NEDO. *Faster Building for Industry.* HMSO, LONDON, 1983.

[141] See BAKER, B.N. *et al.* Factors Affecting Project Success. In *Project Management Handbook* (eds CLELAND, DAVID and KING, WILLIAM R.) Van Nostrand Reinhold, New York, 1982.

[142] See ROWLINSON, S.M. An Analysis of Factors Affecting Project Performance in Industrial Buildings. PhD dissertation, Brunel University, United Kingdom, 1988.

[143] See SHOESMITH, DAVID R. A Study of the Management and Procurement of Building Services Work. *Construction Management and Economics*, 1996, **14**, 93–101.

[144] Clause 21.2 ECC. Cf other references to the applicable law in clauses 11.2(15), 23.1, 40.1 and 84.2 ECC.

bullet points. It is submitted that the use of two bullet points in the Second Edition coupled with the disjunctive 'or' between them underscores that the reasons operate independently of each other. The non-acceptance of the contractor's design for either of these reasons is permissive only. Thus it is not mandatory that the project manager refuse to approve the design if either reason exists as a fact. However, the contractor cannot proceed if this is the case as a matter of course. In this case other procedures in the ECC would become operative and could be relied upon as an alternative to non-acceptance of the design. For instance, the project manager may change the works information to comply with the design.[145] If this course of action is taken it will not amount to a compensation event.[146]

The term 'applicable law' is undefined. It is not unreasonable to equate it with the existing law regarding workmanship and materials and thus the provision could serve to introduce the case law in this regard to govern the matter. It is an open question whether acceptance by the project manager would override the necessity for compliance with the works information or whether the two requirements are cumulative. It may be noted that although the singular 'reason' is used, clause 12.1 is operative and thus, unless it can be argued that the context requires otherwise, words in the singular also mean in the plural. It is clear that the contractor is not to proceed with the works until there has been acceptance of the design by the project manager.[147] Thus no implied obligation to proceed in the absence of acceptance can arise. Once the project manager has accepted the allocation or particulars of the design responsibility any change to it is a compensation event.[148] In general, the contractor's design should correspond to that required under the conditions of tender as this facilitates comparisons by the employer in the evaluation of bids; e.g. the tender conditions may stipulate specifications, methods of measurement, codes of practice or otherwise.

The contractor agrees to an indemnity obligation that is additional to that set out in the risks and insurance core clause.[149] Thus the contractor agrees to indemnify the employer against any claims, compensation and costs due to the design infringing a patent or copyright. The operative wording is identical to clause 83.1 of the ECC. It should be noted that clause 21.4 does not expressly use the term 'design' but it is submitted that this is the meaning of the clause and would be read into or implied in any event. It may be noted that no similar obligation is imposed on the

---

[145] Clause 14.3 ECC. The ECC uses the term 'change' in other conditions including clauses 36.3, 36.4, 44.2 ECC.

[146] Clause 60.1(1) ECC excludes as a compensation event any instruction from the project manager which changes the works provided by the contractor for the design if made at the contractor's request or to comply with other works information provided by the employer.

[147] Clause 21.2 ECC.

[148] For example, under clause 60.1(1) or 60.1(8).

[149] See clause 83.1 ECC.

employer to indemnify the contractor against claims etc. that arise from use of the employer's design.[150] Although the drafting is not specific it may have been the intention of the drafters to pass on the risk of infringement of any form of intellectual property protection rights, e.g. an industrial design that is neither patented nor copyrighted. Even if this is the intention, however, it is still a narrower provision than other indemnity clauses which are not limited to design. The drafting may be contrasted with the copyright licence given under clause 5 of JCT MCWa/ P &T. Clause 5 covers copying, use and reproduction of the documents for any purpose relating to the building contract save extension of the works. In addition, and unlike the ECC, illustrations of the types of uses envisioned are given including letting, advertisement and promotion.

The most important consequence of responsibility for design is that the contractor becomes liable for defects resulting from errors in design. Clause 21.5 anticipates this and makes provision in this way:

> The Contractor's liability to the Employer for Defects due to his design that are not listed on the Defects Certificate[151] is limited to the amount stated in the Contract Data in addition to any damages stated in this contract for delay or low performance.

It may be observed at the outset that responsibility is limited to defects in the works rather than a liability for design *per se*. The definition of 'defect' in clause 11.2(15) of the ECC establishes in one respect that it is works of the design that are not in accordance with the works information. The length that forms now go to in seeking to overcome any diminishing of design responsibility through acceptance may be illustrated with reference to the BPF system which sanctions designs (effectively acceptance) with the words 'returned with no comment' endorsed upon the sanction. The *Manual of the BPF System* describes the method of sanctioning as *nihil obstat* or nothing hinders.[152]

The limitation or cap may be compared, for instance, to the ENAA model forms where the contractor's total maximum liability includes all liability for defects, patent infringement and liquidated damages for delay. The cap on liability in the ENAA forms was maintained, despite objections from the World Bank, for several reasons: the limited availability of insurance for these risks, the size of the risks, and contingency pricing concerns.[153] Several commentators on the provision argue that it goes too far by including defects and patent infringment.[154] It may be noted that loss of profit is a routine exclusion in process plant forms, such as FIDIC E & M, IChemE, and the UNCITRAL *Draft Legal*

---

[150]   Clause 21.4 ECC.

[151]   Clause 11.2(16) ECC.

[152]   *Manual of the BPF System, The British Property Federation System for Building Design and Construction*. British Property Federation, London, 1983, 35.

[153]   See JAYNES, GORDON L. Turnkey Contracts: Japan's Model Forms. *International Construction Law Review*, 1993, 265.

[154]   *Ibid.*, 269, n. 35.

Guide on Drawing Up International Contracts for the Construction of Industrial Works.[155]

Clause 21.5 is a limitation of liability provision and will be construed accordingly. In *Bovis Construction (Scotland) Ltd* v. *Whatlings Construction Ltd*, Lord Jauncey held: '[a] clause limiting liability should state clearly and unambiguously the scope of the limitation and will be construed with a degree of strictness, albeit not to the same extent as an exclusion or indemnity clause'.[156] Apart from the limitation of liability to an amount stated in the Contract Data the parties may also limit liability to exercising reasonable care by the inclusion of secondary option clause M in the conditions. Thus if clause M1.1 applies the contractor will not be liable for defects in the works due to design so far as the contractor proves that reasonable skill and care was used to ensure that the design did in fact comply with the works information.[157] The use of the term 'proves' in clause M1.1 is significant and must be taken to mean that the ordinary burden of proof upon the plaintiff in a negligence action of a breach of the standard of care has been reversed. It should be noted that the contractor need only prove that the requisite degree of care was taken to see that the design complied with the works information alone. Thus no liability would arise with respect to a defect, as defined, under clause M1.1 only because the works contravened the applicable law or the contractor's own design as accepted by the project manager.[158] In these cases the remedies would then arise under other clauses.[159] Where clause M1.1 does not apply, the standard of care, which is otherwise imposed in the conditions – namely fitness for purpose – continues to apply.[160] This conclusion follows, it is submitted, as the only reasonable interpretation that can be imposed when the parties are given a clear choice of a lesser standard of care, but which only applies exceptionally in the

[155] UNCITRAL *Draft Legal Guide on Drawing Up International Contracts for the Construction of Industrial Works* UN Doc A/CN9/WGV/WPG9/Add3.

[156] *Bovis Construction (Scotland) Ltd* v. *Whatlings Construction Ltd* 1995 SLT 1339 (HL) per Lord Jauncey at 1342 citing and applying *Ailsa Craig Fishing Co Ltd* v. *Malvern Fishing Co Ltd* 1982 SC (HL). See lately for illustrations *Copthorne Hotel (Newcastle) Ltd* v. *Arup Associates* (1998) 85 BLR 22 construing a limitation of liability clause, clause 3.21 of JCT 87 narrowly and not so as to protect a management contractor from liability for breach of certain duties; conversely *Moores* v. *Yakeley Associates Ltd* (1999) 62 Con LR 76 upholding a figure inserted in SFA 92 limiting liability of an architect for loss and damage arising from his actions; and *Deepak Fertilisers & Petrochemicals Ltd* v. *Dave McKee (London) Ltd and anor* (1999) 62 Con LR 86 (CA) upholding a clause excluding all liability in tort. See generally 'Limitation Clause: Inapplicable to Repudiatory Breach. *Building Law Monthly*, November 1995, **12**(11), 1. This distinction, although subject to some criticism, has been upheld by the Court of Appeal in *EE Caledonia Ltd* v. *Orbit Valve Co Europe* [1994] 2 Lloyd's Rep 239. Cf *Spriggs* v. *Sotheby Parke Bernet Ltd* [1986] 2 Lloyd's Rep 79.

[157] Clause M1.1 ECC.

[158] See clause 11.2(15).

[159] In particular, clauses 43.1, 44.2, 45.1 ECC.

[160] See the discussion of this topic above.

circumstances. *Reasonableness* as a concept is consistent with relational contract theory. Thus, as a reasonable interpretation test is often applied in the context of the surrounding circumstances, the relational context of the agreement is accommodated in this way.[161]

If the contract does not describe the required standard or level of performance of a product a court may imply a term relating to these matters. An important distinction is made with regard to the standard imposed when terms are implied under statute.[162] Thus, in the case of sale of goods, liability is strict while, in the case of services, the standard is that of reasonable skill and care alone. Liability for breach of statutorily implied terms cannot be excluded save where it is reasonable and only in the case of non-consumer contracts.[163] By way of comparison to the sale of goods 'fitness for purpose' is determined under section 14(3) of the Sale of Goods Act 1979. The test is relevant when the buyer has made known to the seller, expressly or impliedly, any particular purposes for which the goods are intended. However, where the circumstances show that the buyer does not rely, or that it is unreasonable for the buyer to rely, upon the skill and judgment of the seller the term will not be implied. Showing greater knowledge or experience on the part of the buyer may show a lack of reliance on the facts. The lack of reliance can also be shown by virtue of the employer assuming responsibility for choosing particular goods through a specification.[164] If these factors are taken into account in the context of the ECC it is submitted that the detailed provisions in the works information supplied by the employer may serve to preclude any argument by the employer that there has been reliance. Thus it will be less likely rather than more likely that an additional implied term as to the fitness of a particular product will be found. It would be a matter of interpretation of the contents of the works information if the details or specification were incomplete in any respect whether reliance could still be found. It is submitted that the converse is also true and if it is, in fact, the contractor who provides details of the design in contractor supplied works information a term may still be implied that the design or product will be fit for its intended purpose.[165] In general, in construction contracts involving contractor design and

---

[161] Nassar. *Sanctity of Contracts Revisited: A Study in the Theory and Practice of Long-Term International Commercial Transactions.* Martinus Nijhoff Publishers, Dordrecht, 1994, p. 27.

[162] For example, under the Sale of Goods Act 1979, section 13(1) and the Supply of Goods and Services Act 1982, section 3(2) all goods must corrrespond to their description; under the Sale of Goods Act 1979, section 14(6) and the Supply of Goods and Services Act 1982, section 4(2) as amended all goods in which property passes under a contract of sale of goods or work and materials must be of 'satisfactory quality'.

[163] See the Unfair Contract Terms Act 1977.

[164] See e.g. *Comyn Ching & Co Ltd* v. *Oriental Tube Co Ltd* (1979) 17 BLR 47. American case law is to the same effect: see e.g. *Stevens* v. *Parkford* (1920) 48 Cal App 131.

[165] See e.g. *Viking Grain Storage Ltd* v. *T H White and Anor* (1985) 33 BLR 103.

employer reliance, an implied term requiring fitness for purpose is implied in the absence of contrary provision. Recognition of this higher standard in the design and build context may be one reason why the FIDIC Orange Book has recently adopted it.[166]

A limitation of liability itself operates here on two levels; those defects due to the contractor's design which are listed in the defects certificate and those defects which are not. In this regard the defects certificate serves to mark a point in time when the limitation of liability provision in clause 21.5 becomes operative, namely, at the later of the '*defects date*' and the end of the last '*defect correction period*'.[167] The underlying premise is that the contractor is subject to an unqualified obligation to remedy defects up until that time.[168] Further, if the contractor has not corrected a notified defect by that time the project manager can assess the cost of having the defect corrected by other people and then recover the amount from the contractor.[169] Hence clause 21.5 addresses what may be inserted as a limitation on the amount of the contractor's liability for otherwise unremedied design defects beyond the later of the '*defects date*' and the end of the last '*defect correction period*'. The fact that it is unremedied design defects, or those *not* listed on the Defects Certificate, suggests the defects are unknown at the material time. The employer may stipulate any amount but it will be subject to the normal judicial controls in respect of limitations of liability. If no limit is intended to operate this too may be stipulated although a limit seems warranted. David B. Ashely advises:

> [u]se a clause where risk of most consequential damages are retained by the owner when consequential damages are unbearable and grossly out of proportion with contractor profit, a favourable owner-contractor relationship exists and the contract provides sufficient incentive for contractor performance ... [u]se a clause that has a limited risk, a cap on liability exposure, of consequential damages shifted to the contractor with most any project.[170]

In the case of no limit the drafters of the ECC recommend the term 'unlimited' be inserted.[171] Any limitation on the liability of the contractor in this regard is stated to be in addition to the other remedies of the employer to claim damages for delay or low performance.[172] In general, it has been shown in an American study that parties should

---

[166] Clause 4.1 FIDIC Orange Book 1st part I.

[167] Clause 43.2 ECC.

[168] Clause 43.1 ECC.

[169] Clause 45.1 ECC.

[170] ASHLEY, DAVID B. *et al. The Impact of Risk Allocation and Equity in Construction Contracts: An Overview of Indemnification, Consequential Damages, Differing Conditions and Delay Claims*. A Report to the Construction Industry Institute. The University of Austin, Austin, Texas, November 1988, pp. iii–iv.

[171] Guidance notes NEC on clause 21.5 ECC, 34. Cf *Temloc Ltd* v. *Errill Properties Ltd* (1987) 39 BLR 30, 12 Con LR 109, CA.

[172] Clause 21.5 ECC. See also discussion options R and S.

'[a]void the use of consequential damage clauses that shift all the risk onto the contractor. They adversely impact cost and quality in an effort to promote schedule. This clause also greatly inhibits owner-contractor working relations'.[173]

Using the contractor's design

The employer is given an express right to use and copy the contractor's design in these terms:

> The *Employer* may use and copy the *Contractor's* design for any purpose connected with construction, use, alteration or demolition of the *works* unless otherwise stated in the Works Information[174] and for other purposes as stated in the Works Information.[175]

Assuming no particulars have been inserted in the works information in this regard the clause confers broad rights on the employer regarding the contractor's design throughout the lifetime of the works. However, the broad rights themselves must still relate to the conditions which have been imposed, namely: 'construction, use, alteration or demolition'.[176] In comparison, the rights conferred in clause 22 contrast with the more limited licence given to the employer by the designer/(contractor) under JCT 81 and which exclude uses and alteration.[177] In addition, the rights in clause 22 may be contradicted in or removed from the works information and as such are not absolute. While the rights are referred to in these terms it may be noted that the works information may add to them as well thus expanding the employer's rights of use etc. In juxtaposition relational contract theory is less interested in ensuring limited enforceability and narrow rights and duties than in establishing acceptable bounds for the contractual relationship. In summary, while broad rights are given in the first instance they are not immutable, may not be as important as they appear given the other relationships between the parties and may be amended in any event if the parties deem fit.

The clause does not purport to alter the contractor's copyright in the plans and design which would exist as artistic works[178] or by direct analogy to cases involving architects. For example, Uthwatt J in *Meikle* v. *Maufe* held: 'the architect owns the copyright in the plans and also in the design embodied in the owner's building. The building owner may not therefore reproduce the plans or repeat the design in a new building without the architect's express or implied consent'.[179] The clause is not

---

[173] ASHLEY, DAVID B. *et al.*, iv.
[174] Clause 11.2(5) ECC.
[175] Clause 22.1 ECC.
[176] Clause 22.1 ECC; see also FC 22 ECC; cf ICE 6th clause 6 which gives the engineer 'full power to reproduce and use the [the design] ... for the purpose of completing operating maintaining and adjusting the Works'.
[177] See clause 9 JCT 81 on copyright, royalties and patent rights.
[178] See e.g. the Copyright, Designs and Patents Act 1988, sections 1, 3 and 4.
[179] Uthwatt J in *Meikle* v. *Maufe* [1941] 3 All ER 144 at 152.

tantamount to a licence to reproduce the design in new works and is expressly limited to 'any purpose connected with ... the *works*'. This wording is narrower than the original wording in the Consultation Document permitting the employer to 'copy the *Contractor's* design for carrying out or reconstructing the *Works*'. Reconstruction was undefined and arguably could have included replication of the works at another site and as such a licence to reproduce. Reproduction is envisaged under certain standard forms of appointment of architects[180] and now planning supervisors.[181] The contractor's remedies for a breach of copyright would include damages and injunctive relief.[182]

The licence to use the contractor's design may be contrasted with the use of the consultant's documents in the PSC. First, while the employer may use the consultant's documents, it may only be for uses stated in the brief in the First Edition and scope in the Second Edition.[183] Secondly, the use may only take place after the employer has paid the consultant.[184] It may be inferred from this, and the presence of a transfer of copyright provision among the secondary option clauses in the PSC First Edition, that the consultant retains copyright in the documents under the core clause.[185] Under the PSC even if copyright is transferred to the employer the consultant may still use designs and retain copies of documents unless restrictions have been agreed.[186] Any such restrictions on the consultant's use of designs and retention of copies of documents must be set out in the optional statements of part one of the Contract Data of the PSC.[187] The Second Edition of the PSC makes significant changes to the provisions beginning with the replacement of the heading 'Title' for the core clause with 'Rights to material'. Following on from this change the use of the term 'documents' previously is replaced by the broader term 'material' in the amended Second Edition. This also serves to better distinguish the subject matter of the clause from the contractual documentation. It is submitted that the term 'documents' used in the PSC is broad enough to include drawings, designs and plans. However, there is a use in the PSC

---

[180]   For example, clause 2.3.1 of the *Standard Form of Agreement for the Appointment of an Architect* (1992 RIBA). See generally WHEELER, PATRICK. Copyright in Construction Drawings and Works of Architecture. *Construction Law Journal*, 1991, **7**, 75.

[181]   For example, clause 10 of the *Form of Appointment as Planning Supervisors* (FOA 97/1). Association of Planning Supervisors, London, 1997.

[182]   See generally Copyright, Designs and Patents Act 1988, sections 1, 3 , 4, 10, 12, 96, 97 and *Meikle* v. *Maufe* [1941] 3 All ER 144.

[183]   Clause 70.1 PSC First Edition.

[184]   Clause 70.1 PSC First Edition. Payment of the consultant is determined with reference to the 'Price for Services Provided to Date' or 'PSPD': see clauses 11.2(15), 11.2(16), 11.2(17) in the PSC First Edition.

[185]   See secondary option clause G, 'Transfer of copyright', in the PSC First Edition and cf secondary option clause X9 'Transfer of rights' in the PSC Second Edition.

[186]   See clause G2 PSC First Edition.

[187]   Cf clause 13.4 PSC First Edition on the retention of copies of drawings, specifications and other documents by the consultant in other circumstances.

which is inconsistent with this interpretation when both 'designs' and 'documents' are referred to in the same clause such as clause G2 of the PSC. This may have been one of the reasons that the wording was changed to 'materials' in the Second Edition of the PSC.

Design of equipment

The design of equipment in clause 23 is addressed separately from the contractor's design in clause 21 although the two clauses bear significant similarities and dissimilarities. At the outset it is noteworthy that clause 21.2 alone is broad enough to encompass designs for equipment and would have done if clause 23.1 were not present. The inclusion of a separate clause for design of equipment could arguably be taken as evidence of an intention by the drafters to treat the design of equipment separately from design in general. This view is supported in several respects. First, the phrase '*Contractor's* design' appears almost as a term of art in the contract. It is used in both the marginal notes and consistently in clauses 21 and 22. Secondly, the phrase is also used independently in clause 23.1 itself; e.g. one of the three reasons given in clause 23.1 of the ECC for not accepting the design of an item of equipment is that it will not allow the contractor to provide the works in accordance with 'the *Contractor's* design ...'. Thirdly, acceptance of the contractor's design in clause 23.1 is not a prerequisite to proceeding with the design save where an instruction is given to this effect.[188] Fourthly, as clause 22 follows clause 21 and precedes clause 23 it is logical to assume it was only meant to apply to clause 21. Fifthly, the contractor's design under clause 21.1 pertains only to the '*works*' but 'equipment' is defined exclusively of the works.[189]

All of these reasons support the argument that the contractor's design, as it is used in clause 22.1, *excludes* the design of equipment and therefore the employer has no express right to the use etc. thereof. This argument seems plausible, particularly in the civil engineering context, although it is still only an argument and the intention of the drafters may well have been for the employer to have the same broad rights of use over equipment designs as over designs in general. If this were the intention then out of an abundance of caution that right might usefully be stipulated in the works information.

Clause 23.1 provides as follows:

The *Contractor* submits particulars of the design of an item of Equipment[190] to the *Project Manager* for acceptance if the *Project Manager* instructs him to. A reason for not accepting is that the design of the item will not allow the *Contractor* to Provide the Works[191] in accordance with

---

[188]   See clause 23.1 ECC.
[189]   Clause 11.2(11) ECC: 'Equipment is items ... which the Works Information does not require him to include in the *works*'.
[190]   Clause 11.2(11) ECC.
[191]   Clause 11.2(4) ECC.

- the Works Information,[192]
- the *Contractor's* design which the *Project Manager* has accepted, or
- the applicable law.[193]

Thus an instruction is required at the outset prior to the procedure for approval being invoked and unlike the procedure under clause 21.2 which applies automatically.

Three reasons are given for not accepting the design. The key to distinguishing these three reasons from the two reasons given in clause 21.2 is to *read in* the definition of 'Provide the Works' from clause 11.2(4) and distribute it over each reason in clause 23.1. If one does this each of the three reasons for non-acceptance is broadened to include 'all incidental work, services and actions which the contract requires'; clearly much broader than the clause 21.2 reasons. In addition, clause 22.3 appears to operate prospectively. Thus, even though the design of the equipment may technically comply at the time with the works information, if the design will not allow the contractor to provide the works, *viz.* 'complete the works in accordance with this contract',[194] non-acceptance of the design by the Project Manager is justified. Clause 21.2 does not support a prospective interpretation in this regard. It is significant that the second reason for non-acceptance entitles the project manager to overrule an earlier acceptance under clause 21.2. This clearly has implications for clause 21.2 in that it supports the interpretation of the meaning of acceptance, which is less than binding and conclusive. Acceptance of design, at least in relation to design of equipment, may be viewed as subject to a condition subsequent that it may be rescinded or revoked. The narrow meaning of acceptance is further reinforced by reference to part of clause 14.1, namely the project manager's acceptance of the contractor's work does not change the contractor's responsibility to provide the works or liability for the design. To reach this conclusion one need only read the meaning of 'work' in this clause as synonymous with contractor's design.

The interpretation used in clause 23.1 is repeated throughout the ECC and while one would expect to construe each clause individually one would also be entitled to expect that the drafters were striving for some uniformity of approach. The question that the drafting raises in each instance[195] is whether the reasons must all be present in each case for the

---

[192] Clause 11.2(5) ECC.
[193] The applicable law would include the Construction Products Directive, 89/106/EEC (OJ L40, 11 February 1989), implemented in the United Kingdom under the Construction Products Regulations 1991, SI 1991/1620, which cover products produced for incorporation in a permanent manner in both building and construction works and insofar as the essential requirements dictate.
[194] Clause 11.2(4) ECC.
[195] See for examples of clauses stipulating 'a reason' followed by singular or plural examples: clauses 13.4, 13.8, 15.1, 21.2, 23.1, 24.1

clause to operate. In most cases[196] the reasons are those of the project manager and are with respect to 'not accepting' something deriving from the contractor. Thus, it may be a reason for not accepting a proposal,[197] the contractor's design,[198] or the contractor's design of equipment,[199] a person,[200] a subcontractor,[201] a programme,[202] a revision,[203] policies and certificates,[204] a performance bond,[205] or a bank or insurer.[206] As a general matter it would seem that the reasons must be treated singularly and that the existence of any one or singular reason would entitle the action envisaged by the clause to be taken. This interpretation is consistent with the broadest grant of authority to the project manager to act under the form. The stipulation of reasons for refusal of approval and the indication of a time frame for approvals to be given are also two successful means of reducing disputes in the drafting of contracts.[207] In general, the project manager has no implied authority to warrant the accuracy of plans, specifications or quantities on behalf of the employer.[208]

People

Qualified people[209] at each level in the organization of a project are a fundamental tenet of management philosophy. In practice today few contracts on large projects are agreed without some knowledge on the part of the employer who will be representing the contractor. This requirement extends beyond corporate reputation and the contractor's ability to meet rigorous pre-qualification criteria to knowledge of the contractor's key personnel. However, while this is the norm standard forms of contract have at best recognized this in only a general fashion. Thus the obligation of the contractor in this regard under JCT 80 and JCT 81 is simply to 'keep upon the site a competent person-in-charge ...'.[210] Recognition that

---

[196] For example, clauses 13.4, 13.8, 35.3 ECC are exceptions.
[197] Clause 15.1 ECC.
[198] Clause 21.2 ECC.
[199] Clause 23.1 ECC.
[200] Clause 24.1 ECC.
[201] Clauses 26.2, 26.3, 26.4 ECC.
[202] Clause 31.3 ECC.
[203] Clause 54.3 ECC.
[204] Clause 85.1 ECC.
[205] Clause G1.1 ECC.
[206] Clause J1.2 ECC.
[207] SCHNEIDER, MICHAEL E., n. 92 above, 405.
[208] See *Scrivener* v. *Pask* (1865) LR 1 CP 715; *Sharpe* v. *San Paulo Rly Co* (1873) LR 8 Ch App 597.
[209] The ECC uses the term 'person' in the singular and 'people' in the plural without distinction. See clause 28.1 and part two of the Contract Data. See also clause 12.1 ECC. The heading for clause 24 is '**People**' in bold as are all marginal note headings. The July version used the boldfaced term incorrectly in four instances (clauses 25, 26, the Shorter Schedule of Cost Components and part two of the Contract Data) but has been corrected in the November version.
[210] Clause 10 JCT 80 and JCT 81.

such a general obligation may be insufficient can be argued on the basis of the far more extensive alternative supplementary provisions in JCT 81. The supplementary provisions in JCT 81 pertain to the appointment of a full-time site manager who acts as a representative of the contractor on the site and as the person in charge of the works.[211] The JCT 81 provision shares several features with those in the ECC including limitations on removal and replacement;[212] obligations to attend meetings convened by the employer;[213] and obligations to keep records,[214] which are available for inspection.[215] Although these provisions set out some important criteria neither of them extends as far as the detailed list of services provided by a management contractor pursuant to clause 1 of JCT 87 and listed in the Third Schedule to the form. Other forms have adopted still other approaches. FIDIC 4th adopts variable requirements depending upon the person and role to be fulfilled; thus if superintendence is performed by the 'Contractor' competence is assumed; conversely, only if the superintendence is to be performed by the contractor's delegate do the conditions (clause 15.1) then state that this person needs to be 'competent and authorised'. Hence, 'Technical assistants' must be 'skilled and experienced in their respective callings' while 'foremen and leading hands' need be 'competent'; and 'skilled, semi-skilled and unskilled labour' are referred to without specific qualification save that implied by the number necessary for proper and timely execution of the contractor's obligations[216] (clause 16.1(a), (b)). However, arguably competence of the labourers would be either assumed if the clauses are read together giving the engineer liberty to object to any person on various grounds including 'incompetence', or implied in any event.[217]

The weakness in a clause such as that in JCT 80 is that, while no contractor would admit to incompetent personnel on site, without criteria to assess competence (e.g. relevant qualifications and experience),[218] the ability to inspect records and the like, the clause becomes meaningless in practice. In addition, although there is a common law duty to provide competent staff, the duty does not appear to have been developed by the courts with much detail.[219]

---

[211] Clause S3.2 JCT 81.

[212] Clauses S3.2 JCT 81 and 24.1 ECC.

[213] Clauses S3.3 JCT 81 and 16.2 ECC. See generally The Aqua Group. Progress and Site Meetings. *Contract Administration for the Building Team*, 8th edn. Blackwell Science, London, 1996, 32–42.

[214] Clauses S3.4 JCT 81 and 52.2 ECC. See generally SCOTT, S. *Record Keeping for Construction Contractors*. CIOB, Ascot, 1995, Construction Paper 50.

[215] Clauses S3.4 JCT 81 and 52.3 ECC.

[216] FIDIC 4th clause 16.1(a), (b).

[217] See *Hudson* v. *Ridge Manufacturing Co Ltd* [1957] 2 QB 348, [1957] 2 All ER 229.

[218] Clause 24.1 ECC.

[219] See *Hudson* v. *Ridge Manufacturing Co Ltd* [1957] 2 QB 348, [1957] 2 All ER 229, one of the few cases affirming the duty and lately *Gloucestershire Health Authority and ors* v. *M A Torpy & Partners (t/a Torpy & Partners) and anor* (1997) 55 Con LR 124.

Turning to the mechanics of the provision in part two of the Contract Data the contractor can name up to two key people citing their job (description), responsibilities, qualifications and experience. Clause 24.1 states: 'The *Contractor* ... employs each key person ... in the Contract Data ...'. Hence key persons are only those so described in part two of the Contract Data. The proforma suggests only two will be named although clearly this number could be increased. No key persons, as this term is used, are referred to in part one of the Contract Data although clearly the contractor will be naming certain important individuals, e.g. the project manager, the supervisor and the adjudicator. Although the contractor need not necessarily complete this, in practice, employers who now have this option drawn to their attention and are aware of its importance will stipulate in the tender conditions that it be completed on submission or during any tender negotiations. Thus, although key people are included in part two of the Contract Data, in many cases the employer will dictate all details regarding the contractor's key people. The contractor is not contractually bound to employ these key people throughout the job. The term 'key' must be read into clause 24.1 of the ECC to give it this meaning. In comparison under clause 24.2 the term 'key' would not presumably be read in and thus the employer's right would be to instruct the removal of any employee of the contractor whether or not a key employee. This also differs from '*key person*' which is an identified term in clause 22.1 of the PSC, First Edition and with reference to those named in part two of the Contract Data of the PSC. It would seem the ECC provision should have adopted the PSC approach for consistency and thus used and italicized '*key person*' instead of 'key people' in part two of the Contract Data.

Thus a replacement for any one or more key people may be put forward but the replacement(s) must be acceptable to the project manager; providing the replacement's name would be regarded as a submission and that process, as well as acceptance, must comply with clause 13 of the ECC requirements. Acceptability is judged on the basis of the replacement's relevant qualifications and experience only. Although presumably the key person's job (description) would also have been relevant to their initial acceptance by the employer it is not referred to when the employer considers any replacement put forward under clause 24.1, and thus one may assume that the job description must remain unchanged for the replacement. The name itself will be clearly unimportant. This does not mean that the replacement's relevant qualifications and experience must be identical or even comparable to the person to be replaced.[220] However, if these attributes are not as good as those of the person to be replaced the project manager is still entitled not to accept the person put forward as the replacement.[221] Thus, in practice while one can expect the project manager to set high standards in the replacement of any key person, the ECC recognizes that some

[220] Clause 24.1 ECC.
[221] Clause 24.1 ECC.

allowances may have to be made and the project manager is thus given discretion in this regard. Assuming that no acceptable replacement(s) could be found it would constitute a breach of contract on the part of the contractor with the usual consequences. In contrast, clause 22.1 of the PSC, First Edition provides alternatively that the replacement may not be accepted because the replacements relevant qualifications and experience are not as good as those of the person who is to be replaced.

Apart from the issue of competency the project manager may also instruct the contractor to remove an employee whether or not a key person. The power of removal is both direct and onerous. Thus, in the case of such an instruction, the contractor must take steps to see that removal is effected within one day of the instruction and, in addition, that the employee then has no further connection with the contract work.[222] The project manager is under an obligation to state reasons supporting this instruction but no examples are given in the conditions. However, three possible reasons are given in the guidance notes: security; health and safety (communicable diseases), and disorderly behaviour prejudicing the employer's operations. Reasons stated in the guidance notes are treated differently from reasons stated in the conditions, for instance, withholding acceptance for a reason stated in the contract is not a compensation event (clause 13.8) but this provision would not cover a withholding for a reason stated in the guidance notes.[223] An analogy could be drawn with employment law and the notion of just cause to impose some additional limits on the reasons, which would be found to be supportable.[224]

Co-operation

In this book, co-operation has been held out as the single most important feature of the NEC. The fundamental principle of co-operation governing relations between the employer, contractor, project manager and supervisor[225] also finds expression in terms of the contractor's relations with others.[226] 'Others' is a defined term and refers to people or organizations who are *not* the '*Employer*', the '*Project Manager*', the '*Supervisor*', the '*Adjudicator*', the '*Contractor*' or any employee,

---

[222]   Clause 24.2 ECC. Cf clause 8.6 JCT 80: 'The Architect may (but not unreasonably or vexatiously) issue instructions requiring the exclusion from the site of any person employed thereon'. This power is not always given to the architect: e.g. JCT 81. FIDIC 4th clause 16.2 gives the engineer liberty to object to and require the contractor to remove any person who the engineer believes is responsible for misconduct, or is incompetent, or negligent, or even simply undesirable.

[223]   See guidance notes NEC on clause 24.2 ECC, 35.

[224]   See WAGAR, TERRY H. and JAMES, GRANT D. Dismissal for Incompetence: Factors used by Canadian Courts in Determining Just Cause for Termination. *Labor Law Journal*, 1993, **44**, 171–177; and FABIANO, MICHAEL D. The Meaning of Just Cause for Termination when an Employer Alleges Misconduct and the Employee Denies It. *Hastings Law Journal*, 1993, **44**, 399–420.

[225]   Clause 10.1 ECC.

[226]   Clause 25.1 ECC.

'Subcontractor' or supplier of the *'Contractor'*.[227] The number of positive examples where co-operation may be relevant is quite broad; for instance, a duty to co-operate in the obtaining of planning permission or other statutory consents,[228] or under clause U1.1 when the CDM Regulations apply.[229] A similar obligation may arise under a compliance with laws clause or one necessitating fulfillment of statutory obligations but the duty is not described in terms of co-operation. The guidance notes give the example of public utilities but clearly the duty is not limited to public utilities alone. However, the duty cast upon the contractor under clause 25 is narrower than its use in clause 10.1 of the ECC. Thus, under clause 25 the duty is limited on its wording to situations involving obtaining and providing of information that the others need in connection with the works, and to sharing of the working areas with others as stated in the works information. The other contractors and others as defined in the contract should be expressly referred to in the works information as well as what parts of the works they will occupy and for what period of time.[230] The emphasis upon co-operation and the implicit relational content that the provision entails stands in contrast to more decidedly legal bases for action.[231] The PSC contains another manifestation of the duty of co-operation, although the term itself is not used. Thus, where it is viewed as necessary to provide the services the consultant must hold or attend meetings with others.[232] The consultant must also inform the employer of the meetings and is given a right to attend.[233]

Subcontracting

The main provisions on subcontracting are contained in clause 26 of the ECC. There are three subclauses in the clause[234] and a fourth subclause in main options C, D, E and F.[235] The provisions generally provide that the contractor may subcontract if the project manager approves or ECC documents are used, specifically the NEC Engineering and Construction Subcontract (ECSC) or the NEC Professional Services Contract

---

[227] Clause 11.2(2) ECC.

[228] See guidance notes NEC on clause 25.1 ECC, 35.

[229] The CDM Regulations impose a duty upon designers to co-operate with the planning supervisor in Regulation 13(2).

[230] Guidance notes NEC, 22. Cf clause 23.1 PSC First and Second Editions which obliges the consultant to co-operate with others in obtaining and providing information rather in the scope.

[231] Cf the subcontractor's legal right to require a statement of contractual authority from the architect through the contractor under clauses 4.2 JCT 80 and 3.11 JCT NSC/C.

[232] Clause 23.2 PSC First and Second Editions.

[233] Clause 23.2 PSC First and Second Editions.

[234] That is clauses 26.1, 26.2 and 26.3 ECC.

[235] Clause 26.4; clause 26.3 was added to the 2nd Edition of the ECC, 'which is intended to encourage the use of the NEC sub-contract. This is still not a compulsory form': BIRKBY, GILLIAN. The New Engineering Contract. *Civil Engineering Surveyor Construction Law Review*, 1996, 26.

[236] Clause 26.3 ECC.

(PSC).[236] The ECSC and the PSC were both recommended in general terms in the Latham Report under paragraph 5.18: '3 A wholly interrelated package of documents ...', and paragraph 5.20: '6 A full matrix of consultants' and adjudicators' terms of appointment should be published, interlocked with the main contract'. The recommendation was adopted by the drafters.[237] However, in any case and notwithstanding whether the contractor subcontracts work, the contractor remains responsible for performing the contract as if he or she had not subcontracted and the main contract conditions apply as if the subcontractor's employees and equipment were the contractor's.[238] A subcontractor is defined in clause 11.2(9) of the ECC as 'a person or corporate body who has a contract with the *Contractor* to provide a part of the works or to supply Plant and Materials which he has wholly or partly designed specifically for the *works*'. The 'as if's would seem to operate like deeming provisions insofar as subcontractual arrangements are concerned. The intention is effectively to look past any subcontract arrangements and confirm the principal liability of the main contractor in all respects for performance of the main obligations. The continuing responsibility of the contractor for performing the contract notwithstanding subcontracting has other precedents.[239]

The main obligations of the contractor, once again, are defined with reference to the agreement to provide the works under clause 20. The employer has deemed the subcontractor's employees and equipment to be those of the contractor thus underscoring the intention once again to look past the subcontract arrangements that have been made. Hence, for example, if the employer sought and the project manager instructed the removal of an employee under clause 24.2, the contractor could raise no objection to the instruction on the ground that the employee belonged to the subcontractor. But, before the deeming provisions would operate it must still involve a subcontractor as defined in the contract, as third parties would be excluded.[240] The deeming provisions may also have extra-contractual implications although these are less well defined. It should be noted that, notwithstanding a similarly worded provision in the ECSC, the clauses together will still not override the necessity for privity of contract if the project manager and contractor were to have been given direct rights of action against subcontractors and sub-subcontractors respectively. It should be noted that, while there is no prohibition on subcontracting in general, as discussed above it is always open to the employer to vary this rule in the works information. Thus the employer

---

[237] Guidance notes NEC on clause 26.3 ECC, 36.
[238] Clause 26.1 ECC. A similar provision is contained in clause 18.2.2 JCT 81.
[239] For example, clauses 19.2.2 JCT 80 and 3.14 JCT NSC/C. The contractor–subcontractor relationship is problematic in general and has been exacerbated in practice by methods often utilized by contractors to place subcontractors at risk. See on these problems from the subcontractor's point of view: HINZE, H. and TRACEY, A. The Contractor–Subcontractor Relationship: The Subcontractor's View. *Journal of Construction Engineering and Management*, 1994, **120**, 274–287.
[240] Under clause 11.1(9) ECC.

could also list subcontractors which may not be acceptable; or work itself which is not to be subcontracted.[241]

The clause differs in one material respect from the Consultation Document and the First Edition. The Consultation Document expressly prohibited assignment in these terms: '[t]he *Contractor* does not assign the Contract'.[242] Although this reflects the wording prohibiting assignments in many of the standard forms[243] and technically only the benefit of a contract may be assigned, not the burden according to Lord Browne-Wilkinson in *Linden Gardens Trust Ltd* v. *Lenesta Sludge Disposals Ltd*,[244] clearly drafted prohibitions on assignment may render purported assignments by either party invalid.[245] The ECC acknowledges this distinction in (at least) one instance when it states in part in clause 96.2 P2: 'The Employer may instruct the Contractor to ... assign the benefit of any subcontract ...'.

The deletion of the provision from the Consultation Document is significant, for, in the absence of an express prohibition, assignment of the contract should be permitted. Cornes has commented on this omission as follows:

> [t]here is no requirement to obtain consent for an assignment from the other party, or even to notify the other party of an assignment by one party. Such notification is, of course, necessary to perfect a *legal* assignment[246] (as opposed to an *equitable* assignment). It follows that the benefit (but not the burden) of a party's obligation under the Second Edition can be freely assigned with no interference from the other party or, indeed, without the other party's knowledge.[247]

However, it would seem that this position accords with the general principle in law that a party to a contract may validly assign his or her rights under the contract to a third party without the consent of the other party, and, unlike the transfer of obligations by novation, requiring the consent of all concerned.[248] Thus, in general, even though the contractor could assign the contract the primary obligation to provide the works in accordance with the works information could not be novated.[249] The wording in this regard may be contrasted with other forms.[250]

---

[241] Guidance notes NEC, 26.
[242] Clause 26.1 ECC Consultation Document.
[243] See e.g. clause 9.1 JCT 80, clause 3 ICE 6th.
[244] *Linden Gardens Trust Ltd* v. *Lenesta Sludge Disposals Ltd* [1993] 3 All ER 417 at 427, HL, per Lord Browne-Wilkinson.
[245] *Helstan Securities Ltd* v. *Hertfordshire County Council* [1978] 3 All ER 262.
[246] CORNES. The Second Edition of the New Engineering Contract. *International Construction Law Review*, 1996, 100 citing Law of Property Act 1925, section 136.
[247] *Ibid.*
[248] *Nokes* v. *Doncaster Amalgamated Collieries Ltd* [1940] AC 1014, [1940] 3 All ER 549, HL.
[249] Clause 20.1 ECC; *Tolhurst* v. *Associated Portland Cement Manufacturers Ltd* [1903] AC 414, HL.
[250] See e.g. FIDIC 4th clause 3.1 prohibiting assignment without prior consent otherwise than by way of charge or concerning insurance.

There is no language in clause 26 which suggests that novation, that is, the replacement of the contractor by the subcontractor, is intended. In the usual course of events in a design and build situation, it would be more likely that the contractor would replace the employer's designers by novation.[251] Rather, the opposite intention appears in the language, which preserves the contractor's responsibility for performing the contract as if the contractor had not subcontracted and the application of the contract *as if* the subcontractor's employees and equipment were the contractor's.[252] To support this interpretation one should read the 'performing' of the contract in clause 26.1 as synonymous with providing the works in clause 20.1. The wording is also more consistent with vicarious performance by a subcontractor, in which case the contractor would remain liable for any defects of the subcontractor.[253] Hence it would seem no serious issue over the discharge of the liability of the contractor should arise if this interpretation is accepted.

With no prohibition on assignment in the ECC conditions assignment may be done by either the employer or the contractor and could be classified as either legal or equitable. The requirements for a legal assignment will differ in individual jurisdictions.[254] Where the requirements for a legal assignment are not satisfied it may still be valid as an equitable assignment.[255] Any assignment by either party would operate to transfer the assignor's rights to the assignee but subject to any pre-existing equities or defences that existed toward them as assignors. Assuming a valid assignment, a contractor under the ECC should be able to assign the right to present or future payments at the agreed assessment intervals,[256] any right to an advanced payment,[257] or retention money.[258] The employer, on the other hand, could also assign rights under the contract.[259] The employer's right to assign may comprise the right to

---

[251] See generally McNICHOLAS, PAUL. Novation of Consultants to Design Build Contractors. *Construction Law Journal*, 1993, **9**, 263

[252] Clause 26.1 ECC.

[253] *British Waggon Co and Parkgate Waggon Co* v. *Lea & Co* (1880) 5 QBD 149; *Nokes* v. *Doncaster Amalgamated Collieries Ltd* [1940] AC 1014, [1940] 3 All ER 549, HL; *Davies* v. *Collins* [1945] 1 All ER 247 at 249, CA, per Lord Greene MR.

[254] For example, in the United Kingdom the Law of Property Act 1925, section 136 requires a legal assignment to be absolute, in writing and with notice to the debtor.

[255] *Durham Bros* v. *Robertson* [1898] 1 QB 765, CA; *Brandt's Sons & Co* v. *Dunlop Rubber Co Ltd* [1905] AC 454 at 462, HL. See on the difference between legal and equitable assignments: *Tolhurst* v. *Associated Portland Cement Manufacturers Ltd* [1903] AC 414, HL.

[256] Clause 50.1 ECC; *Tancred* v. *Delagoa Bay and East Africa Rly Co* (1889) 23 QBD 239; *Durham Bros* v. *Robertson* [1898] 1 QB 765, CA.

[257] Clause J1 ECC.

[258] Clause P1 ECC; *G & T Earle Ltd* v. *Hemsworth RDC* (1928) 140 LT 69, CA.

[259] *Tolhurst* v. *Associated Portland Cement Manufacturers Ltd* [1903] AC 414, HL; *Dawson* v. *Great Northern and City Rly Co* [1905] 1 KB 260, CA; *South East Thames Regional Health Authority* v. *Y J Lovell (London) Ltd* (1985) 32 BLR 127; *Linden Gardens Trust Ltd* v. *Lenesta Sludge Disposals Ltd* (1992) 57 BLR 57, CA.

assign any property interest of the employer in the construction contract and should extend not only to the right to commence action in respect of past breaches but also to future performance of the contract as well.[260] The ECC does not state a sanction for breach of the subcontracting provisions requiring acceptance by the project manager unless the exceptions are satisfied; namely when the subcontract entails the use of the ECSC, the PSC or the project manager has agreed no submission of the subcontract conditions is required.[261] It is unclear whether breach is sufficient to justify termination at common law[262] but the employer is nevertheless authorized to terminate the contract for any reason[263] whatsoever and which could include a breach of clause 26.

The absence of a prohibition on assignment in the ECC may be contrasted with the inclusion of such a prohibition in the PSC. Pursuant to clause 24.1 of the PSC neither party shall assign any benefit of the contract in whole or in part.

There is no provision for nomination of subcontractors in the ECC. In general, outside the ECC subcontractors (and suppliers) which are chosen by and answerable to the main contractor are called 'domestic', while those who are chosen by and answerable to the employer are called 'nominated'. If they are nominated subcontractors the main contractor will enter into the subcontracts on the instructions of the employer. The absence of a provision for nomination is not unusual but not unique.[264] The reason for this choice was the perceived legal and practical problems arising from nomination.[265] The ECC seeks to achieve the objective of nomination in other ways. That is, the contractor is responsible for providing the works[266] and this responsibility remains even though the contractor may subcontract work.[267] Conversely, if work is subcontracted the employer, through the project manager, retains control over the selection of the subcontractors or the conditions of subcontract.[268] It is also open to the employer to list acceptable subcontractors for particular tasks, and either state work, which should either not be subcontracted or must be subcontracted.[269]

---

[260]   *Linden Gardens Trust Ltd* v. *Lenesta Sludge Disposals Ltd* (1992) 57 BLR 57, CA.

[261]   Clause 26.3 ECC.

[262]   *Thomas Feather & Co (Bradford) Ltd* v. *Keighley Corpn* (1953) 52 LGR 30.

[263]   Clause 94.2 ECC.

[264]   See e.g. the JCT MW form which makes no provision for either nomination or naming.

[265]   Guidance notes NEC on clause 26.2 ECC, 36. See generally for illustrations involving problems surrounding nomination: *North West Metropolitan Regional Hospital Board* v. *T A Bickerton & Son Ltd* [1970] 1 All ER 1039, [1970] 1 WLR 607, HL; *Percy Bilton Ltd* v. *Greater London Council* [1982] 2 All ER 623, HL; *Fairclough Building Ltd* v. *Rhuddlan Borough Council* (1985) 30 BLR 26, CA; and the Latham Report paragraphs 4.14–4.21, 27–30.

[266]   Clause 20.1 ECC.

[267]   Clause 26.1 ECC.

[268]   Clause 26.2 ECC.

[269]   Guidance notes NEC clause 26, 35–36.

Strong similarities may be drawn here between 'listing' and naming subcontractors under certain other forms as well as strong differences under other forms which cede the choice of subcontractors to the contractors. With regard to the acceptance of the subcontractor, no appointment may be made until that acceptance has been forthcoming from the project manager. Thus, under clause 26.2 the '*Contractor* submits the name of each proposed Subcontractor[270] to the *Project Manager* for acceptance'. Submission and consideration thereof must satisfy ECC, clause 13 requirements. It may be observed that it is only the 'name' that is required. This contrasts with the necessity to submit the qualifications and experience of key people under clause 24.1 of the ECC. It would improve the assessment process if these details were also required to be submitted for subcontractors. The project manager may refuse to accept the subcontractor if it is believed that this appointment will not allow[271] the contractor to provide the works.[272] By comparison to clause 24.3, the PSC First Edition, first bullet point would appear a broader ground for non-acceptance of the appointment of a subconsultant than a subcontractor; namely it would not allow the consultant to provide the services 'in accordance with this contract' when the consultant's principal obligation is rather to provide the services 'in accordance with the brief'. It may be noted that the grounds for non-acceptance of subconsultants under the PSC are generally broader than for subcontractors under the ECC. In this regard the reasons for non-acceptance in the case of the PSC substantially reproduce the reasons for not accepting replacement persons rather than for subcontractors[273] (see clauses 22.1, 22.2 and 24.3 of the PSC, First Edition and compare clauses 24.1 and 26.3 of the ECC). It must be recalled that this is the case even though the obligation to provide the works is the responsibility of the contractor alone.[274] This power of acceptance relates in part to a recommendation in the Latham Report that 'it should be a mandatory condition of the Core Clauses that the main contractor will only use the NEC subcontract in employing any subcontractor when using a formal document and will not amend any of the Core Clauses'.[275] Martin Barnes in reply noted how the recommendation was acted on. 'This has been adopted in principle but the client's project manager has the authority to waive the requirement where its effect would be harmless or pointless.'[276] The recommendation continued to add:

---

[270] Clause 11.2(9) ECC.

[271] The term 'allow' may have as wide a meaning as 'permit' and necessarily involves knowledge, consent or connivance of the person concerned: see *Crabtree* v. *Fern Spinning Co Ltd* (1901) 85 LT 549 at 553 per Darling J; *Gilbert* v. *Gulliver* [1918] VLR 185 at 189 per Cussen J; and *De Kuyper* v. *Crafter* [1942] SASR 238 at 243 per Richards J.

[272] Clause 26.2 ECC.

[273] See clauses 22.1, 22.2 and 24.3 PSC First Edition and cf clauses 24.1 and 26.3 ECC.

[274] Clauses 20.1 and 26.1 ECC.

[275] Latham Report paragraph 5.20(5), 39 in part (n. omitted).

[276] BARNES, MARTIN. The New Engineering Contract – An Update. *International Construction Law Review*, 1996, 92–94.

[t]hey [the Core Clauses] should only include those main and secondary options which are contained in the maincontract, unless both parties agree to changes in the options in the subcontract document. Subcontractors should accept similar restrictions on their contractual dealings with sub-subcontractors. If this spirit of co-operation which the NEC wishes to foster is achieved, such provisions should in practice be unnecessary. But in the present adversarial atmosphere, and with the need to change deep rooted cultural attitudes, it will add to confidence if they are included.[277]

The procedure for acceptance will vary depending upon whether the ECSC or PSC is being used for the subcontract and if so under which option. Thus, assuming that the ECSC or PSC is being used, then in the case of main options A or B the subcontractor can be appointed without more. There is an issue as to the degree of any amendments to either the ECSC or the PSC. Thus without a qualification in this regard substantially amended conditions may be put forward which would defeat the intent of back-to-back conditions. Presumably a point is raised where, in the project manager's view, the amendments could preclude the provision of the works in which case they would not be considered acceptable. In contrast if the ECSC or PSC is being used with either main options C, D, E or F then the contractor has no right to acceptance without more and instead may face an instruction from the project manager to submit the proposed Contract Data for acceptance for each subcontract.[278] The project manager may then not accept the proposed Contract Data if he or she states that its use will not allow the contractor to provide the works.[279] The submission for and acceptance of the proposed Contract Data must satisfy clause 13 requirements and the contractor should expect to be able to appoint the contractor if the reason noted is not given. The project manager would be unlikely to withhold acceptance on any other ground save more information being needed as it would be a compensation event under clause 60.1(9) of the ECC. Cornes[280] raises the question of the position of the project manager if he or she refuses a contractor permission to subcontract under certain conditions. He concludes[281] that the project manager would have no right to terminate the contract and, in the absence of another sanction, could claim nominal damages at best. However, this view overlooks the clear right given to the employer to terminate for any reason and which, it is submitted, would be an effective sanction against onerous subcontract conditions.

It has been assumed for the purpose of this discussion that the ECSC or the PSC was being used for the subcontract. However, if either is not being used and in any case where the project manager has not agreed that

---

277   Latham Report paragraph 5.20(5), 39.
278   Clause 26.4 ECC.
279   Clause 26.4 ECC.
280   CORNES, see n. 246 above, 97.
281   *Ibid.*

no submission is required for the subcontract, then the contractor must not appoint the subcontractor on the proposed subcontract conditions until the project manager has accepted them.[282] Thus, just as the contractor had alternatively to submit the proposed Contract Data for the subcontract under main options C, D, E or F, under main options A or B the contractor may have to submit the proposed subcontract conditions. Two reasons are given as exemplars for the project manager's refusal to accept the proposed subcontract conditions. The first is similar to that in relation to refusal to accept the proposed subContract Data; thus they will not allow the contractor to provide the works.[283] The second ground for non-acceptance of the proposed conditions of subcontract is unique and it is when they do not include a statement that the parties to the subcontract shall[284] act in a spirit of mutual trust and co-operation.[285] This statement is, of course, both critical and mandatory to the operation of the subcontract and the relationship between the contractor and subcontractor. If the project manager does accept the proposed subcontract conditions then the contractor can appoint the subcontractor. The submission for acceptance must meet clause 13 requirements in general. As no period for reply by the project manager is given, thus it falls to be determined according to the general period for replies agreed to by the parties in part one of the Contract Data. The withholding of an acceptance of a subcontractor or approval of a subcontractor's non-ECC conditions of subcontract for any other reasons, save that more information is needed,[286] constitutes a compensation event.[287] In general it can be expected that the parties will work together in ensuring acceptance. The notifications should be made as early as possible during the tender stage and either acceptance by the project manager be given or agreement of the parties be reached. The subcontractor should be particularly careful to reflect in the subcontract conditions additional clauses inserted by the employer in the main option chosen as well as any secondary options clauses. It is also possible that the subcontract may contain specialist provisions absent from the main option. Indeed there is much that would be expected to be imported by amendment into any subcontract conditions accepted that were not ECSC, otherwise the contractor would be assuming a very large and potentially unqualified obligation toward the employer. It has been suggested by Ernest J. Bayton that amendments to non-ECSC conditions might need to include importation of early warning procedures, sub-subcontracting, access to the work, programme requirements, defects correction, compensation

---

[282] Clause 26.2 ECC.
[283] Clause 26.3 ECC.
[284] BAIRD, ANDREW. The New Engineering Contract – A Management Summary for Plant Industry Users. *International Construction Law Review*, 1994, 118 notes the use of the term aligns with modern 'goal-directed' motivational planning techniques.
[285] Clause 26.3 ECC.
[286] Clause 13.4 ECC.
[287] Clause 60.1(9) ECC.

event procedures, title provisions, insurance requirements and dispute resolution to name certain provisions.[288]

In summary, although the broad grant of discretion to the project manager to refuse to accept a subcontractor will not achieve precisely the same result as if a nomination provision had been included in the contract it can be used to almost similar effect. However, the grant of discretion to the project manager is new and he should be aware of his new responsibility in this regard and in contrast to roles comparable under traditional forms. The employer also has other means to influence the choice of subcontractor notably in the conditions of tender or through other criteria for the award of subcontracts contained in the works information. Although there is no express requirement for the contractor to comply with any such requirements in the works information,[289] if lists of acceptable subcontractors were included in the works information then the contractor would be obliged to respect these in accordance with the principal obligation.[290] This raises an open question: would a court regard the listing of acceptable subcontractors in the works information as tantamount to nomination? Once again no precise answer is given and as noted this may entail considerable legal and practical problems if construed as such.

The employer may prefer separate contracts with the subcontractors as an alternative means of control and leave the project manager to deal with both the time and physical interfaces across them.[291] Baird has commented on the improvements that are derived through a single form of contract in this regard. 'Contract interfaces on multicontract projects, subcontracting to different trades and disciplines, office productivity, training, administration support procedures, staff mobility and legal support are all made easier and therefore less costly.'[292] In terms of staffing generally the NEC does not anticipate overall higher staffing rates in running the contract over its entire duration compared with other contracts; however, the staffing levels at different stages of the work will depart from that under other contracts. Thus staffing levels are initially higher at the early stages of the work given the necessity for thorough design information but later fall below other comparable staffing levels for other contracts. This has been shown typically to be the case in the maintenance period where there are often fewer claims to deal with than under other traditional forms.[293] In main options C, D, E and F subclause 4^{294} deals with subContract Data rather than subcontract conditions in

---

[288] BAYTON, ERNEST J. An Introduction to the Engineering and Construction Contract. A course given at Altrincham on 3 March 1998. Thomas Telford, London, 1998, p. 38.

[289] It may be noted that this was an express requirement in the main options C, D, E and F of the Consultation Document that was subsequently deleted.

[290] Clause 20.1 ECC.

[291] Guidance notes NEC on clause 26.2 ECC, 36.

[292] BAIRD, ANDREW. The New Engineering Contract – A Management Summary for Plant Industry Users. *International Construction Law Review*, 1994, 117.

[293] Ernest J Bayton comment made based on experience of NEC Users' Group members.

[294] Clause 26.4 in each of these main options.

subclause 3. The two subclauses superficially resemble each other but subclause 4 actually reverses the requirement for submission to the project manager when ECC documents are involved.[295] Thus when the stipulated documents are used the proposed subContract Data must be submitted to the project manager for acceptance. The inclusion of this requirement in only four of the main options indicates that greater control over the works is vested in the project manager with respect to these options than with main options A and B, and only one reason, that of not allowing the contractor to provide the works, is then given for the project manager not accepting the proposed subContract Data.[296]

Approval from others

The ECC uses both the terms 'acceptance' and 'approval' in the form.[297] 'Acceptance' is used in a very wide variety of situations ranging from acceptance of communications[298] and defects,[299] to acceptance of programmes,[300] and replacement persons[301] among others.[302] In contrast, 'approval' is used in only one sense; that is, in clause 27.1 regarding the requirement of the contractor to obtain approval of his or her design from others where necessary.[303] This distinction must be taken to be deliberate. This contention is underscored regarding the subject of clause 27 – design – when it is noted that it is also dealt with in terms of acceptance. Thus under clause 21.2 acceptance of the contractor's design by the project manager is a prerequisite to proceeding with the works. Similarly acceptance of the design of items of equipment may also be subject to the necessity of acceptance by the project manager if so instructed.[304]

To invoke clause 27, approval from others as defined in the contract[305] must be necessary. The party responsible for obtaining[306] approvals under

---

[295] For example, the ECSC or the PSC.

[296] Clause 26.4 ECC.

[297] See discussion of these terms above.

[298] Clauses 13.1 and 13.4 ECC.

[299] Clause 44 ECC.

[300] Clauses 31.1 and 50.3 for first programmes and clauses 32.2, 36.3, and 64.2 ECC of revised programmes.

[301] Clause 34.1 ECC.

[302] For example, clauses 21.2, 26.2, 26.3, 62.3, 65.1, 85.1, 87.1, 87.2 and 95.2 ECC.

[303] Clause 27.1 ECC. Cf clause 25.1 PSC First Edition where the consultant is obliged to obtain approval from others where stated in the brief, and under clause 25.1 PSC Second Edition the similar but broader worded obligation to obtain such approvals where necessary to provide the services.

[304] See clause 23.1 ECC.

[305] 'Others' are defined in clause 11.2(2) ECC as 'people or organisations who are not the *Employer*, the *Project Manager*, the *Supervisor*, the *Adjudicator*, the *Contractor* or any employee, Subcontractor or supplier of the *Contractor*'.

[306] To 'obtain' primarily means to come into possession or enjoyment of something by one's own effort or by request; to procure or gain as the result of purpose and effort, hence generally, to acquire, to get: see *Re Woods, Woods* v. *Woods* [1941] St R Qd 129 at 137 per Philp J.

the clause is the contractor where *necessary*. Thus if the approval cannot be said to be necessary the contractor is under no obligation pursuant to clause 27 to obtain it. If there are approvals which are perhaps advisable but not necessary the responsibility shifts to the employer. Although the clause is thus drafted using very open drafting, if the parties wish they could always agree on which approvals are in fact necessary and set them out in the works information and provided they are exhaustive of the contractor's obligation to seek approvals. This would, of course, have the effect of once again reallocating any unassigned approvals, which are subsequently required to the employer. Returning to approvals in general, under the procedure to be followed, and assuming that an approval is necessary, the contractor will be expected to lodge the application. If the application is successful, the contractor will have satisfied the responsibility under the clause. However, if the application is unsuccessful, the contractor may wish to consider whether the failure merits invoking the early warning procedure.[307] The prudent contractor will err on the side of caution and give the early warning. The outcome will then depend upon how the project manager views the failure to obtain the approval. If it is decided that the contractor was responsible for obtaining the approval the project manager may suggest to the contractor at the early warning meeting that the application be revised and resubmitted for approval. If the contractor agrees with this decision then he or she may be expected to take the action. Proposals are considered and decisions taken at the early warning meeting, particularly in terms of which actions will be taken and who will take them and this course of pursuit is thus probable. However, a decision could also be taken to pursue some alternative to approval in which case clause 27 would no longer be relevant to the process. The early warning procedure is particularly appropriate because of the power of either the contractor or the project manager to instruct 'other people' to attend the meeting. There is no express limitation on those defined as 'Others' in clause 11.2(2) being included in any such instruction. Depending upon the nature and complexity of the approval sought further revisions and reapplication cannot be ruled out.

Access

The ECC sets out rights of access in favour of both parties to the contract. The absence of such a provision in favour of both parties would otherwise be addressed by implying the right. Access would be limited to property under their control and thus would not extend, for instance to adjoining or adjacent property.[308] Thus the contractor is under a dual access obligation to provide access to work being done and to provide access to plant and materials being stored for the contract.[309] The contractor must give access

---

[307] Clause 16 ECC.
[308] See lately on implied rights of access *Milburn Services Ltd* v. *United Trading Group (UK) Ltd* (1997) 52 Con LR 130.
[309] Clause 28.1 ECC.

to the project manager, supervisor and others notified to the contractor by the project manager.[310] The right to access on the part of those named seems to exist without more, at least with respect to the access of the project manager and supervisor, and no qualifications on the right of access are given.[311] However, there is a notice requirement in respect of others. In addition, the project manager must notify the contractor of their access.[312] Notification in this way would follow normal clause 13 requirements. Access given by the employer is arranged through the project manager in respect of those parts of the works that the employer has taken over.[313] This latter right of access extends to use of those parts of the works given although only for the purpose of correcting defects.[314] The wording of the dual access obligation acknowledges the fact that works may be carried out in working areas separate from the site. Access to work being done and to plant and materials may be important for various reasons, e.g. carrying out tests and inspections[315] or marking same for the purpose of passing title.[316] This obligation is carried forward in ECSC provisions. Thus, in addition to the project manager and supervisor, the subcontractor must also provide access to the contractor and others notified by the contractor or the project manager.[317]

Instructions

An affirmative or mandatory obligation is imposed upon the contractor to obey instructions which are given in accordance with the contract and whether given by the project manager or the supervisor. Thus, clause 29.1 of the ECC provides: '[t]he *Contractor* obeys an instruction which is in accordance with this contract and is given to him by the Project *Manager* or the *Supervisor*'.[318] In addition to this general exhortation to obey instructions the contractor may also be under a more specific duty to 'put the instruction ... into effect'.[319] There are a large number of clauses in the ECC that authorize either the project manager or supervisor to issue instructions to the contractor. These provisions may be listed, for instance, in relation to changing the works information;[320] attending an early

---

[310] Clause 28.1 ECC.

[311] See clause 28.1 ECC.

[312] Clause 28.1 ECC.

[313] Clause 43.3 ECC.

[314] See discussion of clause 43.3 below.

[315] See section 4 'Testing and Defects'. The entitlement of access for the supervisor reinforces this rationale.

[316] See section 7 'Title'.

[317] Clause 28.1 ECSC. See also clause 26.1 stating that the contract applies *as if* a subcontractor's employees and equipment were the contractor's.

[318] Cf clause 3.5 JCT MW which imposes no limitations on the instructions which the architect may order. Cf also clause 21.3 PSC Second Edition which obliges the consultant to comply with instructions given by the employer to change the brief only insofar as it is practicable.

[319] Clause 61.1 ECC.

[320] Clauses 14.1, 19.1, 44.2 ECC. See also clause 60.1(1) ECC.

warning meeting;[321] resolving an ambiguity or inconsistency in contract documents;[322] requiring submission of design particulars;[323] removing an employee;[324] stopping or not starting work;[325] submitting quotations;[326] searching;[327] dealing with objects and materials within the site;[328] and leaving the site.[329] The power to issue instructions generally and in relation to one or more of these matters is given routinely in all standard forms. The instructions given with regard to stopping or not starting work may both be countermanded under clauses 60.1(4) and 95.6 of the ECC. If the instruction pertains to either all work or substantial work and the instruction countermanding the original instruction is not issued with 13 weeks termination rights also arise.

The requirement for the instruction to comply with the contract acts as a limitation on the scope of instructions that the architect may issue. It can be contrasted with the absence of limitation in the JCT MW form. Clause 3.5 of the JCT MW provides simply: '[t]he Architect/Contract Administrator may issue written instructions which the contractor shall forthwith carry out'. No procedure is outlined giving the contractor a right to object to an instruction. The failure of the contractor to obey an instruction entitles the employer to engage another contractor, without terminating the original contractor, to execute a portion of the works and recover the cost from the original contractor. Similar powers are given to the employer under clause 4.1 of the JCT 81. The time frame for compliance with the instruction is unqualified[330] although in certain instances the terms of the contract will stipulate a time frame for acting on an instruction.[331] The giving of the instruction may also have to be accompanied by reasons.

No obligation is imposed upon the contractor to comply with any instruction that is not in accordance with the contract. However, unless certain that this is the case, the contractor would be better advised to obey the instruction and dispute it using the adjudication procedures. In this way the contractor lessens the risk of an unjustified repudiation of the contract. The adjudication procedures themselves assume the status quo in any event unless and until there is a settlement by either the parties themselves or the adjudicator.[332]

---

[321]   Clause 16.2 ECC.
[322]   Clause 17.1 ECC. See also clause 63.7 ECC.
[323]   Clause 23.1 ECC.
[324]   Clause 24.2 ECC.
[325]   Clause 34.1 ECC.
[326]   Clauses 36.1, 61 and 62 ECC.
[327]   Clause 42.1 ECC. See also clause 60.1(10) ECC.
[328]   Clause 73.1 ECC. See also clause 60.1(7) ECC.
[329]   Clause 96.2 P2 ECC.
[330]   Cf JCT 80 clause 4.1 that the Contractor shall 'forthwith' comply with all instructions; that is, as soon as reasonably can be: *Hillingdon London Borough Council* v. *Cutler* [1968] 1 QB 124, [1967] 2 All ER 361, CA.
[331]   For example, under clause 62.3 the contractor must submit a quotation within three weeks of being instructed to do so.
[332]   Clause 90.2 EEC and clause 90.9 amended 2nd ECC.

8. Time

The industry is dysfunctional. The symptoms are the delivery of projects late and over budget, low productivity and poor returns, and slow take-up of new technology.

Roger Flanagan, Ian Ingram and Laurence Marsh,
A Bridge to the Future. Profitable Construction for Tomorrow's Industry and Its Customers

General

The ECC core clause entitled only 'Time' is remarkable in its simplicity and unmatched by other forms in this regard. The clause centres upon the key concepts of starting and completion, programme, possession of the site and take over. The clause also addresses instructions in relation to stopping or not starting the work, and acceleration. The theme of time in relation to and its importance with regard to these concepts is underscored by the titling. In terms of the project management literature time, cost and quality are 'linked parameters'. Time and cost factors can also be used to measure project performance and both factors correlate well with project success in certain circumstances under management contracting in particular.[1] The concepts addressed in the third core clause, particularly when read with those in the fourth core clause, 'Testing and Defects', makes that linkage abundantly clear. These concepts and linkages are discussed below.

Starting and completion

Standard form contracts normally impose a fixed date for completion of the works. In the ECC both start and completion dates are given. However, pursuant to one short provision the contractor is *not* to start work on the site until the first possession date. The possession dates are inserted in part one of the Contract Data, section 3 and may pertain to parts of the site. The employer must give the contractor possession of the site in accordance with clause 33. In electrical and mechanical plant contracts the possession

---

[1] See NAOUM, G. Critical Analysis of Time and Cost of Management and Traditional Contracts. *Journal of Construction Engineering and Management*, 1994, **120**, 687–705.

of the site may not be required for much of the period of the contract as offsite design and fabrication is carried on after the starting date but prior to the first possession date. Under the ECC partial possession of the site is also envisaged and in this regard parallels clauses 42.2 of the FIDIC 4th and 42(1),(2) of the ICE 6th.[2] It has been noted that time and cost factors can also be used to measure project performance and both factors correlate well with project success in certain cases. Conversely, the contractor must also do the work so that completion is achieved on or before the completion date itself.[3] Several observations may be made concerning the prohibition on starting work. First of all, it pertains only to the work on the site; thus, while working areas would normally include everything within the boundaries of the site, it is also possible for the contractor to stipulate additional working areas that fall *outside* the site and hence begin work there. Provision is made for this eventuality in part two of the Contract Data; therefore, quite apart from work on the physical site much other work can, of course, still be done.

Secondly, moving to the affirmative obligation that is then imposed on the contractor in clause 30.1 he or she must do the work, or complete the work, on or before the completion date. The 'Completion Date' is defined simply as 'the *completion date* unless later changed in accordance with this contract'[4] and must also be read with clause 11.2(13). Thus, 'Completion is when the *Contractor* has done all the work which the Works Information states he is to do by the Completion Date and corrected notified Defects which would have prevented the *Employer* from using the *works*'. The operative phrase or act in both clauses 11.2(13) and 30.1 is 'to do'. It is submitted that this choice of wording is both deliberate and (although the wording is not definitive) significant. Thus, it is argued here that current wording in these two clauses may be contrasted to wordings under other standard forms which oblige the contractor to progress the works; in particular to proceed regularly and diligently in carrying the works out. The contrast arises from the fact that the ECC wording is *unqualified*. Thus if the contractor is not doing the work such that timely completion will be achieved, a breach is committed which is remediable under the contract. The obligation in this regard stands in addition to the principal obligation to provide the works. Significantly the project manager decides the actual completion date and must certify this fact within one week of completion.[5] Determining completion and the completion date must also be considered in relation to the secondary option clauses; thus if option L applies, the references to these two terms in the conditions of contract may refer to either the whole of the works or any section of the works. There are other instances when

---

[2] By comparison while JCT 80 and IFC 84 require possession of the site to be given to the contractor on a date stated, the JCT Minor Works form allows for the date of possession to be on a date to be inserted.
[3] Clause 30.1 ECC.
[4] Clause 11.2(12) ECC.
[5] Clause 30.2 ECC. See also the discussion of clause L1.1 ECC below.

the project manager must decide matters under the contract such as those under clauses 50.1, 61.4 and 61.5 of the ECC as well as certify matters under clauses 35.4, 51.1 and 94.4 of the ECC.

The ECC seeks to achieve a measure of flexibility regarding the completion date so that it works well across the various methods of procurement. In general, two options were available to the drafters. One was to follow the route taken by JCT forms and specify the actual date for completion,[6] the other to adopt the ICE route, which requires that the works be completed within a specified period of time from the commencement date.[7] The drafters of the ECC have opted for the ICE route. Thus no fixed period of time is stated during which the contractor is to provide the works. Rather, part one of the Contract Data lists the starting date and the completion date. Depending upon the conditions of tender either one or both of the dates may be inserted by the employer and may or may not be subject to negotiations with the contractor. Clearly changes to the completion date would have an effect on prices.

Certain consequences follow from agreement on a completion date. If for any reason a completion date were not inserted in part one it might be possible to imply a term for a date certain on evidence of the parties' presumed intentions.[8] In the absence of a time for completion, and where the court is unable to imply a date, the contractor's obligation will be to complete within a reasonable time. In this case, time is said to be 'at large'.[9] Time may be set at large for a number of reasons including acts of prevention or interference by the employer[10] when no extension of time can be awarded. The most important consequences of this occurring are that provisions for extension of time, and provisions for liquidated and ascertained damages – delay damages in the language of the ECC may well fail.[11] By comparison, under clause 1.1(c)(i) of FIDIC 4th, 'time for completion' is defined as 'the time for completing the execution of and passing the Tests on Completion of the Works or any Section or part thereof as stated in the Contract ... calculated from the Commencement Date'.

These issues follow directly from the contractor's principal obligation to provide the works.[12] They are influenced by the secondary option clauses the parties have chosen. Once the project manager has decided the

---

[6] For example, the appendix to the JCT 80 leaves a blank for insertion of the completion date.

[7] Clause 43 of the ICE 6th, and clause 1.1(c)(i) of FIDIC 4th.

[8] See *Bruno Zornow (Builders) Ltd* v. *Beechcroft Developments Ltd* (1990) 51 BLR 16.

[9] *Holme* v. *Guppy* (1838) 3 M & W 387 at 389 per Parke B.

[10] See generally *Holme* v. *Guppy* (1838) 3 M & W 387; *Roberts* v. *Bury Improvement Comrs* (1870) LR 5 CP 310; *Peak Construction (Liverpool) Ltd* v. *McKinney Foundations Ltd* (1970) 1 BLR 114, CA; *Rapid Building Group Ltd* v. *Ealing Family Housing Association Ltd* (1984) 29 BLR 5, CA.

[11] See *Wells* v. *Army & Navy Co-operative Society Ltd* (1902) 86 LT 764, CA; *Peak Construction (Liverpool) Ltd* v. *McKinney Foundations Ltd* (1970) 1 BLR 114, CA.

[12] See clause 20 ECC.

date of completion,[13] the contractor is under a mandatory obligation to achieve completion on or before that date.[14] Completion as noted may also be in respect of a part of the works. If the deadline is not met and the parties have chosen option L, the contractor would have to pay delay damages at the rate stated in the Contract Data from the completion date until the earlier of completion and the date the employer takes over the works.[15] No subsequent change to the completion date is assumed for these purposes. While this is the negative scenario for the contractor it may also happen that completion is achieved before the completion date. If so, and the parties have chosen option Q to apply, the contractor may be paid a bonus calculated at a rate stated in the Contract Data for each day from the earlier of completion and the date on which the employer takes over the works until the completion date.[16] In both the delay damages and bonus for early completion cases it may be expected that the project manager will issue the completion certificate at the end of the process and within one week of completion itself.[17] Failure on the project manager's part to do so may entail recourse to the early warning procedure in clause 16. This clause, and numerous others in the ECC, uses the term 'within'. The general rule in cases where an act is to be done *within* a specified time, is not to count the day from which something runs.[18] An American study has concluded parties should '[s]hare delay risk where each party is responsible for its own delays and concurrent delays are shared to the extend each party is responsible'.[19]

Programme

'Only recently has the industry awakened to the usefulness of the programme in the administration and control of the contract'.[20] Programming as a discipline is relatively new and Robert R. Kumlin states that it did not emerge as a separate discipline until 1966 with the publication of a booklet by the American Institute of Architects.[21] The

---

[13] Clause 30.2 ECC.

[14] Clause 30.1 ECC.

[15] Clause R1.1 ECC.

[16] Clause Q1.1 ECC.

[17] Under clause 30.2 ECC.

[18] See *Goldsmith's Co* v. *West Metropolitan Railway Co* [1904] 1 KB 1, [1900–03] All ER Rep 667. A requirement that something be done within a specified period means that the full amount of that period, up to midnight on the last day, is available: see *Manorlike Ltd* v. *Le Vitas Travel Agency and Consultancy Services Ltd* [1986] 1 All ER 573, (1986) 278 *Estates Gazette* 412.

[19] ASHLEY, DAVID B. *et al*. *The Impact of Risk Allocation and Equity in Construction Contracts: An Overview of Indemnification, Consequential Damages, Differing Conditions and Delay Claims*. A Report to the Construction Industry Institute. The University of Austin, Austin, Texas, November 1988, p. v.

[20] McGOWAN, PAUL H. *et al*. *Allocation and Evaluation of Risk in Construction Contracts*, CIOB, Ascot, 1992, Occasional Paper 52, 4 n. 20 citing The Need For and Features of the NEC.

[21] KUMLIN, ROBERT R. *Architectural Programming Creative Techniques for Design Professionals*. McGraw-Hill, New York, 1995, pp. 3–6, by the AIA and called

role of the programme in traditional contracting from a legal perspective is slight.[22] Very often the programme is not a contract document and as a result it can be difficult to enforce adherence to it. One consequence of this is that contractors often pay little attention to programmes and their importance is diminished, although this does not accord with good practice.[23] While this view can be put forward from the legal perspective it contrasts markedly with the importance of the programme to the actual measured progress of the works; that progress may be understood in three respects: historically, as-built, and as forecast. Poor monitoring and control, as individual factors, have been ranked, based on a study by Majid and McCaffer, as the fourteenth most significant factor in causing non-excusable delay.[24] On site the programme, howsoever represented, is critical for an accurate understanding of progress on site. The NEC does not limit the form which the programme may take and thus it could include bar charts, critical path routines, precedence diagrams, schedules, network analysis or otherwise; in fact no limit is placed upon two or more of these forms serving in combination as the programme. In contrast the FIDIC Orange Book 1st part 1, clause 4.14 expressly mandates that precedence networking techniques be used. The Orange Book provision moves the debate onto new ground with this specificity.

> Delay in completion can be the greatest cause of extra cost, and of loss of financial return and other benefits from a project. The first estimate of cost and benefits should be based on a realistic programme for a project. On this basis the potential effects of delays can be predicted realistically.[25]

The ECC attempts a reconciliation of the legal and on site views toward programmes by permitting the parties to include a programme as one of the contract documents either upon acceptance or when later prepared and

---

Emerging Techniques of Architectural Practice. AIA Press, Washington, 1966. The pioneering AIA work was followed up shortly in 1969 with another AIA publication *Emerging Techniques 2: Architectural Programming.* AIA Press, Washington, 1969 and thereafter with many other titles.

[22] For example, under JCT forms of contract, although exceptions do exist, most notably the BPF form of contract: see section 2.5, 'Master programme', the *Manual of the BPF System*, 27; see also *Construction Management Forum Report and Guidance.* University of Reading, Reading, 1989, section 7.0, 39–40. More recently MF/1 Revision 3 has significantly increased the detail that is required in the Contractor's programme under clause 14.1.

[23] See *Programmes in Construction – a Guide to Good Practice.* CIOB, Ascot, 1984.

[24] MAJID, M.Z. ABD and McCAFFER, RONALD. Factors of Non-excusable Delays that Influence Contractors' Performance. *Journal of Management in Engineering*, May/June 1998, **14**(3), 48.

[25] CAPPER, PROFESSOR PHILLIP. Management of Legal Risks in Construction. A paper given to the Society of Construction Law at a meeting in Wales on 21 September 1994 referring to and summarizing the conclusions from THOMPSON, P.A. and PERRY, J.G. *Engineering Construction Risks.* SERC, 1992, in Annexe 1 of his paper at 11.

submitted by the contractor in the early stages of the work. The programme may be designated as a contract document in the Contract Data. In one of the optional statements in part two of the Contract Data the contractor may identify the programme itself which would form part of the contract at acceptance. Alternatively in one of the employer's optional statements in part one of the Contract Data and where no programme is identified by the contractor, the employer may require the contractor to submit a programme for acceptance within a given number of weeks of the 'Contract Date'. Once again the intention would appear to render the programme a contract document in either case.[26] Similarly, the PSC introduces a change in paradigm regarding the timely performance of the consultant's work. Just as a contractor's dilatory responses may slow work so too may the consultant's. Thus some of the programming aspects of the ECC are also found in the PSC[27] with a view to encouraging better management by all involved in the work.[28] In fact 'acceptance' of the programme should mean that it is never more than two weeks out of date thereafter.

The approach of many standard forms toward programming as a legal requirement has been ambivalent. Clause 5.3 of JCT 80 requires the contractor to provide the architect with a 'master programme' for execution of the works but which is optional only and a footnote to the clause indicates that it may be deleted. The BPF system also uses the same term to describe the client representative's schedule of main activities. ICE 6th requires the contractor to submit a programme showing the order for carrying out the works.[29] FIDIC 4th goes further than either of these other two forms and imposes a duty on the contractor to submit 'a programme, in such form and detail as the Engineer shall reasonably prescribe, for the execution of the works'.[30] The FIDIC Orange Book imposes a mandatory obligation upon the contractor to submit a programme and outlines the detail that it must contain.[31] None of the forms, however, makes the programme a contract document.[32] The

---

[26] See Consultation Document guidance notes NEC on clause 32.1 ECC, 30. Contra Michael O'Reilly, *Civil Engineering Construction Contracts*. Thomas Telford, London, 1996, 321: '[e]ven where it [the progamme] is included in the Contract Data, it does not represent an invariate term of the contract', contrasting in n. 21 the ICE Conditions of Contract and the status of the programme in these conditions as construed in *Yorkshire Water Authority* v. *Sir Alfred McAlpine & Son (Northern) Ltd* (1985) 32 BLR 114.

[27] Clauses 31 and 32 PSC.

[28] See BROOME, JON C. and PERRY, JOHN G. Experiences of the Use of the New Engineering Contract. *Engineering, Construction and Architectural Management*, 1995, **2**(4), 277–278.

[29] Clause 14 ICE 6th.

[30] Clause 14.1 FIDIC 4th.

[31] Clause 4.14 FIDIC Orange Book 1st part I.

[32] Clause 1.3 of JCT 80 defines 'contract documents' without reference to the programme while clause 1(1)(e) of ICE 6th and clause 1.1(b)(i) of FIDIC 4th similarly omit any reference to programme.

Orange Book expressly indicates it is submitted 'for information' only.[33] It may be argued that by making this choice the true importance of the programme is diminished. Clause 5.3.2 of JCT 80 in particular detracts from the importance of the programme by stating that nothing 'in the master programme ... shall impose any obligation beyond those imposed by the Contract Documents'.[34] It seems that any importance the programme might have is also lessened in the absence of any obligation to comply with it. Thus, to take JCT 80 as an example, notwithstanding calling for a master programme, the consequences of failing to comply with it are not necessarily a breach of the contract. It would seem that the traditional view of programmes is that, whilst they may assist in planning, they count for little beyond that.[35] Despite these views of programmes in the traditional forms research indicates pre-project planning, of which programming could form an integral part, along with accurate risk analysis can reduce overall costs by as much as 20%.[36]

A partial explanation for the ambivalence of the standard forms toward the programme may stem from the deference that employers have paid to contractors in terms of their selection of working methods. It can be argued from a contractor's point of view that strict programme requirements impinge on their freedom of action in terms of choosing working methods. The contractor also likes to believe, perhaps too optimistically at times, that even if he or she falls behind he can still make up for it somehow and has until completion anyway. This assumes no sectional or like limitations have been imposed upon the contractor. The employer, while necessarily concerned about the programme, still knows that the contractor's overall responsibility for completion of the works remains. Hence neither side has tested the issues in the extremes. The traditional standard forms may represent a compromise on these and other programme issues. To address the problems that arise from complacency and waiting until the completion date before acknowledging delays, it is submitted that a more robust approach to the programme issues was necessary. The NEC appears to have taken this approach.

The drafters start from the premise that the programme is a cornerstone of the NEC. Thus at the outset it is clear that a programme is unmistakably required. As a result the first issue arising under the NEC is not whether a programme is required but whether the project manager has accepted the programme. The project manager may accept a programme

[33] Clause 4.14 FIDIC Orange Book 1st part I.
[34] Cf Clause 39 of the Red Book which envisions completion of a schedule and agreed programme for payment of the contract price instalments.
[35] See *Kitsons Sheet Metal Ltd* v. *Matthew Hall Mechanical & Electrical Engineers Ltd* (1989) 47 BLR 82.
[36] *Pre-Project Planning: Beginning a Project the Right Way.* University of Texas at Austin, Construction Industry Institute, Austin, 1994, Construction Industry Institute, Pre-Project Planning Research Team, Publication 39–1. There is a role for specialists in this regard see LENARD, D.J. and ROBERTS, C.F. The Cost Manager in the Building Procurement and Delivery Process. *Building Economist*, June 1992, 12–14.

identified in the Contract Data[37] by the contractor.[38] In this regard the programme becomes the 'Accepted Programme'[39] for contract purposes.[40] Contract purposes would pertain to such matters as programme revisions under clause 32.1; setting the time frame for delivery of possession of the site by the employer to the contractor under clause 33.1; setting retention under clause 50.3; revising activity schedules under clauses 54.2 and 54.3; deciding compensation events under clauses 60.1(2),(3) and (5); and assessing compensation events under clauses 63.3 and 63.6. The accepted programme becomes the benchmark against which the contractor's progress and methods of works are measured[41] and is an essential tool for the assessment of compensation events.[42] The accepted programme may also be adjusted in assessing whether the completion date should be delayed.[43]

The measurement referred to is flexible and the programme will change just as the works and their parameters do[44] and this is recognized. Hence, as progress or methods vary against the accepted programme so too will the programme through the required revisions. The term 'Accepted Programme' reflects this updating as it is used variably in the contract to refer to not only the first accepted programme but also all subsequent accepted programmes. In each case the later accepted programme supersedes the earlier accepted programme and becomes the new measure of progress and methods. Revisions to the programme will also be strictly controlled[45] and must ultimately be accepted by the project manager as well.[46] The revisions to the programme would be made pursuant to the procedures contained in clause 32. In practice revisions to the programme have been averaging four weeks under many NEC contracts; however, time frames relating to revisions turn upon project complexity and duration of the work and thus have also been found to vary from one to thirteen weeks between revisions.[47] The

---

[37] Clause 11.2(14) ECC.

[38] See optional statements in part two of the Contract Data.

[39] See again clause 11.2(14) ECC; the 'Accepted Programme' is an identified term.

[40] Cf FIDIC 4th clause 14.1 which refers instead to the 'consent' of the engineer to the programme.

[41] It is interesting that the programme has been chosen for a central role in the NEC in this regard when one of the drafters, Dr Martin Barnes, is also so closely associated with means of measurement and payment for work in heavy construction involving use of the Civil Engineering Standard Method of Meaasurement: see BARNES, M. *CESMM3 Handbook.* Thomas Telford, London, 1994.

[42] See clauses 64.1 and 64.2 ECC.

[43] See clause 63.3 ECC.

[44] See generally SCOTT, S. Checking the Project Plan. *Construction Management and Economics*, 1995, **13**(2), 127–136 outining a single procedure for verfying the contractor's programming in practice.

[45] See discussion below.

[46] Under clause 31 ECC.

[47] BAYTON, ERNEST, J. An Introduction to the Engineering and Construction Contract. A course given at Altrincham on 3 March 1998. Thomas Telford Training, London, 1998.

significance of the accepted programme can also be seen under the PSC with the obligation that is imposed on the employer as well to provide information in accordance with it.[48] In comparison the JCT has made recent moves to improve the flow of information under JCT 98 by requiring the employer to provide an 'Information Release Schedule' under clause 5.4.1.

There are some timing issues regarding the submission of programmes. Thus, for example, the contractor may not provide a programme that is capable of acceptance at the outset but only shortly thereafter. In this case, the contractor's obligation, while still to submit a programme for acceptance, is now to submit a programme instead within the delay period stated in the Contract Data. The drafters in this regard have not stipulated the submission of a programme as a prerequisite to proceeding with the works unlike the submission of the contractor's design. This arguably supports design over programme in any hierarchical importance. It is suggested that this is less a concession to the importance of the programme than a consequence of certain information being unavailable at the tender stage, for instance, dates for work of the employer and others that may have to be later agreed but which nevertheless must still be included in the programme.[49] Such details are not insignificant, as once agreed the failure to meet them may be compensable.[50] Broome and Perry have conceded that NEC time periods are tight and that once a programme has been accepted both parties are committed to it and to the ensuing risk that compensation events may be found for any transgression.[51] Broome and Perry have also noted, however, that this appears to have generated some benefits as well and thus write:

> [w]hile the time periods are tight, they have been found to be achievable in practice. The benefits to the Employer of having tight time periods appear to be greater security and certainty over the finish date and final price at any point in the contract. For the Contractor the benefits are more security over what he is paid for a change, and a much improved cash flow. Additionally, problems are being solved as they occur and are not being left to sour relationships, which should bring long-term benefit to both parties.[52]

The importance of the programme is underscored when the contractor subsequently fails to meet the delay period for its submission. In this case, one-quarter of the price for work done to date will be retained from the contractor in assessments of the amount due.[53] This sanction is significant and marks a clear departure from other standard forms. This sanction is

---

[48] Clause 20.1 PSC Second Edition.
[49] See clause 31.2 ECC. This is notable in particular in main options E and F.
[50] For example, under clause 60.1(5) ECC.
[51] BROOME, JON C. and PERRY, JOHN G., see n. 28 above, 280.
[52] *Ibid.*
[53] Clause 50.3 ECC; see also secondary option clause L.

not used for any failure to submit a revised programme as required by the contract. Rather, breach in this respect may adversely affect the assessment of compensation events. In contrast to traditional forms, GC/Works/1 3rd also uses the programme for various purposes including assessing the contractor's performance under clause 34; assessing extensions of time under clause 36; and determining claims for disruption and prolongation under clause 46. The importance of submitting a revised programme with regard to requests for extensions of time and the fact that the NEC differs from JCT 80, ICE 6th, FIDIC 4th and PSA/1 in this regard has been noted by John R. Evans.[54] Professor Phillip Capper makes a similar point:

> it is a further weakness of the traditional JCT and ICE forms of construction contract that the contractual provisions on programming of activities involve little obligation. Unlike GC/Works/1 and NEC, the traditional forms make little contractual provision to integrate the programming of activities into the structural obligations.[55]

In early research into use of the form it was found that some contractors have not understood the use of the accepted programme and the importance of providing complete information in their own interest and so that they are placed in as strong a position as possible in the assessment of compensation events.[56] Overcoming this is in part a function of training, understanding and recognition of the central role that progammes play only under the NEC.

The detail, which is expected of the programme, is patent. Clause 31.2 provides as follows:

> The *Contractor* shows on each programme which he submits for acceptance
>
> - the *starting date*, *possession dates* and Completion Date,
> - for each operation, a method statement which identifies the Equipment[57] and other resources which the *Contractor* plans to use,
> - planned Completion,[58]
> - the order and timing of

---

[54]   EVANS, JOHN R. Fair and Reasonable? Ordered Variations and the Standard Forms of Contract. MSc dissertation, University of London, Centre of Construction Law and Management, King's College, September 1995.

[55]   CAPPER, PROFESSOR PHILLIP. Why Are There So Many Disputes for Arbitration in Construction?. *The Building of Construction Law*. A paper presented at the Tenth Annual Construction Conference on 19 September 1997, by the Society of Construction Law and the Centre of Construction Law and Management. King's College, London, 1997, 11.

[56]   BROOME, JON C. and PERRY, JOHN G., see n. 51 above, 275.

[57]   Clause 11.2(11) ECC.

[58]   Clause 11.2(13) ECC.

- the operations which the *Contractor* plans to do[59] in order to Provide the Works[60] and
- the work of the *Employer* and Others[61] either as stated in the Works Information[62] or as later agreed with them[63] by the *Contractor*,
- the dates when the *Contractor* plans to complete work needed to allow the *Employer* and Others[64] to do their work,
- provisions for
  - float,
  - time risk allowances,
  - health and safety requirements and
  - the procedures set out in this contract,
- the dates when, in order to Provide the Works in accordance with his programme, the *Contractor* will need
  - possession of a part[65] of the Site[66] if later than its *possession date*,[67]
  - acceptances[68] and
  - Plant and Materials[69] and other things to be provided by the *Employer* and
- other information which the Works Information requires the *Contractor* to show on a programme submitted for acceptance.

In addition to being required to show these details on each programme that the contractor submits for acceptance, and when either main option A or C is used, the contractor must also show the start and finish of each activity on the '*activity schedule*',[70] and additional details for main options A and D, pursuant to clause 31.4 and for all revised programmes under clause 32.1.

Before turning to what the programme requirements reveal, some observations may be made on the significance of the terminology. The submission itself will fall within clause 13.1. The '*starting date*' and

---

[59] A distinction is made in the conditions between 'doing' the work and 'providing the works'; see discussion of clause 30.1 above. This distinction should presumably apply to operations also as opposed to work.

[60] Clause 11.2(4) ECC.

[61] Clause 11.2(2) ECC. In particular the necessity for third party design approval where necessary: clause 27.1 ECC.

[62] Clause 11.2(5) ECC.

[63] Agreement may be either with the employer or others individually.

[64] Clause 11.2(2) ECC.

[65] For example, under clause 33 ECC or as referred to in section 3 of part one of the Contract Data.

[66] Clause 11.2(7) ECC.

[67] Possession dates are also referred in section 3 of part one of the Contract Data.

[68] For example, under clauses 21.2, 23.1, 24.1, 26.2, 26.3, 26.4, 31.3, 32.2, 36.3, 36.5, 54.2, 85.1, 87.1, G1.1, J1.2 ECC.

[69] Clause 11.2(10) ECC.

[70] Clause 31.4 ECC.

'*possession dates*' are inserted in section 3 of part one of the Contract Data while the 'Completion Date' is defined in section 11.2(12). The flexibility in the use of a starting date borrows from both engineering and building forms. From the ICE 6th form a works commencement date can be specified in the appendix to the tender just as the starting date can be specified in part one of the Contract Data in the ECC. However, unlike ICE 6th the contractor under the ECC would not then have any latitude in starting other than on the starting date. In this regard the form is closer to JCT forms, e.g. JCT 80, clause 23.1.1.

If the contractor is to decide the completion date for the whole of the works the date would then be inserted by the contractor in the optional statements of part two of the Contract Data. The term 'operation' is undefined, although it is used again in clause 32.1 and appears to be broader than 'activities'. As it is not included within the definition of 'Provide the Works' although incidental work, services and actions are, it does not fall within the contractor's principal obligation in this regard under clause 20.1. This interpretation is reinforced by the bullet point below asking for the order and timing of 'the operations which the *Contractor* plans to do in order to Provide the Works'.

The use of the term 'method statement' may be contrasted with the use of the term 'method of working' in clauses 35.3 and 54.2. It is arguable that the two terms are used interchangeably in these clauses and as the guidance notes are exceedingly broad. 'Method statements for the Contractor's operations consist of descriptions of the construction methods as well as the resources, including Equipment, he intends to use.'[71] Such inconsistent use of terminology also appears in the ICE 6th in relation to this topic with 'methods of construction' in clauses 8(3) and in 13(2) 'mode manner ... of construction'. Methods too could also easily fall within the meaning of 'constraint' in clause 11.2(5) and thus impose an obligation to refer to them in the works information on this basis.

Identification is a process under clause 71.1 and in relation to payment. The statement using the term 'resources' would appear to exclude both 'Equipment' and 'Plant and Materials'.[72] Planned completion could be considered to be the completion date less the contractor's provision for float, which is also shown on the programme. D.G. Valentine views the term 'planned completion', in contrast to the date for completion, to support the possibility of accelerating the completion date.[73] The term 'provisions' has a double meaning. Clause 31.2 could have been introduced with a requirement that the '*Contractor* show on each programme which he submits for acceptance *provisions for ...*'. The term is also used in the sense of a time allowance. In this regard all bullet points save 'health and safety requirements' would accord with both meanings.

---

[71] Guidance notes NEC on clause 31.2 ECC, 39.
[72] See clause 11.2(30) ECC.
[73] VALENTINE, D.G. The New Engineering Contract: Part 2 – Claims for Extensions of Time. *Construction Law Journal*, 1991, **12**, 322.

Float is an important concept. The 'float' is the spare time in the programme after time risk allowances have been taken into account. There is a distinction between these two which Gillian Birkby describes as follows:

> a useful distinction is made between time risk allowances which are essentially the contractors's float, and which can be applied to individual activities. This is to be compared with what is called 'float' which is the employer's and which is available to mitigate any delay caused by compensation events.[74]

In general, float may yet be divided further into 'total float', 'free float' and 'independent float'.[75] 'Float', as Birkby notes, is intended to be used to accommodate the potential effects of compensation events on planned completion.[76] Under the ECC 'float' is owned by the contractor. By way of contrast, most other standard forms do not expressly address float and some commentators are critical of this omission.

> In view of the importance of float, it is essential for employers and contractors alike that it is properly identified in a structured programme ... with any necessary adjustment made to the programme. In view of the ever-increasing complexity of construction disputes, this is an issue that clearly needs to be examined by lawyers and addressed in contracts.[77]

As noted, the 'time risk' allowances are the contractor's. They would be expected to be shown on the programme for parts or sections of the works, or activities if main option A or C applied. Under clause 63.5 time risk allowances are included in the assessment of compensation events for matters which have a significant chance of occurring.[78]

'Health and safety requirements' are referred to in clause 18.1 as those in the works information but could also include statutory requirements as well.[79]

Reference is made to 'procedures' in the clause but few procedures are actually referred to as such in the contract, although reference is made to the acceptance or procurement procedures in the works information in clause 11.2(29), (30) and reference is also made to the first assessment

---

[74] BIRKBY, GILLIAN. The New Engineering Contract. *Civil Engineering Surveyor Construction Law Review*, 1996, 26.

[75] See for further explanation LOCK, DENNIS. Resource Scheduling. In *Gower Handbook of Project Management*, 2nd edn. Gower, Aldershot, 1994, pp. 127–130.

[76] Guidance notes NEC on clause 31.2 ECC, 39.

[77] WISHART, IAIN and GIBSON, ROGER. 'Float' – A Valuable Support in Construction Programmes. *Construction Law*, February/March 1994, 454.

[78] Cf clause 2.3 JCT NSC/C allowing an extension of time to be claimed under clause 2.3 for a delay beyond the period stated in an agreed programme thus contemplating extensions being granted in advance of the actual completion date.

[79] See clause 95.3 ECC; and see generally WRIGHT, FRANK. *Law of Health and Safety at Work*. Sweet & Maxwell, London, 1997.

date being decided to 'suit the procedures of the Parties' in clause 50.1. The reference may thus also be taken to refer to the procedures which are *implicit* in the contract and its administration.

The phrase 'other information which the Works Information requires the *Contractor* to show on a programme submitted for acceptance' appears. It is suggested that on multi-contract projects this should probably include boundary data, foundation design data, hook-up data and similar information pertaining to the contractor's design for both the Employer's and other contractors' uses. Such information too should be stated to be submitted in accordance with the programme and identified as a separate activity.[80] Other information could even extend to pricing and which the BPF system by comparison comprehends.

Turning to the contents of the clause in general a cursory review of the programme requirements reveals that eight broad categories are set out; however, a closer review of them will reveal in essence four essential categories:

- dates;
- methods, operations or procedures;
- provisions; and
- information.

Examining these categories in turn it can be remarked that dates are the hallmark of the programme. Some of these dates are known, e.g. the starting date and the possession date, others planned[81] and possibly both.[82] The dates may or may not be solely within the contractor's control and thus can set out deadlines for the employer or others to fulfil if the contractor is to proceed toward and ultimately be able to meet the obligation to provide the works. Methods, operations or procedures encompass not only the equipment and resources that will be used, but their ordering and timing as well. The programme requirements ask something additionally for the contractor's provisions. These are not details that are disclosed as a matter of course by all contractors but which are sought in the interests of transparency. Lastly, the programme asks for other information which the works information requires. In summary, the ECC programme requirements contain some familiar but also unfamiliar details. The result may be reluctance on the part of some contractors to comply fully with them and as such some education may be required in this regard if the programme is to work as intended. The fact that the programme also imposes additional new obligations on employers as well may serve to foster acceptance by contractors.

The inclusion of the 'method statement' as part of an accepted programme has some important consequences. In particular, it will require a revision to the programme whenever the method statement changes. Further, as the method statement is required to identify both

---

[80] Guidance notes NEC, 22.
[81] For example, the dates the contractor plans to complete work.
[82] For example, planned completion and the completion date.

equipment and resources, any change to either would entail the same result; namely revision to the programme. For the most part method statements have not formed part of the contract documents under the standard forms and contractors as a result have had a certain degree of freedom in their planning of methods of work. A corollary to this has been that contractors have normally had to bear any additional costs that a change of methods of work at their discretion might entail. It has not been possible simply to request an instruction and claim compensation as of right from the contract administrator.[83] This assumes, however, that the difficulty does not arise from a matter which may be the responsibility of the employer; for instance, the design, and in which case it may be in the employer's interest to have the contract administrator issue an instruction so as to avoid consequent delays. Delays are often categorized in contract conditions according to whether they are attributable to the employer (compensable), or the contractor (non-excusable), or otherwise (excusable).[84] The number of method statements will, in practice, be far fewer than the number of activities. This follows as method statements are only needed and referable to each operation and that many activities will normally be grouped together to constitute one operation.

By comparison if a power is given to an engineer to order changes in methods of work then such changes will not be treated as variations.[85] However, it has also been held regarding a similar provision to clause 31.2 in the ECC that when a method statement is part of the contract the contractor must follow it although, if the works become impossible as a result, it may also entitle the contractor to a variation order and compensation.[86] This case illustrates the dilemma that can arise from imposing more controls over the contractor by incorporating method statements into the contract either through the programme or otherwise; that is, greater liability for variations which arise when changes to the method statement have to be made. It is submitted that a similar result to that in the case law would result under the ECC, as impossibility within the meaning of clause 19.1 would be likely to necessitate the project manager giving an instruction to change the works information. In general no obligation is imposed upon the contractor to work to a method which proves illegal or impossible (clause 19.1). This wording may be contrasted with clause 13.1 of FIDIC 4th which excuses (non) performance when it is 'legally or physically impossible'. In conclusion tying the method statement, *viz.* methods of working or methods of

---

[83] See *C J Pearce & Co Ltd* v. *Hereford Corpn* (1968) 66 LGR 647.

[84] See e.g. MAJID, M.Z. ABD and McCAFFER, RONALD. n. 24 above, 42–49.

[85] See *Neodex Ltd* v. *Swintom and Pendlebury Borough Council* (1958) 5 BLR 34. It also seems there may be no implied authority to warrant the practicability of any proposed methods of work on behalf of the employer: see *Thorn* v. *London Corpn* (1876) 1 App Cas 120, HL.

[86] *Yorkshire Water Authority* v. *Sir Alfred McAlpine & Son (Northern) Ltd* (1985) 32 BLR 114 at 126 per Skinner J construing clause 8(3) of ICE 5th. See also *Holland Dredging* v. *Dredging & Construction Co* (1987) 37 BLR 1 CA.

construction together with the programme still seems warranted despite the attendant risk of a compensation event arising as the overall benefits associated with the increased planning arguably outweigh these other risks.[87]

Methods of working assume an additional importance in options using activity schedules (namely main options A and C) as the change may mean that the activity schedule will no longer comply with the accepted programme.[88] If the change has this effect then the contractor has to revise the activity schedule and submit it to the project manager for acceptance.[89] Three reasons are given in this case justifying the project manager not accepting the revision:

- it [the revised activity schedule] does not comply with the Accepted Programme,[90]
- any changed Prices are not reasonably distributed between the activities, or
- the total of the Prices is changed.[91]

Thus choice of method of working is not solely at the contractor's discretion and requires acceptance by the project manager.[92] It may be noted that it is not a change of planned method of working itself that is subject to acceptance but only a change which renders the activity schedule in non-compliance with the 'Accepted Programme'. Changes to the 'method statement' itself are additional to this and rather governed by clauses 31.2 and 32.1. It would appear that the intention would be to maintain the overall integrity of the methods of working with the activity schedule and the pricing.

Each programme submitted by the contractor to the project manager for acceptance must show the details set out in clause 31.2. However, it is not just the failure to show any one of the details referred to that would support the non-acceptance of the programme by the project manager but any one of four broad reasons that are given in clause 31.3. The four reasons are:

- the *Contractor's* plans which it shows are not practicable,
- it does not show the information which this contract requires,
- it does not represent the *Contractor's* plans realistically or
- it does not comply with the Works Information.

Initially, the term 'plans' is undefined and may be given a narrow or broad meaning. Narrow meanings are often given in terms of a

---

[87] Compare the views of US contractors towards risks: KANGARI, R. Risk Management Perceptions and Trends of US Construction. *Journal of Construction Engineering and Management*, 1995, 422–429.

[88] See clause 54.2 ECC.

[89] See clause 54.2 ECC.

[90] Clause 11.2(14) ECC.

[91] Clause 54.3 ECC.

[92] Cf clause 14(7) ICE 6th.

contractor's scale drawings, while broad meanings would include planning in the popular sense. The context, it is submitted, suggests a broad meaning was intended here. 'It' would refer to the programme and, in the case of the second bullet point, would plainly cover information which the contractor must show under clause 31.2 itself. Non-compliance with the works information would appear to be a broader ground than simply not showing that which the works information requires as the latter would be covered by the second bullet point.

The term 'information' as first used above in the clause appears to be primarily intended to refer to and be equated with the details that clause 31.2 requires. This is supported by the reference to 'other information' in the final bullet point in clause 31.2 and the right to withhold one-quarter of the PWDD in assessments of the amount due until the contractor has submitted a first programme to the project manager 'showing the information which this contract requires' in clause 50.3. However, it is also broad enough arguably to refer to any information which the contract requires. If so it would seem that the requirement must at least be in respect of the programme. Therefore, the project manager could not withhold acceptance of the programme because it did not show information which the contractor is required to provide to others under clause 25. This uncertainty could be removed by adding the term 'information' to the opening sentence in clause 31.2. It may be contrasted with the use of the term in clause 20.1 of the PSC imposing an obligation on the employer to provide information which the PSC contract requires the employer to provide in accordance with the accepted programme.

It would seem that 'represent' as used in the clause means more than simply 'show', which the contractor is already under an obligation to do, and thus may imply an element of judgment on the part of the project manager as would be the case in judging practicability. The term 'realistically' and its use must be distinguished from 'practicability' in the first bullet point. Practicability is determined with reference to the contractor's plans while 'realisticability' is narrower. Realisticability coined here, would be determined with reference to the *representation* of the plans as this bullet point is worded. Hence realisticability as a ground would be narrower than practicability, though both refer to plans alone which has been argued above should be interpreted broadly.

Two of the above grounds require additional comment in that they exceed what may normally be expected to be the employer's agent's role toward programmes supplied by the contractor. In particular, it is not usual that the project manager will retain such broad rights of non-acceptance or rejection over matters typically left to the contractor. However, by extension, the argument made above regarding the rationale for greater employer control – through the agent – of the contractor's working methods, applies here with greater force. Thus, when the employer is commited to compensating fully the contractor for a wide range of risks under the compensation event procedure, those risks may be offset to some extent in other provisions of the contract. It would seem that the right not to accept the programme on these bases might amount to some of this 'offsetting'. It may also be that, as the parties can agree to cost reimbursement modes of contracting, some additional safeguards were warranted in any event.

The contractor must submit the programme for acceptance on time. The time period is determined with reference to the Contract Data for first programmes[93] and clause 32.2 for revised programmes. Failure on the contractor's part to submit the programme on time may invoke the early warning procedure on the project manager's part.[94] If the programme is submitted timeously then the project manager must either accept it or notify the contractor of reasons for not accepting it and must do so within two weeks of the submission.[95] While it is open to the project manager not to accept it for any reason, he or she can be expected to invoke one of the four reasons given as a matter of course as this would exclude the compensation event procedures.[96] The project manager will be mindful of the employer's objectives that will be stated in the brief. These can form the basis for non-acceptance of the programme on the employer's part.[97] Where the programme is identified in part two of the Contract Data at the outset then by virtue of the definition of 'Accepted Programme' in clause 11.2(14) the acceptance would take place at the contract formation or agreement stage. It would also take place in the same way as other details put forward by the contractor in part two. Thus details would have to be acceptable to the employer or they would continue to be subject to negotiations once again until final agreement was reached.

The ECC does not grant the project manager an express power to instruct the contractor to change an accepted programme. This contrasts markedly with the PSC, First Edition where the employer was given discretion to instruct the consultant to change the accepted programme.[98] This position was at the far end of the spectrum and perhaps for this reason is no longer found in the Second Edition of the PSC. The effect of the exercise of the discretion would include changes to the order and timing of operations of the consultant or the work of the employer and others. These effects follow from what the accepted programme is required to show under clause 30.3 of the PSC, First Edition. Under the Second Edition of the PSC the requirements for the accepted programme are far more extensive and much closer to those requirements in clause 31.2 of the ECC. The obligation of the consultant to comply with the instruction to change the programme was not unlimited, however, and the consultant could refuse to act on the grounds of impracticability.[99] This right to so instruct, and the limitation that referred to it, have both been removed in the Second Edition of the PSC.

[93] See clause 31.1 ECC.
[94] See clause 16 ECC.
[95] Clause 31.3 ECC. The submission must satisfy clause 13 ECC requirements.
[96] See clauses 13.8 and 60.1(9) ECC.
[97] See clause 30.2 PSC.
[98] Clause 31.1 PSC.
[99] See clause 31.1 PSC First Edition.

Various reasons may be put forward as to why the programme has not had the use made of it that could have been made under many standard forms. It is submitted one of these reasons pertains to the failure of drafters directly to relate the programme's provisions to progress of the works. In the leading forms the duty to make progress in the construction of the works has been left vague and open-ended. Clause 23.1 of JCT 80, for example, stipulates the contractor shall 'regularly and diligently' proceed with the works. Clause 41.2 of the ICE 6th states that the contractor shall 'proceed with due expedition and without delay'. These phrases have proved very difficult to construe in practice and notwithstanding that failure to comply with these obligations themselves can be a ground for termination.[100] The difficulties have been exacerbated by the dearth of authority construing the provisions.[101]

Recently the courts have moved to provide more substantive content to these types of duties and, in so doing, have shifted the case law under the traditional forms more *toward* the ECC baseline. In *West Faulkner Associates* v. *London Borough of Newham*, Simon Brown LJ remarked in *obiter*:

> Taken together, the obligation upon the contractor is essentially to proceed continuously, industriously and efficiently with appropriate physical resources so as to progress the works steadily towards completion substantially in accordance with the contractual requirements as to time, sequence and quality of work.[102]

Somewhat more detail was provided in this regard in the first instance decision of Judge Newey QC who held that the duty required the contractors 'to plan their work, to lead and manage their work force, to provide sufficient and proper materials and to employ competent tradesmen, so that the works are fully carried out to an acceptable standard and that all time, sequence and other provisions of the contract are fulfilled'.[103]

It is submitted that the operative wording appropriately governs the obligation of the contractor under the ECC to meet programme requirements under the ECC. Hence, the contractor need not meet the programme requirements perfectly insofar as progress is concerned but *substantially*.

---

[100] See *Canterbury Pipelines Ltd* v. *Christchurch Drainage Board* (1979) 16 BLR 76 (NZ CA); and *Lubenham Fidelities and Investment Co Ltd* v. *South Pembrokeshire District Council* (1986) 33 BLR 39, CA.

[101] A notable exception is *Hounslow London Borough Council* v. *Twickenham Garden Developments Ltd* [1971] 1 Ch 233, [1970] 3 All ER 326. Cf clauses 41.1 and 46.1 FIDIC 4th. Clause 41.1 requires the contractor to proceed with the works 'with due expedition and without delay'.

[102] (1994) 71 BLR 1 at 14, CA.

[103] *West Faulkner Associates* v. *London Borough of Newham Construction Law Journal*, 1993, **9**, 249.

Apart from express provision the situation from the employer's point of view is complicated by the refusal of the courts to imply similar duties, e.g. to proceed regularly and diligently. This follows from the contractor only being obliged to complete by the completion date and thus lack of expedition *per se* without more before that date arrives is viewed as no business of the employer. Staughton LJ in *Greater London Council* v. *Cleveland Bridge and Engineering Co Ltd* put it this way: 'in the absence of any indication to the contrary, a contractor is entitled to plan and perform the work as he pleases, provided always that he finishes it by the time fixed in the contract'.[104]

The programme in the ECC is thus arguably one of the best ways of overcoming some of these limitations in interpretation and application. However, before it can achieve some of the objectives that it holds out, the courts will have to see and construe the programme in a new light. Past court decisions have often limited the effects of the programme in part because it has rarely been held to be a contract document. One result has been that the failure to comply with a programme has neither been taken seriously by the parties nor necessarily viewed as a breach of contract without something more. To reiterate, while programmes have usually been mentioned in contract documents they have not formed part of them and accordingly, the parties have paid little attention to them.[105]

The planning aspects of the programme in the ECC and project planning in general have much in common and one acts to reinforce the importance of the other. Thus a typical project plan exhibits some of the same elements as a programme:

- a defined start position in time and relevant knowledge;
- a defined end position consisting of one or more objectives;
- a defined activity or set of activities for advancing from the start position to the end position; and
- an estimate of the time and resource cost or budget required to complete the project activity; i.e. to advance from the start position to the end position.[106]

There are several important reasons why the contractor should plan or programme work meticulously. In large part, and aside from any intrinsic value that can be shown, it is because best practice dictates that problems and a range of different solutions should be explored and evaluated before resources are committed to a particular course of action. Thus, programming and planning enables accurate estimates of scarce resources

---

[104]   (1986) 34 BLR 50 at 66.

[105]   See e.g. *Kitsons Sheet Metal Ltd* v. *Matthew Hall Mechanical and Electrical Engineers Ltd* (1989) 47 BLR 82; and see also clause 5 of JCT 80 that the (master) programme imposes no obligations beyond those in the contract documents.

[106]   LANIGAN, MIKE. *Engineers in Business, The Principles of Management and Product Design.* Addison-Wesley, Wokingham, 1994, pp. 197–198. Project planning is often considered as an aspect of operations management.

to be employed. In addition, programming and planning can be used to motivate individuals. In general, the individuals involved in a programme or plan will be motivated to work toward their objectives. In this way ownership of the goals is shared among them. Finally, the programme or plan provides a baseline for evaluation of the project thereby enabling better control to be taken over changes.[107]

In summary the programme provisions in the ECC provide an excellent context for some of the drafting principles underlying the form. Throughout clause 31.2 there are repeated references to the work of others as well as the employer. The contractor is asked to plan work mindful of the fact that there will be others on site who also have work to do. Each will have roles. Ultimately, not only must the contractor take their work and those roles into active consideration but must also demonstrate awareness of the effect of his or her own work upon them in turn if the programme is to be maintained.

Revising the programme

The importance of the programme would be lost if adequate provision were not made for its updating as the work progressed. Recognition of this fact is given in the clauses on revising the programme.[108] Revised programmes are neither a defined nor an identified term as such although, as the term is used in the Contract Data, it would have been consistent with usage under clause 11.2 if it had been identified and in italics.[109] A revised programme falls within the definition of 'Accepted Programme'[110] when superseding a previous accepted programme.

The contractor's obligation is to submit a revised programme to the project manager within certain set time frames, either when instructed, or when agreed in the Contract Data. The time frames are expressed in this manner in clause 32.2:

- within the *period for reply* after the *Project Manager* has instructed him to,
- when the *Contractor* chooses to and, in any case,
- at no longer interval than the interval stated in the Contract Data from the *starting date* until Completion[111] of the whole of the *works*.

These time frames are not wholly alternative and the regular interval agreed in the Contract Data for the submission of revised programmes must be respected in all cases. As a communication any instruction from

---

[107] *Ibid.*, p. 199.
[108] Both FIDIC 4th clause 14.2 and clause 8.5 of the FIDIC Orange Book 1st part I also make specific provision on revising the programme depending upon the overall rate of progress of the contractor.
[109] In section 3 of part one of the Contract Data the contractor is obliged to submit revised programmes at intervals no longer than an agreed number of weeks.
[110] Clause 11.2(14) ECC.
[111] Clause 11.2(13) ECC.

the project manager to submit a revised programme would have to be replied to by the contractor within the *'period for reply'* in any case.[112] Whatever the basis for the submission of the revised programme it must still show the same details:

- the actual progress achieved on each operation and its effect upon the timing of the remaining work,
- the effects of implemented compensation events and of notified early warning matters,
- how the *Contractor* plans to deal with any delays and to correct notified Defects[113] and
- any other changes which the Contractor proposes to make to the Accepted Programme.[114]

The contractor's obligations in these terms may be contrasted with what must be shown on a programme in general in clause 31.2. It can be seen that the revised programme assumes much of the detail that is contained in the first or subsequent accepted programmes. The intention is to permit comparisons to be drawn and this is plain on the language of clause 32.1. For instance, the actual progress achieved on operations has to be documented. The operations referred to are those that required method statements in carrying them out as well as details of their order and timing in the programme or accepted programme.[115] Demonstration of the actual progress, if any, would be revealed in the manner most appropriate for the type of programme chosen, for example, network analysis or a variety of other techniques.[116] Network analysis techniques were first used in America during the 1960s and since that time have grown in popularity to where all federal construction projects now require their use.[117] Lastly, the contractor would also have to show the effect of any operations upon the timing of the 'remaining work'.

The express reference to the 'remaining work' in the first bullet point above is a suitable lead into the second bullet point that deals in part with compensation events. Thus the revision of the programme must take into account the effects of implemented compensation events. Even if this directive were not given here it would fall upon the contractor under clause 62.2 which provides '[i]f the programme for remaining work is affected by the compensation event, the *Contractor* includes a revised programme in his quotation showing the effect'. In fact it is critical for the

---

[112]   Clause 13.3 ECC.
[113]   Clause 11.2(15) ECC.
[114]   Clause 11.2(14) ECC.
[115]   See clause 31.2 ECC.
[116]   For example, whether bar charts, critical path routines, precedence diagrams, schedules, network analysis or otherwise.
[117]   This growth is outlined by WICKWIRE, JON M. *et al*. Use of Critical Path Method Techniques in Contract Claims: Issues and Developments, 1974 to 1988. *Public Contract Law Journal*, 1989, **18**, 338; and referring in particular to another Wickwire article, WICKWIRE, J. and SMITH, R. The Use of Critical Path Method Techniques in Contract Claims. *Public Contract Law Journal*, 1974, **7**, 1.

contractor to see that the revised programme has been submitted in this regard as it could otherwise adversely affect the assessment of the compensation event by the project manager. Pursuant to clause 64.2 the project manager's own assessment would be used if the contractor had not submitted the revised programme.

Under the second bullet point the contractor is directed to show the effects of early warning matters, e.g. delayed completion.[118] The early warning procedure contemplates something of what is set out in clause 31.2. Thus under the early warning procedure the contractor should make and consider proposals for how the effect of each matter notified can be avoided or reduced, while in the revision to the programme it must be shown how the contractor plans to deal with any delays. Defects also may 'impair the performance of the *works* in use'.[119] Formal 'proposals' in the early warning procedure[120] would also be a consistent use with regard to that which the contractor 'proposes' to make to the accepted programme.[121] Once a revised programme has been accepted it is incumbent upon both parties to see that all of their obligations in relation to it howsoever changed are then acted on accordingly. In the case of the employer particularly this should be recognized, as a failure to do so may then entail a compensation event.

In summary the early warning procedure and the revising of the programme are very closely related not only as clearly indicated but also as clearly suggested. The programme is unquestionably designed to be used as a tool in the early warning meeting. Even when it is not being revised for early warning purposes much of the information that it must show is still pertinent for such purposes. In practice the programme will not only inform, but also explain and ultimately resolve early warning matters.

Possession, access and use of the site

The ECC addresses the issues of possession, access and use of the site together with the provision of facilities and services in two short subclauses.[122] Examples of 'facilities' are given in the guidance notes as follows: access roads, scaffolding, cranes and hoists, welfare, security arrangements, storage, power supplies, water, compressed air and telephone.[123] The clauses may be viewed as shorter still by virtue of the absence of any definitions for these terms. In brief, and according to clause 33.1, the employer must give possession of each part of the site to the contractor on or before the possession date or the date for possession

---

[118]   Clause 16.1 ECC.
[119]   Clause 16.1 ECC.
[120]   Clause 16.3 ECC.
[121]   The fourth bullet point clause 32.1 ECC.
[122]   The failure to provide facilities or services as agreed is a compensation event: clause 60.1(3) ECC.
[123]   Guidance notes NEC on clause 33.2 ECC, 40; cf the express reference to 'facilities' in clauses 31 and 42(4) and the example of traffic in clause 29 in ICE 6th.

shown on the accepted programme, whichever is later. Clause 33.2 addresses the separate but related topics of access to and use of the Site.

One may take as given the fact that the contractor will need possession of the site at some point. Thus the issues are when the point arises and whether it has been satisfied. In the ECC the point is set as on or before the later of its possession date[124] and the date for possession shown on the 'accepted programme'.[125] Thus the employer is under an express obligation to give the contractor possession of the site, or any part thereof as agreed, by one eventual due date; that is, in the end by the later of either the possession date or the date for possession shown on the accepted programme under clause 33.1. It will be a matter of interpretation whether clause 33.1 precludes the employer giving possession earlier than the last possible due date. The interpretation will turn upon the meaning of 'on or before' and whether it should be read limitatively or not. It is submitted that the employer should not be precluded from giving early possession particularly when the contractor may achieve the same end if a revised programme is submitted that is accepted. It can be remarked that the site may be given in parts as noted and while possession of the whole site may be given on or before the same date as the *'starting date'*,[126] it does not have to be. This giving of partial possession in the ECC is similar to provisions in ICE 6th and FIDIC 4th but differs from those in JCT 80. According to clauses 42 of ICE 6th and 42.1 of FIDIC 4th the contractor is entitled to possession only of so much of the site as is required to commence the works in accordance with the programme. In contrast, clause 23(1) of JCT 80 entitles the contractor to possession of the whole site from the outset. Under JCT/MT[127] possession of the site is not exclusive.

The *'possession dates'* will normally serve as the cornerstone of the contractor's programme but need not necessarily. In some circumstances the contractor may not commence work until some time after either the giving of whole or partial possession. If this were the case the date(s) of the later taking of possession by the contractor would replace the date(s) in part one of the Contract Data and bind the employer. This flexibility is similar to ICE 6th which obliges the contractor to commence work only as soon as is reasonably practical after the commencement date although without prejudice to the employer's rights to the agreed completion date.[128]

---

[124] The *'possession dates'* are an identified term and set out in section 3 of part one of the Contract Data with reference to parts of the site. The proforma makes reference to three possession dates.

[125] Clause 33.1 ECC. The accepted programme is determined in accordance with clause 31; see also clause 11.2(14) ECC.

[126] The starting date is an identified term and is also inserted in section 3 of part one of the Contract Data.

[127] Clause 3.4.1 JCT/MT.

[128] Clause 41 ICE 6th.

In general, the giving of the site by the employer to the contractor is a condition precedent to the obligation to commence work[129] although, as with other conditions for one's benefit, it may be waived if the contractor accepts late possession.[130] If late possession is accepted the contractor may still claim damages for breach of contract. The late giving of possession of a part of the site, that is the later of the possession date itself and the date required for the accepted programme, may invoke the early warning procedure and would also be a compensation event.[131]

The nature of the contractor's interest in the site has occasionally been controversial.[132] Thus, perhaps, the guidance notes seek to qualify the right to possession by the contractor through the definition.

> 'Possession' does not mean exclusive possession since there may be other contractors who need to be present on parts of the site to carry out their work. 'Possession' means the authority to occupy the Site[133] in order to carry out the obligations which the *Contractor* has under the contract.

This definition, once again, does not appear in the ECC but rather the guidance notes and as such is not binding on the parties.

It will normally be a matter of interpretation of the contract whether the contractor is entitled to exclusive possession of the site and with regard to what physical area. In the absence of provision to the contrary a contractor is entitled to possession of the whole area to be covered by a building and sufficient area surrounding it to be able to carry out the work.[134] Applying this principle to the provisions in the ECC it can be seen that there has been both provision to the contrary and a limitation on what is seen as necessary for the contractor to be able carry out the work. The ECC has adopted a dual regime of defined '*working areas*' as well as the 'Site'. Under clause 11.2(7): '[t]he Site is the area within the *boundaries of the site* and the volumes above and below it which are affected by work included in this contract' and under clause 11.2(8): '[t]he Working Areas are the *working areas* unless later changed in accordance with this contract'. A similar result is achieved in the ICE 6th which, although not defining a works area, defines the 'site' very broadly: clause 1(1)(v) states:

---

[129] *Arterial Drainage Co Ltd* v. *Rathangan River Drainage Board* (1860) 6 LR Ir 513.
[130] *Roberts* v. *Bury Improvement Comrs* (1870) LR 5 CP 310.
[131] Clause 60.1(2).
[132] For example, *Hounslow London Borough Council* v. *Twickenham Garden Developments Ltd* [1971] 1 Ch 233, [1970] 3 All ER 326; *Mayfield Holdings Ltd* v. *Moana Reef Ltd* [1973] 1 NZLR 309; *Graham H Roberts Pty Ltd* v. *Maurbeth Investments Pty Ltd* [1974] 1 NSWLR 93; *Surrey Heath Borough Council* v. *Lovell Construction Ltd and Haden Young* (1988) 42 BLR 25, 51; and *Tara Civil Engineering Ltd* v. *Moorfield Developments Ltd* (1989) 46 BLR 72, 79.
[133] Clause 11.2(7) ECC.
[134] *R* v. *Walter Cabott Construction Ltd* (1975) 69 DLR (3d) 542 at 549; cf the qualified possession of the site which is given to a contractor under clause 42 of ICE 6th.

'Site' means the lands and other places on under in or through which the Works are to be executed and any other lands or places provided by the Employer for the purposes of this Contract together with such other places as may be designated in the Contract or subsequently agreed as forming part of the Site.

Part one of the Contract Data, section 1 finally provides for the insertion of the precise *boundaries of the site*.

Pursuant to the dual regime of working areas and site the contractor may submit a proposal to the project manager for adding to the working areas, for instance, if the contractor's mobility on the site were hampered by limited space. Reasons for the project manager not accepting the proposal are that the proposed addition is not necessary for providing the works or the proposed area will be used for work not in the contract.[135] If the space necessary to fulfil works requirements cannot be fulfilled it is recommended that details be inserted in the works information of any physical limitations on the contractor's possession or when others will also occupy and share the site. In particular, details of any common facilities and precisely who has their maintenance obligations should also be clearly set out. If this is not done the employer is at risk of a dispute with the contractor over alleged interference.[136] The provision and sharing of facilities and services between the employer and the contractor is expressly stated in the contract and as the parties have agreed in the works information.[137] However, as noted it should also prudently be addressed *vis à vis* anyone else who will share the site or works area during construction. If the employer incurs costs as a result of the contractor not providing facilities and services which the contractor has agreed to provide the project manager contractor.[138] This is a reciprocal obligation and could equally fall upon the employer with the same consequences. It may also be observed that the Contract Data makes no express reference to 'facilities and services' as such and thus agreement on their content will have to be reached by the parties.[139]

The contract addresses access to and use of the site independently from but in addition to possession. Thus clause 33 in effect governs three separate legal and factual issues. Clause 33.2 provides in part as follows: 'While the *Contractor* has possession of a part of the Site, the *Employer* gives the *Contractor* access to and use of it ...'. It seems reasonable to infer that it would be the party in possession who would normally be expected to afford access to the other party. However, the employer may

---

[135] Clause 15.1 ECC.
[136] See the discussion of interference in Chapter 6 above.
[137] Clause 33.2 ECC.
[138] Clause 33.2 ECC.
[139] However reference to both facilities and services independently is made in the SCC in clauses 43 and 44; facilities alone in clauses 40.2, 42.1 and 60.1(16); and services alone in 11.2(4).

not have possession of the site, but only control the area around the site. In this case it would then be reasonable to impose an obligation upon the employer to provide access through or across this area to enter the site.[140] The obligation is not framed reciprocally in clause 33 but an access obligation is nevertheless imposed on the contractor in favour of the project manager and supervisor in clause 28.1. The contractor must provide access to both the work being done, which would presume the work is being done on the site, and to plant and materials being stored for the contract. The latter access obligation of the contractor is broader than that of the employer. Hence the contractor must also provide access to others notified by the project manager as well.[141] Access itself is viewed as a more limited right than possession.[142]

While the failure of the employer to not give possession of a part of the site by the ultimate due date is an express compensation event the failure to give access to or use of the site is dealt with only generally. Thus a contractor denied either access or use would have to rely upon the failure falling within clauses 60.1(3) or 60.1(18) for redress. The failure would be compensable under the first provision if the access or use fell within the meaning of the word 'something' and it was also noted on the accepted programme. To succeed or be compensable under the second provision noted the contractor would have to show the failure was a breach of an express or implied term of the contract.

The contractor will retain possession of the site until the employer takes over. Up until take over any wrongful interference[143] by the employer with the contractor's possession of the site or ejectment[144] by the employer of the contractor from the site may amount to repudiation. Once there has been a valid take over of the site by the employer the employer must still permit, through arrangements made by the project manager, the contractor to be given access to and use of any part of the works taken over for correcting defects.[145] The project manager must arrange the access within the '*defect correction period*'[146] and it must also be suitable.[147] If such access has not been arranged the project manager then has to extend the period to permit the correction of the defect as necessary.[148] The procedure for the acceptance or otherwise of the defect would then continue under the clause.[149] While the clause is framed with respect to the correction of a defect only there is no reason why the access could not also be given in respect of any outstanding work.

---

[140]   Cf clause 42(1) ICE 6th.
[141]   See clause 28.1 ECC.
[142]   See *LRE Engineering Services Ltd* v. *Otto Simon Carves Ltd* (1981) 24 BLR 127.
[143]   See *Earth & General Contracts Ltd* v. *Manchester Corpn* (1958) 108 LJ 665.
[144]   See *Roberts* v. *Bury Improvement Comrs* (1870) LR 5 CP 310, Ex Ch; *Felton* v. *Wharrie* (1906) 2 *Hudson's BC*, 4th edn 398, CA.
[145]   Clause 43.3 ECC.
[146]   Clause 43.3 ECC. See also section 4 of part one of the Contract Data.
[147]   See clause 43.3 ECC.
[148]   See clause 43.3 ECC.
[149]   See clause 43.3 ECC.

Both the contractor and the employer are under an express obligation to provide facilities and services as stated in the works information.[150] The reverse of this obligation may be the necessity to state any constraints on how the contractor provides the works in the works information as well under clause 11.2(5), e.g. access. The obligation on the contractor's part appears only to pertain to that time when the contractor is in possession of a part of the site. The obligation does not entail access *per se* but the provision of facilities and services. However, where the facilities and services are to be used jointly or by the non-providing party it is submitted that the court would imply a right of access to them. The failure of either party to provide the facilities and services may give rise to an early warning notice.[151] The clause anticipates that the failure to provide the agreed facilities and services may give rise to additional costs and any such costs incurred by the employer in this regard can be assessed by the project manager and paid by the contractor.[152] The employer makes no similar provision in clause 33.2 in respect of any such failure in this regard and giving rise to additional costs being incurred by the contractor. The employer's failure would thus fall to be considered under the compensation event procedures.[153]

The access obligations in the ECC may be contrasted with those in the PSC, First Edition. Pursuant to clause 32.1 the employer is obliged to provide access to 'areas of land and buildings'. The precise nature of the access is qualified in at least two and possibly more respects. Clause 32.1 of the PSC, First Edition also states that any restrictions which apply to the consultant's access must be stated in the brief. It is unusual to purport to give a general right, e.g. access, and at the same time suggest restrictions on it. Thus the right to the access must first be recognized or stated in the brief, and it must be necessary to enable the consultant to provide the services.[154] The employer, in considering any request for access, would apply the test of necessity by the consultant. The access obligation is stated to apply to 'areas' of land and buildings. It is unclear what meaning should be given to this phrase and whether it could operate as a limitation itself. It is also unclear whether it is intended to apply only to land or only to land *and* buildings. A reasonable interpretation would be to read the 'and' disjunctively as well as conjunctively so that the access could pertain to either land or buildings as well as land and buildings. The use of the term 'areas' also appears to detract from the definition of the site in the ECC, which refers to both the area of and volumes above and below.[155] For instance, in a project involving tunnelling work, the PSC access obligation could arguably be used to deny the consultant access to the the work below the areas of land and

---

[150] Clause 33. 2 ECC.
[151] See clause 16 ECC.
[152] Clause 33.2 ECC. See also clause 50.2 ECC.
[153] For example, under clauses 60.1(3), 60.1(5) and, in particular clause 11.2(16) ECC.
[154] See clause 32.1 ECC.
[155] Clause 11.2(7) ECC.

buildings.[156] The PSC, First Edition guidance notes do not add anything on these points. In fact, it may be asked whether they detract for two reasons. The guidance notes refer to 'any land or properties'. Hence, there is no reference to areas, and secondly 'properties' appears to be equated with 'buildings'. This may be the intention but one cannot assume a court would move so quickly to the same conclusion. In addition, the guidance notes see the access for the purpose of carrying out 'the *services*'. In this regard the guidance notes equate 'Provide the Services' with the 'the *services*'. The contention here is rather that the former should be construed to be broader than the latter.

Instructions to stop or not to start work

The project manager and supervisor are given wide-ranging powers to issue instructions in various cases. The power of the project manager to issue instructions to the contractor to either stop work or not to start any work is one important example[157] that, in certain circumstances, can lead to the termination of the contract. It is submitted that the exercise of the power amounts to a general power to order the suspension of the work. If this interpretation is correct it is a power that is not generally given in JCT forms.[158]

There is no established general right to suspend performance in English law.[159] This has led to difficult questions arising surrounding what rights are available to a party upon a breach of contract and what amounts to repudiation. While standard forms have sought to deal with these difficulties by providing express rights of termination they have been less likely to include rights of suspension. The NEC moves away from an ambivalent position on suspension and provides clear situations when it may be invoked.[160] While the practice of including rights of suspension is not universal in forms of contract since such rights have now been given in the Housing Grants, Construction and Regeneration Act 1996 it may be expected that it will serve to promote their wider acceptance.

The issue of suspension of performance has been looked at recently by J.W. Carter.[161] Carter, an advocate of the recognition of a general right to suspend performance for certain breaches of contract as well as generally for repudiation, puts forward several arguments in support of his position; two in particular are central here. The first point Carter makes is that more

[156] See generally clauses 60.1(12), 73.1 and 80.1 ECC.

[157] Clause 34.1 ECC.

[158] However, most JCT forms do empower the architect to issue instructions to postpone work: see e.g. clause 23.2 JCT 80.

[159] *Channel Tunnel Group Ltd* v. *Balfour Beatty Construction Ltd* [1992] 1 QB 656 at 666 per Staughton LJ.

[160] Clause 8.7 FIDIC Orange Book 1st part I also empowers the employer's representative to instruct the contractor to suspend progress of part or all of the works. Clauses 8.8 to 8.11 in part I deal with further issues arising from the suspension.

[161] CARTER, J.W. Suspending Contract Performance for Breach. In *Good Faith and Fault in Contract Law*, (eds BEASTON and FRIEDMAN) p. 485

generous discharge rules encourage defendants to withhold information pertinent to discharge so as to protect their contracts. Thus, he reasons, the adoption of a suspension regime instead may encourage, if not require, defendants to provide more non-performance information. This can also be accomplished without exacerbating defendant-orientated risk factors. Carter's second point is based on commercial practice. That is, good business practice suggests cancellation of a contract be routinely preceded by attempts at negotiation to preserve the bargain.[162] Contrasting some of the work of Ian Macneil,[163] Carter states that the 'law should not ignore the parties' interest in co-operation'.[164] After looking at the current rules for suspension under both English and Australian law, he concludes that both 'doctrinally and in practice, the principal advantage of the right to suspend performance lies in bridging the gap between termination for breach of a condition and termination for repudiation or serious breach'.[165] The NEC, in providing rights to suspend performance, has demonstrated a willingness to lead in this way. The rationale for suspension articulated by Carter is particularly suited to the NEC with its emphasis upon thoughtful risk allocation and co-operation by the parties.

It may be observed that there has been a tendency to equate smaller contracts with commensurately shorter eligible periods of suspension. Thus under ICE 6th the relevant period is 3 months[166] while under ICE MW 2nd it is 60 days.[167] The 13-week period in the ECC concedes this equation and thus one may ask whether the period is too long if the contract is used on a project with a small monetary value.

Where an instruction is given to stop or not to start any work it must initially comply with clause 13 requirements as the instruction is categorized as a communication. The instruction may be given for any reason, however, once given it will amount to a compensation event[168] save any normal exceptions that might apply.[169] The contractor in turn will be under an affirmative obligation to obey the instruction if it is given

---

[162]   See generally LOWRY, S.T. Bargain and Contract Theory in Law and Economics. *Journal of Economic Issues*, 1976, **10**, 1.

[163]   MACNEIL, I.R. Efficient Breach of Contract: Circles in the Sky. *Virginia Law Review*, 1982, **68**, 968. KRONMAN, A.T. Mistake, Disclosure, Information, and the Law of Contracts. *Journal of Legal Studies*, 1978, **7**, 1; although this argument is discounted by FABRE-MAGNAN, MURIEL. Duties of Disclosure and French Contract Law: Contribution to an Economic Analysis. In *Good Faith and Fault in Contract Law*, see n. 161 above, pp. 107–111.

[164]   CARTER, J.W., see n. 161 above, p. 499.

[165]   *Ibid.*, p. 520. Carter draws considerable support from the *Uniform Commercial Code* section 2–609, article 71 of the Vienna Convention on International Sales Law *International Legal Materials*, 1980, **19**, 671 and section 251 of the *Restatement (Second) of the Law of Contracts* for his position.

[166]   Clause 40 ICE 6th.

[167]   Clause 2.6(2)ICE MW 2nd.

[168]   Clause 60.1(4).

[169]   See e.g. discussion clause 61.1 ECC.

in accordance with the contract.[170] There is no qualification regarding the magnitude of the work subject to the instruction by the project manager.

The project manager may later instruct the contractor either to restart the work or to start it in the first instance. This is a second instruction and presupposes there was an earlier instruction either to stop or not to start the work respectively. If the project manager gives such an instruction the clause 13 requirements must be met and the contractor remains under the same affirmative obligation to obey the instruction.[171]

Pursuant to clause 95.6 if the original instruction of the project manager involved *substantial* work or *all* work, and no second instruction has been given within 13 weeks, termination may follow in three cases:

- the *Employer* may terminate if the instruction was due to a default by the *Contractor* (R19),
- the *Contractor* may terminate if the instruction was due to a default by the *Employer* (R20) and
- either Party may terminate if the instruction was due to any other reason (R21).[172]

The question is only academic regarding an instruction that pertains to all work but issues do arise regarding an instruction to stop or not to start *substantial* work. For example, a starting date independent of separate possession dates for parts of the site as well as sectional completion of portions of the works underscores the possible segmentation of the works. If an instruction is given in respect of such a segment, and if it remains in effect while other segmented work is carried out concurrently by the contractor, an issue may arise whether the instruction was in respect of 'substantial' work. If it were not substantial, even though it may amount to a compensation event, it would not necessarily entail a right to terminate the contract. In certain circumstances the contractor may prefer to have a reason to terminate the contract. If so and where the project manager disputed that substantial work was involved, the matter would have to be referred to the '*Adjudicator*' for decision.

To assist in giving meaning to the term 'substantial' guidance could be gleaned from case law regarding substantial performance and a test put forward on this basis. That test could be framed in this way: if the work in respect of which the instruction either to stop or not start was sufficient in itself, and if such work would otherwise constitute substantial performance of the contract without reference to the concurrent construction that the contractor had undertaken, then a right to terminate the contract has arisen. The right to terminate itself is qualified by default. In summary, if the original instruction was due to default by the contractor the employer may terminate the contract.[173] If the original instruction was due to default by the employer the contractor may

---

[170] Clause 29.1 ECC.
[171] Clause 29.1 ECC.
[172] Clause 95.6 ECC.
[173] Clause 95.6 (R19) ECC.

terminate the contract.[174] Outside a default scenario either party may terminate the contract.[175]

Take over

Partition of the site is envisaged under the ECC and provided for in part one of the schedule of Contract Data.[176] Pursuant to clause 35.1 '[p]ossession of each part of the Site[177] returns to the *Employer* when he takes over the part of the *works* which occupies it'.[178] The term 'take over' is popularly used for resumption of legal possession of all or a portion of the site or the works. It is also given legal expression in a number of other standard forms.[179] In strict terms it is the take over of a part of the works,[180] which works occupy a part of the site in turn, that triggers a change in legal possession. The project manager must certify the date upon which the employer takes over any part of the works and its extent within one week of that date.[181] Apart from the take over of parts of the works, a take over of the whole site occurs whenever the project manager certifies termination.[182] Take over in both these respects operates to transfer respective legal possession to the employer and hence responsibility for loss or damage.[183] In general take over may also operate as the time from which certain obligations end or run for agreed periods.[184] The notion of take over may be contrasted with the taking of partial possession of the works by the employer under other standard forms.[185]

The timing of the certification of completion, either in respect of the whole or a part of the works, is relevant in other respects. Depending upon whether the certification was more than two weeks before the completion event different results may follow. The different results also depend in part upon whether the Contract Data states whether the employer is not willing to take over the works before completion. If so, and the employer nevertheless decides to take over a part or the whole of the works before the completion date, the take over occurs within two weeks of completion but, if not, the take over is on the completion date itself.[186]

---

[174] Clause 95.6 (R20) ECC.

[175] Clause 95.6 (R21) ECC.

[176] Section 1. The right to resume partial possession of the site is not given as a matter of course in all standard forms, e.g. JCT MW makes no such provision.

[177] Clause 11.2(7) ECC.

[178] Clause 35.1 ECC.

[179] For example, both ACA 2 clause 12 and FIDIC 4th clause 48.1 'taking-over certificates' may be issued by the architect or engineer respectively.

[180] The works are identified in part one of the Contract Data, section 1.

[181] Clause 35.4 ECC. Take over is also certified under clause 12.1 of ACA 2.

[182] Clause 35.1 ECC.

[183] Clause 80.1 ECC.

[184] See e.g. *ENS Ltd (formerly Ebasco Ltd)* v. *Derwent Cogeneration Ltd* (1999) 62 Con LR 141 where liabilities for defective work under a turnkey contract ran for a period of three years after take over.

[185] See e.g. clause 23.2 JCT 80 but not IFC 84 under clause 2.1.

[186] Clause 35.2 ECC.

The provisions on taking over do not purport to give the employer a right to resume possession of any part of the site other than those previously agreed.[187] In doing otherwise the employer risks interference with the contractor's performance and the sanctions this may entail both at law[188] and under the contract. It will be a compensation event if viewed as a breach of contract under clause 60.1(18). Any take over of the works which has not been agreed by the parties in advance and incorporated in the works information, and whether later agreed or not, amounts to a compensation event.[189] This provision is thus distinct from that envisaged by the employer's agreed taking over of a section of the works and as provided by the works information read together with the sectional completion secondary option clause.[190] The effect of inclusion of the sectional completion secondary option clause is that the employer must take over that section of the works within two weeks of its completion.

The employer may use any part of the works before completion has been certified. The effect of the employer using any part of the works before certification of completion amounts to a take over of that part of the work save in two cases; that is, for a reason stated in the works information or to suit the contractor's method of working.[191] Another way of putting this is that if there is no reason stated in the works information for the use or if the use is not to suit the contractor's method of working, the employer then takes over whatever part of the works the employer uses from the beginning of that use. Certification of the take over before completion and the completion date would then invoke the early warning event procedure and a possible compensation event.[192]

In any circumstances where the employer does take over a part of the works or a section of the works in advance of that agreed, consideration should also be given to the effect on any agreed delay damages. Thus, any delay damages should be reduced to represent the proportion of the cost of the reduction of delay by the early taking over of that part or section of the works. The reduced damages should be separately calculated on a basis similar to the damages stated in the contract rather than pro rata according to the value of the part or section taken over and

---

[187] This is the same situation that pertains under JCT 81 clause 17.

[188] *William Cory & Son Ltd* v. *City of London Corpn* [1951] 2 KB 476 at 484, CA, per Lord Asquith; *London Borough of Merton* v. *Stanley Hugh Leach Ltd* (1985) 32 BLR 51 at 79. See generally for a seminal article on the topic FRIDMAN, G.H.L. Interference with Trade or Business – Part 1. *Tort Law Review*, 1993, **1**, 19; Interference with Trade or Business – Part 2. *Tort Law Review*, 1993, **1**, 99.

[189] Clauses 60.1(5) or (15). But see clause 35.3 ECC also allowing early take over without giving rise to a compensation event if it was to suit the contractor's method of working. Cf JCT 80 clause 18.1 which provides for partial possession of the works by the employer with the consent of the contractor.

[190] Option L ECC. This is similar to the sectional completion supplement in JCT 80.

[191] Clause 35.3 ECC.

[192] See clauses 16 and 60.1(15) ECC. The terminology of 'take over' and 'taking over certificate' are also both used in FIDIC 4th, see clause 48.

which may be too arbitrary to represent a genuine estimate of the reduced damages.[193]

It has been noted above that certification of termination may also operate in addition to take over to return legal possession of the whole site to the employer.[194] In this case, a take over certificate may or may not have to be issued. If so the project manager will certify the date upon which the employer takes over any part of the works and its extent within one week of the date.[195] The certification must be done timeously or the project manager risks invoking the early warning procedure.[196] The giving of the certificate as a communication must satisfy the requirements of clause 13.

Acceleration
The ECC makes express provision for acceleration. Pursuant to clause 36.1 the project manager may instruct the contractor to submit a quotation for an acceleration to achieve completion before the completion date. Accelerated completion procedures are also found in FIDIC 4th, ICE 6th and JCT 87 forms.[197] These provisions should also be contrasted with the power of the architect under clause 25.3.3 of the JCT 80 to bring forward the completion date from that previously fixed by the architect but not such as to accelerate the completion date ahead of that originally agreed by the parties. The JCT 87 provisions in clause 3.6 recognize not only acceleration but any alteration of sequence or timing of any work and whether it effectively moves up a current completion date or cancels or reduces the length of any previous instructed extension of time. Under JCT PCC, clause 2.5.10, the completion date may also be moved forward by written agreement between the parties but without the need to vary the contract, unlike clause 25.3.3 of the JCT 80. The FIDIC conditions present a different scenario. Thus, although express agreement by the contractor is not required,[198] the contractor may treat the request for acceleration as a variation to the works. This would entitle the contractor to seek additional compensation or an extension of time even though such actions by the contractor seemingly contradict part of the wording of the clause.[199]

The ECC provisions seek to address the more problematic features of the engineering form precedents; in particular consent and disagreement.

---

[193] Guidance notes NEC on clause 35.1 ECC, 41. See also *Philips Hong Kong* v. *A-G of Hong Kong* (1993) 61 BLR 41, PC, and the discussion on the calculation of liquidated and ascertained damages.

[194] Clause 35.1 ECC.

[195] Clause 35.4 ECC.

[196] See clause 16 ECC.

[197] Clause 46.1 FIDIC 4th and clauses 46(1)–(3) ICE 6th.

[198] Clause 46.1 FIDIC 4th: '... the Contractors shall thereupon take such steps ... to expedite progress ...'.

[199] Both clause 46.1 FIDIC 4th and 46(1) ICE 6th state: 'The Contractor shall not be entitled to any additional payment for taking such steps'.

It has been suggested that the inability of the employer to order either the acceleration of the work or to sanction effectively a contractor who is falling behind in the project without more are two explanations for the turn toward milestones or sectional completion requirements.[200] Milestone payments are common in design and build forms. Peter W.G. Morris has suggested that the trend can be expected to continue in the future: '[t]he move towards scheduling and managing by milestones will be consolidated. It fits best with ... project management "best practices"'.[201] The ECC requires the consent of the contractor[202] but differs from consent under the ICE conditions.[203] In the ECC provisions the contractor actively participates in trying to arrive at a solution for recovering lost time or expediting the works. This is achieved through the quotation procedure.[204]

The form of the proposals that the contractor puts forward in a quotation comprises changes to the prices and the completion date all as shown on a revised programme.[205] Depending upon the main option that the contractor is working under the subcontractor(s) may also be involved. Special provision is made in all main options save A and B for the contractor to submit a subcontractor's proposal to accelerate to the project manager for acceptance.[206] The contractor receives the proposal pursuant to the terms of the subcontract with the subcontractor.[207] There are no limitations on the contractor and subcontractor(s) collaborating in this respect. The procedure requiring the submission of subcontractors' proposals for acceleration through the contractor to the project manager ensures the project manager's overall control where the employer's interests are affected. The absence of an employer interest in any acceleration agreed solely between a contractor and subcontractor is reflected by the omission of the necessity to submit any such agreements to the project manager for scrutiny under main options A and B.[208] The provision is exceptional in the overall scheme of the ECC which normally assumes a third party or independent role for the project manager *vis à vis* the actions of subcontractors.

Once the proposals of the contractor or subcontractor(s) are in hand the project manager must decide whether to instruct the contractor to submit a

---

[200]   HOUGHTON, ANTHONY. Milestones and Liquidated Damages. *Construction Law Journal*, 1992, **8**, 232.

[201]   MORRIS, PETER W.G. *The Management of Projects*. Thomas Telford, London, 1994.

[202]   Guy Cottam refers to the acceleration provision as 'weak' as a result: Contract to Suit All Occasions? *Construction News*, 27 May 1993, 14.

[203]   Clause 46(3) ICE 6th.

[204]   BLACKLER, TONY *et al.*, critique a similar acceleration provision in the JCT 87 on grounds of expense or that the contractor who does not wish to accelerate may block it by quoting unreasonably: *Rowe & Maw, JCT Management Contract,* 16.

[205]   Clause 36.1 ECC. Revision to the programme is pursuant to clause 32 ECC.

[206]   Clause 36.5 main options C, D, E, and F ECC.

[207]   Clause 36.5 main options C, D and E ECSC.

[208]   Guidance notes NEC on clause 36.5 ECC, 42.

quotation. If so[209] the contractor then has to submit a quotation or give reasons for not doing so within the *'period for reply'*[210] or risk breaching the contract. The period for reply is inserted in section 1 of part one of the Contract Data. The reasons for not doing so are required under clause 36.1. Both the contractor's reply and any submission for acceptance must satisfy clause 13 requirements. In cases where a quotation is submitted by the contractor and accepted by the project manager the implementation of the acceleration will depend in part on the main option which has been chosen. Under all main options the project manager will change the completion date accordingly and accept the revised programme.[211] Additionally, in the case of main options A, B, C and D, the project manager will also change the prices accordingly.[212] The contractor's duty to provide the works is, of course, qualified to the extent of the changes.[213] Although there is no express cross-reference to the quotation procedures in clause 62 the use of the same terminology suggests that is what is clearly intended.[214] Tying the proposals for acceleration expressly into the familiar quotation procedure would serve to reassure the contractor that his interests would be dealt with fairly.

In summary, the acceleration procedures in the ECC are a good example of how the contractor's interests have been taken into account. Acceleration more often than not would be in the employer's or end user's interest. The contractor has entered into the agreement on the basis of certain resource allocation assumptions. Acceleration would overturn some of those assumptions. It is for this reason that, while the Contractor is given incentives to participate through familiar procedures with certain outcomes, there is still no sanction for failure to do so. The familiar procedures once again are those referred to above and which involve the submission of quotations.[215]

The absence of an employer right to compel acceleration serves not only to focus employer thinking on the most appropriate mode of procurement from the outset but also on whether acceleration is helpful at all.

> As a general rule, projects showing a combination of positive [on schedule] and zero [behind schedule] delta deviations should be left alone, because progress is ahead or on plan by both measures ... transferring resources (people or money) ... should always be approached with caution, especially if the transfer of people is involved ... Adding people to a project does not always correct a progress problem. There is a finite chance, therefore, of turning one

---

[209] The instruction must satisfy clause 13 ECC requirements.

[210] Clause 36.2 ECC.

[211] Clauses 36.3 and 36.4 ECC. All changes are made by instruction, clause 13 ECC in respect of which the contractor is under an obligation to obey, clause 29.1 ECC.

[212] Clause 36.3 ECC.

[213] See clause 20 ECC.

[214] It is a drafting principle of the NEC not to use cross-references.

[215] See discussion clause 62 ECC.

problem into two problems with this approach to problem solving.[216]

A thoughtful employer who notes the likelihood of accelerating the work as a serious prospect, should set a percentage chance on it and then consider those options which support the percentage chance. That is, in order of preference, main option E, followed by C, D or F in no particular order. Using the cost reimbursable contract the contractor would have the greatest incentive or the fewest reservations about acceleration of the work. Similarly, under either of the target contracts or the management contract the combined incentives and disincentives would be more apt to see the contractor participate in the acceleration. One may ask how are matters addressed when the project manager wishes to take no further action here – can the revised quotation procedure be read into the provisions? It would seem the answer is no and that the matter would end there. This follows from the requirement for consent to accelerate the works and that there would be little gained in having the project manager's own assessment in the circumstances. In summary, a prudent combination of forward planning and co-operative action once undertaken should be able to achieve both parties' goals in a significant change such as acceleration of the works.

Sectional completion

The ECC provides for the division or partition of the works into sections with separate completion dates for each section.[217] Sectional completion is catered for as a secondary option clause as follows:

L1.1 In these *conditions of contract*, unless stated as the whole of the *works*,[218] each reference and clause relevant to
- the *works*,
- Completion[219] and
- Completion Date[220]

applies, as the case may be, to either the whole of the *works* or any *section* of the *works*.

Some comments may be made on the terminology. The phrase '*conditions of contract*' is italicized here but once again not in clause

---

[216] LANIGAN, MIKE. See n. 106 above, p. 263.

[217] The term '*section*' is an identified term and as such appears in the Contract Data, part one. Each section of the works is briefly described and a completion date inserted respectively.

[218] A general description of the works should be given in section 1 part one of the Contract Data and which includes general arrangement and location drawings; working, production and other detailed drawings, specifications, models and other means used to describe the employer designed parts of the works; and statements of any constraints imposed on the contractor pertaining to how the contractor will provide the works: guidance notes NEC, 21.

[219] See section 11.2(13) ECC.

[220] See clause 11.2(12) ECC and the optional statements in part two of the Contract Data.

11.2. The sectional completion supplement enables important dates to be agreed by the parties upon which certain sections of the works are to be completed. The sections of the works to be completed are described in part one of the Contract Data and designated as 'sections' of the works. The relevant completion date for a section is entered in part one of the Contract Data. In the proforma for the contract five sections may be described in addition to their respective completion dates. Amendments to part one could add additional sections.[221] The use of the term 'sections' should be contrasted with the term 'parts' in other clauses, notably regarding possession of the site and take over,[222] and section 3 in part one of the Contract Data. The clear implication of this wording is that parts of the site need not be coextensive with sections of the work as described, although where they are then both these clauses[223] and the relevant secondary option clauses[224] should equally apply. It should be mentioned that the use of the term 'description' here is also intentional in that part one of the Contract Data provides only for a description of sections and not parts. This may mean that parts of the work without more should be capable of clear recognition. Lastly, it may be noted that part one of the Contract Data italicizes the terms 'section', 'sections', and 'Section'.

The court will not ordinarily imply a term for sectional completion into a contract containing only one completion date.[225] The sectional completion option in the ECC further supports this conclusion. As such, if the parties have not chosen to include the sectional completion option, it is unlikely a court would imply a term for sectional completion. It is worth noting once again that the ECC does not contain a precedence of documents clause and that it is left to the project manager to resolve any ambiguity or inconsistency that may arise.[226] Questions will inevitably follow as a result. Thus, for example, on this topic, would information suggesting sectional completion in applicable bills of quantities,[227] be sufficient to imply sectional completion?[228] The answer to this and related questions will ultimately be left to the project manager to decide.

Sectional completion dates may be relevant to works to be completed by others. In this case the details would be included in the works information rather than part one of the Contract Data. Details would also be reflected in the contractor's programme. Once part of the contractor's

---

[221] Cf phased completion supplement for Works Contract/2 (JCT 87) as an alternative to sectional completion.
[222] Clauses 33 and 35 ECC.
[223] For example, clauses 33 and 35 ECC.
[224] Secondary options L, P, Q and R.
[225] See *Bruno Zornow (Builders) Ltd* v. *Beechcroft Developments Ltd* (1989) 51 BLR 16.
[226] Clause 17.1 ECC.
[227] For example, a main option B or D as the method of procurement.
[228] See *E Turner & Sons Ltd* v. *Mathind Ltd* (1989) 5 Const LJ 273, CA; but see *M J Gleeson (Contractors) Ltd* v. *London Borough of Hillingdon* (1970) 215 *Estates Gazette* 495; and *Bruno Zornow (Builders) Ltd* v. *Beechcroft Developments Ltd* (1989) 51 BLR 16.

accepted programme, any failure to meet the sectional completion dates by the others or even the employer would become a compensation event under either clause 60.1(3) or (5).

Completion of all sections will be followed by completion of the works. In the absence of provision to the contrary in the works information completion of the last section will not be equated with the whole of the works, which remains separately identified in part one of the Contract Data. The principal obligation of the contractor is, after all, to 'provide the works',[229] not all sections of the works. This obligation, inclusive of incidental work, services and actions[230] that the contract requires is, once again, a different obligation from completing all sections of the works. The sections in this narrower regard are thus closer to what are referred to as milestones in other contracts. Milestones are endorsed in the Construction Round Table's *Declaration of Commitment to Fair Construction Contracts* requiring members to declare their intention to give effect to certain principles in the conduct of their projects and which include: '[w]henever possible to base interim payments on agreed schedules of payments, milestones or activities including payments for off-site activity'.[231] Milestones are also 'important to provide intermediate points throughout the network and resulting schedule that can be used as benchmarks'.[232]

By comparison, the PSC First Edition does not specify what the services shall be, as it is designed to be generic. In practice a list of services will be agreed by the parties. Payment does not follow traditional lines which is often based upon an agreed percentage of the overall construction costs but rather the parties may choose instead from one of four options.[233] In contrast is Schedule 1 to the *Form of Appointment as Planning Supervisors* (FOA 97/1) which provides a very detailed list of services. The distinction arises between the two forms from the fact that stipulated duties are laid upon a planning supervisor under the relevant CDM Regulations and which must be reflected in the appointment unlike in the case of the '*Consultant*' under the PSC.

The sectional completion supplement should be read together and applied with the bonus for early completion[234] and delay damages[235] secondary option clauses which it may often be expected to be used with.

[229]   See clause 20.1 ECC.

[230]   Clause 11.2(4) ECC.

[231]   *Construction Industry Law Letter*, 1995, 1104.

[232]   LOCK, DENNIS. See n. 75 above, p. 134.

[233]   BIRKBY, GILLIAN. One-Stop Shopping for Consultants' Appointments? *Construction Law*, December 1994, 182.

[234]   Secondary option clause Q.

[235]   Secondary option clause R. See also *Bruno Zornow (Builders) Ltd* v. *Beechcroft Developments Ltd* (1989) 51 BLR 16 on the effect that sectional completion supplements may have upon liquidated or delay damages provisions.

Delay damages

The ECC, like most other standard forms of contract,[236] makes provision for damages for delay in completion.[237] Provision is not surprising when some surveys suggest a large percentage of all projects finish late. A major recent poll by the Construction Clients' Forum showed that 58% of clients reported their projects were late, 32% said the work was over budget and 90% reported defects.[238] Delay, or 'negative progress deviation', is thus one of the central problems in planning and control of projects today.[239] The parties may expressly provide for it, however, by the incorporation of the secondary option clause on delay damages. Option R1.1 states:

> The *Contractor* pays delay damages at the rate stated in the Contract Data from the Completion Date[240] for each day until the earlier of
> * Completion[241] and
> * the date on which the *Employer* takes over[242] the *works*
> until the Completion Date.[243]

First of all, with regard to the 'rate' of delay damages, they may be given for the whole of the works as an optional statement in part one of the Contract Data whether or not option L is also used. If options L and R are used together, the delay damages may be given as an optional statement in part one of the Contract Data in respect of individual sections of the works. The proforma allows for five such sectional delay damage rates although more could be added. In each case a description is given and the rate as an amount per day. In comparison, the appendix to JCT 80 contains a similar provision for a rate of liquidated and ascertained damages to be inserted. It has been held in relation to this provision that the insertion of 'nil' precludes both any claim for unliquidated damages for late completion and any implied term arising that the delayed work would be completed within a reasonable time and such as would support a claim for damages at common law under *Temloc Ltd* v. *Errill Properties Ltd.*[244]

The delay damages provisions should be considered together with secondary option clause L1.1 which requires the terms 'Completion' and 'Completion Date' to be read to apply to any section of the works as well. In many cases it may be expected that the employer will use options L and

---

[236] See e.g. clause 24 JCT 80 and clause 47 ICE 6th.

[237] Secondary option clause R ECC.

[238] See RIDOUT, GRAHAM. Clients Frustrated at Industry Performance. *Contract Journal*, 14 April 1999, 1.

[239] See LANIGAN, MIKE, n. 106 above, p. 200. See generally MORRIS, P.W.G. and HOUGH, G.H. *The Anatomy of Major Projects*. John Wiley and Sons, London, 1989.

[240] See clause 11.2(12) ECC.

[241] See clause 11.2(13) ECC.

[242] See clause 35 ECC.

[243] Clause 11.2(12) ECC.

[244] *Temloc Ltd* v. *Errill Properties Ltd* (1987) 39 BLR 30, CA.

R together.[245] If a contractor fails to meet successive sectional completion dates as well as the final completion date, there may be liability for both delay damages in respect of the incomplete sections as well as the whole of the works.

Part one of the Contract Data stipulates that delay damages for the whole of the works are payable per day. Daily or weekly rates are the norm in the construction industry. To be valid and upheld by the court the provision would have to be construed as a 'liquidated', or 'liquidated and ascertained' damages provision (an amount payable in the event of breach agreed to beforehand by the parties[246]) and not a penalty.

This question is determined as a matter of interpretation by the court with recourse to well-established principles.[247] In particular, the court will ask whether the sum represents a genuine pre-estimate of the damage, which the employer would incur in the case of delay in completion. It can be seen that the answer to this question in part will thus turn upon the amount that the parties have stipulated. Therefore, an excessive or extravagant sum in relation to the loss likely to befall the employer would tend toward it being construed as a penalty.[248]

While there is clearly a relationship between the loss occasioned and the amount stipulated, it need not be exact as it is a 'genuine pre-estimate of the damage' that is the test. Thus, in a hypothetical situation where the stipulated sum exceeded the maximum loss possible of the employer it still may not be a penalty on this basis.[249] If, however, the amount was found to be unenforceable as a penalty, the employer may still be able to deduct unliquidated damages although the sum stipulated could still serve as the maximum recoverable.[250] The fact that the ECC describes the sum as 'delay damages' is not conclusive and substance over form would presumably prevail in the court's determination[251] and the extent to which it had recourse to the established jurisprudence. If these tests were applied it would be expected that they would also be material in construing the vesting clauses in the ECC regarding equipment, plant and materials.[252]

In general, in any situation where the contractor fails without excuse to complete the works (or any section of them) within the time prescribed

---

[245] See the optional statements in part one of the Contract Data in this regard.

[246] See discussion of completion above.

[247] *Dunlop Pneumatic Tyre Co Ltd* v. *New Garage & Motor Co Ltd* [1915] AC 79 at 86, HL, per Lord Dunedin.

[248] *Clydebank Engineering Co* v. *Don Jose Ramos Yzquierdo y Castaneda* [1905] AC 6, HL.

[249] *Philips Hong Kong* v. *A-G of Hong Kong* (1993) 61 BLR 41, PC.

[250] *Rapid Building Group* v. *Ealing Family Housing Association Ltd* (1984) 29 BLR 5, CA; *Elsley* v. *J G Collins Insurance Agencies Ltd* (1978) 83 DLR (3d) 1 at 14; cf *Widnes Foundry* (*1925*) *Ltd* v. *Cellulose Acetate Silk Co Ltd* [1931] 2 KB 393, CA; affd [1933] AC 20, HL.

[251] *Public Works Comr* v. *Hills* [1906] AC 368, PC.

[252] See clause 7 and 96.2 P3 ECC; and *Ranger* v. *Great Western Rly Co* (1854) 5 HL Cas 72, HL.

damages for breach of contract would become payable.[253] In such case normal contract law principles and the rules regarding remoteness of damage would govern payment of the award.[254]

Two questions have risen in particular regarding damages clauses. First, is a damages clause an exhaustive remedy? Second, does an agreed sum set a maximum figure allowable for recovery? Case law suggests, with regard to the first issue in situations involving *liquidated* damages clauses, that the clause itself must be properly construed to determine the answer.[255] The reply to the second question is unclear and case law can be found supporting both limiting the parties to any agreed sum as a maximum figure[256] as well as finding the sum imposes no ceiling at all.[257] Hence it is an open question whether any agreed sum in the Contract Data will be construed as a limitation on the maximum figure allowable. It would seem on balance that the additional attention given to this issue in drafting and existence of the precedents referred to tips the scales in favour of finding that if option R, for example, were used then the employer's rights to claim damages would be limited to the amount stipulated.[258] This point, however, is distinct from the remedy of the employer to seek delay damages, which is not exclusive. In addition, the employer would have remedies both at law and under the contract. In particular, the employer has the right to terminate the contractor's appointment if delay amounted to a substantial failure to comply with the contractor's obligations,[259] or substantially hindered the employer or others[260] in the performance of their obligations. Any amounts due to the contractor on termination for these reasons would be reduced by the amount retained by the employer for delay damages and other amounts.[261]

The exercise of the employer's rights in these regards is subject to any other constraints which the conditions impose or the parties may have supplementally agreed to.[262] It is a matter of interpretation whether timely

---

[253] *Young* v. *Kitchin* (1878) 3 Ex D 127.

[254] *Hadley* v. *Baxendale* (1854) 9 Exch 341, [1843–60] All ER Rep 461; *Victoria Laundry (Windsor) Ltd* v. *Newman Industries Ltd* [1949] 2 KB 528, [1949] 1 All ER 997; *Canada Foundry Co Ltd* v. *Edmonton Portland Cement Co* [1918] 3 WWR 866, PC.

[255] *Temloc Ltd* v. *Errill Properties Ltd* (1987) 39 BLR 30 at 39, CA, per Nourse LJ. Cf *Baese Pty Ltd* v. *R A Bracken Building Pty Ltd* (1989) 52 BLR 130 (NSWSC) declining to follow *Temloc*.

[256] *Luen Yick Co* v. *Tan Man Kee Machinery Workshop* [1958] HKLR 405 at 416–417 per Reece J; *Elsey* v. *J G Collins Insurance Agencies Ltd* (1978) 83 DLR (3d) 1 (SCC); and *Pigott Foundations Ltd* v. *Shepherd Construction Ltd* (1993) 42 Con LR 98.

[257] Obiter comments of Bingham and Parker LJJ in *E Turner & Sons Ltd* v. *Mathind Ltd* (1989) 5 Const LJ 273, 281 and 282 respectively.

[258] Cf *Moores* v. *Yakeley Associates Ltd* (1999) 62 Con LR 76.

[259] Clause 95.2 ECC.

[260] Clause 95.3 ECC.

[261] Clause 97 ECC.

[262] For example, under clause 95.2 and 95.3 a four-week notice period is stipulated before termination may be ordered.

completion[263] is a condition precedent to any right of the contractor to be paid for work done. Upon the wording in the ECC this does not appear to be the case and thus, notwithstanding such defaults, the contractor nevertheless would remain entitled to payment less the employer's legitimate deductions.

The far-reaching provisions regarding delay damages and extension of time in the ECC make it unlikely that time for completion would be viewed as the essence of the contract and entitling repudiation for breach simpliciter without regard to its nature and consequences.[264] However, the provisions for notice throughout could have the effect of making time of the essence such that the employer could treat the contractor's failure to complete by the notified date as a repudiatory breach of contract entitling termination.[265] Such entitlement of the employer would exist at law and be judged at law rather than solely under the provisions of their agreement. In this way the right to repudiate the agreement is seen as *additional* to the other remedies of the employer. The court would be likely to impose a reasonable requirement upon the employer in the giving of any notice to overcome delay; whether a four-week time period would be sufficient is a matter of fact for the court.

The NEC, unlike other forms,[266] makes no express provision for reduction of delay damages where there has been either early completion or take over of a part of the works. This omission could result in a court holding that the delay damages were punitive. Similar issues arise in cases involving sectional completion.[267] In part to address this issue the JCT issued a sectional completion supplement for use with JCT forms following *M J Gleeson (Contractors) Ltd* v. *London Borough of Hillingdon*.[268] A delay damages clause upon its proper interpretation may also be viewed as an exemption clause and subject to judicial scrutiny including *contra proferentem* interpretation.[269] However the *contra proferentem* rule itself is increasingly being confined to cases involving ambiguity alone rather than as a general rule of interpretation in

---

[263]   See *Maryon* v. *Carter* (1830) 4 C & P 295.

[264]   See *Lamprell* v. *Billericay Union* (1849) 3 Exch 283; and *Webb* v. *Hughes* (1870) LR 10 Eq 281.

[265]   *Felton* v. *Wharrie* (1906) 2 *Hudson's BC*, 4th edn. 398; *United Scientific Holdings Ltd* v. *Burnley Borough Council* [1978] AC 904 at 937, 944, 958, HL; and *Charles Rickards Ltd* v. *Oppenheim* [1950] 1 KB 616, [1950] 1 All ER 420, CA.

[266]   See e.g. clauses 47.2 FIDIC 4th, 47.1 ICE 6th.

[267]   See e.g. *M J Gleeson (Contractors) Ltd* v. *London Borough of Hillingdon* (1970) 215 *Estates Gazette* 495; *Bramall & Ogden Ltd* v. *Sheffield City Council* (1983) 29 BLR 73; and *Bruno Zornow (Builders) Ltd* v. *Beechcroft Developments Ltd* (1990) 16 Con LR 30.

[268]   *M J Gleeson (Contractors) Ltd* v. *London Borough of Hillingdon* (1970) 215 *Estates Gazette* 495. See generally McINNIS, J.A. *Hong Kong Construction Law*, Div XII paras 228–540.

[269]   See *Bramall & Ogden Ltd* v. *Sheffield City Council* (1983) 29 BLR 73 at 89.

all cases and this is supported by increasing judicial intervention which has made it less likely for the rule to be called in aid.[270]

The procedures for the deduction of liquidated damages under standard form contracts are normally strictly outlined and construed. For instance, a certificate of failure to complete or a notice of intention to deduct damages may be required as conditions precedent to their deduction.[271] The procedures in the ECC for the deduction of the delay damages may be expected to be similarly strictly construed by the courts; however, the ECC does not require these conditions precedent to be satisfied. Rather, the only critical issue is whether completion has occurred. Once again completion may be determined with reference to the whole or any section of the works under the sectional completion supplement. If completion has not occurred as agreed then without more the contractor will have to pay delay damages at the rate stated in the contract data from the completion date for each date until the earlier of completion and the date on which the employer takes over the works.[272] Assessment of the amount due would be made in the ordinary way under clause 50.2 and paid by or retained from the contractor. The same result would pertain if the employer had taken over the works within the meaning of clause 35. That would end the matter save in the case where the completion date ends up being changed after the delay damages have been paid. In this case, and if it changed to a later date, the employer must repay the overpayment of the delay damages with interest.[273] The assessment of the interest would be from the date of payment to the date of repayment.[274] Presumably for the avoidance of doubt the date of repayment is expressly stated to be an assessment date[275] and as such is brought within the meaning of clause 50.1 of the ECC. If this interpretation were correct then interest would run until the payment is made. This interpretation appears to accord generally with the intent that costs be fully recovered. The rate of interest would be that agreed in section 5 of part one of the Contract Data.[276]

Any act of prevention or interference by the employer which is not compensated for with an extension of time will preclude reliance upon the delay damages provisions.[277] Thus an employer in this situation who may

---

[270] See for a unique look at the use of not only the *contra proferentem* rule but three other important rules of interpretation as well in reported American construction cases: THOMAS, H. RANDOLPH *et al.* Interpretation of Construction Contracts. *Journal of Construction Engineering and Management*, 1994, **120**, 321–336.

[271] See *A Bell & Son (Paddington) Ltd* v. *CBF Residential Care and Housing Association* (1989) 46 BLR 102. Cf clauses 2.9 JCT NSC/C and 35.15 JCT 80 for other examples of certificates as conditions precedent to contractual entitlements.

[272] Clause R1.1 ECC.

[273] Clause R1.2 ECC.

[274] Clause R1.2 ECC.

[275] Clause R1.2 ECC.

[276] See also clause 51.5 ECC.

[277] *Wells* v. *Army & Navy Co-operative Society Ltd* (1902) 86 LT 764, CA; *Peak Construction (Liverpool) Ltd* v. *McKinney Foundations Ltd* (1970) 1 BLR 114, CA.

have committed a breach of contract or delayed the contractor through instructions issued by the project manager will wish to extend the completion date for the contractor to preserve the right to seek delay damages as from the new or extended completion date at least.

The employer may rely upon the delay damages provisions without proof of loss; subject to it being valid and the employer having complied with all requisite contractual procedures. However, if the loss is greater than the amount of the delay damages stipulated, the employer may be precluded from not relying upon the clause and seeking to claim general or unliquidated damages instead if the clause is presumed to be exhaustive of the employer's rights.[278] This limitation on the employer's rights, however, pertains only to the damages for delay. If the contractor has independently breached other provisions of agreement with the employer the contractor may still be able to claim general or unliquidated damages in respect of those breaches.[279]

If the completion date is changed to a later date after the contractor has paid delay damages, the employer must repay their overpayment with interest.[280] Case law had earlier reached the same result and thus in *Department of the Environment for Northern Ireland* v. *Farrans (Construction) Ltd* when liquidated damages had been paid for late completion prior to an extension of time being granted the employer was ordered to repay the sum deducted with interest.[281] The interest is assessed from the date of payment by the contractor to the date of repayment by the employer. The date of repayment is an assessment date.[282]

Several clauses in the ECC operate to excuse the contractor from paying delay damages and can also operate to extend the completion date; for instance, weather extremes which exceed those agreed and are in excess of those occurring on average less frequently than once in ten years.[283] In this way a more objective means of dealing with this risk has thus been provided because as Phillip Capper writes:

> The unpredictability of English weather is incontrovertible. That it affects many construction processes is not surprising. Traditional forms of construction contract leave this risk as one to be resolved in the eventual discretion of the contract administrator. But views will differ as to the fairness and appropriateness of the exercise of that discretion. Other solutions could be adopted. The NEC forms seek to base the evaluation of compensation for such events on more

---

[278] *Temloc Ltd* v. *Errill Properties Ltd* (1987) 39 BLR 30 at 39, CA, per Nourse LJ.
[279] *E Turner & Sons Ltd* v. *Mathind Ltd* (1986) 5 Const LJ 273, CA; *M J Gleeson plc* v. *Taylor Woodrow Construction Ltd* (1989) 49 BLR 95 at 107.
[280] Clause R1.2 ECC. A stipulation for interest is also made in ICE 6th clauses 69(7) and (8).
[281] *Department of the Environment for Northern Ireland* v. *Farrans (Construction) Ltd* (1981) 19 BLR 1.
[282] Clause r1.2 ECC.
[283] Clause 60.1(13) ECC.

objective data. Contracts could conceivably be drafted which require the prior pricing of such contingent risks. That has not been the traditional practice of the British construction industry but nor has the postponement of resolution of uncertainties been limited to weather. Therein lies one of the clues to the frequency of construction disputes, eventually demanding arbitration.[284]

However, it should be noted that any amount which the contractor may have to pay as delay damages will not reduce any amount also stipulated to be payable by the contractor in respect of liability for defects due to design and which are not listed on the defects certificate.[285] Defects not listed in this way could be equated to latent defects in contrast to those defects which are due to the contractor's design and hence presumably patent defects. Overall, the number of instances when the contractor will be excused from delays for which he or she is responsible is limited.[286]

Glyn Jones would classify a risk such as weather as a 'speculative risk' – speculative in the sense that the contractor might be willing to assume it on the basis of his profit motive.

> The JCT endeavour to deal with known Speculative Risks in an optimum way wherein the Employer secures the lowest Contract Sum in return for taking certain of the Risks. The Contractor on the other hand although relieved of these risks is also being denied the chance to gain the profit that exists in every Speculative Risk ... Contractors *want* to take Speculative Risks for these are the only ones that grant them the chance to earn profits. Employers ought however to *deny* the Contractor certain of these Risk responsibilities in order to receive lower bids. If however an unknown Speculative Risk materialises there will be a gap in the contract ... If earlier editions of the JCT Contract (or any other construction contract) are compared with today's it can be seen there are provisions which have shifted Speculative Risks from the Contractor's shoulders to those of the Employer.[287]

Bonus for early completion

The parties to the ECC may agree to the payment of a bonus for early completion. The inclusion of the provision marks a departure from traditional forms. No other leading standard forms include such a bonus clause in their general wording although FIDIC 4th includes two

---

[284] CAPPER, PROFESSOR PHILLIP. See n. 55 above, p. 13.

[285] Clause 21.5 ECC. See also Contract Data part one section 2.

[286] See *Computer & Systems Engineering plc* v. *John Elliott (Ilford) Ltd* (1990) 54 BLR 1; cf *Surrey Heath Borough Council* v. *Lovell Construction Ltd* (1988) 42 BLR 25.

[287] JONES, GLYN P. *A New Approach to the 1980 Standard Form of Building Contract.* The Construction Press, Lancaster, 1980, pp. 22–24 and citing CARR, R.I. Paying the Price for Construction Risk. *Journal of the Construction Div ASCE*, March 1977.

examples of such clauses in part II, clause 47.3. The bonus clause is contained in a secondary option clause that provides:

> Q.1 The *Contractor* is paid a bonus calculated at the rate stated in the Contract Data for each day from the earlier of
> * Completion[288] and
> * the date on which the *Employer* takes over[289] the *works*
> until the Completion Date.[290]

The rate or the bonus as such may be given for the whole of the works as an optional statement in part one of the Contract Data. If options L and Q are used together the rate or bonuses may be given as an optional statement in part one of the Contract Data in respect of individual sections of the works. The proforma allows for five such sectional bonuses although more could be added. In each case a description is given and the rate as an amount per day.

It will be a matter of interpretation whether the contractor would be entitled to a bonus payment under the clause if the original completion date was adjusted with the grant of an extension of time[291] or there was early completion or take over of a part of the works. If both options L and Q are used together, as one may expect many parties to do to achieve the full incentive effect of the provisions, then it is submitted that this would be the correct interpretation. In many cases it may be expected that the employer will use options L and Q together. If option L is relied on clause L1.1 would require the terms 'Completion' and 'Completion Date' to be read to apply to any section of the works as well.[292] Thus a contractor would receive the pro rata portion of the bonus for the take over, sectional or early completion reflecting its value relative to the prices. If there were an act of prevention by the employer that precluded the contractor otherwise completing early and as thereby the right to earn a bonus, the contractor would be able to claim damages for the deprivation.[293] However, such damages would not necessarily equal the stipulated amount of the bonus in any case where the likelihood of completion will be discounted.[294] Apart from the contractor's common law rights in this regard where the employer's act of prevention is also a compensation event the normal compensation event procedure would apply and as such the contractor would benefit from both cost and time allowances the latter of which should serve to safeguard any bonus entitlement.

In general the bonus option clause in the NEC is an important advance that affirms the value of positive incentives over disincentives. However,

---

[288] See clause 11.2(13) ECC.
[289] See clause 35 ECC.
[290] See clause 11.2(12) ECC.
[291] *Ware and Jones* v. *Lyttelton Harbour Board* (1882) 1 NZLR 191.
[292] See the optional statements in part one of the Contract Data in this regard.
[293] *Bywaters & Sons* v. *Curnick & Co* (1906) 2 *Hudson's BC*, 4th edn 393, CA.
[294] See *Macintosh* v. *Midland Counties Rly Co* (1845) 14 M & W 548 at 558. See also *Bywaters & Sons* v. *Curnick & Co* (1906) 2 *Hudson's BC*, 4th edn 393 at 397, CA.

as with many of the secondary options the clause should not be used without *first* considering whether it is appropriate in all of the circumstances of the project and after weighing the factors involved. The types of factors worth considering could pertain to the project goals of time, cost and quality. Majid Jaraiedi lists the following factors:

- How can one determine which projects warrant incentive contracts?
- How should the cost of the provisions be determined so that the goals of the employer are met and the contractor is properly motivated?
- How can the success and effectiveness of the incentives be measured?
- How can additional and or unforeseen problems be addressed within the contract to ensure its success?
- How should the magnitude of the incentives be determined such that it can affect time compression?
- Can nonmonetary rewards be used to align contractor goals with those of the employer?
- Can a combination of monetary and nonmonetary considerations be used to develop the incentive provisions?[295]

Other lesser factors could pertain to matters such as administrative burden in setting and measuring performance targets in determining whether the bases for awarding a bonus have been satisfied. Once again, therefore, use of the bonus clause should work not only in the contract but also with the project goals.[296]

---

[295] JARAIEDI, MAJID *et al.* Incentive/Disincentive Guidelines for Highway Construction Contracts. *Journal of Construction Engineering and Management,* 1995, **120**, 114.

[296] A novel example of sharing savings was seen lately when Otis returned 50% of savings on one project attributable to partnering arrangements and reduced man-hours; see SAVVAS, ANTONY. 'Trust' Leads to Give-Back. *Contract Journal,* 10 June 1998, 9.

9. Testing and defects

Every client has the right to expect high quality from the project which it has commissioned.

Sir Michael Latham,
Constructing the Team

General

Clause 4 of the ECC sets out the contractor's responsibility for testing and defects. Formerly, under the Consultation Document, the clause was headed 'Quality'. Although neither the clauses in the Consultation Document sought, nor do the clauses in the Second Edition seek, to impose an obligation on the contractor to fulfil any particular quality assurance programme,[1] the original heading clearly has stronger connotations with such programmes than the current heading of 'Testing and Defects'. The original 'Quality' heading is also arguably closer to the aims of project management and construction management than the narrower heading adopted.[2] The two headings reflect a subtle difference in orientation. Under the former heading attention is focused upon process while under the latter it is focused upon outcomes. Quality suggests that all functions and actions were relevant to achieving the desired outcomes. This is still the case even though no particular form of quality assurance programme was mandated. While no particular programme was or is mandated, incorporation of any applicable quality standard or quality assurance programme may still be effected through the works information if the parties wished. In contrast, the Highways Agency Design and Build Contract 1996 expressly imposes an obligation in clause 28 to comply with a quality management system in accordance with BS EN ISO 9002, as well as prepare a design quality plan and construction quality plan in accordance with the employer's requirements. It is interesting to note,

[1] For example, BS 5750, BS 5882, ISO 9000, BS EN ISO 9000, NQA-1, AQAP 1-10, 10 CFR 50, CSA Z299 or ASME 3.
[2] See generally BARBER, J. *Quality Management in Construction – Contractual Aspects*. CIRIA, London, 1992; and ASHFORD, J.L. *Quality Management in Construction – Certification of Product Quality and Quality Management Systems*. CIRIA, London, 1989, CIRIA Special Publication 72.

however, that ISO 9001 makes no reference to project management and this may be an inhibition to the full implementation of the standard until it is addressed at the standards level.[3] The works information is the appropriate means to introduce such a programme in the ECC because of the essential relationship it has to both tests and inspections. Thus the tests carried out under clause 40.1 by the contractor, supervisor and others; the materials, facilities and samples to be provided under clause 40.2 by both the contractor and employer; the plant and materials to be inspected or tested under clauses 41.1 and 71.1 may *all* be set out in the works information. It may be that an employer would like to see complete details of a quality assurance programme in part two of the Contract Data prior to awarding the contract, or the employer may in turn have stipulated it at the outset in part one of the Contract Data. Thus and notwithstanding that quality objectives may be achieved in the same way under either the provisions of the Consultation Document or the Second Edition, it is still the Consultation Document which had the clearest connotations that such steps should be taken. The ECC provisions now contrast with those in clause 4.8 of the FIDIC Orange Book which imposes an express quality assurance obligation. In view of the increasing importance of quality to the construction process it is suggested here that the ECC provisions should be re-examined in light of this precedent and this trend. For example, clause 4.8 in FIDIC Orange Book 1st, part I provides:

> [u]nless otherwise stated in Part II, the Contractor shall institute a quality assurance system to demonstrate compliance with the requirements of the Contract. Such system shall be in accordance with the details stated in the Contract. Compliance with the quality assurance system shall not relieve the Contractor of his duties, obligations or responsibilities.

It is significant that the duty has been included in part I of the general conditions and thus made it the default rule out of which parties must contract in part II if they do not wish it to apply.[4] In general, the experiences of contractors with quality management programmes further supports their extension.[5]

Notwithstanding the absence of a mandatory quality assurance programme some of the most important principles[6] upon which such a

---

[3] See COUWENBERGH, J.C.H. What is Missing in the International Standard ISO 9001 Regarding to the Building Industry. In Quality Management in Building and Construction. *Proceedings of Eureka Conference Hamar/Lillehammer, June 1994* ed. SJOHOLT, ODD. Norwegian Building Institute, Hamar/Lillehammer, 1994, p. 508.

[4] See again Highways Agency Design and Build Contract 1996, clause 28 referred to above.

[5] See *Quality Management in Construction – Survey of Experiences with BS 5750,* Report of Key Findings. CIRIA, London, 1996. CIRIA Special Publication 132.

[6] See generally on the relationship of risk management to quality assurance. TAYLOR, MALCOLM. Raising Awareness of Risk. *Architects' Journal,* 19 May 1993, **197**(20), 26–27.

programme is based are still reflected in the ECC. The degree to which the conditions of contract promote the meeting of the project's established requirements for materials and workmanship can be an important factor in evaluating the risk associated with the conditions. The ease with which the language of the contract can be understood has been shown to be an important factor in reducing risk.[7] Three important quality management principles have been put forward by Stebbing:

- quality is everybody's business;
- do it right the first time every time; and
- communicate and co-operate.[8]

The ECC reflects these principles in various ways. For instance the tests and inspections obligations in clause 4 reveal specific quality related responsibilities on both the contractor's and project manager's parts within the meaning of the first principle. The mutual early warning requirements in clause 16.2 regarding impaired performance of the works demonstrate the importance of prevention and the role of planning for problems falls within the meaning of the second principle. Lastly, the express communications obligations in clause 13 reinforce what the individuals are to do and with whom they interface within the meaning of the third principle. As such, even without a proactive heading, recognition of the importance of quality can be found in the ECC through the operation of these principles in the contract.[9] In any case, the contractor's obligation to provide the works in accordance with the works information is ultimately an obligation with respect to quality. The standards, objectives and procedures which are set out in the works information, and whether incorporating a quality assurance programme or not, still delimit, define and ensure a generic quality obligation. Ultimately, they provide the basis against which all work is judged.[10]

Dr Peter Morris has outlined some of the reasons why United Kingdom contractors have been slow to take up quality management including frequent absence of strong clients demanding quality; the poor nature of the bidding selection process (localized suppliers and cheapest bid wins); and the highly differentiated nature of the construction project organization.[11] The absence of an explicit reference to a quality assurance programme in the ECC may be contrasted, however, with its mandating in the PSC. Pursuant to clause 40.1 the consultant is expressly required to

---

[7] See BUBSHAIT, ABDULAZIZ A. and ALMOHAWIS, SOLIMAN A., 134.

[8] STEBBING, LIONEL. Project Quality Management. In *Gower Handbook of Project Management*, 2nd edn. ed. LOCK, DENIS. Gower, Aldershot, 1994, 554.

[9] See generally STEBBING, LIONEL. *Quality Assurance: the Route to Efficiency and Competitiveness*, 3rd edn. Ellis Horwood, London, 1993.

[10] See generally clause 11.2(15) ECC defining a 'defect'.

[11] MORRIS, DR PETER. Current Trends in the Organisation of Construction Projects. In *Future Directions in Construction Law*. Proceedings of the Fifth Annual Conference of the Centre of Construction Law and Management. King's College, London, 1992, p. 188.

operate a 'quality management system' for the services to any extent
required by the brief in the First Edition and the scope in the Second
Edition. Today, the term 'quality management system' may be contrasted
with the broader and more current term 'total quality' systems. The latter
phrase is used in an umbrella sense to cover continuous improvement,
quality systems and standards (e.g. ISO 9000), culture change and staff
development.[12] If the employer wishes to have such a system in operation
it need only be stated in the brief. To this end the choice of the system
itself is also left to the employer who may choose from any deemed
appropriate. The significance of imposing a quality management system
upon the consultant is that the likelihood of, if not the necessity for,
comparable requirements also being imposed on the contractors is
increased. While contractors are increasing their use of quality
management systems in their organizations it has been without a
sufficient understanding of how they should be integrated with their use
of standard forms of contract and as a result conflicts have been shown to
arise.[13] The references to a quality management system, and the bias
toward an integrated quality management programme that the NEC still
implies, must reflect in part the intention that the form be used in process
plant construction as well.[14] In this sense it is understood that process
plant contracts provide far more detail in terms of procedures for
performance testing and with their overall higher preoccupation with
quality issues than, for example, building contracts. A fair interpretation
of core clause 4 would enable it to be applied to meet both the more
rigorous procedures in process plant construction as well as the
performance aspects of any specifications or works information details.
Indeed it has been suggested that performance requirements have no place
whatsoever in the conditions of contract and are quite properly dealt with
in the works information.[15]

Quality management
In the past attitudes and practices toward quality systems have been
laissez faire. Some of this ambivalence can be seen in a 1989 CIRIA
Report reflecting division at that time over either the need for or value of
quality assurance as well as third party certification.[16] The prevailing
views at common law, under European Union legislation, and under

---

[12] European Construction Institute, *Implementing TQ*, preface. See generally
ROTHERY, BRIAN. *ISO 14000 and ISO 9000*. Gower, Aldershot, 1996.
[13] NETTO, A.M. *et al*. Legal Implications of ISO 9000 QMS in Standard Forms of
Building Contract. *Training for Quality*, 1997, **5**(4), 169–177.
[14] See SHAW, NIGEL. Operating the NEC in the Power Industry. In *Launch Seminar on
The New Engineering Contract Launch 2nd Edition: Proceedings of a conference in
London on 3 October 1995* by the Institution of Civil Engineers. Thomas Telford,
London, 1995.
[15] See BAIRD, ANDREW. Adversarialism, Pro-active Management and the NEC. In
Commercial Dispute Resolution (eds ODAMS and HIGGINS), p. 39.
[16] See ASHFORD, J.L., n. 2 above.

traditional standards forms have not mandated quality systems as part of the construction contract. This has led to conflicts between quality management systems and the contractual provisions. While contractors are increasing their use of quality management systems in their organizations it has been without a sufficient understanding of how they should be integrated with their use of standard forms of contract and as a result conflicts have been shown to arise.[17]

Professor John Uff QC has written of the ambivalence toward quality at common law.

> The common law has traditionally taken a direct and simplistic view of quality. This is a necessary result of the limited sanctions that the law could apply. Thus, until comparatively recent times, virtually the whole of the considerable body of law on the subject of quality was concerned with simple commercial transactions, typically the sale of goods.[18]

Continuing, Uff writes 'law has, thus, made little contribution to the science of quality control'.[19] It should be observed, however, that standard forms of contract are still drafted based on legal principles bearing a close relationship with the sale of goods.[20] The result, again according to Uff, is that '[q]uality control has developed as a management tool, still virtually divorced from contract law'.[21] Historically, insufficient attention has been focused on quality as one of the key determinants of project success.[22] This has begun to change with recognition of the importance of quality itself.[23] Attention to the details of quality marks a shift from subjective to objective measures of evaluation. This situation pertains quite apart from the fact that the key determinants of contract strategy should be cost, time and quality choices.[24] As for European

---

[17] NETTO, A.M. *et al.*, see n. 13 above, 169–177.

[18] UFF, JOHN. Overview: The Place of Management in Construction. *Management and Construction Law*. A one-day seminar on 23 March 1990 by the Centre of Construction Law and Management. King's College, London, 1990. Uff continues to note that the types of problems the law was typically concerned with were 'arcane' such as with the notions of 'temporary disconformity', p. 12 and citing *P & M Kaye Ltd* v. *Hosier & Dickenson Ltd* [1972] 1 All ER 121, [1972] 1 WLR 146, HL; and *Lintest Builders Ltd* v. *Roberts* (1978) 10 BLR 120, CA.

[19] *Ibid.*, 12.

[20] *Ibid.*, 12. Uff cites as examples clause 8 JCT 80 and clause 39 ICE 6th.

[21] *Ibid.*, 12.

[22] RWELAMILA, R.D. and HALL, K.A. Total Systems Intervention: An Integrated Approach to Time, Cost and Quality Management. *Construction Management and Economics*, 1995, **13**(3), 235–241.

[23] See BENNET, J. and GRICE, T. Procurement Systems for Building. In *Quantity Surveying Techniques: New Directions* (ed. BRANDON, P.S.) Blackwell Scientific Publications, Oxford, 1990; HUGHES, T. and WILLIAMS, T. *Quality Assurance: A Framework to Build On*. BSP Professional Books, Oxford, 1991.

[24] PERRY, J.G. and HOARE, D.J. Contracts of the Future: Risks and Rewards. In *Future Directions*, see n. 11 above, pp. 81–97.

Union legislation, no single policy or directive imposes any direct obligation upon the employer, contractor, or designer to introduce or follow a quality management system. This rather surprising fact pertains despite the number of European Union policies with regard to a single internal market that do impact directly upon quality management in construction: namely, technical harmonization of products;[25] health and safety at work;[26] public procurement[27] and post-construction liability. The impact of these policies and respective directives upon the construction process varies and it is not the intention to seek to outline those effects here but to highlight once again the absence of compulsion with regard to quality management systems in construction at large.[28] In contrast, in Hong Kong, certain conditions of contract mandate quality management programmes, for example, in use on the Port and Airport Development, as well as tendering requirements, and those of the Housing Authority.[29] While the European Union has moved quickly in these areas now that clear policies have been adopted regarding quality management, Europe originally trailed developments in the both the United States and United Kingdom.

One of the first employers to note the relationship between contracts and quality assurance in construction was the Department of Transport which introduced standardized formats for end of contract reporting.[30] The United Kingdom's development of a quality infrastructure relates back at least to 1982 when the White Paper *Standards, Quality and International Competitiveness* was released.[31] Since that time the United Kingdom policy has had the following features:

---

[25] See notably the Construction Products Directive 89/106/EEC (OJ L 40, 11 February 1989), Gas Appliances Directive 90/396/EEC (OJ L 196, 26 July 1990), Electromagnetic Compatability Directive 89/336/EEC (OJ L 139, 23 May 1989), Personal Protective Equipment Directive 89/656/EEC 89 (OJ L 393, 30 December 1989), and the Machinery Directive 89/392/EEC (OJ L 183 29 June 1989). See on the historical background and the need to both revise existing and introduce new product directives concerning construction: PINNEY, ADAM M. EC Legislation in Construction and its Effect on the Construction Industry. *Facilities*, 1993, **11**, 1.

[26] See notably the Workplace Directive 89/391/EEC (OJ L 393, 30 December 1989); Temporary or Mobile Construction Site Directive 92/57/EEC (OJ L 245, 26 August 1992); Work Equipment Directive 89/655/EEC (OJ L 393, 30 December 1989); and Use of Personal Protective Equipment Directive 89/656/EEC (OJL 399, 30 December 1989).

[27] See notably the Public Supplies Directive 93/36/EEC (OJ L 199, 9 August 1993); Public Works Directive 71/305/EEC (OJ L 185, 25 August 1971); and Public Services Directive 92/50/EEC (OJ L 209, 24 July 1992).

[28] See notably the Product Liability Directive 85/374/EEC (OJ L 210, 7 August 1985).

[29] See generally ATKINSON, GEORGE. *Construction Quality and Quality Standards: The European Pespective* E & FN Spon, London, 1995.

[30] MAGGS, M.F. *et al.* introducers, GARNHAM, M.A., reporter, Feedback: Post Contract Information. *Proceedings of the Institution of Civil Engineers* 80, part 1, June 1986, 801–804.

[31] White Paper, *Standards, Quality and International Competitiveness*. HMSO, Department of Trade, London, 1982.

- use of EN29000 series (BS 5750) as the standard for assessment of quality management systems;
- third-party certification of quality management sytems by independent certification bodies;
- accreditation by the National Accreditation Council for Certification Bodies (NACCB) of bodies engaged in product approvals, product conformity assessment, quality management systems assessment, personnel assessment.[32]

In the past quality systems have plainly been seen as separate from standard contractual obligations.[33] Today, however, that view is no longer valid and the benefits of quality management systems are better understood and accepted. The benefits of a quality system today are variously quoted as being greater efficiency, less remedial work, better control of operations, greater management confidence, improved quality and quality awareness, maintenance and improvement of order level, engineering efficiency, improved administration, market stability and increased sales, improved job satisfaction and easier integration of new staff.[34] Quality itself is also increasingly seen as an important employer need. In a report undertaken for the Construction Industry and Research Association, John Barber concluded that quality systems, contracts, and insurance should all be regarded as concurrent means of assuring quality.[35] The CIRIA report, entitled *Quality Management in Construction – Contractual Aspects*, only one of many the Association has undertaken with regard to quality,[36] very clearly addresses the inter-relationship between quality systems and contractual obligations.[37] Responding to a series of broad questions which the report raised at the outset,[38] Barber, who was retained as the research contractor for the project, supported by Professor John Uff QC, looked at the inter-relationship, and in particular the existing 'quality frameworks', in

---

[32] GROVER, R. and LAVERS, A. *Quality Management in Construction – The Impact of European Communities' Policy on Quality Management in Construction.* CIRIA, London, 1993, CIRIA Special Publication 89, 56. See also Royal Institute of British Architects. *Quality Assurance for Architects.* Ribair, London, 1989 for additional background.

[33] BARBER, JOHN, see n. 2 above, 2.

[34] ASHFORD, J.L., see n. 2 above, 18.

[35] BARBER, JOHN, see n. 2 above, 2. See also NIGRO, WILLIAM T. Contract Documents: A Quality Control Guide. *Architecture*, 1987, **76**(1), 82–85.

[36] See e.g. OLIVER, G.B.M. *Quality Management in Construction – Implementation in Design Services Organisations.* CIRIA, London, 1992; CIRIA Special Publication 88; OLIVER, G.B.M. *Quality Management in Construction – Interpretations of BS 5750 (1987) 'Quality Systems' for the Construction Industry.* CIRIA, London, 1990, CIRIA Special Publication 74, in addition to other CIRIA references in this chapter.

[37] CIRIA first identified this issue in 1985 but then left it open for later study: see *Quality Assurance in Civil Engineering.* CIRIA, London, 1985, CIRIA Report 109.

[38] See BARBER, JOHN, n. 2 above, 5. See also by BARBER, JOHN. Quality Management: the Way Forward, 3 November 1992.

leading standard forms of contract. As Barber points out, practitioners have tended to regard quality systems as separate from contractual obligations. However, this has not prevented a *de facto* quality framework within the standard forms. Barber states:

> the quality framework is the contractual approach to assuring quality. It is intended to establish requirements, ensure compliance and avoid defects as far as possible, and deal with defects without recourse to legal proceedings. The aim is both to forestall non-fulfilment of quality requirements and to provide more immediate remedies in the event of non-fulfilment.[39]

Considering the contractual quality framework in the context of quality management systems raised a number of questions again, which the authors sought to answer. Analysing the standard forms selected for the exercise, the authors were able to isolate where and how quality systems could be more explicitly translated into contractual obligations. Based upon that analysis it could be concluded that programme requirements in standard forms present the best means of introducing an express quality system. Barber does not use the NEC Consultation Document as an example but relies instead upon the similar broadly worded programme requirements in GC/Works 1/3rd and describes them in this way:

> [t]hese Conditions are not entirely consistent with the Model Standards for quality systems, but they go a long way in that direction. The 'Programme' is close to including a quality plan, and its contents could readily be extended or adjusted to do so. The duty under 31(1) to 'execute the Works in accordance with the Programme' would then represent the contractual invoking of a quality system.[40]

Further research has provided additional insight into other aspects of construction that support express quality systems. Thus it has been suggested that the design and build method of procurement provides one of the best opportunities for quality systems.[41] This follows from the advantages that derive from single-point responsibility in this form of procurement and which more closely resembles the manufacturing precedent from which quality initiatives derive. Contracts that are intended to operate less adversarially also better support quality systems.[42] The NEC contract system with its ability to assign design responsibility as well as the central role of the programme within the

---

[39]   BARBER, JOHN, n. 2 above, 35.

[40]   BARBER, JOHN, see n. 2 above, 42.

[41]   CORNICK, T.C. and BARRE, N.J. Quality Management and Design-Build: The Opportunities for this Method of Procurement. *International Journal of Quality & Reliability Management*, 1991, **8**(3).

[42]   See McCABE, STEVEN. Creating Excellence in Construction Companies: UK Contractors' Experiences of Quality Initiatives. *The TQM Magazine*, 1996, **8**(6), 14–19.

system confirms both the compatibility and suitability of the NEC for use with quality management systems. The use of the NEC in this way and the trend toward universal standards is likely to be reinforced over time with the fairly recent publication of a new British Standard for the conduct and management of projects.[43] The standard establishes guidelines for the conduct of both public and private projects and builds upon earlier standards pertaining to network techniques, BS 4335 and BS 6046.

Tests and inspections

The principal means by which quality will be achieved is through testing and inspections. Once again, the ECC as a multidisciplinary form will be subject to different practices depending upon the industry that is involved. Thus, for example, in the process plant sector, testing and inspections will be particularly relevant to commissioning. Commissioning also provides an important bridge between construction and operational staff to comissioning teams.[44] Conversely, in the building sector testing procedures are relatively less detailed. These differences reflect different objectives under the respective types of forms but may also reflect different aptitudes and abilities on the part of employers in each industry as well. Professor Phillip Capper has written that the 'competence' of the client may explain in part why there are more effective forms of contract and more effective dispute resolution in this industry and that the process plant industry is also better resourced and more interested in the 'whole life cost' of the project than perhaps other employers.[45] The ECC strikes a balance in this regard in the core clause and then invites the parties to add any necessary detail they require in the works information.

Clause 40 sets out the provisions in respect of and governs the tests and inspections required by the works information and the applicable law.[46] The works information may also be changed by the project manager to vary the tests and inspections set out under clause 14.3 and in which case it will amount to a compensation event under clause 60.1. Three references to the works information in the core clause permit additional details on testing and inspection to be agreed. The references which enable advance provision to be made are set out in clauses 40.1, 40.2 and 41.1. An additional reference to the works information in clause 44.1 contemplates instead post-provision. Clause 40 is read with the definitions for the working areas and plant and materials in clause 11.2. As many of the tests and inspections are in respect of plant and materials which are required by the works information to be delivered to the working areas the definitions for these terms respectively is relevant to tests and inspections.

---

[43] See British Standards Institution *BS 6079 Guide to Project Management*. BSI, London, 1996.

[44] European Construction Institute, *Implementing TQ*, 239.

[45] CAPPER, PROFESSOR PHILLIP. Management of Legal Risks in Construction. A paper given to the Society of Construction Law at a meeting in Wales on 21 September 1994.

[46] Clause 40.1 ECC. Note in civil law jurisdictions the ability to choose an applicable law other than that of the law of the place of the works is often limited.

Thus tests and inspections which the contractor or subcontractors carry out for their own purposes are excluded. However, while these tests are excluded from the operation of clause 40 if the test or inspection reveals a defect the formal procedure for the notification of defects still applies.[47]

Both the terms 'tests' and 'inspections' are undefined.[48] Thus it is the parties themselves, in addition to applicable law requirements, which can set the standards etc. against which the tests and inspections may be measured. Industry standards in every case will presumably be one of the benchmarks against which results can be compared. If the standards refer to specifications it is reasonable to assume that both traditional and complete specifications as well as performance specifications[49] may be utilized in setting benchmarks. Benchmarking is assuming increasing importance in the United Kingdom construction industry with initiatives being taken by a range of firms and benchmarking clubs.[50] The Construction Industry Board is also pursuing or supporting a number of benchmarking and best practice goals through the Construction Productivity Network, joint CIRIA-BREE initiatives and others.[51]

The tests and inspections are directed toward whether a defect can be shown. In general, these testing procedures are both rigorous and lengthy. In brief, however, it is not the tests or inspections which are themselves important but what they reveal. The focus is on the outcome, as noted above, not the process. The outcome is important for two purposes.

- The passage of the test or inspection will entitle the contractor to bring plant and materials to the working areas.[52]
- It will reveal whether or not a defect is present.

A 'Defect' is defined in the ECC as follows in clause 11.2(15):

- a part[53] of the *works*[54] which is not in accordance with the Works Information,[55] or
- a part of the *works* designed by the *Contractor* which is not in accordance with

---

[47] See clause 42 ECC.

[48] In general the term 'inspection' is distinguishable from 'examination', in that it involves a less thorough and scientific process, but is more than a mere casual glance; in effect a careful and critical look: see *Gibson* v. *Skibs A/S Marina* [1966] 2 All ER 476; and *Potato Marketing Board* v. *Merricks* [1958] 2 QB 316.

[49] See lately on performance specifications, LUPTON, SARAH. Performance Specifications: The Legal Implications, *International Construction Law Review*, 1996, 28.

[50] European Construction Institute, *Implementing TQ*, 266.

[51] *Towards a 30% Productivity Improvement in Construction*, Construction Industry Board. Construction Industry Board, Thomas Telford, London, 1996, 23. Cf MOHAMED, SHERIF. Benchmarking and Improving Construction Productivity. *Benchmarking for Quality Management & Technology*, 1996, **3**(3), 50–58 who states that the benefits of benchmarking are still largely unrecognized in the construction industry.

[52] Clause 41.1 ECC.

[53] Contrast the use of the term 'part' in clauses 33 and 35 ECC.

[54] Section 1 part one of the Contract Data.

[55] See clause 11.2(5) ECC.

- the applicable law, or
- the *Contractor's* design which has been accepted[56] by the *Project Manager*.[57]

Thus, if a test or inspection shows that any work has a defect, as defined above and only as defined, the contractor must correct the defect and the test or inspection is repeated.[58] Assuming that the presence of the defect requires no change to the works information,[59] a repeat test will not be treated as a compensation event. The presence of a defect itself may invoke the early warning procedure as well.[60] The early warning in turn may give rise to a possible compensation event under clause 60.1(16) or impact upon the contractor's ability to provide the works within the meaning of clause 20.1. The project manager will assess the cost incurred by the employer in repeating a test or inspection after a defect is found and the contractor will have to pay the amount assessed.[61] These costs may be different than those which would be assessed under clause 60.1(16) and awarded to the contractor for a similar breach by the employer. The '*law of the contract*' is inserted by agreement in section 1 of part one of the Contract Data. This is the first one of five references to when an issue is determined with reference to the applicable law. Selection of the proper law of the contract which may be inserted here by the parties is normally conclusive under English law and can be different from the procedural law of the arbitration.[62]

The conditions outline a code-like procedure with respect to testing. The centrality of such procedures distinguishes the NEC from traditional forms of contract. Research suggests that traditional forms of contracting often overemphasize contractual arrangements at the expense of effective organizational procedures such as clear communications, co-ordination, reporting and interpersonal relationships.[63] Both the contractor and the employer provide materials, facilities and samples for tests and inspections as stated in the works information.[64] No distinction is made

---

[56] Under clause 21.2 ECC.

[57] Clause 11.2(15) ECC. The presence of a defect may also preclude the right to delivery of plant and materials to the working areas, clause 41.1 ECC.

[58] Clause 40.4 ECC. Formal notification of the result of the test or inspection and the presence of a defect as defined is made pursuant to clause 42.2 ECC.

[59] And which could be dealt with under clause 60.1(1) ECC.

[60] See clause 16 ECC.

[61] Clause 40.6 ECC.

[62] See *James Miller & Partners Ltd* v. *Whitworth Street Estates (Manchester) Ltd* [1970] AC 583, [1970] 1 All ER 796, HL.

[63] STOCKS, ROBERT K. and MALE, STEVEN P. Investigation into the Client's Perceptions of Contractual Forms and Procedures: The Instigation of Good Practice. In *Organizing and Managing Construction*. At Proceedings of CIB W 65 4th International Symposium on Organization and Management of Construction, vol 1 Mega Projects, Organization and Management. University of Waterloo, Waterloo, 1984, pp. 291–300.

[64] Clause 40.2 ECC.

between who provides materials versus facilities or samples and, in the absence of details in the works information, the obligation may be assumed to exist both independently and jointly. The duty of co-operation in clause 10.1 assists this interpretation. It is recommended that the tests and inspections described at this stage include all of those to be done before completion.[65] Depending upon the main option chosen the provision of materials, facilities and samples and apparatus by either the employer or contractor will also likely vary. In short, any failure to provide them as agreed may invoke the early warning procedure[66] and entail a possible compensation event.[67] It is interesting to note that 'searching' in clause 42.1 may include providing facilities, materials and samples for tests and inspections done by the supervisor.

It is the supervisor and not the project manager who fulfils the leading role in respect to testing and inspection. Either the supervisor or the contractor will notify the other of each of their respective tests and inspections both before the same are commenced as well as afterward with their results.[68] Results would presumably be in the form produced following the tests and the notifications should satisfy clause 13. Testing and inspection must be capable of being carried out in an unobstructed manner. Thus, the contractor must notify the supervisor in sufficient time not only for a test or inspection to be arranged but also for it to be done before any work that the contractor intends to do which would obstruct the test or inspection.[69] If the contractor fails to give sufficient notice and the work becomes obstructed the supervisor may instruct the contractor to search for defects. The sanction for the contractor failing to give the sufficient notice in this case is the denial of the instruction to search being treated as a compensation event whether or not a defect is found.[70] While the supervisor has a right to watch any test done by the contractor the conditions are silent on the supervisor's right to watch any inspection of the contractor. It is unclear what meaning should be given to this omission. It may have relevance with regard to searching for defects.[71] Failure to permit the supervisor to watch the test may have early warning implications as well.[72]

All tests and inspections must be carried out by the supervisor without causing unnecessary delay to the work, or to any payment, which is conditional upon a test or inspection being successful.[73] Clearly testing and inspection procedures themselves may imply a certain amount of 'necessary' delay which, on the interpretation here, would appear to be

---

[65] Guidance notes NEC, 22.
[66] See clause 16 ECC.
[67] Under clause 60.1(16) ECC.
[68] Clause 40.3 ECC.
[69] Clause 40.3 ECC.
[70] Clause 60.1(1) ECC.
[71] See clause 42 ECC.
[72] See clause 16 ECC.
[73] Clause 40.5 ECC.

acceptable. Failure by the supervisor to carry out the test or inspection without causing this unnecessary delay has early warning implications and is a compensation event.[74]

Presumably no one will wish to cause delay and steps can be taken that seek to preclude it arising. One series of steps that could be taken in this regard could involve specifying from the outset in the works information when tests and inspections will be conducted. For example, a series of key times could include before payment for or marking of equipment or plant or materials; before delivery to the working areas; before completion and after take over but before the *'defects date'*.[75] The defects date itself has been assigned particular significance in the payment procedures following tests and inspections. Under clause 40.5 once the last *'defect correction period'* has passed and where payments are due upon a test or inspection being successful then the payment would become due at the later of the *'defects date'* and the end of the last *'defect correction period'*[76] in two cases:

- if the supervisor has not done the test or inspection; and
- if the delay to the test or inspection is not the contractor's fault.

Today, however, some argue it is increasingly difficult to ascribe *objective* meanings to the term 'fault' and so allocate legal responsibility for an act.[77] This in turn is seen as part of the explanation of a move for the law to be not only more responsive but fair.[78] Another aspect of this is how causes of action which were formerly strict liability are being invaded by fault requirements.[79] The provision can be seen to operate both in favour of as well as against the contractor's interest. In the first place it overcomes the ultimate cost effects of both delayed testing as well as no testing by the supervisor. Thus, if the supervisor tests late or even not at all payment still falls due as indicated. Assessment of the amount due itself would follow in this case in the ordinary course.[80] However, in the second place, the contractor must still wait until the specified due dates before being paid. This may be some considerable time after when testing was supposed to have taken place. Specifying deadlines in the works information in advance of the fallback deadlines in clause 40.5 still

---

[74] Clause 60.1(11) ECC.

[75] Guidance notes NEC on clause 40.2 ECC, 43. The *'defects date'* is an identified term in part one of the Contract Data, section 4 and is inserted as a given number of weeks after completion of the whole of the works.

[76] The *'defect correction period'* is an identified term in part one of the Contract Data, section 4 and is inserted as a given number of weeks.

[77] CORBETT, ANGUS. The Rationale for the Recovery of Economic Loss in Negligence and the Problem of Auditors' Liability. *Melbourne University Law Review*, 1994, **19**, 814.

[78] FINN, PAUL. Statutes and the Common Law. *University of Western Australia Law Review*, 1992, **22**, 7, 16, cited by Corbett, n. 77 above, 818 n. 13.

[79] PARDY, BRUCE. Fault and Cause: Rethinking the Role of Negligent Conduct. *Tort Law Review*, 1995, **3**, 143.

[80] For example, pursuant to clause 50 ECC.

does not appear to overcome this pitfall and to overcome the delay the contractor may have to refer the inaction by the supervisor to the *'Adjudicator'* for settlement.

If a test or inspection shows that any work has a defect the procedure for the notification of defects is invoked.[81] The contractor in such case is under a clear obligation to correct the defect.[82] The test or inspection as such thus needs to be repeated.[83] The conditions do not state who bears the costs of initial inspections – although they clearly give the project manager the power to assess the cost incurred by the employer in repeating a test or inspection after a defect is found, and this cost is the contractor's responsibility.[84] Should we thus assume the costs of inspections otherwise fall where they may? Best practice would assign the cost of carrying out each test and inspection to one party or the other in the works information. However, in addressing this question of responsibility outside the conditions the ECC contrasts with the provisions in both JCT 80,[85] which imposes the costs of all tests and inspections upon the contractor, irrespective of whether defective work is found, and ICE 6th. The ECC conditions impose only the cost of repeat tests and inspections on the contractor.[86] Pursuant to the JCT 80 terms the contractor is only entitled to an extension of time under clause 25.4.5.2.[87] In recognition of the difficulty in addressing the question of work not in accordance with the contract and the opening up and testing of work, clause 8.4.4 of the JCT 80 actually incorporates by reference a Code of Practice for the architect to consider in issuing any instructions in this regard.[88] The purpose of the Code of Practice is stated to be to 'help in the fair and reasonable operation of the requirements of clause 8.4.4'[89] although in practice it may actually add undue complexity to the provision. Donald Keating QC has written of it:

> [c]lause 8.4.4 of JCT 80 [1987 version] ... in its attempts to deal with the problems relating to opening up, requires the architect to take into account a code of practice which contains 14 specific matters he has to have in mind together with 'any other relevant matters'. How this works in practice, I do not know. But it is a classic example of attempting to deal with problems that may arise

---

[81] See clause 42 ECC.

[82] Clause 40.4 ECC.

[83] Clause 40.4 ECC.

[84] Clause 40.6 ECC.

[85] JCT 80 clause 8.4.

[86] Clause 40.5 ECC. This is closer to the approach adopted for instance in FIDIC 4th clause 36.4.

[87] The same entitlement that the contractor receives under clause 8.4.3 of JCT 81.

[88] Clause 8.4.4 JCT 80 in part: 'having had due regard to the Code of Practice appended to these Conditions ... issue such instructions ... to open up for inspection or to test ...'. The Code of Practice is also reproduced as an appendix to the JCT 81 form in respect of instructions issued under clause 8.4.3 of that form.

[89] Section 1 Code of Practice JCT 80.

in great detail and which experience suggests does not always work better than general provisions.[90]

While the Code states that the architect and contractor should endeavour to agree to the amount and method of opening up and testing[91] in any case the architect is required to consider 14 specific criteria listed in the Code.[92] An additional and general criterion to consider 'any other relevant matters' is also listed.[93] It may be noted that DOM/1 too includes a Code of Practice[94] to help in the fair and reasonable operation of the provisions on opening up and testing.

Returning to the ICE 6th provisions, clause 36(3) imposes residual responsibility on the employer to pay for the cost of additional tests if they showed that the workmanship or materials was in accordance with the contract. This narrow drafting in the ICE form would thus leave the employer to pay for the cost of tests which fell short of non-conformity but which otherwise revealed legitimate concerns, for instance, concerning health and safety. Under the ECC form the definition of 'Defect', which is determined by reference to the works information, and which works information may specify health and safety requirements,[95] would close this gap and leave responsibility for the cost of the test still upon the contractor.

Testing and inspection before delivery

Testing and inspection may be carried out before delivery to the site or working areas. However, in the case of tests or inspections to be carried out on plant and materials before delivery to the working areas, and where the works information so provides, the contractor must not bring plant and materials to the working areas until the supervisor has notified the contractor that they have passed the test or inspection.[96] Only the works information would make this provision and there is no express reference to testing and inspection outside the working areas in section 7. Thus passage of the test or inspection is a condition precedent to delivery to the working areas. The tests or inspections themselves must satisfy the requirements of clause 40 in general. For the procedures to operate efficiently the contractor may first have to notify the supervisor of the results of tests or inspections under clause 40.3. It can be seen that it is then the supervisor who has the final authority to say whether those

---

[90] KEATING QC, DONALD. Alwyn Waters Memorial Lecture: the Making of a Standard Form. *Construction Law Journal*, 1995, **11**, 175.

[91] Section 2 Code of Practice JCT 80.

[92] Section 2 sub-section 1 to 14 Code of Practice JCT 80. Sub-section 7 actually requires the architect to consider other relevant Codes of Practice.

[93] Section 2 sub-section 15 Code of Practice JCT 80.

[94] DOM/1 Code of Practice 'B'.

[95] Under section 18.1 ECC.

[96] Clause 41.1 ECC. See also clause 71.1 ECC for the stipulation of plant and materials (cl 11.2(10)) outside the 'Working Areas' which have to be passed before marking by the Supervisor.

results are successful. If successful, the supervisor notifies the contractor in turn of this fact and the delivery may be made. Conversely, failure to pass the test or inspection invokes the procedures for the notification of defects.[97] The notification itself may involve the early warning procedure[98] and impact upon the contractor's ability to provide the works.[99] The purpose of clause 41.1 is to avoid the expense of transporting plant and materials back to their place of manufacture or otherwise before delivery if testing and inspection reveal defects.[100] Transport costs could also be an item of wasted expenditure under the schedules of cost components.[101]

Searching and notifying defects

The supervisor may instruct the contractor to search.[102] While the instruction must be supported by a reason from the supervisor there is no limitation on the motives of the supervisor in requiring the contractor to search. Clearly, the central reason in almost every case will be that work has been completed which does not comply with the works information; in other words, there is a defect. However, on the wording of the clause it is an open question whether or not the searching is limited to or circumscribed by searching for defects as defined only. The answer to this question may turn on an interpretation of clause 40 as a whole. The act of searching is described as follows and may include:[103]

- uncovering,[104] dismantling, re-covering and re-erecting work,
- providing facilities, materials and samples for tests and inspections done by the *Supervisor*, and
- doing tests and inspections which the Works Information[105] does not require.

Thus, on the above wording, these examples are not limitative of what searching includes. Unlike the provisions on tests and inspections in clauses 40 and 41, which are limited with reference to defects, no corresponding limitation is imposed in searching. The use of the term 'include' is rare in the ECC although it is frequently used in both legislative drafting and as a matter of convention in private contracts. The

---

[97] See clauses 40.3 and 42.2 ECC.
[98] Clause 16 ECC.
[99] Under clause 20.1 ECC.
[100] Guidance notes NEC on clause 41.1 ECC, 45.
[101] Section 3, clause 31(b) the cost of plant and materials payments for delivery to and removal from the working areas.
[102] Clause 42.1 ECC. See the definition of 'Defect' in clause 11.2(15) and see also the definition of 'Works Information' in clause 11.2(5) ECC.
[103] Clause 42.1 ECC.
[104] For example, to avoid problems of fraudulent concealment, see for examples: WALLACE QC, IAN DUNCAN. Defective Work: the New Flavours. *Construction Law Journal*, 1990, **6**, 89–90. UFF QC, JOHN saw in 1988 the solution to covering up problems as quality assurance: The Place of Law and the Role of Construction.
[105] Clause 11.2(5) ECC.

effect of the use of the term 'include' depends in part upon where it is located (e.g. whether in a definition section or not) and whether it refers to things which would not normally be included in the meaning of the term it qualifies and thus, depending upon the context, it may be either to enlarge or restrict the meaning of the qualified term, here 'searching'.[106] The use of the word 'includes' is not in itself sufficient to exclude the normal meaning of 'searching'[107] but the 'context' may be sufficient to show that 'includes' is used as equivalent to 'means and includes' and that the qualification is therefore exhaustive.[108] It may be that the inclusion of the phrase 'providing facilities, materials and samples for tests and inspections done by the *Supervisor*', which would not normally be expected to be within the meaning of the term 'searching' and could have the effect of excluding other things that are not ordinarily included within the meaning of the term.[109] Doing tests and inspections which the works information does not require may be a compensation event depending upon whether a defect is found (clause 60.1(10)), or whether it was a second or repeat test or inspection (clause 40.6 of the ECC).

The marginal note for clause 42 is 'Searching and notifying Defects' and the inclusion of two subclauses addressing searching in 42.1 and notifying defects in 42.2 respectively suggests that clause 42.1 is not limited to searching for defects alone. One reason for avoiding such a limitation at the outset is that it may unnecessarily restrict the scope of searching and hence the likelihood that defects which might exist would be found. Conversely, the heading for the core clause itself is 'Testing and Defects'. This suggests a clear emphasis on one or the other of these two issues and that searching must bear a necessary relationship to either one or the other. A related issue of interpretation is also raised and which follows from the wording of clause 40.1. That clause begins '[t]his clause only governs tests and inspection required by the Works Information ...'. How then should 'this clause' be construed?[110] Does it apply to clause 40, 40.1, 40.1 to 40.6 or all of core clause 4 – which would include clause 42.1? It is submitted that it would apply to clause 40 only. This conclusion is reached on the basis that the last two bullet points in clause 42.1 would be unnecessary if this were not the case. That is, with tests and inspections, and the provision of materials, facilities and samples already addressed in the works information and governed by clause 40, it is only when these matters have not been addressed by the works information that searching in respect of them may be necessary. This argument necessarily implies that the tests and inspections carried out under clause 40.1 would be sufficient to reveal the presence of any defects. It follows that searching should be limited to defects as well. This interpretation is

---

[106] *Reynolds* v. *John* [1956] 1 QB 650, [1956] 1 All ER 306, applying *Dilworth* v. *Stamps Comrs* [1899] AC 99, PC.

[107] See e.g. *London School Board* v. *Jackson* (1881) 7 QBD 502, 50 LJMC 134.

[108] *Dilworth* v. *Stamps Comrs* [1899] AC 99 at 107, PC. above at 107.

[109] See *Tallents* v. *Bell and Goddard* [1944] 2 All ER 474.

[110] The phrase 'In this clause' is also used in clause 11.2(25) ECC.

reinforced by the wording in clause 42.2 which requires both the supervisor and the contractor to notify each other 'of each Defect which he finds'. Notification under clause 42.2 is separate from any early warning notice under clause 16.1 and which may be required by virtue of finding the defect. This association between searching and finding in popular terms is also too strong to ignore. In conclusion it is submitted that searching in clause 42.1 is likely to be intended to apply only to searches in relation to defects as defined.[111]

Whether a contractor will be compensated for searching largely depends upon the outcome of the search. Assuming an instruction[112] for the search, if a defect is found which is due to the fault of the contractor, or non-compliance with the works information, no compensation event arises.[113] However, if no defect as defined were found, the instruction would amount to a compensation event. Exceptionally, where the search was needed only because the contractor gave insufficient notice of doing work, which obstructed a required test or inspection, it would not constitute a compensation event.[114] Conversely, a compensation event could arise if, notwithstanding that no defect as defined was discovered, the search revealed that the employer had breached the contract[115] or that the employer's design did not comply with the works information.[116] This distinction is important. It occurs throughout the contract and stands in marked contrast to defects as defined with regard to the contractor's work, design or performance. In either case that involves the employer, the project manager may have to step in and issue an instruction to remedy the situation. This can be done with a separate instruction that may be a further compensation event for the contractor.[117] Until the defects date, both the supervisor and the contractor are under a reciprocal obligation to notify each other of defects which either one finds.[118] Other finders of defects may also notify either the contractor or the supervisor of the defect and they in turn are regarded as the finder of the defect once they have been so notified.[119] The defects date is material as once it has passed no notification can occur.[120] With the formal notification of a defect the contractor must proceed in accordance with clause 43 for its correction.

---

[111] Apart from this uncertainty in the meaning of the clause, it has also been critiqued on word length alone. CORBETT, EDWARD has written of the 1st Edition wording that: ' ... the 151 words and convoluted syntax of the opening sentence of clause 42 ... is enough to deter all but the most determined native English speakers': FIDIC 5th or a New Style Red Book?, 291.

[112] See clause 42.1 ECC. The instruction must satisfy clause 13 ECC as a communication.

[113] Clause 60.1(10) ECC.

[114] Clause 60.1(10) ECC.

[115] Clause 60.1(18) ECC.

[116] See clause 60.1(1) ECC.

[117] For example, an instruction made pursuant to clause 60.1(1).

[118] Clause 42.2 ECC.

[119] See FC 42 ECC.

[120] See clause 42.2.

Correcting defects

The ECC expressly addresses defects in a frank manner. The contract seems to acknowledge defects are an inevitable part of the construction process. Not only are defects inevitable but, Duncan Wallace has suggested, they are often deliberate in the sense of being known or acquiesced in by the contractor's supervisory management.[121] The contract does not pretend that defects never occur or that the standard to be achieved is perfection; rather that standards are variable and reflect conscious decisions about costs, but that positive measures can be taken to anticipate and address the defects that will appear. The 'tone' of the form in this regard is constructive. For instance, if it is agreed that defects can and will occur, the parties' attentions may therefore be directed toward more efficient and cost effective means to redress or correct them. One illustration of this constructive approach can be seen in the provisions of clause 43. The clause 43 provisions expressly impose an obligation on the contractor to correct 'Defects'. It is worth underscoring that it is 'Defects' as defined in the contract alone which is the operative term. The language in this sense is both more direct and less subjective than other forms which may couch the obligations in terms of workmanship or otherwise.

The obligation of the contractor to correct defects arises whether or not the supervisor has notified the contractor of any defects.[122] The absence of a notification requirement by the supervisor reinforces the obligation of the contractor in the first instance to discover and correct defects. This too is a departure from other traditional forms and goes well beyond the passive role which contractors have usually played in this regard. The obligation to correct defects may be equated with express provisions in many forms granting the contract administrator a power to order and the contractor to oblige in the removal and replacement of defective work. The decision whether to remove or rectify defective work can be a difficult one. Thus, for example, DOM/1 includes a Code of Practice to assist in the decision with respect to non-complying work.[123]

The contractor is under an express obligation to correct any *notified* defects before the end of the defects correction period.[124] The same phrase was used to replace, in ICE 6th, 'period of maintenance', from ICE 5th, presumably with the intention of ensuring that the engineer has power to order variations during this time.[125] No time limit is referred to in respect of *unnotified* defects and thus it would appear the contractor remains under

---

[121]   WALLACE QC, IAN DUNCAN, n. 104 above, 87. See for additional background on defects NEDO. *Build: Building Users' Insurance against Latent Defects.* HMSO, London, December 1988.

[122]   Clause 43.1 ECC.

[123]   DOM/1 Code of Practice 'A'.

[124]   Clause 43.1 ECC.

[125]   See GILBERT, JOHN. 'The ICE 6th Edition – Some Initial Thoughts. *Construction Law Journal,* 1991, **7**, 200, 204. In the FIDIC Orange Book, 1st Edition the drafters have included a 'contract period' which, unless agreed otherwise, is in effect a 365-day defect liability period that runs from the commencement date up to completion; clause 1.1.3.5 FIDIC Orange 1st part I.

an indefinite and unqualified obligation regarding time with respect to their correction. The '*defect correction period*' is an identified term, agreed to be a number of weeks, and inserted in section 4 of the Contract Data. For notified defects, the defect correction period begins at the time agreed for completion for defects notified before completion, and when the defect is notified for other defects.[126] The emphasis upon notified defects is consistent with the definition of completion.[127] It may be that either the contractor or the project manager proposes that the defect not be corrected but is rather accepted instead. If so the relevant procedure would then concern that for the accepting of defects under clause 44. Assuming that all of the defects are neither corrected nor accepted, the relevant procedure is then that for uncorrected defects under clause 45. The failure of a contractor to ultimately correct defects may entitle the employer to claim damages for breach of contract.[128]

The express obligation of the contractor to correct defects and liability otherwise in damages for failing so to act should result in the two rights accruing cumulatively to the employer as a result if *Hancock* v. *B W Brazier (Anerley) Ltd* applies.[129] However, the right of the employer to claim damages may be the only remedy once the final defects correction period has expired. These rights of the employer may arise under the general law either expressly or by implication. Other considerations apply at common law in certain limited instances. For example, in a contract for the sale of a house to be erected, terms will be implied that the contractor will do the work in a workmanlike manner, will supply good and proper materials and that the house will be reasonably fit for human habitation.[130] These common law obligations have been codified and extended in the United Kingdom by the Defective Premises Act 1972. These obligations extend to those acquiring an interest in the house or dwelling and bind both contractors and developers. The duty to supply a habitable dwelling arguably extends to architects and surveyors. If so, it should also logically extend to a project manager under the NEC acting qua architect or surveyor.[131]

---

[126] Clause 43.1 ECC. The supervisor issues the defects certificate at the later of the defects date and the end of the last defect correction period: clause 43.2 ECC.

[127] Completion is defined in clause 11.2(13) ECC in part in relation to the correction of *notified* defects.

[128] *Surrey Heath Borough Council* v. *Lovell Construction Ltd* (1988) 42 BLR 25, (1990) 48 BLR 108, CA; *Tompkinson* v. *Parochial Church of St Michael* (1990) 6 Const LJ 319.

[129] *Hancock* v. *B W Brazier (Anerley) Ltd* [1966] 2 All ER 901, [1966] 1 WLR 1317, CA. The *Hancock* case was applied recently in *Milburn Services Ltd* v. *United Trading Group (UK) Ltd* (1997) 52 Con LR 130 in determining whether a common law claim for damages was excluded or limited by the express terms of the contract.

[130] *Hancock* v. *B W Brazier (Anerley) Ltd* [1966] 2 All ER 901, [1966] 1 WLR 1317, CA. See also *Basildon District Council* v. *J E Lesser (Properties) Ltd* [1985] QB 839, [1985] 1 All ER 20.

[131] See *Hudson's*, vol. 1, 218 and see also PALMER, N. and McKENDRICK, E. *Product Liability in the Construction Industry*. Lloyd's of London Press, London, 1993, 180.

In general there is no duty to protect against economic loss and a supervisor should be under no duty to warn of correcting defects at a time when the corrections may be done relatively inexpensively compared to such cost at a later date.[132] In general the contractor is not under an obligation in tort to avoid causing the employer economic loss unless there is a special relationship of proximity and reliance.[133] Similarly the failure of the supervisor to notice a defect should not provide the contractor with a defence to a claim or retention by the employer.[134] Once again, the supervisor will issue a defects certificate at the later of the defects date and the end of the last defect correction period.[135] The defects certificate under the ECC serves a somewhat different purpose than under other traditional forms. Thus, in contrast to the 'certificate of completion of making good defects' in JCT 80[136] or the 'defects liability certificate' in FIDIC 4th[137] the ECC defects certificate is issued *before* the defects are corrected not afterwards. In this way the defects certificate may be compared, in one respect, to a snagging list – a term commonly used on the job site to refer to any list of defects. However, unlike the ECC defects certificate, a snagging list has no contractual effect. The list of defects contains only those defects as defined which the supervisor has notified before the defects date and which the contractor has not corrected, or if there are no such defects then a statement to that effect.[138] The significance of a certificate alone that there are no defects at that date, at a time when the supervisor must certify that fact should not be lost. It arguably serves as the best evidence of the fulfilment of the contractor's obligation to provide defect-free works to that point at time. Thus it is more than simply the time at which the contractor has a right to correct defects. Too often in practice, and in the absence of an unequivocal statement from one or the other of the two parties or their agents, late claims, defences or allegations are raised. The operation of the defects certificate is consistent with other principles of the NEC – progress the works, reduce claims and the likelihood of disputes.

The obligation of the contractor to correct defects continues beyond the transfer in possession of the site from the contractor to the employer. As such provision has been made for renewed rights of access to fulfil the obligation. In short, the project manager will arrange for the employer to give access to and use of any part of the works by the contractor, which the employer has taken over if it is needed for correcting a defect.[139] The access which the project manager arranges must be both suitable and

---

[132]   See *AMF International Ltd* v. *Magnet Bowling Ltd* [1968] 2 All ER 789 at 809.

[133]   *Nitrigin Eireann Teoranta* v. *Inco Alloys Ltd* [1992] 1 All ER 854 at 856–860.

[134]   *East Ham Borough Council* v. *Bernard Sunley & Sons Ltd* [1966] AC 406 at 441–449, HL, per Lord Upjohn. See lately on the duty of supervision *Department of National Heritage* v. *Steenson Varming Mulcahy* (1998) 60 Con LR 33.

[135]   Clause 43.2 ECC.

[136]   Clause 17.4 JCT 80; and which may still be contrasted with the final certificate.

[137]   Clause 62.1 FIDIC 4th.

[138]   See clause 11.2(16) ECC.

[139]   Clause 43.3 ECC.

during the defect correction period.[140] If the project manager does not fulfil these conditions then he or she must extend the period for correcting the defect as is necessary.[141] Although the clause is unclear on its wording it seems sensible that the 'period' referred to is the *'defect correction period'*. This interpretation may not be wholly satisfactory to the contractor whose payment may be delayed as a result.

Close examination of clause 43.3 reveals that there are both important dates and time frames which are relevant to correcting defects: the *'starting date'*, *'completion date'*, the *'defects date'*, and the *'defect correction period'*. These first three dates may in theory (it would be a small job in practice) overlap with the defect correction period time frame. The defect correction period time frame may vary according to the nature of the project. One consequence of this is that a longer defect correction period clearly gives the employer a longer time frame in which to rely upon contractual rather than extra-contractual remedies for the correction of defects. The consultant is under a corresponding duty in the PSC to correct defects that he or she becomes aware of.[142] Similarly, in certain circumstances, the failure of the consultant to correct the defects can result in the employer assessing the cost of having them corrected by others and charging the consultant for it.[143]

The larger issue of the responsibility for and most efficacious means of dealing with defective work has occupied policy makers throughout Europe[144] and the United Kingdom. The Chairman of Justice, Lord Alexander of Weedon QC wrote in a report: 'Over the last quarter-century many attempts have been made by official and semi-official bodies to tackle this problem [defective building work]. They have not succeeded; on the contrary, decisions of the courts have sometimes made things worse'.[145] The report by Justice made a wide variety of recommendations including a compulsory insurance-backed warranty for work to dwellings.[146] Other recommendations included extending the Defective Premises Act 1972; bringing section 38 of the Building Act 1984 into force; and using court annexed arbitration subject to financial limits, and introducing a voluntary registration scheme for builders.[147] Making the

---

[140] See clause 43.3 ECC.This is an improvement over earlier standard form provisions which did not guarantee a right to an extension of time when access was denied by the employer, see e.g. ACA 2.

[141] Clause 43.3 ECC.

[142] Clause 41.1 PSC First and Second Editions.

[143] See clause 41.2 PSC First and 41.3 PSC Second Editions. Unlike the ECC provisions the consultant has a reasonable period of time to make the corrections under the PSC: see again clause 41.2 PSC.

[144] See DALBY, JOSEPH. Liability and Warranties in the Construction Industry Recent Developments – a Framework for Change. *Construction Law Journal*, 1994, **10**, 104 for additional background to recent European Union initiatives.

[145] Justice, *Protecting the Householder Against Defective Building Work*. Justice, London, 1996, the foreword at p. ix.

[146] *Ibid.*

[147] *Ibid.*

scheme compulsory may also serve to overcome some of the difficulties in trying to determine responsibility for the defective work when surveys show that contractors and designers are responsible for approximately one-half of such defective work. 'Statistics published by the Building Research Establishment (BRE) ... and the Property Services Agency, and the Bureau Securitas show that broadly speaking 40–50% of defects in housing are caused by faulty design, and 40–50% by faulty construction; and 10% by faulty materials'.[148] Since the Justice report Latham has also recommended a builders' guarantee scheme to address defective work. To return to one of the themes here, while the problem of defective work is a significant problem the focus in these solutions is remedial in nature. It is argued here that the issue of defective work can and must also be addressed through the conditions of contract. This is not original. In the report *Building Toward 2001* it was stated that what was needed was 'a new form of contract that arranges the resource groups of a construction project so that they all have identical goals of a timely, economical, profitable and high quality product'. This cannot be taken for granted, however, and it has been stated: '[t]hat [it] must involve a radical change to the parties' basic contractual rights and obligations'.[149]

Accepting defects

The ECC is designed to ensure performance in absolute and measurable terms. Thus the principal obligation of the contractor is to provide the works *in accordance with* the works information.[150] The centrality of this obligation is especially reinforced by virtue of the fact that one reason alone may be given by the project manager in every instance to justify refusal to accede to a request from the contractor: it will result in non-compliance with the works information.[151] This is not to say that the parties themselves may not attenuate this standard in the works information but that is a separate matter from the clear obligations imposed in core clauses of the main options. The works information is the yardstick against which standards are measured. If there is non-compliance with the works information the subject matter is treated *prima facie* as a defect and dealt with according to the consequences and procedures that follow as a result of this finding.

---

[148]   *Ibid.*, paragraph 3.1.5. Similar problems have been revealed by the then Department of the Environment report entitled *Beat the Cowboys*. HMSO, Department of the Environment, London, July 1988. See generally BISHOP, D. A Search for a Better Solution to the Overall Management of the Aftermath of Latent Defects in Building. In *Managing Construction Worldwide, vol 1 Systems for Managing Construction*, at The Organisation and Management of Construction, 5th International Symposium held in London on 7–10 September 1987. E & FN Spon, London, 1987, pp. 350–359.

[149]   McGAW, MARK C. Adjudicators, Experts and Keeping Out of Court. *Construction Law Journal*, 1992, **8**, 351.

[150]   Clause 20.1 ECC.

[151]   For example, clause 21.2 ECC.

There is one exception to the paramountcy of the works information. It concerns when defects may be accepted. It is important to note that the exception itself does not entail a change to any classification of a defect which is found, rather a change only to the procedures which govern as a result of finding and then dealing with the defect. Thus, instead of correcting the defect,[152] or treating the defect as an uncorrected defect,[153] the defect is accepted.[154] This issue is distinct from omission of work.[155] According to clause 44.1 the contractor and the project manager may each propose to the other that the works information should be changed so that a defect does not have to be corrected.[156] No time limit is imposed in making the proposal and thus either may presumably make it both after as well as before completion.

Procedurally, if the contractor and the project manager are prepared to consider the change, the contractor will submit a quotation for reduced prices, an earlier completion date or both to the project manager for acceptance.[157] Conversely, if the other is not prepared to consider the proposal, the obligation is permissive only, and then one returns to the other procedures outlined for dealing with defects. No criteria are set out regarding the magnitude of the reduction in prices or the effect on the completion period and instead will presumably be judged by the employer in all of the circumstances. The contractor has some scope for manoeuvring given the quotation may address both price and completion. In theory there is no objection to even a nil price reduction. If the project manager accepts the quotation the instruction will be given to change the works information, the prices and the completion date accordingly.[158] Failing acceptance of the quotation the project manager would return to the procedure for correcting defects under clause 43. The change is expressly stated not to be compensable in favour of the contractor.[159] The contractor is under the usual obligation to obey the instruction.[160] The power of either the contractor or the project manager to propose, and the project manager to accept defective or non-conforming work – materials, facilities and samples – in exchange for reduced prices 'and/or' an earlier completion date is an interesting one and one which does not exist, by comparison, in JCT 81, or even ICE 6th. It follows once again from the implicit acknowledgment in the provisions that defects are an almost inevitable part of the construction process and therefore should be addressed affirmatively and constructively.

---

[152] See clause 43 ECC.
[153] See clause 45 ECC.
[154] Clause 44 ECC.
[155] See clause 60.1 ECC.
[156] Cf clause 8.1.1 of JCT 80 which allows the architect to accept workmanship of a standard appropriate to the works when no actual standard is described in the Contract Bills. This approach is not adopted in all JCT forms, see e.g. clause 1.2 IFC 84 deeming quality to be that set out in the Contract Bills.
[157] Clause 44.2 ECC. The submissions must satisfy clause 13 ECC requirements.
[158] Clause 44.2 ECC.
[159] Clause 60.1(1).
[160] Clause 29.1 ECC.

The approach adopted toward the existence of defects is reinforced by many of the sound reasons why an employer may well prefer to accept a defect rather than require its correction. For instance, the non-compliance may be technical only and not have any real effect on the integrity of the project as a whole, or, where the actual correction of the defect may be outweighed by time or administrative costs. There are numerous other reasons why the employer may prefer to accept the defective work subject to a deduction including not only time considerations or simple amenity breaches but loss of confidence in the contractor as well.[161] The ECC has therefore adopted a pragmatic and flexible approach in this regard.

Uncorrected defects

The ECC contains a sanction in the event of the contractor failing to correct a notified defect *within* its '*defect correction period*' – established under clause 43. If the period has not yet expired then the relevant procedure remains that under clause 43 for the correcting of defects. The project manager will assess the cost of having the defect corrected by other people and the contractor will have to pay this amount.[162] No time frame is given when the contractor must make the payment but the indication of the drafters is that it will be later rather than sooner, e.g. the amounts could accumulate until the defects date unless there has been completion of a section of the works and the end of a defect correction period before completion of the whole of the works.[163] Thus the intention appears not to invoke the assessment procedure under clause 50.1 but simply to set out the right of the employer at a later date, notably upon the release of the second half of any retention monies if held by the employer, to set off this amount.[164]

Low performance damages

The parties may agree to the inclusion of a low performance damages clause.[165] Thus, if a defect included in the defects certificate shows low performance with respect to a performance level stated in the Contract Data or the works information, the contractor will have to pay an agreed level of low performance damages.[166] In this regard the Contract Data provides for a series of amounts in respect of individual levels of low performance. It is recommended in the guidance notes that the details of any test that is to be used to measure the performance of the works or any item of plant for which low performance damages are to be specified be included in the works information.[167]

---

[161] WALLACE QC, IAN DUNCAN, n. 104 above, 89–90.
[162] Clause 45.1 ECC.
[163] Guidance notes NEC on clause 45.1 ECC, 48.
[164] For example, under secondary option clause P1. See again guidance notes NEC on clause 45.1 ECC, 48. This interpretation is contradicted by that given in FC 45 ECC.
[165] Option S ECC. The remedy arises only once the defects certificate has been issued.
[166] Clause S1.1 ECC.
[167] Guidance notes NEC, 23.

The low performance damages clause may be used whether performance specifications govern the contract as a whole or not. Performance specifications are common in process plant forms and in this regard some guidance may be drawn from them.[168] The attraction of a performance specification from the contractor's point of view is that it provides scope for manoeuvering in tender price competition. Care should be exercised, however, for selecting a contractor solely on the basis of the lowest tender which is often outweighed in later delays and cost overruns.[169] The employer may choose performance criteria from any one of a variety of accepted standards. The employer can set the minimum standards to be achieved and then leave the rest to the discretion and good judgment of the contractor.

The employer is reassured in the process by being able to test the end product as against the agreed standards or performance levels. Some care should be taken in setting performance levels, however. In particular attention should be given to the time periods during which continuing low performance levels remain acceptable. Care should also be taken to see that the chosen levels are not inconsistent with other documents which may not be contract documents but which could give rise to ambiguities, such as maintenance manuals. Lastly, both parties should carefully set out any other relevant factors and assumptions upon which the low performance is based. The JCT recognized the move toward performance standards[170] in the building sectors[171] by introducing clause 42 through amendment 12 to JCT 80 dealing with performance specified work. While the amendment is not intended to impose performance specifications across the whole works it does permit specified performance levels to be incorporated in respect of agreed portions of the works.

Procedurally, the low performance of the works in use will be acknowledged in the defects certificate. The low performance is likely to be revealed during tests or inspections carried out by the supervisor following completion and before the defects date. As the contractor is under an obligation to correct defects under 43, the continuance of the low performance thus assumes that no correction either has been or can be made. In many cases, for instance process plants, it will be economically impossible to rectify any low performance. As a result the employer should have some form of remedy and thus, in the ECC, the employer can

---

[168] The use of performance specifications has been increasing. In the building sector amendment 12 issued by the JCT for JCT 80 introducing a new clause 42 in 1993 for performance specified work likely both reflected and accelerated this trend.

[169] BROMILOW, F.J. Building Contract Cost Performance. *Building Economist*, 1971, **9**(4), 126–138; and NEDO, *The Professions in the Construction Industry.* HMSO, London, 1976.

[170] The two reasons which are often cited for the use of performance specifications are as an enabler for innovation and as a means of improving the selection process between products: LUPTON, SARAH. Performance Specification: The Legal Implications, 32.

[171] In contrast to the engineering sector where performance standards are widespread. *International Construction Law Review*, 1996.

claim an amount of liquidated or low performance damages which represents the loss. In this regard normal measures of damages are applicable and a lump sum award for the loss of performance over the expected life of the asset would be appropriate. Part one of the Contract Data anticipates this approach with individual liquidated amounts for set performance levels. In contrast to delay damages in part one, which are set at an amount per day, the amounts for low performance levels must anticipate the actual life of the asset. As pre-estimates of damages the set amounts are subject to the judicial supervision exercised over all liquidated damages provisions. This fact should encourage employers not only to choose carefully the amounts in the first instance but to be cognizant of certain other ramifications which may follow. For instance, whether the set amounts for low performance damages will be viewed as an exhaustive remedy in this regard and whether the amounts set a maximum allowable figure for recovery. It is submitted that the court in answering these questions will be closely guided by the available case law concerning these questions under liquidated damages clauses in general.

Any amount which the contractor may have to pay as low performance damages will not reduce any amount also stipulated to be payable by the contractor in respect of liability for defects due to design and which are not listed on the defects certificate.[172] The employer will also maintain other remedies. These remedies[173] include or pertain to the following:

- recovery of the cost of having defective or low standard work corrected by other people; and
- acceptance of a reduction in price, or agreeing to an earlier completion date with the contractor in exchange for the concession.

In the absence of express provision the payment procedure for low performance damages should be read subject to and as a formal part of the normal rules on payment in clause 5.

---

[172] Clause 21.5 ECC. See also Contract Data part one section 2. The defects certificate is defined in clause 11.2(16) ECC.
[173] See clauses 45 and 44 ECC respectively.

10. Payment

The ... NEC is not just a new set of conditions but a new way of thinking about construction contracts.

P.D.V. Marsh,
Contracting and Engineering for Construction Projects, 4th edn

General

The payment risk is one of the most problematic in construction and accordingly preoccupies attention in standard forms of contract.[1] The NEC has taken this issue further than any other form of contract by providing in effect six different payment mechanisms. In fact, it would not be incorrect to say that the six main options that comprise the NEC are really only distinguished one from another on the *basis* of payment. A careful review of every unique clause that comprises each merged main option will reveal that all of them, with only one exception, relate in one way or another to payment. The exception put forward here is subcontracting. It is put forward as an exception even though the issues may indirectly still relate to payment. The notable clauses in this regard touching on subcontracting alone are clauses 20.3, 26.4 and 36.5. Hence, the distinguishing clauses in each of the six main options that all pertain to payment in one way or another are as follows

- Definitions of the prices, the price for work done to date, actual cost, disallowed cost alone.[2]
- Forecasts of actual costs.[3]
- Entries for the programme and acceleration.[4] The programme relates to payment through designation of the start and finish of activities on the

---

[1] GREENWOOD, DAVID and KLEIN, RUDI. Security of Payment in the Light of the Latham Report: An Opportunity to Remove Unacceptable Risks? *Construction Law Journal*, 1995, **11**, 255, citing GREENWOOD, D.J. *Contractual Arrangements*.

[2] Clauses 11.2(19), 11.2(20), 11.2(21), 11.2(22), 11.2(23), 11.2(24), 11.2(25), 11.2(26), 11.2(27), 11.2(28), 11.2(29), and 11.2(30) ECC.

[3] Clause 20.4 ECC. See lately, for an attempt to bring together in one source the various leading cost models used in construction cost and price forecasting. *Cost Modelling*, (ed. SKITMORE, M.) E & FN Spon, London, 1999, Foundations of Building Economics Series.

[4] Clauses 31.4, 36.3, 36.4, 36.5 ECC.

activity schedule. Acceleration relates to payment through the requirement to change the completion date and/or prices.
- Payment itself; hence there are distinct issues on payment in respect of assessing the amount due (clause 50.6); in relation to accounts for actual cost (clause 52.2); the activity schedule (clause 54); the bill of quantities (clause 55); determining the actual cost (clause 52); and payment on termination (clause 97.4 of the ECC).
- Compensation events, as either their designation under clause 60, their assessment under clause 63 or their implementation under clause 65 of the ECC all impact upon payment.

The underlying theory is that the different procurement methods support different allocations of risk between the parties.[5] Thus under main options A and B the cost risk is largely placed upon the contractor. In effect, the contractor carries all the risks save those reallocated to the employer under the compensation event procedure. Under main options C and D the cost or financial risk is more evenly shared between the contractor and the employer while under main option E the cost risk is largely allocated to the employer. While the theory of these individual allocations is looked at elsewhere some observations on payment in general may be made which are common to all of the options. Overall, even with the different payment mechanisms, the costs of risk allocation are manageable.[6] Conversely, the alternatives to the proper allocation and management of risk are costly and uncertain.[7] Given the cost-to-benefit ratio that studies seem to suggest in favour of the use of better planning and risk allocation tools such costs appear justified.

The contractor's right to payment can only arise in accordance with the express or implied terms of the respective option. The basis for payment, although the amounts and timing will differ under the respective options, is the wording of the contract. To be paid under the contract the contractor must be able to support the contention with contractual references; for in their absence, apart from new rights under the Housing Grants, Construction and Regeneration Act (HGCRA) 1996, the Contractor will have no right to be paid.[8] Section 109(1) of the HGCRA now provides:

> [a] party to a construction contract is entitled to payment by instalments, stage payments or other periodic payments for any

[5] See generally WARD, S. and CHAPMAN, C. Choosing Contractor Payment Terms. *International Journal of Project Management*, 1994, **12**(4), 216–221.

[6] SMITH, ROBERT J. Allocation of Risk – The Case for Manageability. *International Construction Law Review*, 1996, 564 sets out the costs involved in terms of hypothetical projects.

[7] *Ibid.*, 564–566.

[8] *Wilmot* v. *Smith* (1828) 3 C & P 453; *Bottoms* v. *York Corpn* (1892) 2 *Hudson's BC* 4th edn. 208, CA; *Ranger* v. *Great Western Rly Co* (1854) 5 HL Cas 72, HL; *Taverner & Co Ltd* v. *Glamorgan County Council* (1940) 57 TLR 243; *Gilbert & Partners* v. *Knight* [1968] 2 All ER 248, CA.

work under the contract unless – (a) it is specified in the contract that the duration of the work is to be less than 45 days, or (b) it is agreed between the parties that the duration of the work is estimated to be less than 45 days.

Pursuant to sections 114(1) to (3) of the HGCRA the Secretary of State is empowered to make a 'Scheme for Construction Contracts'. Where a 'construction contract', as defined within the meaning of section 104(1) of the HGCRA, does not comply with the HGCRA, then the provisions in the Scheme for Construction Contracts apply. In the case of the payment provisions, this is part II of the relevant Scheme. Hence the entitlement to payment is either found to be express under the ECC or will be implied under the HGCRA and part II of the Scheme for Construction Contracts. If the contractor fails in the contentions payment must be sought outside the contract, for instance, collateral contract, or in restitution. The contractual terms will set out the works that the contractor is to provide in exchange for the employer's obligation to make payment therefor. In addition to construction of the works *per se* the options reserved to the employer or those acting qua employer include the option to vary what constitutes the works; that is add to or subtract from them which, once again, the contractor is entitled to receive payment for.

It should also be noted that while the different main options are devoted to different payment mechanisms certain secondary options might apply to each main option. Hence the provisions with respect to advanced payments, multiple currencies, and price adjustment for inflation and retention should also be considered when discussing payment. So too should the relevant facts provided either by the employer in part one or the contractor in part two of the Contract Data.

In summary, the NEC has taken payment as the most important mechanism for distinguishing between different modes of procurement. This enables one essentially to regard the NEC as one contract with six different payment mechanisms. In so configuring the contract if this innovation is understood it will radically simplify how one regards the choice of form and method of procurement. In short, parties are given the widest possible choice across the narrowest possible spectrum and hence a unique appeal. Before examining the individual payment mechanisms in the six main options the effect of entirety is examined.

Doctrine of entirety

The doctrine of entire contracts is relevant to payment under main options A and C. Pursuant to the doctrine all of a contractor's obligations must be fulfilled prior to any obligation of the employer to make payment.[9] In

---

[9] Upon the proper interpretation of the contract as a whole. The leading authorities on the doctrine of entire contracts are *Cutter* v. *Powell* (1795) 6 Term Rep 320; *Munro* v. *Butt* (1858) 8 E & B 738; *Appleby* v. *Myers* (1867) LR 2 CP 651; and *Hoenig* v. *Isaacs* [1952] 2 All ER 176, CA, per Denning LJ. See lately *Holland Hannen & Cubitts (Northern) Ltd* v. *Welsh Health Technical Services Organisation* (1981) 18 BLR 80 at 122 per Judge Newey QC.

other words, fulfilment of the contractor's obligations is a condition precedent to the employer's liability to make payment. The effect of the doctrine is that a contractor who fails to complete can recover neither any payment nor a reasonable sum for the value of the work done. The application of the doctrine may be considered in relation to these two main options. However, while it may be considered, it should be underscored that the passage of the HGCRA would now influence that discussion in those circumstances where the HGCRA applies.[10] For present purposes the issue may be considered both as it stood before and stands after the passage of the HGCRA. Prior to the passage of the HGCRA, under main options A and C, the priced and target contracts with *'activity schedules'*, there were two open questions: whether the contracts as a whole are entire,[11] and whether individual activities could be construed as being entire. If the answer to either of these questions were affirmative then a contractor who failed to complete or failed to complete individual activities could be denied recovery in total or in part.

To answer these questions the courts would have construed the main options to determine whether any one or more options created entire contracts. The ECC has elaborate payment provisions in the various options. In particular, payment provisions operate at stated *'assessment intervals'*,[12] upon the expiry of certain time frames,[13] following compensation events[14] and upon termination.[15] Such provisions would normally be expected to weigh in favour of a determination that the contract as a whole is not entire. However, and the reason that the issue remained open, is that not one of the provisions was conclusive on the issue of entirety. Thus, notwithstanding these features and the fact that the contractor might enforce rights to payment in accordance with them, the doctrine of entire contracts could still apply to the ECC. It would only be on a proper interpretation by the courts of the main options adopted by the parties that an answer to the question whether the doctrine applies or not could be definitively given.[16] As such, if a court found that the contract was entire, and notwithstanding the features noted which arguably detract from the application of the doctrine, it could apply the doctrine to activities or individual assessment intervals. Such a finding by the court is arguably further supported if the assessment intervals relate to agreed sections of the works; that is, when the parties have agreed to the sectional completion secondary option clause.

---

[10] That is, whenever the ECC is used in England, Wales, Scotland and Northern Ireland the HGCRA will apply.
[11] One could also ask this first question with respect to main options B and D also.
[12] See clause 50.1 ECC.
[13] See clause 50.1 ECC.
[14] See clause 63.2 ECC.
[15] See clause 97 ECC.
[16] Despite the passage of the HGCRA it is still open that this issue could be litigated on facts arising before passage of the legislation.

If, in fact, the doctrine of entire contracts applies for instance to any of the main options then several factors, both in law and under the core conditions, militate against its strict application. First of all, the doctrine is subject to any frustration of contract or supervening illegality at common law, either of which may still entitle the contractor to some payment. The ECC too makes express provision for impossibility as well as illegality[17] and which also gives the contractor certain rights to payment in those circumstances. Secondly, if on a proper interpretation of the main options, payments under the activity schedules were equated with instalment payments under other forms, an employer may be denied their recovery save where the contractor's breach amounted to a total failure of consideration.[18] In fact, the payments currently made for compensation events are not added to the total of the prices but rather first added to the items in the activity schedules.

The doctrine is also subject to mitigation through any waiver[19] by the employer or the employer's express or implied acceptance of incomplete performance. Acceptance has been strictly construed in other cases. Thus, reoccupation of the site and use of the works in certain circumstances has not amounted to acceptance of incomplete performance.[20] In the context of the ECC the express provisions regarding take over of the site would further weaken the applicability of these cases.[21] If it could be argued that there had been waiver or acceptance by the employer of incomplete performance,[22] the employer's actions would remain without prejudice to the rights to deduct, set-off or counterclaim at law for any defective performance.[23] Such rights at common law would also likely be found to be in addition to similar rights extended to the employer under clause 45 of the ECC.[24]

Another means whereby the courts have mitigated some of the doctrine's harshest effects is through the introduction of the notion of substantial performance. Thus a contractor who can be said to have 'substantially performed' all obligations will be entitled to payment

---

[17] See clause 19.1 ECC.

[18] *Fibrosa Spolka Akcyjna* v. *Fairbairn Lawson Combe Barbour Ltd* [1943] AC 32, [1942] 2 All ER 122, HL.

[19] Waiver is only expressly dealt with regarding insurance policies under clause 85.2 ECC.

[20] *Sumpter* v. *Hedges* [1898] 1 QB 673, CA.

[21] For example, *Sumpter* v. *Hedges* [1898] 1 QB 673, CA.

[22] Again, assuming that main options A and B are properly construed to be entire contracts.

[23] See generally *Hoenig* v. *Isaacs* [1952] 2 All ER 176 at 181, CA, per Denning LJ. However, if an employer sought damages for incomplete performance the employer would have to credit the contractor for the value of any completed works: see *Mertens* v. *Home Freeholds Co* [1921] 2 KB 526, CA.

[24] Clause 15(3)(b) FCEC uses the phrase 'without prejudice to any rights which exist at Common Law'. See the *Lockland Builders* case (1995) 77 BLR 38, 46 Con LR 92, CA; and *Milburn Services Ltd* v. *United Trading Group (UK) Ltd* (1997) 52 Con LR 130.

therefor, subject to the employer's normal rights to reduce or abate the contract price on account of defective or omitted work.[25] Whether substantial performance has been achieved is a question of fact in every case. Case law has focused upon both the nature and extent of the defects and their relationship to the contract price and the total cost of rectification.[26] The position of the contractor in reply to this interpretation could be to argue simply that the payments for agreed activities or timed *'assessment intervals'* should be equated with instalment or interim payments, which fall due notwithstanding non-completion.[27] It should be noted that the notion of substantial performance and the necessity for and qualification of certain grounds for termination under core clause 9 accords with relational contract doctrine as well.[28]

In contrast to the situation pre-HGCRA it can now be argued that the legislation has statutorily overridden the doctrine of entire contracts to the extent it is inconsistent with section 109(1) of the legislation and part II of the Scheme for Construction Contracts. Hence under section 109(1): 'A party to a construction contract is entitled to payment by instalments, stage payments or other periodic payments for any work under the contract . . .' save two narrow exceptions.[29]

Today, in England, Wales, Scotland, and Northern Ireland, where a 'construction contract', as defined within the meaning of section 104(1) of the HGCRA, does not comply with the HGCRA, then the provisions in the Scheme for Construction Contracts apply, and in the case of the payment provisions, that is part II. Hence the entitlement to payment is either found to be express under the ECC or will be implied under the HGCRA and part II of the Scheme for Construction Contracts. Once again, this would appear to change the law insofar as the doctrine of entire contracts is concerned in these jurisdictions.

In summary, obligations assumed by the contractor will continue to be judged in many instances against the background of the common law, and

---

[25] *H Dakin & Co* v. *Lee* [1916] 1 KB 566, CA; *Hoenig* v. *Isaacs* [1952] 2 All ER 176, CA. See discussion of set-off and abatement and the meaning of 'substantial' below. See lately on the availability of abatement to a contractor *Mellowes Archital Ltd* v. *Bell Projects Ltd* (1998) 87 BLR 26.

[26] See *Broom* v. *Davis* (1794) 7 East 480n; *Thornton* v. *Place* (1832) 1 Mood & R 218; *Cutler* v. *Close* (1832) 5 C & P 337; *Sumpter* v. *Hedges* [1898] 1 QB 673, CA; *H Dakin & Co Ltd* v. *Lee* [1916] 1 KB 566, CA; *Hoenig* v. *Isaacs* [1952] 2 All ER 176, CA; *Bolton* v. *Mahadeva* [1972] 2 All ER 1322, CA.

[27] See *Newfoundland Government* v. *Newfoundland Rly* (1999) 13 App Cas 199, PC; and *Tern Construction Group Ltd* v. *RBS Garages Ltd* (1993) CILL 844.

[28] See SCOTT, ROBERT E. Risk Distribution and Adjustment in Long-Term Contracts. *The Complex Long-Term Contract Structures and International Arbitration* (ed. NICHLISCH, FRITZ). C.F. Muller Juristischer Verlag, Heidelberg, 1987, p. 51 (ns omitted).

[29] That is, '(a) it is specified in the contract that the duration of the work is to be less than 45 days, or (b) it is agreed between the parties that the duration of the work is estimated to be less than 45 days': section 109(1) HGCRA.

the doctrines that form part of it, save where modified by statute. The creation of a new form without more and in the absence of express reference to the common law issues that arise means it falls back upon the parties to understand their relevance in the context of their contractual relations and later decision-makers sitting in judgment of remaining disagreements.[30]

Housing Grants, Construction and Regeneration Act 1996

In April 1998 the ICE approved amendments prepared by the NEC Panel to address the passage of part 2 of the Housing Grants, Construction and Regeneration Act 1996.[31] Thus whenever the ECC is used in England, Wales, Scotland and Northern Ireland a new secondary option clause, 'Option Y (UK) 2: The Housing Grants, Construction and Regeneration Act 1996' should be used although not in other circumstances. The amendments to the form were originally released as an addendum to the NEC with Notes for Guidance[32] and incorporated into the contract by making a statement in the Contract Data.[33] However, as the core clause will only be amended in those cases where the HGCRA applies, the amendments are optional and are therefore only contained in a secondary option clause, that is Y (UK) 2.

Option Y (UK) 2 comprises eight clauses. Clauses Y2.1 to 2.4 and Y2.8 address the payment provisions of the HGCRA while clauses Y2.5 to Y2.7 deal with the adjudication provisions of the legislation. Both the unamended and amended provisions will be examined here although the amended provisions will be given precedence.[34] The provisions addressing adjudication are considered in relation to core clause 9 below.

Identified and defined terms

The various payment mechanisms in the main options are dependent upon the definitions of numerous important terms[35] but two, in particular, stand

---

[30] Perhaps it was uncertainty such as this which was behind the comment of John Uff QC who wondered whether a go slow approach may have been better. Uff: '... the real debate is whether the NEC represents too great a move towards radicalism; and whether *festina lente* is not to be preferred': Figaro on ICE, 654.

[31] See generally JOYCE, RAYMOND. *A Commentary on Construction Contracts, Part II of Housing Grants, Construction and Regeneration Act 1996*. Thomas Telford, London, 1996.

[32] A reference document was released by the ICE in April 1998: NEC/NECC/Y(UK) 2 April 1998 which contained notes for guidance and the consequential amendments.

[33] 'The conditions of contract are the core clauses for Options ... and U (UK) 2 (published by the ICE April 1998) of the second edition (November 1995) of the NEC Engineering and Construction Contract': Option Y (UK) 2 notes for guidance.

[34] As with the secondary option U, the CDM Regulations, consideration should be given by the NEC Panel to UK and Scottish versions to accommodate these two options. See generally JOYCE, RAYMOND. *The CDM Regulations Explained*. Thomas Telford, London, 1995.

[35] Other important terms examined below include the 'Actual Cost' in clause 11.2(27) and 'Disallowed Cost' in clause 11.2(30) ECC.

out: the 'Prices' and the 'Price for Work Done to Date' (PWDD). Both terms are defined in clause 11.2. In some instances the same definitions may pertain in one or more main options. Thus there are only three definitions for the 'Prices'. In main options A and C the prices are defined as the lump sum prices for each of the activities in the '*activity schedule*'.[36] However, notwithstanding the definition of prices is the same in both main options they are still used to different effect in a priced contract versus a target contract and given their different definitions for the PWDD. In main options B and D the prices are the lump sums and the amounts obtained by multiplying the rates by the quantities for the items in the '*bill of quantities*'.[37] It can be noted that this is a *de facto* division regarding the prices according to whether an activity schedule or a bill of quantities is used. In main options E and F the prices are defined as the 'Actual Cost' plus the 'Fee'.[38] 'Actual Cost' and 'Fee' are also defined terms but differ according to the main option employed. There is no necessary correlation between those main options which use the same definitions for the prices and their definitions for actual cost. Perry and Thompson observe generally that a lump sum fee constitutes a greater incentive to the contractor than other fee alternatives.[39] In each of main options A, B, C and D the definition of the prices may be later changed in accordance with the contract. No similar qualification is made in respect of the definition of the prices in main options E and F. It has been remarked generally that preoccupation with exact cost prediction in the private sector contrasts markedly with the preoccupations with competitiveness, health, safety, the environment and quality in the public sector.[40]

In addition to these definitions of prices it is also significant to note what has remained undefined as well. Thus, there is no definition of the contract price (as that term is used in other forms), priced contract, '*activity schedule*', '*bill of quantities*', cost reimbursable contract, or management contract. In each case the meanings of these terms will have to be ascribed in the context of the contract documents as a whole.[41] Regarding the main options A and B, the priced contracts, the term 'priced' appears to be used as a verb. Thus no contract price is stated but rather it is the process of pricing the works using either an activity schedule or a bill of quantities that is material. It is a non-static process.

---

[36] Clause 11.2(20) ECC.

[37] Clause 11.2(21) ECC.

[38] Clause 11.2(19) ECC.

[39] PERRY, J.G. and THOMPSON, P.A. *Target and Cost Reimbursable Construction Contracts*. A Study of Their Use and Implications. CIRIA, London, 1982, CIRIA Report 85 (formerly CIRIA Report S6), p. 14.

[40] See LUPTON, SARAH. Performance Specification: The Legal Implications, *International Construction Law Review*, 1996, 35. The article is an abridged verion of an earlier report co-authored by LUPTON, SARAH and STELLAKIS, MANOS. *Performance Specification: An Analysis of Trends and Development of a Conceptual Framework*. RIBA Publications, London, 1995.

[41] See *Hume* v. *Rundell* (1824) 2 S & St 174.

Turning to the second critical term, the 'Price for Work Done to Date' and how it is defined under the various main options, there is again some overlap and only four potential definitions are applicable. Both in the case of the 'Price for Work Done to Date', and the 'Prices', the respective definitions are contained in the individual main option clauses for each option. Thus the definitions of PWDD are set out again according to the respective main option. In main option A, PWDD is the total of the prices for each group of completed activities, and each completed activity which is not in a group which is without defects which would either delay or be covered by immediately following work.[42]

In main option B, PWDD is the total of the quantity of the works which the contractor has completed for each item in the bill of quantities multiplied by the rate and a proportion of each lump sum which is the proportion of the work covered by the item which the contractor has completed.[43] In main options C, D and E, PWDD is the actual cost that the contractor has paid plus the fee.[44]

In clause 11.2(25) completed work means 'work without Defects which would either delay or be covered by immediately following work'. The significance of the qualification of the definition of PWDD not only by reference to defects but defects 'which would either delay or be covered by immediately following work' is unclear. The fact that 'Defects' is capitalized means the term is being used as defined. It is submitted, however, that the qualification will operate in favour of the contractor and thus enable work falling within the limitations to be still regarded as completed for the purpose of calculating the PWDD and hence to be paid for by the employer. The wording also suggests that this qualification, referring to the meaning of completed work 'In this clause' operates only in main option B.

Lastly, in main option F, PWDD is the amount of actual cost that the contractor has accepted for payment plus the fee.[45] A distinction can be made on this wording from an accounting point of view. Thus, giving the words 'paid' and 'accepted for payment' their natural meaning, the contractor is in a better cash flow[46] position under main option F than the other main options; payment will be earlier in this case than in the cases of the other three definitions. However, to what extent the short assessment intervals will mitigate adverse cash flow consequences under the main options C, D and E is an open question. It should not be overlooked that even apart from this distinction between costs paid and accepted for payment meaning must be given to 'Actual Cost' too and which meaning is restrictive. While cash flow is often referred to as the

---

[42] Clause 11.2(24) ECC.

[43] Clause 11.2(25) ECC.

[44] Clause 11.2(23) ECC; both 'Actual Cost' and 'Fee' are defined terms.

[45] Clause 11.2(22) ECC.

[46] See generally on cash flow BRISCOE, GEOFFREY. *The Economics of the Construction Industry*. B.T. Batsford, London; CIOB, Ascot, 1988, 61–99 and 252–253.

'lifeblood' of the industry, it is also a sign of a well-managed project. In fact cash flow schedules are routinely used on well-managed projects. Dennis Lock states:

> [t]he project manager may be asked to arrange the preparation of cash flow predictions, either for his own company or as a service to the customer. Whether for use in assembling funds or for DCF ['discounted cash flow'] project appraisal, cash flow predictions are necessarily bound up with project timescale planning. Since money is a basic project resource, cash schedules are an important aspect of resource scheduling for major projects.[47]

Recent research has concluded that cash flow factors are largely responsible for the level of insolvency in the construction industry.[48]

'Actual Cost' and 'Disallowed Cost' are both defined terms themselves and also figure prominently in the meaning of either the prices 'and/or' the PWDD. 'Actual Cost' may have one of three separate meanings depending upon the main option chosen.[49] In main options A and B actual cost is defined as the cost of the components in the schedule of cost components (SCC) whether the work is subcontracted or not but excluding the cost of preparing quotations for compensation events.[50] Similarly the employer is not allowed to claim the cost incurred in making assessments for payment. The SCC is a complete statement of all of the cost components under main options A and B. Although the SCC is capitalized it is not a defined term. It would more appropriately be italicized as it is identified in part two of the Contract Data. The inclusion of subcontractor costs in actual cost may be implied in main options A and B given their express exclusion from main options C, D and E as described in the introductory paragraph of the SCC and the Shorter Schedule of Cost Components (SSCC).

Main options C, D and E define actual cost rather as the amount of the payments due to the subcontractors for work which is subcontracted and the cost of components in the SCC[51] for work which is not subcontracted.[52] Under main options C, D and E the SCC is a complete statement of cost components but as noted additionally includes payments to subcontractors. Disallowed cost becomes relevant to the meaning of actual cost as in each of main options C, D and E as well as main option F

[47] LOCK, DENNIS. Resource Scheduling. In *Gower Handbook of Project Management*, 2nd edn. Gower, Aldershot, 1994, p. 144.

[48] See LOWE, J. Insolvency in the UK Construction Industry. *Journal of Financial Management of Property and Construction*, March 1997, 83–110.

[49] See clauses 11.2(26), 11.2(27) and 11.2(28) ECC for definitions of actual cost in the various main options.

[50] Clause 11.2(28) ECC. See also the discussion below regarding the exclusion of the cost of preparing quotations, and see clause 62.1 ECC.

[51] See generally on the broader issue of cost controls, PILCHER, R. *Project Cost Control in Construction*, 2nd edn. Blackwell Scientific Publications, London, 1994.

[52] Clause 11.2(27) ECC.

actual cost is less disallowed cost.[53] Actual cost itself, in respect of main option F, is the amount of payments due to subcontractors for work, which the contractor is required to subcontract less any disallowed cost.[54] Inasmuch as the contractor, under main option F, is required to subcontract all design, construction, installation and other works which the works information requires, actual cost would appear to thus exclude work the contractor carries out.

First of all definitions of 'Disallowed Cost' are set out in clause 11.2(29) in respect of main option F and 11.2(30) in respect of main options C, D and E. The power of disallowance is one which the project manager exercises in other instances; for example, the disallowance of payments to subcontractors regarding compensation events. 'Disallowed Cost' may have one of two separate meanings again depending upon the main option chosen. The intention is to indicate which costs will be excluded from recovery under main options C, D, E and F. The definitions are lengthy and merit reproduction in full. Thus, in respect of main options C, D and E only the definition is as follows:

11.2(30) Disallowed Cost is cost which the *Project Manager* decides
- is not justified by the *Contractor's* accounts and records,
- should not have been paid to a Subcontractor[55] in accordance with his subcontract,[56]
- was incurred only because the *Contractor* did not
    - follow an acceptance or procurement procedure stated in the Works Information or
    - give an early warning[57] which he could have given or
- results from paying a Subcontractor more for a compensation event than is included in the accepted quotation[58] or assessment[59] for the compensation event,

and the cost of
- correcting Defects[60] after Completion,[61]
- correcting Defects[62] caused by the *Contractor* not complying with a requirement for how he is to Provide the Works[63] stated in the Works Information,[64]

---

[53] Clause 11.2(27) for main options C, D and E, and clause 11.2(26) for main option F.
[54] Clause 11.2(26) ECC.
[55] Clause 11.2(9) ECC.
[56] See e.g. clause 51 ECSC. This wording would apparently leave open negotiated or *ex gratia* payments.
[57] See clause 16 ECC.
[58] Under clause 62.3 ECSC.
[59] Under clauses 64.1, 64.2 ECSC.
[60] Clause 11.2(15) ECC.
[61] Clause 11.2(13) ECC.
[62] Clause 11.2(15) ECC.
[63] Clause 11.2(4) ECC.
[64] See clause 20.1 ECC; read with the immediately preceding bullet point this cost presumably is intended to apply to the cost of correcting defects before completion.

- Plant and Materials[65] not used to Provide the Works[66] (after reasonable wastage)[67] and
- resources not used to Provide the Works (after allowing for reasonable availability and utilization) or not taken away from the Working Areas[68] when the *Project Manager* requested.

Some comments may be made on the terminology. First of all 'costs' arise and are described in the ECC in relation to certain issues including indemnities (clauses 21.4, 83.1 and 83.2); failing to provide facilities and services (clause 33.2); repeating tests or inspections (clause 40.6); and employer's risk (clause 80.1). It would not seem that cost as used in clause 11.2(30) is limited with respect to these issues. As to 'decisions', most decisions of the project manager will be taken in relation to and under the compensation events core clause. The 'records' referred to may be those the contractor is under an obligation to keep pursuant to clause 52.2. It is submitted that the necessity for the cost to have been incurred 'only because the *Contractor* did not ...' do certain things will operate in practice as a limitation on disallowance by the project manager.

With regard to not 'follow[ing] an acceptance or procurement procedure stated in the Works Information' contractors will presumably seek to limit this ground to only those procedures stated in the works information not additional procedures that might be required under or implied by the contract itself. It may also be noted that the failure to follow such acceptance or procurement procedures could also pertain to a matter already addressed in clause 11.2(30), e.g. plant and materials. Reference is made to 'not complying with a requirement', although it may be noted that no definition is given for the meaning of 'requirement'. The root word 'requires' is only used in relation to provide the works in clause 11.2(4) and not the definition of works information and thus may be used generally to refer only to 'incidental work, services and actions'.

The 'resources' which the contractor plans to use in providing the works are required to be shown on the programme under clause 31.2 of the ECC. Both the allowance for reasonable wastage of plant and materials and the allowance for reasonable availability utilization of resources should operate in favour of the contractor and reduce the total of the disallowed cost in each case. Lastly, with regard to the use of the term 'requested', it may be asked what is the nature of this request? The use of the term would seem to make it unlikely that a formal instruction was intended rather than some other form of communication, as a request also appears to fall outside of clause 13.1 of the ECC and the meaning of a communication.

---

[65] Clause 11.2(10) ECC.
[66] This follows from the assumption that plant and materials in general are intended to be included in the works, clause 11.2(10) ECC.
[67] See also section 31(a) and (b) SCC.
[68] Clause 11.2(8) ECC.

The differences between this definition of 'Disallowed Cost' in clause 11.2(28) and 'Disallowed Cost' in clause 11.2(29) in respect of main option F only, may be summarized briefly. The first bullet point differs slightly and is worded instead: 'is not justified by the accounts and records provided by the *Contractor*'; while the last four bullet points are omitted from clause 11.2(29). The omission of certain items of disallowed cost in main option F follows from the fact that all work will normally be subcontracted.

Thus the subcontractor has the responsibility to correct the subcontractor's own defects and, under the subcontract main options C, D and E, disallowed cost as defined includes the four omitted items in any event. Clearly, the most significant of the four omissions pertains to correcting defects and, as such, underscores the management contractor's lesser obligation in this regard compared to the contractor's obligation under the other main options. It would be unusual for a management contractor to correct defects on behalf of subcontractors.

The significance of the right of the project manager, and the right of the contractor by extension, under the equivalent ECSC provisions,[69] to disallow costs from recovery by the contractor is to motivate efficient working.[70] Upon examination it can be remarked that the substance of the clause is procedural in the first instance and substantive in the second. Thus, with regard to the first six bullet points above respectively, best practice under the NEC dictates in effect that documentation must be in order, performance should fulfil the contract, procedures must be followed, requisite notices should be given and quotations should be accurate. Further, with regard to the substantive provisions that follow in the remaining four bullet points in the clause, it is clear that both commitments to quality from and responsibility by the contractor are sought. In one final respect the disallowed cost provision is also punitive and seeks an alternative way of punishing for breach of contract.

In summary, best practice or good management has set forth ways and means to move the works forward. The clause operates both as an incentive and disincentive. The disincentive is clearly the disallowance of costs; on the other hand the clause could also be seen as an incentive to recovery of full or actual cost if the procedures agreed are respected. A well-rounded understanding of the true import of these aspects of the clause in operation may require attitudinal change itself. '[T]he concepts of provisional sums and quantities, bill rates, and the various allowances built into ICE remeasurement contracts need to be forgotten and the implications of "actual costs" in NEC activity schedule contracts understood.'[71]

---

[69] Clause 11.2(30) ECC is identical so far as material to clause 11.2(30) ECSC and the subcontract main options C, D and E.

[70] Guidance notes NEC, 95.

[71] WILLIAMS, DAVID H. Using the NEC: A Client's View. New Engineering Contract Conference Proceedings in Hong Kong, 28 November 1994. *Asian Law Journal*, Hong Kong, 1994, p. 16.

The meanings of 'Actual Cost' and 'Prices' delimit the PWDD in main options C, D, E and F. However, the interrelationship between actual cost and disallowed cost is an important factor in determining the PWDD. This follows as a result of the exclusive definition of the actual cost in *terms of* disallowed cost. The significance of actual cost in relation to both the assessment and payment procedures is returned to below.[72]

Assessing the amount due

A contractor is paid according to assessments that are carried out by the project manager in accordance with clause 50. One commentator has suggested that the assessment procedure 'requires the computation to be fair between the parties'.[73] Fairness is not a neutral factor and is sometimes included as a positive factor in the reduction of risk associated with the conditions of contract.[74] The assessment procedure, along with the compensation event procedure, is one of the two most complicated procedures in the ECC. The complexity follows from three factors in general:

- the large number of factors which must be considered;[75]
- the number and length of material definitions;[76] and
- the number of material secondary option clause considerations.[77]

The importance of these things and their relationship to assessment are considered in the discussion below.

In general, the project manager will assess the amount due to the contractor at each relevant assessment date. The amount due PWDD plus other amounts to be paid to the contractor less amounts to be paid by or retained from the contractor.[78] Any value added tax or sales tax, which the governing law would require the employer to pay to the contractor, should be included in the amount due.[79] The obligation this clause imposes on the project manager to take VAT into account has been criticized as 'difficult'.[80]

Assessment begins with reference to what is referred to as an *'assessment interval'*. The assessment interval is stated in section 5 of part

---

[72] See discussion of actual cost below.

[73] O'REILLY, MICHAEL. *Civil Engineering Construction Contracts*, 314, n. 5.

[74] See BUBSHAIT, ABDULAZIZ A. and ALMOHAWIS, SOLIMAN A. Evaluating the General Conditions of a Construction Contract. *International Journal of Project Management*, 1994, **12**(3), 134.

[75] For example, corrections, time frames and programme requirements.

[76] For example, the 'Prices', the 'Price for Work Done to Date', 'Actual Cost', 'Disallowed Cost', and the 'Fee'.

[77] For example, under secondary option clauses J, K, N, P, Q, R and S.

[78] Clause 50.2 ECC, and see discussion of these terms below.

[79] Clause 50.2 ECC.

[80] See CORNES. The Second Edition of the New Engineering Contract. *International Construction Law Review*, 1996, 97.

one of the Contract Data as a given number of weeks and must not exceed five weeks.[81] The first assessment interval will be determined with reference to the first 'assessment date'.

The assessment date *per se* is neither an identified nor a defined term nor does it appear anywhere in the Contract Data. Rather assessment dates occur at certain fixed times or following certain agreed intervals as stipulated in the contract itself. The first assessment date is decided by the project manager and to suit the parties' procedures[82] but must not be later than the assessment interval after the starting date.[83] This wording suggests that the project manager consults with the contractor but the wording is not imperative. A series of later assessment dates occur under clause 50.1 and are respectively:

- at the end of each *assessment interval* until Completion[84] of the whole of the *works*,
- at Completion of the whole of the works,[85]
- four weeks after the *Supervisor* issues the Defects Certificate[86] and
- after Completion of the whole of the *works*,
  - when an amount due is corrected[87] and
  - when a payment is made late.[88]

It can be noted from these '*assessment intervals*' that the assessment dates will occur regularly throughout the contract period but may increase in frequency with shorter assessment intervals occurring as completion is first approached and then passed. The assessment dates in this sense stand as interim assessment dates in contrast to the first assessment date which the project manager decides upon taking into account the parties' procedures. The last assessment dates occur again as noted above upon completion and four weeks after the issuance of the defects certificate. Contractors may initially seek to equate the first and subsequent assessment dates with interim payments, and the last assessment date with the final payment under traditional forms; however, the peculiarities of the assessment and payment procedures as discussed here suggest otherwise. The assessments may be summarized as in Table 1.

No further assessment dates need occur after these final assessments but they can occur in situations involving correction of a certified amount; when interest is assessed on a late payment; or where one of the applicable secondary option clauses applies.[89] The first two situations are

---

[81] Section 5 of part one.
[82] Clause 50.1 ECC.
[83] Clause 50.1 ECC. Both '*assessment interval*' and '*starting date*' are italicized terms and as such are identified for purposes of the Contract Data.
[84] Clause 11.2(13) ECC.
[85] It would appear 'works' here is unintentionally not italicized.
[86] Clause 11.2(16) ECC.
[87] See also clause 51.3 ECC.
[88] Clause 50.1 ECC.
[89] For example, under secondary option clauses J, K, N, P, Q, R and S.

Table 1. Summary of assessments

Main option and clauses	Interim assessment	Final assessment
A – clauses 11.2 and 11.2(24)	Total of the prices for completed activities	Total of the prices for all activities
B – clauses 11.2(21) and 11.2(25)	Quantities of completed work at bills rates and proportions of lump sum prices	Remeasurement of quantities of completed work at bills rates
C – clauses 11.2(20) and 11.2(23)	Actual cost paid plus fee	Tender price plus share of saving or excess compared to target
D – clauses 11.2(21) and 11.2(23)	Actual cost paid plus fee	Remeasured value of the work in accordance with the bills plus any saving or excess
E – clauses 11.2(19) and 11.2(23)	Actual cost paid plus fee	Actual cost paid plus fee
F – clauses 11.2(19) and 11.2(22)	Actual cost accepted for payment plus fee	Actual cost paid plus fee

those referred to above in clause 50.1 and follow plainly from the wording of the clause. If neither of these situations occurs and there are no applicable secondary option clauses then the last assessment date will be four weeks after the issuance of the defects certificate by the project manager. Pursuant to clause 50.1 the project manager will assess the cost of correcting defects listed on the defects certificate which is issued under clause 43.1. This date assumes that no reference to either the 'Adjudicator' or the tribunal follows and which entails a reassessment.[90]

With regard to assessments and the length of payment times under the First Edition the Latham Report states that:

> the objective under the NEC is to pay both contractor and subcontractor from the assessment date rather than the certificate date. The authors of the NEC believe that this gives protection to both main contractors and subcontractors. It is also the case that the NEC is drafted to facilitate payment on a 4-4-5 week cycle and the normal payment interval is expected to be one month.[91]

Since this statement the Second Edition of the NEC has now effectively reduced the payments to a 3-3-4 week cycle.[92] Early experience under the form indicates that the payment periods are being met and settlement of

---

[90] See clauses 92.2 and 93.2 ECC.
[91] Latham Report, paragraph 5.20(3), 39.
[92] See BARNES, MARTIN. The New Engineering Contract – An Update. *International Construction Law Review*, 1996, 92–94.

the final account is commonly taking place within a few months of completion and well ahead of many other forms of contract.[93]

Assessment and the programme

The assessment procedures include consideration of an important component of the NEC scheme – the programme. In this regard a right to retain a sum of money from an amount due to the contractor under an assessment is expressly given when the contractor has failed to fulfil all of the programme commitments. The retention is dependent upon whether the contractor has submitted a first programme to the project manager at the outset. Thus, if no programme is identified in the Contract Data and the contractor has not submitted a first programme to the project manager for acceptance, one-quarter of the PWDD as defined will be retained from the contractor in assessments of the amount due.[94] The effect will be to reduce the amount of the certificate by as much as 25% although it may also be less than this depending upon the calculation of the amount due under clause 50.2, that is, plus 'other amounts to be paid to the *Contractor*'. Conversely, if the contractor has submitted that first such programme but it does not show the information which the contract requires, the effect is the same and the project manager will again withhold one-quarter of the PWDD from the contractor in assessments of the amount due.[95] Emphasis is placed upon the wording to conclude that these two reasons are the only bases for the retention. Thus, retention would not be justified if the programme was submitted and it showed the information required but the project manager simply did not wish to accept the programme and notwithstanding this power under other provisions of the contract.[96] It should be noted that under the amendments to the Second Edition as a result of the HGCRA the retention would now have to satisfy clause 56.2 also. Clearly the clause makes no attempt to address any necessity of the project manager to *accept* the programme. Acceptance is both a separate topic and a separate procedure, and is dealt with in clause 31.3 regarding programmes in general and clause 13.4 and 13.5 if a further submission is required. The intention in limiting clause 50.3 in this way was to avoid retention being imposed as a result of any delay by the project manager in deciding whether to accept the programme or not.[97] Similarly, the fact that the retention is limited to the submission of the first programme only means that clause 50.3 would have no application to a subsequent programme which would rather be treated instead as a revised programme.[98] Because submission and non-

---

[93] BROOME, JON C. and PERRY, JOHN G. Experiences of the Use of the New Engineering Contract. *Engineering, Construction and Architectural Management*, 1995, **2**(4), 281.

[94] Clause 50.3 ECC.

[95] Clause 50.3.

[96] Clauses 13.8 and 31.3 ECC.

[97] Guidance notes on clause 50.3 ECC, 52.

[98] See clauses 32 and 64 ECC.

acceptance is addressed in clause 50.3, it is really designed to serve as an important incentive for the timely submission of programmes by the contractor, not a guise for withholding funds from the contractor. Eggleston describes the withholding provision as punitive[99] while Cornes[100] describes it as 'draconian' and adds it is 'likely ... a penalty in law and therefore unenforceable'.[101] However, it seems that before one could come to that conclusion the provision would have to be looked at more in context and read against all aspects of the *Dunlop Pneumatic Tyre*[102] test. Further, this view also seems to underestimate the true importance of the programme in the NEC system. It is not simply a matter of convenience but is essential to the project manager's decision-making. Without the programme the project manager's decisions are not only less well informed but also entail greater risk from the employer's perspective.

Ultimately, the contractor's compliance with the programme requirements will be measured against the specifics in clause 31. Clause 50.3 only addresses the case where no programme is identified in the Contract Data. In any other case in which a programme has been so identified the contractor would then still be obliged under clause 31.1 to submit the first programme to the project manager for acceptance within the period stated in the Contract Data. In practice it is likely that the programme would have been accepted at that time,[103] although if it had not been, clause 50.3 and the one-quarter retention of the PWDD would operate in those circumstances as well.

The programme requirements are considered in advance of and stand as effective conditions precedent to the project manager receiving an application for payment. The application for payment is submitted pursuant to clause 50.4. To be considered the application should be submitted on or before the relevant assessment date. Then, in assessing the amount due, the project manager would consider the application. To what extent the project manager considers it may in part be dependent upon how much in advance of the relevant assessment date the application was made. One might expect a more considered approach if given well in advance of the deadline than if given on the date itself. The same two questions are asked by the project manager in each case pertaining to the correctness of the amount previously assessed and whether or not the amounts previously certified were paid within the assessment intervals or periods stated in the contract. If corrections are necessary the project

---

[99] EGGLESTON. *The New Engineering Contract, A Commentary.* Blackwell Science, London, 1996, pp. 175–176.

[100] CORNES. The Second Edition of the New Engineering Contract. *International Construction Law Review*, 1996. 105.

[101] CORNES, 105 and citing *Dunlop Pneumatic Tyre Co Ltd* v. *New Garage and Motor Co Ltd* [1915] AC 79, HL.

[102] *Dunlop Pneumatic Tyre Co Ltd* v. *New Garage and Motor Co Ltd* [1915] AC 79, HL; note that the retention was actually one-half under the First Edition.

[103] See clause 11.2(14) ECC.

manager will correct any wrongly assessed amount due in the next later payment certificate.[104] To determine when a wrong assessment has been made clause 50.5 must be read with clause 51.3. In this case, as well as any involving previously certified payments being paid outside the agreed assessment intervals of periods stated in the contract, interest on either the correcting amount or the late payment respectively may also be owed. The interest is calculated according to the clause 51 procedures. Reference may also be made by the project manager to the fee percentage in the Contract Data with regard to the assessments.

Progress and stage payments[105] *per se* present problems of measurement, particularly in relation to intangible tasks such as design or inspections. Thus, from a project management point of view, the employer may wish to seek to provide greater specificity in measuring the progress which has been made before making a payment. One recommended means of accomplishing this is through 'achievement analysis' which involves choosing work elements involved in the activity and subjecting them to measurement and reporting requirements. The activities become susceptible to work values in a convenient form of unit. An activity will only be completed once the designated number of units has been achieved. At that point a comparison may be made against the budget for the activity. It may also be a useful method to update the programme or even any networks being used that similarly call for monitoring and updating. In general, the achievement analysis approach can provide greater precision in payments based on solely time-related predictions. This is to meet the assumption that is often made on projects that if expenditures are being incurred as predicted that progress must be made correspondingly.[106] Achievement analysis seeks to address the time delay that can arise between expenditure and accounting entry. It is thus a means of financial control in the overall management of the project.

Assessment of the amount due

With the '*assessment intervals*' and assessment dates clearly demarcated the project manager is able to assess the actual amount that is due to the contractor. The basis for assessing this amount is the PWDD. Almost all other payments to the contractor are arrived at on the basis of the PWDD and will be either added to or deducted from it. Advanced payments are an exception to this. In addition, if option P regarding retention is adopted once the retention free amount is reached an amount will be retained that is equal to the retention percentage stated in the Contract Data applied to the excess of the PWDD above the retention free amount under clause P1.1. Clause 50.2 provides as follows:

---

[104] Clause 50.5 ECC.
[105] Cf the BPF system which stipulates stage payments to both consultants and contractors.
[106] See generally LOCK, DENNIS. n. 47 above, pp. 322–352.

The amount due is the Price for Work done to Date[107] plus other amounts to be paid to the *Contractor*[108] less amounts to be paid by [the Contractor][109] or retained from the *Contractor*. Any value added tax or sales tax which the law requires the *Employer* to pay to the *Contractor* must be included in the amount due.

The amount due would exclude advanced payments. Amounts retained from the Contractor could arise for various reasons, e.g. if programme requirements were not met an amount may be retained under clause 50.3; or if secondary option P is used, once the PWDD reaches the retention free amount, an amount may be retained from the contractor in each amount assessed due. It is recommended that if a contractor's invoice for VAT or sales tax is used that it be given to the project manager for attachment to the certificate.[110]

Assessment and applications for payment

Pursuant to clause 50.4: '[i]n assessing the amount due, the *Project Manager* considers any application for payment[111] the *Contractor* has submitted on or before the assessment date'. The language of clause 50.4 is ambiguous when read with the intentions of the drafters as to how it should be construed. The drafters intend that the project manager 'takes account of any submissions by the *Contractor*'.[112] However, the wording of the clause mandates instead that the project manager considers the 'application', not submission *per se*, of the contractor. There is nothing that necessarily equates an application to make payment with a right to make submissions in respect of it. In the absence of such an equation it seems the two phrases should be given separate meanings. If this interpretation were correct then procedure under the clause would differ from other forms that require an application as a *precondition* for payment. In fact, the wording of the contract suggests the contrary because an 'application' is not a 'communication' within the meaning of clause 13.1. It is only as a communication that an application would receive the right to a reply and the implicit 'taking account thereof' that a reply entails. If it is not a communication any other obligation of the project manager to take account of the application must be found elsewhere in the contract. No provisions exist in clause 50.4 in this regard although once again this appears to be the purported interpretation that the drafters would seek to place upon it.

---

[107] Defined respectively for each main option and discussed below.

[108] For example, under the compensation event procedure in core clause 60.

[109] For example, under clauses 40.5, 40.6, 45.1, 94.4 ECC. 'A payment is made by the *Contractor* to the *Employer* if the change reduces the amount due': clause 51.1 ECC.

[110] Guidance notes NEC on clause 50.2, at 52.

[111] Cf the Green Book conditions which transfer money to the contractor as and when necessary so that the works may be properly funded. This is sometimes referred to as a cash 'neutral' position: WILCOCK, CHRIS. The I Chem E Standard Forms – Model Conditions? *Construction Law*, 5 December 1994, 172.

[112] Guidance notes NEC on clause 50.4 ECC, at 52.

In summary, while the contractor does not appear to have been given any express contractual right to make submissions with or at the time of any application for payment under clause 50.4, nevertheless a large and liberal interpretation is still put forward for the provision. It is contended that it is only through such an interpretation that the true intentions of the drafters will be achieved. One step toward this end may be taken if the project manager treats the application for payment itself as a *submission* by the contractor and thus one falling within the protections afforded such a communication under clause 13. Treating the application as a submission at least suggests a case may be made at that time or later in support of the application. Further, when the project manager gives a reply to the submission it will then have to give the contractor details of how the amount due has been assessed.[113] With this obligation being imposed upon the project manager it will also be in the project manager's interest to hear the details of any submission that the contractor may think relevant at the time of the application. That would still appear to be the case notwithstanding that any wrongly assessed amounts due could still be corrected by the project manager in later payment certificates.[114]

Payment

Assessment dates are relevant not only to the calculation of payments to the contractor but to their certification as well.[115] Under the unamended Second Edition of the ECC, the right to payment is recognized by a certificate given by the project manager within one week of each assessment date.[116] Under the amended Second Edition of the ECC, the project manager certifies a payment on or before the date on which a payment becomes due.[117] The ECC thus adopts the most common method of making provision for payments to the contractor in the standard forms but also, it would seem, the most complex. These complex payment provisions could be improved with fuller descriptions of the requirements for applications for payment with sample documents; especially given how the NEC flow chart provisions resemble the flow charts set out in the approval and review work procedure under the ENAA Model Form of Contract.[118]

No distinction is made in the ECC between interim payment certificates and final payment certificates. In addition, in the case of main options C and D, neither the '*activity schedule*' nor the '*bill of quantities*' is utilized to assess interim payments but rather only to assess compensation events and calculate the contractor's share. In fact, this terminology itself has been eschewed by the NEC in favour of 'assessments' as a general rule. Under

---

[113]   Clause 50.4 ECC.
[114]   Clause 50.5 ECC. Interest is payable on corrected amounts: clause 51 ECC.
[115]   See clause 51 ECC.
[116]   Clause 51.1 ECC.
[117]   Clause 51.1 amended 2nd ECC.
[118]   For example, ENAA Model Form, 1992, vol. 4, Work Procedure 3, Approval and Review Procedure.

the unamended Second Edition it will be a question of interpretation whether the issue of the payment certificate creates a debt due immediately,[119] or simply entitles the employer to make an advance payment to the contractor which is not otherwise legally due until completion.[120] The better view, given the secondary option of an express advanced payment to the contractor, is that the issuance of the certificate creates a debt due immediately. This view is supported by the contractual provisions in favour of the contractor on interest for late payments,[121] as well as practice under most standard forms. Notwithstanding this view, however, the employer is accorded significant rights to defeat payment under the case law. In particular, a contractor's claim for summary judgment on the value of a certificate may be defeated by putting forward a defence of set-off,[122] or arguing that the certificate was overvalued.[123] Under the amended provisions of the ECC[124] and under the HGCRA,[125] while the contractor does not have an immediate right to payment, right to payment still arises once the final date for payment, as understood within the meaning of both the ECC and HGCRA, has passed. Early practice under the provisions in the legislation suggest that it is working and has shortened payment cycles.[126] Section 110(1)(a) of the HGCRA requires an adequate mechanism for determining what payments become due under the contract and when they become due under the contract. Under the ECC the 'adequate mechanism' is the project manager's certificate. Thus, 'the *Project Manager's* certificate is the notice of payment from the *Employer* to the *Contractor* specifying the amount (if any) of the payment made or proposed to be made, and the basis on which that amount was calculated'.[127] The relationship of the ECC provision to the HGCRA is made clear by the opening words of clause 56.1 which read: 'For the purpose of Sections 109 and 110 of the Act'. The date on which a payment then becomes due following the giving of the certificate is seven days after the assessment date.[128] Section 110(1)(b) of the HGCRA stipulates there

---

[119] *Pickering* v. *Ilfracombe Rly Co* (1868) LR 3 CP 235.

[120] *Tharsis Sulphur and Copper Co* v. *McElroy & Sons* (1878) 3 App Cas 1040, HL.

[121] Clause 51.2 and 51.3 ECC.

[122] See generally DERHAM, RORY. *Set-Off*, 2nd edn. Oxford University Press, Oxford, 1996.

[123] *C M Pillings & Co Ltd* v. *Kent Investments Ltd* (1985) 30 BLR 80, CA.

[124] Clause 56.1 amended 2nd ECC.

[125] Sections 109(1) and 110(1) HGCRA. See on the possible effect of the HGCRA provisions on rights of set-off: BARRETT, KEVIN J. Withholding Payment under the Housing Grants, Construction and Regeneration Act 1996. *Construction Law Journal*, 1998, **14**, 180; and KENNEDY, P. *et al.* Resolution of Disputes Arising from Set-off Clauses between Main Contractors and Subcontractors. *Construction Management and Economics*, 1997, **15**, 533–534.

[126] MORBY, AARON and GREEN, BRIAN. Contractors Clean Up Act on Payment. *Construction News*, 19 August 1999, 1.

[127] Clause 56.1 amended 2nd ECC.

[128] Clause 56.1 amended 2nd ECC. It may be noted that clause 56 is a new clause in the amended Second Edition and not simply an amended clause.

must be a 'final date for payment in relation to any sum which becomes due'. Also pursuant to the provision, the parties are free to choose how long the period is to be between the date when a sum becomes due and the final date for payment. Under the amended ECC, the period chosen is 21 days. Thus clause 56.1 provides the final date for payment is 21 days or, if a different period for payment is stated in the Contract Data, the period stated after the date on which payment becomes due. Reading the two parts of clause 56.1 together it can be seen there is a maximum 28-day interval between the assessment date and the final date for payment. The employer is obligated to pay on or before the agreed and defined final date for payment or the contractor's remedies come into play, *viz.* the right to suspend performance and claim as a compensation event.[129] To return to the point made above and the absence of any distinction between interim payment certificates (interim assessments) and final payment certificates (final assessments) it is interesting that the HGCRA similarly now makes no distinction either. Every payment, whether construed as 'interim' or not, gives rise to a 'final date for payment'. That final date for payment has nothing to do with whether the completion date has passed, save in the one case where the assessment interval is determined with reference to completion.[130]

The first payment to the contractor is the amount due. Other payments reflect the *change* in the amount due since the issuance of the last payment certificate.[131] This is one of only two references to the 'payment certificate' which also includes clause 50.5. In the Consultation Document clause 50.1 actually used this heading. However, in the Second Edition the term is not used in this way nor identified nor defined in the contract or Contract Data; in this respect it contrasts with the 'Defects Certificate'. The contractor makes a payment to the employer if the change reduces the amount due. Other payments are made by the employer to the contractor and are in the '*currency of this contract*' unless otherwise stated in the contract.[132] In general, the payments will be due within three weeks of each assessment date unless stated otherwise.[133] The time frame is the same under the amended Second Edition only the payments would be viewed as due within '21 days'.[134] Generally, in the NEC, time periods are set out in weeks and in this regard reinforce the multi-jurisdictional character of the form by not having to allow for holidays which vary from country to country. However, under the HGCRA, time periods are expressed in days and this has had to be accommodated in the amendments incorporated under secondary option Y (UK) 2. Thus time periods in the amendments are stated in days. References here to 'three weeks' may be taken to mean 21 days in relation to the amended Second Edition. Clause

---

[129] Section 112(3) HGCRA, and clause 60.7 ECC.
[130] See the discussion above.
[131] Clause 51.1 ECC.
[132] Clause 51.1 ECC. '*Currency of this contract*' is an italicized term and identified as such for purposes of the Contract Data: see section 5 part one.
[133] See clause 51.2 ECC.
[134] Clause 56.1 amended 2nd ECC.

Y2.1 provides in part 'periods of time stated in days are reckoned in accordance with Section 116 of the Act'. The provision for payment to or repayment by either party is a somewhat different approach from that under many other traditional forms but does serve to underscore the inherent adjustability of payment certificates.[135] The tendency of the courts is to regard the issuance of a certificate as a condition precedent to the contractor's right to payment, but in every case it will still be a matter of interpretation whether this is so. If the provision were construed as a condition precedent the contractor would be without a clear right to payment in the absence of the certificate.[136]

The contractor's principal remedy under the traditional forms is to seek immediate arbitration.[137] This remedy is also available under the ECC following the adjudication procedure. By comparison, under the amended Second Edition, in the absence of the project manager's certificate, which serves as the 'adequate machinery' required under the HGCRA, the provisions of the Scheme for Construction Contracts would come into play by default.[138] In this way the contractor would not lose the right to an interim payment solely on the basis of no certificate.

Payment and the award of interest

Recognition of the right to payment of interest has been slow coming under certain traditional forms. The ECC moves forward with a stipulated right to compound interest[139] not only in respect of late payments as discussed above but also in respect of corrections to payments on broad grounds and even the withholding of a certificate or a failure to certify. However, it should be noted that while the entitlement is to compound interest, only simple interest accrues for periods less than one year.[140]

Each certified payment is made within three weeks of the assessment date or, if a different period is stated in the Contract Data, within the period stated.[141] The time frames for the assessment intervals are precise. If no provision is made to the contrary in the Contract Data the time frames for assessment can be set out.

- An assessment interval will end on an assessment date.
- The assessment interval will not exceed five weeks.

---

[135] See generally *Lamprell* v. *Billericay Union* (1849) 3 Exch 283.

[136] *Morgan* v. *Birnie* (1833) 9 Bing 672; *Glenn* v. *Leith* (1853) 1 CLR 569; *Grafton* v. *Easter Counties Rly Co* (1853) 8 Ex 699; *Westwood* v. *Secretary of State for India in Council* (1863) 7 LT 736; *Stevenson* v. *Watson* (1879) 4 CPD 148; *Wallace* v. *Brandon and Byshottles UDC* (1903) 2 *Hudson's BC*, 4th edn. 362, CA; *Eagleshaw* v. *McMaster* [1920] 2 KB 169.

[137] See *Lubenham Fidelities and Investments Co Ltd* v. *South Pembrokeshire District Council* (1986) 33 BLR 39, CA.

[138] Section 109(3) HGCRA.

[139] The compound entitlement was recognized though only in the Second Edition of the NEC.

[140] See discussion below.

[141] Clause 51.2 ECC.

- Payments due must be certified within one week of each assessment date.
- The certified payment must be made within three weeks (or 21 days)[142] of the assessment date.
- Late payments will attract interest.

It has been argued by Eggleston that one consequence of the use of ECC assessment intervals is that if the contractor does work after completion the wait for payment may be as long as twelve months.[143] The example given in support of this contention is that if the assessment intervals are applied to payments for repair or emergency work after completion, even at the employer's expense, it will be a hardship. However, if one refers to clause 82.1 on repairs it can be seen that the repair obligation imposed on the contractor under this clause operates only *until* the defects certificate has been issued. In this case the contractor would benefit from an assessment four weeks after the issuance of the defects certificate. Interest, although only simple, would still be paid on any late payment.[144] The assessment interval for interest for late payments is between the date by which the late payment should have been made and the date when the late payment is made.[145] The amount of the interest is included in the first assessment after the late payment is made.[146]

Four general areas recognize a right to interest and set out '*assessment intervals*' during which the interest will accrue:

- late payments;
- corrections of wrongly assessed amounts;
- following dispute resolution; and
- failure to certify.

The interest assessment intervals are all independent but there is no limitation on them running consecutively. Hence late certification may attract interest, as may late payment in respect of the certificated amount. This accords with the Construction Round Table's *Declaration of Commitment to Fair Construction Contracts* requiring members to declare their intention to give effect to certain principles in the conduct of their projects and which include: 'To make interim payments in the period in which they become due as agreed in our contracts and to provide compensation for delay in making any payment at an appropriate rate'.[147] Interest is due in all cases of late payment and the principle is applied consistently across the contract. The fact that interest may be payable by not only the employer but the contractor as well serves to increase the overall acceptability of the provisions. Equally, the uniformity of the

---

[142] Clause 56.1 amended 2nd ECC.
[143] Eggleston, see n. 99 above, p. 175.
[144] Clause 51.2 ECC.
[145] Clause 51.2 ECC.
[146] Clause 51.2 ECC.
[147] *Construction Industry Law Letter*, 1995, 1104.

principles and whether applied in the first instance by the project manager or second or third instances by the adjudicator or tribunal similarly enforce acceptability and overall administration. The fairness of this situation and the general trend toward recognition of rights to finance charges or interest as a principle may also be reflected in recent amendments to FIDIC 4th.[148]

Turning to the second of the general areas that recognize a right to interest, interest may be awarded when there has been correction of an amount assessed. Under clause 50.5, the project manager is under an obligation to correct any wrongly assessed amount due in a later payment certificate. To give this clause meaning one must read it with clause 51.3 which provides that, if an amount due is corrected in a later certificate by the project manager, then interest on the correcting amount is paid. The only two cases where such interest would accrue concerning the project manager's correction arise from a mistake or a compensation event.[149] It is the use of the root word 'correct' which gives meaning to a reading of the two clauses together. The fact that the wrongs may pertain to not only 'mistakes' but also compensation events suggests no aspersions are cast in using this language. Mistake itself should be given its ordinary meaning. It would seem that the reference to a 'later certificate' in clause 51.3 may preclude the automatic termination of the project manager's authority once what is believed to be the final payment certificate has been issued. The assessment interval in the case of a corrected later certificate runs between the date when the incorrect amount was certified and until the date when the correcting amount is certified.[150] The amount of the interest is included in the corrected assessment.[151] David Cornes[152] has raised whether the word should be given a narrow interpretation. It is submitted that this would be the wrong interpretation to place upon clause 51.4 as there is sufficient material both in the guidance notes, and the express references to not only interest, but to it compounding as well under clause 51.1 to warrant a liberal interpretation.

The third area is also framed in terms of a correction; however, unlike the second area, there is no attribute of error or wrongfulness. Thus, if an amount due is corrected in a later certificate following a decision of the adjudicator or the tribunal, then interest again is paid on the correcting amount.

The fourth general area or case where interest may accrue is where the project manager does not issue a certificate that should have been issued.[153] In this case the interest assessment interval runs between the

---

[148] FIDIC 4th Supplement, 1st 1996 provides for amendment to clause 60.10 to grant the contractor a remedy in the form of interest when the engineer fails to certify interim payments timeously.
[149] Clause 51.3 ECC.
[150] Clause 51.3 ECC.
[151] Clause 51.3 ECC.
[152] CORNES, see n. 100 above, 105.
[153] Clause 51.4 ECC.

date on which the project manager should have certified the amount due and the date when it is actually certified.[154] The interest is included in the amount that should have been certified.[155] The interest is calculated at the *'interest rate'* and is compounded annually. As the compounding is calculated on an annual basis only simple interest is payable at the agreed *'interest rate'* for periods of less than one year.[156] This fact should be borne in mind when selecting the *'interest rate'*. It may be one reason perhaps why section 5 of part one of the Contract Data stipulates: '[t]he *interest rate* is ... % per annum (not less than 2) above the ... rate of the ... bank'. Clearly, the *'interest rate'*, as an identified term in this way, must be inserted in the Contract Data[157] to be meaningful. No reason for the minimum choice of 2% over the rate is given although presumably it was felt to be representative of average returns. The interest rate will be determined with reference to a selected base rate or minimum lending rate from one or perhaps more banks.[158] As noted the interest will be compounded but only annually. The endorsement of a compound rate of interest in the ECC accords with the general practice of the courts in the award of interest at commercial rates in building contract cases.[159] However, the restriction on assessing the compound rate in favour of a simple rate for periods of less than one year seems outside current trends and contrary to some commentary and authority. David Cornes, for instance, notes that compounding upon each assessment interval rather than annually would be closer to the practice now followed under ICE 5th and 6th form provisions in accordance with *Morgan Grenfell (Local Authority) Finance Ltd* v. *Sunderland Borough Council and Seven Seas Dredging*.[160] The interpretation, however, could be given to cases arising under the First Edition of the NEC inasmuch as no provision was made for annual compounding. The award of interest in these situations at least meets, and may even exceed, the recommendations in the Latham Report given the number of situations that are addressed and the entitlement to compound interest. The Latham Report provides that an effective form of contract should '[c]learly set ... out the period within which interim payments must be made to all participants in the process, failing which they will have an automatic right to compensation, involving payment of interest at a sufficiently heavy rate to deter slow payment'.[161]

---

[154] Clause 51.4 ECC.

[155] Clause 51.4 ECC.

[156] Guidance notes NEC on clause 51.5 ECC, at 53.

[157] Section 5 part one Contract Data.

[158] See section 5 part one Contract Data; see also e.g. *Tate & Lyle Food and Distribution Ltd* v. *Greater London Council* [1981] 3 All ER 716 at 722, [1982] 1 WLR 149 at 154 per Forbes J.

[159] See e.g. *Tate & Lyle Food and Distribution Ltd* v. *Greater London Council* [1981] 3 All ER 716 at 722, [1982] 1 WLR 149 at 154 per Forbes J.

[160] CORNES, see n. 100 above, 106 citing *Morgan Grenfell (Local Authority) Finance Ltd* v. *Sunderland Borough Council and Seven Seas Dredging* (1989) 49 BLR 31.

[161] Latham Report, paragraph 5.18(9).

Actual cost

'Actual Cost' is both relevant to and an integral part of the assessment procedures. 'Actual Cost' is defined for each of the main options in clause 11.2. Thus, in respect of main options A and B, actual cost is the cost of the components in the SCC components whether work is subcontracted or not and excludes the cost of preparing quotations for compensation events.[162] Under main options C, D and E actual cost is the amount of payments due to subcontractors for work which is subcontracted and the cost of components in the SCC for work which is not subcontracted less any disallowed costs.[163] Lastly, under main option F, actual cost is the amount of payments due to subcontractors for work that the contractor is required to subcontract less any disallowed cost.[164] In short, all the contractor's costs that are not included in the defined actual cost are deemed to be included in the fee percentage.[165] The primary function of the word 'deem' is to bring in something which would otherwise be excluded.[166] The *'fee percentage'* is an identified term in part two of the Contract Data and important from the employer's point of view in assessing tenders.

It can be observed from the above discussion that an important aspect of the definitions of actual cost are the assumptions about financial or cost risk for subcontractors. It should be underscored that under main options A and B payments to subcontractors are excluded from actual cost. Clause 11.2(28) only treats the issue of subcontracting as immaterial to arriving at actual cost. As such, subcontractors' costs are also included in the assessment of compensation events. The effect in this case is that payment risk for subcontractors remains with the contractor. Greenwood and Klein state that payment risk in general centres upon four issues: agreement of the amount due, prompt payment of the amounts agreed, security of deferred payment in the event of insolvency and security of retention funds.[167] Main options C, D and E exhibit a different allocation of cost risk regarding subcontractors. Thus, actual cost includes payments due to subcontractors both in relation to the calculation of the price and in assessing compensation events.[168] This leaves cost risk for these three main options upon the employer. Lastly, although a shorter definition of actual cost pertains to main option F, it too leaves the cost risk for payments to subcontractors upon the employer. In part, on the assumption of this risk, the employer retains a necessary measure of control over the selection of

---

[162]   Clause 11.2(28) ECC.
[163]   Clause 11.2(27) ECC. 'Disallowed Cost' is also a defined term in clause 11.2(30).
[164]   Clause 11.2(26). 'Disallowed Cost' is also a defined term in clause 11.2(29) and differs from its definition and use in relation to main options C, D and E.
[165]   Clause 52.1 ECC.
[166]   *Barclays Bank Ltd* v. *Inland Revenue Commissioners* [1961] AC 509 at 523, [1960] 2 All ER 817 at 820, HL, per Viscount Simonds.
[167]   GREENWOOD, DAVID and KLEIN, RUDI, see n. 1 above, 255.
[168]   Clause 11.2(27) ECC.

subcontractors,[169] notification of compensation events[170] and the protections afforded under clause 52.1 of the ECC.

The actual cost as defined fulfils primarily one of two functions in the six main options. That is, in main options A and B it is relevant to and forms the basis of assessment for compensation events; while in main options C, D, E and F it is used in the calculation of PWDD inclusive of the fee percentage. The relationship of actual cost to the assessment of compensation events follows as a result of their effect on prices.[171] The definition of actual cost in main options A and B expressly excludes the cost of preparation of quotations for compensation events unlike and in contrast to main options C, D, E and F which include this cost.

The amounts included in the actual cost are at open market or competitively tendered prices with all discounts, rebates and taxes, which can be recovered, deducted.[172] This provides a measure of protection for the employer in respect of the costs. Under main options C, D, E and F, the contractor is obliged to keep accounts of payments of actual cost. Thus, records showing that the payments have been made, records of communications and calculations relating to the assessment of compensation events for subcontractors, and other accounts and records as stated in the works information must be maintained.[173] Further, in respect of those same main options, the contractor must allow the project manager to inspect the requisite accounts and records at any time within working hours.[174] The record-keeping requirements and attendant inspection rights do not apply to main options A and B.

Contractor's share

The 'Contractor's share' provisions are a feature only of the two target contract main options C with 'activity schedule' and D with 'bill of quantities'. The target contract may be used where the extent of the work is uncertain or where the employer wishes to share a larger part of the construction risks with the contractor. In return for assuming a larger portion of the risk than under a priced contract, for example, the contractor is given a right to share in any cost savings. Both this risk of loss and risk of higher return are addressed through the mechanism of the 'Contractor's share'.

---

[169] See discussion clauses 26.2, 26.3.
[170] For example, the contractor may not extend time for notification of a compensation event by a subcontractor without the project manager's consent, clauses 62.5 ECC, 62.5 ECSC.
[171] See discussion section 63.1 ECC.
[172] Clause 52.1 ECC.
[173] Clause 52.2 ECC.
[174] Clause 52.3 ECC.

Procedure

The contractor will tender target price or target prices for the contract that should be inclusive of anticipated costs. In coming to the tender price the contractor will be mindful of the definition of actual cost for the main option chosen and thus will wish to include those items covered plus any other costs which are expected to be covered in the contractor's fee. It may be based on either an activity schedule (main option C) or a bill of quantities (main option D). The analogy in traditional contracting would be to a contractor who is paid prime cost. Under the target cost mode of procurement the contractor would not necessarily be paid prime cost alone but that sum plus or minus an agreed percentage (or percentages as in the ECC) in relation to the tendered target cost. J.G. Perry and P.A. Thompson write:

> [a] target cost must be realistic and should be the best estimate of the probable actual cost of completing the work. Whatever method is used to set the target it is essential that it should offer a genuine incentive to the Contractor. There is no advantage in beating down the target if this results in the removal of positive incentive from the Contractor.[175]

The agreed percentage (or percentages) which are inserted in part one of the Contract Data in this way represent a 'sharing' of the increase over or decrease below the prime cost sum. The ECC *'Contractor's share percentage'* provisions seek to achieve similar ends. The employer will assess the target prices which have been tendered as well as the *'fee percentage'* against other tenderers. From a comparative point of view the provisions indicate a high degree of flexibility.

The ECC provisions on contractor's share are contained in clauses 53.1 to 53.5. The provisions are identical in both main options C and D and it is only in respect of these two main options that the share issue will arise. Clause 53.1 provides the general method of calculation for the *'Contractor's share percentage'*. As with the expression of any essentially mathematical formula, in words it is not easily followed.[176] The procedure begins with the project manager assessing the contractor's share of the difference between the total of the prices and the PWDD.[177] The difference is then divided into increments falling within each of the share ranges that are stated in the Contract Data.[178] The *'share ranges'* is an identified term and appears in part one of the Contract Data. The proforma indicates four share ranges:

- less than an agreed percentage;
- a range between two agreed percentages;

---

[175] PERRY, J.G. and THOMPSON, P.A., see n. 39 above, p. 16.
[176] The drafters must have recognized this for three separate examples of how to perform the calculations are included in the guidance notes NEC on clause 53 ECC, at 54.
[177] Clause 53.1 ECC.
[178] Clause 53.1 ECC.

- a further range between two agreed percentages; and
- greater than an agreed percentage.

The limits of any of the shares ranges are the PWDD divided by the total of the prices expressed as a percentage.[179] The contractor's share equals the sum of the products of the increments within each share range and the corresponding '*Contractor's share percentage*'. The contractor's '*share percentage*' is also an identified term and refers to the agreed share percentages inserted opposite the agreed respective share ranges in part one of the Contract Data. Once again with regard to the proforma there are four such percentages that are applicable although the number could be either more or less than this. The share percentages can vary anywhere inclusive of and between zero and 100%.

The intention in this formula is to see that the contractor is given a share in any cost savings in completing the contract or pays a share of any excess of the final cost over the original tender price albeit at the times agreed. The formula states this in effect in the wording of the ECC. It becomes clearer when the material definitions comprising both the 'Prices' and PWDD are also borne in mind. The definition of 'Prices' is peculiar to each of the two main options (C and D) while the PWDD is the same in respect of each one. Adjustment to the prices themselves may occur in other circumstances relevant to the contract, e.g. compensation events; or the parties' agreement, e.g. price adjustment for inflation or '*retention*'. Hence the formula sets out the calculations for giving the contractor a share of either the excess or the shortfall of the final price for work done to date (defined as 'Actual Cost plus the Fee') compared to the tendered target cost.

The contractor will only be paid actual cost plus the fee during the contract for routine assessments. These assessments are made pursuant to the general assessment procedures in clause 50.[180] The assessments referred to in clause 53 thus address only those taking place upon completion and post-completion. The choice of leaving assessments of the contractor's share until completion and post-completion was a policy decision by the drafters based upon the perceived danger of a serious under- or overpayment of any contractor's share paid on an interim assessment interval basis.[181] Two main reasons were given by the drafters:

- as the prices tendered by the contractor are for the main purpose of establishing the total of the prices, it is not intended that they necessarily provide a realistic forecast of cash flow or would be comparable to the PWDD at interim stages; and
- forecasts of the final PWDD and the final total of the prices are expected to be uncertain at early stages of the contract.

---

[179] Clause 53.1 ECC.
[180] See discussion above.
[181] Guidance notes NEC on clause 53.4 ECC, at 55.

Assuming then that any other assessments which are required to have been made have in fact been made and that completion has been achieved, the project manager will then assess the contractor's share upon completion.[182] The reference to an assessment at completion is imposed under both clauses 50.1 and 53.3. The share is included in the amount due following completion and would have to be paid within either three weeks (or 21 days)[183] of the assessment or other period provided in the Contract Data.[184] The assessment will be made using the project manager's own forecasts of the PWDD and the final total of the prices.[185] The project manager will ascertain whether the PWDD is less than the total of the prices;[186] if so, the contractor will be paid a share of the saving.[187] Conversely, the contractor will have to pay a share of the excess.[188] The share will be included in the amount due following completion of the works.[189]

The contractor's share will be assessed a second and final time once the final PWDD and the final total of the prices have been determined. At that time the project manager will assess the contractor's share in a similar manner to the first time only, instead of using forecasts in so doing, the final PWDD and final total of the prices themselves will be used.[190] The project manager will ascertain whether the PWDD is less than the total of the prices,[191] and, once again if so, the contractor will be paid a share of the saving.[192] Conversely, the contractor will have to pay a share of the excess.[193] This time the share is included in the final amount due to or owed by the contractor or the final total of the prices.[194] In practice the final amount due will be included in the amount due four weeks after the supervisor issues the defects certificate. While the prospect of contractor payments to the employer is exceptional it is nevertheless open on the wording and given the reciprocal obligations the parties have assumed toward each other.

The contractor's share provisions also contain an incentive[195] for the contractor to consider and propose changes to the employer's works

---

[182]   Clause 53.3 ECC.
[183]   Clause 56.1 amended 2nd ECC.
[184]   Clause 53.3 ECC.
[185]   Clause 53.3 ECC.
[186]   Clause 53.2 ECC.
[187]   Clause 53.2 ECC.
[188]   Clause 53.2 ECC.
[189]   Clause 53.3 ECC.
[190]   Clause 53.4 ECC.
[191]   Clause 53.2 ECC.
[192]   Clause 53.2 ECC.
[193]   Clause 53.2 ECC.
[194]   Clause 53.4 ECC.
[195]   The Latham Report paragraph 5.18(12), 37 recommended that a modern form of contract should provide 'for incentives for exceptional performance'. See also SINGLETON, D. Winning Performance. *Contract Journal*, 6 April 1995, 33 summarizing the advantages of incentive-based contracts.

information that would reduce actual cost. If the contractor makes such a proposal, and it is accepted by the project manager, and results in the reduction of actual cost, then, notwithstanding the reduction, the prices remain *unchanged*.[196] The incentive thus operates as an exception as it were to the general rule contained in clause 63.2 that reductions in the total actual cost result in corresponding reductions of the prices. The effect of not reducing the prices is to increase the contractor's share. The incentive only applies to proposals from the contractor to change the employer's works information and not the contractor's own works information. The explanation for this distinction is found in clause 60.1 which would have governed and similarly dictates that only a change to the employer's works information is compensable, not a change by the contractor to the contractor's own works information.

There is also a separate provision for payment on termination when a target contract is used. In this case the project manager will assess the contractor's share after termination has been certified. The assessment in this instance will be based on the PWDD at termination and the total of the prices for the works done before termination.[197]

Value management

The contractor's share provisions implicitly introduce *value management* to the NEC. *Value management* is an inclusive term given to a variety of value techniques applied during all stages of a project to audit value and realize the maximum functional value of decisions taken against a value system determined or agreed by the client.[198] Two of the principal techniques employed are *function analysis*[199] and *life-cycle costing.*[200] The contractor is under a general obligation to provide the works or complete the works in accordance with the contract as well as all incidental work, services and actions that the contract requires.[201] However, there are also certain limitations on the contractor's actions such as those with regard to acceptance of the contractor's design by the project manager[202] and the necessity to obey instructions given by the project manager and supervisor.[203] Under the target contracts in the NEC provision is made for the contractor to share in agreed savings or pay a

---

[196] Clause 53.5 ECC.
[197] Clause 97.4 ECC.
[198] See NORTON, BRIAN R. and McELLIGOTT, WILLIAM C. *Value Management in Construction: A Practical Guide*. MacMillan, London, 1995, pp. 3–8; and CONNAUGHTON, JOHN N. and GREEN, STUART D. *Value Management in Construction: A Client's Guide*. CIRIA, London, 1996.
[199] See SNODGRASS, T.J. and KASI, M. *Function Analysis*. University of Wisconsin, Madison, 1986.
[200] See DELL'ISOLLA, A.J. and KIRK, S.J. *Life Cycle Costing for Design Professionals*. McGraw-Hill, New York, 1991; FERRY, D.J.O. and FLANAGAN, R. *Life Cycle Costing: A Radical Approach*. CIRIA, London, 1991, CIRIA Report 122.
[201] See clauses 11.2(4) and 20.1.
[202] Clause 21.2 ECC.
[203] Clause 29 ECC.

share of any excess over stipulated prices.[204] The actual contractor's share percentages and share ranges are agreed and specified in part one of the Contract Data when using either main option C or D. The shares are determined with reference to the PWDD or actual cost plus the fee. The obligation of the contractor to provide the works in accordance with the contract as well as the way in which the works are specified and described in the works information serves as a further limitation on the contractor's actions.[205] The procedures effectively operate to constrain the contractor from failing to provide what has been agreed contractually. However, in recognition of the fact that the contractor is in an excellent position to perceive savings, clause 53.5 on the contractor's share, enables the contractor to investigate and propose changes to the employer's works information which will reduce the defined actual cost. When this procedure is invoked it has the effect of improving the contractor's share position and thus profits. In short, it is a form of value management.

Value management has its forebears in the United States and during the last five decades has evolved to take in successive variations including 'value analysis',[206] 'value engineering',[207] and more recently 'value management'.[208] The latter term is often used today in a blanket sense to include these other value techniques.[209] However, it is more closely associated with evolving United Kingdom and European views[210] in this area rather than the American preference for value engineering. The importance of the subject and the increasing attention being given to it is a reflection of the changes in the British construction industry.[211] In particular, it reflects competitive fee bidding for consultants, diversity in procurement routes, redefinition of roles in industry and moves toward

---

[204] Clause 53.2 ECC.

[205] See clauses 11.2(4), 11.2(5) and 20.1 ECC.

[206] See GAGE, W.L. *Value Analysis.* McGraw-Hill, New York, 1967; FALLON, C. *Value Analysis to Improve Productivity.* Wiley, New York, 1971; MILES, L.D. *Techniques of Value Analysis and Engineering.* McGraw-Hill, New York, 1972; O'BRIEN, J. *Value Analysis in Design and Construction.* McGraw-Hill, New York, 1976; and SPRINT. *The European Market for Value Analysis.* Commission of the European Communities, Luxembourg, 1992.

[207] See ZIMMERMAN, L.W. and HART, G.D. *Value Engineering: A Practical Approach for Owners and Designers and Constructors.* Van Nostrand Reinhold, New York, 1982; DELL'ISOLLA, A.J. and KIRK, S.J. *Value Engineering in the Construction Industry,* 3rd edn. Smith, Hinchman and Grylls, Washington, 1988.

[208] NORTON, BRIAN R. and McELLIGOTT, WILLIAM G. *Value Management in Construction. A Practical Guide.* MacMillan, London, 1995, pp. 4–7.

[209] *Ibid.,* 6.

[210] KELLY, JOHN and MALE, STEVEN. *Value Management in Design and Construction The Economic Management of Projects.* E & FN Spon, London, 1993, p. 4. In the United Kingdom a number of important surveys or reports have been done and include BURT, M.E. *A Survey of Quality and Value in Building.* BRE, London, 1975; NEDO. *Faster Building for Commerce.* HMSO, London, 1987; and GREEN, S.D. and POPPER, P.A. *Value Engineering: The Search for Unnecessary Cost.* CIOB, Ascot, 1990, CIOB Occasional Paper 39.

[211] KELLY, JOHN and MALE, STEVEN, n. 210 above, pp. 4–7.

single-point responsibility and management of the total construction process.[212] This process and these forces of redefinition are also concurrently both shaping and being shaped by the NEC. In summary, while the NEC implicitly admits of value management through the contractor's share provisions, more emphasis should be devoted to the subject. The emphasis would ideally be made in the conditions but alternatively could at least be made within the guidance notes. It is only by drawing the attention of parties to value management that the best use of and fullest implications from the concept will be realized.[213]

Activity schedules

Main options A and C require additional payment provisions because they comprise 'activity schedules'. The provisions in respect of both options are identical. The activity schedule itself is a means of allocating the parties' respective shares and arriving at payment due. Thus the information contained in the activity schedule is not works information or site information.[214] It is a flexible tool that may accommodate a variety of activities whether physical or otherwise; for instance, preliminaries could be accommodated as recurring payments on a monthly or bi-monthly basis. It is also an essential tool in ensuring correspondence between methods and the programme. As such, if a planned method of working is changed at the contractor's discretion, the change may mean that the activity schedule no longer complies with the 'Accepted Programme'. If so, the contractor is obliged to revise the activity schedule and submit[215] it to the project manager for acceptance.[216] The changes to planned methods of working involve only those changes made at the contractor's discretion and, perhaps as the project manager already exercises a degree of control over methods of working, under the procedure for acceptance of the programme. While there is some administrative burden it should be able to be offset by computer software programs and remains an important project management tool. Brian Eggleston has been critical of this aspect and writes: '... the administrative burden is obvious. In some cases the amount of detail is so great that only computers can keep pace with changes to the activity schedule and the programme'.[217] It is submitted that the trend toward greater use of information techology is clear and desirable and that some automation may be warranted and should form no impediment.[218] The

---

212 *Ibid.*, pp. 4–5.
213 Express provision for value engineering is made in clause 14.2 of the FIDIC Orange Book.
214 Clause 54.1 ECC.
215 See clause 13 ECC.
216 See clause 54.2 ECC.
217 EGGLESTON, BRIAN. *The New Engineering Contract, A Commentary.* Blackwell Science, London, 1996, p. 17.
218 See generally CHURCHER, D.W. *et al. IT in Construction – Quantifying the Benefits.* CIRIA, London, 1996, CIRIA Report 160.

number of software programs promoting project management is now quite large and in one recent survey some 25 such programs were listed.[219]

Various reasons may be given by the project manager for not accepting the revised activity schedule including that it does not comply with the accepted programme, changed prices are not reasonably distributed between the activities, or the total of the prices is changed.[220]

Bills of quantities

Main options B and D with '*bills of quantities*' require an additional payment provision to assess the contractor's share. The provision, which is identical in both main options, provides that information in the bill of quantities is not works information or site information.[221] The effect of this provision is simple. It serves clearly to draw a line between the bill of quantities, and its primary purpose as a *quantitative* measuring tool, and the works information as a *qualitative* measuring tool. This contrast may be pointed out by comparing the clause to a provision in JCT 80. Clause 14.1 of JCT 80 states: 'The quality and quantity of the work included in the Contract Sum shall be deemed to be that which is set out in the Contract Bills'. Thus in JCT 80, where bills of quantities versions[222] are used, clause 14.1 indicates that *both* the quality and quantity of the work are determined with reference to the Contract Bills.[223] However, in the ECC main options with bills of quantities – the priced contract and target contracts – it is the works information that is paramount. The bills of quantities cannot modify a contractor's principal obligation to provide the works in accordance with the works information. This is unlike clause 14.1 that effects a modification of the contractor's principal obligation under JCT 80 to complete the works. On monthly payments and measurement under traditional bill arrangements it has been observed:

> [s]ome clients are increasingly doubtful that monthly payments in accordance with certification procedures based on measurement are the best way to ensure satisfactory progress on contracts.[224] The system has no particular advantages for them, and does not reflect payment methods in other sections of business or industry.[225]

---

[219] TIGHE, STEPHEN. Project Management – A Guide to the Systems Available. *Construction Computing*, July/August 1997, 18.

[220] Clause 54.3 ECC, although changes to the prices could occur as a result of compensation events.

[221] Clause 55.1 ECC.

[222] JCT 80 With Quantities.

[223] In the JCT 80 Without Quantities versions similar provision is made only with respect to the Specification and Schedule of Rates contract documents.

[224] Unlike JCT 80 and IFC 84 the JCT MW form makes provision for progress payments where so requested by the contractor for the value of the works properly executed and for the value of goods and materials properly on site.

[225] *Trust and Money*, Interim Report of the Joint Government/Industry Review of Procurement and Contractual Arrangements in the United Kingdom Construction Industry. HMSO, London, 1993, 32.

Secondary option clauses and assessment
The selection of various secondary option clauses may also be relevant to the assessment procedure; namely, those concerning price adjustment for inflation, '*retention*', advanced payment, value added tax and sales tax, multiple currencies, bonus for early completion, and delay damages or low performance damages. The selection of certain secondary option clauses is dependent upon which main option is chosen. Not every secondary option clause is apposite or recommended for all options. Bonus for early completion and delay damages or low performance damages present no peculiar assessment concerns and therefore are discussed elsewhere. These options, as relevant, are examined below.

Price adjustment for inflation
Formulae methods of calculating fluctuations in civil engineering contracts date back to 1973 and work done by NEDO. As a result fluctuations formulae are sometimes still referred to as the NEDO indices or also occasionally by the names of the two chairmen who oversaw their development for NEDO; first J.W. Baxter for engineering, and secondly J.G. Osborne for building, hence the 'Baxter Formula' and the 'Osborne Formula' respectively.[226] It is not surprising that some method of dealing with rises and falls in inputs is utilized in construction given the long duration of construction projects which make them especially susceptible to inflationary trends. As a result traditional forms have increasingly had to address the issues raised, in particular through fluctuations clauses and the use of formulae.[227] The ECC secondary option clause is one recent illustration of attention given to the subject. It is interesting to note that the option clause itself was originally the first listed in the secondary option clauses in the Consultation Document, option G. Although no explanation was given for its removal to a later part of the clauses in the Second Edition it may reflect a slowing of inflationary pressures since the Consultation Document was released and a consequent lessening of attention toward it.

---

[226] Construction Sponsorship Directorate, Department of the Environment. *Price Adjustment Formulae for Construction Contracts Users Guide 1990 Series of Indices*. Department of the Environment, HMSO, London, 1995. Other guidance on the use of formulae is available including the Department of the Environment, HMSO. *Monthly Bulletin of Indices*. HMSO, Department of the Environment, London; HMSO. *Updating Percentages for Measured Term Contracts*. HMSO, London; and HMSO and DOE. *Price and Cost Indices for Public Sector Building Works*. HMSO, Department of the Environment, London. The Beama Contract Price Adjustment Clauses and Formulae are well known in the engineering industry: see PIKE, ANDREW. *I MechE/IEE Conditions of Contract: A Commentary on five I MechE/IEE Model Forms of General Conditions of Contract, and on the Beama Contract Price Adjustment Clauses and Formulae*. Sweet & Maxwell, London, 1984.

[227] Cf and contrast the fluctuation provisions in JCT 81, JCT 87, ICE 6th and the applicable rules for formulae previously separately issued for NSC/C, NAM/SC, DOM/1 and DOM/2.

The method of price adjustment adopted in the ECC was one of three considered originally by the drafters in developing the NEC. Based on NEC risk allocation principles the inflation risk would normally be assigned to the employer as it is outside the control of the contractor. The other two choices considered involved:

- applying a price adjustment to the appropriate part of the total of the prices; and
- adjusting (reducing) the actual cost to the base date and then basing the target share on the difference between the adjusted (reduced) actual cost and the uninflated total of the prices.[228]

The first method required the measurement of work done during the payment period which was additional to the assessment of actual cost but was rejected as the least accurate of the three methods considered.[229] The second method produced a target share in base date terms which was unacceptable to the drafters who would have preferred shares in current money values.[230] The third method, which was ultimately adopted, determines the inflationary component of actual cost during the payment period and adds it to the total of the prices. Application of the method in practice depends upon the main options chosen. The attraction of this method is clearly the accuracy it offers when suitable indices are used.

Definitions

The price adjustment for inflation secondary option clause is the only option, save for the trust fund secondary option clause, that has separate provisions on defined terms. It is a measure of both the complexity and the importance of precise terminology in both options that this is the case. It is also the only secondary option that consists of four separate clauses, clauses N1–N4; as well as separate provisions for different main options, clauses N4.1 and N4.2. Although the marginal note is 'Defined terms', the provisions both define as well as identify terms and this usage is consistent with that under clause 11. Definitions are given for three terms: the 'Base Date Index', the 'Latest Index', and the 'Price Adjustment Factor'.[231]

The definitions of 'Base Date Index' and 'Latest Index' serve only to indicate which index or indices are being chosen for comparative assessment purposes. In general, cost indices are used not only in construction but in the general economy as well and are critical in planning and managing building projects. They are routinely used to forecast building dates within expected completion time frames. They are important both to the contractor and the employer with regard to any adjustment to the contract. For instance, adjustments may pertain to contract costs, changing economic conditions, forecasting future costs and

---

[228] Guidance notes Consultation Document G4, 47.
[229] Guidance notes Consultation Document G4, 47.
[230] Guidance notes Consultation Document G4, 47.
[231] As defined terms they are capitalized in the form.

updating past costs. The 'Base Date Index' – abbreviated to B – is the latest available index before the *'base date'*.[232] The *'base date'* is an identified term as it is italicized in the form and in the Contract Data.[233] The 'Latest Index' – abbreviated to L – is the latest available index before the date of assessment of an amount due.[234] It can be seen that the base date index and latest index are thus one and the same appropriately updated. Their relationship is an important variable in determining 'Price Adjustment Factor' for inflation for the work in question. The 'Price Adjustment Factor' itself is defined as the total of the products of each of the proportions stated in the Contract Data multiplied by (L–B)/B for the index linked to it.[235] The proportions referred to are those chosen to calculate or reflect what percentage is being attributed to each of the various indices, for instance, 20% to a labour cost index, 35% to a retail price index etc. The proportions must add to 100%.[236] A contractor may be expected to seek to weight the proportions so that they correspond to the proportions in the tender and contract itself for the total value of the works. There is also a non-adjustable portion that must be taken into account in arriving at the total and which represents the contractor's risk for inflation.[237] The drafters recommend that the non-adjustable portion not exceed 10%.[238]

Price adjustment factors

The premise behind option N is that the assessment of the amount due includes adjusting prices for inflation. To achieve this, certain 'Price Adjustment Factors' must be calculated for relevant assessment dates.[239] The indices, respective portions for the indices and the base date are set out in part one of the Contract Data.[240] The 'Price Adjustment Factor' itself is a defined term; namely the total of the products of each of the proportions stated in the Contract Data multiplied by (L–B)/B for the index linked to it.[241] When the completion date for the whole of the works occurs the 'Price Adjustment Factor' calculated at that time is used for calculating price adjustments after that time.[242] Hence inflation would become a contractor's risk after the completion date. Parties must also consider the effect of including the sectional completion secondary option clause in their agreement. In this case under clause N2.2 of the ECC the

---

[232] Clause N1.1(a) ECC.
[233] See the optional statements in part one of the Contract Data. The base date will normally be a short time before the submission of tenders.
[234] Clause N1.1(b) ECC.
[235] Clause N1.1(c) ECC.
[236] The Schedule of Contract Data has the proportions adding instead to one.
[237] Guidance notes NEC on clause N1.1 ECC, 85. See also the comment on the effect of the non-adjustable portion on payments for compensation events.
[238] Guidance notes NEC on clause N1.1 ECC, 85.
[239] See generally clause 50.1 ECC.
[240] See also the relevant definitions in clause N1.1 ECC.
[241] Clause N1.1(c) ECC.
[242] Clause N2.2 ECC.

contractor will still receive a price adjustment for inflation on payments for late completion of sections of the work if the last completion date has not passed.[243] The adjustments may come in respect to changes to the relevant indices, e.g. changes between their base date index and latest (base date) index or the assessment of compensation events. If an index is changed after it has been used in calculating a price adjustment factor, the calculation is then repeated and a correction will be included in the next assessment of the amount due.[244] The actual determinations of the amounts due will depend upon the main option chosen.[245]

Compensation events

The assessment of compensation events is dealt with exceptionally in the ECC. Clause N3.1 changes the definition of 'Actual Cost'[246] in the relevant four main options for the purpose of assessing compensation events. Assuming that actual costs have in fact increased the changes in the definition of actual cost serve to reduce it as follows to:

- Actual costs current at the time of assessing the compensation events adjusted to *base date* by dividing by one plus the Price Adjustment Factor for the last assessment of the amount due and
- Actual Costs at *base date* levels for amounts calculated from rates stated in the Contract Data for employees and Equipment.[247]

The rationale for this change in the definition of actual costs is to permit the adjustments of the amounts due for inflation to be made under clauses N4.1 or N4.2 according to the relevant main options rather than clause 63. In general, the assessment of compensation events will involve both actual costs and forecast actual costs. As such, under the prevailing definitions of actual cost both base date values and current (e.g. effectively latest index) values are used in assessment. Therefore, clause N3.1 reduces all current actual costs to base date values so that changes to the prices for compensation events are made in base date terms and thus can be adjusted for the effects of inflation under clauses N4.1 and N4.2.

The price adjustment

The price adjustment for inflation is used only with main options A, B, C and D. The intention behind the price adjustment option is to allocate the risk of inflation in the contract to the employer. When the option is not adopted the risk of inflation in the cost of inputs remains with the contractor. This risk for the contractor is not present in main options E and F as the risk of cost increases is already borne by the employer as

---

[243] See discussion guidance notes on clause N2.2 ECC, 42.
[244] For example, perhaps where an index was provisional only and later changed.
[245] See discussion of price adjustment below.
[246] See clauses 11.2(28) and 11.2(29) ECC.
[247] Clause N3.1 ECC. 'Equipment' is defined in clause 11.2(11) ECC.

payments are made to the contractor in respect of actual costs incurred. These actual costs will reflect current inflation costs.

Main options A and B

The calculation of the price adjustment in main options A and B is simpler than for main options C and D. This is because it reflects the regular payment of the amount due and not the target share under options C and D. Under main options A and B each amount due will also include an amount for price adjustment. This amount is the sum of three figures:

- the change for the PWDD since the last assessment of the amount due multiplied by the Price Adjustment Factor for the date of the current assessment;
- the amount for price adjustment included in the previous amount due; and
- correcting amounts, not included elsewhere, which arise from changes to indices used for assessing previous amounts for price adjustment.[248]

The amount due is the total of these three figures and becomes the price adjustment up to each assessment date.[249]

Main options C and D

The calculation of the price adjustment under main options C and D differs from that for main options A and B. It can also be seen to be more complex. The additional complexity stems from the use of a formula in the calculation and the need to adjust the price with reference to the contractor's share rather than the actual payment due to the contractor. This follows from the definition of the PWDD in clause 11.2(23); that is, the actual cost which the contractor has paid plus the fee.[250] Hence, as actual costs are current costs (e.g. effectively latest index values) any inflation since the base date is already included. In contrast, the project manager assesses, and the contractor's share is calculated, under clause 53.1 with reference to the difference between the total of the prices and the PWDD. As the prices have not been inflation adjusted at this point clause N4.2 permits a comparison between them.

Under main options C and D each time an amount due is assessed, an amount for price adjustment is added to the total of the prices.[251] This price adjustment is the sum of two figures:

- the change in the PWDD since the last assessment of the amount due multiplied by $(1-1/(1 + PAF))$ where PAF is the Price Adjustment Factor for the current assessment; and

---

[248] Clause N4.1 ECC.

[249] See clause 51.1 ECC.

[250] Cf the definitions of PWDD in clause 11.2(24) and 11.2(25) in main options A and B respectively.

[251] The prices will determined as follows: with reference to the activities in the activity schedule in main option C, see clause 11.2(2) ECC; and with reference to the bill of quantities in main option D, see clause 11.2(21) ECC.

- correcting amounts, not included elsewhere, which arise from changes to indices used for assessing previous amounts for price adjustment.[252]

The amount due is the total of these two figures and becomes the price adjustment. Thus the price adjustment is added to the total of the prices.

Retention

Retention provisions in standard and other forms of construction contracts are common.[253] The '*retention*' provision in the ECC is included as a secondary option clause for use with all main options save F – the management contract – and sets out when the employer begins holding retention money and the time when the contractor becomes entitled to the release of the retention money. It is not unusual to have no retention on a management contractor's fee; for instance, under clause 4.8.1 of the JCT 87 there is similarly no retention on the management contractor's fee. However, under this form, while 3% of the management contractor's total fee is withheld for 28 days following payment of the final certificate it is not held in trust. In any case the employer may have the benefit of retention provisions in subcontracts. The retention procedures in the ECC are novel. The novelty in part stems from the attempt by the drafters to balance the withholding of sums for the purposes noted against maintaining the largest possible cash flow for the contractor.[254] To seek to achieve a proper balance a '*retention free amount*' has been introduced to the procedures. While a retention free amount will increase the contractor's cash flow, it is open to the employer to set the amount at nil and thus revert to a more conventional mode of retention.[255] A maximum amount of retention may then be inserted. Other contracts have sought to achieve similar objectives using different tools. Thus JCT NAM/SC[256] provides for a cash discount of 2.5% while DOM/1[257] provides for a 2.5% cash discount and retention.[258]

The '*retention free amount*' is an identified term for purposes of the Contract Data and will be inserted as a set figure. Once the retention free amount has been reached in terms of the PWDD, retention begins and an amount is retained in each amount assessed as due.[259] The '*retention percentage*' is an identified term and stated in the Contract Data as a given percentage. Retention becomes operative once the PWDD has reached the retention free amount. The amount retained is the retention

---

[252] Clause N4.2 ECC.

[253] See e.g. FIDIC 4th clauses 60.2, 60.3. See generally NHENKORAH, K. Rethinking the Retentions Rule, arguing in favour of retention bonds *Chartered Quantity Surveyor*, November 1993, 8–9.

[254] Cf clause 14.3 FIDIC 4th, which requires quarterly cash flow estimates to be provided by the contractor to the engineer.

[255] See Guidance Notes on clause P.1 ECC, 87.

[256] Clause 19.8.2 JCT NAM/SC.

[257] Clause 21 DOM/1.

[258] See *Team Services plc* v. *Kier Management and Design Ltd* (1993) 63 BLR 76, CA.

[259] Clause P1.1 ECC.

percentage applied to the excess of the PWDD above the retention free amount.[260] The retention free amount is also an identified term and given in the optional statements in part one of the Contract Data along with the retention free percentage. It is an amount that is withheld or retained from payments to the contractor. The retention amount continues to accrue in this way with each payment until the earlier of either of two events occurs; that is until 'Completion of the whole of the *works*' and the date on which the employer takes over the whole of the works.[261] Once either of these events occurs then the amount retained is halved; that is, released, either in the assessment made at 'Completion of the whole of the *works*' or in the next assessment after the employer has taken over the whole of the works. In the latter case that is only if this is before 'Completion of the whole of the *works*'.[262] Conversely, if neither completion nor take over has occurred, the retention amount continues to be withheld in each amount assessed due.[263] The same retention percentage applies as does the method of calculation for retention amount. The status quo is maintained until the 'Defects Certificate' is issued. Once the defects certificate is issued no amount is retained in the assessments made.[264] If the defects certificate has not been issued the amount retained remains at this amount until it is issued. An assessment interval occurs under clause 50.1 four weeks after the supervisor issues the defects certificate and it would be appropriate for the remaining half of the retention amount then to be released.

Unlike other retention clause provisions in the standard forms, the ECC does not state that the employer's interest in the retention money is as trustee. The significance of impressing the retention money with a trust can be seen in *P C Harrington Contractors Ltd* v. *Co Partnership Developments Ltd* under JCT 87 which held that sums the employer held in trust for the works contractors could not be set-off against.[265] This fact serves to distinguish the authorities that have granted injunctions to contractors to compel the payment of retention money into separate accounts, for instance, in the face of employer insolvency.[266] The grant of injunctions in retention situations though has been sporadic and in many instances they have been defeated[267] although not in all instances.[268]

---

[260] Clause P1.1 ECC.
[261] Clause P1.1 ECC.
[262] Clause P1.2 ECC.
[263] Clause P1.1 ECC.
[264] Clause P1.2 ECC.
[265] *P C Harrington Contractors Ltd* v. *Co Partnership Developments Ltd* (1998) 88 BLR 44 (CA).
[266] *Rayack Construction Ltd* v. *Lampeter Meat Co Ltd* (1979) 12 BLR 30; *Wates Construction (London) Ltd* v. *Franthom Property Ltd* (1991) 53 BLR 23, CA.
[267] See *Henry Boot Building Ltd* v. *Croydon Hotel & Leisure Co Ltd* (1985) 36 BLR 41, CA; *GPT Realisations Ltd* v. *Panatown Ltd* (1992) 61 BLR 88.
[268] *Concorde Construction Co Ltd* v. *Colgan Co Ltd* (1984) 29 BLR 120 (HC of HK); *J F Finnegan Ltd* v. *Ford Sellar Morris Developments Ltd* (1991) 53 BLR 38.

Retention provisions empower the employer to retain an agreed percentage of each payment due to the contractor as security for performance of the works and as some protection against insolvency of the employer. Insolvency is an important variable in the construction industry and there are many factors that are relevant to determining whether insolvency has occurred or is likely to occur.[269] However, of late a separate set of factors has come in for increased attention as a means of reinforcing the traditional indicators. The area chosen is managerial ability and thus it has been hypothesized and proven in research results that financial difficulties routinely relate to inadequate management ability and errors.[270] One conclusion that may be drawn from such research is to underscore the importance of sound management-based decision making in construction firms if the risk of financial difficulties is to be reduced.

The retention provisions in the ECC should now be read subject to the provisions of the HGCRA and secondary option Y (UK) 2. Pursuant to section 110(2) of the HGCRA the employer is under an obligation to give notice not later than five days after the date on which a payment becomes due from the employer to the contractor specifying the amount, if any, of a payment made or proposed to be made and the basis on which that amount is calculated. While the obligation is imposed upon the employer in the legislation it is fulfilled by the project manager under the ECC. Then, pursuant to section 111(1), a potential second notice provision is invoked as follows:

> A party to a construction contract may not withhold payment after the final date for payment of a sum due under the contract unless he has given an effective notice of intention to withhold payment.

Reading the provisions of sections 110(2) and 111(1) together, the withholding of retention money cannot be done unless an effective notice of the employer's intention to do so has been given. These provisions have been addressed in clause 56.2 of the amended Second Edition of the ECC which provides in part:

> If the *Employer* intends to withhold payment after the final date for payment of a sum due under this contract, he notifies the *Contractor* not later than seven days (the prescribed period) before the final date for payment by specifying ...

The seven-day time frame is reasonable and is also the same default time period under section 111(4)(a) of the HGCRA. The intention of the time frame would be to encourage negotiation to resolve contentious withholdings. Although the wording of sections 110(2) and 111(1) would suggest two notices in this regard, the remainder of section 111(1)

---

[269] See discussion of clause 95 ECC in Appendix 1 Division 9 below.

[270] ABIDALL, A.F. and HARRIS, F. A Methodology for Predicting Company Failure in the Construction Industry. *Construction Management and Economics*, 1995, **13**(3), 189–196.

includes a savings provision. Thus, 'the notice mentioned in section 110(2) may suffice as a notice of intention to withhold payment if it complies with the requirements of this section'. Section 111(2)(a), and (b) then finishes by setting out the specific requirements for the notice to be effective. The subparagraphs are adopted verbatim in clause 56.2:

- amount proposed to be withheld and the ground for withholding payment or
- if there is more than one ground, each ground and the amount attributable to it.

Thus, to ensure that there is compliance with the provisions the project manager's certificate should make reference to the agreed retention sum as at least one of the grounds for the withholding and in this respect all of the provisions will be satisfied.

Set-off and abatement

The retention provisions raise the issue of set-off and abatement. At common law the leading test regarding the right of an employer to set-off amounts otherwise due the contractor is stated in *Gilbert-Ash (Northern) Ltd* v. *Modern Engineering (Bristol) Ltd* and which right would arise if the employer could show that entitlement to leave to defend on an application for summary judgment of an amount certified due under the contract and brought by the contractor.[271] Clause 50.2 provides in part: 'The amount due is the Price for Work Done to Date plus other amounts to be paid to the *Contractor* less amounts to be paid by or retained from the *Contractor*'. The question this wording raises is whether it gives the employer express rights of abatement and set-off; both equitable and common law. One begins with the presumption that parties to a contract do not intend to abandon their remedies that arise by operation of law. Both set-off and abatement arise in this manner. Thus to rebut the presumption very clear words must be used.[272] In the absence of such express provision one may presume that the employer continues to enjoy these rights. By way of contrast contractors' rights at common law are expressly preserved. The rights are of course now subject to the provisions in the HGCRA.

---

[271] *Gilbert-Ash (Northern) Ltd* v. *Modern Engineering (Bristol) Ltd* [1974] AC 689, [1973] 3 All ER 195, HL. See generally for a discussion of the topic McINNIS, J.A. *Hong Kong Construction Law*, Div VI paragraphs 226–677.3; and DERHAM, R. *Set-off*, 2nd edn. Oxford University Press, Oxford, 1996; TAN, EUGENE Y.C. The Common Law Right to Set-off in Construction Contracts. *Malayan Law Journal*, 1995, **3**, cxxv; JONES, N.F. Set-off in the Construction Industry. *Construction Law Journal*, 1991, **7**, 84; and lately *BOC Group plc* v. *Centeon LLC* (1999) 63 Con LR 104 (CA).

[272] *Gilbert-Ash (Northern) Ltd* v. *Modern Engineering (Bristol) Ltd* [1974] AC 689 at 717, [1973] 3 All ER 195 at 215, HL, per Lord Diplock; *C M Pillings & Co Ltd* v. *Kent Investments Ltd* (1985) 30 BLR 80 at 92, CA; *Sonat Offshore SA* v. *Amerada Hess Development Ltd* (1987) 39 BLR 1 at 22, CA; *NEI Thompson Ltd* v. *Wimpey Construction UK Ltd* (1987) 39 BLR 65, CA; and see *Mottram Consultants Ltd* v. *Bernard Sunley & Sons Ltd* (1974) 2 BLR 28, HL, and *Barrett Steel Building Ltd* v. *Amec Construction Ltd* (1997) 15-CLD-10-07.

The ECC wording makes no express reference to set-off and invokes rather the notion of retention. By comparison FIDIC 4th, although not referring to 'set-off' expressly, does give the engineer a right to deduct 'any sums which may have become due and payable' by the contractor to the employer (clause 60.2) and thus confers comparable rights upon the engineer. The effect of the ECC wording is to return the employer at this stage to the common law. It will be a matter of argument whether this drafting was directed specifically to retention funds alone. However, as retention is a secondary option only which may not be agreed to by the parties there is no reason to refer to it in the core clauses. Hence there is an argument that can be made in favour of a broad interpretation of 'retaining' being capable of encompassing set-off and abatement. A broad interpretation would then entitle the set-off of any mutual demands which are capable of being liquidated or ascertained at the time of pleading, or common law set-off.[273] It would also entail equitable set-off which may act as a defence to any claim by the contractor for payment. An equitable set-off may be raised when a cross-claim is so closely connected with the claim opposite that it would be manifestly unjust not to take it into account.[274] The equitable set-offs may be sound in either tort or contract. They will usually be restricted to claims arising from the same and not separate contracts;[275] although this restriction and the necessity for a close connection are not relevant to common law set-off.[276] The significance of these defences is especially relevant in the context of applications for summary judgment or interim payment that may be defeated if the defences are successfully raised.[277] The fact of certification itself may be irrelevant to the success of the contractor's claim.[278]

In addition to the matters discussed above[279] the HGCRA expressly rules out 'set off or abatement ... by reference to any sum claimed to be due under one or more other contracts'.[280] However, there is an argument to be made that because this express ruling out of set-off occurs only

---

[273] *Morley* v. *Inglis* (1837) 4 Bing 58 at 71 per Tindal CJ; *Stooke* v. *Taylor* (1880) 5 QBD 569; *Henriksens Rederi A/S* v. *P H Z Rolimpex* [1974] QB 233 at 246, [1973] 3 All ER 589 at 593, CA, per Denning LJ; *Axel Johnson Petroleum AB* v. *MG Mineral Group AG* [1992] 2 All ER 163, [1992] 1 WLR 270; *B Hargreaves Ltd* v. *Action 2000 Ltd* (1992) 62 BLR 72, CA.

[274] *Hanak* v. *Green* [1958] 2 QB 9 at 24, [1958] 2 All ER 141 at 150, CA, per Morris LJ.

[275] *Anglian Building Products Ltd* v. *W & C French (Construction) Ltd* (1972) 16 BLR 1, CA; *B Hargreaves Ltd* v. *Action 2000 Ltd* (1992) 62 BLR 72, CA.

[276] See *Morley* v. *Inglis* (1837) 4 Bing 58 at 71 per Tindal CJ and *Stooke* v. *Taylor* (1880) 5 QBD 569.

[277] *Acsim (Southern) Ltd* v. *Danish Contracting and Development Co Ltd* (1989) 47 BLR 55, CA; *A Cameron Ltd* v. *John Mowlem & Co plc* (1990) 52 BLR 24, CA; *Slater* v. *C A Duquemin Ltd* [1992] CILL 761; *Smallman Construction Ltd* v. *Redpath Dorman Long Ltd* (1988) 47 BLR 15, CA.

[278] *C M Pillings & Co Ltd* v. *Kent Investments Ltd* (1985) 30 BLR 80, CA; *R M Douglas Construction Ltd* v. *Bass Leisure Ltd* (1990) 53 BLR 119.

[279] See discussion of retention above.

[280] Section 110(2)(b) HGCRA.

under section 110(2)(a) and not under section 111 as well that set-off may still be argued. Raymond Joyce writes as follows:

> The inability to deduct sums from the section 111(2) notice by reference to one or more other contracts is not repeated for the purposes of the section 111 notice. Therefore, provided that a contract permits the withholding of payment, in part or otherwise, by reference to another contract, or contracts, this may be another ground to withhold payment. Even if there are no cross-contractual rights to withhold payment, the section does not exclude the possibility of an equitable set-off where the circumstances are sufficiently connected, that to oust the right to withhold payment under the contract would be inequitable.[281]

Joyce's position remains only one interpretation of the sections and contrary views could also be put forward. For example, one could emphasize instead how section 111(1) of the HGCRA can be read together with section 110(2) to satisfy the former section's notice requirement. Thus, one may argue that a court should be inclined to read sections 110(2)(a) and 111(1) together as well for the purpose of excluding an equitable set-off claimed to be due under one or more other contracts. Both interpretations are open to a court and it will be interesting to see how the contractual, common law and statutory interfaces are dealt with on this issue.

Advanced payment to the contractor

The parties may agree that the employer will make an advanced payment to the contractor.[282] The reasons for this vary widely from the financial situation of the contractor to the level of investment required in anticipation of commencing the contract. To accommodate these or other reasons[283] an advanced payment to the contractor may be arranged. The amount of the advanced payment, the repayment amounts and the time frame for repayment will normally be stated in the Contract Data.[284] The proforma Contract Data provisions indicate that the contractor will repay the instalments in assessments starting not less than a given number of weeks after the 'Contract Date'.[285] Although the term 'assessments' is used in the Contract Data it differs from the use of the term in clause 50

---

[281] JOYCE, RAYMOND, see n. 31 above.

[282] Similar provision is made in other forms, e.g. clause 60 part II FIDIC 4th.

[283] BALLARD, D.E. put forward some convincing reasons in favour of advanced payment guarantees in exchange for the right to early payment for goods and materials in Payment for Materials or Goods Not Yet Incorporated in the Works. A paper delivered to the Society of Construction Law in London on 8 December 1992.

[284] Clause J1.1 ECC. The same are inserted in the optional statements portion of part one of the Contract Data. Cf the use of the term 'advances' in clause 40 of GC/Works/1 3rd with reference to payments made to the contractor during the course of the works at periods not less than monthly.

[285] See part one of the Contract Data.

which implies some uncertainty in arriving at the amount due. Assessments in contrast and as understood in relation to advanced payments are certain and given either as an agreed amount or a percentage of the payment otherwise due; as seen in the proforma for option J in part one of the Contract Data. The instalments are given as either a stated amount or a percentage of the payment otherwise due.[286] In normal circumstances the advances would be repaid earlier rather than later into the contract period and in most cases well before completion.

The advanced payment may be made at either of two points in time. It can be made either within four weeks of the 'Contract Date' or, if the employer requires security for making the advanced payment,[287] within four weeks of the later of the 'Contract Date' and the date when the employer receives the advanced payment bond.[288] The giving or not of an advanced payment bond is referred to in the optional statements of part one of the Contract Data. An advanced payment bond must be issued either by an approved bank or insurer. The employer's right of approval is exercised through the project manager's right to accept the bank or insurer for the purposes of issuing the bond.[289] The project manager on one exemplar ground may not accept the proposed bank or insurer. That is, its commercial position is not strong enough to carry the bond.[290] This determination should be objective and it is suggested that standard criteria may be utilized to assess the institution's commercial position. Criteria could include capital adequacy, asset quality, management quality, earnings and liquidity. However, even with resort to standard indices the non-acceptance by the project manager carries certain risks. Thus, for example, assuming non-acceptance is a decision, a change of view by the project manager would be a compensation event under clause 60.1(8). The value of any bond required will correspond to that of the advanced payment. The form of the bond if required will be set out in the works information.[291] The failure to provide a bond within four weeks of the time agreed for its provision is a ground for termination.[292] On the other hand, any delay in making an agreed advanced payment is a compensation event.[293] In this regard the early warning procedure in clause 16 would be applicable. The reason for treating the failure of the employer timeously to deliver an agreed advanced payment as a compensation event is that the financial consequences for the contractor may be significant. Thus the potential consequences of this failure requires the additional scope that

[286] See part one of the Contract Data.
[287] Such as when an advanced payment bond is required by the employer.
[288] Clause J1.2 ECC. See generally NEWMAN, PAUL. *Bonds, Guarantees and Performance Security in the Construction Industry.* Jordan, Bristol, 1998.
[289] Clause J1.2 ECC. The submission for acceptance follows the communications procedures in clause 13 ECC.
[290] Clause J1.2 ECC.
[291] Clause J1.2 ECC.
[292] Clause 95.2 ECC.
[293] Clause J1.2 ECC.

the compensation event procedure offers and enables fuller redress.[294] If the compensation event procedure were not appropriate then interest alone would have been put forward as the remedy.

The repayment of an advanced payment by the contractor to the employer is done by instalments in accordance with the Contract Data. The procedure dictates that the certified amount assessed as due to the contractor will be less the amount of the repayment instalment. The assessment intervals are those originally set out in the Contract Data, normally as a minimum number of weeks, and until such time as the full amount of the advanced payment has been repaid.[295] As noted above it is anticipated in the ordinary course that repayment will be effected earlier rather than later in the construction period although the objective in setting the repayment instalments should be to achieve total repayment measuredly rather than hastily.

The advanced payment procedure carries a risk of duplication with it and thus instructions to tenderers should clearly indicate that any activity schedule or bill of quantities should not be priced to achieve an advanced payment as well.[296]

Multiple currencies

The NEC is an international form[297] and recognition of this is seen in the secondary option clause on multiple currencies.[298] The secondary option clause K is used only with main options A and B. With main options C and D clause 50.6 pertains while with main options E and F clause 50.7 pertains. Hence the parties are only given a choice on this issue under main options A and B as the other main options are addressed in the core clauses. The provisions of secondary option K seek to address exchange rate risk when payments may be made in more than one currency by placing them squarely on the employer.

In general the employer will choose the base currency for the contract and insert this choice in section 5 of part one of the Contract Data. It may be noted that the choice of base currency itself, unlike secondary option K alone, clearly applies to all main options. Procedurally, by the agreement on what currency should be selected for the contract, and then by fixing

---

[294] See guidance notes on clause J1.2 ECC, 83.

[295] Clause J1.3 ECC.

[296] Guidance notes on clause J1.1ECC, 82.

[297] Other forms of contract in use outside of the United Kingdom are reviewed in SMITH, N.J. and WEARNE, S.H. *Construction Contract Arrangements in EU Countries: A Review of the Contract Arrangements for the Construction of Buildings, Infrastructure and Industrial Projects in France, Germany, Greece, Italy, the Netherlands, Spain and the United Kingdom.* European Construction Institute, Loughborough University of Technology, Loughborough, Leicestershire, United Kingdom, 1993. See also BURR, ANDREW. *European Construction Contracts.* Wiley Chancery, London, 1994. An early work on many of the special problems involved in international projects are discussed in STALLWORTHY, E.A. and KHARBANDA, O.P. *International Construction and the Role of Project Management.* Gower, Aldershot, 1985.

[298] Secondary option clause K.

the '*exchange rates*' in advance for all other employer payments to the contractor when made in other currencies, both the currency risk and the exchange rate risk are removed for the contractor from the submission of the contractor's tender or the formation of the contract. Both '*currency of this contract*' and '*exchange rates*' are identified terms for purposes of the Contract Data. The intention is that the contractor will then be protected in effect from the submission of the tender or the contract date when the contract comes into existence.

Main options C or D pertain to when the contractor makes payments falling within the meaning of actual cost in a foreign currency. A foreign currency is one other than the currency of the contract. They are included in the amount due as payments to be made to the contractor in the same currency.[299] However, in this case such payments may be converted to the '*currency of this* [the] *contract*' so as to calculate the fee and any contractor's share, which are paid in the currency of the contract, using agreed '*exchange rates*'.[300] In the case of main options E or F a near identical provision to that for main options C or D applies save there is no reference to the '*Contractor's* share' as that term is understood in the contract. This should also be read with references to the '*Contractor's share percentages*' and '*share ranges*', both of which are identified terms and appear in the optional statements of part one of the Contract Data with reference to main options C and D. The '*exchange rates*' are referred to as an identified term and optional statement in part one of the Contract Data. The project manager will give the contractor details of how the amount due has been assessed under each one of the main options.[301] Payment follows the assessment.

The multiple currencies provision seeks to reconcile the fact that actual cost to be as precise as possible should be the actual cost in the foreign currency with the reality that employers are neither in the business of speculating on foreign currencies nor acting as foreign exchanges brokers.

Clause K1.1 provides that the Contract Data may list work that is to be paid in currencies other than the agreed currency for the contract. When an amount assessed as due includes some of this work the multiple currencies clause becomes operative. The contractor will then be paid in those currencies and which are other than the currency of the contract for the listed work. The parties' agreed '*exchange rates*' are used to convert from the currency of the contract to the other currencies.

The parties may agree in the Contract Data to stated maximum amounts which the other currency payments are not to exceed.[302] Whenever any excess pertains it will be paid in the currency of the contract.[303] With the benefit of the knowledge of the agreed exchange rates the contractor may even choose to make payments in currencies

---

[299] Clause 50.6 ECC.
[300] Clause 50.6 ECC.
[301] Clause 50.4 ECC.
[302] Clause K1.2 ECC.
[303] Clause K1.2 ECC.

other than the currency for the contract; the risk of loss but also gain on the transaction is then assumed. The ECC procedure mirrors that employed in World Bank funded development projects.[304] It is a flexible procedure and one that admits of modification by the parties themselves. Thus in the optional statements in part one of the Contract Data it may be stipulated that the employer will pay for certain items[305] or activities[306] in designated currencies up to any set maximum amounts. By so doing it is once again the employer who assumes the exchange rate risk. The contractor in turn can then decide whether to reverse this allocation of risk by paying in a currency other than that designated. In summary the multiple currencies provision operates creatively and openly.

---

[304] Guidance notes on clause K1 ECC, 83.
[305] For example, equipment, plant and materials.
[306] For example, those with reference to activity schedules.

11. Compensation events

NEC has … simplified the management of risk. Risk allocation is
explicit. The full list of compensation events is set out clearly, and
the facility exists to append further options. Each risk now takes
both cost and time effects into consideration and, most importantly,
cost and time are valued and adjusted collectively instead of being
treated in isolation.

Paul H. McGowan *et al.*,
Allocation and Evaluation of Risk in Construction Contracts

General

The ECC introduces the concept of 'compensation events'. The concept is
new and central to the operation of the contract in that it is one of the three
pillars on which unexpected risk allocations are made. The other two
pillars are risk allocation by insurance, and risk allocation by termination.
While the term 'unexpected' is used here it is not with reference to any
class of compensation events occurring rather only the likelihood of an
individual compensation event itself taking place in the facts of a given
case. The drafters recognized this implicitly with the statement, for
example, with regard to the first compensation event that '[t]here may be
many reasons for changing the Works Information'.[1]

Compensation events are risks or events stated in the contract, whether
in the core or secondary option clauses, which entitle the contractor to
compensation for both time and cost effects when the employer carries the
risk. It may be noted that certain compensation events provide only time to
the contractor and could be thought of as neutral events. The converse of
this is also relevant and as such events which have neither time nor cost
effects would seem impliedly to be excluded from this definition. There are
other limitations that arise to circumscribe the contractual right to
compensation. Therefore, excluded from the meaning of compensation
events are also those events or risks that arise from a fault of the contractor,
which have not happened nor are expected to happen, and which have no
effect on actual cost or completion as defined. By choosing to compensate
the contractor for both the time and cost effects of compensation events as a
matter of policy the ECC makes a significant departure from traditional

---

[1] Guidance notes NEC on clause 60.1 ECC, at 57.

forms which have seen this relationship (time and cost) as dichotomous. The decision to compensate the contractor for both these time and cost effects significantly challenges some conventional practices; however, while this choice is exceptional it is not wholly without precedent under standard forms in other jurisdictions.[2] The choice was premised upon acceptance of the principle that compensation events as defined entail both time and costs. While acceptance of this premise has been very slow in coming to standard forms of contract perhaps not surprisingly it has been taken to be an axiom of project management for some time. 'A project plan is a model of a project created before the project is launched ... a simple but universal model for all projects. It illustrates that specific project activities ... will take time and cost money ... [and that] plan progress and plan cost [always] vary with time'.[3] Thus, *time*, *cost* and *progress* are referred to in project management literature as 'linked parameters'. Viewing the choice from a risk allocation perspective it is assumed that, the contractor, should be indifferent to the risk and that, on occurrence, employers should be expected to pay for it in full. As acceptance and understanding of the premise grows it may not be too long before it becomes the norm under all forms.

> Change in the delivered scope, or in the manner or sequence in which it is carried out, must to some degree be inevitable ... The cumulative effect of such instructed changes can undermine the whole economy of a project. A weakness of the traditional JCT and ICE forms (beginning to be corrected under the influence of more modern forms such as eg NEC) is that these contracts provide for changes to be implemented before their impacts in time and/or cost have been resolved. Ex post facto claims, arguments, justifications, and eventual disputes over what is an appropriate adjustment to the contract programme and contract price are hardly surprising results. These form, perhaps more than anything else, the stuff of arbitrated construction disputes.[4]

The decision made with respect to time and cost is not the only innovation that is introduced in the sixth core clause. The second policy issue the sixth core clause raises concerns how any entitlement to extra time and money would be calculated and whether the pre-pricing of compensation events should be adopted. Edward Corbett sees as

---

[2] Thus the practice is also a feature of standard forms in Canada and the United States for example. Clause 6.2.1 CCDC 2-1994: 'When a change in the Work is proposed or required ... the Consultant shall present ... a method of adjustment or an amount of adjustment for the Contract Price, if any, and the adjustment of the Contract Time, if any ...'. Clause 7.2.1of AIA A 201 is much the same.

[3] LANIGAN, MIKE. *Engineers in Business. The Principles of Management and Product Design*. Addison-Wesley, Wokingham, 1994, p. 198.

[4] CAPPER, PROFESSOR PHILLIP. Why are There So Many Disputes for Arbitration in Construction? *The Building of Construction Law*. A paper presented at the Tenth Annual Construction Conference on 19 September 1997, by the Society of Construction Law and the Centre of Construction Law and Management, pp. 10–11.

significant that there are no neutral events in terms of risk allocation which would allow the contractor only time but no money, thus leaving losses where they fall.[5] This contrasts with the NEC which does admit of neutral events. Once again it may be noted that, while this choice on the part of the drafters is exceptional it too has precursors in other forms.[6] The policy the drafters adopted was that assessment of a risk event would be based on the forecasted effect on the contractor's actual costs (as defined) and programme (as accepted).[7] It would follow a bidding or quotation procedure – in effect a means of negotiated agreement or solution of the problem. Although the bidding or quotation can be described as single stage or uncompetitive the view of the drafters was that this was a second order effect that was more than offset by the primary benefits which follow from the policy.[8] The process can give the employer greater control than the role traditionally had. Paul H. McGowan writes:

> [u]nder the terms of NEC and GC/Works/1, quotations are provided on the basis of revised price and programme. The requirement for and use of detailed programmes will assist both the contractor in the preparation of the quotation and the engineer in its assessment.[9]

A.A. Kwakye too sees quotation procedures as advantageous:

> [t]he pre-estimation of the time and financial effects of instructions enables the client to know the overall position of his or her project as a result of an engineer's instruction ... [and] [s]ubject to the acceptance of and agreement to a contractor's quotation, the client can request the acceleration of the project at any time during production on site.[10]

---

[5] CORBETT, EDWARD. FIDIC 5th or a New Style Red Book? *International Construction Law Review*, 1993, 289.

[6] Clause 6.2.2 CCDC 2-1994: 'When the Owner and the Contractor agree to the adjustment ... such agreement shall be effective and shall be recorded in a Change Order, signed by the Owner and Contractor ...' (cf 7.2.1 of AIA A 201 but which deems agreement on the parties' part). See generally for a comparison of the variations clauses in the ICE 6th, FIDIC 4th and the AS 2124-1986, and AS 2124-1994, STAUGAS, JOANNE. Variations. *Building and Construction Law*, 1995, **11**, 156. The AS 2124-1994 form is reproduced and commented upon by DORTER, JOHN B. Australian Construction Contracts: Time for a Change, likewise the CCDC-2 form is reproduced in and discussed by KNUTSON, ROBERT. Standard Canadian Construction Contracts. In *Comparative Studies in Construction Law: The Sweet Lectures* (ed. ODAMS, A.M.) Construction Law Press, London, 1995, PP. 49–72 and 37–48 respectively.

[7] PERRY, JOHN G. The New Engineering Contract: Principles of Design and Risk Allocation. *Engineering, Construction and Architectural Management*, 1995, **2**(3), 206.

[8] *Ibid.*

[9] McGOWAN, PAUL H. *et al. Allocation and Evaluation in Construction Contracts.* CIOB, Ascot, 1992, Occasional Paper 52, p. 5.

[10] KWAKYE, A.A. *Construction Project Administration in Practice.* Addison Wesley Longman, Harlow; CIOB, Ascot, 1997, p. 105.

The employer can ask for alternative quotations and prefer either cost or time oriented solutions. The result should be that the determination of the true costs involved should be better reflected than the use of tendered rates under other forms of contract.

There are other reasons that commend the approach; in particular by adopting quotation procedures the drafters have opted for an 'open book' to pricing and valuation that again is missing from many other forms. Norris, Perry and Simon put the issue in these terms.

> The central question is whether the contractor should have a right to compensation of both money and time in all cases. The principle adopted in the NEC is that he should (although he will not receive either unless it is demonstrated that a loss has been suffered). The argument for this has two stages. Firstly, that, in general, any of the risk events listed could affect both cost and time. Secondly, the Contractor should be indifferent to whether the risk occurs or not and the Employer should expect to pay for the full cost and time implications of a risk event that he carries. This policy puts a strong motivation on the Employer to minimise the occurrence of those risks, which are under his control. (The assessment procedures built into the NEC also motivate the Contractor to prepare realistic programmes and keep them updated.)[11]

Perry has written that the procedures adopted for assessing the effects of risk events were intended to achieve the following benefits:

- early certainty to the employer of the price to be paid for the occurrence of a risk event and a choice over how it is managed;
- improved cash flow for the contractor; and
- the likelihood of greater collaboration over how to respond to the risk event as the method of assessment should leave the contractor indifferent as to how it is dealt with.[12]

Perry and Hoare have also commented upon the effect of single tender quotation procedure as opposed to the original competitive tender procedure. 'This is an example of balancing principles in practice to which Abrahamson[13] referred. The perception of the authors is that, in relative terms, this is a second order effect which is more than offset by the primary benefits to the contract . . .'.[14] It is significant that the JCT has adopted a quotation procedure with the release of JCT 98[15] which implicitly endorses the direction taken earlier in the NEC.

---

[11] NORRIS, C. *et al. Project Risk Analysis and Management*. The Association of Project Managers, London, April 1991, p. 89.

[12] PERRY, JOHN G. See n. 7 above, p. 206.

[13] That is, ABRAHAMSON, MAX. Risk Management. *International Construction Law Review*, 1984, 241.

[14] PERRY, J.G. and HOARE, D.J. Contracts of the Future, 91.

[15] Clause 13.4.1.1 JCT 98. See on the quotation procedure and contractor's price statements BINGHAM, TONY. Quite a Racket over Fair Play. *Building*, 3 July 1998, 37.

Compensation events are enshrined in core clause 6 which lists some 18 separate events qualifying for compensation. Some commentators have viewed the provision favourably; Schneider, for example, sees clause 60.1 as 'well-balanced' in terms of dispute avoidance.[16] In addition to these 18 listed events there are additional compensation events listed in main options B and D[17] and certain of the secondary option clauses.[18] This listing is not exhaustive and the employer or project manager may add further compensation events in the Contract Data if that is wished. The optional statements in part one of the Contract Data proforma leaves space for three additional compensation events although there is no provision either here or in the core clause for their deletion. The effect of adding further compensation events in this way serves to reallocate risks from the contractor to the employer in the same way as all other compensation events.[19] Prior to looking at the individual compensation events in the core clause the procedures with respect to them bear mentioning.

Procedure

How do compensation events arise? At the outset the circumstances themselves will suggest that a possible compensation event has arisen or is about to arise. The event may be any one of the 18 separate events listed in clause 60 or any of the other provisions that add to the list. The fact of their inclusion in one single clause is an improvement in the overall clarity of the form.[20] The majority of the potential compensation events will arise from an instruction or a changed decision of the project manager. In these cases the procedure in clause 61 regarding the notification of compensation events becomes relevant.[21]

During the notification process certain assumptions with regard to the compensation event are tested and will in turn affect the quotation procedure.[22] Numerous factors are relevant to the quotation; in particular, whether the compensation event arose from the project manager giving an instruction or changing a decision;[23] whether there was any fault involved on the part of the contractor;[24] and whether an early warning was required.[25] Further or alternative quotations may be required and

---

[16] SCHNEIDER, MICHAEL E. Mastering the Interfaces – Construction Contracts Drafting for Dispute Avoidance. *International Construction Law Review*, 1993, 412.

[17] Clauses 60.4, 60.5 and 60.6 ECC.

[18] Clauses J1.2, T1.1 and U1.1 ECC.

[19] Examples of possible additional compensation events are given in the guidance notes NEC, see clause 60 ECC, at 57.

[20] BROOME, JON C. and PERRY, JOHN G. Experiences of the Use of the New Engineering Contract. *Engineering, Construction and Architectural Management*, 1995, **2**(4), 275, 278 come to this conclusion based on research into use of the form.

[21] See discussion below. BROOME, JON C. and PERRY, JOHN G. *Ibid.*, 275.

[22] See discussion below.

[23] See discussion clauses 60.1(1) and 61.1 ECC below.

[24] See discussion clause 61.1 ECC below.

[25] See discussion clauses 16 and 61.5 ECC.

throughout the whole quotation process time frames in these and other regards will be especially relevant.[26] In the end result, if a compensation event is acknowledged, then it falls to be assessed. This procedure will be carried out by the project manager and may impact on the prices, completion date and works information.[27] Once again various assumptions will be tested, including the competency of the contractor in reacting to the event.[28] When the assessment of the compensation event is complete it will be implemented.[29]

It can be seen from this brief introduction to the compensation event provisions and their procedures that they are among the most complex of any provisions in the NEC.[30] The attention to details and their overall scope seems warranted. The drafters have sought to break from past traditions where 'variations' themselves have been dealt with variably and perfunctorily. Research is providing a better understanding of the factors that give rise to variations in construction.[31] The inevitable result of such past approaches has been an increased incidence of disputes. By seeking to address more fully the subject pragmatically and purposefully the drafters have moved closer to their objective of reducing disputes. It has been suggested that the early warning and compensation event procedure will reduce disputes.

> [T]he events giving rise to the claim often do not allow an early assessment and agreement on their effects in time and money. Procedures for management and cost control should then be followed comparable to those in cost-reimbursement contracts. Fixed price contracts rarely contain provisions to this effect. A notable exception is the New Engineering Contract with its procedures for early warning and anticipated assessment of Compensation Events. It may well be expected that the procedures stipulated there, if properly applied, will make a major contribution to avoiding or limiting disputes in this difficult area of construction contracts.[32]

Likewise, by seeking to more openly acknowledge and address the actual or full costs of variations through the compensation events provisions, both parties to the contract end up being better informed about these costs. Mike Lanigan has written that: '[n]o project ever launched has totally conformed to its initial plan, so it is quite normal for deviations [used synonymously with variations in much project management

---

[26] See discussion clauses 62.1 to 62.5 ECC.
[27] See discussion clause 63 ECC below.
[28] See discussion clause 63.6 ECC below.
[29] See discussion clause 64 ECC below.
[30] The assessment procedures under clause 50 are also reasonably complex.
[31] See e.g. lately AKINSOLA, A.O. Identification and Evaluation of Factors Influencing Variations on Building Projects. *International Journal of Project Management*, 1997, **15**(4), 263.
[32] SCHNEIDER, MICHAEL E., see n. 16 above, 421.

literature] to arise between plan and actual performance'.[33] Robert E. Cox similarly writes: '[t]he litmus test for successful management should not be whether the project was free of change orders and claims – few projects would pass that test – but, rather, if change orders and claims were resolved in a timely manner to the benefit of all the parties and the project'.[34] The implication is that the parties should thus be more realistic about dealing with these costs than has perhaps often been the case. Justin Sweet, noting that the NEC chose a generous pricing formula, wrote: '[a] compensation method for changes that is too parsimonious can act as a disincentive to working out the design in advance and may discourage competent contractors from bidding'.[35] With this introduction the details of the compensation procedures may be turned to.

Compensation events

Clause 60.1 sets out 18 compensation events that are applicable to all main options. They will be examined in turn. The first compensation event addresses changes in the Works Information. Although no priority or hierarchy of compensation is referred to it is likely that the first compensation event, changing the works information, will in practice be the one most often invoked.

Changing the works information

> 60.1(1) The *Project Manager* gives an instruction changing the Works Information ...[36]

Clause 60.1(1) is one of only two compensation events[37] that may involve an actual reduction of the prices.[38] This clause is 'equivalent' to variations clauses under other standard forms of contract, although this statement is made quite apart from the theoretical reductions in prices that could be made in other instances. The elements may be broken down as follows:

- it is the project manager alone who acts, *not* the employer;
- the act referred to is the project manager's giving of instructions;[39]
- a change[40] is involved to the works information.[41]

---

[33] LANIGAN, MIKE, see n. 3 above, p. 200.
[34] COX, ROBERT E. Managing Change Orders and Claims. *Journal of Management in Engineering*, January/February 1997, **13**(1), 24–29.
[35] SWEET, JUSTIN. Judging Contracts: Some Reflections on the Third International Construction Law Conference. *International Construction Law Review*, 1994, 427–428.
[36] 'Works Information' is defined in clause 11.2(5) ECC.
[37] The other is clause 60.1(17) ECC.
[38] See also clause 63.2 ECC.
[39] For example, the project manager gives instructions under clauses 17.1, 19.1 ECC. and instructs alone under clauses 61.1, 61.4, 62.4, 73.1 ECC.
[40] See e.g. clauses 36.3, 36.4, 44.2 ECC.
[41] The works information is defined in clause 11.2(5) and the contractor must provide the works in accordance with clause 20.1 ECC.

Thus the ECC does not deal singularly with the power to order variations as it is commonly referred to but only in relation to a number of other actions that the project manager performs under the contract. In addition to these provisions, which it is submitted should be read together, the project manager's authority to so act is again underlined in clause 14.3. According to this clause the '*Project Manager* may give an instruction to the *Contractor* which changes the Works Information'. While there are other reasons why the works information may be changed[42] clause 14.3 will likely be the most often resorted to and one of the most significant of the clauses referred to here. Once the instruction has been given the contractor is under a concomitant obligation to obey it.[43]

The clause creates two exceptions to the general rule that a change to the works information constitutes a compensation event. These exceptions are as follows:

- when the change is made in order to accept a defect; and
- when the change is made to works information provided by the contractor for his or her design and made at the contractor's request, or to comply with other works information provided by the employer.[44]

Therefore, with regard to the first exception, any instruction to change the works information after a quotation from the contractor has been accepted, to accept a defect will not amount to a compensation event.[45] This is the case even though acceptance by the project manager of the quotation may entail changes not only to the works information but possibly the prices and completion date as well. Why is this the case? Simply because the change is not a true compensation event as defined, more an accommodation toward the contractor. Turning to the second exception it concedes the possibility of a divergence between parts one and two of the Contract Data and thus asks how that should be dealt with.

The answer, at least in the case of part one of the Contract Data – or information provided by the employer – is to make it paramount. As a result it becomes the contractor's responsibility to ensure that any works information provided with the contractor's tender in part two of the Contract Data *is consistent with and can be read subject to* the employer's information. In this context, and if it cannot be so construed, the project manager may refuse to accept the contractor's design. The exception speaks to this situation. Thus, while the works information may be changed to reconcile information contained in parts one and two of the Contract Data, in so doing no liability of the employer toward the contractor for compensation is assumed.[46] This provision would appear to operate similarly to that in clause 5.8 of the FIDIC Orange Book 1st, part

---

[42] See again clauses 17 and 19 ECC.
[43] Clause 29.1 ECC.
[44] Clause 60.1(1) ECC.
[45] See discussion clause 44 ECC.
[46] See also discussion clause 21.2 ECC.

I, concerning errors by the contractor. In this case the errors are corrected at the contractor's cost. The absence of any mention of incorrect data provided by the employer suggests it remains the contractor's responsibility based upon the obligation under clause 4.1 of the Orange Book to check the employer's design.[47]

In general, under standard forms of contract, the power to order changes to the works must be given expressly in the contract. This stems from two things: the absence of a power at common law to order changes to the contract; and the fact that the principal obligation of the contractor is to complete (or provide) the works. If an employer could change the contract or its description or contents of the works at will and without recompense the contractor would be placed in an impossible position. Legal certainty might also be lacking if the employer could alter the contents of the contractor's obligations without more. Hence express powers are required and normally included in most standard forms. The expression of the power assumes some *quid pro quo* on the part of the employer; normally time or money. The ECC as noted has given the contractor the benefit of both time and money[48] in exchange for the grant of the right to make variations to the description of the works in their agreement. In the absence of clause 60.1(1), read with the other clauses referred to above, the employer would have had to have the contract varied by agreement or entered into a new contract.[49] Traditionally, the completion of work additional to the contract has carried no immediate right to payment.[50] It is for these reasons that the right to order the extra work and make the commensurate payment is now express in traditional standard forms.

The power given to the project manager is that of 'changing' the works information and this term is precisely used in both clauses 14.3 and 60.1(1). However, the fact that only 'change' is used as the operative verb in the ECC, unlike certain other traditional forms, should not be viewed as limitative. Typically, variation clauses, as they are often referred to, are drafted in conventional repetitive styles which seek to address a wide variety of circumstances, e.g. clause 13.1 of the JCT 80 defining 'variation' as meaning or including alteration, modification, addition, omission, substitution, alteration and removal. The ECC wording is simply representative of the drafting style adopted in the contract.

[47] *Guide to the Use of FIDIC Conditions of Contract for Design-Build and Turnkey, First Edition.* FIDIC, Lausanne, 1996, pp. 66–67.

[48] EGGLESTON. *The New Engineering Contract, A Commentary.* Blackwell Science, London, 1996, sees this as a problem in at least one respect: '[o]ne characteristic of the compensation event procedure which exacerbates its administrative burdens is that it covers both time and money', 195.

[49] *Holland Hannen & Cubitts (Northern) Ltd* v. *Welsh Health Technical Services Organisation* (1981) 18 BLR 80; *Blue Circle Industries plc* v. *Holland Dredging Co (UK) Ltd* (1987) 37 BLR 40, CA.

[50] *Wilmot* v. *Smith* (1828) 3 C & P 453; *Kirk* v. *Bromley Union Guardians* (1848) 12 Jur 85; *Ranger* v. *Great Western Rly Co* (1854) 5 HL Cas 72, HL; *Bottoms* v. *York Corpn* (1892) 2 *Hudson's BC*, 4th edn. 208, CA; *Taverner & Co Ltd* v. *Glamorgan County Council* (1940) 57 TLR 243; *Gilbert & Partners* v. *Knight* [1968] 2 All ER 248, CA.

Accordingly, it should be given the widest possible interpretation. Although there are not express limits in clause 14.3 itself the scope and extent to which changes may be ordered would be limited by both other contractual provisions[51] and case law.

Hence, it is submitted that the meaning of 'changing' should be construed to encompass extra work (save that which is so different in kind or extent from that agreed that it was outside the contemplation of the parties),[52] changes to the specifications,[53] and the omission of work.[54] The instruction mandating the change should be communicated in a form in writing.[55] This is a procedural restriction which must be complied with and will likely be treated as a condition precedent to the contractor's right to be paid for any changed work.[56]

The compensation event procedure mirrors certain of Latham's assumptions about an effective form of contract. Thus, the fact that the contractor is fully compensated for certain employer driven changes to the works information, although not the employer's own changes, is consonant with both parties 'taking all reasonable steps to avoid changes to pre-planned works information'.[57] It seems significant that Latham adopts NEC terminology with this recommendation or assumption. In addition, and where the changes still occur, 'they should be priced in advance, with provision for independent adjudication if agreement cannot be reached'.[58] This corresponds to both the present quotation and adjudication procedures under the ECC.

Possession of the site

(2) The *Employer* does not give possession of a part of the Site[59] by the later of its *possession date* and the date required by the Accepted Programme.[60]

---

[51] See e.g. discussion of clause 60.4 below.

[52] *Pepper* v. *Burland* (1792) 1 Peake NP 139 per Lord Kenyon CJ; *Goodyear* v. *Weymouth and Melcombe Regis Corpn* (1865) 35 LJCP 12; *Thorn* v. *London Corpn* (1876) 1 App Cas 120, HL; *Sir Lindsay Parkinson & Co Ltd* v. *Comrs of Works and Public Buildings* [1949] 2 KB 632, [1950] 1 All ER 208, CA; *Blue Circle Industries plc* v. *Holland Dredging Co (UK) Ltd* (1987) 37 BLR 40, CA; *McAlpine Humberoak Ltd* v. *McDermott International Inc (No 1)* (1992) 58 BLR 1, CA.

[53] See *Howard de Walden Estates Ltd* v. *Costain Management Design Ltd* (1991) 55 BLR 124.

[54] See e.g. *Carr* v. *Berriman Pty Ltd* (1953) 27 ALJ 273; *Comr for Main Roads* v. *Reed & Stuart Pty Ltd* (1974) 12 BLR 55.

[55] Clause 13.1 ECC.

[56] See *Russell* v. *Viscount Sa da Bandeira* (1862) 13 CBNS 149; *Taverner & Co Ltd* v. *Glamorgan County Council* (1941) 57 TLR 243.

[57] Latham Report paragraph 5.18(7) in part, 37.

[58] *Ibid*.

[59] Clause 11.2(7) ECC.

[60] Clause 60.1(2) ECC. The 'Accepted Programme' is defined in clause 11.2(14) ECC; cf the ICE MW 2nd form which makes no express provision and only gives the contractor a right to claim an extension of time or recourse to common law remedies.

The employer is under an express obligation to give the contractor possession of the site or each part of the site as agreed.[61] The time limit for the giving of the possession is stated to be the later of either the relevant possession date and the date stipulated in the 'Accepted Programme'. The *'possession dates'* as noted is an identified term, agreed by the parties and inserted in the Contract Data.[62] The proforma allows for three parts of the site to be given respective possession dates without further amendment. The 'Accepted Programme' is also an identified term and either that in part two of the optional statements in the Contract Data or the latest programme accepted by the project manager.[63] If no programme is identified in part two the contractor will be obliged to submit a first programme for acceptance within an agreed number of weeks of the Contract Date according to the optional statements in part one of the Contract Data. Provided the compensation event does not arise from the project manager or supervisor giving an instruction or changing an earlier decision then the failure of the employer is compensable. Notification itself will follow the procedure in clause 61.

Provision by the employer

(3) The *Employer* does not provide something which he is to provide by the date for providing it required by the Accepted Programme.[64]

Subclause (3) underscores the responsibility of the employer to perform obligations timeously. Thus, where the employer has agreed to provide 'something', and recognition of this fact can be found in the 'Accepted Programme', this will be held to. The term 'something' has to be given a broad interpretation and thus would extend to facilities and services stated in the works information provided they are also recognized in the accepted programme. Failure to fulfil the obligation is compensable.[65]

There are a host of matters which the programme must contain to be accepted. These are set out in clause 31.2 and, for the most part, are matters the delivery of which is within the employer's control. However, in a few cases there are matters that the employer is to provide although the contractor is still responsible for showing the dates for their provision on the programme. These matters include the order and timing of the work of the employer, either as stated in the works information or as later agreed with the contractor, plant and materials, and other things to be provided by the employer.[66] In general, all matters which the employer is to provide should be stated in the works information. Pursuant to clause 31.2 it is incumbent upon the contractor to include their details in the programme put forward for acceptance. Once they are accepted the

---

[61] Clause 33.1 ECC.
[62] Section 3 of part one of the Contract Data.
[63] Clause 11.2(14) ECC.
[64] Clause 60.1(3) ECC.
[65] Clause 60.1(3) ECC.
[66] Clause 31.2 ECC.

employer is bound by the agreed dates for their provision and any failure to meet them entitles the contractor to compensation.[67]

Stopping work
(4) The *Project Manager* gives an instruction[68] to stop or not to start work.[69]

The project manager has authority under clause 34.1 to instruct the contractor either to stop or not to start work and the project manager's actions in this regard may result in compensation being paid to the contractor. At the outset there must be an instruction from the project manager to this effect. The express reference to only the project manager arguably excludes any similar instruction by the supervisor from consideration under this head. However, a compensation event may arise in relation to this subclause if the project manager *or the supervisor* gives an instruction or changes an earlier decision within the meaning of clause 61.1. The instruction is also relevant to termination of the contract.[70] Notification follows pursuant to clause 61.

Work of the employer or others
(5) The *Employer* or Others[71] do not work within the times shown on the Accepted Programme[72] or do not work within the conditions[73] stated in the Works Information.[74]

The obligations of the parties to the ECC are, as noted above,[75] reciprocal. It has been remarked that the employer is already under other obligations with respect to the 'Accepted Programme'. The employer must give all or part possessions of the site and provide those things agreed to timeously and in accordance with the accepted programme as well.[76] In the case of subclause (5), the employer must also work within times shown on the accepted programme. The employer was added as an amendment to the Second Edition of the form.

This means that where the employer's own workmen are carrying out work onsite at the same time as the contractor, and cause him delay or disruption, this will be a compensation event. If the

---

[67] See also clause 60.1(5) ECC below.
[68] For example, the project manager gives instructions under clauses 17.1, 19.1 ECC and instructs alone under clauses 61.1, 61.4, 62.4, 73.1 ECC.
[69] Clause 60.1(4) ECC.
[70] See clause 95.6 ECC.
[71] Clause 11.2(2) ECC.
[72] Clause 11.2(14) ECC.
[73] Cf the use of the word 'requirements' in other instances; e.g. health and safety requirements in clause 31.2 ECC.
[74] Clause 60.1(5) ECC.
[75] See clause 60.1(3) ECC above.
[76] See discussion clauses 60.1(2) and 60.1(3) ECC above.

employer uses his own direct contractors, these will be classified as 'Others' and were already covered by this compensation event.[77]

In fact it is not only the employer who must do so in this case but exceptionally 'Others' as that term is understood in the contract. 'Others' is defined in the contract as people or organizations that are not the *'Employer'*, *'Project Manager'*, *'Supervisor'*, *'Adjudicator'*, *'Contractor'*, or any employee, 'Subcontractor' or supplier of the *'Contractor'*.[78]

Notwithstanding these exclusions there is still some considerable scope for the term and it would seem reasonably to include public utility undertakings and the like. In fact it is not the identity of the others that is the most important factor but whether their work was recognized on the accepted programme. If so, the effect of the clause is to affirm the right of the contractor to compensation whenever he or she does not work within the times shown on the accepted programme.

The subclause is much broader than its counterpart in subclause (3) above. It is broader as it addresses not only working to fixed dates but working to all the relevant intervals between them. In addition to this it adds that the work must be done in accordance with all relevant conditions in respect thereof in the works information. Once again it is not only the employer's own liability in this regard but the responsibility for all 'Others' as understood within the meaning of the term for which the employer also bears the risk of cost and time. To be compensable in respect of the same the work must only be referable to a time frame on the accepted programme or qualified in some sense by the works information. It is submitted that the true breadth of this provision will be revealed as and when tested in the courts. Notification of the event proceeds in accordance with clause 61.

Reply to a communication

(6) The *Project Manager* or the *Supervisor* does not reply to a communication from the *Contractor* within the period required by this contract.[79]

Throughout the ECC, various time periods are stipulated for making replies to the contractor. The time periods may be unique for a particular clause[80] or the general *'period for reply'* that is given in part one of the Contract Data.[81] This subclause should be read as coming within the general *'period for reply'* imposed on the project manager and supervisor in clause 13.3.[82] Looking at the elements in the subclause to be

---

[77] BIRKBY, GILLIAN. The New Engineering Contract. *Civil Engineering Surveyor Construction Law Review*, 1996, 26.
[78] Clause 11.2(2) ECC.
[79] Clause 60.1(6) ECC.
[80] See e.g. clauses 31.3, 61.4 and 62.3 ECC.
[81] See e.g. clauses 13.3–13.5, 32.2 and 32.6 ECC.
[82] See discussion clause 13.3 ECC above.

compensable a failure to reply must originate with or be the responsibility of the project manager or supervisor, be in response to a communication[83] from the contractor and exceed the relevant time period. If these conditions are fulfilled the contractor may recover both time and cost consequences in respect of the same. As a result it can be expected to motivate the project manager to meet the obligation for timely replies. John R. Evans has observed the importance of the time and cost relationship from a project management perspective. Evans reviewed the provisions on variations in JCT 80, ICE 6th, FIDIC 4th, PSA/1 and NEC and compared them against a set of criteria to see whether they admitted of a clear *relationship* between time and cost. In Evans' conclusions *only* the NEC clearly recognized the relationship of the two as well as to payment and progress monitoring. In Evans' view there were decided advantages from a project management and programme management perspective once this relationship between time and cost was recognized.[84] The procedure for the notification of the event follows that in clause 61.

Objects of value

(7) The *Project Manager* gives an instruction for dealing with an object of value or of historical or other interest found within the Site.[85]

The ECC sets out how objects of value or of historical interest are to be dealt with in clause 73. In particular, title to such objects may be in issue and instructions with respect to them may be called for. Even though the contractor has no title to an object of value or of historical or other interest within the site issues may still arise. For instance, is the object of historical interest? Was it found within the site as defined? The drafting of subclause 60.1(7) makes no mention of materials from excavation and demolition that is also dealt with in clause 73. A proper interpretation given to this may be to exclude an instruction with respect to materials from excavation and demolition from falling within the literal meaning of the subclause.

What actions can be expected from the contractor in these circumstances? At the outset the contractor would be expected not to move the object without instructions.[86] Upon its finding the contractor would be placed under an obligation to notify the project manager of it.[87] Notification would follow the procedures in clause 61. The project manager in turn may be expected to give an instruction either in respect of

---

[83]   As defined in clause 13.1 ECC.

[84]   EVANS, JOHN R. Fair and Reasonable? Ordered Variations and the Standard Forms of Contract. MSc dissertation, University of London, Centre of Construction Law and Management. King's College, London, 1995. See also McGOWAN, PAUL H., n. 9 above.

[85]   Clause 60.1(7) ECC.

[86]   Clause 73.1 ECC.

[87]   Clause 73.1 ECC. Notification falls within and must comply with clause 13 ECC.

moving it at the outset or how to deal with it otherwise. Any such instruction would amount to a formal communication and would have to comply with the clause 13 procedures. The contractor in the ordinary course would then be under an obligation to obey the instruction if it were given in accordance with the contract.[88]

Changing a decision

(8) The *Project Manager* or the *Supervisor* changes a decision which he has previously communicated to the *Contractor*.[89]

There are three issues under subclause (8) which are material to whether compensation may be payable to the contractor. All three issues pose their own difficulties from either a legal or factual point of view. In the first instance there is the issue of what constitutes a 'decision' of the project manager or supervisor, as the term itself is undefined.[90] It may be that a decision should refer only to the narrow range of decisions of the project manger alone and which are expressly referred to in the contract. Alternatively, a decision could pertain to any resolution by the project manager in a broad or general sense. Somewhere in between these two poles lies a middle ground as well. That is, based on the use of the term 'communicated' in clause 13.1, it seems that a decision could also reasonably be understood to include at least the eight forms of communication referred to in that clause. Ultimately, whether the term 'decision' may be more broadly construed as it is in ordinary usage would depend not only on the circumstances of the case but the court's approach to the form as whole.

It would seem that, as plain language drafting principles have been employed in the form, a court might wish to admit any interpretation that accords with general usage as well as the more limited interpretations set out here. In summary, given this subclause involves a financial responsibility which operates as an exception to the general rule that risk lies with the contractor, as an exception it must be given a restricted meaning. Therefore, on this analysis a decision would be limited only to those clauses that refer to decisions expressly, or alternatively to clauses referring to communications as defined. By implication the decision would not extend to any resolution by the project manager or supervisor.

Turning to the second issue under the subclause it would appear to hinge upon the meaning of 'changes'.[91] The difficulties inherent in deciding whether an individual decision has been changed follow from the number of other possible characterizations that one may have for a decision. As entitlement to compensation is the result one may prefer to

---

[88] Clause 29.1 ECC.

[89] Clause 60.1(8) ECC.

[90] Although undefined, 'decisions' may be made by the project manager under clauses 16.4, 30.2, 50.1, 61.4, 61.5, 63.4, 64.1; as well as changed by the project manager under this clauses, 61.1 and 62.3 ECC.

[91] Cf the use of the term in clauses 36.3, 36.4, 44.2 ECC.

view the decisions as not being changed but explained or clarified. In strict terms a clarification of a decision previously communicated to the contractor by the project manager would seem to fall outside of the subclause.

The final issue is factual. That is, has the decision in question previously been communicated to the contractor? The resolution of this issue requires proof of receipt itself. Clause 13.2 addresses only the question of *when* a communication is effective and thus receipt is assumed. As such receipt will have to be proved as a question of fact, recourse to the general law may assist in this regard.[92]

Apart from the interpretation issue raised above in relation to the subclause, the provision itself supports the finding of a general jurisdiction residing in both the project manager and supervisor to change decisions they have made previously. This jurisdiction may be illustrated in numerous specific instances[93] and while it is implied in clause 61.1 it is not otherwise given as a general grant of authority to them.[94]

Withholding an acceptance

(9) The *Project Manager* withholds an acceptance (other than acceptance of a quotation for acceleration or for not correcting a Defect) for a reason not stated in this contract.[95]

Subclause (9) may be reworded in an effort at simplification as follows:

- if the project manager withholds an acceptance for a reason not stated in this contract it is a compensation event;
- if the project manager withholds an acceptance of a quotation for acceleration it is not a compensation event; and
- if the project manager withholds an acceptance of a quotation for not correcting a defect it is not a compensation event.

For the subclause to be fully understood it must be read with the provisions in clauses 13.4 and 13.8. The clauses are somewhat difficult to apply for a number of reasons. In this context some of the difficulties stem from the fact that both clauses yield rules of both general and specific application. Hence clause 13.8 addresses 'communications' – a rule of

---

[92] By analogy to jurisprudence developing the 'postal acceptance rule'; see EVANS, DAVID M. The Anglo-American Mailing Rule. *International and Comparative Law Quarterly*, 1966, **15**, 553; and GARDNER, SIMON. Trashing the Trollope: A Deconstruction of the Postal Rules in Contract. *Oxford Journal of Legal Studies*, 1992, **12**, 170.

[93] For example, clauses 11.2(14) in effect a constructive change, 14.2, 34.1, 36.3, 50.5, 51.3, 51.5 and 60.6 ECC.

[94] FC 61 ECC, 52 classifying this clause as a type of compensation event which arises from the project manager or supervisor giving an instruction or changing an earlier decision also supports the jurisdiction.

[95] Clause 60.1(9) ECC.

general application at the same time as it addresses a rule of specific application – the contractor's submission. Some of the difficulty in construing the clause is attributable to the use of overlapping terminology including 'submission', 'submit' and 'communication'. This fact has been alluded to elsewhere in this book.

Turning to these points concerning clause 13.8 it too can be said to be a rule of both general and specific application. Thus in all cases the project manager may withhold acceptance of a submission – in fact the specific case. However, it is submitted that to give the clause its intended meaning 'submission' must be read as 'communication' – the general case. The subclause also provides a general rule insofar as the withholding of (an) acceptance is concerned; that is, for a reason stated in the contract. It can be noted that this rule of general application would apply equally to clause 13.4 where a reason is stated in support of withholding acceptance of a communication; namely more information is needed to assess it. As such it can be said that there is overlapping of these rules as currently drafted. The overlap is also expressly tied into the compensation event procedure itself. Thus clause 13.8 closes by stating the withholding of (an) acceptance for a reason stated in the contract 'is not a compensation event'. The point is thus made forcefully by the drafters as they have only rarely used the text in the core clauses outside of core clause 6 to give or refute a right to compensation.

There is one additional aspect of the drafting that should be clarified. It concerns whether the phrase 'not acceptance' was intended to mean the same thing as 'withholding acceptance'. It may be recalled that clause 13.4 provides in part: 'If his [the project manager's] reply is not acceptance, he states his reasons ... A reason for withholding acceptance is that ...'. Aside from the meaning intended in the clause it is arguable that not acceptance – or non-acceptance – is different from withholding acceptance without more. Non-acceptance suggests a negative reply communicated to the other party. Conversely, withholding acceptance suggests no reply, whether affirmative or negative. While this would appear to be a reasonable interpretation of these two terms it is suggested that was not the likely intent of the drafters when the clause is read as a whole. In reading clause 13.4 as a whole it appears that the drafters equate not (or non-) acceptance with withholding acceptance. This interpretation follows as a result of giving the same meaning to the term 'reason(s)' in the two sentences in which the other terms appear. The term 'reason(s)' bridges the meaning between the two terms and it follows that the two terms should be equated.

Returning to subclause (9) it can now be read such that 'non-acceptance' for a reason not stated in the contract is a compensation event. The same interpretation may be placed upon clause 13.8 so that it too would read 'non-acceptance' for a reason stated in the contract is not a compensation event. The meaning behind this concerns the allocation of risk. It is just that clauses 60.1(9) deals with it in a slightly more complex way than most other compensation events in clause 60.1. The complexity arises from one of the very same reasons affecting the interpretation of clauses 13.4 and 13.8. In all three clauses the provision addresses both a rule of general and specific application. This point has been made above in relation to clauses 13.4 and 13.8. It can be explained in relation to clause 60.1(9) on two bases: risk and the exceptions themselves.

The general rule in the ECC is that the risk is upon the contractor save provision to the contrary. The compensation event procedure reverses or provides an exception to this general allocation of risk. It places the risk upon the employer with events falling within one of the relevant clauses. Thus, when a compensation event occurs, the risk is upon the employer without more. However, even though one is dealing with compensation events (the exception to the general rule in relation to any risk) the risk of withholding of acceptance of a submission whenever a reason is given in the contract for the withholding is returned to the contractor. The argument has been made that withholding of acceptance may be equated with non-acceptance or, for that matter, refusal.

Thus the contractor remains at risk for the subject matter of events which may give rise to submissions whenever: reasons for the withholding of acceptance in respect of such submissions are given in the contract, and any ultimate withholding of acceptance is for one of these reasons. On this interpretation it remains the case that the employer is at risk for the withholding of an acceptance of a submission for any other reason than that stated in the contract. The exceptions may now be summarized briefly as follows:

- The risk of the project manager withholding an acceptance for a reason *not* stated in the contract is on the employer.
- The risk for a project manager withholding an acceptance for a reason *stated* in the contract is upon the contractor.
- The risk for the project manager withholding an acceptance of a quotation for acceleration or a quotation for *not* correcting a defect is also upon the contractor.

The reason that the risks in respect of the third point above remain upon the contractor is to ensure the complete discretion of the project manager to withhold acceptance in respect of them for any reason whatsoever. Thus, the project manager may withhold acceptance in respect of quotations for acceleration or not correcting a defect even though no reasons for so doing are given in the contract. Without creating these exceptions the withholdings would be compensable under clause 11.2(9). Further, the cases where both types of quotations arise entail choices on the part of the project manager. If the costs of acceleration are too high the project manager may drop it without more. Similarly if the cost of not correcting a defect – which is in fact rather the acceptance of defects of procedure that is being referred to[96] – is too high it may similarly be dropped without more. In both cases no explanations or reasons within the meaning of the clause would need to be given. The explanation is simply that the risks remain where they always were.

---

[96] Clause 44 ECC.

In summary, although subclause (9) confirms the principles supporting the allocation of risk in the ECC it does so with some unnecessary complexity. It is submitted that the same objectives could have been achieved and the clause simplified by merely giving an exemplar reason for the withholding of acceptances in each of the clauses involving the two quotations. As a result the parenthetical reference 'other than acceptance of a quotation for acceleration or for not correcting a Defect' could have been omitted and in this way the subclause simplified to a small degree. The allocation of the risks overall would have been more consistently maintained in this way.

Searching

(10) The *Supervisor* instructs the *Contractor* to search and no Defect[97] is found unless the search is needed only because the *Contractor* gave insufficient notice of doing work obstructing a required test or inspection.[98]

This clause must be read with the general power of the supervisor to instruct the contractor to search under clause 42.1.[99] Pursuant to this power the supervisor may instruct the contractor to search for any reason. A reason for the instruction will be presumed.[100] The result of the instruction may be that a defect as defined[101] is either found or is not found. Where no defect is found compensation occurs unless the search was only needed because the contractor gave insufficient notice of doing work obstructing a required test or inspection.[102] Whether a test or inspection is required depends upon whether the same must be done pursuant to the works information. Clause 40.1 of the ECC applies only to tests and inspections 'required by the Works Information'. As such, any tests or inspections which are not required pursuant to the works information and which are rather carried out as a matter of discretion by the contractor could not give rise to an obstruction[103] within the meaning of the clause. With regard to the notice aspect of the subclause alone any insufficiency in this regard on the contractor's part would preclude a compensation event arising.

Delayed tests and inspections

(11) A test or inspection done by the *Supervisor* causes unnecessary delay.[104]

---

[97] Clause 11.2(15) ECC.
[98] Clause 60.1(10) ECC.This clause differs from the wording in the First Edition.
[99] See discussion clause 42.1 ECC above.
[100] The giving of the instruction itself must satisfy the requirements of clause 13 ECC.
[101] See clause 11.2(15) ECC.
[102] Clause 61.10 ECC.
[103] Several standard forms address obstruction in the context of certificates, see e.g. clause 28.1.2 JCT 80, clause 7.5.2 IFC 84.
[104] Clause 60.1(11) ECC.

Pursuant to the terms of the works information it can be expected that the supervisor will carry out a wide variety of tests and inspections. Clause 40.5 requires the supervisor to perform those tests without causing unnecessary delay.[105] Where a test or inspection done by the supervisor causes unnecessary delay a compensation event may arise. It does not arise as such from the project manager or supervisor giving an instruction or changing an earlier decision.[106]

The delay in clause 40.5 may be either in respect of the work or of a payment, which is conditional upon a test or inspection being successful. However subclause (11) does not make this connection explicit; rather the delay is left at large. It is arguable that the delay is meant to refer to either the work or payment. While reading these aspects of clause 40.5 into subclause (11) assists in its meaning the question of the magnitude of the delay insofar as the work is concerned remains open. Clause 40.5 stipulates when a payment conditional upon a successful test or inspection is due and thus delay beyond these dates is arguably unnecessary and compensable. In contrast, and assuming no provision has been made in the works information in this regard, it is once again an open question when a normal or necessary delay which some will associate with tests and inspections becomes abnormal or unnecessary. The difficulty of this point is illustrated by trying to determine what constitutes necessary delay. The clause in this regard merits reconsideration.

Physical conditions

(12) The *Contractor* encounters physical conditions which
- are within the Site,[107]
- are not weather conditions and
- which an experienced contractor would have judged at the Contract Date to have such a small chance of occurring that it would have been unreasonable for him [the experienced contractor] to have allowed for them.[108]

Some observations may be made on the terminology. As the term 'contractor' is not capitalized it is intended to not refer to the 'Contractor'; hence an objective standard. The Contract Date is the date when the contract came into existence under clause 11.2(3) of the ECC. There is no attempt to quantify the size of the 'chance' of occurrence save by the wording that follows in the clause. If construed strictly it is open to argue that even a 1% allowance would take it outside of the provision. The subject of site or ground conditions[109] has traditionally been a source of disputes between parties and expense.

---

[105] See discussion clause 40.5 ECC above.
[106] Clause 61.1 ECC. Notification follows the procedure in clause 61 ECC.
[107] Clause 11.2(7) ECC.
[108] Clause 60.1(12) ECC.
[109] See generally SANDERS, STEVEN C. Unanticipated Environmental Costs in Construction Contracts: The Differing Site Conditions Clause as a Risk Allocation Tool. *International Construction Law Review*, 1994, 466.

A statistical review of projects ... revealed that fifty percent of
commercial buildings and thirty-seven percent of industrial
buildings experience delay due to unforeseen ground conditions.
All developments on second-hand sites met unexpected ground
during construction. Such events increase construction costs and
may lead to disputes between the involved parties. Also the effect on
the project's whole life financial performance can be significant,
particularly if commissioning is delayed. Reports from NEDO state
that the most frequent origins of overruns and long delays (defined
as being in excess of 10 weeks) are unforeseen obstacles in the
ground.[110]

Robert J. Smith also suggests that poorly or inappropriately drafted
ground conditions clauses in contracts attract a risk premium of, perhaps,
3%.[111] Controversy surrounding subclause (12) of the ECC suggests very
little has changed in that regard. It is some evidence of the difficulties
involved in this issue that the ICE has prepared a wholly distinct set of
conditions of contract for ground investigation in mitigation – ICE
Conditions of Contract for Ground Invesigation.[112] The Conditions are
prepared on the basis of the ICE 5th conditions and comprise some 72
clauses, forms of tender, agreement, and bond, as well as a looseleaf
contract price fluctuations provision. Case law has exacerbated the
traditional problem in two principal respects:

- it generally imposes the cost risk for adverse physical conditions and
  obstructions on the contractor;[113]
- the employer's obligations regarding both site suitability[114] and
  accuracy of the pre-contract or tender information[115] have been
  minimal.[116]

The few situations when the contractor has been able to secure some
reassigning of the responsibility for these issues to the employer have

---

[110] ALHALABY, N.M.H. and WHYTE, I.L. The Impact of Ground Risks in
Construction on Project Finance. *Risk and Reliability in Ground Engineering.*
Proceedings of a conference held in London on 11 and 12 November 1993 by the
Institution of Civil Engineers (ed. SKIPP, B.O.). Thomas Telford, London, 1994, p.
54.

[111] SMITH, ROBERT J. Allocation of Risk – The Case for Manageability. *International
Construction Law Review*, 1996, 550.

[112] ICE Conditions of Contract for Ground Investigation, 1st edn. 1983.

[113] For example, under JCT forms of contract no relief is expressly provided the
contractor in these events arising.

[114] *Bottoms* v. *York Corpn* (1892) 2 *Hudson's BC*, 4th edn. 208 CA; *McDonald* v.
Workington Corpn (1892) 2 *Hudson's BC*, 4th edn. 228; CA; *Re Nuttal and Lynton
and Barnstable Rly Co's Arbitration* (1899) 82 LT 17, CA.

[115] See *Sharpe* v. *San Paulo Rly Co* (1873) LR 8 Ch App 597. Case law has tended away
from the implication of terms with regard to employer obligations in both (1) and (2).

[116] See e.g. *S Pearson & Son Ltd* v. *Dublin Corpn* [1907] AC 351, HL; and *Morrison-
Knudsen International Co Inc* v. *Commonwealth of Australia* (1972) 46 ALJR 265.

typically involved negligent or fraudulent misrepresentations which are difficult and costly to prove. These two factors leave very little margin for the contractor; particularly when working in a competitive environment which may result in underestimating the degree of risk which the contractor should reasonably have been expected to price or allow for. The question that must be asked is whether the changes in subclause (12) address these principal issues. Subclause (12) is also radically shorter than site or ground conditions clauses in other standard forms. In terms of length one of the closest comparisons would be to clause 3.8 of ICE MW 2nd but the ECC provision is still shorter than this one.

The wording of the clause invokes a pot-pourri of legal concepts: knowledge, which is implied judgment; assumptions, experience, and reasonableness, which are express. In addition, in analogy to tort, chance is also invoked. It is difficult to imagine the combining of more legal concepts in one short clause. Perhaps surprisingly there is no express reference to foreseeability although the clause may still be construed in this manner as noted below. Despite the number of legal concepts involved the wording draws upon familiar terminology from engineering forms. Thus the phrase 'physical conditions' borrows from ICE 6th and FIDIC 4th which also use the same phrase. Clause 12(1) of the ICE 6th uses both this phrase and 'artificial obstructions' while clause 12.2 of the FIDIC 4th uses the phrases 'physical obstructions' and 'physical conditions'.[117] As a general matter, clause 60.1(12) appears almost to be the converse of clause 12 of the ICE 6th. In effect, the test has changed under clause 12 from conditions that could not have been reasonably foreseen (and as such with no need to allow for them) to conditions that had such a small chance of occurring that it would have been unreasonable to have allowed for them under clause 60.1(12). Thus, one test is framed positively and one is framed negatively. On this aspect alone the ECC test is *broader* than the test under clause 12 as the contractor's risk has been *extended* to conditions which it may have been unreasonable to allow for but which may have been reasonably foreseen.

The phrase has been construed under other forms as not being limited to conditions external to the works (as defined) and may include conditions which arise from the physical characteristics of the materials being used in the works.[118] A similar interpretation might be expected to

---

[117] See generally WIEGAND, CHRISTIAN. Allocation of the Soil Risk in Construction Contracts: A Legal Comparison. *International Construction Law Review*, 1984, 282; JONES, GLOWER W. The US Perspective on Procedures for Subsurface Ground Conditions Claims. *International Construction Law Review*, 1990, 155–186; MARSTON, DONALD L. The Impact of Subsurface Ground Conditions on Project Participants – a Canadian Perspective. *International Construction Law Review*, 1990, 186–197; and MERONI, RUDOLF. Sub-surface Ground Conditions – Risks and Pitfalls for Project Participants: Civil Law Projects – Legal and Contractual Approach in Switzerland. *International Construction Law Review*, 1990, 198–209.

[118] See *Holland Dredging (UK) Ltd* v. *Dredging and Construction Co Ltd* (1987) 37 BLR 1, CA; and *Humber Oil Terminals Trustee Ltd* v. *Harbour General Works (Stevin) Ltd* (1991) 59 BLR 1, CA.

be placed upon this phrase in the ECC; in particular, if the facts giving rise to the dispute arise in an engineering context. The effect of this in practice is that contractors have assumed quite different risks in this respect depending upon the form that they have used. Physical conditions themselves are those which arise *within the site*. The site is, of course, the 'Site' as defined in the contract and the ECC definition again distinguishes itself from building forms by including a definition and aligns itself with engineering form practice.[119] The ECC definition gives an extended meaning to the term which encompasses not only the area within the boundaries of the site but also the volumes above and below it which are affected by work included in the contract.[120] The *'boundaries of the site'* is an identified term in section 1 of part one of the Contract Data. In line with engineering form practice, the ECC also allows for further extension of the meaning of 'site' by agreement of the parties.[121] Extension in the ECC is achieved by extending the *'boundaries of the site'* as identified. Taken out of the definition, however, are what are referred to as 'weather conditions'. This term is undefined and may best be understood by reference to what the parties have agreed will be taken as *'weather measurement'* and *'weather data'*.[122] The term itself is also capable of ordinary meaning and which would not be likely to contradict that suggested here in relation to the weather measurements and weather data.

The test which is to be applied in judging this matter is objective. The language refers to 'an experienced contractor'. The absence of a capital initial indicates it is not the contractor as party to the contract and that contractor's knowledge or experience that is intended as the touchstone for the test, rather a third party in the contractor's circumstances. The test should be applied at the 'Contract Date' and thus excludes the wisdom that often comes with hindsight. The experienced contractor is expected to exercise judgment is assessing the likelihood that the physical conditions encountered had such a small chance of occurring that it would have been unreasonable for the experienced contractor to have allowed for them. The extent of the investigations will depend to some degree on the attitude of the contractor toward risk as well as the type of project. Researchers are endeavouring to determine effective levels of and durations of pre-contractual investigation through analytical frameworks.[123]

---

[119] Both ICE 6th and FIDIC 4th contain definitions of the site unlike for instance JCT 80, JCT/MW or JCT 81.

[120] Clause 11.2(7) ECC. Clause 1(1)v in ICE 6th covers that 'on under in or through' while FIDIC 4th clause 1.1(f)(vii) refers to 'places' only. SCHNEIDER, MICHAEL E., see n. 16 above, 410 refers to earlier editions of the clause as 'well-balanced'.

[121] See clauses 1(1)v ICE 6th and 1.1(f)(vii) FIDIC 4th.

[122] Clause 11.2(13) see discussion below.

[123] BROCHNER, J. Precontractual Investigations and Risk Aversion. *Engineering, Construction and Architectural Management*, 1994, **1**(2), 91–101.

This test, it can be remarked, is not based solely on foreseeability as there might be risks which the experienced contractor foresees but assesses as having virtually no chance of occurring but which, if they do occur and despite their foreseeability, still entitle the contractor to compensation. Instead, the right to the compensation turns upon whether it was reasonable for the contractor to have so discounted the likelihood of occurrence of that risk so as not to have allowed for it. No figure is placed upon what constitutes a 'small chance' and certainly in practice this will be subject to variation among contractors. However, once again, it is not how the contractor who is party to the contract evaluated the chance but how some other experienced contractor would have. The courts will presumably tell us what a small chance is although it will almost certainly be fact-dependent on and heavily qualified by the circumstances of the individual case. Arriving at suitable qualifications for the experienced contractor may be assisted by the minimum experience which the parties themselves agree to in the Contract Data.

The seeming intractability of problems surrounding site or ground conditions is perhaps one explanation for the lengths which the contract drafters have gone to in addressing the topic. For instance, under American federal construction contracts a process of *equitable adjustment* of the contract price or time period is carried out by contract administrators in the case of unforeseen ground conditions.[124] To illustrate the point in the case of the ECC it may be noted that of the eighteen compensation events only one merits further attention in clause 60, that is, physical conditions. In fact, physical conditions are addressed on two further occasions in clauses 60.2 and 60.3. According to NEC flow chart 60, sheet 3 of 6, to qualify as a compensation event the physical conditions in clause 60.1(12) must meet the criteria in clause 60.2. Thus, in judging the physical conditions referable to subclause (12) the contractor is assumed to have taken into account:

- the Site Information,[125]
- publicly available information[126] referred to in the Site Information,
- information obtainable from a visual inspection of the Site and
- other information which an experienced contractor could reasonably be expected to have or to obtain.[127]

These assumptions as to the level of knowledge which the contractor is assumed to have taken into account seek to address one of the more contentious issues which has often been litigated: that is the *foreseeability* of the risk. Notwithstanding the use of the word 'assumed' in clause 60.2 it is submitted that the intention is to bind the employer to disclose the

---

[124] See e.g. *Great Lakes Dredge & Dock Co* v. *US* 96 Fed 923 Supp, 924; and *Turnbull Inc* v. *US* 389 F 2d 1007 (CT CL, 1967) 1011.
[125] Clause 11.2(6) ECC.
[126] A variety of possible meanings for the term 'information' are discussed above.
[127] Clause 60.2 ECC.

information in his or her possession and which is referred to in the site information. This interpretation is consistent with the policy of disclosure imposed on both parties in the conditions generally.

Clause 60.2 imposes a similar obligation upon the contractor to be familiar with the site, as do other forms. Notwithstanding this obligation, contractors routinely fail to conduct the necessary investigations and in practice it is often a basis for refusing claims. Past drafting provisions under engineering forms as well as past case law under building forms have struggled with this question. Research indicates that unclear contract wording or drafting results in uncertainty and a higher number of claims and variations.[128]

The ECC seeks to overcome some of the uncertainty associated with foreseeability tests by stating what assumptions will be made about the contractor's degree of knowledge of the risk, setting a clear standard against which it will be measured and offering the employer an incentive to disclose fully information to the contractor. Requirements to disclose site information are well known in other jurisdictions and in this regard the ECC provision moves closer to them.[129]

The contractor's knowledge is based not only on the 'Site Information' as defined but any publicly available information referred to *in* the site information. The definition of 'Site Information' is extended not only by the reference to and incorporation of the definition of 'Site' itself but also the inclusion of the 'surroundings' in the definition. Thus *prima facie* the references to such information by the employer effectively serve to shrink the employer's risk while increasing the contractor's risk. However, in fact, it rather serves to shrink both their risks because the contractor has not only more information with which to assess the risk, but information which in the past when it has come from the employer, the contractor has not always been able to rely upon. Once again, practice and drafting under the engineering form, e.g. clause 11(1) of the ICE 6th and clause 11.1 of the FIDIC 4th, and building forms differ, and while the engineering forms seem to impose a disclosure obligation on the employer, the issue is not beyond doubt. The result is that the contractor should be able to take better account of the risk. The result should be a 'win-win' situation as described by Latham. The 'win-win' perspective was present in the drafter's intentions from the outset. John G. Perry states:

> [d]evelop the terms of the contract to embody the interests of both owners and contractors, recognising the goals of each and the ability of each to control and reduce specified risks and costs. Develop a formal contracting plan in depth as a means of arriving at a logical approach to risk management based on the desired project objectives.[130]

[128] CHOY, W.K. and SIDWELL, A.C. Sources of Variations in Australian Construction Contracts. *Building Economist*, 1991, **30**(3), 25–30.

[129] See e.g. *Morrison Knudsen Company Inc* v. *Alaska* 519 P 2d 834 (S Ct Alaska) 1974; and Alberta in *Opron Construction Co Ltd* v. *Alaska* (1994) 14 CLR (2d) 97; and *Begro Construction Ltd* v. *St Mary River District* (1994) 15 CLR (2d) 150.

[130] PERRY, JOHN G., see n. 7 above, p. 204.

The provision serves to overcome the limitations which past practice and case law have imposed; that is, less disclosure as a matter of course with the ensuing higher risk. The result should be better informed decision making.

The intent to achieve more sharing[131] of the responsibility for determining and assessing physical conditions is evident in other aspects of the provision as well as the risk allocation rules that were adopted by the drafters in formulating the provision. In the first instance, the contractor too must take some steps to be informed of the site conditions. At a minimum a visual inspection of the site is required. No necessity for physical tests or boreholes etc. is imposed as a matter of course; however, if such tests and the like would provide 'information which an experienced contractor could reasonably be expected ... to obtain'[132] then they should be undertaken as the contractor will be assumed to have their results in any case with the consequent effect on any later claim for a compensation event under subclause (12) that may be made. Turning to the motivation of the drafters, the clause was based on two of the six leading principles adopted for risk allocation in the NEC. That is, risks which are outside the contractor's control should usually be allocated to the employer; and to a lesser degree, that risks should not be allocated to a party who may be unable to sustain the consequences if the risk occurs.[133]

The second occasion when physical conditions are referred to in clause 60 concerns inconsistencies in the site information. Thus, if there is an inconsistency within the site information the contractor is assumed to have taken into account the physical conditions more favourable to doing the work.[134] The drafters see this provision as simply a restatement of the *contra proferentem* rule but in fact it is actually more than this. The *contra proferentem* rule means 'against the party putting forward' and is a rule of interpretation of a document in case of ambiguity against the party whose document it is or who has drafted it.[135] Eggleston suggests that clause 60.3 has the effect of overruling all four factors in clause 60.2 when there is an inconsistency in the site information.[136] The four factors once again are those the contractor is assumed to have taken into account in judging physical conditions: the site information; publicly available information referred to in the site information; information available from

---

[131] KORNHAUSER, LEWIS A. has done some early work on the how risk averse parties view contract choice: see Kornhauser. Reliance, Reputation and Breach of Contract. *Journal of Law and Economics*, 1983, **26**, 691; and Kornhauser. An Introduction to the Economic Analysis of Contract Damages. *University of Colorado Law Review*, 1986, **57**, 683.

[132] Clause 60.2 ECC.

[133] PERRY, JOHN G., see n. 7 above, p. 204.

[134] Clause 60.3 ECC.

[135] BURKE, JOHN. *Jowitt's Dictionary of English Law*, 2nd edn. Sweet & Maxwell, London, 1997, vol. 1, p. 477; see also the guidance notes NEC on clause 60.3 ECC 59.

[136] Eggleston, see n. 48 above, p. 208.

visual inspection of the site; and other information which an experienced contractor could reasonably be expected to obtain. However, this interpretation appears to go further than necessary.[137] Two of the four factors – information from the visual inspection, and other information which an experienced contractor could be expected to obtain – will normally be outside what is included in the site information. This is because site information is intended to contain only factual information.[138] In addition, the contractor's knowledge with respect to these two factors will likely be construed as that existing prior to formation of the contract or the 'Contract Date'. This follows in part from the limitation of the experienced contractor's judgment to that known at the contract date under clause 60.1(12). This too would seem to suggest the *contra proferentem* rule would really only have a role to play on the first two of the four factors stated.

There is a second point, which Eggleston also makes, in that clause 60.3 'appears to be wholly contrary to the contractor's duty to use reasonable skill and care when he is responsible for design'.[139] The point had been developed, albeit somewhat differently, by the commentator earlier in his text when he wrote:

> [clause 60.3] states that if there is inconsistency in the site information the contractor is assumed to have taken into account the physical conditions more favourable to doing the work. Perfectly reasonable, if not perhaps a little generous to the contractor, for employer's design and where the contractor is simply building the works. But apply the clause to contractor's design and what then are the consequences? Surely the essence of sound design is that it should cater for the worst conditions which might be expected not the best.[140]

A reply may be given to this proposition. That is, the intention behind clause 60.3 is to address inconsistencies in the site information *alone*. To seek to apply the provision to inconsistencies in relation to design and which are rather more appropriately addressed in the works information strains the meaning of the provision. In addition, the design inconsistency may also be addressed through the mechanisms in clause 17.1; namely ambiguities and inconsistencies, and in clause 60.1, compensation events. The *contra proferentem* rule notwithstanding insofar as design is concerned, the drafters have stated:

> [i]f an inconsistency becomes apparent between the Works Information provided by the *Employer* and a design which is part

---

[137] It has been noted that Eggleston's interpretations (*ibid.*) have largely been made without the benefit of experience using the form: see JONES, DAVID, review of *The New Engineering Contract, A Commentary*, by Brian Eggleston, *Construction Law Journal*, 1997, **13**, 139, 140.

[138] Guidance notes NEC on clause S1.1, 23.

[139] Eggleston, see n. 48 above, p. 208.

[140] Eggleston, see n. 48 above, pp. 110–111.

of the Works Information provided by the *Contractor* and included in part two of the Contract Data, the instruction [under clause 17.1] would be to require the design to comply with the *Employer's* Works Information. Such change would not be a compensation event ...[141]

Both clauses, it may be argued, are more specific in their application and hence should govern over the more general provisions in clause 60.3 that address site information.

There are other criticisms of clauses 60.1(12) and 60.2 that may be made. In particular, two foreseeability tests unnecessarily complicate the application of the tests in practice and when reading the two clauses together. It is also unclear under the provisions at what point in time the tests should be applied: pre-contract, or as at the contract date? In addition ambiguity is introduced by virtue of two contractors being involved: one the party contractor and one notional and experienced third party contractor. In effect, the knowledge or experience of the party contractor is thereby equated with the *notional* experienced contractor in every instance in judging physical conditions. In addition, there is too much repetition in clause 60.2, even if only for emphasis.

Thus, it is possible to encounter the same 'information' at least three times. That is, as 'Site Information'; or as publicly available information 'referred to' in the 'Site Information'; or as information which the experienced contractor could 'reasonably be expected to have or to obtain' in any event. Notwithstanding the qualification in the third bullet point with regard to this last type of information being 'other' information, the same reading of the clause, hence the triplication, can be argued. These two clauses, it should be underscored, are not the only provisions that address site information either. Thus the clauses must also be construed as defined in clause 11.2(6). The result is that a good case may be put forward that the term 'Site Information' could have been simplified by either removing the definition altogether from clause 11.2 or further consolidating these three references and reducing some of the repetition.

Taking the consolidation suggestion such action would not have to materially affect the few other references to site information in the form and could actually improve the application of the tests in the more problematic physical conditions clause. The other references to site information are in clauses 54.1 and 55.1. The following three *redrafted* subclauses may thus be suggested:

11.2(6) Site Information is information available to the *Contractor* and which
- describes the Site and its surroundings or
- is obtainable from a visual inspection of the Site or
- is in the documents which the Contract Data states it is in.

---

[141] Guidance notes NEC on clause 17.1 ECC, 31.

60.1(12) The *Contractor* encounters physical conditions which
- are within the Site,
- are not weather conditions and
- which an experienced contractor would not have allowed for.

60.2 The *Contractor* takes account of Site Information in judging physical conditions.

It can be remarked that the concepts of 'assumptions' and 'reasonableness' have been dropped from these redrafts and it is submitted without any loss in intended meaning. The wording is simpler and should be easier to apply. Discretion is maintained in the interpretation of the provision by retaining the express references to judgment and experience and the implied reference to knowledge. Once again, an experienced contractor may reasonably be expected to have or to obtain other information in making judgment.

If one leaves the reference to 'experience' in clause 60.2 the need specifically to include a reference to other information referred to in the 'Site Information' would not appear to be necessary. This is because an experienced contractor should presumably be expected to refer to it – *viz.* 'have it or to obtain it'. To have not allowed for it as well suggests a very small risk as sophisticated tendering practices today should realistically take account of every risk in bidding no matter how small.[142] In summary, while the physical conditions clauses still remain difficult to apply in practice, even after the suggested simplification, the risk allocation performed thereby should still be mitigated somewhat by the other important procedures in the contract, in particular those on early warning.

Weather

(13) A *weather measurement* is recorded
- within a calendar month,
- before the Completion Date[143] for the whole of the *works* and
- at the place stated in the Contract Data

the value of which, by comparison with the *weather data*, is shown to occur on average less frequently than once in ten years.[144]

Building contracts are designed to operate in all climates and across all seasons. Thus, as a general rule, adverse weather conditions will not excuse delays or lack of performance.[145] Notwithstanding the benign attitude of the law toward adverse weather conditions the drafters of the NEC have sought to balance the risks which the weather presents in an

---

[142]   SMITH, ROBERT J., see n. 111 above, 550 referring to *No Dispute: Strategies for Improvement in the Building and Construction Industry*. National Public Works Conference, National Building and Construction Council, Sydney, 1990 has written about the benefit-to-cost ratio of using better contracting practices.

[143]   Clause 11.2(12) ECC.

[144]   Clause 60.1(13) ECC. This wording differs from that in the First Edition.

[145]   *Maryon* v. *Carter* (1830) 4 Car & P 295, 172, ER 711.

objective fashion. This has been achieved by moving away from subjective assessments of when the weather has affected the contractor's performance to empirical measures of what conditions the contractor should generally expect to prevail and thus in which conditions the contractor must be able to perform work without hindrance. This is wholly consistent with the meaning of the term 'risk' and clearly differs with events which have uncertain outcomes; R.F. Fellows states:

> Often the word 'risk' is assumed to relate to circumstances where the outcome is not known for certain; in consequence all forecasts contain some elements of risk. The differentiation between risk and uncertainty is not always appreciated, yet it can be critical. *Risk* is where the outcome of an event, or each set of possible outcomes, can be predicted on the basis of statistical probability. (For example will it rain tomorrow? How much rain is expected tomorrow? How much rain is expected tomorrow between 8 am and 6 pm?). Other events have outcomes which are *uncertain*; they cannot be predicted via statistical probability and the probability of their occurrence is unknown/unquantifiable. Clearly, as records become more extensive, areas of uncertainty become areas of risk and so their treatment in construction projects, and in construction contracts, alters.[146]

The parties agree to certain weather parameters that can be compared to the actual weather conditions that existed on site.[147] The parameters are referred to as the '*weather measurements*'[148] in section 6 of part one of the Contract Data. The weather measurements will be recorded for each calendar month on site, for instance, for:

- the cumulative rainfall (mm)
- the number of days with rainfall more than 5 mm
- the number of days with minimum air temperature less than 0 degrees Celsius
- the number of days with snow lying at ... hours GMT
  and these measurements.

The guidance notes point out that these parameters have been selected as having the most significant effect on construction work in the United Kingdom. However, sites in other countries will undoubtedly prefer to amend and add alternative measurements depending upon their location. For instance, wind speeds may be exceedingly relevant, snow may not

---

[146] FELLOWS, R.F. *The Management of Risk*, (ed. HARLOW, PETER). CIOB, Ascot, 1996, Construction Papers 65.

[147] The importance of choosing the weather parameters very carefully to avoid unintentional risk allocations and ensure fairness to both parties is illustrated by some examples. VALENTINE, D.G. The New Engineering Contract: Part 2 – a New Language. *Construction Law Journal*, 1991, **12**, 313–314.

[148] '*Weather measurements*' is an identified term in this respect.

fall on site and both cumulative and daily rainfall totals may have to be adjusted upward. These weather measurements may then be compared to agreed weather data[149] that are compiled by weather agencies and inserted in section 6 of part one of the Contract Data. The weather data *per se* are the records of past weather measurements for each calendar month, which were recorded at an agreed place and which are made available by the weather agency.[150] If there are no recorded weather data available, assumed values for a ten-year return period for each weather measurement for each calendar month are made.[151] The weather measurements may then be compared to the assumed values.

The place where the weather is to be recorded by the parties is agreed and the ten-year return period is taken as the norm. If the weather conditions exceed the levels in the weather data this is treated as a compensation event under subclause (13). Weather conditions that the weather data indicates are likely to occur within any given ten-year time period are at the contractor's risk. The contractor is assumed to have submitted the tender with knowledge of these conditions and priced accordingly.[152]

Therefore, some balance had to be struck in these choices. The word 'month' has several meanings. It may mean one of the twelve unequal parts into which the calendar year is divided; it may mean the period which, beginning on any day of a calendar month other than the first, ends on the day next before the corresponding day of the next month; or it may denote a lunar month, that is to say, a period consisting of 28 days.[153] The use of the term 'calendar month' in the ECC is still exceptional and almost all time frames are referred to in weeks in the other clauses save those concerning weather. 'Month' is defined in the Interpretation Act 1978, Schedule 1 to mean 'calendar month' and as such the qualification does not add anything on United Kingdom contracts.[154]

Determining whether a compensation event has occurred will be done using the testing procedures in the contract. Thus one can expect that either the supervisor will carry out tests when the issue arises or the contractor will carry them out with the supervisor in attendance if the supervisor wishes.[155] The testing and the measurements must be precise. The time frame in question will be the day – measured on a 24-hour basis – when the weather measurements are said to have exceeded, within a calendar month, those which do not occur on average less

---

[149] 'Weather data' is an identified term.

[150] Section 6 part one Contract Data.

[151] Section 6 part one Contract Data.

[152] NORRIS, C. *et al. Project Risk Analysis and Management.* The Association of Project Managers, London, April 1991, p. 91.

[153] See *Halsbury's Laws of England*, 4th edn, vol. 45, paragraph 1107. See generally on the reckoning of calendar months, *Migotti* v. *Colvill* (1879) 4 CPD 233.

[154] See generally on the reckoning of calendar months, *Migotti* v. *Colvill* (1879) 4 CPD 233.

[155] See generally clause 40 ECC.

frequently than once in ten years. It becomes a comparison of the weather measurements to the weather data. If the weather data are exceeded using this test the matter proceeds as a notifiable compensation event and may be assessed accordingly. The weather compensation event is ultimately a good example of the principles of probability in action. To illustrate that there is still arbitrariness in the drafting decision made, Perry notes, with regard to the choice of one calendar month and a ten-year return period, that the 'adoption of a 2-calendar month period would reduce the contractor's risk whilst a 20 year return period would increase it'.[156]

The NEC provisions regarding the weather have been developed in consultation with the United Kingdom Meteorological Office.[157] This Office, or its equivalents in other jurisdictions, may serve as the agency providing weather data for part one purposes. Their operation, in practice, has been good and the objective probabilistic criteria adopted have all but eliminated arguments over this issue on the job site.[158]

Employer's risk events

(14) An *Employer's* risk event occurs.[159]

The employer's risks are listed in clause 80.1 of the ECC. Broadly, the risks fall into six general categories:

(1) claims and proceedings;
(2) certain loss of or damage to plant and materials supplied to the contractor until receipt and acceptance;
(3) certain loss of or damage to the works, plant and materials;
(4) certain loss of or damage to parts of the works with exceptions;
(5) certain loss of or damage to the works and equipment, plant and materials retained on site after termination with exceptions; and
(6) additional risks as agreed – these additional employer's risk events may be agreed and inserted in the optional statements of part one of the Contract Data. The proforma leaves space for three such events.[160]

The contractor, from the starting date, carries those risks which are not carried by the employer until the defects certificate has been issued.[161] Any employer's risk event within the meaning of clause 80.1 that occurs is compensable according to subclause (14). Notification of the compensation event follows the procedures in clause 61.

---

[156] PERRY, JOHN G., see n. 7 above, 207.
[157] Guidance notes NEC on clause 60.1(13) ECC, at 60. Details of the agency and the services it provides may be obtained from one of its offices whose addresses are contained in Appendix 6 of the guidance notes NEC, 130. BROOME, JON C. and PERRY, JOHN G. Experiences of the Use of the New Engineering Contract. *Engineering, Construction and Architectural Management*, 1995, **2**(4), 278.
[158] BROOM, JON C. and PERRY, JOHN G. *ibid.*, 278.
[159] Clause 60.1(14) ECC.
[160] See discussion clause 80.1 ECC below.
[161] Clause 81.1 ECC.

An interesting point arises in the interpretation of clause 60.1(14); does it conflict in operation with clause 83.1?[162] Different remedies are provided under each clause. Thus, under clause 60.1(14), the normal assessment procedures under clause 63 govern; however, under clause 83.1, the compensation given is a full indemnity. Hence there is the possibility of two potentially different remedies being open. It is submitted that if two remedies are found to pertain then they should be treated as alternative and a clear election required as to which of the remedies a party intends to rely upon.

Employer's use of the works

(15) The *Project Manager* certifies take over of a part of the *works* before both Completion[163] and the Completion Date.[164]

The employer's use of the works is also a compensation event under subclause (15) in limited circumstances. To understand the operation of the subclause it must be read with clause 35. Pursuant to clause 35 possession of parts of the site returns to the employer when the employer takes over[165] those parts of the works which occupy the site. No mention is made initially of certification with respect to the taking over. However, and notwithstanding there may be no take over of either any part or the whole site, the whole site still returns to the employer upon certification. Take over may also occur or be deemed to occur in certain circumstances when the employer makes use of any part of the works before completion has been certified.[166] The intention of the employer in this regard may be notified at an early warning meeting.[167] This in itself is not compensable under subclause (15). However, the project manager must ultimately certify that date, and the extent of the take over, and also do so within one week of the date.[168] If the use is not for a reason either stated in the works information or to accommodate the contractor's methods of working then the take over is compensable under subclause (15). Apart from use, take over in general as well is compensable under subclause (15) upon certification and provided, once again, it is before both completion and the completion date as defined. Notification of the compensation event follows the usual procedures in clause 61.[169]

---

[162] Eggleston, see n. 48 above, p. 206 raises the point but leaves it open and invites employers to consider with their lawyers and insurers whether clause 60.1(14) is either necessary or desirable.

[163] Clause 11.2(13) ECC.

[164] Clause 60.1(15) ECC. The 'Completion Date' is defined in clause 11.2(12) ECC. This clause is new compared to the First Edition.

[165] Cf 10.1 FIDIC Orange Book 1st part I.

[166] Clause 35.3 ECC.

[167] See clause 16 ECC.

[168] Clause 35.4 ECC.

[169] Other consequences also follow including those in relation to the contractor's rights of access under clause 43.3 ECC.

Further provision by the employer

(16) The *Employer* does not provide materials, facilities and samples for tests as stated in the Works Information.[170]

Both the employer and the contractor are required to provide materials, facilities and samples for tests and inspections as stated in the works information[171] under clause 40.2.[172] The failure of the employer to act accordingly is compensable under subclause (16).[173]

Assumptions by the project manager

(17) The *Project Manager* notifies a correction to an assumption[174] about the nature of a compensation event.[175]

Clause 60.1(17) is a new provision that was added to the Second Edition. It is one of only two compensation events[176] that may involve an actual reduction of the prices.[177] During the course of the compensation event procedure the project manager may have to make certain assumptions about the event itself and for the purpose of giving instructions to the contractor in submitting quotations. The assumptions will be made when the project manager decides that the effects of the compensation event are too uncertain to be forecast reasonably.[178] The project manager's assessment of the event will be based upon these assumptions. Practice under the form has revealed that project managers are quite willing to rely upon the use of such assumptions.[179] If, however an assumption about the nature of the event is later found to be have been wrong a correction must be issued in respect of it.[180] Subclause (17) gives the contractor a right to recompense if the assumption was with respect to the 'nature' of the event. It has been suggested that there is an incompatability in the wording of the clauses in this way: 'clause 60.1(17) refers to assumptions about the "nature" of a compensation event whereas clause 61.6 is about assumptions on the "effects" of a compensation event'.[181] A careful reading of both clauses reveals this interpretation is unsustainable. Both clauses refer to assumptions about the nature of (compensation) events although only clause 61.6 deals with when those assumptions about the nature of the events must be made, that is, when effects of the compensation event are too uncertain to be forecast reasonably.

---

[170] Clause 60.1(16) ECC.
[171] Clause 11.2(5) ECC.
[172] Cf the wording in clause 60.1(10) 'a required test or inspection'.
[173] See discussion clause 40.2 ECC above.
[174] The assumptions are made under clause 61.1 ECC.
[175] Clause 60.1(17) ECC.
[176] The other is clause 60.1(1) ECC.
[177] See clause 63.2 ECC.
[178] Clause 61.6 ECC.
[179] Clause 61.6 ECC. BROOME, JON C. and PERRY, JOHN G., see n. 157 above, 278–279.
[180] Clause 61.6 ECC.
[181] Eggleston, see n. 48 above, p. 207

While subclause (17) would thus appear to be narrower than clause 61.6 in respect of which it is directed, it is arguable that no distinction should be made insofar as its application is concerned for this reason. While the project manager may well make assumptions expressly or impliedly in the taking of the many other decisions that must be made regarding the works, a compensation event will only arise if the assumption itself is in respect of a compensation event. It is noteworthy that one event may be susceptible to recovery on two bases if an assumption in respect of it proves to be incorrect.

A reason for the project manager making assumptions about the nature of the event is clearly to expedite the procedure and provide some basis upon which a quotation may be given by the contractor and remedial action taken. Early reports confirm that project managers are stating their assumptions in practice for reasons relating to cost control.[182] The contractor is encouraged to proceed with the actions agreed comfortable with the knowledge that if the matter proves to be different than expected the contractor still need not bear the risk of agreeing to take the action. The risk remains on the employer throughout in the ordinary course. With actions being taken of this sort employers undoubtedly have a strong interest in the most experienced project managers. Those project managers with long experience will justifiably be cautious in the assumptions that they have to make. In those cases where assumptions have to be made they will be of limited scope to reduce the magnitude of the risk carried. In practical terms the project manager will seek to address the event only insofar as it needs to be addressed on the strength of or given the information available. In other words, given a choice the project manager will not work any further ahead than actual foresight extends. The result may be that further quotations from the contractor will be called for as the effects of the event are dealt with in smaller portions but the project manager has this power to do so and it may better serve the interests of the employer. It has been noted that the alternative quotation procedure is consistent with modern programme analysis software.[183]

There is an important distinction to be made between the forecasts that the project manager makes in respect of the event and assumptions made regarding those forecasts. Once again, it is only when the assumptions prove incorrect that the event will be compensable under subclause (17). With no definition for either the term 'assumption' or 'forecast' nor a generally accepted usage, it will be incumbent upon the project manager to ensure, for the contractor's sake, precisely when either of the two terms is being used. Failure to state clearly and accurately which assumptions are being made will lead to uncertainty and potential disputes. Incorrect forecasts, or forecasts shown by later recorded information to have been wrong, and that were used in the assessment of a compensation event, give no equivalent right to additional compensation. Once again, as this contrasts with the case of an incorrect

---

[182] *Ibid.*, 215.
[183] EVANS, JOHN R., see n. 84 above, pp. 9 and 57.

assumption *regarding* the forecast,[184] extra care will have to be taken throughout.

Breach of contract by the employer

(18) A breach of contract by the *Employer* which is not one of the other compensation events in this contract.[185]

Subclause (18) is an unusual but interesting provision that is intended to operate as an 'umbrella' to bring breaches of contract by the employer within the compensation event procedures.[186] The unusual aspect of the provision stems from the implication that it clearly gives rise to; that is, compensation events themselves are or amount to breaches of contract. It may seem peculiar to treat events that are anticipated and expressly provided for as breaches of contract. For the most part the compensation events are rather part of the *application* of the contract and not a breach of it.

> This is a useful sweep-up clause, covering any events which do not fall neatly within any of the other events. It is an advantage to the employer because if such an event occurs, it can be dealt with under the terms of this clause, thus preserving for the employer the delays damages provisions, if these have been used. The ambit of the clause is not limited to 'acts of prevention' by the employer, but it will probably not cover the full extent of what would otherwise be breaches of contract by the employer.[187]

The most interesting aspect of the subclause may be gleaned if one focuses not on the characterizations which are made of compensation events but the genuine attempt it makes to address unforeseeable events. In this regard the subclause shares more in common with hardship and similar type clauses than at first may be noticed. In fact, the umbrella provision coupled with the full compensation event procedure permits the renegotiation of the contract as a matter of course in respect of every technical or substantive breach of contract by the employer. Although this was not likely to have been the original intention of the drafters that fact need not detract from the utility of the provision in circumstances where its use is warranted. In those cases it can and may be expected to offer a significant means to overcome breaches of contract that might have otherwise ended the parties' relationship. Certainly, if it does operate in this fashion, it will be very important indeed and fully accord with the relational theoretical framework developed for the form.

This perspective on the provision contrasts markedly with that of Brian Eggleston. Eggleston seems to see the clause rather as a belated attempt by the drafters to shore up their drafting.

---

[184] See clause 65.2 ECC. Forecasts may also be made in other respects but once again are outside the compensation event procedure: see e.g. clauses 20.4, 53.3 and 65.3 ECC.
[185] Clause 60.1(18) ECC.
[186] Guidance notes NEC on clause 60.1(18) ECC, at 61.
[187] BIRKBY, GILLIAN, see n. 77 above, 26.

> There can be little doubt that when the NEC was first produced its promoters thought or hoped that they had devised a scheme which would eliminate end of contract claims ... And when the promoters realised that the list of compensation events in the First Edition of the NEC was by no means comprehensive of the employer's possible defaults, they revised the list for the Second Edition and included most significantly event number 18.[188]

Eggleston's view, however, seems beside the point. It also does not accord with the facts, which suggest a different perspective when first addressing the rationale behind compensation events and an evolution in the number of events which would be listed and where. With regard to the rationale one must return to the drafting objectives set out for the new form; one of which pertained to seeking greater clarity and simplicity in its operation and procedures and which was based upon flow charts.

> One of the benefits of using this approach to drafting has been that opportunities could be taken for simplifying the structure of the Contract as well as making sure that all procedures were not open ended or conflicting. For example, almost all circumstances, which may give rise to additional payment to the Contractor, are identified as Compensation Events. The procedure for dealing with these events is mainly set out in the Core Clauses ... This is in contrast to traditional forms of contract in which the procedure for compensation is different depending upon the nature of each event.[189]

The compensation event procedure does not distinguish between payment for work and payment as compensation nor does the procedure distinguish between events giving rise to either extra time or extra money. This procedure contrasts markedly with other leading forms. For example, under JCT forms variations, payments for loss and expense, and extensions of time are dealt with in different ways.[190] As suggested by the drafters, compensation events are now also set out in main options B and D,[191] certain secondary option clauses,[192] and may even be added to by the employer or project manager in the Contract Data.[193] Not just the possibility but the *advisability* of adding such additional compensation events is adverted to by the drafters – in fact, five examples are given in the guidance notes.[194]

---

[188] EGGLESTON, see n. 48 above, p. 197. CHEVIN, DENISE. No Claims Bonus. *Building*, 12 August 1994, 16–17 equates the compensation event procedure with claims procedures.

[189] Guidance notes Consultation Document, 3.

[190] For example, clauses 13, 25 and 26 respectively of JCT 80.

[191] Clauses 60.4, 60.5 and 60.6 ECC.

[192] Clauses J1.2, T1.1 and U1.1 ECC.

[193] See the optional statements in part one of the Contract Data where the proforma leaves space for three such cases.

[194] Guidance notes NEC on clause 60 ECC, at 57.

Thus, far from suggesting the list of compensation events in the clause was comprehensive, even before the eighteenth event was added in the Second Edition, it was seen very early on to be rather the minimum number of events which the drafters recommend be carried as employer risks. If one looks to the original NEC specification it can also be remarked that just eleven compensation events were listed.[195] As such it can be seen that the increase in the number of events occurred after more reflection than suggested by Eggleston. Cornes on the other hand takes a more traditional view of the significance of the clause in relation to the problem area of employer extensions of time and for whose benefit such clauses are intended – contractor or employer – and concludes in favour of their enforceability.

> [O]n the First Edition ... a breach of contract by the Employer did not enable the Project Manager to extend time for completion, unless the breach was also a compensation event. The effect would be to render unenforceable the 'delay damages' provision and to replace the obligation of the Contractor to complete in the time originally required under the contract with an obligation to complete in a reasonable time. Those consequences are avoided on the Second Edition by making the Employer's breaches compensation events.[196]

This view is significant in overcoming previous limitations in the case law.

Extension of time provisions are inserted in contracts to benefit *both* the employer and the contractor.[197] Previously it was wrongly assumed, based on dicta in *Peak Construction (Liverpool) Ltd* v. *McKinney Foundations Ltd*,[198] that extension of time provisions were only inserted for the benefit of the employer. In the *Peak* case, Salmon LJ construed an extension of time provision against the employer using the *contra proferentem rule* of interpretation and which assumed that the clause was thus inserted to benefit the employer.

Compensation events in the bill of quantities options
In addition to the compensation events in clause 60.1, further events are set out in the priced and target contracts with '*bill of quantities*' in clauses 60.4 to 60.6. The clauses address three separate issues: changes in quantities in general, difference in quantities that delay completion, and mistakes in the bills of quantities.

---

[195] BARNES, DR MARTIN *Specification and Partial Draft for a New Style Conditions of Contract*. Martin Barnes Project Management, Deloittes, London, December 1986, p. 50.

[196] CORNES. The Second Edition of the New Engineering Contract. *International Construction Law Review*, 1996. 107.

[197] *Hudson's*, vol. 2, pp. 1172–1173.

[198] *Peak Construction (Liverpool) Ltd* v. *McKinney Foundations Ltd* (1970) 1 BLR 111, CA.

For clause 60.4 to operate in the first instance there must be a variation in the quantities in the bill of quantities where either the priced or target contract is being employed. If so, the result will turn upon which of the clauses in clauses 60.4 to 60.6 is applicable.

If there is a difference between the total quantity of work done and the quantity stated for an item in the bill of quantities[199] at the contract date a compensation event occurs under clause 60.4 if two tests are satisfied concurrently:

- if the difference causes the actual cost[200] per unit of quantity to change; and
- the product of the rate in the bill of quantities for the item at the contract date and the final total quantity of work done exceeds 0.1% of the total of the prices at the contract date.[201]

Hence, while a simple change in quantities itself is not sufficient for a compensation event to occur it is a necessary condition in addition to satisfying the two tests. Both tests address quantitative measures. The first test simply sets out to determine whether a change has occurred. If so, the second test sets out a threshold for the change which must be met if it is to result in a compensation event. The threshold, set at 0.1% as referred to above, serves to preclude very small changes which are really *de minimus* or too small to be significant. As in the case of changes in the law that reduce the total actual cost and the prices correspondingly,[202] if the actual cost per unit of the quantity is reduced so is the affected rate. In this regard both clause T1.1 and clause 60.4 operate reciprocally either to increase or reduce the prices[203] and thus benefit either the contractor or the employer respectively.

The clause is intended to apply only to changes which do not result from changes to the works information which are governed by and remain subject to clause 60.1 irrespective of the effect on quantities.[204] Under main option D, the employer assumes the risk for changes in quantities and which results in adjustment to the target price.

In contrast to clause 60.4, under clause 60.5, if the difference between the final total quantity of the work done and the quantity stated for an item in the bill of quantities at the contract date simply delays completion, quite apart from any change to actual unit costs irrespective of their

---

[199]   The bill of quantities is an identified term for purposes of the optional statements of part two of the Contract Data.

[200]   'Actual cost' is a defined term and differs according to whether the priced or target contracts are being used, see clauses 11.2(28) and 11.2(27) ECC respectively.

[201]   Cf clause 52.3 FIDIC 4th providing for the addition to or subtraction from the contract price of a sum when a notional 15% figure is exceeded.

[202]   See discussion clause T1.1 ECC above.

[203]   See also clause 60.6; these are the only secondary option clauses permitting a reduction in the prices.

[204]   Guidance notes NEC on clause 60.4 ECC, at 66. See generally GOULD, NICHOLAS. 'Automatic Variations Exist': The Engineer's Power to Re-Rate. *Construction Law Journal*, 1986, **2**, 95.

magnitude, a compensation event also occurs. Here it is the delay to completion which is central to the occurrence of a compensation event and not any differences *per se* between various versions of the bills of quantities themselves and which are not compensable. This non-compensability for such changes in any differing versions of bills of quantities follows from the definitions given to the price for work done to date in both the priced and target contracts. In respect of the priced contract it is based in part on the actual quantity of the work which the contractor has completed[205] while in the target contract it is based on the actual cost which the contractor has paid plus the fee.[206]

The third case giving rise to a compensation event involves mistakes in the bill of quantities. In this situation, if the project manager corrects such a mistake and it is either a departure from the agreed method of measurement or is due to ambiguities or inconsistencies, each such correction is a compensation event which may lead to reduced prices.[207] The method of measurement is an identified term in the optional statements of part one of the Contract Data in respect of both the priced and target contracts in main options B and D. The ambiguities and inconsistencies referred to should be understood to refer to those described in clause 17.1 and namely in or between the documents which form part of the contract[208] and presumably would not extend to construing the documents.

The clause gives only one ground for complaint; mistakes in the bill of quantities. However, it gives two bases upon which the contractor may argue that a mistake exists. In the first instance, and which case may be more readily and objectively established than the second case, the mistake is determined with reference to the parties' agreed method of measurement. In the second case, a 'mistake' is said to exist due to an ambiguity or an inconsistency in the bill itself or the bill as construed in relation to one of the other contract documents. It can be seen that this second category could be said to be *subjective* versus the more *objective* first category. It is likely that the second category will lead to more alleged compensation events from contractors than the first category because of its broader scope. The check on the second category is that the project manager must actually correct the mistake in the bill for it to be compensable. This implies acceptance on the project manager's part in the manner envisaged by clauses 13 and 14. In effect, without the project manager's 'correction', to be read as acceptance that a mistake exists, the matter will end; assuming compliance with the other relevant provisions in clauses 13 and 14 of the ECC if necessary. Conversely, if the correction is made it is treated as a compensation event and may lead to reduced prices.[209] It may lead to the reduced prices as a result of the outcome of

---

[205] Clause 11.2(25) ECC.
[206] Clause 11.2(230 ECC.
[207] Clause 60.5 ECC.
[208] See discussion clause 17.1 ECC above.
[209] Clause 60.6 ECC.

the notification procedure in clause 61. The provisions in clause 60.6 are consistent with the absence of a formal hierarchy or precedence of documents clauses. Justin Sweet notes this topic raises the issue of 'coherence' in the contract documents and how the parties must take into account complicated performance relationships across the documents.[210]

Secondary option compensation events

In addition to the eighteen compensation events which are set out in clause 60.1, and any other compensation events which may be defined in part one of the Contract Data, four compensation events are also set out in the secondary option clauses, namely J1.2, T1.1 U1.1 and Y2.4. They may be referred to in turn.

Secondary option clause J governs advanced payments to the contractor.[211] Once an advanced payment has been agreed by the parties it is incumbent upon the employer to fulfil the obligation to make the advanced payment and any delay in respect thereof is a compensation event.[212] In this regard the matter falls to be considered under the routine compensation procedure under core clause 60. This procedure follows notwithstanding that the matter could have been dealt with alternatively through the award of interest on the late payment but this was viewed by the drafters as inappropriate given the potential significance of the financial consequences for the contractor.[213]

Pursuant to secondary option T1, a change in the law of the country in which the site is located is a compensation event if it occurs after the 'Contract Date'.[214] Unlike the other compensation events, which operate as a matter of course to shift the risk for the event from the contractor to the employer, option T may reallocate the risk to either party depending upon the effect of the change in the law. The drafters intended 'law' to be construed broadly inclusively of statutes, ordinances, decrees, regulations and bylaws.[215] Thus, if the effect of the change in the law is to reduce the total actual cost for the contract the prices will be reduced.[216] One check on the procedure is that generally applicable to compensation events in clause 63.1; only changes which affect the contractor's 'Actual Cost' are included. Examples of changes in the law which do not go to actual costs would include revenue law changes affecting the contractor's profits. Conversely, any change in the law which does affect actual costs, namely those impacting directly on the items contained in the SCC and SSCC, would be relevant.

---

[210] SWEET, JUSTIN, see n. 35 above, p. 419. A further means of ranking contract documents that Sweet notes is simply assigning the power to make binding interpretations to a designated third party.

[211] See discussion clause J1 ECC.

[212] Clause J1.2 ECC.

[213] Guidance notes NEC on clause J1.2 ECC, 83.

[214] Clause T1.1 ECC. The 'contract date' is the date when the contract came into existence: clause 11.2(3) ECC.

[215] Guidance notes NEC on clause T1.1 ECC, 89.

[216] See clause T1.1 ECC. Both 'actual cost' and 'prices' are defined terms.

The procedures regarding notification of an option T event are also unusual in that they do not necessarily have to follow those set out in clause 61 of the ECC. Thus, notification to the contractor of an actual change in the law may originate with the project manager who can also instruct the contractor to submit quotations.[217] Although option T provides no further details regarding the procedure or timing, it is submitted that it is again reasonable to assume that the clause 6 procedures would also apply.

Clause T1.1 was originally contained albeit in shorter form in a core clause of the Consultation Document which provided: 'The law governing the Site is changed after Acceptance'.[218] However, this wording was problematic in at least two senses. It was ambiguous and in its resemblance to a choice of law clause may have caused additional confusion. Under the current provision a change in the law now operates only exceptionally as a compensation event, unlike formerly when it would have operated in all cases falling within the core clause. It may have been felt that the provision was too generous as a result and was therefore circumscribed in subsequent operation.

Under U1.1 any delay to the work or additional or changed work caused as a result of the application of the Construction (Design and Management) Regulations 1994 is treated as a compensation event if an experienced contractor could not reasonably have been expected to have foreseen it.[219] The specific application of the Regulations to United Kingdom construction work alone resulted in the clause being included as a secondary option clause only.

The final secondary option clause for compensation events is contained in secondary option Y (UK) 2 and provides that suspension of performance is a compensation event if the contractor exercises the right to suspend performance under the Housing Grants, Construction and Regeneration Act 1996.

Notifying compensation events

The procedures for the notification of compensation events are some of the most complex in the contract. The complexities arise for various reasons. The subject matter first of all deals largely with unknowns. Lack of knowledge, either hindsight or foresight, in how the matter was or is to be dealt with, can necessitate the making of assumptions about the event. These assumptions themselves may prove either uncertain or wrong. Quotations in respect of the event add complexity as does the whole instruction procedure; instructions it may be noted, which follow consequent upon other instructions which have proved to be either wrong or in need of correction. When the intricacies of the early warning

---

[217] Clause T1.1 ECC. The contractor would notify the project manager of such an event rather pursuant to clause 61.3 ECC.

[218] Consultation Document clause 60.1(17). Other changes in terminology to note include that to 'Contract Date' (cl 11.2(3)) from 'Acceptance'.

[219] Clause U1.1 ECC.

procedure are added to the notification procedures it can be seen why they are so complex. Those procedures are the subject of the remainder of this section.

The notification procedure broadly breaks down along three lines for actual or anticipated compensation events involving the following:

- prior instructions or changes to a decision of the project manager or supervisor;
- potential instructions from the project manager; and
- notices from the contractor.

Beginning with the first category, a relevant compensation event may arise under any of subclauses (1), (4), (7), (8), (10), (17), although further compensation events could be added in this category by the parties in part one of the Contract Data. In every case but subclauses (10) and (17) an instruction from the project manager is involved. Under subclauses (10) and (17) the instruction comes from the supervisor. Two other potential compensation events which may be relevant to this classification arise under subclause (15) and clause 60.6 in main options B and D. However, in these cases unlike the others in this category, it is moreover the actions of the project manager in certifying and correcting the bill of quantities respectively rather than the giving of an instruction *per se* that is material. As will be noted below in both this category and the second category, for notification of compensation events the project manager will notify the contractor of the event and instruct the contractor to submit quotations.

The second category for notification of compensation events concerns primarily potential instructions from the project manager but which may also involve potential changed decisions as contemplated by clause 61.2. The instruction may pertain to matters either within the project manager's or the supervisor's normal jurisdiction. In a usual case the project manager would apprehend a compensation event and thus invite a quotation from the contractor to address it. The rationale is that, by giving the project manager the power to call for a quotation from the contractor in respect of a proposed instruction or changed decision, the time and cost involved in the course of action may be better assessed. 'This procedure follows from the view that the employer will want greater control in contracts of the future.'[220] Thus, the employer through the project manager will be able to prefer effects on time as opposed to cost and hence whether to pursue alternative quotations. This means not only is the contractor indifferent to the occurrence of the event but the method of dealing with it as well. The *quid pro quo* of giving the employer this degree of control was to assure the contractor of compensation for the full effects.

The third category of compensation event involves notices from the contractor to the project manager that an event which has either happened or which is expected to happen is a compensation event.[221] For the most

[220] NORRIS, G. *et al.*, see n. 152 above, pp. 89–90.
[221] Clause 61.3 ECC.

part these events would simply be those outside the first or second categories,[222] including clauses 60.4 and 60.5 in main options B and D, the secondary option clauses,[223] and any further compensation events added by the parties in part one of the Contract Data. The drafters envisage the events dividing into three categories themselves within this third category: those involving the failure of the employer, project manager, supervisor or others to fulfil their obligations under subclauses (2), (3), (5), (6), (11), (16) and (18); the project manager withholding an acceptance under subclause (9); and a happening not caused by any party under subclauses (12) or (13). This classification *omits* the compensation events in main options B and D as well as those in the secondary option clauses. The categories and the events which would fall within them do so only as a general rule and they are not intended to be viewed as wholly mutually exclusive. Thus, for instance, subclause (1) could exceptionally fall in *both* the first and second categories of compensation events.

One unusual example of a further compensation event that could be added by the parties in part one of the Contract Data, would be the obligation of the contractor to give notice of a change in the law if option T were adopted and the contractor believed that it was a compensation event. This could be quite an onerous obligation given the number of laws which change in countries, the contractor's potential unfamiliarity with foreign laws, the uncertainty often surrounding when laws come into force and the short time period for notice itself from the contractor.

To qualify as one of the events in respect of which the contractor must give notice to the project manager, three conditions in clause 61.3 must be satisfied:

- a belief by the contractor that the event is a compensation event;
- it is less than two weeks since the contractor became aware of the event; and
- the project manager has not notified the contractor of the event.

It may be noted that the current wording in clause 61.3 has changed from that in the First Edition. Formerly, one had to notify a compensation event within two weeks of becoming aware of it or lose the right. The question it raises is whether a different interpretation was intended. David Cornes suggests that the wording, when read with clause 61.4, does not require compensation events to be notified within two weeks of becoming aware of them and that, even if it did, whenever a quotation was sought from the contractor by the project manager would amount to waiver by the employer.[224]

These three conditions may be examined in turn. The first of the three conditions to be satisfied adds little to the operation of the clause as the contractor's belief in the event constituting a compensation event would

---

[222] For example, subclauses (2), (3), (5), (6), (9), (11), (12), (13), (14), (15), (16) and (18) ECC. Cf the division of compensation events in FC 61.

[223] For example, clauses J1.2, T1.1 and U1.1 ECC.

[224] Clause 61.3. CORNES, see n. 196, 107.

seem to be understood in any case based upon the fact of giving notice. However, it can be contrasted with the notice given under the early warning procedure that omits any reference to compensation events. The second condition is significant and, it is submitted, would appear to operate as a bar to the contractor giving late notice of the event. In the event of a refusal by the project manager to entertain late notification, the contractor could invoke the dispute procedures in clause 9. The third condition to be satisfied in clause 61.3 and referred to briefly once above is simply that the project manager must not have notified the contractor of the event.

It is the second condition that presents the most difficult issues. Several arguments can be advanced both in favour of as well as against an interpretation of the clause such that it would operate as a bar to the contractor giving late notice of the event. First, can clause 13.5, dealing with extending the period of reply to a communication, be used to extend the time period for notice of compensation events by the contractor? To try and answer this question clause 61.5, which deals with the failure of the contractor to give the early warning, should also be looked at, e.g. one outside the two week time limit in clause 61.3. This clause seems to suggest, on the one hand, that late notice is possible; however, limitations on the subject matter and the language used in the early warning clause itself would appear to contradict this assertion. That is, while an early warning should be given in respect of 'matters' which could increase the total of the prices, delay completion as defined or impair the performance of the works in use, these matters need not necessarily involve a compensation event.

Hence it may be asked whether clause 61.5 is only relevant if the matter giving rise to the early warning proves to be a compensation event as well? No clear answer appears on the wording of the form. In early practice under the form, and with regard to the early warning procedures, Broome and Perry found that the procedures were not always being followed even though the concept itself was endorsed.[225] It is suggested here that initial unfamiliarity with the use of the procedures as well as some of their inherent complexity may be partly responsible for the researchers' observations.

There are further real limitations on the argument that clause 13.5 supports any interpretation of clause 61.3 that it is not a bar. In particular, the fact that the project manager has no power to extend the time limit unless the parties have agreed to an extension before the reply is due is a real limitation. Clause 13.5 would also seem to be excluded by implication as a result of the third condition in clause 61.3 that the project manager has not notified the event to the contractor. That is, in the absence of notice by the project manager to the contractor of the event in question, a 'reply' as it were from the contractor appears to be excluded by definition. Similarly, and insofar as the project manager's power to

---

[225]   BROOME, JON C. and PERRY, JOHN G., see n. 157 above, 276.

extend time frames under clause 62.5 is concerned, it too fails a test of direct relevance. Clause 62.5 would seem to apply only to the submission of quotations for a compensation event and, as clause 61.3 in point of time *precedes* the quotation procedure, clause 62.5 does not assist the argument either.

Contrary to this argument Cornes finds significance in both the quotation procedure and the change in wording in the clause from that in the First Edition. Formerly, under the First Edition, one had to notify a compensation event within two weeks of becoming aware of it or lose the right.[226] The question that the change raises is whether a different interpretation was intended. Cornes suggests that the wording, when read with clause 61.4, does *not* require compensation events to be notified within two weeks of becoming aware of them.[227] Further, he argues that even if compensation events had to be notified within this time frame, whenever the project manager sought a quotation from the contractor would amount to waiver by the employer.[228] For Gillian Birkby the issue under the clause is rather the potential for difficulties in meeting the time frames.

> Clause 62.5 . . . allows the project manager to extend the time for the contractor to submit his quotation and for the project manager to make his reply, as long as they both agree on this before the end of their respective periods. Clearly, this need to assess compensation events immediately [when] they occur or in anticipation of them can cause difficulties, and unless adequate resources are devoted to this aspect of the project, it can itself cause further delay.[229]

In conclusion, while there is some support to the contrary, it is impossible to say that the project manager clearly has either the power or would be able to extend in favour of the contractor the two-week time limit for notice imposed in clause 61.3. Therefore, based upon some of the more favourable arguments that could be put forward in support of the late notice by the contractor, and the fact they may be countered on other interpretations, one may conclude the failure of the contractor to meet the notification time limit would preclude a compensation event arising. Such a conclusion is consistent with the policy of both early assessment as well as full and final assessment of compensation events which is generally held out under the ECC. It is also consistent with the wording of the same clause in the First Edition of the form which stated that the contractor 'may not notify a compensation event more than two weeks after he became aware of it'. The immediate question this interpretation raises if correct is whether it will operate harshly or unfairly on the contractor.

In reply, and at the outset, it may be noted that most standard forms impose time limits or notice requirements of one sort or another on the

---

[226]   Clause 61.3 NEC First Edition.
[227]   CORNES, see n. 196, 107.
[228]   *Ibid.*
[229]   BIRKBY, GILLIAN, see n. 77 above, 26.

contractor bringing claims for financial compensation under the contract. It is a question of interpretation in each case whether compliance with the notice provisions is a condition precedent to acceptance of the claim and recovery.[230] The ECC does not use the word 'claims' in its drafting in this sense although clearly the intent is that the compensation event procedure addresses this issue.[231]

The word 'claims' is used in the indemnity provisions in clauses 21.4, 80.1, 83.1 and trust fund provisions in clause V3.1(3) of the ECC. Conversely, the FIDIC Orange Book 1st part I uses the term 'claim' in its ordinary sense in clause 20 underscoring a fundamental difference in drafting philosophy with the NEC. The NEC has studiously avoided terms of art in its drafting in preference to a 'clean slate' approach. The drafters have sought to remove the background and context of the common law in this way. However, while the drafters could choose new terminology and thus seek to further their intention to remove the contract from the influence of the common law they could never do so entirely. In addition, and notwithstanding that many previous construction cases would have been decided under the wording of other ad hoc or standard forms of contract, those cases nevertheless provide the *context* in which the NEC will always be situated. Courts will be cognizant of these precedents and may still either directly borrow from or simply be inspired by them in their reasoning. Thus the NEC as shown in this discussion is paradoxically freed and yet still limited by previous jurisprudence and interpretations of other standard forms which have preceded it.

The intention behind the compensation event procedure is that the parties are motivated to assess the events quickly; but the drafters, framing the clause as they have, have left open the issue whether timely notice is a condition precedent to compensation. All the drafters say is that the 'stated time limit is intended to expedite the procedure so that dealing with compensation events a long time after they have occurred is avoided'.[232] However, this objective itself may not be achieved as the test in clause 61.3 is based upon the contractor's awareness of the event. The test is the same in this regard concerning early warning of matters with described potential consequences. As such it is a subjective not an objective test and no right to give notice and seek compensation under the contract will be or need be lost if the contractor acts within two weeks of becoming *aware* of the putative compensation event. This could, of course, be 'a long time after' the event occurred. On this interpretation the clause may not be as strict as perhaps the drafters intended but arguably still too strict or harsh in its operation for some.

---

[230] See *Blackford & Son (Calne) Ltd* v. *Christchurch Corpn* [1962] 1 Lloyd's Rep 349; *Tersons Ltd* v. *Stevenage Development Corpn* [1965] 1 QB 37, [1963] 3 All ER 863, CA; *London Borough of Merton* v. *Stanley Hugh Leach Ltd* (1985) 32 BLR 51.

[231] See lately on the topic of claims in general TRICKEY, G. *Presentation and Settlement of Contractors' Claims*, 2nd edn. E & FN Spon, London, 1999.

[232] Guidance notes NEC on clause 61.3 ECC, at 61.

A choice has been made and a balance has been struck. It would appear that the perceived advantages on site of settling issues one way *or the other* and thereby refocusing the parties' attention on looking forward rather than backward was seen as outweighing any potential hardship that could come from the contractor failing to give notice timeously. Once again, the loss of any right to give the notice would only arise after the contractor became aware of the right in the first place. The situation may thus be compared to that of limitation in the general law and which does not begin counting the period of limitation until the person had the knowledge to bring the action[233] as well as the right to do so.[234] While the notice period is indeed much shorter than that under the general law it is no more harsh or unfair in principle than the way in which the longer limitation also operates.

In addition to this, one must also refer to the right of the contractor to dispute loss of the right to give notice of a compensation event under the adjudication provisions of the contract. The dispute could be referred in respect of any failure by the project manager in the first instance to have made a notification – and thus not having taken an action – or as 'any other matter' all within clause 90.1. This too serves to mitigate the potential harshness of the time limit. Therefore, it is submitted that it is not only the timetable in general for the assessment of compensation events which is strict but the time limit for giving their notice as well. Apart from the time limit in clause 61.3, a general time limit or long stop pertains to the notification of all compensation events. Thus a compensation event cannot be notified after the '*defects date*'.[235] The intent here would clearly be to limit the types of claims that are often submitted long after completion of the works. Assuming no time limits problems arise the compensation event procedures may continue to be turned to.[236]

The notification procedure assumes that a compensation event has been identified as described above.[237] If so, one of the first questions for the project manager is whether the effects of the compensation event are too *uncertain* to be forecast reasonably.[238] Where they are the project manager will make assumptions about the event and must state them in any instruction to the contractor to submit a quotation in respect of it.[239] The project manager's eventual assessment[240] of the event will be based

---

[233] See the Limitation Act 1980 section 14A(6)–(10).

[234] Limitation Act 1980 s 14A. See lately *Birmingham Midshires Building Society* v. *Wretham and ors* (1999) 63 Con LR 93.

[235] Clause 61.7 ECC.

[236] If notice requirements or time limits were not met then it would have consequences as discussed below. In comparison to and unlike the ICE 6th form failure to timeously give notice of a claim under clause 54(2) may result in no sanction at all.

[237] The '*defects date*' is an identified term and inserted by agreement in part one of the Contract Data as a given number of weeks after the completion date.

[238] Clause 61.6 ECC.

[239] Clause 61.6 ECC.

[240] Under clause 63 ECC.

upon these assumptions.[241] Depending upon the circumstances the project manager's assumption may, in effect, correct a previous wrongly held assumption and in which case compensation occurs.[242] Examples of the likely compensation events which would arise either from the project manager giving an instruction or changing an earlier decision have been noted in what is referred to as a first category of compensation events above.

The project manager may instruct the contractor to submit a quotation for a proposed instruction or a proposed changed decision.[243] If so, the contractor moves not to act on the basis of the proposal but rather to submit the quotation itself. Thus, it is at this stage a two-step procedure. Conversely, if the project manager does not act to issue the proposed instruction or correction at the outset the outcome will depend upon whether the compensation event arises from the project manager or supervisor giving an instruction or changing an earlier decision within the meaning of clause 61.1. If so, the project manager will notify the contractor of the compensation event, and the contractor should move to put the instruction or changed decision into effect with a quotation either in hand or an instruction to that effect from the project manager to follow. If not, then the three conditions to be fulfilled in clause 61.3 and set out above must be satisfied for notification and the procedures, which follow it, to continue.

The project manager must take, at this point, four decisions, which operate as conditions *subsequent* to the event.[244] Thus, a finding by the project manager that any of the four decisions operates means that neither the prices nor the completion date are changed. This is a somewhat curious result as to this point inquiries have principally centred upon a finding of whether a compensation event has been validly notified. These decisions address rather two potential outcomes after a compensation event has been validly notified. The decisions concern whether the event notified by the contractor alone:

- arises from a fault of the *Contractor*,
- has not happened and is not expected to happen,
- has no effect[245] upon Actual Cost[246] or Completion[247] or
- is not one of the compensation events stated in the contract.[248]

---

[241] Clause 61.6 ECC.

[242] Clauses 61.6 and 60.1(17).

[243] Clause 61.2 ECC.

[244] Clause 61.4 ECC.

[245] This wording has changed considerably from that in the First Edition where the project manager considered instead whether the event 'could have an effect upon Actual Cost or Completion'.

[246] The meaning of actual cost as defined is dependent upon the main option chosen.

[247] Clause 11.2(13) ECC.

[248] Clause 61.4 ECC.

This simple wording belies the true difficulties that will arise in the interpretation of this clause. Some comments may be made on that wording. The meaning of the term 'arise' in the JCT form of contract, for example, was construed in *Ashville Investments Ltd* v. *Elmer Contractors Ltd* as being relevant to a finding of jurisdiction.[249]

The clause itself is 'defensive'; that is it will be used in defence of alleged compensation events that are put forward by contractors and the defences are considerable. Most significant of the defences which have been granted to the project manager is the introduction of a *fault*-based system of responsibility. The implications of the express inclusion of fault are profound and will serve as an inroad to negligence law and all of its complexities: fault 'includes negligence in the ordinary acceptation of the term' according to Cockburn, CJ in *London & North Western Rly* v. *Grace*.[250] This seems a rather noticeable lapse by the drafters when their intention for the most part has been to try and eschew terms that have a specific legal meaning or are subjective.[251] In drawing this conclusion fault is placed in the same subjective category of terms as 'fair' and 'reasonable'. It would seem that a preferable approach would have been to preclude valid notification of the event if it arose as a result of the failure of the contractor to fulfil obligations under the contract in any material respect. This suggestion has the merit of remaining consistent in terms of a contractual solution as opposed to the extra-contractual solution adopted by the introduction of a fault-based system.[252]

The second decision to be taken by the project manager is also nettlesome. It asks the project manager to decide whether an event – already notified by the contractor – has either not happened or is not expected to happen. It will not be surprising if the contractor and the project manager differ on this point especially with regard to the retrospective view. The prospective view may be more defensible although, it is submitted, could still have been improved by using instead the language of uncertainty in clause 61.6.

The project manager may decide that the event has no effect upon actual cost or completion. The wording of the phrase is disjunctive and hence no effect as a result of the event upon either should be sufficient to preclude a change to either the prices or the completion date. What meaning, however, should be given to an event which does clearly impact upon one but not the other of the terms in the phrase? Once again it would

---

[249] *Ashville Investments Ltd* v. *Elmer Contractors Ltd* [1989] QB 488, [1988] 2 All ER 577, CA.

[250] *London & North Western Rly* v. *Grace* (1858) 2 CBNS 559 Cf *Manufacturers' Mutual Insurance* v. *Queensland Government Railways* (1968) 42 ALJR 181 which held that 'faulty' design did not require an element of blameworthiness. See also FINN, PAUL. Statutes and the Common Law. *University of Western Law Review*, 1992, **22**, 16.

[251] Guidance notes NEC, 2.

[252] The complexities that often surround allegations of fault can be seen lately in *W Lamb (t/a The Premier Pump & Tank Co)* v. *Jarvis & Sons plc* (1998) 60 Con LR 1 where neither party was able to establish fault resulting in an equal apportionment of liability.

seem the project manager might still disavow it, even though this may have other implications for the contractor in terms of the contractor's own position.

The final decision to be taken by the project manager is whether the event is not one of the compensation events stated in this contract. The language first of all implies that there are other compensation events as it were outside the contract. This is perhaps anomalous, as the intention was to replace 'claims', as they are generally known, with the compensation event procedure.[253] By using language that implicitly acknowledges this suggestion the intention is undermined. The language is also arguably inconsistent or incongruous with subclause (18).[254] The subclause provides that a breach of contract by the employer, which is not one of the other compensation events in the contract, is a compensation event. Thus, and quite apart from the suggestion immediately above that compensation events are implied and may exist outside the contract on the strength of this language, any breach of contract (not one of the other compensation events in the contract) is still a compensation event. This exclusion will serve along with other provisions to reduce the likelihood that any additional compensation events would be implied. It is, therefore, arguable that the language in clause 61.4 is perhaps broader than intended.

If the project manager 'decides otherwise', the contractor is instructed to submit quotations to address the effect of the event.[255] The project manager's decisions are not limited in fact and thus any decisions other than four negative replies to the conditions subsequent obliges the project manager to instruct the contractor to submit quotations in respect of the event. The project manager notifies the decision to the contractor or instructs the contractor to submit quotations within either one week of the contractor's (original) notification or a longer period with the consent of the contractor.[256] Agreement to extend the period would presumably have to be reached before the expiry of the one-week period of notification.[257] This one-week time frame should be distinguished from the three-week time limit for the actual submission of quotations under clause 62.3. Where the contractor disputes one or more of the project manager's decisions in these respects, recourse may be had to the adjudication procedures in clause 90.1.

If the project manager decides that the contractor did not give an early warning of the event which an experienced contractor could have given, the contractor will be notified of this decision when instructed by the

---

[253] Guidance notes Consultation Document on clause 60.1 ECC, at 53: 'The NEC does not use the term claims. The events for which the Contractor is entitled to be compensated for any increase in his costs or time to complete are identified as Compensation Events'. In fact the term 'claims' was used in the Consultation Document in clause 81.1(a) and is still used in clause 80.2 ECC.

[254] Clause 60.1(18) ECC.

[255] Clause 61.4 ECC.

[256] Clause 61.4 ECC.

[257] See clause 13.5 ECC.

project manager to submit a quotation.[258] Thus, while the outcome in either case is the same in one respect – that is, an instruction to submit a quotation[259] – it differs in that only where the contractor has failed to give the early warning is it a factor in the project manager's later assessment of the event. The early warning procedure is that envisaged under clause 16. The objective comparison of the contractor's conduct to that of an experienced contractor is also utilized in clause 60.2.[260] The notification procedure then gives way to the quotation procedure in clause 62. There are no unique clauses that pertain to any of the individual main options.

The early warning procedures underscore that the compensation event procedures, like so many under the NEC, are intended to be used by all parties working together. Early experience in the use of the form confirms this and Broome and Perry have observed:

> [i]t is the authors' view, based on comments from interviewees, that for medium to large compensation events, more joint effort should be spent agreeing the problem, defining its solution and stating assumptions that are to be made before the Contractor builds up his quotation, rather than after the Project Manager has commented on it.[261]

Quotations for compensation events

The quotation procedure for compensation events is a significant innovation but was pioneered in the United Kingdom in the BPF form and is now used in numerous other forms, for example, SEACC,[262] GC/Works/1 3rd and PSA/1. Amendment 13 to JCT 80, before it became JCT 98, also added clause 13A while clause 13.4.1.1 of NSC/C also provided for the contractor to quote for any adjustment to the contract sum, extension of time and loss/expense resulting from a proposed variation instead of straightforward valuation by the quantity surveyor.

The quotation procedure for compensation events opens either with the project manager having already instructed the contractor to submit a quotation for a compensation event or being in the process itself of considering a quotation already submitted by the contractor. Assuming that the project manager has already instructed the contractor to submit a quotation then, according to clause 62.1, the project manager may also instruct the contractor to submit alternative quotations. If the project manager has not, and is actually considering a quotation already submitted by the contractor, the reply will then be in accordance with

---

[258] Clause 61.5 ECC.
[259] See clause 13 ECC.
[260] See discussion clause 60.2 ECC above.
[261] BROOME, JON C. and PERRY, JOHN G., see n. 157 above, 279.
[262] The SEACC procurement system was published in 1993 by the Electrical Contractor's Association and called the Specialist Engineering and Construction Contracts. See BROOME, JON C. and PERRY, JOHN G., *ibid.*, 279.

clause 62.3 and following. The alternative quotations should be based upon different ways of dealing with the compensation event, which are practicable. The quotations are different in the sense that they proceed upon other bases than those given in an earlier instruction or instructions. While this obligation of the contractor to fulfil the terms of the instruction is mandatory, a discretion is also given to submit further 'alternative' quotations premised upon still other methods of dealing with the compensation event and, once again, which the contractor considers to be practicable.[263] The flexibility, which the alternative quotation procedure recognizes, should enable the parties to maximize their preferences in terms of effects of the event on various outcomes such as the completion date or the prices.

The ECC sets out a prescribed minimum content for the quotations. They must comprise the contractor's proposed changes to the prices and any delay to the completion date that is assessed.[264] It is any expected delay to the completion date that is 'assessed' and in this regard the contractor must submit details of the assessment with each quotation. Research has shown that there is little similarity in how delay claims are perceived and dealt with under United Kingdom conditions of contract.[265] Clearly, the onus is upon the contractor to support his or her assertions and this must be done with details. In this respect, and inasmuch as the compensation procedure is again meant to displace claims, similar evidentiary considerations should apply.[266] In general, the failure of a party to show loss can result in dismissal of a claim (*Linden Gardens Trust Ltd* v. *Lenesta Sludge Disposals Ltd*). There are similarities in proof of claims both under contracts as well as for breach of contract. Thus, a putative claimant will normally be expected to prove the particular facts alleged in support of the claim; causation; compliance with procedures both under the contract and in any forum in which the claim is sought to be enforced; and lastly proof of quantum, loss or damage. The details should be given in respect of each quotation.[267] The wording in this regard would seem to preclude global or composite quotations being put forward.

The principle of global or composite claims in the litigation context was first recognized in English case law in *J Crosby & Sons Ltd* v. *Portland Urban District Council*.[268] The terminology itself is variable and may also be called 'rolled up claims'[269] and in the United States 'actual

---

[263]   Clause 62.1 ECC.

[264]   Clause 62.2 ECC.

[265]   See SCOTT, STEPHEN. Delay Claims in UK Contracts. *Journal of Construction Engineering and Management*, 1997, **123**, 238.

[266]   *Linden Gardens Trust Ltd* v. *Lenesta Sludge Disposals Ltd* [1993] 3 All ER 417, 63 BLR 1, HL. See generally on proof of claims, McINNIS, J.A. *Hong Kong Construction Law*. Butterworths, Singapore, 1995, Div X 'Claims'.

[267]   Clause 62.5 ECC.

[268]   *J Crosby & Sons Ltd* v. *Portland Urban District Council* (1967) 5 BLR 121 at 133–134 per Donaldson J.

[269]   The term 'rolled up claims' was used by Vinelott J in *London Borough of Merton* v. *Stanley Hugh Leach Ltd* (1985) 32 BLR 51 at 102

total cost,' 'total cost claims', or 'modified total cost claims'.[270] The subject has attracted both academic comment[271] and numerous cases.[272] Whether or not the clause wording would seem to preclude global or composite quotations in practice such types of quotations are being put forward in respect of multiple compensation events. Brian Eggleston reported this was an early problem: '[r]eports from early users of the NEC are hundreds of compensation events on comparatively straightforward schemes'.[273] There are various explanations for this occurring including choice of the wrong main option at the outset.[274] The putting forward of global or composite compensation events is borne out by the experience of NEC users. Take, for example, BAA. Following their use of the NEC they recommend the grouping of compensation events and performance criteria, that is, groundworks and risk allocation.[275] David H. Williams has said:

> The NEC Guidance Notes and Flow Charts strongly imply that 'Notifications' lead to 'Compensation Events' on a one to one basis. In practice 'Notifications' are being grouped together into 'problem areas' by agreement which are defined as a specific Compensation Event leading to one Actual Cost Quotation and one Programme Evaluation.[276]

Based upon the experience of BAA a procedure may be outlined for grouping and dealing with multiple notifications of compensation events and instructions together.[277]

---

[270] Justice Byrne in Total Costs and Global Claims. *Building and Construction Law*, 1995, **11**, 397 uses these terms.

[271] See AAEN, BERNHARD A. The Total Cost Method of Calculating Damages in Construction Cases. *Pacific Law Journal*, 1991, **22**, 1185; CARNELL, N.J. *Wharf Properties* v. *Eric Cumine Associates*: The Effect on Rolled-up Claims. *Construction Law Journal*, 1991, **7**, 303; WILSON, MARK. Global Claims at the Crossroads. *Construction Law Journal*, 1995, **11**, 15.

[272] See *G A B Robins Holdings Ltd* v. *Specialist Computer Centres Ltd* (1999) 15 Const LJ 143; *Inserco Limited* v. *Honeywell Control Systems* (1998) CILL 1368; *Bernhard's Rugby Landscapes Ltd* v. *Stockley Park Consortium* (1997) 82 BLR 39; *Amec Building Ltd* v. *Cadmus Investments Co Ltd* (1997) 51 Con LR 105; and *John Holland Construction and Engineering Pty Ltd and anor* v. *Kvaerner R J Brown Pty Ltd and anor* (1996) 82 BLR 81.

[273] EGGLESTON, see n. 48 above, p. 195

[274] Comments of BAYTON, ERNEST J. An Introduction to the Engineering and Construction Contract. A Course given at Altrincham on 3 March 1998. Thomas Telford Training, London, 1998.

[275] WILLIAMS, DAVID H. Using the NEC: A Client's View. New Engineering Contract Conference Proceedings in Hong Hong, 28 November 1994. *Asian Law Journal*, Hong Kong, 1994, p. 22.

[276] *Ibid*. In BAA's case one example was the grouping together of thirty notifications and two instructions.

[277] Based upon suggestions of WILLIAMS, DAVID H., *ibid.*, p 23.

(1) The contractor notifies the project manager as and when the contractor identifies an issue that might become a compensation event and as the contract requires.

(2) As notifications are received by the project manager, and in the light of day-to-day knowledge of the works, the project manager decides that a particular 'problem area' has arisen and agrees with the contractor to its identification as a compensation event.

(3) The project manager, with the contractor's agreement, allocates subsequent eligible notifications to relevant compensation events.

(4) Individual notifications are evaluated on a prime cost basis within their individual two-week periods.

(5) The contractor is paid in the interim payment for work done on the agreed prime cost evaluations.

(6) Once the problem area has been fully defined, and a solution and plan of work agreed, the project manager instructs the contractor to submit a quotation.

(7) The contractor submits the (prime cost) notification evaluations, revises programme and methods as necessary and submits a time and cost quotation.

In summary, notwithstanding once again the implication that compensation events are discrete, establishing a mechanism to address multiple compensation events, notifications, and quotations should facilitate the project work. Returning to the programme for the remaining work if it is affected by the compensation event the contractor must include a revised programme in the quotation showing the effect[278] and complying with clause 31.1. The contractor will complete the assessment in accordance with clause 63.

Clause 62.3 and not clause 32.2 would govern the period for submission of the quotation by the contractor inclusive of the revised programme.[279] That is, within three weeks of being instructed to do so by the project manager. It is open to the project manager to extend the time allowed for the contractor to submit the quotation when it involves a compensation event provided both agree to the extension before the actual submission is due.[280] Notwithstanding their agreement, the project manager is still under an obligation to notify the contractor formally that the extension has been agreed to.[281] This 'double agreement' provision in the clause will serve to lessen the risk of misunderstanding over whether agreement has, in fact, been reached.[282] If the contractor meets the period agreed for the submission of the quotation, as originally framed or extended by agreement, the project manager will begin the formulation of a reply. If the contractor has

---

[278] Clause 62.2 ECC.

[279] Clause 13.3 ECC.

[280] Clause 62.5 ECC. The clause was absent in the First Edition and adds considerable flexibility to the quotation procedure.

[281] Notification must satisfy the clause 13 ECC requirements.

[282] See clause 62.5.

failed to meet the deadline the project manager will instead have to make an assessment of the event.

The options for reply open to the project manager are prescribed. Thus, the project manager's reply is limited to:

- an instruction to submit a revised quotation,
- an acceptance of a quotation,
- a notification that a proposed instruction or a proposed changed decision will not be given or
- a notification that he will be making his own assessment.[283]

The project manager in turn is obliged to reply within two weeks of the submission.[284] These time frames concern the submission of the actual quotations from the contractor and the project manager's replies. They are distinct from the time frame discussed above in relation to the project manager's decision to instruct the contractor to submit quotations under clause 61.4 of the ECC. However, once again the time frame for reply, on this occasion the extension, operates in favour of the project manager.[285] The same provision permits the time for reply to be extended in favour of the contractor for the submission of quotations as well. The wording itself leaves open the application of the clause to revised quotations also. The period can be extended by consent if both the project manager and the contractor agree to do so before the submission date.[286] A 'double agreement' provision again applies and thus the project manager must also formally notify the contractor that the extension has been agreed.[287] One may question whether the notification in this instance should not have come from the contractor as the extension operates in favour of the project manager and inasmuch as failure to reply within the period required by the contract is a compensation event.[288] However, how far does the compensation event procedure extend? By leaving the project manager with the responsibility of notifying the contractor of the extension, it would seem that the contractor has to object to any failure by the project manager in this notification. The question it raises is whether the notice to extend the time limit itself is subject to the *'period for reply'*. Hence, not only a 'double notice' requirement but a 'double period for reply' as well. If this is the case then the project manager is at risk of late reply to both the original submission and, even if they have agreed to extend this time limit, for late notice of their agreement to extend the time as well. As either carries the sanction of the compensation event procedure it would seem that the contractor should logically have carried this second risk and the responsibility to notify formally the project manager of the contractor's assent to extending the time for reply.

---

[283] Clause 62.3 ECC.
[284] Clause 62.3 ECC.
[285] Clause 62.5 ECC.
[286] Clause 62.5 ECC.
[287] Clause 62.5 ECC. Notification must satisfy the clause 13 ECC requirements.
[288] Clause 60.1(6) ECC.

The instruction to submit a revised quotation should be distinguished from that of requiring an alternative quotation under clause 62.1. A revised quotation presupposes that the basis of the original quotation is broadly acceptable and thus requires only the revision, which the clause suggests. Of the four replies that may be given only the instruction to submit a revised quotation necessitates an explanation to the contractor on the part of the project manager of the reasons for doing so. Thus, only this reply contemplates further dialogue. The second reply, e.g. acceptance of a quotation, follows the remainder of the quotation procedures, namely implementation.[289] In the case of the third reply, e.g. with a notification under clause 13 of the ECC, that a proposed instruction or a proposed changed decision will not be given, no implementation ensues. In the case of the fourth reply, e.g. a notification under clause 13 of the ECC that the project manager will be making an assessment under clause 64, then implementation is under clause 65 of the ECC. Both the third reply and fourth reply would end further dialogue on this construction. The explanation is warranted not only on management grounds, as it must serve to increase the chances of the two reaching agreement on a quotation, but also in furthering broader NEC objectives such as co-operation.[290]

The contractor must submit the revised quotation within three weeks of being instructed to do so[291] although the project manager may extend the time frame and, once again, to do so they must agree to the extension before the submission is due.[292] The 'double agreement' provision discussed above applies, as may the 'double notice' provision if the interpretation placed on the clause applies as well. Agreement in advance of the time limit to extend it is also the general rule in the contract under clause 13.5. Once the quotation has been revised the procedures follow that for the contractor's original submission under clause 62.5 and following. There is no reason in theory why a second or even further reply of the project manager could not be to submit revised quotations again with the whole process repeating itself, although in practice there will most certainly be a limit reached.

The quotation procedure is an integral part of the NEC and to work effectively must be given sufficient resources. Latham concluded that there was 'widespread – but not unanimous – support for pricing variations in advance of the work being carried out, as a matter of normal practice'.[293] This fact has been tacitly acknowledged with the contractor's cost of preparing quotations for compensation events in main options C, D E and F expected to be included in the actual cost as defined in each respective option and thus in the price for work done to date.[294] However,

---

[289]   Clause 64 ECC.
[290]   See clauses 10.1 and 25.1 ECC.
[291]   Clause 62.4 ECC.
[292]   Clause 62.5 ECC.
[293]   *Trust and Money*, 31.
[294]   Guidance notes NEC on clause 62.1 ECC, at 62.

the cost of preparing quotations for compensation events is specifically excluded from the definition of actual cost in main options A and B.[295] The drafters consciously adopted this policy toward these two main options to retain the certainty of the prices relative to the work done.[296] However, even if there is certainty in the prices in this respect the drafters' suggestion that tenderers should allow in their tendered fee percentage for the costs of preparing quotations shows the certainty is illusory in this respect from the contractor's perspective. A further rationale for excluding the cost of preparing quotations in main options A and B would be that these options from a procurement strategy point of view should occasion the least likely number of compensation events. Therefore, the cost with regard to preparing quotations in these options relative to main options C, D, E and F would be less and also, therefore, less justifiable. The drafters concede, however, that some employers are making other arrangements to reimburse the cost of preparing quotations in special circumstances.[297] This practice would seem to warrant the drafters considering a new provision as a secondary option so that this may be taken into account and uniformly dealt with. The absence of an express provision with respect to the other main options is also likely to mean that the practice is not being uniformly followed. The related question of recovery of the cost of the preparation of claims has also attracted recent interest and with a higher profile for the topic it would again seem worthwhile considering a uniform express provision in the form.

Assessing compensation events

The assessment of compensation events in the ECC is intended to be complete and thus address all effects on price[298] and completion.[299] Significantly, the intention is to address even the disruption accompanying the events. In this regard the NEC makes a dramatic departure from the accepted practices in compensating variations under traditional forms of contract. To achieve this the effect of the compensation event is considered in three different respects: completion as shown on the 'Accepted Programme',[300] matters which have a significant chance of occurring and which are at the contractor's risk,[301] and prices.[302] These effects, when taken into account generally, operate in favour of the contractor but in many cases also operate in the employer's favour as well. Thus the employer may be entitled to reductions in prices, for example, and presumably, if option P applied, the employer would

---

[295] Clause 11.2(28) defines actual cost in part as 'excluding the cost of preparing quotations for compensation events'.
[296] Guidance notes NEC on clause 62.1 ECC, at 62.
[297] For example, when the effect is very large or when multiple quotations are being sought for significant design changes, guidance notes NEC on clause 62.1 ECC, at 62.
[298] In particular under clauses 63.1 and 63.2 ECC.
[299] In particular under clause 63.3 ECC.
[300] See clause 63.3 ECC.
[301] See clause 63.5 ECC.
[302] See clause 63.1 ECC.

retain the agreed percentage on the value of any compensation event. The *quid pro quo*, which the employer has obtained, is based upon one notice principle and four assumptions about the contractor's conduct: the principle of early warning,[303] and the assumptions of competence, promptness, reasonableness and 'changeability'.[304] One further measure mutually agreed seeks to maintain the balance between the two parties with regard to the resolution of ambiguities or inconsistencies in the works information.[305] In summary, the scope and fairness of these provisions presents a significant reordering of the traditional employer/ contractor relationship.

The first respect in which the effects of a compensation event are assessed concerns completion as shown on the accepted programme. Thus, where a compensation event occurs which delays the completion date, it will be assessed as the length of time that, due to the compensation event, planned completion is later than planned completion as shown on the accepted programme.[306] It is only a delay to the completion date that is relevant under this clause as any earlier completion date for which additional compensation would become due would have to arise under the acceleration provisions.[307]

The second respect in which the effects of a compensation event are assessed concerns a consideration of both cost and time risk allowances for matters which have a significant chance of occurring and which are at the contractor's risk under the contract.[308] This notion has been expressed in a similar fashion by Capper with regard to the employer: '[o]n most construction projects, the client deceives himself if he uses single figure estimates of cost and time for appraisal and funding decisions. Ranges of estimates should be used, including specific contingencies and tolerances for uncertainty'.[309]

Dennis Lock sets out the importance of accurate estimates in another respect:

> [a]n accurate estimate of project costs provides a proper basis for management control. Ideally such estimates should be based on a well-defined project specification. The degree of estimating accuracy achieved will determine the element of risk taken in pricing decisions, and the effectiveness of subsequent working cost budgets and resource schedules.[310]

[303]   See clauses 16.1 and 63.4 ECC.
[304]   See clause 63.6 ECC.
[305]   See clause 63.7 ECC.
[306]   Clause 61.3 ECC. See also clause 11.2(13), (14) and (15) for relevant definitions.
[307]   See clause 36 ECC.
[308]   Clause 63.5 ECC.
[309]   CAPPER, PROFESSOR PHILLIP. Management of Legal Risks in Construction. A paper given to the Society of Construction Law at a meeting in Wales on 21 September 1994.
[310]   LOCK, DENNIS. Resource Scheduling. In *Gower Handbook of Project Management*, 2nd edn. Gower, Aldershot, 1994, p. 40.

Realistic estimates are also relevant to systematic risk management generally as Patrick S. Godfrey has written: '[s]ystematic risk management encourages you to itemise and quantify risks and consider risk containment and risk reduction policies. Instead of relying on a single value project cost estimate, you produce a distribution of project costs, with confidence levels, making the estimating process realistic because it recognises the uncertainties that exist'.[311]

The allowances will normally be included in the forecasts of actual cost and completion to address uncertainties much in the same way as a contractor uses margins in bidding. The contractor, in the quotation, could show the allowances and yet the project manager may be expected to accept them if they satisfy assumptions about the contractor's conduct. While there are many factors that will of course be relevant here, the contractor's own experience will serve as one of the best measures for determining the amount of the allowance that should be included in the quotation. While these factors will all be relevant, and generally weigh in favour of the contractor, they will be tested against the assumptions that the project manager holds in respect of the contractor's conduct and the notice principle of early warning.

The assumptions that the project manager holds toward the contractor's conduct concern *competence, promptness, reasonableness* and *changeability*. Clause 63.6 provides:

> Assessments are based upon the assumptions that the *Contractor* reacts competently and promptly to the compensation event, that the additional Actual Cost and time due to the event are reasonably incurred and that the Accepted Programme can be changed.

With regard to *competence*, there is no standard against which competence is to be measured. The use of the term stands in contrast to that of 'an experienced contractor' in the same clause.[312] This fact, the oversight exercised by the employer in terms of 'key people' named in part two of the Contract Data and the limitations on the hiring of replacements requiring a *de facto* minimum level of competence suggest the test here is of a lower magnitude than that of the experienced contractor. Similarly, *promptness*, with the sanctions available to the project manager to secure the timely performance of the contractor in general, would appear to be a minimum standard. Reluctance on the part of project participants to deal promptly with changes and unexpected conditions is a common cause of disputes.[313]

The test or assumption with regard to both the additional cost and the time due to the event is that they are reasonably incurred. *Reasonableness*, as a standard, is by the drafters' admission, one 'used

---

[311] GODFREY, PATRICK S. Sir William Halcrow and Partners Ltd. *Control of Risk: A Guide to the Systematic Management of Risk from Construction.* CIRIA, London, 1996, 19.

[312] Clause 63.4 ECC. See also clause 60.2 ECC.

[313] SMITH, G.A., see n. 77 above, n. 1 references omitted.

as little as possible'.[314] The implication is that subjective terms such as 'reasonable' may be more productive of disputes than the use of objective standards. However, here the open-ended nature of both cost and time factors may have constrained the drafters in the use of their preferred terminology. The interpretation of the term may be expected to rely upon other precedents so far as material.

Changeability, as the word is used here, refers to the assumption underlying the assessment that the accepted programme can be changed. This in itself need not necessarily prove a significant obstacle to making the assessment. The accepted programme does have a different status from that of either the first or any subsequent programmes. The programmes may be accepted in turn and in each case the last accepted programme supersedes previous accepted programmes.[315] Thus, it is submitted, that the wording of the clause in this respect suggests something more in the nature of a requirement that the contractor make such changes to the accepted programme – which can itself entail compensation events[316] – than a limitation on being able to do it. In summary, the assumptions in clause 63.6 upon which assessments in part are based put forward minimum general standards that should be observed and complement the objective criteria in the ECC which they overlap with.

The project manager in the ordinary course during the notification procedure will have given the early warning.[317] At that time, if the project manager decided that the contractor did not give an early warning of the event which an experienced contractor could have given, he or she would have told the contractor when first instructed to submit quotations.[318] Thus, at the assessment stage, if the result of that notification was that the contractor had not given such an early warning, that is an early warning which an experienced contractor could have given, the event is still assessed as if such warning had been given.[319] This would mean in practice that any additional costs or delays as a result of the failure to give the early warning would be denied to the contractor and would be directly relevant to the basis of the assessment for the event.

The general rule for the assessment of compensation events regarding their effects on prices is set out in clause 63.1; that is, it is based upon:

- the Actual Cost of the work already done,
- the forecast Actual Cost of the work not yet done and
- the resulting Fee.

Two critical factors are thus material in the above formulation: the meanings of 'Actual Cost'[320] and 'Fee'.[321] The two factors are also

---

[314] Guidance notes NEC, 2.
[315] Clause 11.2(14) ECC.
[316] See clauses 60.1(2), (3) and (5).
[317] Clause 61 ECC.
[318] See discussion clause 61.5 ECC.
[319] Clause 63.4 ECC.
[320] See the discussion of actual cost above.
[321] Clause 11.2(17) ECC.

interrelated in that the definition and amount of the fee is calculated by reference to the actual cost, that is, by applying the *'fee percentage'* to the amount of the actual cost.[322] There are three distinct definitions of 'actual cost' under the various main options.[323] The definitions differ under the respective main options to reflect varying allocations of the financial or cost risk of subcontractors. A material component in the definition of actual cost under each main option is comprised in one of the two Schedules of Cost Components (SCC and SSCC).[324] These schedules define the cost components which are included in an assessment of changed costs arising from compensation events under all main options save F, and define the cost components which a contractor and subcontractor[325] will be directly reimbursed for.[326] Thus, costs are either within the SCC or SSCC and potentially directly recoverable or not. Where the cost components are not within either the SCC or SSCC they may still be indirectly recoverable under the fee. Thus a division has been drawn in terms of where individual cost components fall and as such, how they must be taken into account into bidding. The division may be changed, however, and an employer could add or delete individual cost components in the schedules. Under the drafting scheme deletion would add such components' costs to the fee[327] which could impact upon the value of the bid. The most significant component of the fee would normally be the contractor's profit and thus it is understandably important to ensure it is included in assessments of compensation events.

The assessment of a compensation event in the ECC is different from that for the assessment of variations under other forms which are primarily based upon the existing rates and prices in the contract. The selection of this method of assessment reflects clear drafting decisions that have been taken. That is, by specifically excluding events which arise through the contractor's fault and those which are at the contractor's risk in any event, the likely average number of compensation events that one may expect to arise in the use of the contract should be less than that under other forms. As such, and with this clearer allocation of risk, it seems appropriate that the contractor is reimbursed for actual additional costs or forecast additional costs where work has already been done as a result of the compensation event.[328]

The comprehensive nature of the compensation event procedure in general, with its reliance upon notifications, instructions, further

---

[322] Clause 11.2(17). Cf the use of the term 'fees' in clause 6.2 JCT 80 meaning sums payable statutorily.

[323] Clauses A and B11.2(28); C, D and E11.2(27); and F11.2(26) ECC.

[324] The guidance notes Consultation Document referred to the Schedule as the 'Schedule of Actual Cost', 63.

[325] A materially identical SCC and SSCC are contained in the ECSC.

[326] Guidance notes SCC, 93; however, the SSCC cannot be used for this purpose under main options C, D and E: guidance notes SSCC, 101.

[327] See clause 52.1 ECC.

[328] See guidance notes NEC on clause 63.1 ECC, at 63.

notifications followed by a detailed quotation and instructions, will result in most assessments being made in respect of forecast actual costs for work not yet done.

The general rule is intended to operate in respect of 'changes' to the prices only rather than their replacement as a result of the effect of the event. Hence forecast costs do not supersede the original prices in respect of unchanged work. This is not clear in the drafting of clause 63.1 and the wording of the clause could be improved if attention was drawn to the fact that it is the 'differences' between the prices before and after, or more likely in anticipation of compensation events, that form the basis of the assessment along with the addition of the fee.

There is a final stage in the assessment procedure in clause 63 which applies generally to all of the main options but which will likely only occur in the rare instance where a change to the works information has to be made to resolve an ambiguity or inconsistency. The terms for dealing with this case are set out in clause 63.7 and really serve two purposes. That is, the clause effectively adds an additional compensation event to the list of 18 events in clause 60.1 as well as adds a new rule of interpretation – the *contra proferentem* rule. In both respects the inclusion of the clause with the assessment provision rather than either clause 60.1 itself or the short interpretation (construction) provisions in clause 12 is open to question but does not materially affect its application. The provision seems to raise more questions than it answers.

Specifically, the provision provides that an instruction to change the works information in order to resolve an ambiguity or inconsistency is assessed as follows: if the works information provided by the employer is changed, the effect of the compensation event is assessed as if the prices and the completion date were for the interpretation most favourable to the contractor.[329]

Conversely, if the works information provided by the contractor is changed, the effect of the compensation event is assessed as if the prices and the completion date were for the interpretation most favourable to the employer.[330] At the outset the provision seems far too long to achieve its modest objectives. Economies in the number of words used would have been better served by removing the repetitious phrasing. Overall drafters seem to have achieved their goal of limiting the number of sentences which were over 40 words in length.[331] Similarly, another objective of the drafters has been to use ordinary language, (even though the provision sets out what is legally referred to as the *contra proferentem* rule) it could have still been described using plain language. Thus clause 63.7 could have been worded simply: 'The effects of changes to the Works Information are construed against the drafter'; or alternatively: 'The effects of changes to the Works Information are construed against the person who provided the Works Information'.

---

[329]   Clause 63.7 ECC.
[330]   Clause 63.7 ECC.
[331]   Guidance notes NEC, 2.

Another example may be given. Thus, the references to the 'Prices' and 'Completion Date' are understood and would follow from the application of clauses 63.1 and 63.3. The designation as a compensation event in subclause 60.1 itself would have also served to reduce the wording and improve the overall clarity of the drafting. The clause could provide: '(19) An instruction to change the works information (in order) to resolve an ambiguity or inconsistency'. It is understood to be a compensation event when read with the introductory phrase to clause 60.1. Focusing on the substance of the provision it addresses ambiguities or inconsistencies in only the works information. However, clause 17.1, which it must be read with, pertains to the same arising 'in or between the documents that are part of this contract'. As the ECC contemplates the contractor supplying other documents which may form part of the contract there is no logical reason not to extend the application of the rule to all of the contract documents. In fact, logically it could be extended to all documents provided by a party irrespective of whether they are contract documents or not. This would have the advantage of consistency and serve as an additional incentive to providing accurate documents.

As the provision stands at present it may serve more as an incentive for the contractor to detect ambiguities or inconsistencies in works information provided by the employer with a view to securing an instruction to resolve it through a compensation event which would act in the contractor's interest more than anything else. Reserving in the project manager an express power to refuse to issue the instruction if the ambiguity or inconsistency was not material may lessen this possibility, however, and serve as at least one check on the procedure.

To this point review of the assessment procedure in clause 63 has been relevant to all main options. However, in addition to these provisions further assessment provisions are also contained in the secondary option clauses. Thus, in respect of main options A and C, the assessments for changed prices for compensation events are in the form of changes to the 'activity schedule';[332] while in respect of main options B and D such assessments are in the form of changes to the 'bill of quantities'.[333] Thus, when read with clause 11.2(20), it is the changed activity schedule which is now relevant in assessing either the price for work done to date or the contractor's share; and when read with clause 11.2(21) it is the changed bill of quantities which is now relevant in assessing either the price for work done to date or the contractor's share. If the project manager and the contractor agree, however, rates and lump sums in the bill of quantities may be used as a basis for assessment instead of actual cost and the resulting fee.[334] The assessment of a compensation event under main options A and B which is or includes subcontracted work will have the contractor's fee percentage added to the actual cost but the fees paid or to

---

[332] Clause 63.8 ECC.
[333] Clause 63.9 ECC.
[334] Only with regard to main options B and D, clause 63.9 ECC.

be paid by the contractor to the subcontractors are not added.[335] Thus, only the contractor's fee is material in this respect. Two reasons are given for this: to avoid the employer paying fees twice on work which is also subcontracted; and because the employer has no control over fees tendered by subcontractors.[336] Once these assessments have been taken into account the focus shifts to the SCC and SSCC.[337]

A common issue in respect of all options concerns whether the project manager will make an assessment of the compensation event or not.[338] If so, the SSCC may be used.[339] If the project manager does not take this decision and pursues this action unilaterally, the project manager may still agree on the same end with the contractor and that the SSCC again will be used.[340] Where this agreement is reached the contractor may then assess the compensation event using the SSCC. 'As Project Managers become used to operating the NEC procedure it can be expected that they will quickly learn to gather appropriate cost and productivity data which will enable them to reject with confidence any excessive quotations by contractors'.[341]

The inclusion of time risk in the assessment of compensation events means that each event is potentially a ground for the extension of time. Listing grounds for the extension of time occurs in other standard forms, e.g. clause 25 of the JCT 80, not in others, e.g. JCT MW, with still others, e.g. ICE 6th, adopting a mid-course both listing specific grounds for extension of time as well as including a general reference when 'other special circumstances of any kind' occur.[342] This also marks a change from a number of forms that do not accept that the grant of an extension of time necessarily entitles the contractor to additional costs as a result. For example, under JCT MW there is no provision allowing the contractor to claim loss and expense for matters justifying an extension of time and which readily lends itself to a claim for breach of contract to recover alleged losses. When the rule operates, contractors who feel that an extension of time alone does not fully compensate them for their increased costs can be forced to commence action for breach of contract or claim additional compensation.

The assessment procedure contains its own default provisions in respect of all main options and thus the failure of the contractor to act in accordance with the contract results in the project manager taking remedial action; that is, through the project manager's assessments.[343] In

---

[335]   Clause 63.10 ECC.
[336]   Guidance notes NEC on clause 63.10 ECC, at 66.
[337]   There are no additional secondary option clauses regarding assessment in main option F.
[338]   See 63.11 ECC.
[339]   Clause 63.11 ECC.
[340]   See clause 63.11 ECC.
[341]   NORRIS, C. *et al.*, see n. 11, p. 91.
[342]   Clause 2.2 JCT MW and clause 44 ICE 6th.
[343]   Clause 64.1 ECC.

comparison, under FIDIC 4th regarding delays, the contractor's entitlement to an extension of time is not dependent upon any action on the contractor's part to seek to offset the effect of the delay and in this regard would not be expected to encourage co-operation. There are no additional default provisions in respect of the project manager's assessments in the secondary option clauses.

Fairness and the cost basis of valuation

The use of an agreed cost basis for valuing variations should be *fair*. This much would appear to follow if the recommendations in Latham are acceptable. However, cost based valuations have also been criticized. Thus, Eggleston writes 'firstly there is a records problem, and secondly there are the complexities of notional assessments'.[344] With regard to the first point Eggleston writes as follows:

> [clause 63.1] requires that a compensation event should be made between the value of the work completed as if the compensation event had not occurred and the value of the work completed including the effects of the compensation event – in both cases using the actual cost formula of the contract to provide a common base for comparison. Now the one thing that any contractor using main options A or B is unlikely to have in his records is the value of the work in accordance with the actual cost formula. What he will have are records of real costs – and for the most part they are likely to be subcontractor's accounts – a category of cost not recognised in the definition of actual cost for main options A and B. He will also know the value of the work completed in accordance with his activity schedule or his bill of quantities. These are of no help to him. What he has to do is a notional calculation of what the work he has completed would have cost, with and without the compensation event, using the contractual actual cost formula.[345]

Eggleston's critique serves to focus attention on very difficult aspects of the assessment procedure. However, what it fails to take into consideration are some of the other contractual provisions, which have also been inserted in the contract to mitigate these difficulties. Initially, Eggleston's criticism should not be taken to apply generally to all main options. Under main options C, D, E and F, the contractor is under an express obligation to keep accounts of payments of actual cost as defined and records which show whether the payments have been made.[346] With regard to main options A and B, although not under this express obligation, a contractor may wish to consider such account and record

---

[344] EGGLESTON, n. 48 above, p. 219.

[345] *Ibid.*, pp. 219–220. Eggleston also argues that the same records and notional assessment problems apply with regard to the forecast of actual costs for work not yet done. However, the rebuttal made to the point here above applies equally to forecast actual costs.

[346] Clause 52.2 ECC.

keeping as a matter of *best practice* precisely to avoid the problems that may materialize. Concerning subcontractors, once again, an express obligation is imposed on the contractor to keep records of communications and calculations relating to the assessment of compensation events for subcontractors.[347] Once again these records are integral to the assessment of actual cost and it is the contractor who must keep them.

The same argument as above could be made concerning best practice and the recommendation that they also be kept by the contractor under main options A and B. If the employer is alive to this issue of record keeping, further obligations on the part of the contractor in the works information may be specified. The obligations need not necessarily entail additional or duplicative administrative or paperwork burden for the contractor but rather a reorientation of the current organization so that the contract is satisfied. The incentive for the contractor is, of course, the entitlement to be compensated according to the records in this regard. The drafters do impose a separate obligation on the contractor to maintain separate accounts for subcontractors. However, they also provide that, to achieve satisfactory assessment of compensation events, 'the Subcontractors' costs should be available in the same way as the *Contractor's* costs'.[348] The drafters continue to note that payments to subcontractors could not be included in actual cost as defined for main options A and B because to do so would have the effect of removing subcontractor's costs from the assessement of compensation events and also absolving the contractor of any payment risk toward subcontractors.[349]

The differences in assessment under main options A and B have also been recognized by clause 63.9. Thus, if the project manager and contractor agree, the rates and lump sums in the bill of quantities may be used as a basis for assessment *instead* of actual cost and the fee.[350] This can operate as a strong alternative if the accounts and records are not available. In assessing compensation events it must also be noted that actual cost is but one determinant and is, of course, not referred to in isolation. Thus, when Eggleston writes above that neither the activity schedule nor the bill of quantities is of any help to the contractor it should be noted that in both the case of main options A and B respectively the assessments for changed prices themselves are in the form of changes to the activity schedule or the bill of quantities.[351] Thus in this regard they help in providing a reference for the assessments (notional and agreed) of the changed prices.

To return to the issue of fairness under the provision and one final criticism of the clause, it has also been argued that the records and

---

[347]   Clause 52.2 ECC.
[348]   Guidance notes NEC, 94.
[349]   Guidance notes NEC, 94.
[350]   Clause 63.9 ECC.
[351]   Clauses 63.8 and 63.9 ECC.

notional assessment problems apply and that '[f]or claims it might not be so fair to the contractor since claims valued on cost may not provide as good a remedy as claims valued as damages'.[352] However, in reply, agreed valuation procedures have many precedents. Thus clause 13.5 of the JCT 80 sets out certain valuation rules which rely heavily upon notions of fairness. In addition to the payment made to the contractor under the valuation rules set out in the clause 13.2 JCT 80 also permits the contractor to claim for direct loss and/or expense incurred as a result of a variation. Similarly GC/Works/1 endorses certain valuations at fair rates and prices, while clause 3.6 of the JCT/MW uses fair and reasonable valuations, and clause 6.1 of the ICE MW, 2nd Edition uses the terms 'fair and reasonable' when referring to additions to or deductions from payments to the contractor by the engineer. The NEC has in fact taken these procedures further than these other forms by setting out a *formal and agreed basis for valuation* that is dependent upon agreed definitions and criteria. While it may be technically accurate to state that it remains a 'notional assessment' it should still more closely approximate the costs that either will or are likely to be incurred than providing as have these other forms. While all or every single cost incurred – hence 'real actual cost' – could also have been the measure adopted it would have left a larger margin of error on the part of the employer.

Thus by limiting actual cost to the parties notional but agreed 'actual cost' a reasonable or *fair* apportionment of those costs has been made. Thus one should not examine the provision only from one perspective but from both perspectives – that of the contractor *and* the employer. In more general terms, fairness can be seen to be an underlying principle in the FIDIC conditions of contract,[353] is deeply rooted in the reasons underlying the movement toward standard forms,[354] reflects important issues in the past such as express requirements for fair wage clauses[355] and makes an important contribution to a theoretical understanding of the NEC.

---

[352] EGGLESTON, see n. 48 above, p. 219.

[353] John Bowcock, then chairman of the FIDIC and ACE contracts committee: '... fundamental to all FIDIC Conditions is a fair allocation of risk and responsibilities between the parties to a contract', in The FIDIC Contract Forms: The Present and Future. *The Patrick McCreight Memorial Lecture*. A paper given in London on 7 November 1995 by the Society of Construction Law. Society of Construction Law, London, 1995, p. 4.

[354] See discussion on this in Chapter 1.

[355] See e.g. clauses 17A JCT 63, 19A JCT 80, 51 GC/Works/1 1st then implementing the Fair Wages Resolution (14 October 1946) of the House of Commons and not rescinded until August 1983. It has been remarked that when this policy change was introduced through for instance amendments to the Local Government Act 1988 that it operated contrary to fairness and as a result of which fair wage clauses were deleted from JCT forms: see *JCT Newsletter*, May–November 1988, **3**, 2.

Project manager's assessments

There are four occasions under clause 64.1 when the project manager may make an assessment of a compensation event by default:

- if the *Contractor* has not submitted a required quotation[356] and details of his assessment[357] within the time allowed,
- if the *Project Manager* decides that the *Contractor* has not assessed the compensation event correctly in a quotation and he does not instruct the *Contractor* to submit a revised quotation,
- if, when the *Contractor* submits quotations for a compensation event,[358] he has not submitted a programme which this contract requires him to submit[359] or
- if when the *Contractor* submits quotations for a compensation event[360] the *Project Manager* has not accepted the *Contractor's* latest programme[361] for one of the reasons stated in this contract.[362]

All of the occasions referred to above make it possible, whether viewed independently or collectively, for the project manager to assess the effect of the compensation event as a *fallback* position. This, in fact, is one of the more significant aspects of the compensation event procedure as a whole. That is, it expects the contractor to participate constructively, *co-operate* one could say, in the resolution of the difficulties the event presents and gives the contractor both the initial and foremost responsibility in achieving this end. In short, the project manager is not simply on site to 'tell the contractor what to do', rather the contractor must take on that responsibility.

In the first instance, the solutions of the contractor must meet minimum procedural standards as it were. Thus, the quotation must in fact be submitted, it must contain the details required for a quotation as understood in the ECC and it must be done timeously. Failure to reach this threshold results in the project manager assuming the primary responsibility from the contractor for assessing the effects of the compensation event.[363]

The 'correctness' of the assessment of the compensation event is also a measure of the contractor's continued involvement in the process. The ECC does not provide any explicit guidance on correctness; rather it follows from a reading of clause 63 as a whole. Thus, the measure of correctness with regard to the respective assessments will be determined

---

[356] For example, under clauses 36.1, 61.1, 61.2, 61.4, 62.1, or 62.4 ECC.
[357] For example, under clause 62.2 ECC.
[358] Cf the absence of commas in the identical phrase in the next paragraph.
[359] For example, under clauses 31.1, 32, 1, 31.4, 32, 2, 36.2, 50.3, or 62.2 ECC.
[360] For example, under clauses 36.1, 44.2, 61.1, 61.4, 61.5, 61.6 or 62.5 ECC.
[361] For example, under clauses 31.3.
[362] Clause 64.1 ECC.
[363] The failure to submit a quotation at all in the first instance precludes any opportunity for a revised quotation to be submitted, e.g. as in the second paragraph.

as follows: with reference to prices under clause 63.1 and 63.2; completion under clause 63.3; and matters which have a significant chance of occurring and are at the contractor's risk under clause 63.5. Where the event arises in relation to a change to the works information to resolve an ambiguity or inconsistency under clause 63.7, to be correct the assessment must have been construed against the drafter. It is submitted that a correct assessment would respect *all* of the assumptions in clause 63.6. Thus, while any one or all of these bases could be put forward in justification of the project manager's own assessment of the compensation event, the absence of a direct reference to them concerning 'correctness' still leaves open other bases on which the project manager could so act. The action assumes that no instruction to submit a revised quotation has been given.[364]

The imperative of the submission of either a first programme[365] or a later or revised programme[366] is demonstrated by the third and fourth paragraphs in clause 64.1.[367] A tenet of the ECC is the assessment of both the cost and time effects of a compensation event. Thus, where there is a delay to the completion date, the time element must have an agreed point of reference for the assessment. That point of reference is the programme,[368] at whatever stage.

The necessity for and centrality of the programme are carried over into the project manager's assessment where the project manager's own assessment must be used if there is no accepted programme or, once again, the contractor has not submitted a required revised programme for acceptance.[369] The assumption of the contractor's responsibility in this regard comes with the time frame the contractor was originally given for submitting the quotation. Thus the project manager will notify the contractor of the assessment and give details of it within the period allowed for the contractor's submission of a quotation for the same event. That time frame would normally have been within three weeks of having been instructed to do so by the project manager.[370] The details as well would be those same details that would have been expected from the contractor under clause 62.2 of the ECC. In actual fact, the project manager will have longer than the three weeks mentioned, as the time frame will not begin to run until the 'need for the *Project Manager's* assessment becomes apparent'.[371]

The assessment procedure operates with its checks and balances. The contractor carries the primary responsibility for the assessment of

---

[364] For example, under clauses 62.3, 62.4, or 64.1 ECC.
[365] For example, under clauses 31.1 or 50.3 ECC.
[366] For example, under clauses 11.2(14), 32.1, 36.1, 36.3, or 36.4 ECC.
[367] There is once again unnecessary repetition in the drafting which could have been met with a subparagraph; see e.g. the double 'bullet points' in clause 31.2 ECC.
[368] See, in particular, clause 32 ECC.
[369] Clause 64.2 ECC.
[370] See clause 62.3 ECC.
[371] Clause 64.3 ECC.

compensation events. However, failure to carry it out at all, carry it out correctly, or carry it out without reference to the requisite programme can result in the contractor's forfeiture of the responsibility to the project manager. At that time the project manager would not only assume the contractor's rights in relation to the assessment but also the contractor's responsibilities for carrying out all the requirements as described and, ultimately, which responsibilities could be tested if need be by a reference to the adjudicator. In summary, the assessment procedure can operate in one's favour as a result of the way control is ceded to either the contractor or project manager in respect of it but, and as illustrated, even that control is not without checks and balances.

Implementing compensation events[372]

The final stage of the compensation event procedures concerns their implementation. Initially the course of action to be followed on implementation is dependent upon whether the project manager has notified the contractor of the quotation which has been accepted.[373] The timing of the implementation, as it is understood in clause 65.1, will occur when the project manager accepts a quotation or completes an assessment or when the compensation event occurs, whichever is the latest. Conversely, if the project manager has not so notified the contractor, implementation will then rather occur when the contractor is notified of the project manager's own assessment of the compensation event under clause 64.3.[374]

According to the ECC drafting it appears to be a principle that compensation events are not reassessed once implemented save in very limited circumstances and notably involving wrong assumptions. The limited circumstances when a review may be made are set out in clause 61.6. This principle is taken further with regard to assessments based upon forecasts. Thus, in the case of assessments based upon forecasts, even when the forecast is shown by later recorded information to have been wrong, it will still not be revised.[375] This wording and use of 'recorded information' suggests that neither the satisfaction of this standard nor means of proof will overcome the stated proposition that forecasts are unassailable for error. It is noteworthy that the provision is expressly limited to forecasts and hence the issue that arises is whether revision is possible in other circumstances. It is submitted that such an interpretation would run contrary to the general drafting intent in the ECC and that the reason for the express provision in this case is to rule out any entitlement that a contractor would have otherwise had at common law if an error had been shown to have been made. In practice, the effect of the provision could also really only be intended to equate the risks of forecast

---

[372] The drafters have used this phrase when in fact the actual implementation is of assessments and quotations rather than compensation events.
[373] Clause 65.1 ECC.
[374] See clause 65.1 ECC.
[375] Clause 65.2 ECC.

assessment procedures with those carried generally in pricing or tendering in the first instance. It shows that the failure to forecast assessment precisely has been addressed in the overall risk allocation much in the same way as profit forecasts in the original tender will have been. The failure to realize one's expectations is not a ground at common law for overturning one's bid any more than one's forecast under the ECC.

The provision on later recorded information is significant and may be used to entice co-operation in the quotation procedure, as it will not be used in subsequent adjudication and arbitration to revise assessment. An adjudicator would simply review the project manager's decision and decide if it was properly taken. The review would be done in the light of the information provided to the project manager at the time, not in the light of what subsequently developed. The simplest reason for this is that the contract has provided that it is the contractor who has assumed the risk of the forecast cost being more or less than what materializes. Thus the contractor's forecast is treated in the same way as the contractor's tender price in the first instance. It is offered and may be more or less than the costs that materialize. This means the forecast price is, as a general rule, at least as firm if not more so than at the time of tender. Exceptions to this could include wholly unforeseen or additional work to that envisaged at tender time. This follows as the contractor would have better knowledge of the project and resources in relation to it than at the time of tender.

In the case of main options A, B, C or D, the project manager must include the changes to the prices and the completion date from any accepted quotation or from the project manager's own assessment in the notification implementing the compensation event.[376] It is, in fact, this change to the prices and the completion date that is the critical component of implementation in respect of these main options. In contrast, under main options E or F, the project manager has to include the changes to the forecast amount of the prices and the completion date in the notification to the contractor implementing a compensation event.[377] An additional approval is also required in respect of compensation events involving subcontractors and inasmuch an election may have to be made 'based upon different ways of dealing with the compensation event'.[378] Hence, there would be no implementation in this respect until such agreement of the project manager had been given.[379]

---

[376] Clause 65.4 ECC.
[377] Clause 65.3 ECC.
[378] Clause 62.1 ECSC.
[379] Clause 65.5 ECC main options E and F only.

12. Title and bonds

I may be allowed to remark that it is difficult to understand why businessmen persist in entering upon considerable obligations in old-fashioned forms of contract which do not adequately express the true transaction.

Lord Atkin,
Trade Indemnity Co Ltd v. *Workington Harbour and Dock Board*

General

Core clause 7 in the ECC is headed 'Title'. The clause addresses title issues in relation to equipment, plant and materials either individually or together in each of the clauses save 73.1 which pertains to 'objects of value or of historical or other interest'. The term 'title' is undefined but in general may be thought of as the evidence of a right that a person has to possess property. The meaning of 'title' varies depending upon the context but is most commonly used in relation to real property and conveyancing law. It may be contrasted with the term 'property' that was originally used in the heading of this clause in the Consultation Document. The term is no longer used either in the heading for the core clause or in any of the clauses themselves. 'Property' is the broader term, for not only does it encompass title but unrestricted rights to possess, use, dispose of and exclude.[1] However, there are limitations on the grant of injunctions in aid and thus they have been denied after the commencement of insolvency proceedings against the employer.[2] Whether the difference in these meanings should be understood as the reason for the change in the heading of the clause is an open question. The consistent use of the term 'title' itself throughout the clause in both the Consultation Document and the ECC suggests the change may be more stylistic than substantive.[3] The issue is not academic, as the courts have construed clauses which purport to transfer 'property' restrictively in the past.[4]

---

[1] 1 Bl Comm 138; 2 Bl Comm 2, 15.

[2] *Re Jartay Developments Ltd* (1982) 22 BLR 134; *Mac-Jordan Construction Ltd* v. *Brookmount-Erostin Ltd* (1991) 56 BLR 1, CA.

[3] Cf JCT 80 clauses 16.1 and 16.2 which use the term 'property' alone and not 'title'.

[4] See e.g. *Re Winter, ex p Bolland* (1878) 8 Ch D 225 and *Re Keen, ex p Collins* [1902] 1 KB 555.

Employer's title to equipment, plant and materials

Clause 70 establishes the employer's title to two categories of inputs: equipment, plant and materials in either of two cases. While two categories of input are referred to here there is some overlap. Thus the SCC include as components of 'Plant and Materials' delivery to and removal from the working areas, providing and removing packaging, and samples and tests, while examples of 'Equipment' include materials, fuels and other consumables, scaffolding, machinery, testing equipment, transport, construction plant, temporary works, cabins and workshops.[5] The definitions of plant and materials and equipment differ as well from comparable definitions in most traditional forms of contract. The two cases address inputs which are either inside or outside the working areas. 'The Working Areas are the *working areas* unless later changed in accordance with this contract' under clause 11.2(8) while the '*working areas*' is an identified term in part two of the Contract Data, is inclusive of the site and is especially important to the operation of clauses 70 and 71.[6] In the case of inputs *outside* the working areas they must be marked – or appropriated – by the supervisor as belonging to the contract and title passes in this way. With inputs *inside* the working areas, no specific marking is required; rather title passes to the employer once it is brought within a working area. The significance of the delineation of the working areas in relation to payment in this way should not be lost on the contractor. Title returns or passes back to the contractor in only one circumstance; that is, if it is removed from the working areas with the project manager's permission. The requirement of the supervisor's permission means removal alone is insufficient to return the title in the input to the contractor.

It is somewhat unusual to have title dependent upon permissions in this way as, for the most part, passage in and title to property is normally determined according to operation of law. Although the wording is not express, if this right of removal upon permission extends to materials which had been incorporated into the works then it adds to the contractor's rights under the common law.[7] It would appear to be distinct from the revesting of surplus materials in the contractor upon the completion of the works.[8]

No provision is made in the ECC for an effect on title as a result of an affixing of an input to the works. This contrasts with the JCT forms[9] that continue with the use of this language so predominant in property law.

---

[5] Guidance notes SCC, 96.

[6] Cf JCT 80 clause 16.1 and JCT 81 clause 15 using a broader concept in their distinctions than the working areas encompassing that area 'adjacent to the Works' as well.

[7] *Lyde* v. *Russell* (1830) 1 B & Ad 394.

[8] See *Hart* v. *Porthgain Harbour Co Ltd* [1903] 1 Ch 690.

[9] For example, clauses 16.1 and 16.2 JCT 80 and clause 15.1 JCT 81 which both refer to 'unfixed materials' although the JCT 80 provisions do not expressly address ownership itself. JCT 81 sets out detailed provisions in Appendix 2 regarding payment for off-site materials or goods.

According to the law in this area property in the materials at least supplied by a contractor passes to the employer upon their incorporation in the works or affixing.[10] Blackburn J in *Appleby* v. *Myers*[11] said 'materials worked by one into the property of another become part of that property. This is equally true whether it be fixed or moveable property'. The principle is reflected in the maxim *quicquid plantatur solo solo cedit*, 'whatever is affixed to the soil belongs to the soil'.[12] It is paramount to rights the contractor might seek to exercise. Richard Davis has been critical of the failure to overturn the rule based on recommendations made in the Latham Report. Davis writes:

> Latham's proposals made up a balanced package, the cornerstone of which was the construction trust. By failing to include the trust in the Act, the Government has yielded to pressure from employers to maintain the *quidquid plantatur* rule. In doing this, Parliament has ... up[held] the interests of landowners.[13]

The title referred to in clause 70 is that of the contractor *alone*. It does not purport to cover inputs that may belong to subcontractors, parent companies if the contractor is a subsidiary or for that matter other members of a corporate group. In this regard the wording marks a change from the Consultation Document. Clause 70.1 in the Consultation Document provided: '[w]hatever title the Contractor or a subcontractor or the parent company of either or another part of a group with the same parent company as either has or later acquires ...'. In comparison, clauses 53(1) of the ICE 6th and 55.1 of the FIDIC 4th refer to the contractor's equipment without qualification. Only the ECC wording seems to leave open title in the contractors which may be less than complete title, or legal and beneficial ownership. The significance may be greater than cross-holdings as the point also goes to whether leased or hired inputs are also excluded from the provisions. While this deletion from the Consultation Document has been made, it is compensated for to a degree in the SCC. Thus, in section 2 of the SCC the cost of equipment *includes* payments for the hire of equipment not owned directly by the contractor, but which is owned by the contractor's parent company, or by another part of a group with the same parent company. In addition, the SCC makes provision for depreciation and maintenance of equipment.

This result pertains irrespective of whether the contractor owns the equipment, purchases or hires it at arm's length from a third party, or at non-arm's length from a parent company or another part of a group with

---

[10] *Elwes* v. *Maw* (1802) 3 East 38; *Tripp* v. *Armitage* (1839) 4 M & W 687; *Sims* v. *London Necropolis Co* (1885) 1 TLR 584.

[11] *Appleby* v. *Myers* (1867) LR 2 CP 651, 659.

[12] Broom, Max 401–431.

[13] DAVIS, RICHARD. Payment Issues and Legislation. In *Contemporary Issues in Construction Law, vol 1 Security for Payment* (eds DAVIS, RICHARD and ODAMS, MARTIN A.). Construction Law Press, London, 1996, p. 25. See generally *Benjamin's Sale of Goods*, 4th edn. Sweet & Maxwell, London, 1992.

the same parent company.[14] The SSC is intended to be a full statement of actual cost components under all main options save option F. Thus, bringing equipment on site, or marking or identifying it for payment will pass 'whatever' title the contractor has to the employer. This occurs irrespective of ownership by the contractor. It is submitted that the use of the term 'whatever' in clause 70 was deliberate and reflects the fact that the contractor may have a conditional title to the equipment under a lease or hire purchase agreement. The difficulties in addressing this issue while removed from the core clause are still alluded to by the drafters when discussing cost components. The drafters write: '[t]his category [hire purchase or lease agreement] is included because the question of "ownership" is legally complex and treated differently under the law of different countries'.[15] As such, the recommendation of the drafters is that a special condition may be required to address the vesting issue that arises with equipment.[16] Thus an employer who is apprehensive that equipment which is not owned by the contractor is being included in the costs and which could vest in the employer raising potential disputes over ownership is advised to consider precluding the contractor from bringing such equipment to the working areas.[17] However, inasmuch as leased equipment is a feature of the industry, it would be difficult to require, let alone enforce, on many sites.

The inclusion of a provision on title in the core clauses in the ECC correctly assumes that disputed ownership is often an issue in building and engineering contracts. Thus, from the outset, title is assumed to be in issue and a means whereby title problems may be resolved is provided for. As noted above the means centre upon a clear distinction between inputs within or without the working areas,[18] and clear means of appropriation through either marking or payment.

The definitions for 'Plant and Material' and 'Equipment' given in clause 11.2 reinforce these distinctions. Thus 'Plant and Materials' are grouped together and defined as: 'items intended to be included in the works';[19] while 'Equipment' is defined as: 'items provided by the *Contractor* and used by him to Provide the Works and which the Works Information[20] does not require him to include in the *works*'.[21] This

---

[14] See section 22 SCC. This would extend to subsidiaries.

[15] Guidance notes section 2 SCC, 96.

[16] Guidance notes SCC section 2, 96. The SSCC does not provide this detail regarding equipment costs.

[17] Guidance notes section 2 SCC, 96.

[18] See clause 11.2(8) ECC defining the 'Working Areas' as 'the *working areas* unless later changed in accordance with this contract'. The '*working areas*' alone would be those set out in part two of the Contract Data and including the 'Site'. The 'Site' itself is also defined in clause 11.2(7) *inter alia* as the area within the '*boundaries of the site*'. It can be seen from this how words are given extended meanings through their definitions which are often inclusive of *other* identified or defined terms.

[19] Clause 11.2(10) ECC.

[20] Clause 11.2(5) ECC.

[21] Clause 11.2(11) ECC.

definition should also be read with clause 26.1 applying the conditions of contract on equipment to subcontractors' equipment as well if the contractor subcontracts work. The definitions differ somewhat from more traditional definitions and thus will require the parties to pay particular attention to their use. Traditional terminology may distinguish between 'goods', inputs that are separately identifiable both during and after construction and 'materials' which often lose their separate identity during construction. Under many forms of building contract 'materials' may also include 'goods'. 'Plant' is more typically viewed as including both equipment and tools used by the contractor during construction and which are not incorporated in the works. The term 'plant' is sometimes used to include portable buildings and cranes and at times ambiguously to refer to mechanical and electrical components in certain forms of contract.[22]

Given the definitions which have been put forward the works information can be expected to identify which items will be marked for inclusion in the works. It is recommended that 'Plant and Materials' at least include materials and workmanship specifications; requirements for their delivery and storage before incorporation in the works; and details on provision of spares and the vendors.[23] The failure to identify adequately inputs in this way could lead to uncertainty. The ECC definitions should facilitate a clear answer to the question when inputs are either within or without the working areas, although the introduction of an intention element itself distinguishing the two categories is also a potential source of uncertainty insofar as proof is concerned. This aspect of the definition will serve to limit what falls to be classified as plant and materials, for in the absence of intent to include the plant and materials within the works, they may either be classified as equipment or paid accordingly or not paid for at all. The answer to whether the plant and materials could still be paid for if unintentionally included in the works could turn on provisions that had been made in the Contract Data.

The determinations and the procedures are straightforward. If the item has been brought *within* the working area whatever title the contractor has to the equipment, plant and materials will pass to the employer.[24] Similarly, if the item is located *outside* the working area but it has been *marked* as for the contract by the supervisor it will also pass to the employer.[25] The title passing upon marking is whatever title the contractor has to the item.[26] If the item is removed from the working area then only in the case when it was so removed with the project manager's permission will title pass back to the contractor.[27]

---

[22] See BARBER, P. Title to Goods, Material and Plant under Construction Contracts. In *Interests in Goods* (eds PALMER, NORMAN and McKENDRICK, EWAN). Lloyd's of London Press, London, 1993, pp. 101–102.

[23] Guidance notes NEC, 21.

[24] Clause 70.2 ECC.

[25] Clause 70.1 ECC.

[26] Clause 70.1 ECC.

[27] Clause 70.2 ECC.

There are similar consent requirements for removal once either inputs have been brought onto the site or have vested in the employer in other traditional forms.[28] It can be seen that the central question with regard to clause 70 is *location* of the item and marking is secondary. Pursuant to clause 71 the focus shifts to *marking* and *identification* for payment. Before leaving this provision attention should be redrawn to the rather modest objective of the clause to pass only the title that the contractor has. The provision differs from provisions in other forms of contract that often purport to pass an absolute title in the input to the employer irrespective of any competing third party interests. Although provisions of this nature are fairly routine their operation is anything but routine, particularly in the event of insolvency.[29]

Clause 70.2 indirectly raises the issue of retention of title. What gives rise to this issue is that it is necessary for the project manager to permit the removal of equipment, plant and materials if title is to pass back to the contractor. It follows from the necessity for such permission that if any such items were removed without the permission and purportedly passed to a third party the employer's interests could be asserted over the third party on the basis of this clause and the absence of the permission. The employer may have to argue that the provision is in effect a retention of title clause. While the validity of such clauses has been generally upheld,[30] the lack of clear drafting in the ECC clause complicates the employer's position and may make the clause very difficult if not impossible to enforce.[31] The clear choice of the drafters to seek to pass only the title that the contractor has may be a concession recognizing the inherent difficulties in dealing with the rights of third parties. By not leaving either party with any false sense of security with respect to the inputs the employer may be more vigilant in dealing with the contractor and verifying title as a result.

The tentativeness in the ECC may simply reflect a similar tentativeness that the JCT initially exhibited toward the issue when trying to decide how it should amend the JCT forms. At the time, the JCT declined to amend its forms with regard to main contractors as, among other reasons, it saw this giving rise to a significant increase in costs.[32] However, a

---

[28] See e.g. clauses 16.1 JCT 80, 15 JCT 81, 54.1 FIDIC 4th, and 53(1) ICE 6th.

[29] See generally BARBER, P., n. 22 above, 101.

[30] *Aluminum Industrie Vaassen* v. *Romalpa Aluminum Ltd* [1976] 2 All ER 552, [1976] 1 WLR 676, CA; *Re Peachdart Ltd* [1984] Ch 131, [1983] 3 All ER 204.

[31] See *Archivent Sales & Developments Ltd* v. *Strathclyde Regional Council* (1984) 27 BLR 98 (Ct of Sess); *Sauter Automation Ltd* v. *Goodman Mechanical Services Ltd* (*in liquidation*) (1986) 34 BLR 81 (Ch D); *W Hanson (Harrow) Ltd* v. *Rapid Civil Engineering Ltd* (1987) 38 BLR 106, 11 Con LR 119; *Stroud Architectural Services Ltd* v. *John Laing Construction Ltd* (1993) 35 Con LR 135; and DE LACY, JOHN. Romalpa Theory and Practice in the Sale of Goods. *Anglo American Law Review*, 1995, **24**, 327.

[32] WILLIAMS, G. ANTOINETTE. Reservation of Title in the Construction Industry: Who Wins? – Some Economic Perspectives on Risk Allocation. *Construction Law Journal*, 1987, **3**, 271. See also Royal Institute of British Architects. *Retention of Title (Ownership) by Suppliers of Building Materials and Goods*. RIBA, London, 1978.

different result pertained with the JCT view toward subcontractors after the *Dawber Williamson* case.[33] The *Dawber Williamson* case held that an express provision in a subcontract that property in materials will not pass until the subcontractor has been paid will prevail over a term in the main contract which purports to transfer property to the employer on payment of interim certificates. After the case, amendment 1 replaced clause 19.4 of JCT 80 which required the contractor to ensure that subcontract provisions passed ownership of materials delivered to site to the client when paid for. In addition, the amendment stipulated that property in materials delivered to the site passed to the contractor if the contractor paid the subcontractor before receiving payment from the employer. It has been argued that the reasons for not amending the forms initially were still as true after the *Dawber Williamson* case was decided as before and thus defeating the actions of the JCT.

Marking equipment, plant and materials outside the working areas

The supervisor must mark inputs that are outside the working areas in either of two cases:

- if the contract identifies them for payment;[34] and
- if the contractor has prepared them for marking as the works information requires.[35]

The second case could involve passing tests specified in the works information or satisfying conditions for their storage or insurance. When either of these two conditions is satisfied, *viz.* the contract identifies items for payment or the contractor has prepared items for marking as per the works information, the supervisor will then mark the items under clause 71.1.

The powers given to the supervisor to mark equipment, plant and materials outside the works area is arguably equivalent to the vesting clauses which operate to appropriate inputs under certain other forms.[36] The FIDIC and ICE forms both contain vesting clauses. In the FIDIC 4th form, where vesting of the contractor's equipment, temporary works and materials is required, an additional clause may be added.[37] The ICE 6th

---

[33] *Dawber Williamson Roofing Ltd* v. *Humberside County Council* (1979) 14 BLR 70.

[34] The identification for payment has antecedents in certain other standard forms: see e.g. clause 15 JCT 81 and Appendix 2. See also clauses 16.1 and 16.2 JCT 80 but which rather proceed not just on the basis of an inclusion of the value of the materials and goods in an interim certificate for property to pass but also payment as well for this to occur.

[35] Clause 71.1 ECC.

[36] Although in certain standard forms, e.g. JCT 80 there are no provisions on evidence of ownership of off-site materials and goods; cf JCT 81 clause 15. Vesting clauses, unlike retention of title clauses, purport to operate only between the parties to the contract.

[37] Clause 54.2 FIDIC 4th.

form too uses the express term 'vesting'[38] and also extends to goods as well as the items referred to in the FIDIC clause. Materials vesting clauses are the most common but equipment and plant vesting clauses also exist. Vesting clauses purport to offer security to the employer and to facilitate the employer taking over the contract in the event of contractor default.[39] Under other forms it is not marking *per se* that operates to vest inputs in the employer rather delivery to site or the contractor's default which are the normal mechanisms. The advantage of the ECC provision is that the contract will identify the items for marking and hence payment. It is not simply left to the discretion of the project manager. The fact that while items are outside the working areas they are even able to be paid for at all compares favourably, from the contractor's point of view, to other forms as well.[40] A vesting clause is intended to operate to pass full ownership in and property to the input.[41] It can be strongly contended that this is the presumed intention behind clause 71. However, more recent authority has called some of the earlier authority on the effect of vesting clauses into question.[42] As a result, vesting clauses are now more likely to be regarded as 'only a part of the machinery of interim payment ... and, it is submitted, cannot be regarded ... as outright purchases of the materials'.[43] Notwithstanding this view it can still be contended that on the wording of clause 71 and despite any passage of property, the contractor still retains a right to use of the inputs in the construction of the works.[44] In *Re Cosslett (Contractors) Ltd* it was held that a deeming clause did not pass the general property in a plant to an employer merely upon being brought on to the site.[45]

No objection would appear to be able to be made on the part of a trustee in bankruptcy or a liquidator of the contractor as such clauses normally operate independently of insolvency and other similar grounds for termination, such as those set forth in clause 95.1a and 95.1b of the contract.[46] The meaning of 'determined' as against 'terminated' under individual standard forms may vary although they are used inter-changeably here and the two terms have been equated under clause 16(1)

---

[38] Clause 53.1 ICE 6th which concerns on site items, although clause 54 addresses vesting of items not on site.

[39] *Hart* v. *Porthgain Habour Co Ltd* [1903] 1 Ch 690 at 696.

[40] For example, neither JCT/MW nor GC/Works/1 3rd provides for payment of materials and goods which are off the site.

[41] See *Reeves* v. *Barlow* (1884) 12 QBD 436, CA; and *Brown* v. *Bateman* (1867) LR 2 CP 272.

[42] See White J in *Egan* v. *State Transport Authority* (1982) 31 SASR 481 questioning in particular *Banbury and Cheltenham Direct Rly Co* v. *Daniel* (1884) 50 LJ Ch 265.

[43] *Hudson's*, vol. 2, p. 1128.

[44] See *Bennett & White (Calgary) Ltd* v. *Municipal District of Sugar City (No 5)* [1951] AC 786, PC.

[45] *Re Cosslett (Contractors) Ltd* [1996] 4 All ER 46.

[46] *Re Waugh, ex p Dickin* (1876) 4 Ch D 524; see also *Re Walker, ex p Barter* (1884) 26 Ch D 510, CA.

of the FCEC form and mean that one or both parties are excused from further performance.[47]

Removing equipment

The removal of equipment is treated separately under the contract in clause 72. In the first instance the provision assumes that the item of equipment is located on site. This is unlike the title provisions in clauses 70 and 71 that refer to working areas, which is defined inclusively of the site.[48] The contractor removes[49] equipment from the site when it is no longer needed unless the project manager allows it to be left in the works.[50] This is a straightforward proposition that informs the contractor of the obligation to remove equipment that is no longer needed. If the item is not still needed the project manager may allow it to be left behind in the works.[51] If the project manager does not allow it to be left behind then the contractor must remove it from site.[52] Contractors are thus encouraged to obtain approvals in advance of using certain work methods that entail leaving equipment behind or risk running afoul of their obligation to remove unneeded items of equipment. The use of the term 'equipment' alone may act as a saving provision in this regard, and if separate meanings are attributed to all three categories of inputs, *viz.* plant and materials as well. This follows also from the fact that a contractor is more likely to leave materials on site than equipment. Hence, if the contractor must leave it behind and is unable to obtain permission to do so, the arguable classification of the item as rather plant or materials may mean relief from an obligation that could otherwise arise.

Objects and materials within the site

The contractor acquires no title to objects of value or those which have some historical or other interest within the site.[53] This resembles in short form clause 34 of JCT 63 and JCT 80.[54] The term 'object', it is submitted, should be taken broadly to include fossils and other antiquities as described in other forms.[55] The clause is declarative of the absence of interest in the

---

[47] Per Lord Wilberforce in *Photo Production Ltd* v. *Securicor Transport Ltd* [1980] AC 827, [1980] 1 All ER 556, HL. See also *E R Dyer Ltd* v. *The Simon Build/Peter Lind Partnership* (1982) 23 BLR 23.

[48] See the respective definitions of 'Working Areas' and 'Site' in clauses 11.2(8) and 11.2(7).

[49] See on the meaning of 'remove' *Arrow Co* v. *Tyne Commissioners* [1894] AC 508; and *Barraclough* v. *Brown* [1897] AC 615; and *Smith* v. *Wilson* [1896] AC 579.

[50] Clause 72.1 ECC.

[51] Clause 72.1 ECC.

[52] Clause 72.1 ECC.

[53] Clause 73.1 ECC. Cf the meaning the parties give to the '*working areas*' in part two of the Contract Data.

[54] Clause 34.1 JCT 80 provides in part 'all fossils, antiquities and other objects of interest or value ... become the property of the Employer ....

[55] For example, clause 34 of the JCT 63 and 80 and clause 32 of the ICE 6th the latter of which also refers to coins. The right to ownership of fossils found under one's land is

contractor but does not purport to be creative of any such interest in the employer.[56] However, clause 73.1 will operate as the general rule and the contractor would only acquire a title to any materials arising from excavation or demolition if so stated in the works information.[57] Clear provision is necessary in this regard to overcome any disputes which may arise between the parties as to property and hence the right to dispose at a profit of surplus excavation and demolition materials.

The clause establishes a procedure to be followed if a qualifying object is found. That is, the contractor should notify the project manager who in turn will instruct the contractor how to deal with it.[58] No movement of the object lest it be damaged is permitted without instructions from the project manager. A clear drafting intent in this regard may be inferred from the change in wording and replacement of 'may' with 'does' in clause 73.1 of the amended Second Edition. Clause 73.1 now reads: 'The Contractor does not move the object without instructions'. The replacement of the word 'may' with 'does' suggests that a more affirmative obligation is placed upon the contractor as the latter may be used synonymously with 'shall'. Presumably the project manager will become informed as to the nature of the object and any prudent steps to take for its safeguarding. The instruction to deal with the object qualifies as a compensation event under clause 60.1(7). If such objects were likely to be encountered and the parties have anticipated them, additional provisions may be included in the works information. Their foreseeability is more likely, for instance, in certain areas of archaeological importance.[59] However, in this case if such advance provision is made then the contractor would not be entitled to treat the removal of the object as a compensation event.

At common law, if the object were classed as treasure trove, it would belong to the Crown but these rights are now subject to the Treasure Act 1996.[60] Treasure trove normally entails money or coin, gold, silver, plate or bullion hidden in the earth or some other private place and the owner must be unknown.[61] By way of contrast, the contractor can acquire title to materials from excavation and demolition but only insofar as stated in the works information.[62] It should be noted that 'materials' as used in clause 73.2 is uncapitalized and thus distinct from 'Plant and Materials' as used in and defined by clause 11.2(10).

recognized under the general law in any case and would vest ownership in the employer or owner.

[56] See again clause 34.1 JCT 80.

[57] Clause 73.2 ECC.

[58] Clause 73.1 ECC.

[59] For example, those areas designated as such by the Secretary of State for the Environment under the Ancient Monuments and Archaeological Areas Act 1979, section 33.

[60] Seven hundred years of common law authority in this area though is now subject to the recently passed Treasure Act 1996.

[61] 1 Bl Comm 295.

[62] Clause 73.2 ECC.

Advanced payment to the contractor

The parties may agree that the employer will make an advanced[63] payment to the contractor. It is the type of provision that has been endorsed in the Latham Report. The Latham Report recommends that an effective modern form of contract should make 'provision where appropriate for advance mobilization payments (if necessary bonded) to contractors and subcontractors . . .'.[64] The parties may do so by agreeing to adopt the secondary option for advanced payment to the contractor.[65] The employer may, but need not necessarily, require security for making the advanced payment. If security is to be provided under the ECC it will normally be by way of an advanced payment bond.[66] The requirement for the bond would be stipulated in the Contract Data and from that point on would be governed by the provisions in option J. In part one of the Contract Data the optional statements for option J indicate whether the advanced payment bond is or is not required. In general, both HM Treasury and the Central Unit on Procurement have recommended that advance payments should be avoided. Where they cannot be avoided the government practice is to require a reducing on-demand advance payment bond issued by a bank.[67] Under the ECC, any advanced payment bond must be issued by either an approved bank or insurer. The employer's right of approval is exercised through the project manager's right to accept the bank or insurer put forward for the purposes of issuing the bond.[68] The contractor puts forward the bank or insurer formally in a submission complying with clause 13.

The project manager gives one exemplar reason for the non-acceptance of either the proposed bank or insurer. That is, its commercial position is not strong enough to carry the bond.[69] This determination should be objective and various indices may be utilized to assess the institution's commercial position. If the institution is not accepted the contractor may wish to revise the submissions and resubmit them. Assuming they are then accepted the bank or insurer would proceed to issue the bond.

---

[63] Cf use of the term 'advances' in GC/Works/1 3rd clause 40 to refer to payments made to the contractor during the progress of the works.

[64] The Latham Report paragraph 5.18(13), 37.

[65] Option J ECC.

[66] Clause J1 ECC. A variety of payment obligations may be supported by bonds, see generally *Oastler* v. *Pound* (1863) 7 LT 852; *Wardens and Commonalty of the Mystery of Mercers of the City of London* v. *New Hampshire Insurance Co Ltd* [1992] 1 WLR 792, (1992) 60 BLR 26, sub nom *Mercers Co* v. *New Hampshire Insurance Co* [1992] 3 All ER 57, CA. For references to *Mercers* and other recent cases see WALLACE QC, IAN DUNCAN. Bonds and Guarantees: Recent Developments and Cases. In *Contemporary Issues in Construction Law* (eds DAVIS and ODAMS), vol. 1, p. 99.

[67] See *Bonds and Guarantees*. HM Treasury, Central Unit on Procurement, London, August, 1994, guidance note 46.

[68] Clause J1.2 ECC.

[69] Clause J1.2 ECC.

The value of any advanced payment bond required will correspond to that of the advanced payment. The form of the bond will be set out in the works information. Time limits are imposed on both sides. Thus the failure to provide the bond within four weeks of the time agreed for its provision is a notifiable default, a ground for termination[70] and may amount to repudiation of the agreement.[71] On the other hand, the advanced payment itself must be must be made within four weeks of the later of the 'Contract Date' and the date when the employer receives the bond.[72] This time limit assumes that a bond was required; had it not been required the time limit once again would have been rather within four weeks of the contract date. Any delay in making an agreed advance payment is a compensation event.[73] Where there is such delay the early warning procedure is relevant.[74] The discharge of a bondsman under an advance payment bond may occur on grounds similar to those discharging a surety under a contract of guarantee.

The employer may have a cause of action in negligence against the project manager for failure to ensure that a bond,[75] when agreed by the parties, or insurance[76] has been taken out.

Performance bond

The parties may agree to enter into a performance bond as security for fulfilment of contractual obligations. Although the bond is expressly stated to be for 'performance', bonds may be entered into by contracting parties for a wide variety of obligations. The ECC follows both the ICE 6th and FIDIC 4th forms in this regard and stands in contrast to JCT 80 which makes no such provision. FIDIC 4th, however, uses the term 'performance security' (clause 10.1) and includes example forms. Concerns surrounding the use of bonds by United Kingdom government departments gave rise to the release of a formal policy with regard to them in an address given on 26 November 1996 by then Minister of State for Construction and Planning at the Department of the Environment, Robert Jones, MP.[77] The policy recommended that only conditional performance

---

[70] See clause 95.2 ECC, and see also the discussion on the four week time frame below.

[71] *Swartz & Son (Pty) Ltd* v. *Wolmaransstad Town Council* 1960 (2) SA 1. Separate issues may also arise as to the potential liability of the bond issuer see e.g. *Laing Management Ltd (formerly Laing Management Contracting Ltd) and Morrison-Knudson Ltd (formerly Ferguson Morrison-Knudsen River Ltd)* v. *Aegon Insurance Co (UK) Ltd* (1998) 86 BLR 70.

[72] Clause J1.2 ECC.

[73] Clause J1.2 ECC. See also advanced payment to the contractor above.

[74] See clause 16 ECC.

[75] See *Convent Hospital* v. *Eberlin & Partners* (1989) 23 Con LR 112.

[76] *Pozzolanic Lytag Ltd* v. *Bryan Hobson Associates* (1999) 63 Con LR 81. The allocation of insurance responsibilities were also examined recently in *British Telecommunications plc* v. *James Thomson & Sons (Engineers) Ltd* (1999) 61 Con LR 1 (HL).

[77] See for a short comment on the policy, 'Performance Bonds – Government Policy Announced,' 1997, 14–CLD–v.

bonds, retention bonds and advance payments bonds be used. Performance bonds in general are often divided into two categories; conditional or unconditional.[78] A bond issued under the ECC may be either conditional or unconditional, as there is no limitation imposed. Under a conditional bond, conditions that pertain to the right of the employer to call the bond, most commonly the necessity for either default or proof of loss,[79] or notice[80] should be set out in the works information. In contrast, under an unconditional (or demand) bond, the employer may call upon it without more. Although a court will require strict compliance with the terms of an unconditional bond[81] it will not lightly interfere with an employer's rights to call upon it.[82]

The provisions that govern the terms of the parties' agreement on the performance bond are similar to those governing advanced payment bonds. A bank or an insurer acceptable to the project manager must provide the bond. The amount of the bond will be stated in the Contract Data, and the form of the bond should be set out in the works information.[83] The same reason for non-acceptance of the bank or insurer is also given as in the case of an advanced payment bond; namely its commercial position is not strong enough.[84] The time frame for the giving of the bond is as of the 'Contract Date'; however, it may be given as late as four weeks after the 'Contract Date'.[85] No express provision is made for extending this time frame and the failure to provide a bond as agreed within four weeks is a notifiable default[86] and as such may lead to termination under the contract[87] and even repudiation at law.[88] However, this four-week time frame may become eight weeks on another interpretation. The notice preceding termination which may either identify particular matters of complaint or require steps to be taken to remedy the complaint or breach is often referred to as a 'notice to show

---

[78] See MILNE, M. *Contracts under Seal and Performance Bonds*. CIOB, Ascot, 1993, CIOB Construction Papers 16.

[79] See e.g. *Nene Housing Society Ltd* v. *National Westminster Bank Ltd* (1980) 16 BLR 22; *Tins Industrial Co Ltd* v. *Kono Insurance Ltd* (1987) 42 BLR 110 (HKCA).

[80] See e.g. *Oval (717) Ltd* v. *Aegon Insurance Company (UK) Ltd* (1998) 85 BLR 97.

[81] *I E Contractors Ltd* v. *Lloyds Bank plc and Rafidian Bank* [1990] 2 Lloyd's Rep 496, 51 BLR 1, CA.

[82] *R D Harbottle (Mercantile) Ltd* v. *National Westminster Bank Ltd* [1978] QB 146, [1977] 2 All ER 862; cf the recent decision in *Tower Housing Association Ltd* v. *Technical & General Guarantee Co Ltd* (1998) 87 BLR 74.

[83] Clause G1.1 ECC. The NEC contains no sample or model forms of bonds despite a recommendation to the contrary in the Latham Report: see paragraph 5.20(6), 40.

[84] Clause G1.1 ECC.

[85] Clause G1.1 ECC.

[86] Clause 95.2 ECC: 'The *Employer* may terminate if the *Project Manager* has notified that the *Contractor* has defaulted in one of the following ways and not put the default right within four weeks of the notification … [n]ot provided a bond or guarantee which this contract requires (R12)'.

[87] Clause 95.2 ECC.

[88] *Swartz & Son (Pty) Ltd* v. *Wolmaransstad Town Council* 1960 (2) SA 1.

cause'.[89] This position contrasts with ICE 6th, which, while potentially imposing a mandatory obligation upon the contractor to post-performance security, still does not list the failure to arrange the security as a ground for termination but rather leaves that issue to the discretion of the employer under clause 10.

Thus, reading the provision on termination and the apparent requirement of the four weeks' notice of the default prior to termination *together with* the four-week period for providing the bond following the 'Contract Date' suggests instead an eight-week period. This interpretation leaves unaffected a breach of contract occurring when the initial four-week period following the 'Contract Date' alone is exceeded and in which case the above mentioned remedies would continue to apply.

The parties themselves agree upon the stated percentage for the performance bond. In practice this amount is often set at 10% of the tender price.[90] The approval requirement in the ECC is similar to that under both the ICE and FIDIC conditions.[91] The cost of providing the bond, although silent in the ECC, will be borne by the contractor. The cost of providing the bond is expressly imposed on the contractor under both the ICE 6th and FIDIC 4th forms. The ECC makes no provision for expiry of the performance bond and rather will end according to its terms. Normally such bonds end either upon completion or upon the contractor's obligation to rectify defects; here either with the issue of or four weeks following the defects certificate.[92] The parties may thus wish to specify the expiry period for greater certainty. In addition, as no provision is made for the costs of the bond, they are not to fall upon the contractor in the ordinary course either as part of the prices or the fee as defined unless provision is made to the contrary.[93]

Parent company guarantee

In certain circumstances, for instance, if another company owns the contractor, the employer may require, when the contractor agrees, a guarantee by the contractor's parent company.[94] The ECC makes provision for this with a parent company guarantee secondary option clause.[95] If the option is chosen it will be governed by the terms of clause H1.1. To invoke the provision the contractor first of all must be owned by a parent company. No details are given of how that issue should be

---

[89] See generally WILLIAMS, MARK. Notices to Show Cause and the Building Contract – Requirements, Validity and Interpretation. *Building and Construction Law*, 1995, **11**, 169.

[90] For example, under clause 10(1) of ICE 6th.

[91] Clause 10(1) ICE 6th and clause 10.1 FIDIC 4th.

[92] See clauses 50.1, 81 and 82 ECC. See generally *Lewis* v. *Hoare* (1881) 44 LT 66, HL.

[93] See generally MAHTANI, N. Issues Concerning Performance Guarantees and Related Remedies in Construction Contracts. *International Construction Law Review*, 1994, 363.

[94] Clause H1.1 ECC.

[95] Option H ECC.

determined and arguably general company law principles would apply. No reference is made in the Contract Data to the parent company guarantee itself although the form for it should be governed by details set out in the works information.[96] The time frame for the giving of the guarantee is as of the 'Contract Date';[97] however, it may be given as late as four weeks after the 'Contract Date'.[98] No express provision is made for extending this time frame and the failure to provide a bond as agreed initially is a notifiable default and a ground for termination.[99]

Trust fund

The Second Edition of the NEC contains a trust fund provision following a recommendation to this effect in the Latham Report. The Latham Report recommends a modern form of contract should provide 'for secure trust fund routes of payment';[100] and insofar as the NEC itself is concerned in part: '[p]rovision should [sic] made, as a Core Clause, for a secure trust fund to be arranged, into which the client deposits payments for each milestone, activity schedule or interim payment period before the commencement of the relevant period'.[101] Martin Barnes has noted that the trust fund was added only as a secondary option so that administrative costs would not be incurred where and when trust funds were not needed abroad.[102] The provisions are unique and clearly go further than any other leading standard forms in seeking to provide security for payment, although there are still other precedents which provide for secure trust funds, e.g. the Specialist Engineering and Construction procurement system produced by the Electrical Contractors' Association which was adopted by the Specialist Engineering Contractors Group setting out secure trust funds for separate client payments to main contractors and specialists at the end of each instalment period. The drafters have stated they had only one objective in mind when the provision was included; that is the protection of the firm, at any tier in the supply chain, against insolvency of its employer.[103] Despite this wording the liability for insolvencies in the supply chain,

---

[96] Clause H1.1 ECC. The works information should also provide the form for other options which the parties agree to such as the performance bond, see clause G1.1 ECC; and the advance payment bond, clause J1.2.

[97] The contract date is the date when the contract came into existence: clause 11.2(3) ECC.

[98] Clause H1.1 ECC.

[99] Clause 95.2 ECC. See also the discussion on the four-week time frame above.

[100] Latham Report, paragraph 5.18(10), 37

[101] Latham Report, paragraph 5.20(2), 39. The New Engineering Contract – An Update. *International Construction Law Review*, 1996, 92–94. See generally GREENWOOD, DAVID and KLEIN, RUDI. Security of Payment in the Light of the Latham Report: An Opportunity to Remove Unacceptable Risks? *Construction Law Journal*, 1995, **11**, 255; and JENKINS, JANE. The Latham Trust Fund Proposals. *Construction Law Journal*, 1995, **11**, 262.

[102] BARNES, MARTIN. *ibid.*, 92–94.

[103] Guidance notes NEC option V, 90.

which is inclusive of subcontractors and suppliers and sub-subcontractors etc., remains upon the employer. It is the employer who initially funds the trusts and subsequently replenishes the trust fund in favour of the defined beneficiaries. This objective is clearly reflected in the drafting of the provisions. The drafters have expressly excluded the use of the trust fund to protect against late payment on the basis that adequate protection is already given under the terms of the ECSC.[104] Thus the scope of the trust fund provisions is narrow in part on the expectation that additional protections will be afforded in other interlocking NEC documents or other secondary option clauses.[105] While trust funds are one mechanical means of assessing client generated risks the literature suggests that more sophisticated means of assessing those risks are available to predict project outcomes.[106]

Defined terms

The trust fund secondary option clause is the only option, save for the price adjustment for inflation secondary option clause, that has separate provisions on defined terms. It is a measure of both the complexity and the importance of precise terminology in the establishment and administration of the trust fund that this is the case. It is also the longest secondary option and the only one that has a sample document included in a dedicated appendix to the guidance notes. The Sample Trust Deed also contains two schedules, on administrative powers and the initial trust fund. Although the marginal note is 'Defined terms', the provisions both define as well as identify terms, which is consistent with usage in clause 11. Definitions are given for seven terms: the trust fund, trust deed,[107] initial value, insolvency of an individual,[108] insolvency of a company,[109] the beneficiaries,[110] and a trust payment.

---

[104] Guidance notes NEC option V, 90. See also New Housing Grants, Construction and Regeneration Act 1996.

[105] For example, secondary option clause P on retention.

[106] See SKOMETA, SIMON T. *et al.* Validation of the Model for Evaluating Client-generated Risk by Project Consultants. *Construction Management and Economics*, 1996, **14**(2), 131–145. See DAVIS, RICHARD. Payment Issues and Legislation. *Contemporary Issues in Construction Law, vol. 1 Security for Payment.* (eds DAVIS, RICHARD and ODAMS, A. MARTIN). Construction Law Press, London, 1996, pp. 31–47 for a short comparison of the NEC trust fund provisions to the SEACC form provisions and those in the case of *Lovell Construction Ltd* v. *Independent Estates plc* [1994] 1BCLC 31.

[107] Clause V1.1(2) ECC: 'The Trust Deed is a deed between the *Employer* and the *Trustees* which contains the provisions for administering the Trust Fund. Terms defined in this contract have the same meaning in the Trust Deed'.

[108] Clause V1.1(4) ECC: see discussion of definition in clause 95.1 ECC.

[109] Clause V1.1(5) ECC: see discussion of definition in clause 95.1 ECC.

[110] Clause V1.1(6) ECC: 'The Beneficiaries are the *Contractor* and • Subcontractors, • suppliers of the *Contractor*, • subcontractors of whatever tier of a Subcontractor and • suppliers of whatever tier of a Subcontractor or of his subcontractors [ ] who are employed to Provide the Works'.

Some observations may be made with regard to the definitions. First of all, clause V1.1(1) provides: '[t]he Trust Fund is a fund held and administered by the *Trustees*'. The *'Trustees'* is an identified term in the optional statements in part one of the Contract Data. The proforma allows for two trustees to be named, although more could be added. No limitations are imposed upon who may serve as trustees and both individuals and trust corporations or companies may be expected to act. The Contract Data example recommends that trustees should be chosen from several professional groups including, in particular, one from a group experienced in insolvency law.

The meaning of initial value in clause V1.1(3) is as follows: '[t]he Initial Value of the Trust Fund is an amount which is the total of the Prices at the Contract Date multiplied by 1.5 and divided by the number of months in the period between the Contract Date and the Completion Date'. This wording suggests that the term being defined is 'The Initial Value of the Trust Fund', although subsequent clauses V2.2 and V3.1(4) reconfirm it is only 'The Initial Value' which is being defined in fact. The amount of the initial value payment was chosen by the drafters on the basis of previous experience as to what the likely maximum payment would be.[111] The initial value chosen may have to be amended if main option A is used and only a small number of milestone payments are planned.[112] The Sample Trust Deed shows the initial value as representing the initial trust fund itself.[113]

The definitions of insolvency of an individual and insolvency of a company are identical to the provisions in clause 95.1, although the definitions will vary outside the United Kingdom and amendment may be required to reflect local laws. The definition of beneficiaries will only protect a beneficiary from an insolvency in the immediately preceding tier of the subcontractual or supply chain of contracts.[114]

Lastly, the meaning of trust payment in clause V1.1(7) of the ECC: '[a] Trust Payment is a payment made by the *Trustees* out of the Trust Fund' may be contrasted to the description of trust payment in the Sample Trust Deed: '[a]ny payment or application of any part of the Trust Fund as the Trustees think fit'. The latter arguably provides the wider meaning notwithstanding the provisions of clause V1.1(2) giving the terms defined in the contract the same meaning as in the trust deed.

Trust fund
The contractual provisions on the trust fund in clause V2 are contained separately from those on the trust deed.[115] The responsibility to establish the trust fund is imposed on the employer who must act to do so within one week of the 'Contract Date'.[116] The contract date is the date when the

[111] See guidance notes NEC on clause V1.1(3) ECC, 90.
[112] Guidance notes NEC on clause V1.1(3) ECC, 90.
[113] Schedule 2 to the Deed, 137.
[114] Guidance notes NEC on clause V3.1(6) ECC, 90.
[115] See clause V3 ECC below.
[116] Clause V2.1 ECC.

contract came into existence under clause 11.2(3). No express provision is made in the clause for the employer's failure to do so and thus the normal rules regarding failing to take action would apply. Three modes of establishment are given in clause V2.2. Two of the modes are given alternatively while the third mode applies to government departments or public authorities in the United Kingdom. Trust funds and retention can be separate issues under different forms; for instance, under the ICE MW 2nd there is no provision for retention moneys to be held on trust or kept in a separate bank account.

Prompt payment has had increasing attention of late and a series of prompt payment measures may be referred to. In particular, a new British Standard for Prompt Payment, BS 7890 – *Method for Achieving Good Payment Performance in Commercial Transactions.*[117] BS 7890 has set out the basic principles of credit management best practice. In addition, league tables published by the Economic Secretary to the Treasury since 17 December 1996 reflect greater departmental prompt payment requirements and targets. The Audit Commission too has required local authorities to publish their bill payment record as a performance indicator as from the 1997–1998 financial year. The Department of Trade and Industry Consultation Document *Tackling Late Payment: Stating Payment Practice in the Directors' Report* was also important and now with the provisions in the HGCRA 1996 and the passage of the Late Payment of Commercial Debts (Interest) Act a new legislative framework has been superimposed.[118]

Private employers may establish the trust fund by making a payment to the trustees equal to the initial value of the trust fund.[119] Alternatively, they may provide the trustees with a guarantee in the same amount from a bank or other financial institution that is acceptable to the trustees.[120] Where the payment mode is chosen the trustees must hold the trust fund in an interest bearing account.[121] The clear segregation of a trust fund is a critical element in its establishment.[122] The term 'private' employers is used here in contrast to non-government department or non-public authorities reading clause V2.2 of the ECC *a contrario*. The guidance notes use the term 'public sector' collectively to refer to these terms also. The guidance notes also state that public sector employers are likely to use the second or third modes.[123] This also implies that public sector employers could use the first mode as well. However, this interpretation is

---

[117] BS 7890. *Method for Achieving Good Payment Performance in Commercial Transactions.* British Standards Institution, London, 1996.

[118] The Late Payment of Commercial Debts (Interest) Act 1998 became law on 11 June 1998 and came into force on 1 November 1999.

[119] Clause V2.2 ECC.

[120] Clause V2.2 ECC.

[121] Clause V3.1(8) ECC.

[122] See HAYTON, DAVID. The Significance of Equity in Construction Contracts. *Construction Law Yearbook*, 1994, 19.

[123] Guidance notes, clause V2.2, 91.

not supported either by the drafting in clause V2.2 or the flow chart in respect of it, FC V, 99.

The guarantee to be given by the employer may be compared to and contrasted with the parent company guarantee given under secondary option H and even the performance and advanced payment bonds given under secondary options G and J respectively. The forms of the parent company guarantee and bonds in the contract must be set out in the works information. No similar requirement exists for the trust fund guarantee. The form of the bonds given in secondary options G and J are also required to be set out in the works information.[124] The parent company guarantee may be given up to four weeks after the 'Contract Date' while the trust fund guarantee must be given within one week. A four-week limit is also the standard used when a performance bond or advanced payment bond is being given.[125] There is no element of discretion exercised toward the acceptability of the guarantor. The parent company is the only potential guarantor and must provide the security. With the trust fund the trustees exercise a degree of control over the selection of the guarantor. There is no requirement for reasons to be given for any non-acceptance of a bank or other financial institution.[126] Broad acceptability is also the rule in the giving of bonds under the contract. In the cases of both secondary options G and J, the bank or insurer issuing the bond must be accepted by the project manager. No express requirement is given for the parent company guarantee to be payable unconditionally or on demand. The trust fund guarantee is required to be payable on the trustees' first written demand. The guarantees differ in their objectives; with the parent company guarantee supporting a performance obligation against the trust fund supporting a payment obligation. In summary, the similarities of the trust fund guarantee to, and its differences from, broadly comparable secondary options place the trust fund provisions no higher nor lower in status than those provisions governing the giving of these other securities.

The third mode of establishing the trust fund pertains expressly to public bodies. Thus, if the employer is a government department or other public authority in the United Kingdom the trust may be established by the employer entering into certain irrevocable undertakings with the contractor and the trustees.[127] The undertakings are given with respect to paying the trustees promptly. Promptness is a requirement under certain other clauses in the ECC including clauses 63.6 and 82.1. There is considerable case law surrounding the interpretation of the term 'promptly' and similar time stipulation clauses which have given rise to an overall hierarchy of strictness. Catherine Morton writes:

---

[124] Clauses G1.1 and J1.2 ECC.
[125] Secondary options G and J respectively.
[126] Cf clause G1.1 and J1.2 ECC.
[127] Clause V2.2 ECC.

[a]t the lowest level are expressions such as 'within a reasonable time' ... [and at] a slightly more stringent level are expressions such as 'as soon as possible', 'forthwith' and 'promptly'. These expressions have been interpreted to mean 'reasonable in all the circumstances' and not what a party may consider reasonable. At the highest level are expressions such as 'within [14] days' and 'immediately'. Depending on the context in which these expressions are used, the Courts could infer that 'time is of the essence' ...[128]

The payments to the trustees must be made on demand in such amounts as they request for trust payments as well as their fees and expenses for administering the trust fund.[129] 'Trust payments' are payments made by the trustees out of the trust fund under clause V1.1(7) of the ECC. This definition may be contrasted with that of 'trust payment' in the Sample Trust Deed: 'Any payment or application of any part of the Trust Fund as the *Trustees* think fit'. Additional provisions are illustrated in the 'Sample Trust Deed' in clause 5.4: 'The *Employer* pays the *Trustees* their fees and expenses for administering the Trust Fund and pays any guarantor's fees'; and clause 5.5: 'The *Trustees* may engage professional advisers and consultants to help them with the administration of the Trust Fund and may make Trust Payments for their fees and expenses'.

While the irrevocable undertakings take the place of a trust deed they would form the principal basis of any such deed if one were drafted.[130] The undertakings would have to be drafted separately, and without more would not constitute a contract document. The drafters recommend that the contractor also be a party to the undertakings in addition to the department or public authority and the trustees.[131] It is unclear why this recommendation is given when the contractor is not a party to the trust deed itself as the rationale for including the contractor as a party in both cases would be the same, *viz.* giving the contractor a clear right of action to enforce the agreement. The availability of undertakings as a mode of establishment of the trust fund has been limited to government departments and public authorities in recognition of the potential difficulties in enforcement and the risk of insolvency.[132] It is interesting to note that only the undertaking mode of establishment appears without limitation in terms of amount. Both the payment and guarantee modes are limited in terms of amount to the initial value of the trust fund. Whether this is intended to impose a greater potential trust liability upon a government or public authority employer is an open question.

---

[128] MORTON, CATHERINE. Time Bars and Conditions Precedent. *Building and Construction Law*, 1995, **11**, 303–304.
[129] Clause V2.2 ECC. See also the administrative powers of the trustees in Schedule 1 to the Sample Trust Deed, clauses 2, 3 and 7.
[130] Cf the Sample Trust Deed and Schedule 1 to it.
[131] Guidance notes NEC on clause V2.2 ECC, 91.
[132] Guidance notes NEC on clause V2.2 ECC, 91.

A loose disclosure obligation is imposed upon the contractor. Thus, the contractor must *inform* suppliers and subcontractors of the terms of the trust deed and the appointment of the trustee.[133] While the giving of a copy of the trust deed itself would clearly satisfy the obligation the contractor need not strictly go that far and may not have a copy of the trust deed in any case. The contractor is a beneficiary under the trust deed only with the employer and the trustees as the parties under clause V1.1(2) and the Sample Trust Deed. The guidance notes state the employer will need to provide a copy of the trust deed to the contractor (clause V2.3 of the ECC, 91), but nowhere in the contract is this intention expressed. This may be contrasted with clause 16.4 requiring the project manager to give a copy of the record to the contractor. This obligation to inform, as it were, may present practical difficulties where there are a large number of subcontractors on the project and thus some mechanism or means should be in place to see that the obligation has been carried out. The notification of the appointment of the trustees themselves should follow as a matter of course with subcontractors who are engaged under the ECSC form as it contains an optional clause naming the same trustees.[134]

The contractor must also arrange that subcontractors ensure that their suppliers and subcontractors, of whatever tier, are also informed. This last requirement is somewhat exceptional in that it asks for the fulfilment of an obligation by the contractor beyond the normal contractual chain of responsibility. One may have expected that this obligation would rather have been imposed upon the subcontractors themselves. However, it would appear that the attempt to extend the obligation to subcontractors of whatever tier might have made that difficult to attain in practice. Hence, the contractor may have been chosen to overcome this and perhaps achieve greater accountability at least at the initial point of control with the contractor.[135]

Trust deed

The trustees in accordance with the trust deed administer the trust fund. The trust deed in turn includes eight mandatory provisions that are set out in full in clause V3.1 of the ECC.[136] The employer and the trustees enter into the trust deed.[137] The beneficiaries[138] in the trust deed are the contractor, subcontractors, suppliers of the contractor, subcontractors of whatever tier of a subcontractor, and suppliers of whatever tier of subcontractor or of his or her subcontractors who are employed to

---

[133]   Clause V2.3 ECC.
[134]   See ECSC part one optional statements. For present purposes appointment is equated with choosing trustees and indicating same in part one.
[135]   The same obligation is nevertheless imposed upon the subcontractor in any case: see clause V1.3 ESC.
[136]   Clause V3.1 ECC, and see clauses V3.1(1) to (8) ECC.
[137]   Clause V1.1(2) ECC.
[138]   'Beneficiaries' is a defined term in clause V1.1(6) ECC.

provide the works.[139] The definition does not mention suppliers *to* suppliers of the contractor. However, such a group is identified as a beneficiary in the Sample Trust Deed as follows: 'suppliers of whatever tier of a supplier of the *Contractor*'. The drafters concede their intention was to include this group under clause V1.1(6) of the ECC, 91. However, it is submitted this may be insufficient to achieve this intent, particularly given clause V1.1(2) of the ECC stating '[t]erms defined in this contract have the same meaning in the Trust Deed'. Thus this express provision may preclude their drafting intention being given effect to. In comparison the definition of 'Subcontractor' in clause 11.2(9) of the ECC excludes many suppliers.

To trigger recourse to the trust deed by a beneficiary requires firstly the insolvency of an individual or of a company to arise.[140] Once this condition has been satisfied the beneficiary still has the burden of satisfying the trustees of several additional conditions before a claim becomes successful.

- The trustee has not received all or part of a payment properly due under the contract. While the payments due to a beneficiary may be those assessed under core clause 5 of the ECC or ECSC and its equivalents in other subcontracts, clause V3.1(3) suggests an independent power of assessment in the trustees.
- The trustee's contract relates to the works. The works would include not only those identified in section 1 of part one of the Contract Data but also the subcontract works in section 1 of part one of the Contract Data in the ESCC and their equivalents in other subcontracts.
- The payment was unpaid at the time of the insolvency. The Sample Trust Deed contains a helpful definition of 'Unpaid Sum': 'The value of the payment which in the opinion of the *Trustees* the Beneficiary will not receive or is unlikely to receive in respect of the works as a result of events referred to in subclause 3.3. That amount excludes any interest on such sum and excludes any payment in compensation for any other financial or other loss which may be suffered by the Beneficiary in consequence of such events'.
- The reason for the failure to pay was the insolvency of the party which should have made the payment.

The conditions comprise two bullet points in the contract but would seem to be more accurately set out as four points, numbered here. All the conditions must be satisfied or the claim will fail.

The beneficiary must establish that the payment said to be due was unpaid *at the time of the insolvency*. One possible limitation on the operation of the trust fund is the decision in *British Eagle International Airlines Ltd* v. *Cie Nationale Air France*[141] which held that clauses which

---

[139] Clause V1.1(6) ECC.
[140] See clauses V1.1(4) and V1.1(5) ECC.
[141] *British Eagle International Airlines Ltd* v. *Cie Nationale Air France* [1975] 2 All ER 390, [1975] 1 WLR 758, HL.

distort the pari passu principle in liquidation are contrary to public policy and therefore void. The Latham Report recommended the effective overturning of the *British Eagle* judgment.[142] Tony Bingham has written with regard to the ECC provision: 'If the courts agree that under the new NEC trust fund scheme, the money in a trust is now owned by a bust company, then the scheme will work'.[143] The last point to note is that causation must also be shown. This may prove difficult, for the inability of a creditor to meet payments as they come due also suggests other problems. Distinguishing the other potential causes for the failure to make the payment from the fact of the insolvency itself also seems unnecessary notwithstanding insolvency law.

It is material to the claim that the beneficiary advances to know whether the defects certificate has been issued or not, for only when it has not will the conditions referred to above be capable of satisfaction. Thus the issuance of the defects certificate acts as an effective bar to a claim by a beneficiary being paid.[144]

Assuming that the beneficiary has satisfied all of the conditions referred to, the trustees may make a trust payment to the beneficiary at their discretion.[145] The amount may not exceed the value of the payment that the beneficiary has not received.[146] Thus the amount due to the beneficiary acts as a limitation on the value of any claim which the trustees will entertain. Conversely the trustees in their discretion may pay an amount less than this maximum as well.

An obligation is imposed on the beneficiary in respect of amounts received from the trustees. Thus, if the beneficiary subsequently receives a payment from another party in respect of which a trust payment has been made, the beneficiary 'passes on that amount' to the trustees. 'Party' is undefined. It is in the beneficiary's interest that it be construed narrowly, e.g. party to the contract, and in the trustees interest that it be construed broadly, e.g. party to the contract or any third party. The Sample Trust Deed is less ambiguous and refers instead to a payment from another 'person' under clause 3.5. 'Person' in turn is also defined in clause 1.1 of the Sample Trust Deed as '[a]ny individual, Trustee, company, partership or incorporated or unincorporated body'.[147] The obligation to pass on the amount appears to be in respect of the payment from the other party. In this sense the obligation may not be restitutionary *per se*, as the contractor is not repaying money originally received from the trustees by again 'passing on' the proceeds of the second payment.

---

[142] Latham Report, 27, n. 92, 97.
[143] BINGHAM, TONY. Insolvency Juggling Act. *Building*, 18 August 1995, 25. See generally for a discussion of the topic and some of the exceptions that have been developed in the case law with regard to retention and trust funds McINNIS, J.A. *Hong Kong Construction Law*. Butterworths, Singapore, 1995, Div VI, paragraphs 721–1080.
[144] Clause V3.1(5) ECC.
[145] Clause V3.1(1) ECC.
[146] Clause V3.1(1) ECC.
[147] Clause V3.1(2) ECC.

The drafters refer to the trust fund being 'reimbursed'. It would appear to be a popular use of the term only given this fact. Contractors can be expected to argue strenuously whenever arguable that such second payments were not in respect of anything for which a trust payment has been made. The trust provisions note parenthetically that the obligation to pass on the payment is up to the value of the trust payment only.[148]

The trustees may take steps to safeguard trust assets following payment. In particular, the trustees may require either an assignment of rights or an undertaking with respect to the payment from the beneficiary before making a trust payment.[149] No details are given of the nature of the assignment of rights and in this regard they are completely open-ended and more detail may have been expected on this question. Further clarification is offered, however, by the wording of the Sample Trust Deed.[150] The offer of an undertaking is also oddly out of place when it was rejected in the first instance as an option available to private employers in establishing the trust fund. However, the significance of both provisions is diminished by their optional nature.

The trustees are given a characteristic broad grant of discretion in deciding the amount and timing of all trust payments.[151] The trust payments may either be made on account or withheld until the trustees have assessed the total amount of any debts owing to a beneficiary arising out of insolvency.[152] Reference to the trustees carrying out the assessment suggests that they have a power to assess amounts owing to the contractor independent to that of the project manager; indeed the trustees will be assumed to be independent throughout.

It is a condition precedent to the payment of a claim that the beneficiary satisfies the trustees that the reason for a preceding failure to be paid *is the insolvency* of the party that should have made the payment.[153] This has been referred to as causation. However, the power of the trustees to withhold payments from the beneficiary concerning debts owing 'arising out of' an insolvency is much broader than this.[154] The result may be that the trustees will thus require the contractor to seek payment from others before paying a claim out of trust funds.

The trustees may take into account any claims that the party suffering from insolvency may have against the beneficiary.[155] The reference, it

---

[148] See clause V3.1(2) ECC.

[149] Clause V3.1(2) ECC.

[150] Clause 3.5 of the Sample Trust Deed at 133 provides in part: 'to assign to the *Trustees* on such terms as the *Trustees* think fit all its rights in relation to the receipt from another person of any sum to which the proposed Trust Payment directly or indirectly or in whole or in part relates'.

[151] See clause V3.1(3) ECC.

[152] See clause V3.1(3) ECC.

[153] Clause V3.1(1) ECC.

[154] See MUSTILL, SIR MICHAEL and BOYD, STEWART. *Commercial Arbitration*, 2nd edn. Butterworths, London, 1989, p. 120 discussing the breadth of the phrase in the arbitration context.

[155] See clause V3.1(3) ECC.

may be noted, is to claims not debts and a parenthetical reference includes claims by way of set-off as well. In general, the common law rules on set-off will apply subject to the provisions of the HGCRA. The trustees may also take into account the likely liability of the liquidator or other administrator[156] of the insolvent party to meet the claims of unsecured creditors from funds in his hands. This suggests that the trustees may require the contractor to seek payment from the liquidator or other administrator before paying a claim out of trust funds.

After having taken all of the relevant factors into account the trustees may decide to make a trust payment. The route they will take in this regard is somewhat dependent upon whether a government department or other public authority is involved. If so, the trustees will issue a demand to the employer for the amount of the trust payment. The employer is expected to pay the demand promptly[157] although no contractual remedy in the event of failure to do so is given. Where a private employer is involved the trustees will make a payment from the trust fund.[158] The payment has consequences for the trustees in terms of the preservation of the capital or assets of the trust as well. Thus if the trust fund was established under the first mode – payment – the employer must maintain the trust fund at the initial value. The employer will be notified of the responsibility to do so within one week of the trustees making the trust payment.[159] Successive trust payments will entail successive notices. If, on the other hand, the trust fund was established by the second mode – guarantee – the employer 'ensures that the guarantor maintains the Trust Fund at the Initial Value'.[160] The trustees once again will notify the Employer or the guarantor within one week of making a trust payment.[161] The responsibility of the employer or the guarantor is then to restore the trust fund to the initial value within two weeks of the notification.[162]

In summary, the payment of trust funds triggers a form of dual obligation on the part of the employer or the guarantor to maintain at and restore the trust fund to its initial value.[163] The dual obligation is given effect to in the Sample Trust Deed as an undertaking by the employer with regard to each obligation.[164] In this way it can be seen that the potential liability of the employer or guarantor is unlimited. It is submitted that the intention of the drafters can be seen in these provisions but they assume a great deal; particularly regarding the true role of a

---

[156] Cf references to the receiver, receiver and manager or administrative receiver in clause V1.1(5) ECC.
[157] See clause V2.2 ECC.
[158] Clause V1.1(7) ECC.
[159] Clause 3.1(4) ECC.
[160] Clause 3.1(4) ECC.
[161] Clause 3.1(4) ECC.
[162] Clause 3.1(4) ECC.
[163] See clause 3.1(4) ECC. See clause 5.1, 133.
[164] See clause 3.1(4) ECC. See clause 5.1, 133.

guarantor, in this case a bank or other financial institution. The liability of the guarantor is secondary to that of the employer. The guarantor's obligation is to make payment upon the failure of the employer to do so. If the ECC provisions seek to reverse this, as it appears they do, it should have been clearly stated in the contract or the notes that accompany them. The contract does state that the guarantee given by the employer is payable on 'their first written demand'.[165] But whether a prior demand upon and failure of the employer to meet the demand is still required is unclear. Further, the nature of a guarantee does not easily admit of obligations framed in terms of either maintenance or restoration. In other words, the guarantee itself should be independent of liabilities of the underlying construction contract. If properly drafted as a continuing guarantee the protection if affords would remain in place without the necessity to refer to its value being restored. Conversely, if it were not drafted to be a continuing guarantee then it would likely have to be replaced rather than restored. The ECC provisions do not sufficiently distinguish between these two types of guarantees and the independent nature of the liability; something more is still required.

The Sample Trust Deed has offered more in its attempt to reflect the drafters' intent. Thus, in schedule 2 to the Sample Trust Deed, an 'Initial Trust Fund' is created. It evidences the agreement of the parties to establish the Trust Fund at an amount equal to the initial value agreed to and defined in the ECC. The initial trust fund agreement refers in the alternative to a guarantee and an irrevocable undertaking. Both documents are drafted separately and attached to the initial trust fund agreement. The operative provisions in the initial trust fund agreement clearly indicate that it is the *benefit* of the guarantee or irrevocable undertaking that the trustee receives and which benefit is given by way of assignment.[166] One may expect that the guarantee or irrevocable undertaking would then contain the payment obligations under the securities. In conclusion, some clarification regarding recourse to the securities referred to in the ECC, the guarantee and irrevocable undertaking is warranted. Parties to and others affected by the contract may seek to introduce some of this clarification through the ancillary documentation.

The trustees may wish to engage consultants regarding the issues raised above or more generally concerning the administration of the trust fund. They are given the power to do so in the trust deed.[167] When they do so they may make trust payments to any consultants engaged by them for their fees and expenses.[168] No limitation is imposed upon the disciplines the consultants may be engaged in or the professions or otherwise they may belong to. The criteria for the making of a trust payment in respect of fees and expenses are in fact the same as for the

---

[165] Clause V2.2 ECC.
[166] See again Appendix 2 to the Sample Trust Deed, 137.
[167] Clauses 3.1 and 3.1(7) ECC.
[168] Clause V3.1(7) ECC.

making of a trust payment to a beneficiary. Both trust payments are governed by clause V3.1(3).[169] Even when the trustees engage no consultants they will nevertheless incur their own fees and expenses in administering the trust fund. However, these costs are borne directly by the employer.[170] This obligation forms part of the trust deed under clause V3.1 and is also independently one of the undertakings given by a government department or public authority under clause V2.2 of the ECC.

Closing the trust fund will depend upon the mode of establishment. If the trust fund was established by payment the trustees will pay any amount remaining in it inclusive of accrued interest to the employer.[171] If the trust fund was established by guarantee it will simply be returned to the employer.[172] No limitation on the duration of the trust fund itself is contained in the ECC. A limitation of one sort is found in the prohibition of paying claims that are received after the defects certificate has been issued.[173] Clause 6 of the Sample Trust Deed has chosen a maximum period of ten years after the trust deed was entered into or any earlier period specified in advance by deed by the trustees.[174] The power of revocation itself is expressly given in clause 9 of the Sample Trust Deed.

Provision is made in closing in the Sample Trust Deed in clause 10 for referral of any dispute arising in connection with the trust to a single arbitrator. In this regard the parties should be mindful of the dispute provisions in core clause 9 of the ECC and work to ensure that they may operate together where warranted.

---

[169]   See discussion clause V3.1 ECC above.
[170]   Clause V3.1(7) ECC.
[171]   Clause V3.1(5) ECC.
[172]   Clause V3.1(5) ECC.
[173]   Clause V3.1(5) ECC.
[174]   See the Sample Trust Deed, clause 1.1, 132.

13. Risks and insurance

Contractual documents are tools for managing risks. Their purpose is to determine the consequences of particular risks which you must previously have identified.

Professor Phillip Capper,
Management of Legal Risks in Construction

General

The assessment and allocation of risk through the conditions of contract on a construction project is of fundamental importance. A major American study concluded that:

[c]areful and thoughtful selection of indemnity, consequential damage, differing conditions and delay clauses that do not grossly and inequitably allocate risk to the contractor, positively impacts overall project performance and the owner-contractor working relationship.[1]

The allocation of risk in a construction project is in part a function of the standard form that will be chosen and in part the method of procurement itself. The NEC, through its various main options, allows some basic choices to be made at the outset regarding these questions. Each main option assumes the identification, classification and allocation of certain risks. Max Abrahamson, an early authority on the analysis of risk, shortly outlined an approach to risk in this way – list the risk, place the risk and measure the risk.[2] Based upon the choices that have been made in these regards in the various main options, a contractor is able to cost a project.

To a certain degree the outcomes may be influenced through a mix of secondary option clauses and the contents of other contract documents. In

---

[1] ASHLEY, DAVID B. *et al. The Impact of Risk Allocation and Equity in Construction Contracts: An Overview of Indemnification, Consequential Damages, Differing Conditions and Delay Claims.* A Report to the Construction Industry Institute. The University of Austin, Austin, Texas, November 1988, p. ii.

[2] ABRAHAMSON, MAX. Risk Management. *International Construction Law Review*, 1984, 241.

addition, the risks may be attenuated through other documents such as sureties, bonds, guarantees, indemnities and most importantly insurance.[3] The core clause 8 provisions address the allocation of risk for generally accepted categories of legal and insurable risks. Thus, while they are limited in this sense and do not purport to address all construction risks and which are dealt with in other provisions in the contract documents, the provisions are still very important. As a matter of principle the clause sets forward a category of risks that belong to the employer and leaves the contractor with all other risks not so defined. This is an interesting drafting technique that reverses the approach in other forms of contract that set out the employer's risks as the 'excepted risks'. As a general matter Abrahamson lists some sixty-four construction risks which fall under ten general headings as follows: the physical works, delay and disputes, direction and supervision, damage and injury to persons and property, shortage of resources, government policy, conflict, labour demands and unrest, inflation, and arbitration and law.[4] While the construction risk can be transferred by insurance, hence allowed for by only the cost of the premium, it is still one of the most important factors in costing projects.

The effect of making, upon one interpretation, the employer's risks the general case and the contractor's risks a remaining or residual category of risks, is open to interpretation. Whether construed narrowly or broadly the intention is clearly to see that no risks are left unallocated.

Employer's risks

The ECC sets out *six broad categories of events* which fall as risks upon the employer:

(1) claims, proceedings, compensation and costs which are payable due to the event;
(2) loss of or damage to plant and materials supplied to the contractor;
(3) loss of or damage to the works, plant and materials;
(4) loss of or damage to parts of the works taken over by the employer;
(5) loss of or damage to the works and any equipment, plant and materials retained on site by the employer after termination; and
(6) additional employer's risks stated in the Contract Data.[5]

---

[3] See generally NEWMAN, PAUL. *Bonds, Guarantees and Performance Security in the Construction Industry.* Jordans, Bristol, 1998; HUGHES WILL *et al. Financial Protection in the UK Building Industry.* E & FN Spon, London, 1998; and ANDREWS, GERALDINE and MILLET, RICHARD. *Law of Guarantees.* FT Law & Tax, London, 1995.

[4] ABRAHAMSON, MAX, see n. 2 above, 241–244. See also with regard to the spectrum of risks in construction specifically from an insurance perspective, BUNNI, NAEL G. *Construction Insurance.* Elsevier Applied Science Publishers, London, 1986, pp. 41–99.

[5] Clause 80.1 ECC. It can be noted that the First Edition referred instead to 'other' employer's risks rather than 'additional' employer's risks.

A perusal of these six categories of events reveals four entail loss of or damage[6] – either in whole or part – to the equipment 'and/or' plant and materials. The classifications adopted in this sense reflect traditional insurance terminology that is shared with many other standard forms even though the assigning of the risks to the employer in this way differs from other precedents. For example, the ICE 6th form imposes a general obligation on the contractor to take care of the works (clause 20(1)) and insure in respect of the works (clause 21); then certain 'excepted risks' fall outside of the assigned liability and belong to the employer. While the contractor has the general liability for loss of or damage to the works etc. under both the ECC and ICE 6th, only the ICE 6th deliberately sets out the employer's liabilities moreover as *exceptions* themselves. Such drafting may have implications for the interpretation of the provisions.[7] The term 'excepted risks' is used in many forms of contract to indicate employer's risks. The choice of traditional phrases with a specific legal meaning by the drafters in the insurance provisions was deliberate.[8] Notwithstanding the similarities of the categories as a whole they merit individual attention and will be commented upon in turn.[9]

Claims, proceedings, compensation and costs which are payable due to the event

The first category of event which is assigned to the employer is the broadest category and entails all claims, proceedings, compensation and costs payable which are due to any of *three general cases*. With regard to this terminology in general, and prior to the recent civil reforms in the United Kingdom, the term 'proceedings' could be expected to extend to all matters instituted in court, i.e. pleadings and interlocutory hearings, as well as the trial itself. The term 'compensation' is undefined in the ECC. Its use may be compared to that in clause 6 of the ECC dealing with 'compensation events'. In cases where the legislature authorizes interference with the rights of private persons, provision is generally made for the payment of 'compensation' to persons injured.[10] Lastly, with regard to the term 'costs' this is one of the rare cases where the drafters have had to use legal terms of art with distinct meanings to reflect one concept. The tendency in the ECC is to replace such terms with one term and ascribe a collective meaning to it, e.g. payments. In general, 'costs' includes fees, charges, disbursements, expenses and remuneration.[11] Once

---

[6] See discussion below.

[7] See generally EAGLESTONE, F.N. The ICE Conditions of Contract (6th Edition) and Insurance. *Arbitration*, 1993, 191.

[8] See guidance notes NEC, 2.

[9] Cf JONES, GLYN P. *A New Approach to the 1980 Standard Form of Building Contract*. The Construction Press, Lancaster, 1980 who classifies risks into four categories: fundamental, pure, particular and speculative.

[10] *Metropolitan Asylum District Managers* v. *Hill* (1881) 6 App Cas 193 at 203, HL.

[11] See *Halsbury's Laws of England*, 4th edn., vol. 37 paragraph 1712. Cf the use of the phrase 'claims, compensation and costs' in clause 21.3 ECC; 'claims, proceedings, compensation, and costs' in clause 83.1 ECC.

again, then, the first category of event which is assigned to the employer entails all claims, proceedings, compensation and costs payable which are due to any of *three general cases*:

- use or occupation of the site by the works or for the purpose of the works which is the unavoidable result of the works;
- negligence, breach of statutory duty or interference with any legal rights by the employer or by any person employed by or contracted to the employer except the contractor; or
- a fault of the employer or a fault in the employer's design.[12]

Referring to the three general cases in turn, while the principal issue in respect of all categories is the same – is the event an employer's risk? – the drafting in many cases raises other issues as well as can be seen, notably breach of statutory duty and occupier's liability. In the first case, breach of statutory duty and negligence give rise to distinct causes of action.[13] The imposition of a statutory duty will not without more normally relieve the person upon whom the duty is placed of an ordinary duty of care in relation to the same subject matter and, therefore, as a matter of pleading, breach of statutory duty and negligence are often raised together.[14]

The language of 'use or occupation of the Site' is a broad phrase and hence confers a wide area of risk upon the employer in general. A similarly worded excepted risk, 'use or occupation by the Employer . . .' is used in clause 20(2)(a) of the ICE 6th. The phrase 'use or occupation' also has broad connotation in the area of occupier's liability. The Occupiers' Liability Act 1957 itself has no definition of 'occupier', but it seems that in general a person is an occupier if he or she has a sufficient degree of control over the state of the premises or over the activities of the persons on the premises. In order to be an occupier, it is not necessary for a person to have *complete* control over the premises, but it is sufficient to share the control with others. *Occupier* includes a person who has a licence entitling them to possession.[15] A contractor may be in occupation of the site for the purposes of the Occupiers' Liability Act 1957. Where the contractor is in occupational control of the premises, there is a duty to allow lawful visitors to see that the premises are safe for the purpose of their visit unless excused under the Act. In discharging this duty an occupier may be able to rely upon a visitor guarding against special risks ordinarily incident in the exercise of the visitor's calling.[16]

---

[12] Clause 80.1 ECC.

[13] *Caswell* v. *Powell Duffryn Associated Collieries Ltd* [1940] AC 152 at 177, [1939] 3 All ER 722 at 739, HL, per Lord Wright.

[14] See *Franklin* v. *Gramophone Co Ltd* [1948] 1 KB 542, [1948] 1 All ER 353, CA.

[15] *Stevens* v. *London Borough of Bromley* [1972] Ch 400, [1972] 1 All ER 712, CA; *R* v. *Tao* [1977] QB 141, [1976] 3 All ER 65, CA.

[16] Occupiers' Liability Act 1957, section 2(3). The duties of occupiers and the common duty of care under the Occupiers Liability Act 1957, section 2(1) have been considered in a large number of cases.

Thus, whether the employer expressly agreed to assume risks in respect of such use or occupation is not material if occupier's liability legislation in a particular jurisdiction imposed it in any event.[17] Where the drafters may have attempted a change is in their subtle reference to the use or occupation being by the '*works*' rather than the employer.

It is submitted that this wording would not affect liability being imposed on the employer as a result of being an occupier and that a court would look past a contractual designation that it is instead the works which occupy a site. The qualification that the use etc. is the unavoidable result of the works is a difficult phrase to construe. There are similar antecedents[18] but they do not appear to have been judicially considered. One issue the qualification arguably raises, notwithstanding provisions that suggest the contrary, is whether the employer thereby assumes the risk of design faults of the contractor. Although the employer would clearly contest this interpretation it is arguably open to the contractor if the issue arose.

Loss of or damage to plant and materials supplied to the contractor

The second general category of *cases* deals with loss of or damage to plant and materials supplied to the contractor by the employer or others on the employer's behalf until the contractor has received and accepted them. It raises, in fact, three separate legal issues: negligence, breach of statutory duty and interference with legal rights or it would seem interference with contractual relations. All three cases involve torts. As in the case of occupier's liability, tort liability may be imposed irrespective of the contractual allocation agreed between the parties, at least insofar as third parties are concerned and which case this provision addresses. Each of the three cases poses its own individual problems in terms of establishing a successful cause of action.[19]

It is reasonable for the employer to assume the risk of their own negligence or that of their employees.[20] This follows from the statutory provisions in many jurisdictions that limit the extent to which a person can exclude their liability for loss or damage as a result of their, or their employees', negligence in any case.[21] Similarly, attempts to argue one party to a contract has waived liability of the other party for the consequences of negligence attributable to them have met with little success. Some of the same issues have been canvassed in particular in

---

[17] For example, under the Occupiers' Liability Act 1957. See also *Wheat* v. *E Lacon & Co Ltd* [1966] AC 552, [1966] 1 ALL ER 582, HL.

[18] See, in particular clause 22(2)(d) ICE 6th: 'damage which is the unavoidable result of the construction of the Works in accordance with the Contract'; see also clause 22.2 FIDIC 4th.

[19] See HEUSTON, E.V. and BUCKLEY, RICHARD A. *Salmond & Heuston on the Law of Torts*, 21st edn. Sweet & Maxwell, London, 1996.

[20] See generally on negligence *Halsbury's Laws of England*, 4th edn. reissue, vol. 33, paragraphs 601ff.

[21] See e.g. the Unfair Contract Terms Act 1977.

cases involving indemnity provisions.[22] To achieve this result the courts have consistently held that very clear drafting is required before liability for negligence is either assumed or transferred to someone else. In *Smith v. South Wales Switchgear Ltd* an indemnity in respect of 'any liability, loss, claim or proceedings whatsoever' did *not* extend to negligence.[23]

This situation may be contrasted with that in clause 80.1 where the employer is expressly assuming the sole risk of negligence. This assumption of risk is stated to be without limitation save for the fact that has given rise to a claim, proceedings, compensation or costs being payable. The employer may or may not have taken out insurance in respect of the risk, and liability in this regard is unaffected as a result. It is submitted that the provision would result in the employer bearing the whole risk of negligent actions by persons employed by or contracted to the employer – save the contractor. This is an extremely wide liability as can be seen on the basis of just one class of cases of risk by fire.[24] Pure risks such as fire affect both individuals and individual projects. If the event occurs and loss arises then there is no prospect of gain but only reimbursement. Most standard form contracts deal with pure risks conventionally and require at least one party to formally insure for them. There is no reasonably practicable means of preventing pure risks and although their risk of occurrence is low their impact is potentially great.

Breach of statutory duty is a less well-known concept than negligence and one for which the employer has assumed all risk.[25] The ECC is unclear in terms of the precise scope that was intended by the phrase and whether it was to pertain narrowly or broadly. In a narrow sense breach of statutory duty is normally used in the construction context as referring to a breach of the relevant statutory building legislation[26] but does appear in some standard form insurance provisions as well.[27] As such, it is a matter

[22] See the discussion of indemnity below. See generally WRIGHT, D. Subrogation: Risk and Responsibility in Construction Contracts. *Construction Law Journal*, 1995, **11**, 355.

[23] See *Smith* v. *South Wales Switchgear Ltd* [1978] 1 All ER 18 at 22, [1978] 1 WLR 165 at 168, HL.

[24] See *Scottish Special Housing Association* v. *Wimpey Construction UK Ltd* [1986] 2 All ER 957, [1986] 1 WLR 995, HL; *Welsh Health Technical Services Organisation* v. *Haden Young* (1987) 37 BLR 130; *Norwich City Council* v. *Harvey* (1988) 45 BLR 14, [1989] 1 ALL ER 1180, CA; *Surrey Heath Borough Council* v. *Lovell Construction Ltd and Haden Young Ltd* (1990) 48 BLR 108, CA; and *National Trust for Places of Historic Interest or Natural Beauty* v. *Haden Young Ltd* (1993) 66 BLR 88.

[25] As to the remedies for failure to perform a statutory duty see generally *Halsbury's Statutes*, 4th edn., vol. 1, pp. 487–489; *Halsbury's Laws of England*, 4th edn. reissue, vol. 1(1), paragraphs 132, 201, 211; *Halsbury's Laws of England*, 4th edn. reissue, vol. 44(1) paragraphs 1353ff; as to actions for damages for breach of statutory duty, see *Halsbury's Laws of England*, 4th edn. reissue, vol. 45 paragraphs 1279ff; and for a recent example of a successful cause of action *Skandia Property (UK) and anor* v. *Thames Water Utilities Ltd* (1998) 57 Con LR 65.

[26] For example, in the United Kingdom the Building Act 1984.

[27] See e.g. clause 20.2 JCT 80.

of interpretation of that relevant legislation whether a private law right of action is also accorded by it. Thus, as the material portions of the relevant legislation in the Building Act are not yet in force, the risk assumed by the employer under the ECC provision in this regard is minimal. Section 38 of the Building Act 1984 does provide that breach of a duty imposed under the building regulations is actionable subject to the limitations referred there but again is not yet actionable. It must be noted that breach of statutory duty is considered independently here of any liability which the breach itself may separately entail in negligence.

Construed broadly, and with respect to any statutes that could apply to the parties, the provision may have a different import and notwith-standing that in the United Kingdom there is, in fact, very little support in favour of an independent common law liability for breach of statutory duty.[28] The issue turns upon an interpretation of the statute. Initially, there is no general rule to determine whether any such statute creates a right of action for breach of statutory duty. Ordinarily, a breach of statutory duty without more will not give rise to a private law cause of action. However, a cause of action for breach of statutory duty may be shown to exist on a proper interpretation of the statute. That is, when the statutory duty is imposed for the protection of a limited class of the public and when Parliament intended to confer a private right of action on members of that class.

There are a number of indicators that aid in the interpretation of the statute. Thus, if the statute provides no other remedy for its breach and the parliamentary intention is to protect a limited class, it is more likely that it gives rise to a private right as in that case the interests of the class would otherwise be unprotected. Conversely, if the statute did provide some other means of enforcing the duty that would mean, as a matter of interpretation, that the statutory right was intended to be the sole means of enforcement over a private right of action.[29]

The difficulty in determining whether there is a statutory right of action is compounded in two significant ways. That is, by the way in which litigants have pleaded their causes of action in the reported cases; and by the reluctance of the courts to intervene when it is the exercise of statutorily conferred discretion that is at the heart of the allegation.

Concerning the first case, at times the actions have been framed as breach of statutory duty, while at other times they have been framed in negligence or breach of a common law duty of care. Negligence and common law duties of care cannot be wholly equated without more. A careless performance of a statutory power will not in itself amount to a breach of the statutory duty. Before it could be taken further, a litigant

---

[28] *Murphy* v. *Brentwood District Council* [1991] 1 AC 398 at 490, [1990] 2 All ER 908 at 937, HL, per Lord Oliver.

[29] *Cutler* v. *Wandsworth Stadium Ltd* [1949] AC 398, [1949] 1 All ER 554, HL; *Lonrho Ltd* v. *Shell Petroleum Co Ltd* (*No 2*) [1982] AC 173, [1981] 2 All ER 456, HL; cf *Groves* v. *Lord Wimborne* [1898] 2 QB 402, CA, holding on the true interpretation of a statute a protected class was given a private right of action.

would have to show a breach of the statutory duty itself or that the carelessness amounted to a breach of the common law duty of care.[30]

With regard to the second case, if the exercise of the statutory discretion is found to be within the authority's jurisdiction, then once again a court will be very reluctant to intervene. Further, as so much of the exercise of discretion today is clothed in terms of policy it becomes almost impossible for the court to intervene on that basis. The end result is that litigants are often forced back to ordinary principles of negligence to seek to establish their claims.[31]

The third *case*, where the employer assumes the risk in terms of claims etc., is when there is fault on the employers part or fault in the employer's design. This meaning can be compared to that given to the term 'default' in an indemnity clause in a JCT form, namely that arising when one person did not do that which ought to have been done or did what ought not to have been done in all the circumstances providing that the conduct in question involved something in the nature of a a breach of duty.[32] The ECC clause is capable of a disjunctive interpretation pertaining to either faults in general by the employer or faults specifically in relation to the employer's design. With regard to the first case of fault it has been argued elsewhere that an express reference to fault – albeit in the context of the contractor's actions – invoked concepts of negligence law and all of its complexities. This arguably goes further than the employer would have needed to but perhaps it reflects a willingness to admit such liability which could be expected to follow as a result of any negligence action. In this sense express recognition of and liability for fault caused events may be more pragmatic. If responsibility is so readily conceded when fault is clear the parties may rather devote their time to finding solutions. With regard to faults in design it is submitted that the provision could be construed broadly and exceeding the mere failure of the employer as designer to comply with accepted standards of care, skill and knowledge in the design sectors.[33] It should again be noted that the responsibility of the employer as designer is assumed under the contract on the part of either one or both the employer and contractor and inasmuch as the ECC does not describe either party expressly as a designer *per se*.

A second narrower interpretation of the third case could be put forward for a non-disjunctive interpretation and one that would limit the employer's fault in this regard to that arising solely in relation to the designs. The omission to address fault in general by the drafters in their explanation of the clause would seem to support this, but is a weak argument overall.[34] The

---

[30] See *Home Office* v. *Dorset Yacht Co Ltd* [1970] AC 1004, [1970] 2 All ER 294, HL.

[31] See for a recent illustration of the courts' hesitancy to grant a private right of action for an alleged breach of statutory duty by a local authority *X (Minors)* v. *Bedfordshire County Council and others* [1995] 2 AC 633, [1995] 3 All ER 353, HL, a conjoined appeal.

[32] *City of Manchester* v. *Fram Gerrard Ltd* (1974) 6 BLR 70.

[33] See *Queensland Government Railways* v. *Manufacturers' Mutual Insurance Ltd* [1969] 1 Lloyd's Rep 214.

[34] Guidance notes NEC on clause 80.1 ECC, 71.

assumption of the risk is at least consistent, however, with provisions elsewhere in the ECC; for example, under clause 60.1 where a compensation event includes change to the works information as a result of the employer's design, and when read with clause 80.1 could thus include those changes involving fault on the employer's part.

Loss of or damage to plant and materials supplied to the contractor

The second category of *event*, which is assigned to the employer, is that of loss of or damage to plant and materials supplied to the contractor by the employer or by others on the employer's behalf; for example, the contractor and employer under clause 84.2 of the ECC and the contractor and subcontractor under clause 84.2 of the ECSC. It may be observed in *Petrofina (UK) Ltd* v. *Magnaload Ltd*.[35] Lloyd J construed 'subcontractor' as including sub-subcontractors as the *insured* in the policy in issue. These insured would seek as wide a description as possible when identified.[36] Particular risks, those associated with specific or particular activities often have restricted consequences, are similar to pure risks in that they offer no prospect of gain and are also often insured in joint names.[37] The liability remains with the employer until the contractor has received and accepted the plant and materials.[38] This is the first of four of the six categories in clause 80.1 which specifically refer to 'loss of or damage' in respect of the risk. The Insurance Table refers to 'Loss of or damage to the works, Plant and Materials', 'Loss of or damage to Equipment', and 'Liability for loss of or damage to property' etc. The terminology in this sense is familiar and used in the majority of policies issued and described as construction insurance. Loss or damage or material damage provisions are also routine in contractors' all risk, or 'CAR' or builders' risk insurance.[39]

The commitment of the insurer is to pay compensation when insurable in respect of either the specific loss or damage occurring. Construction insurance of this type, as clause 84.2 confirms, is often taken out in joint names. Increasingly, however, such policies are being taken out by employers in respect of whole projects. 'Project insurance' is a generic term to refer not only to loss or damage coverage but other types of coverage as well. It may be taken out by the employer either individually or jointly with the contractor or subcontractors and even consultants. By purchasing project insurance some of the duplication inherent in separate coverage and the premiums they entail may be overcome. Significantly, it can also overcome the separate apportionment of risks in respect of the

---

[35] See *Petrofina (UK) Ltd* v. *Magnaload Ltd* (1984) 25 BLR 37 at 46 per Lloyd J.

[36] See *St Paul Fire & Marine Insurance Co (UK)* v. *McConnell Dowell Constructors Ltd* (1993) 67 BLR 72, [1993] Lloyd's Rep 503, 37 Con LR 96 (QBD).

[37] Clause 80.1 ECC.

[38] Clause 80.1 ECC.

[39] See MONKMAN, D. *Insurances for the Construction Industry*. CIOB, Ascot, 1993, Construction Paper 26; and see generally *Colinvaux's Law of Insurance*, (ed. MERKIN, PROFESSOR ROBERT), 7th edn. Sweet & Maxwell, London, 1997.

coverage. The employer's construction insurance may be drafted with separate floaters for the risks regarding equipment, plant and materials. Any policy taken out by the employer in these regards may be carefully tailored to cover only those time frames agreed in the contract. For instance, plant and materials supplied to the contractor only until the employer has received and accepted them; or the same when retained on the site by the employer after termination.[40] Careful drafting would be required, as most insurance policies will be worded using the existing wording and time frames in other forms. Hence, coverage is more likely to be provided from possession, practical or substantial completion, than the periods which are noted here. However, these changes should still be easily accommodated with the insurer.

Loss of or damage to the works, plant and materials
The third category of *events* entails certain loss of or damage to the works or plant and materials in any of *three cases* namely due to:

- war, civil war, rebellion, revolution, insurrection, military or usurped power;
- strikes, riots and civil commotion not confined to the contractor's employees;
- radioactive contamination.[41]

A construction risk policy will routinely exclude certain risks as uninsurable. Thus even assuming that it would be the employer's intention to insure for as many of the risks in clause 80.1 as possible, the cases in this third category would not normally be expected to fall within the terms of coverage. The fact that either party may terminate the contract in two of these circumstances, war or radioactive contamination, is consistent with this, although the events are qualified and must substantially affect the contractor's work for 26 weeks.[42] Such risks would also be expected to relieve the parties of continuing liabilities toward each other in any case in most legal systems.[43] These are typical fundamental risks that are dealt with under many standard forms of contract by making them 'excepted risks'. Hence they are not the responsibility of the contractor. Even when these types of risks are insurable their magnitude often precludes purchasing cover for them. As a result they may either remain with the employer or with the government or an appropriate government agency. It is noteworthy that the term *force majeure* itself is not used in the clause although certain of these risks would normally be expected to fall within such wording. This type of drafting choice has been given support in a commentary on the UNCITRAL *Draft Legal Guide on Drawing Up International Contracts for the Construction of Industrial Works* UN by Dr Eugen Salpius, who

---

[40] See the second and fifth categories of employer's risks in clause 80.1 ECC.
[41] Clause 80.1 ECC.
[42] See clause 95.5.
[43] See clause 95.5.

has written: '[t]he draft legal guide avoids terminology such as *force majeure*, frustration, fault or recklessness on the grounds that they have a special meaning in some legal systems and lead to unintended and undesired results in cases where the contract provisions have to be interpreted'.[44]

Loss of or damage to parts of the works taken over by the employer

The fourth category of *events* involves certain loss of or damage to parts of the works, which have been taken over by the employer, except loss or damage occurring before the issue of the defects certificate due to any of three *causes* (or in three cases as discussed above) namely that due to:

- a defect which existed at take over;
- an 'event' occurring before take over which was not in itself an employer's risk; or
- the activities of the contractor on the site after take over.[45]

This category of events must clearly be read with the provisions on, and is dependent on take over of the works, by the employer.[46] The take over referred to contemplates merely parts of the works and thus is not limited to take over of the whole of the works as on termination or two weeks after completion.[47] The effect of the take over is thus to return property in the works to the employer. This property in the works gives the employer not only an insurable interest in the works but a personal interest to see that coverage is effected.[48]

It should be observed that it is take over which operates as a general rule to transfer the risk[49] in the works to the employer. However, notwithstanding take over there are some risks still remaining with the contractor. The intention is that these risks remain with the contractor until the defects certificate is issued. The defects certificate thus operates as a limitation on the risks that remain with the contractor. It is a

---

[44] UNCITRAL *Draft Legal Guide on Drawing Up International Contracts for the Construction of Industrial Works* UN Doc A/CN9/WGV/WPG9/Add3; and SALPIUS, DR EUGEN. Exemptions from Liability for Non-performance Examined in the Context of the UNCITRAL Draft Legal Guide on Drawing up International Contracts for the Construction of Industrial Works. In *The Liability of Contractors* (ed. LLOYD), 171–172. In contrast to this view BAIRD, ANDREW Pioneering the NEC System of Documents. *Engineering, Construction and Architectural Management*, 1995, **2**(4), 249 expresses reservations about the omission of the term from the form.

[45] Clause 80.1 ECC.

[46] See discussion clause 35 above.

[47] Clauses 35.1, 35.3 and 35.4 ECC all admit of and address partial take overs of the works; cf clause 35.2 ECC.

[48] See *Hopewell Project Management Limited and Hopewell Energy (Philippines) Corp v. Ewbank Preece Limited* (1997) CILL 1310 discussing the meaning of insurable interests.

[49] SCOTT, ROBERT E. Risk Distribution and Adjustment in Long-Term Contracts. *The Complex Long-Term Contract Structures and International Arbitration* (ed. NICHLISCH, FRITZ). C.F. Muller Juristischer Verlag, Heidelberg, 1987, pp. 57–60.

necessary limitation, for the risks themselves are cast very broadly and could not reasonably be left with the contractor otherwise. The language of the exceptions refers to both an 'event' and 'activities', both of which, it can be noted, are susceptible to potentially very broad meanings. However, while it operates as a limitation, it exceeds the liability under other forms of contract, which would have the contractor's obligations end upon completion.

Loss of or damage to the works and any equipment, plant and materials retained on site by the employer after termination

The fifth category of *events* involves loss of or damage to the works and any equipment, plant and materials retained on site by the employer after a termination.[50] However, loss and damage due to the activities of the contractor on the site after the termination are expressly excluded.[51] Termination, in contrast to that of take over in the fourth category,[52] is pursuant to clause 94.

Additional employer's risks stated in the Contract Data

The sixth and final category of events is simply any additional employer's risks that are stated in the Contract Data.[53] These could include a range of speculative risks. These are typically risks that offer the possibility of profit or loss and so would be expected to interest the contractor. Many of these risks, such as physical conditions, inflation and adverse weather, could also be addressed and formally classified as employer's risks in any event under the clause 6 compensation events. Where none of the above categories of events applies the event is not categorized as an employer's risk and accordingly falls to be classified as a contractor's risk and carried by the contractor.[54]

The employer may seek to offset any one or more of the risks assumed in clause 80.1 through insurance coverage. Such coverage may already be required to be obtained pursuant to clause 84.2. The provisions in clauses 80.1 and 80.2 generally avoid duplication and although the same risk may be referred to in both clauses, e.g. loss of or damage to equipment, it pertains to different time frames. Where there is no obligation to insure it would still normally be in the employer's interest to obtain insurance coverage in respect of the risk. Thus, as the employer has assumed the risk of fault in the design, coverage may also be sought for the risk under an appropriate professional indemnity insurance policy. Professional indemnity insurance (PII) is taken out by many design professionals. In general, it covers liability for negligent acts, errors and omissions in respect of their professional work. If the employer insured with regard to clause 80.1 of the ECC, it should be established that the

---

[50] Clause 80.1 ECC.
[51] Clause 80.1 ECC.
[52] See clause 35 ECC.
[53] Clause 80.1 ECC.
[54] Clause 81.1 ECC.

coverage wording and the clause are consistent, e.g. reference to 'fault', for while PII policies would normally cover 'claims' they could be expected to exclude negligence or faults *per se*. It may be noted that forms do not routinely require PII to be taken out in respect of design roles, for example, the ICE 6th and FIDIC 4th.[55]

Contractor's risks

The contractor's risks are shortly set out in one clause and are all those risks which arise from the starting date[56] until the defects certificate has been issued[57] and which are not carried by the employer.[58] The scheme for the allocation of risks can thus be seen to be procedurally uncomplicated. To identify who carries the risk several steps may be followed:

- ascertain first whether it falls between the starting date and the issuance of the defects certificate;
- confirm it is not one of the employer's risks in the six broad categories of events which the employer has assumed, and, if so, the risk will fall upon the contractor.

The risks are in addition to those which are expressly assigned to the contractor in the insurance clauses[59] and whether or not the employer takes out the coverage in respect of them.[60]

In any case where the responsibility for insuring is upon the contractor and such insurance is not effected, the employer is entitled to deduct the costs as well as any costs which the employer may have to pay as a result to the contractor's insurers.[61] It follows that such cases are at the contractor's risk.[62]

Repairs

The contractor is under an express obligation to replace promptly losses or repair damage to the works, plant and materials. By comparison, the term 'rectify' is used in clause 20(3) of ICE 6th and clause 20.2 of FIDIC 4th regarding the contractor's obligation to reinstate the works etc. while the

---

[55] See generally Neil F. Jones & Co. *Professional Negligence in the Construction Industry*. Lloyds of London Press, London, 1998; DUGDALE, A.M. and STANTON, K.M. *Dugdale and Stanton: Professional Negligence*. Butterworths, London, 1996; and PATTERSON, FRANCES A. *Professional Indemnity Insurance Explained*. RIBA Publications, London, 1995.

[56] The starting date is an identifed term and inserted as agreed in section 3 of part one of the Contract Data.

[57] The 'Defects Certificate' will be issued on the '*defects date*' as agreed in section 4 of part one of the Contract Data unless a defect has been earlier notified which has the effect of extending the defects correction period.

[58] Clause 81.1 ECC.

[59] See clause 84 ECC.

[60] For example, under clause 86.1 ECC.

[61] SCC section 7 ECC.

[62] See clause 85.4 ECC.

JCT MW form uses 'restore or replace' in clause 6.3A and requires the contractor to begin the restoration or replacement immediately and prior to acceptance of any insurance claims. The contractor's obligation runs until the defects certificate[63] has been issued and must be fulfilled whether or not the project manager has given an instruction to that effect. However, if an instruction has been given to that effect the contractor is under an express obligation to obey it under clause 29.1. The obligation, although included among the insurance provisions, pertains not only to repairs arising from the contractor's own actions – or those at the contractor's risk – but also any arising from the employer's actions or which are at risk.[64] The inclusion of such repair provisions among the insurance clauses is not unusual. If an instruction were thus required it could operate as a countermand of the contractor's obligation to effect the repairs.

The brevity of the clear obligation of the contractor to repair may be contrasted with the detailed provisions in the ICE 6th. The repairing obligation of the contractor under the ICE form covers the same time frame[65] as the ECC but is more comprehensively worded. Thus it pertains not only to all work of repair but also 'amendment reconstruction rectification and making good defects of whatever nature'.[66]

The obligation to repair under the ICE 6th arises by instruction unlike the ECC. The value of work under the ICE 6th form is ascertained for and paid as if additional work only was not necessitated by the neglect or fault of the contractor or the contractor's failure to use conforming materials or workmanship.[67] The ECC provision adopted the language of defects correction in the ICE 6th. Previously it referred to 'maintenance' in terms of the obligation. The ICE clause incorporates both the repair obligation and completion of outstanding work. This contrasts with the ECC provision that is both narrower and broader than this. It is narrower in that it assigns the responsibility to complete outstanding work in the defects correction provisions of the contract.[68] It is broader in that the obligation it imposes on the contractor is in respect of 'loss of and ... damage to' the works, plant and materials. In one sense, of course, this view turns upon how this phrase is to be construed but it is arguably capable of very broad meaning. Neither clause would have any effect on the rights of the employer to claim general damages from the contractor for breach of obligation to effect repairs.

The clause points out a distinction at common law that can be drawn between obligations to *repair* as opposed to obligations to *construct* buildings. The obligation to construct places the risk upon the contractor until completion and the destruction of the subject matter of the contract

---

[63] Defined in clause 11.2(16) and issued under clause 43.1 ECC.

[64] For example, events falling within clause 80.1 ECC.

[65] For example, until the expiry of the relevant defects correction period under clause 49(2) in the ICE 6th and the issuance of the defects certificate in the ECC: clause 82.1 ECC.

[66] Clause 49(2) ICE 6th.

[67] See clause 49(2) ICE 6th.

[68] Clause 43 ECC.

without fault on the part of the contractor will not excuse performance. However, in the case of the obligation to repair, the continued existence of the subject matter of the contract is assumed[69] (it is normally treated as an implied condition in English law) for purposes of their agreement and thus destruction for repairing purposes would frustrate the contract.[70] It may be observed that the difficulties this distinction raises may have been a factor in amendments to JCT forms and the introduction of clauses 22A, 22B and 22C. These alternative clauses admit of a distinction between insurance of existing structures and extensions to existing structures (clause 22C) and insurance for the erection of new buildings (clause 22A and 22B) e.g. in JCT 80. However, the first release of JCT 87 suggests a rapprochement of these alternatives. Thus more provisions in JCT 87 now apply irrespective of whether the contract is for the erection of new buildings or the alteration of or extension to an existing structure.[71] The doctrine of frustration of contract could thus be relevant to the proper interpretation of clause 82.1 in circumstances involving destruction of the works, or plant and materials and whether the clause is sufficiently worded to overcome the common law position which would favour the contractor. In general, questions of liability for defects and latent damages are the subject of intense debate and considerable disagreement and until some consensus is reached on these issues attempts to address them in standard forms will remain tentative. Disagreement can be seen following the Latham Report recommendations (paragraph 11.24) that legislation should be introduced for compulsory latent defects insurance.[72] Working Group 10 of the Construction Industry Board, reporting on this and related issues, was unable to come to any agreement on whether a statutory requirement for the recommendation with regard to certain forms of building work was advised.[73] The direction of attempts to deal with the issue in future appears to be toward voluntary insurance cover.[74]

---

[69] Cf the American law which views the issue in terms of a warranty by the employer: *Butterfield* v. *Byron* 153 Mass 517 (1890); 27 NE 667 (1891).

[70] *Appleby* v. *Myers* (1867) LR 2 CP 651. See in particular n. [g] and clause 6.4 JCT 87. See generally on JCT insurance provisions, Royal Institution of Chartered Surveyors. *Introductory Guidance to Insurance under JCT Contracts*. Royal Institution of Chartered Surveyors, RICS Books, London, 1991; and for a recent decision considering the effect of clause 22C *Kruger Tissue (Industrial) Ltd (formerly Industrial Cleaning Papers Ltd)* v. *Frank Galliers Ltd and Ors* (1998) 57 Con LR 1.

[71] See in particular n. [g] and clause 6.4 JCT 87. See generally on JCT insurance provisions, Royal Institution of Chartered Surveyors. *Introductory Guidance to Insurance under JCT Contracts*. Royal Institution of Chartered Surveyors, RICS Books, London, 1991; and for a recent decision considering the effect of clause 22C *Kruger Tissue (Industrial) Ltd (formerly Industrial Cleaning Papers Ltd)* v. *Frank Galliers Ltd and Ors* (1998) 57 Con LR 1.

[72] Latham Report, paragraph 11.24.

[73] See *Liability Law and Latent Defects Insurance*, Construction Industry Board. Thomas Telford, London, 1997, vi.

[74] See Department of the Environment. *Latent Defects Liability and 'BUILD'* Insurance. Department of the Environment, HMSO, London, 1997.

Indemnity

Indemnity provisions in standard form construction contracts are routine. Nael G. Bunni, in *The FIDIC Form of Contract, The Fourth Edition of the Red Book*, sets out the characteristics of construction contracts that necessitate indemnity provisions as including the obligation to complete, financing considerations, uniqueness, hazards, and tender analysis.[75] Thus, the ECC contains express indemnity obligations; that is, each party agrees to indemnify the other against claims, proceedings, compensation and costs due to an event that is at that party's own risk.[76] Thus, for purposes of construing the clause the event causing the loss must be identified as the responsibility of one or the other of the parties – that is at the contractor's or employer's risk – for the obligation to arise. An express reference to 'costs' is advisable as it is not necessarily covered in an indemnity obligation.[77]

The employer's and the contractor's risks are separately identified in clauses 80 and 81 respectively. Details of their insurance cover are contained in an insurance table in clause 84. The requirements for insurance are intended to reflect the extent of coverage that is normally available in the market and the way that it is purchased.[78] Similarly, specific references to the detailed coverage provisions have been left out of the insurance table and thus would be decided by the parties and their underwriters. If the event causing the loss can be identified as the responsibility of one or the other of the parties there may be a reduction in liability.

Pursuant to clause 83.2, the liability of each party to indemnify the other will be reduced if the event is at the other party's risk and contributed to the claims or otherwise.[79] Looking at the parties individually it means a contributing event can be precisely attributed to either an employer's risk event within the meaning of clause 80.1 or an event which is carried by the contractor within the meaning of clause 81.1. Once again, the clause does not purport to address claims or otherwise wholly attributable to third parties or others, e.g. those neither the contractor nor employer has any vicarious liability toward. If such a contributing event can be established on the part of one party to the contract the liability of the other party to indemnity the counterpart will be reduced. The reduction will be in proportion to the extent that the relevant event, which was at the other's risk contributed, and taking into account each parties' responsibilities under the contract.[80]

[75] BUNNI, NAEL G. *The FIDIC Form of Contract, The Fourth Edition of the Red Book*, 2nd edn. Blackwell Science, London, 1997, p. 105.
[76] Clause 83.1 ECC. See also use of these terms in clause 80.1 and the discussion above.
[77] See *Richardson* v. *Buckinghamshire County Council* (1971) 6 BLR 58, CA.
[78] In the view of MAIDMENT, DAVID. Insurance and the Engineering and Construction Contract. In *Launch Seminar on The New Engineering Contract Launch 2nd Editions*. Proceedings of a conference in London on 3 October 1995 by the Institution of Civil Engineers. Thomas Telford, London, 1995.
[79] Clause 83.2 ECC.
[80] See clause 83.2 ECC.

The general rule in the allocation of risk in the ECC is that the contractor carries all risks which are not carried by the employer.[81] The rule operates in both the insurance provisions and the contract as a whole. Examples of the allocation of risk as a whole within the contract may be seen in both the compensation event and termination procedures and certain secondary option clauses as well, e.g. clause 83.1. The question this raises is how broadly should the indemnity clause be construed? That is, to cover only the risks referred in core clause 8 or with respect to all of the risks that arise in the contract. The wording of the indemnity clause itself is broad and does not specify that it is an indemnity against third party claims only. Although that is the effect given to other standard form indemnity clauses[82] they need not be limited in this sense and may rather be construed as a whole in the context of all the parties' rights and obligations. One limitation that may arise, however, in relation to giving the clause a broad interpretation is the absence of any reference to the term 'loss'. Typically, no liability arises under an indemnity clause until the loss suffered has been proven.[83] It is an open question whether clause 83 would be given such a meaning.

Indemnity clauses in traditional forms of contract are usual.[84] It is a question of interpretation whether the surety obligation arises as a matter of guarantee or indemnity. Very often indemnity clauses involve the contractor alone agreeing to indemnify against limited or specific liabilities. The scope of the surety's liability will depend upon an interpretation of the clause and any contract of guarantee that supports it. Indemnity clauses are construed strictly by the courts[85] although the courts for this reason may use the mutuality present in the ECC clause to argue against too strict an interpretation. The effect of a strict interpretation may serve to deny recovery for loss caused by negligence.[86] An express reference to 'negligence' is the most certain method of ensuring that this type of loss is covered,[87] although if no other possible type of loss could reasonably have been in the contemplation of the

---

[81] Clause 81.1 ECC.

[82] See e.g. clause 22(3) ICE 6th.

[83] *Collinge* v. *Hayward* (1839) 9 Ad & El 633; *County and District Properties Ltd* v. *C Jenner & Son Ltd* (1976) 3 BLR 41, [1976] 2 Lloyd's Rep 728.

[84] See e.g. clauses 20.1, 20.2 JCT 80; clause 22 ICE 6th, 22.1 FIDIC 4th.

[85] See *City of Manchester* v. *Fram Gerrard Ltd* (1974) 6 BLR 70; and *Re Bayley-Worthington & Cohen's Contract* [1909] 1 Ch 648, in particular construing the meaning of the term 'default'.

[86] *Walters* v. *Whessoe Ltd* (1960) 6 BLR 23, CA; *A M F International Ltd* v. *Magnet Bowling Ltd* [1968] 2 All ER 789, [1968] 1 WLR 1028; *EE Caledonia Ltd* v. *Orbit Valve Co Europe* [1993] 4 All ER 165. See also *City of Manchester* v. *Fram Gerrard Ltd* (1974) 6 BLR 70.

[87] See *Smith* v. *South Wales Switchgear Ltd* [1978] 1 All ER 18, [1978] 1 WLR 165, HL; and see generally *A E Farr Ltd* v. *The Admiralty* [1953] 2 All ER 512, [1953] 1 WLR 965. An express reference to 'negligence' is contained in clause 80.1 ECC. See generally PERCY, R.A. and WALTON, CHRISTOPHER. *Charlesworth & Percy on Negligence*, 9th edn., Common Law Library, Sweet & Maxwell, London, 1996.

parties it may still be covered.[88] The indemnity provisions should be read with the general insurance obligations also imposed in the ECC and in particular the amounts inserted in the Contract Data for the indemnities.

In general, a surety may be discharged on numerous grounds including completion;[89] alteration of the obligations which have been guaranteed;[90] misconduct on the part of the employer;[91] breach of the contract of guarantee by the employer;[92] or overpayment.[93] The express or implied terms of the contract of guarantee may remove or qualify any of these grounds for discharge, for instance, through the requirement of materiality. A right to make alterations to the guaranteed obligations is also often expressly reserved in the contract of guarantee. The question of fraud on the part of the contractor is also a relevant consideration but is not generally a factor in discharging the surety.[94]

The liability of each party to indemnify the other can be reduced if the events at the other party's risk contributed to the claims, proceedings, compensation and costs.[95] Any reduction on this basis would be made in proportion to the extent that the events that were at the other party's risk contributed to it.[96] It must also take into account each party's responsibilities under the contract.[97] The provision gives express recognition to the right of either party to reduce their respective liability for events at the other's risk. The drafting in this regard is subtle but clearer than the JCT provisions, for instance. Amendment 2 to JCT 80 added an exception to the indemnity obligation that the contractor is under toward the employer in clause 20.1 but the language does not expressly use the term 'contribution' although that would appear to be the aim when the event is due in part to the employer or those the employer is responsible for. The references are to the risks themselves, not the fault of the other party in contributing to the outcome. In this way, the language avoids a blameworthy tone, which can stand in the way of amicable

---

[88] *Alderslade* v. *Hendon Laundry Ltd* [1945] KB 189, [1945] 1 All ER 244, CA; *Canada Steamship Lines Ltd* v. *R* [1952] AC 192, [1952] 1 All ER 305, PC; *Dorset County Council* v. *Southern Felt Roofing Co Ltd* (1989) 48 BLR 96, CA; *E E Caledonia Ltd* v. *Orbit Valve plc* [1995] 1 All ER 174, [1994] 1 WLR 1515, CA.

[89] See *Lewis* v. *Hoare* (1881) 44 LT 66, HL.

[90] *Holme* v. *Brunskill* (1877) 3 QBD 495; *Hoole UDC* v. *Fidelity and Deposit Co of Maryland* [1916] 2 KB 568, CA; *Wardens and Commonalty of the Mystery of Mercers of the City of London* v. *New Hampshire Insurance Co Ltd* [1992] 1 WLR 792, (1992) 60 BLR 26, sub nom *Mercers Co* v. *New Hampshire Insurance Co* [1992] 3 All ER 57, CA.

[91] *Bank of India* v. *Patel* [1983] 2 Lloyd's Rep 298, CA.

[92] For example, failure to effect a policy of insurance: *Watts* v. *Shuttleworth* (1871) 7 H & N 353.

[93] *Warre* v. *Calvert* (1837) 7 Ad & El 143; *Calvert* v. *London Dock Co* (1838) 7 LJ Ch 90; *General Steam Navigation Co* v. *Rolt* (1858) 6 CBNS 550, Ex Ch.

[94] See e.g. *Kingston-upon-Hull Corpn* v. *Harding* [1892] 2 QB 494, CA.

[95] Clause 83.2 ECC.

[96] Clause 83.2 ECC.

[97] Clause 83.2 ECC.

settlements. It is similar to the ICE 6th form provisions in this way. Clause 20(3)(c) addresses concurrent loss precisely, using both the language of risk (the employer's risks being those referred to as 'Excepted Risks') and the term 'apportion' in respect of them. It is crafted to be a factual determination at this stage even if perhaps more emotive decisions had to be taken in the earlier assigning of the risks based upon the event.[98] The language too would seem implicitly to invoke the notion of contribution so often associated with the undertaking to indemnify another, e.g. as in the right to recover contribution from another or joint tortfeasor often through third party proceedings. If this is the intention it is submitted that the interpretation of the provisions can only be rendered more certain as the notion is generally well known and understood. It may also serve to overcome precedents that have conceded complete defences in respect of partial liabilities for losses that involved both parties.[99] The prospect of discretion would appear to still exist in applying the notion of indemnity to the circumstances of any case, as the determination of the liability must 'tak[e] into account each Party's responsibilities under th[e] contract'.[100]

From a procedural point of view the indemnity clause would appear to support the right of either party to join the other as a third party to a claim or proceeding brought against it by another person. The identification of the event itself is also relevant for limitation purposes and time will normally begin to run for these purposes from the crystallization of the liability or event.[101]

Insurance cover

The contractor is under a clear obligation to obtain insurance cover.[102] In particular, the insurance stated in the Insurance Table in clause 84.2 must be obtained.[103] The only exception to the obligation is optional and pertains to any insurance that the employer must provide in accordance with the Contract Data.[104] The proforma in this regard leaves open to the contractor to provide up to three additional insurances, to each which the level of cover/indemnity must be indicated. No deductibles are included. Similarly, the obligation of the contractor may be augmented in accordance with the Contract Data,[105] once again the proforma suggests or leaves it open to the contractor to provide additional insurances and the

---

[98] Under clauses 80.1 and 81.1 ECC.

[99] See e.g. *A M F International Ltd* v. *Magnet Bowling Ltd* [1968] 2 All ER 789, [1968] 1 WLR 1028; *Wayne Tank & Pump Co Ltd* v. *Employers' Liability Assurance Corpn Ltd* [1974] QB 57, [1973] 3 All ER 825, CA.

[100] Clause 83.2 ECC.

[101] See *County and District Properties Ltd* v. *C Jenner & Son Ltd* (1974) 3 BLR 41.

[102] Clause 84.1 ECC.

[103] See generally MADGE, P. *A Guide to the Indemnity and Insurance Aspects of Building Contracts*. RIBA Publications, London, 1985.

[104] Clause 84.1 ECC.

[105] Clause 84.1 ECC.

level of cover/indemnity. Recognition that the employer may have a mutually agreed and clear obligation to insure is exceptional in comparison to other standard forms. All insurance must be in the joint names of the parties and provide cover for events that are at the contractor's risk from the starting date until the defects certificate has been issued.[106] The precise time frame is that for which the contractor is also obliged to replace loss of and repair damage to the works, plant and materials.[107]

The joint names requirement reflects the clear fact that insurance coverage is normally in the interests of both parties.[108] The employer's interest arises for varying reasons, not the least of which is the fundamental interest in securing completion of the project and the contract which can easily be jeopardized by any loss or damage with respect to the works or associated inputs. Even though only the parties to the contract are referred to as those to be jointly named, the lenders to the project may also want their interests recognized in the contract. They may thus seek assurances from the parties regarding the continuity of the project or additional protections for their contributions and may be given rights in relation to the proceeds of the insurance policies. The fact of joint names on the policy of course entitles either contractor or employer to sue as principals in their own name. Like the insurable obligations that may be imposed upon the employer in the works information, both accord with the partnering aspect or joint endeavour of work under the NEC.

David Cornes[109] critiques the absence of any express obligation on the employer to insure the building, as opposed to the works, on refurbishment projects. Given the contractor's current obligation to provide joint names insurance for the employer's existing building rather than the works under clause 84.2, Cornes doubts[110] whether it is appropriate or possible for the contractor to carry such insurance or even whether a Contractor's All Risk (CAR) policy would extend to it. As such, he recommends the parties agree to amend the provision and provide for the employer to insure both buildings and the works with one insurer.

Insurance table
An insurance table in clause 84.2 provides as follows.

---

[106] Clause 84.2 ECC.

[107] See clause 82.1 ECC.

[108] See generally the early case of *Gold* v. *Patman & Fotheringham Ltd* [1958] 2 All ER 497, [1958] 1 WLR 697, where the Court of Appeal refused to construe a JCT clause imposing a duty on the contractor to insure as necessarily implying the insurance should be effected in joint names. JCT forms today now expressly impose joint names policy requirements, see e.g. clauses 21.2.1, 22A.1, 22B.1 and 22C.1.

[109] CORNES. The Second Edition of the New Engineering Contract. *International Construction Law Review*, 1996, 97.

[110] *Ibid.*, 109.

Table 2   Insurance table

Insurance against	Minimum amount of cover or minimum limit of indemnity
Loss of or damage to the *works*, Plant and Materials.[111]	The replacement cost, including the amount stated in the Contract Data for the replacement of any Plant and Materials provided by the *Employer*.
Loss of or damage to Equipment.[112]	The replacement cost.
Liability for loss of or damage to property (except the *works*, Plant and Materials and Equipment) and liability for bodily injury to or death of a person (not an employee of the *Contractor*) caused by activity in connection with this contract.	The amount stated in the Contract Data for any one event with cross liability so that the insurance applies to the Parties separately.
Liability for death of or bodily injury to employees of the *Contractor* arising out of and in the course of their employment in connection with this contract.	The greater of the amount required by the applicable law and the amount stated in the Contract Data for any one event.

The ECC includes an insurance table (Table 2) which sets out the types of insurance that the contractor must provide. There are some similarities to the coverage which the employer may be expected to purchase for employer risks although different time frames will apply to avoid double coverage. Four types of insurance are referred to in the insurance table and broadly comprise policies for loss or material damage and liability. Both the insurance as described and the two types of policies in the table overlap. One factor that distinguishes them more than any other appears to be the required minimum amount of cover or minimum limit of indemnity stipulated. These minima in respect of loss of or damage to the works, plant and materials are set out as the *replacement cost*, including the amount stated in the Contract Data for the replacement of any plant and materials provided by the employer.[113] It should be noted that the amounts are stipulated as minima and as such there is no reason why the contractor could not insure for a sum greater than that stated in the Contract Data. Replacement cost, as the drafters wish the term to be understood, is stated to be that of similar age and condition rather than new for old,[114] particularly as regards equipment. Other standard forms may use other amounts for the agreed minima. In comparison, clause 21.1 of the FIDIC 4th uses 'full replacement cost' which is stated to include profit plus an additional 15% of such replacement cost to cover additional

---

[111] Clause 11.2(10) ECC.
[112] Clause 11.2(11) ECC.
[113] Clause 84.2 Insurance Table ECC.
[114] Guidance notes NEC on clause 84.2 ECC, 73.

costs for rectification, including professional fees plus a sum to cover the contractor's equipment brought on site, and clause 21(2) of the ICE 6th uses 'full replacement cost' to include an additional 10% for rectification including professional fees. The table anticipates the fact that the employer may freely issue plant and materials to the contractor. As such, the contractor should not only insure for the replacement cost of the contractor's own inputs in these regards but also for that of the employer. While the contractor is expected to know the value of his or her own inputs, the agreed value of the employer's free inputs will be given by the employer in the optional statements of part one of the Contract Data. Replacement cost is also the measure adopted for the minimum in respect of loss of or damage to the equipment, although no provision is made in this instance for any freely issued contribution by the employer. The insurance for loss of or damage to equipment, plant and materials makes no distinction between these inputs depending on whether they are inside or outside the working areas or marked by the supervisor. As these factors are relevant to title to the inputs within the meaning of core clause 7,[115] but have not been referred to in assigning responsibility to the contractor to insure for them, save indirectly for the allowance in the Insurance Table, clause 84.2 of the ECC of an amount in the Contract Data for plant and materials provided by the employer. The contractor should see that all these inputs are insured notwithstanding their location or marking. In comparison, the provisions in clauses 6.3A and 6.3B of the JCT MW expressly impose an obligation on the contractor to insure off site inputs, namely 'all unfixed materials and goods delivered to, placed on or adjacent to the Works and intended therefor'.

The Contract Data states the agreed minimum with regard to the liability for loss of or damage to property and liability for bodily injury to or death of individuals save employees of the contractor when caused by activities in connection with the contract. A causal link would have to be shown to invoke the provision. In general, the notion of 'cause' involves some degree of dominance or control, or even a positive mandate.[116] The agreed minimum sum is framed as an indemnity and limited with respect to one event only.[117] Cross-liability is stipulated so that the insurance taken out will apply to each party separately.[118] Thus either party would be able to claim respectively and as separate insureds notwithstanding the responsibility for the liability for the loss or damage rested with the other party to the contract.[119] The reference used here is to 'property' exclusively. The works, plant and materials and equipment are expressly

---

[115] See clauses 70.1, 70.2 and 71.1 ECC.

[116] See *McLeod (or Houston)* v. *Buchanan* [1940] 2 All ER 179 at 187, HL, per Lord Wright; *Shave* v. *Rosner* [1954] 2 QB 113, [1954] 2 All ER 280; *Lovelace* v. *DPP* [1954] 3 All ER 481, [1954] 1 WLR 1468.

[117] See section 8 part one Contract Data.

[118] See clause 84.2 Insurance Table ECC.

[119] Cf similar requirements in clause 23(2) ICE 6th, and clause 23.3 FIDIC 4th.

excluded.[120] In this way the contractor is put on notice and required to insure against this liability for the property, which may but need not necessarily be owned by the employer, surrounding, near or adjacent to the working areas. CAR policies can easily result in gaps in coverage in this respect. The insurance table provision seeks to address such a limitation or exclusion.

The fourth insurance referred to in the insurance table is that generally taken out and required by law to insure one's employees.[121] Referred to as employees' or workers' compensation or their equivalents, it is still reasonable to require that the insurance be in place under the contract as well as statutorily. A minimum limit is set on the indemnity insurance for death of or bodily injury to the contractor's employees arising out of and in the course of their employment in connection with the contract. The limit is set out as the greater of the amount required by the applicable law and the amount stated and agreed in the Contract Data.[122] Thus, any statutory provision operates as the minimum liability and the parties may only increase, not decrease, it by agreement. A CAR policy will routinely exclude any double coverage if in respect to employees' compensation; limit payments to the insured; and provide for apportionment of loss among the insurers if permitted by law.

The insurance table once again sets out certain minimum requirements insofar as coverage is concerned. However, and as the provisions for additional insurance in the Contract Data clearly imply, there can and will be other instances when extra insurance is advised. A good example in this regard is the absence of any express requirement for the contractor to obtain insurance coverage for design liability. This is advisable notwithstanding that the parties may have addressed the question of liability by agreeing to include option M in the contract; that is, the limitation of the contractor's liability for design to that of reasonable skill and care. It would seem a suitable professional indemnity policy might be appropriate in this case. Any design liability amount could be based on either the amount of insurance one is able or not able to obtain.[123] It may be noted that the comparable JCT 81 provision does not expressly address insurance in this regard either. It is an interesting point that may be contrasted with the recent comment of Lord Lloyd of Berwick in *Marc Rich & Co AG* v. *Bishop Rock Marine Co Ltd* lately when he said:

---

[120] Cf *Surrey Heath Borough Council* v. *Lovell Construction Ltd and Haden Young Ltd* (1990) 48 BLR 108, CA, construing the phrase 'any property real or personal' under JCT 81 holding that they included property of the employer and the works.

[121] For example, in the United Kingdom pursuant to the Employer's Liability (Compulsory Insurance) Act 1969.

[122] See section 8 part one of the Contract Data.

[123] BAIRD, ANDREW. The New Engineering Contract – A Management Summary for Plant Industry Users. *International Construction Law Review*, 1994, 124. Cf FIDIC 4th which imposes no obligation on the Contractor to take out professional indemnity insurance for design liability.

[t]raditionally the courts have regarded the availability of insurance as irrelevant to the question whether a duty of care should be imposed. Even if this traditional view is gradually being displaced, it cannot be right that the courts should reach conclusions on the availability of insurance, or the impact of imposing a fresh liability on the insurance market generally, without proper material.[124]

The insurance that would in all likelihood be taken out by the contractor if the contractor alone were to insure for the loss or damage to the works, equipment, plant and materials, would be a form of CAR insurance.[125] It may also reasonably be expected to cover the liability for bodily injury or death referred to in the insurance table as well. CAR policies are primarily designed to cover what is referred to as 'first party' loss only, e.g. to property of the contractor as insured. It is for this reason that an additional amount is prudently stipulated for any plant and materials provided by the employer, although separate floaters could also be provided in this regard. Notwithstanding that CAR policies are referred to as 'all risks' insurance, they do not cover all risks and can be expected to include a range of general and special exclusions. CAR policies provide a broad range of coverage but often do not address all risks as such. Those types of risks excluded by CAR policies may be covered in other types of insurance, e.g. specified perils policies. The risks covered in specified perils policies are also sometimes referred to as 'fundamental risks'. Coverage for such fundamental risks may have to be arranged separately.[126] The general exclusions would reasonably include certain of the employer's risks noted in clause 80.1.[127] As already mentioned, some of these risks also provide good grounds for termination of the contract.[128] The exclusions themselves are often the subject of litigation and have proved difficult, not only for the parties and insurers to apply fairly, but for the courts as well. This has especially been true of exclusions extending to the cost of replacing defective works or any work executed or any site materials lost or damaged as a result of its own defect in design. Three such routine exclusions address such matters:

- limiting the cost of replacing defective works or any work executed or any site materials lost or damaged as a result of their own defect in design;

---

[124] Lord Lloyd of Berwick in *Marc Rich & Co AG* v. *Bishop Rock Marine Co Ltd* [1996] AC 211 at 228–229, [1995] 3 All ER 307 at 320, HL, and also referring to MARKESINIS, B. and DEAKIN, S. *Tort Law*, 3rd edn. Oxford University Press, Oxford, 1994, p. 114.

[125] JCT 80 abbreviates the type of policy to simply 'All Risks Insurance': see clause 22.

[126] See also n. [h.1] JCT 81 providing in part: '[p]olicies issued by insurers are not standardised and there will be some variation in the way the insurance for those risks is expressed' and see generally JCT Practice Note 22.

[127] For example, war, civil war, riots and radioactive contamination.

[128] See clause 95.5 ECC.

- limiting the making of claims for defective works from the time the damage becomes apparent rather than when an insured became aware of it; and
- limitations for wear and tear.[129]

It has been noted that it is the contractor who obtains the insurance even though it will be taken out in the joint names of the parties. The joint names requirement appears only to be imposed on the contractor in clause 84.2 of the ECC and with respect to those risks listed in the insurance table. Thus, in the event of default by the contractor to insure and insurance having to be taken out by the employer by default pursuant to clause 86.1, it would presumably have to be in the sole name of the employer. Notwithstanding these facts, and the likelihood that a contractor would obtain a form of CAR policy, there are often good reasons for the employer taking out the insurance or a single policy in respect of the whole project. Thus, for instance a single point of coverage may significantly reduce costs, premiums or both. It may also serve to limit the prospect of a conflict in the insurance provisions across policies or those that arise from their differing approaches to claims. Some of the ECC provisions anticipate this with waivers of the insurers' normal rights of subrogation but an employer could still go much further with negotiated project insurance coverage. In the end it is the employer who will ultimately bear the cost of any coverage and the only question becomes in what form will that cost be borne; that is through premiums directly or through the contractor's tender price indirectly. It is for these and other reasons that some employers have begun to take more proactive roles toward their coverage. The ECC has recognized this trend and gone some way to accommodating it. The ECC accomplishes this by affording the employer the right, in the optional statements of part one of the Contract Data, to provide *any* insurance that is listed in the insurance table and which the contractor has traditionally provided.[130] The provisions addressing insurance by the employer advance this right.[131]

In comparison to other forms, JCT 87 uses the terms 'project' and 'project insurance' (in the marginal notes) although the primary responsibility for insuring still remains with the management contractor not the employer. FIDIC 4th notes that in certain circumstances, e.g. where a number of separate contractors are employed on a single project, or even where phased take overs are involved, it may be preferable for the

---

[129] In respect of this first type of exclusion see generally *Cementation Piling and Foundations Ltd* v. *Aegon Insurance Co Ltd and Commercial Union Insurance* [1993] 1 Lloyd's Rep 526; Damage under Contractors All Risks Policy. *Building Law Monthly*, December 1993, 4; *Hitchins (Hatfield) Ltd* v. *Prudential Assurance Co Ltd* (1991) 60 BLR 51 CA.

[130] See the optional statements; the proforma leaves space for three separate insurances to be provided with additional insurance in the next optional statement if the need arises.

[131] Clause 87 ECC.

employer to arrange all works and third party liability insurance. An example clause in FIDIC 4th is given in this regard as follows:

> Without limiting his or the Contractor's obligations and responsibilities under Clause 20, the Employer will insure: (a) the Works, together with materials and Plant for incorporation therein, to the full replacement cost (the term 'cost' in this context shall include profit) and (b) an additional sum to cover any additional costs of and incidental to the rectification of loss or damage including professional fees and the cost of demolishing and removing any part of the Works and of removing debris of whatsoever nature.

Other subclauses in the example provide for the contractor's insurance of his or her own equipment in clause 21.2 and the scope of cover and that it is to be in joint names under clause 21.3.

Insurance policies

There is a procedure for effecting the insurance. In general, responsibility is imposed upon the contractor to effect the insurance. The contractor is also under an express obligation to submit[132] policies and certificates of insurance for the insurance that is to be provided. This wording was omitted in the original Second Edition, which referred instead to insurance alone and which was less clear in intent. Core clause 8, in fact, refers to 'insurances'; 'policies and certificates for the insurance'; 'policies and certificates for insurances'; 'policies and certificates'; 'insurance policies'; 'policies'; and 'insurance policy or certificate' without differentiation. The critical factor from the parties' perspectives is that their liabilities are covered by their insurances, as contained in their policies and evidenced by their certificates.

The submission is made to the project manager for acceptance before the starting date,[133] and afterwards as the project manager instructs.[134] The provision underscores that insurance coverage must be in place and accepted or agreed to before the starting date for the contract. This necessity for acceptance may be equated with approval. While no criteria are given upon which the project manager will decide to accept the policies and certificates, the project manager may not accept them on the general ground that they do not comply with the contract.[135] The requirement for acceptance of the policies and certificates by the project manager goes further in this regard than is the case under most JCT forms. The JCT forms may give the employer either a right of approval only over the insurers themselves and not the policies[136] or may only require the submission of documentary evidence that the policies have been taken out

---

[132] Submission must satisfy the requirements of clause 13 ECC.
[133] See section 3 of part one of the Contract Data for the starting date.
[134] Clause 85.1 ECC.
[135] Clause 85.1 ECC.
[136] See e.g. JCT 80 clause 22A.

or are being maintained.[137] The ECC provisions clearly give the employer more control over the terms of the policies themselves rather than simply relying upon amounts of agreed minimum levels of coverage or indemnity. The reason for this is that the policies themselves may still vary quite considerably in terms of the general or specific exclusions from cover and the attendant risks in these regards for the employer.[138] In this way a sound relationship between the risk and the control of the risk is sought. 'If you attempt to transfer risk to others but resist the transfer of control of that risk, it will generally lead to an overall increase in the cost of the risk. It can also mean that you end up paying not only for the transfer but also for the consequences of the risk if it materialises'.[139] The employer may also rely upon clause 86 to effect the insurance as if the contractor has not insured in those circumstances where the project manager refuses to accept the policies and certificates put forward by the contractor. This right is in addition to the obligation of the employer to effect the insurances contemplated by clause 87 of the ECC. The requirement for acceptance by the project manager raises the issue of the legal consequences of this action and whether it can give rise to liability in negligence.[140]

The insurance policies must include a waiver by the insurers of their subrogation rights against the directors and other employees of every insured except where there is fraud.[141] The complex relationship involved with insurance and indemnity clauses in standard form contracts has given rise to apparently conflicting decisions. One factor relevant to an explanation of these decisions is that the courts have often construed such clauses as imposing a responsibility to insure as if it were a clause that actually allocated the insured risk to the party responsible for insuring.[142] The inclusion of directors in the waiver reflects current trends regarding increased directors' liabilities in general.[143] An identical provision operates in the insurance policies the subcontractor must obtain.[144] As such, the clause should preclude the exercise of subrogation rights by the

---

[137] For example, JCT 80 clauses 21, 22B.2, 22C.3; IFC clause 6.22; and JCT MW clause 16.4. However, clause 6.4.2 JCT 87 requires deposit of the policies themselves and the employer has to instruct different definitions of cover under clauses 6.4.1.1 or 6.4.3.1.

[138] JCT 87 addresses one aspect of this albeit in a footnote to clause 6.4; n. [i] notes that 'cover should not be reduced by the terms of any exclusion written in the policy beyond the terms of clause 6.2, paragraph 2'.

[139] GODREY, PATRICK S. *et al. Contraol of Risk. A Guide to the Systematic Management of Risk from Construction.* CIRIA, London, 1996, p. 14.

[140] See the further discussion of this topic below. The duty of an architect to advise in relation to insurance provisions was considered in *Tompkinson* v. *Parochial Church Council of St Michael* (1990) 6 Const LJ 319.

[141] Clause 85.2 ECC.

[142] See WRIGHT, JOHN D. Subrogation: Risk and Responsibility in Construction Contracts. *Construction Law Journal*, 1995, 11, 360.

[143] See generally RILEY, MARY L. Director's Liability. *Asian Commercial Law Review*, 1998, **3**(4), 115–124.

[144] Clause 85.2 ECSC.

insurers against the subcontractors save in the exceptional case given.[145] The waiver of subrogation rights should also serve to limit insurer sponsored litigation against the parties: employer, contractor and subcontractors, and their employees when claims arise. Such provisions are not uncommon in the other forms and in some cases are listed as an option to naming the subcontractors themselves as insureds under the original joint names policies.[146]

The parties must comply with the terms and conditions of the insurance policies[147] and in this way avoid, or at least limit, the likelihood that the insurers would deny coverage for a breach of any of the policies. The provision has counterparts in other standard forms and may operate in part to overcome denial of coverage on this basis.

The responsibility for deductibles[148] – or that portion of the liability retained by the insured – is addressed indirectly. Thus, any amount not recovered from an insurer will be borne by either the employer or the contractor respectively in accordance with whether they bore the original risk for the event.[149] Those events at the contractor's risk are the contractor's while those events that are the employer's risk are the employer's. The deductibles which the parties agree to will have an important effect on the level of premiums.[150] The requirement for agreement over the levels of deductibles gives the employer another measure of control over the true cost and value of the insurance and in this regard differs from typical JCT provisions.[151]

In determining which party carries the risk for amounts not covered by insurance, clause 85.4 must be referred to. In essence, whether it will fall upon a party will depend upon who bore the risk originally – the employer or contractor.[152] If the employer bore the original risk any amount not recovered from the insurer so remains as the employer's risk.[153] The same result pertains for risks, which were originally the contractor's, who too will continue to bear the risk in respect of those amounts.[154] Hence, the unavailability of insurance proceeds does not affect the allocation of the risk in this regard.

If the contractor does not insure

There may be occasions when the contractor fails to insure a risk that the contract requires. If so, and a required insurance policy or certificate is not

[145] See *Petrofina (UK) Ltd* v. *Magnaload Ltd* [1984] QB 127, [1983] 3 All ER 35.
[146] For example, clause 22.3 JCT 81; clause 6.3 JCT 87.
[147] Clauses 85.3 ECC and ECSC.
[148] Deductibles are referred to as 'excesses' in certain standard forms, e.g. clause 25(2) ICE 6th; clause 6.4 JCT 87.
[149] See clause 85.4 ECC.
[150] The guidance notes discuss a number of common reasons why deductibles are used: see clause 85.4 ECC, 73.
[151] See e.g. clauses 6.2, 6.3 IFC 84; clause JCT 81.
[152] See again clauses 80.1 and 81 ECC.
[153] See clause 85.4 ECC.
[154] See clause 85.4 ECC.

submitted, the employer retains a right to insure the neglected risk.[155] Default provisions, such as clause 86.1, are intended to overcome any gap in the insurance coverage that can result when there is a breach of the obligation to insure.[156] While this is likely, the intent the drafting used to achieve such an objective has to be construed in a roundabout fashion if it is to succeed. The circularity may be explained in this way. The right of the employer to insure arises if two conditions are satisfied: first, the contract stipulates a risk that the contractor is required to insure; and secondly, the contractor does not submit a required policy or certificate.[157] The stipulation that the contractor is required to insure may be implicit in that the contractor's obligation to insure may arise merely as a result of the event not being found to be an employer's risk.[158] The absence of either one of these conditions would preclude the employer insuring because the latter assumes or is conditional itself upon the former occurring. To overcome this one must construe the 'required' aspect of the policy or certificate as referring to the risk in question in the first condition; in the wording of the clause that 'risk which this contract requires'.[159] Otherwise it would be open to an obstreperous contractor to contradict the right of an employer to insure on the ground that notwithstanding a given risk remains uninsured the provision has still been complied with by *submitting* the policy or certificate required by the contract. Support for such an argument can be found in the provisions regarding the submission of programmes, the relationship to payment and the absence of any necessity for the project manager to accept the programmes in certain cases.[160] Once again, to overcome this the project manager should construe the required aspect of the policy or certificate as referring to *the* risk which the contract requires.[161]

The contractor pays the cost of any insurance that the employer takes out on behalf of the contractor. The 'payment' anticipates the use of the assessment procedure[162] by the project manager to recover the cost of the insurance from the contractor.

---

[155] See clause 86.1 ECC. This type of provision is similar to clauses 22B and 22C in JCT 80 which gives the employer an option to take out insurance cover and unlike clause 21(1) of ICE 6th which assumes that the contractor will take out the specified insurance.

[156] An argument has been dealt with in several recent cases that the person with the obligation to insure also bears the risk: see *Surrey Heath Borough Council* v. *Lovell Construction Ltd and Haden Young Ltd* (1990) 48 BLR 108 at 121, CA, per Dillon LJ; *National Trust for Places of Historic Interest or Natural Beauty* v. *Haden Young Ltd* (1994) 72 BLR 1 at 10, CA, per Nourse LJ; and *Callaghan and Welton (t/a R W Construction)* v. *Hewgate Construction Ltd* (1995) 75 BLR 11 at 19, CA, per Beldam LJ.

[157] See clause 86.1 ECC.

[158] See clauses 80.1 and 80.1 ECC.

[159] Clause 86.1 ECC.

[160] See discussion clauses 13, 31 and 50 ECC above.

[161] Clause 86.1 ECC.

[162] Clause 50.2 ECC.

Insurance by the employer

The employer has a right to effect his or her own insurance, both in the
first instance and with the agreement of the contractor, or as a result of the
contractor's default. There are reasons why it may be more appropriate for
the employer to assume the responsibilities for insurance. In general, the
employer must provide the insurance as agreed to in the Contract Data.[163]
Where the employer does so the contractor is given a right to accept the
policies. Thus, the project manager must submit those policies and
certificates of insurance that the employer is to provide to the contractor
for acceptance.[164] The submission must be made by the project manager
before the starting date and afterwards as the project manager instructs.[165]
The contractor must accept the policies and certificates if they comply
with the contract. The necessity for and the requirement of acceptance by
the contractor differ from the acceptance of policies and certificates for
insurance of the project manager when they are submitted by the
contractor.[166] In this latter regard the project manager may either accept
or reject the contractor's submission.[167] The right to do so is confirmed by
the giving of an express reason or basis on which the project manager may
not accept the submission, e.g. the policies and certificates of insurance
do not comply with the contract.[168] This would not appear to be the
drafting intention. The drafters would prefer to equate the requirement for
acceptance by the contractor with that of the employer. However, this
view does not appear to give sufficient weight to the general right of the
project manager to *withhold* acceptance of a submission by the
contractor.[169] Notwithstanding the contractor's acceptance of an
insurance policy or certificate, which has been provided by the employer,
the responsibility of the employer to provide the insurance stated and
agreed upon in the Contract Data remains.[170] The wording here is very
clear when referring to 'does not change'. For that matter, the employer's
provision of certain insurance agreed to be additional does not detract
from the contractor's obligations to insure. A similar default clause to that
available to the employer in the event of the contractor not insuring[171] is
also available to the contractor if the employer does not insure. As such,
in this case the contractor may insure the relevant risk or risks. The
drafting of clause 87.3 is materially identical to clause 86.1 and thus gives
rise to the same questions regarding its correct meaning and
interpretation.

---

[163]   Clause 84.1 ECC.
[164]   Clause 87.1 ECC.
[165]   Clause 87.1 ECC.
[166]   Under clause 85.1 ECC.
[167]   Clause 13.8 ECC.
[168]   Clause 85.1 ECC.
[169]   See guidance notes NEC on clause 87.1 ECC, 73.
[170]   See clause 87.2.
[171]   See clause 86.1 ECC.

Lastly, the employer pays the cost of any insurance that the contractor takes out on behalf of the employer.[172] The 'payment' anticipates an adjustment to the amount due[173] by the project manager for the cost of the insurance. No provision exists requiring the employer to make payments directly to the insurers themselves for any insurance that the contractor effects.[174]

---

[172] Clause 87.3 ECC.
[173] Clause 50.2 ECC.
[174] Contra guidance notes NEC on clause 87.3 ECC, 74.

14. Disputes and termination

Construction projects inevitably involve conflict situations. Problem situations arise from technical, climatic and logistic events, but disputes are caused by people and the motivational, behavioural and cultural implications of their actions will play an important, if not always visible, part in their creation – and so of their resolution.

Ron Baden Hellard,
Project Partnering: Principle and Practice

General

The NEC is premised upon the present need for greater co-operation among parties to contracts and for fewer disputes. There is unquestionable evidence of conflict in many of the surveys carried out in the industry.[1] The NEC, proponents argue, can operate at an organizational level to influence the behaviour of individuals involved in a project through the leadership of the project manager operating under a uniform and dedicated set of contract documents.[2] While NEC proponents have made the argument referred to here they have also quite bluntly raised the issue in this way: 'Does the NEC create trust and co-operation between people, or does it need these ingredients to be present at the outset of a project in order to operate successfully?' The reply, or more accurately, surmise of the same proponents is that '[w]hile there is some evidence to suggest that the use of the NEC does encourage a co-operative attitude on site, there is a great deal to suggest that it helps to perpetuate, reinforce and, with time, enhance the spirit of co-operation established at the outset of the project'.[3]

---

[1] See MURDOCH, I.I. and OSBORNE, A.N. *Survey of Current Practice, The Exercise of Market Power and the Boundaries of Market Structure as Determinants of Inter-Organisational Conflict*. CIB, London, 1995, CIB Publication 196 pp. 1–11; and FENN, P. *et al.* Conflict and Dispute in Construction. *Construction Management and Economics*, November 1997, **15**, 513–518.
[2] See BAIRD, ANDREW. Adversarialism, Pro-active Management and the NEC. *Commercial Dispute Resolution* (eds ODAMS, A. MARTIN and HIGGENS, JOANNA). Construction Law Press, London, 1996, pp. 25–29.
[3] BROOME, JON C. and PERRY, JOHN G. Experiences of the Use of the New Engineering Contract. *Engineering, Construction and Architectural Management*, 1995, **2**(4), 283.

The predicament the construction industry finds itself in though is that 'disputes are more likely to arise through the use of traditional United Kingdom standard forms. As Thompson & Perry found "existing models do not greatly help the achievements of objectives i.e. they do not make a significant contribution to reducing the effects of risk"'.[4] Once again, however, while the form of contract is significant the attitudes of the parties have also been shown to be exceedingly important in the reduction of disputes and thus the forms must offer appropriate incentives and shared benefits as well if the change is to be realized.[5] Many of the principles upon which the NEC has been drafted presuppose these goals of greater co-operation, fewer disputes and a clearer allocation of risk. Simple language, clear communications, and improved management procedures, among other features of the NEC, are designed in substantial part to address these present needs. Some of the other features of the NEC are designed to achieve the reduction of disputes as well. Thus, where it is understood that an issue has been problematic or productive of disputes, attention or special provision has often been given to it in the form.

Various studies into the causes of construction disputes have been carried out. One such survey compiled a top ten list of specific construction disputes as follows:

(1) unrealistic and unfair contract clauses which shift project risks to parties who are not prepared or able to assume them;
(2) unrealistic expectations and lack of financing;
(3) ambiguous contract provisions;
(4) unrealistically low bids;
(5) poor communications;
(6) deficient management, supervision and co-ordination on the part of the contractor;
(7) reluctance on the part of the project participants to deal promptly with changes and unexpected conditions;
(8) the absence of team spirit among project participants;
(9) a predisposition toward adversarial relationships on the part of some or all of the parties to the project; and
(10) contract administrators who avoid tough decisions and pass along problems to a higher authority.[6]

---

[4] CAPPER, PROFESSOR PHILLIP. Management of Legal Risks in Construction. A paper given to the Society of Construction Law at a meeting in Wales on 21 September 1994, p. 3, and citing Thompson and Perry, *Engineering Construction Risks: A Guide to Engineering Construction Risks: A Guide to Project Risk Analysis and Risk Management.* Science and Engineering Research Council, Thomas Telford, Swindon, 1993, p. 36.

[5] See discussion NEDO. *Faster Building for Industry.* HMSO, London, 1983, p. 4 and following.

[6] SMITH, G.A. Beyond ADR – Dispute Resolution in the Construction Industry through Realistic Contract Risk Allocation. *The Organization of Management of Construction: Shaping Theory and Practice* (eds LANGFORD, D.A. and RETICK, A.). E & FN Spon, London, 1996, vol. 2, n. 1 references omitted. See more recently on attitudes

Examples may be given of how the NEC has been designed to address some of these principal types of disputes. Thus, the right to and valuation of certain types of cost inputs has typically been productive of disputes so the SCC has been introduced to seek to reduce the number of such disputes on this issue with regard to the cost reimbursement main options.[7] Other examples may be noted. For instance, the requirement now to submit an activity schedule with the tender seeks to reduce disputes regarding the payment interface. The NEC has also chosen to address both aspects of significant contractual detail and procedures in the works information rather than the conditions of contract. One benefit that should follow from this choice is that fewer legal disputes will be likely to arise over the meaning and contents of the works information than had the detail and procedures been left as part of the conditions of contract. Hence, by both transferring and reducing the legal content of the conditions of contract it is strongly arguable that it will also serve to reduce disputes. The diminution of the legal content of the conditions has been achieved in more obvious ways as well. Thus, there are only nine core clauses and sixteen additional or secondary option clauses that may be 'negotiated' between the parties. The intention is thus to keep the parties focused upon the mutual completion of the works rather than just the independent formulation of their respective legal obligations. The principal reason behind this intention once again is both the desire and need of many clients to reduce the wastage of resources caused by disputes.[8] One last illustration of the attention given to the issue of disputes may be noted; that is, the ECC is almost wholly back-to-back with the conditions of contract in the ECSC. This provides significant advantages over most traditional forms of contract and will, it is submitted, reduce the likelihood of disputes. Thus the dispute and termination provisions in the ECC must not be looked at in isolation. They are an integral part of a contract system and stated drafting objectives which have addressed these topics in other ways as well.

The ninth core clause in the ECC is entitled 'Disputes and termination'. The provisions on disputes and termination in core clause 9 are the most extensive of any of the core clauses in the ECC. They have already been substantially rewritten twice; once following the release of the First

toward ADR, BROOKER, PENNY and LAVERS, ANTHONY. Perception of Alternative Dispute Resolution as Constraints upon its Use in the UK Construction Industry. *Construction Management and Economics*, 1997, **15**, 519–526; and on the practice involved MACKIE, KARL *et al. Commercial Dispute Resolution: An ADR Practice Guide*. Butterworths, London, Dublin, Edinburgh, 1995.

[7] SCHNEIDER, MICHAEL E. Mastering the Interfaces – Construction Contracts Drafting for Dispute Avoidance. *International Construction Law Review*, 1993, 407 n. 17 referring to the IChemE Reimbursable and supporting guidance notes, and the UNIDO-Contract, Cost Reimbursable version, Annexure XXVII.

[8] PERRY, J.G. and HOARE, D.J. Contracts of the Future: Risks and Rewards. In *Future Directions in Construction Law*. Proceedings of the Fifth Annual Conference of the Centre of Construction Law and Management, King's College, London, 1992, pp. 81–97.

Edition[9] and a second time following the passage of the Housing Grants, Construction and Regeneration Act 1996. Clause 9, according to the drafters, 'describes the procedures for dealing with disputes and the circumstances under which the Parties may terminate the contract and the subsequent procedures'.[10] It is unusual to group the topics of disputes and termination together in a standard form in this way because there is not a necessary correlation between the two in all cases.[11] Some recognition of this fact has come lately with extensive amendments to clause 9 to comply with the HGCRA. In fact, the changes to clause 9 suggest that a new heading for the clause would now be appropriate. The amended core clause is now more conciliatory in tone and focused upon dispute *avoidance* rather than dispute *settlement*. A suggested new heading for clause 9 could thus be 'Dispute avoidance and termination'. This assumes that it is desirable to continue to address both the avoidance of disputes and termination of the contract in the same core clause. It is an interesting choice of the drafters that termination would be so clearly dealt with when contract formation has been given a lesser degree of attention.[12] The importance of this change, and perhaps an implicit attempt to *move away* from the view that conflicts (if not disputes) are inevitable in construction, is progressive. There is some early evidence which may suggest a degree of success in this regard; only six adjudications that had been heard to 1998 under the NEC.[13] Until recently few reported cases considered adjudication provisions in other forms although the reasons for this are not entirely clear. Mark C. McGaw notes four cases up until 1992 and some might say that this is some evidence that adjudication has been a 'modest success'.[14] It may be concluded that, if the results of adjudication

---

9 The Latham Report paragraph 5.20(7), 40 noted that 'the adjudication procedures may need some amendment to bring them within the principles of Chapter 9 [Dispute Resolution] of this Report'.

10 Guidance notes NEC, 75. See also The New Engineering Contract: Need For and Features, 4; Consultation Document and the comments of Dr Barnes reported following a meeting with the Hong Kong Institute of Engineers: More on the New Engineering Contract. *Hong Kong Engineer*, January 1992, 7.

11 EGGLESTON. *The New Engineering Contract, A Commentary*. Blackwell Science, London, 1996, p. 261 makes this point but suggests that the reason for the conjunction was that it was 'probably done simply to avoid the need for a Section 10 which would upset the clause numbering system of the contract'.

12 See generally WHITFIELD, JEFF. *Conflicts in Construction: Avoiding, Managing, Resolving*. Macmillan, Basingstoke, 1994; and a comparative international view on the issue of disputes in construction given in *Dispute Resolution and Conflict in Dispute Resolution and Conflict Management in Construction: An International Perspective* (eds DAVIS, EDWARD *et al.*) E & FN Spon, London, 1998.

13 BAYTON, ERNEST J. An Introduction to the Engineering and Construction Contract. A course given at Altrincham on 3 March 1998. Thomas Telford Training, London, 1998.

14 McGAW, MARK C. Adjudicators, Experts and Keeping Out of Court. *Construction Law Journal*, 1992, **8**, 336 n. 17; n. 23 at 338, and referring to both Ron Denny, formerly deputy director of the BPF, quoted in *Construction News*, June 13, 1991 and SHILSTON, ALAN. Reconciliation in the Construction Industry. *Arbitration*, 1988, 187.

were not generally seen to be positive, such provisions would never have been mandated in the HGCRA. The number of adjudication cases, however, both referrals and reported, with the passage of the legislation has exploded and thus, the force of these arguments may be blunted. From another angle, however, there is also evidence that the perception of construction professionals, toward the NEC is one of minimal expectancy of dispute when operating according to its terms. In a large survey of construction professionals researchers asked respondents to rate forms of contract according to their perceived expectancy of disputes if using it. The NEC form was ranked third overall in a list of fourteen standard forms suggesting a very low expectation of disputes, with the two forms ranking ahead of the NEC being the JCT MW form and the IChemE Green Book.[15] This too is a positive indicator. The inclusion of a dispute avoidance tier is also consistent with a sound conceptual framework for dispute management[16] and the dispute avoidance tier now better reflects one of the original intentions of the drafters:

> One of the motivations behind the NEC contract is also to reduce the occurrence of disputes. However, under the NEC, possible sources of dispute are treated in a fundamentally different way from that in more conventional contracts. Under the NEC, the intention is that disputes are to be avoided through good management practice, which reduces the incidence of conflict. While it does address the matter of how disputes may equally be resolved, its primary emphasis is on how they can be avoided. The aim is transparency, bad management is to be penalised, not insured against.[17]

Housing Grants, Construction and Regeneration Act 1996

The Housing Grants, Construction and Regeneration Act 1996 (HGCRA) has been introduced above.[18] As a result of the passage of the HGCRA, whenever the ECC is used in England, Wales, Scotland and Northern Ireland a new secondary option clause, 'Option Y(UK)2: The Housing Grants, Construction and Regeneration Act 1996' should be used, although not in other circumstances. The amendments to the form were first released as an Addendum with notes for guidance.[19] They are

---

[15] FENN, PETER *et al.* Conflict and Dispute in Construction. *Construction Management and Economics*, 1997, **15**(6), 513–518.

[16] See SHI, XINPING and GIBSON, HARRY L. Development and Significance of Business Dispute Management to Managers. *Journal of General Management*, 1997, **22**(4), 81 whose framework is set out in three states: (1) pre-dispute prevention; (2) alternative dispute resolution; and (3) post-dispute evaluation.

[17] ROOKE, JOHN and SEYMOUR, DAVID. The NEC and the Culture of the Industry: Some Early Findings Regarding Possible Sources of Resistance to Change. *Engineering, Construction and Architectural Management*, 1995, **2**(4), 297.

[18] See generally ARDEN QC, ANDREW *et al. Housing Grants, Construction and Regeneration Act 1996.* Sweet & Maxwell, London, 1996.

[19] A reference document was released by the ICE in April 1998: NEC/NECC/Y(UK) 2/ April 1998 which contained guidance notes and the consequential amendments.

incorporated into the contract by making a statement in the Contract Data.[20] However, as the core clause will only be amended in those cases where the HGCRA applies, the amendments are optional and are, therefore, only contained in a secondary option clause, that is Y (UK) 2. Option Y (UK) 2 comprises eight clauses. Clauses Y 2.5 to Y 2.7 deal with the adjudication provisions of the legislation. Both the unamended and amended provisions will be examined here, although the amended provisions will be given precedence.[21]

Avoidance and settlement of disputes

Adjudication can be viewed as a contractual procedure that stimulates the methodology of managerial decision-making to resolve disputes. It is, therefore, in theory at least, a pragmatic solution to the problem of managing disputes arising out of the interaction of individuals from separate organisations tending to have conflicting interests.[22]

The object of adjudication as referred to in the Construction Industry Council's *Model Adjudication Procedure* provides: 'The object of adjudication is to reach a fair, rapid and inexpensive decision upon a dispute arising under the Contract and this procedure shall be interpreted accordingly'.[23] The first heading in the unamended Second Edition of the ECC is 'Settlement of disputes'. In this regard the heading sets forth a clear policy choice on the part of the drafters in favour of adjudication as the first tier of a two-tier procedure for dealing with disputes under the form. This classification assumes 'formal' dispute resolution tiers. However, the most important tier in the dispute avoidance process may well be the informal tier involving the parties' ongoing co-operation. Dr Martin Barnes states: 'The adjudication procedure is a commercial/technical process not a quasi-legal procedure as is arbitration'.[24]

The choice of adjudication as a first tier in the unamended Second Edition stands in contrast to FIDIC 4th and ICE 6th procedures.[25] Under both clauses 67.1 of the FIDIC 4th and 66(3) of the ICE 6th, the first tier

---

[20] 'The conditions of contract are the core clauses for Options ... and Y(UK)2 (published by the ICE April 1998) of the Second Edition (November 1995) of the NEC Engineering and Construction Contract': option Y(UK)2 guidance notes.

[21] As with the secondary option U, the CDM Regulations, consideration should be given by the NEC Panel to United Kingdom and Scottish versions to accommodate these two options.

[22] McGAW, MARK C. See n. 16 above, 357 and citing in n. 82 also HELLARD, R.B. ADR in Technical Contracts by Multi-Disciplinary Contract Adjudication. *Arbitration*, 1988, 108.

[23] Construction Industry Council's *Model Adjudication Procedure*, 1st edn., February 1998, 1.

[24] BARNES, DR MARTIN. The New Engineering Contract – An Update. *International Construction Law Review*, 1996, 91.

[25] See generally STEPHENSON, DOUGLAS A. *Arbitration Practice in Construction Contracts*, 3rd edn. E & FN Spon, London, 1993, pp. 8–20.

of dispute resolution involves a reference to the engineer for decision. Under FIDIC 4th, the reference to the engineer may be made at any time. The engineer has 84 days to give notice of a decision. It is interesting to note the credibility of the engineer acting as a first tier dispute resolver is said to be 'challenged' by the substitution of a third party independent adjudicator for the engineer.[26] Following the delivery of the engineer's decision under these forms, or the expiry of the time for delivery, either party may refer the dispute to a second tier. In ICE 6th, this tier is the ICE Conciliation Procedure, while under FIDIC 4th it is a less formal means described as 'amicable settlement'.[27] Under the ICE 6th, the reference to conciliation may be made at any point following the engineer's decision, or the expiry of the time for delivery of the decision provided that the dispute has not then been referred to arbitration. Where an amicable settlement has not been reached under the FIDIC procedures the dispute may be ultimately referred to a third and final tier of dispute resolution; namely, arbitration under the Rules of Conciliation and Arbitration of the International Chamber of Commerce.[28] The final tier in the ICE 6th dispute resolution process is also arbitration only in accordance with the ICE Arbitration Procedure.[29] Thus under both FIDIC and the ICE a formal three-tier dispute process is in place.

The three tier FIDIC and ICE procedures may be contrasted with the two-tier process in the ECC. The essential difference among these three forms is that, under the ECC, the reference to the engineer in the first instance is a reference to the engineer's quasi-arbitral role. The separation of the engineer's traditional roles under the NEC necessitated this change. Another difference that may be noted in the forms concerns the role of choice. Thus, while one of the optional statements in part one of the Contract Data allows the parties to choose the arbitration procedure, no similar optional statement is included for the adjudication procedures; rather, the procedures will ordinarily be governed by those set out in the Adjudicator's Contract. Other precedents do exist, for instance, the Construction Industry Council's *Model Adjudication Procedure*, as potential models for the adjudication procedures.

The amendments to the Second Edition of the ECC move the form further away still from ICE and FIDIC. Hence, in the amended ECC, a formalized meeting procedure is adopted as a new first tier of dispute resolution. The removal of the quasi-arbitral role of the engineer (or architect) remains the same, however, under the amended version. The

---

[26] CAPPER, PHILLIP and BUNCH, ANTHONY. Construction Industry Arbitrations. In *Handbook of Arbitration of Practice* (eds BERNSTEIN, RONALD *et al.*), 3rd edn. Sweet & Maxwell and the Chartered Institute of Arbitrators, London, 1998, p. 345.

[27] Clauses 67.2 FIDIC 4th and 66(5) ICE 6th.

[28] Clause 67.3 FIDIC 4th. The International Chamber of Commerce has released new Arbitration Rules for 1998: International Chamber of Commerce, *ICC Rules of Arbitration*, in force as from 1 January 1998. ICC Publications, Paris, 1997.

[29] Clause 66(6), (7), and (8) ICE 6th. The ICE has lately updated its arbitration procedures replacing the ICE Arbitration Procedure (1983) with the ICE Arbitration Procedure (1997) to conform to changes made in the Arbitration Act 1996.

change in the ECC and the second tier adjudication procedure reflects an innovative approach to dispute resolution in comparison to the traditional ICE and FIDIC procedures.

This innovation follows recent trends, such as expert determination, partnering,[30] dispute review advisers,[31] dispute review boards[32] and mediation. In construction the Red Book uses expert determination for a wide variety of disputes as does the ENAA Model Form of Contract for Power Plant Construction 1996.[33] It also follows changes to FIDIC 4th which introduced for the first time a dispute adjudication board.[34] This is a significant change that FIDIC has made introducing adjudication either by one or three individuals largely in place of arbitration. While the parties nevertheless maintain an ultimate right to arbitrate disputes that are either unresolved amicably in the first instance, or under the dispute adjudication procedure, it is clearly the intention to discourage arbitration. In the guide to the amended clause 67 it provides in part:

> [a]lthough some disputes may have ultimately to be decided by arbitration, the Board provides a procedure for the settlement of disputes where direct discussions between those involved have failed. In order to maximize the Board's chances of success in avoiding arbitration, its member(s) must be suitably qualified, impartial, and accepted and trusted by both parties.[35]

Similarly, the World Bank has been innovating in its large contract documentation and dispute resolution procedures. Thus, as from January 1995, it became mandatory to refer disputes in the first instance not to an engineer but either to a three-member dispute review board or a one-member dispute review expert.[36] The World Bank has also adopted the

---

[30] See GAEDE JR, A.H. Partnering: A Common Sense Approach to Preventing and Managing Claims. *International Construction Law Review*, 1995, 81; BADEN HELLARD, RON. *Project Partnering: Principle and Practice*. Thomas Telford, London, 1995.

[31] See notably CHEUNG, SAI-ON and YEUNG, YUET-WA. The Effectiveness of the Dispute Resolution Advisor System: A Critical Appraisal. *International Journal of Project Management*, 1998, **16**(6), 367–374; LUK, JOHN W.K. and WONG, W.T. The Current Practice of Dispute Resolution Adviser in the Construction Industry of Hong Kong. *Arbitration*, 1995, 253.

[32] PIKE, ANDREW. Dispute Review Boards and Adjudicators. *International Construction Law Review*, 1993, 157.

[33] The Red Book – IChemE 3rd 1995 e.g. clauses 33.7, 36.7, 38.5, 42.5 and 43.9; as does the ENAA Model Form of Contract for Power Plant Construction 1996. See lately *Dixon's Group plc* v. *Jan Andrew Murray-Oboynski* (1998) 86 BLR 16; and *Davies Middleton & Davies Ltd* v. *Toyo Engineering Corporation* (1998) 85 BLR 59 (CA).

[34] FIDIC 4th Supplement, First Edition 1996 supersedes clause 67 on disputes and arbitration in FIDIC 4th. See MOLINEAU, CHARLES B. Real Time Dispute Resolution: Updating FIDIC. *International Construction Law Review*, 1994, 263–266.

[35] FIDIC 4th Supplement, First Edition 1996, A–5.

[36] JAYNES, GORDON L. Dispute Review Boards: The World Bank is Aboard. *International Construction Law Review*, 1996, 17.

NEC model for small contracts worth US$10 million or less in their
Procurement of Works (Smaller Contracts), which now uses an
adjudicator to resolve disputes. The *Smaller Contracts* form is a model
form of contract and thus it is left to the parties whether to adopt a
disputes review board or disputes review expert. The latter was intended
to replace the adjudicator in the *Smaller Contracts* form.[37] Despite the
encouraging growth in these trends, research in the United Kingdom
construction industry suggests *attitudes* toward alternative modes of
dispute resolution still act as a constraint upon its use.[38]

Returning to the ECC provisions the option Y (UK) 2 amendments
return to a drafting style that is closer to the other core clauses. In the First
Edition the style of clause 9 conformed broadly to or matched that in the
other core clauses. The drafting was perfunctory, descriptive and
declaratory. Hence, characteristic NEC action verbs such as 'implement',
'provide', 'decides', 'makes', and 'notifies' were used in the First Edition.
In contrast, the unamended Second Edition purported to lay down a
procedure to be followed and thus introduced the settlement of disputes
with this provision: 'Any dispute arising under or in connection with this
contract is submitted to and settled by the *Adjudicator* as follows'.[39] It
was unusual in NEC drafting to describe something both in prospective
terms and with reference to the '*Adjudicator*' and not the 'Parties'
directly. This fact may have been realized by the drafters subsequent to
the release of the Second Edition and could have been a factor, quite apart
from the HGCRA, in the deletion of clause 90.1 and its substitution.
However, if that were the intent, the drafters have still failed to adopt fully
the existing drafting style for the other core clauses. They have done so by
referring to a 'procedure' to be followed for the avoidance and settlement
of disputes. There is no reason why a procedure had to be set out. Indeed,
and presumably if the previously adhered to means of drafting had been
followed, the clause would have simply reflected flow charted procedures.
It may be noted, however, that there were no flow charts in the First
Edition to support the procedures in the core clause and that they were
only introduced in the Second Edition. Indeed the NEC is intended as a
set of procedures to reinforce better management under the contract and
no individual set of procedures should be singled out for special
treatment. The procedures themselves are far less elaborate than those

---

[37] See JAYNES, GORDON L. *ibid.*, 18–19. See also PIKE, ANDREW n. 32 above, 157.
[38] See BROOKER, PENNY and LAVERS, ANTHONY. Perceptions of Alternative
Dispute Resolution as Constraints upon its Use in the UK Construction Industry.
Construction Management and Economics, 1997, **15**(6), 519–526. See generally
KWAKYE, A.A. *Alternative Dispute Resolution in Construction*. CIOB, Ascot, 1993,
CIOB Construction Papers 21; MYERS, JAMES J. Resolving Disputes in Worldwide
Infrastructure Projects. *International Construction Law Review*, 1995, 431; ROGERS,
JUSTICE A. Alternative Dispute Resolution in Construction Disputes in Australasia.
Building and Construction Law, September 1992, 168; HOLLANDS, DAVID E.
Alternative Dispute Resolution in Construction. *Arbitration*, 1992, 57.
[39] Clause 90.1 2nd ECC.

addressing payment or compensation events and again for that reason need not have been given special attention.[40]

Dispute categories

Disputes are divided into three categories under both the unamended and amended Second Edition, which may be summarized as follows:

- actions taken by the project manager or supervisor;
- actions not taken by the project manager or supervisor; and
- a general category comprising any other matter.

Under the First Edition disputes could be raised only with respect to the first two categories. However, the First Edition clause dealt not simply with actions that had not been taken, in an unqualified sense, but also actions 'not in accordance with the contract' or 'outside the authority given by this contract'. The former qualification parallels clause 29.1 of both the First and Second Editions obliging the contractor to obey 'an instruction ... which is in accordance with this contract'. The prospect that actions may be other than instructions would justify the language in clause 9, at least from a drafting point of view. The second qualification is more problematic. The absence of an express reference in the clause to a right to refer 'any other matter', as appears in the Second Edition version, would appear to be an equivalent means of conferring a residual right to refer disputes to the '*Adjudicator*'. The application of the section invoking notions of authority or jurisdiction is potentially quite broad. It would appear to be broader than the Second Edition version which, once again, was confined to disputes 'arising under or in connection with this contract'.[41] It may be noted that, in the unamended Second Edition, reference is made in the adjudication table to the project manager or supervisor 'not having taken an action' while clause 90.2 of the ECC refers to 'inaction'. In comparison, the amended Second Edition uses only the phrase 'failure to take action'. The latter phrasing is more precise than 'inaction' and should also be easier to determine with reference to what failure relates.

The division of disputes into three categories underscores the overall importance of 'actions' in the scheme of the ECC. It may be recalled that actions have been held out here as the generic term for instructions, submissions, proposals, records, acceptances, notifications and replies

---

[40] The importance of consistent drafting in relation to dispute avoidance is developed by DELAUME, GEORGES R. The Effectiveness of Conflict Avoidance. In *Law and Practice of Transnational Contracts*. Oceana, New York, 1988, section 402 The Perils of Draftsmanship, 102–106.

[41] CHATTERJEE, S.K., in a short article and after a review of the jurisprudence on these and similar phrases suggests use of the words 'in connection with' should be avoided although use of the words 'arising under' is generally acceptable: Do Disputes Arise 'out of' or 'under' or 'out of and under' a Contract? *Arbitration*, 1994, 117. See lately *Strachan & Henshaw Ltd* v. *Stein Industrie (UK) Ltd and GEC Alsthom Ltd* (1998) 87 BLR 52 (CA) construing an almost identical provision in clause 44.4 MF/1.

that the project manager will take. Thus, for instance, the project manager has the power through the terms of the contract to change the works information, and vary or accelerate the manner in which the contractor carries out the works. Any one of these actions may give rise to a dispute 'arising under or in connection with this contract'.[42] There are instances throughout where the project manager or supervisor may also *not* take an action. It could be said that their response is negative in this regard. Thus, in response to a proposal from the contractor to add to the working areas, the project manager has two clear options: not to accept the proposal or not to take the action. Reasons for so doing may include that the proposed addition is not necessary to provide the works or that the proposed area would be used for work not in the contract.[43] These illustrations would appear to fall logically within cases where the project manager or supervisor has not taken actions. However, there may be other instances as well when an omission or failure to act on their part gives rise to a dispute within the meaning of this second category of dispute. Even if the dispute falls outside this category it may still be raised under the final category of dispute which the arbitrator has jurisdiction to hear, namely, 'any other matter'.

Only the contractor may invoke the procedures for dealing with the action or inaction of the project manager or supervisor as a dispute. Neither the procedure for settlement of disputes under clause 90.1 of the unamended Second Edition nor that for avoidance and settlement of disputes under clause 90.2 of the amended Second Edition is intended to deal with disputed actions or inactions on the part of the project manager or supervisor from the employer's perspective. In contrast, under both the unamended and amended versions, either party, which includes the employer, is entitled to invoke the procedures for dealing with 'any other matter'. These clauses are not designed as the basis for raising disputes solely between the employer and the project manager or supervisor, however, and such issues would be better dealt with under the consultant's terms of engagement and the dispute provisions of the PSC. Provision is made for the adjudicator under the main contract to resolve certain matters that could arise between the project manager and employer and any subconsultant to the project manager under clause 91.3 of the PSC First Edition.

Timing

Under the unamended clause 90.1 all disputes may be submitted to the adjudicator between two and four[44] weeks after notification of the dispute either to the project manager by the contractor or to the other party and the project manager by the contractor or employer. In the

[42] Clause 90.1 ECC.

[43] Clause 15.1 ECC. Other examples include clauses 21.2, 23.1, 24.1, 26.2, 26.3, 31.3 etc.

[44] COTTAM, GUY. Covering all the Options. Construction News, 3 June 1993, 13 critiques the short four-week time frame and states that it will result in many unneccessary arbitrators being appointed.

categories of disputes involving actions or inactions by the project manager or supervisor, the contractor must make the notification not more than four weeks after becoming aware that the disputed action was or was not taken.[45] Under the amended version of clause 90 a different time frame pertains to reflect the introduction of a new first tier of dispute resolution. The procedure under the amended clause may be briefly outlined.

In general, if the contractor is dissatisfied with an action or a failure to take action by the project manager, this dissatisfaction must be notified to the project manager no later than:

- four weeks after becoming aware of the action; or
- four weeks after becoming aware that the action in question had not been taken.[46]

The project manger and contractor are then obliged to attend a meeting within two weeks of the notification to discuss and seek to resolve the matter.[47] An identical procedure and time frame pertains with regard to the third category of 'any other matter'.[48] The parties agree to *postpone* the crystallization of a 'dispute', which is expressly stated to include a difference, unless the notice of dissatisfaction has been given and the matter has not been resolved.[49] The parties' agreement that no matter shall be a 'dispute', unless a notice of dissatisfaction has been given and the matter not resolved within four weeks, differs from the ICE 6th procedure. Under clause 66(2) of ICE 6th, before there can even be a first-tier reference to the engineer, there has to be an *existing* dispute or difference.[50] The meaning or effective defining of a dispute in this way renders fulfilment of the procedures a condition precedent to invoking adjudication. These initial time frames permit a minimum further period of two weeks after the holding of the one and only meeting required in an effort to seek to resolve the impasse. During this time frame it would be open to the parties to take whatever steps they wish, including additional meetings, in their efforts to overcome the disagreement. To this point in the procedures none of the changes that were introduced to clause 90 were specifically required as a result of the passage of the HGCRA.

Either party may give notice to the other party at any time of an intention to refer a dispute to adjudication.[51] In this regard the notice may be wholly prospective although once given the reference must then be made to the adjudicator within seven days of the notice.[52] No provision is

---

[45] The short time limits in which a decision of the project manager must be communicated to the contractor may also be contrasted with the 84-day period of reply in FIDIC 4th, clause 67.2.

[46] Clause 90.2 amended 2nd ECC.

[47] Clause 90.2 amended 2nd ECC.

[48] Clause 90.3 amended 2nd ECC.

[49] Clause 90.4 amended 2nd ECC.

[50] See *Monmouth County Council* v. *Costelloe and Kemple Ltd* (1965) 63 LGR 429, CA.

[51] Clause 90.5 amended 2nd ECC.

[52] Clause 90.5 amended 2nd Edition ECC.

made for the extension of the seven-day time frame in the event of its expiry; however, in the absence of any time limit in the first instance it would appear to be open to the parties to submit disputes to adjudication long after the completion date. The prospective notice provision and further seven-day time frame provides a final opportunity for the matter to be resolved amicably if possible. Both the absences of a time limit for the notice of the intention to refer and the later seven-day time limit derived from the HGCRA.[53]

In the unamended Second Edition, an adjudication table summarizes the three categories of disputes that may be referred to the adjudicator. Reading the adjudication table it can be remarked that it provides a scheme for the submission of disputes from actions or inactions of the project manager or the supervisor directly to the adjudicator. In comparison, the BPF system sends all disputes to adjudication but, unlike the NEC, the adjudicator is appointed only after the need for adjudication arises. This introduces an unnecessary element of delay under the BPF. In the ECC there is no intermediate reference of a dispute about an action of the supervisor to the project manager first or as a condition precedent to its submission to the adjudicator. The actions of the project manager and the supervisor are independent of each other and the provisions on adjudication regard them as such. This contrasts sharply with both the FIDIC and ICE procedures, which impose an additional intermediate dispute resolution tier, namely amicable settlement and conciliation respectively.[54] It has been observed that clause 67 of the FIDIC conditions has proved problematic based upon a majority of ICC references under those conditions raising matters of compliance with that clause.[55] An evolution can thus be seen in the available tiers of dispute resolution under the various editions of the NEC.

Dispute tiers
The use of tables in the NEC has been inconsistent. For example, in the First Edition, a table format was shown in clauses 94.2, 96.2 and 97.2. However, in the unamended Second Edition a table was added in clause 90.1, remained in clause 94.2 but was deleted from clauses 96.2 and 97.2. Finally, in the amended Second Edition the table in clause 90.1 has been deleted. Notwithstanding the substance of the clauses has not been changed, save clause 90.1, the changes in format detract from familiarity in use of the form.

Procedures and information
Some minimal procedural requirements are set out in clause 91.1 of the unamended Second Edition and clause 90.6 of the amended Second Edition. Thus, the party submitting the dispute to the adjudicator must

---

[53] Section 108(2)(a), and (b) respectively.
[54] Clause 67.2 FIDIC 4th and clause 66(5) ICE 6th.
[55] See UFF, JOHN and JEFFORD, NERYS. European Harmonisation in the Field of Construction. *International Construction Law Review*, 1993, 130.

Table 3   Dispute tiers and their effect

	First Edition	Second Edition	Amended Second Edition
First tier	Adjudication	Adjudication	Meeting
Second tier	Arbitration	Review by Tribunal	Adjudication
Third tier	N/A	N/A	Review by tribunal
Procedure	Notice	Notice	Notice
Effect of first tier	Not stated	Decision final and binding unless and until revised by tribunal	Postpones dispute arising
Effect of second tier	Turns on chosen arbitration law and procedure	Settles dispute. Power to review and revise. Also turns on chosen tribunal and procedure	Settles dispute. Power to review and revise. Also turns on chosen tribunal and procedure
Effect of third tier	N/A	N/A	Settles dispute. Power to review and revise. Also turns on chosen tribunal and procedure

include with the submission any information to be considered by the adjudicator. Any further information from a party to be considered by the adjudicator must be provided within four weeks from the submission under clause 91.1 and within 14 days under clause 90.6.[56] Both clauses address important issues in relation to later disclosure and discovery of evidence. An express discovery obligation is imposed upon the parties to see that any communication that passes between a party and the adjudicator is also communicated to the other party.[57] This practice serves to reassure parties that justice is being fairly done and that each in turn would be able to raise a full answer and defence to the communication if need be and at the relevant time.

The disclosure and discovery of evidence issues would be clearer if the term 'evidence' had been used rather than 'information' in these clauses but it has not been and attention should be drawn to it. Awareness that it may be evidence one is discussing in this context[58] and its importance prompts a reconsideration of the meaning and significance of the term in the ECC as a whole.[59] The breadth of meaning can be demonstrated by listing the categories of information which arise under the ECC.

[56] Similarly provision is made in clause 2.1 AC.
[57] Clause 92.1 unamended 2nd ECC.
[58] Evidence is only referred to explicitly in clause 93.2 ECC.
[59] The term 'evidence' is used along with 'information' in clause 93.2 ECC.

- There are *affirmative* direct references to information. This refers principally to the 'Site information' and the 'Works Information', both of which are defined as 'information' which fulfils certain stated criteria.[60] If the stated criteria are fulfilled, and it is noted that they are limitative, the site information and works information will be regarded as 'information' for the purposes of the contract.
- There are *negative* direct references to information. Thus, 'information' in the '*activity schedule*'[61] or the '*bills of quantities*'[62] is *not* 'Works Information' or 'Site Information'.
- There are *indirect* references to information in both the 'Works Information' and the 'Site Information'. The indirect references broaden what may be regarded as information.[63]
- There are *specific* references to information *inside* the contract. Thus the programme to be accepted must 'show the information which this contract requires'.[64]
- There are *specific* references to information *outside* the contract. In particular, that information which the contractor is *assumed* to have taken into account in judging the physical conditions of the site. That is, 'information obtainable from a visual inspection of the site'; and 'other information which an experienced contractor could reasonably be expected to have or to obtain' (clause 60.2 of the ECC). An analogous category of information but which is not referred to specifically as such in the contract is weather data under clause 60.2(13). Similar wording to clause 60.2 can be seen in the ICE 6th form. Clause 12(5) of the ICE 6th sets out a similar standard which is expected of contractors regarding their foreseeing of adverse physical conditions and artificial obstructions; that is, they should be 'reasonably foreseen by an experienced contractor'.
- There are *physical data* emanating from the contractor and are referred to in the contract although not specifically as 'information'. This category, it is submitted, includes the following: submissions, proposals, records, acceptances, notifications, replies; quotations;[65] forecasts;[66] proposed subContract Data;[67] accounts, records which show that payments have been made, and records of communications and calculations relating to assessment of compensation events for subcontractors.[68]

[60] See clauses 11.2(5) and (6) ECC.
[61] Clause 54.1 main options A and C ECC.
[62] Clause 55.1 main options B and D ECC.
[63] See clauses 31.2 ECC, 'other information which the Works Information requires ...'; and 60.2, 'publicly available information referred to in the Site Information'. See also clause 52.2 requiring the contractor to keep 'other accounts and records as stated in the Works Information'.
[64] Clause 31.3 ECC. The precise content of this information is contained in clause 31.2. See also clause 50.3.
[65] Clause 61 ECC.
[66] Clause 20.4 main options C, D, E and F ECC.
[67] Clause 26.4 main options C, D, E and F ECC.
[68] Clause 52.2 main options C, D and F ECC.

- There are *physical data* emanating from the employer and referred to in the contract although not specifically as 'information'. This category includes, it is submitted, instructions, certificates, proposals, records, acceptances, notifications and replies.
- There are *physical materials, facilities and samples* provided by both parties and which yield test and inspection results or, it is submitted, information.[69]
- There is *generic* information referred to in the contract. The reference to this category of information is coupled with an affirmative duty not only to procure such information but also to disclose and produce it to others as well. Thus, the 'Contractor co-operates with Others[70] in obtaining and providing information which they need in connection with the works'.[71] A more limited form of disclosure and production obligation pertains in relation to the Contractor's accounts and records, which form part of the works information.[72]

From a legal perspective what information entails under the contract is significant for several reasons.

- It may be relevant to later admissibility or weight at any proceedings subsequent to those before the tribunal.
- Disclosure or discovery, either before the adjudicator or tribunal, may similarly affect use or weight subsequently.
- It may affect any attempt to preclude or circumscribe later use if characterized in any way such as 'without prejudice' information; or information used in settlement negotiations.
- The information may have unintended legal consequences such as in relation to admissions in pleadings, or matters of estoppel or waiver.

The ECC does not purport to address these issues but leaves them to the general law instead. Therefore, one should be aware of the plethora of types of information surrounding the ECC provisions and their real importance.

Time limitation

There is a time limitation on the submission of further information to be considered by the adjudicator. That is, it must be provided within either 4 weeks or 14 days of the original submission depending upon the version used. The time limitation is likely inserted as a practical matter or the parties could seek to continue to introduce new information until the very moment the adjudicator notifies the decision. That moment is within four weeks of the end of the period for providing information under the amended Second Edition or within 28 days under the amended Second Edition.[73] Under clause 90.9, the parties may agree to extend the period,

---

[69] Clause 40.2 ECC.
[70] Clause 11.2(2) ECC.
[71] Clause 25.1 ECC.
[72] Clauses 52.2 and 52.3 ECC.
[73] Clause 91.1 unamended 2nd ECC, and clause 90.9 amended 2nd ECC.

or the adjudicator may extend the period by up to 14 days with the consent of the notifying party alone. The 28-day requirement derives from section 108(2)(c) of the HGCRA, while the 14-day period of extension derives from section 108(2)(d) of the HGCRA. Hence the adjudication period envisaged is 8 weeks in total from submission to decision. Whether this period of time is reasonable will depend upon the nature and size of the given dispute. It can relatively easily be said that in some cases it will be too long and in others too short. This time frame as well, it should be noted, does not include the between 2- and 4-week delay that is required after notification of the dispute has been given to the other party 'and/or' the project manager. It can be observed that the 8-week time period under the unamended Second Edition version itself is also a compromise on the much shorter 4-week period that was originally given in the Consultation Document.[74] It is ironic that the shorter periods required under the HGCRA, as reflected in the amended Second Edition version, are very close to the shorter time periods in the NEC Consultation Document.

The question a limitation period normally raises is whether it is to operate as a bar. The short answer is that the time frame is permissive only. This follows from the power of the adjudicator to extend the periods in both the unamended and amended versions of the Second Edition. This, it is submitted, is the proper interpretation of the uncertain wording of clause 91.1 which provides in part: 'The four week periods in this clause may be extended if requested by the *Adjudicator* in view of the nature of the dispute and agreed by the parties'.[75] This wording implies that it is the adjudicator who requests the extension of time *ex mero motu* or of mere motion rather than the parties and which thus puts some considerable pressure upon them to agree. However, this interpretation may not be as plausible under clause 90.9 which does not give the adjudicator a similar power to suggest an extension of time, and even though the adjudicator may have wider powers under clause 90.8 for dealing with the facts and the law.

One further qualification on the right of the adjudicator to extend the time period, save consent, can also be seen; that is, the 'nature of the dispute'. With regard to the nature of the dispute it seems out of place that this qualification exists when either party may submit 'any other matter' as a dispute in the first instance. There is also no guidance on how the nature of disputes should be classified. What will distinguish the nature of one dispute from another such that it becomes amenable to the grant of an extension of time is unclear. A case could be made, it seems, for the inclusion of exemplar reasons for refusal as in so many other sections of the ECC.[76] As to the apparent necessity for agreement of the parties to the extension of time, it is more common that extensions of time in arbitrations at least are by decision of the arbitrator alone.[77] It is unusual

---

[74] Clause 90.3 ECC CD. Cf clause 4.30 JCT NSC/C similarly providing for short time limits in which the adjudicator's decision has to be given.

[75] Clause 91.1 ECC.

[76] See e.g. clauses 21.2, 23.1, 26.3, 31.3. ECC.

[77] See e.g. article 23 Uncitral Arb Rules.

that agreement of the parties themselves to the extension would be needed.[78] The better course seems to rely upon their vesting of jurisdiction in the adjudicator at the outset and for all relevant purposes without the necessity to reconfirm those rights in specific instances.

An interesting point of interpretation arises under the unamended clause 91.1 that does not arise under the amended clause 90.9. Thus, the right to extend the 'four week periods in this clause' implies that the adjudicator has no power to extend the time frames in clause 90.1. That is, the between two- and four-week period after the notification of the dispute in the first instance either to the party 'and/or' the project manager for notification to the adjudicator; or the original four-week period in which the project manager must be notified once the contractor has become aware of the dispute. Both these time periods are not 'in this clause', that is, clause 91.1; only one of the time periods is a four-week time period in a strict sense, and neither presupposes the involvement of an adjudicator in the first instance. Thus, it appears that the time frames in the unamended clause 90 are strict and when they have been exceeded a reference to the adjudicator would not lie. Further, the adjudicator could also refuse to entertain a submission on the basis of a lack of jurisdiction. If the adjudicator were to entertain the dispute in this situation, then the adjudicator should address the question of jurisdiction at the outset and any participation by the project manager should clearly be stated to be without prejudice to rights to contest jurisdiction; hence a conditional appearance. This interpretation, while strict, also follows from the ECC objective that procedures are logically complete.[79]

The unamended clause 91 makes a major departure from the Consultation Document. In the Consultation Document the project manager provided the adjudicator with the information upon which the dispute was based. It can be quickly seen how this could lead to serious objections on the part of the contractor.[80] This would have been the wrong approach, to have given the project manager, a party adverse to the contractor as it were, the right of choosing, perhaps selectively in an egregious case, the information upon which the dispute should be determined. It would have been tantamount to a limitation on the adjudicator's jurisdiction as well as potentially leaving the project manager in a position to be influenced by the employer.

Pending and post-decision

The status quo is preserved under both the unamended and amended versions of the Second Edition pending the adjudicator's decision. Thus the parties should not use their dispute as an excuse to delay or stop work

---

[78] Cf the Arbitration Act 1979, section 1(4) which required consent, in one instance, for leave to appeal an arbitration award.

[79] The New Engineering Contract: Need For and Features, 15. Cf the language of clause 93.1 in even stricter terms: 'It is not referable to the *tribunal* unless the dissatisfied Party notifies his intention within four weeks'.

[80] Clause 90.2 ECC CD.

as: '[u]nless and until there is a settlement, the Parties[81] and the *Project Manager* proceed as if the ... matter were not disputed'.[82] This has been seen as advantageous. Under the unamended Second Edition the adjudicator will settle the dispute by notifying the parties and the project manager of the decision together with reasons within the time allowed by the contract.[83] The amendments to the Second Edition have altered this time frame, as section 108(2)(c) of the HGCRA provides the contract shall 'require the adjudicator to reach a decision within 28 days of referral or such longer period as is agreed by the parties after the dispute has arisen'. Hence the ECC could not have continued to permit a time frame earlier agreed between the parties and inserted in the Contract Data to override the statutory time. The intention of the drafters in this regard would be the same as their intention with regard to all of the amendments, namely that the Scheme for Construction Contracts (England and Wales) Regulations 1998 would not apply. 'The intention of the new clauses is to retain the principles of adjudication provisions in the ECC in managing disputes, and at the same time comply with the Act so that the fall-back "Scheme for Construction Contracts" does not apply'.[84] Section 2 of the Regulations stipulates that where a construction contract (as that term is defined and which would include the NEC in most applications) does not comply with the requirements of section 108(1) to (4) of the HGCRA, the adjudication provisions in part I of the Schedule to the Regulations apply. (It may be noted that in a recent survey respondents generally did not wish to see architects and engineers with any power to make final and binding decisions unless agreed between the parties after the dispute had arisen.[85]) Returning to Clause 90.2 by the insertion of this provision in the parties' agreement, the adjudicator, under the terms of engagement in the PSC, agrees to be bound by it indirectly and thus the time frame becomes an enforceable obligation *vis-à-vis* the adjudicator also. Clause 2 of the Form of Agreement in the PSC First Edition provides in part: 'The Adjudicator accepts this appointment and undertakes to carry out the Adjudicator's duties described in the *contract between the Parties*'.

The decision of the Adjudicator is final and binding unless and until revised by the tribunal under the unamended Second Edition.[86] The amended version of the equivalent clause provides the decision is binding

---

[81] Clause 11.2(1) ECC.

[82] Clause 90.2 unamended ECC. The amended Second Edition ECC similarly provides: 'Unless and until the Adjudicator has given his decision on the dispute, the Parties and the Project Manager proceed as if the action, failure to take action or other matters were not disputed'.

[83] Clause 90.2 ECC. CAPPER, PHILLIP N. The Adjudicator under NEC 2nd Edition: A New Approach to Disputes. *Engineering, Construction and Architectural Management*, 1995, **2**(4), 317.

[84] NEC/ECC/Y(UK)2/April 1998, 2.

[85] See STIPANOWICH, T.J. Dispute Avoidance and Resolution: Which Techniques Work Best? The Results of a Major Study. *Constructor*, January 1997, 26.

[86] Clause 90.2 ECC. Cf clause 4.30 JCT NSC/C setting out that the adjudicator's decisions were not binding on the Arbitrator.

until the dispute is finally determined by the tribunal or by agreement.[87] In general the restriction of the number of grounds upon which an expert could be challenged would serve as a significant means to reduce disputes.[88] It can be remarked that the latter provision appears to offer less finality than the earlier version on the quality of decision of the adjudicator. In part the explanation for this may be due to the omission from clause 90 of the right of the parties, given under section 108(3) of the HGCRA, to accept the decision of the adjudicator as finally determining the dispute. Previously there were issues surrounding the enforceability of adjudicators' decisions;[89] however, in a series of recent decisions the courts have unreservedly affirmed and thereby reinforced respect for them.[90]

Trend toward adjudication

Adjudication is the name given to a procedure where, by contract, a summary interim decision-making power in respect of disputes is vested in a third party individual (the 'adjudicator') who is usually not involved in the day-to-day performance or administration of the contract, and is neither an arbitrator nor connected with the state.[91]

The adjudication provisions in the ECC were originally part of a trend toward this form of dispute resolution in standard forms of contract.[92]

It is important in certain types of contracts, such as those for long-term construction projects, to try to ensure that the parties continue to perform their substantive obligations under the contract even after a dispute has arisen between them. Without provisions of this nature, the overall objectives of the contract can be jeopardised whilst the parties resort to litigation or arbitration to settle the dispute.[93]

---

[87] Clause 90.11 amended 2nd ECC.

[88] See UFF QC, JOHN. Control of Disputes within the Contract Framework. *Future Directions in Construction Law: Proceedings of the Fifth Annual Conference of the Centre of Construction Law and Management.* King's College, London, 1992, pp. 197–219.

[89] See *A Cameron Ltd* v. *John Mowlem & Co plc* (1990) 25 Con LR 11, 52 BLR 24, CA. See generally on adjudication COTTAM, GUY *Adjudication under the Scheme for Construction Contracts: Including Payment Provision.* Thomas Telford, London, 1998; GORDON, KATE *Adjudication in the Construction Industry.* FT Law & Tax, London, 1997; and HIBBERD, PETER R. and NEWMAN, PAUL. *Alternative Dispute Resolution.* Blackwells, London, 1996.

[90] See *Macob Civil Engineering Ltd* v. *Morrison Construction Ltd* (1999) 64 Con LR 1 per Dyson J; *Outwing Construction Ltd* v. *H Randell and Son Limited* (1999) 15 Const LJ 308 per Lloyd J; and *Rentokil Ailsa Environmental Ltd* v. *Eastend Civil Engineering Ltd* (1999) CILL 1506.

[91] McGRAW, MARK C., see n. 14 above, 332.

[92] SCHNEIDER, MICHAEL E. proposed a review certifier in Arbitration of Construction Disputes. *International Construction Law Review*, 1984, 319.

[93] HUNTER, MARTIN *et al. The Freshfields Guide to Arbitration and ADR Clauses in International Contracts.* Kluwer Law and Taxation Publishers, Deventer, 1993, p. 48.

While the BPF and ACE system had already introduced an adjudication mechanism, as Baden Hellard notes, the 'NEC has developed the principles and application still further'.[94] Illustrations from other forms such as JCT 81, NSC/C, DOM/1, and GC/Works/1[95] may be given. However, adjudication provisions can be seen in United Kingdom standard forms beginning with the 1976 Green Form of nominated subcontract used in conjunction with JCT 63 and shortly thereafter the Blue Form of domestic subcontract. The innovation was retained in the new forms of building subcontract replacing both the Green and Blue Forms, that is NSC/4, NSC/4a and DOM/1.[96] Even prior to the recent Construction Contracts legislation the adjudication mechanism could be found across the whole range of subcontract forms used with JCT main contract forms; that is, at the time of introduction DOM/2 (1981) for use with JCT 81, NAM/SC and IN/SC (1984) for use with IFC 84 and the JCT 87 Works Contract for use with JCT 87. Adjudication is also in the ACA Form of Building Agreement as an option, 1982, the BPF System, 1983, the ACA Form 1984 edition as an option, JCT 81, as an option from 1988 and GC/Works/1 3rd from 1989 and in certain non-JCT subcontracts such as GW/S subcontract for use with the old GC/Works/1 2nd (1985). Henry J. Brown and Arthur L. Marriott note that adjudication provisions (prior to the HGCRA) have varied from form to form but do share some common threads such as a third party neutral; disputes heard before completion; procedure is more summary, informal and inquisitorial than arbitration; interim binding quality of the decision unless or until set aside subsequently or varied by agreement; and rights to refer.[97] It is noteworthy that separate adjudication under JCT 80 was actually opposed by the architectural profession in a submission to Latham on the basis it was inconsistent with the duty of impartial contract administration that JCT 80 imposes upon architects.[98]

The provisions share some characteristics, for instance, the adjudicator fulfils a separate function from the contract administrator – whether a project manager, architect or engineer. The adjudicator's decisions are binding on the parties until challenged in arbitration or a court. In the ECC 'the decision is final and binding unless and until revised by the tribunal'.[99] The jurisdiction of and the procedures which are followed by the adjudicator are set out in the contract and as referred to above.[100] In summary, while the ECC helped lead the trend toward adjudication, in

[94] HELLARD, RON BADEN. *Project Partnering: Principle and Practice*. Thomas Telford, London, 1995, p. 106.
[95] See JCT 81 clauses 4.30–4.37 NSC/C, clause 24 DOM/1 and clause 59 GC/Works/1 3rd.
[96] See McGRAW, MARK C., n. 14 above, 334.
[97] BROWN, HENRY J. and MARRIOTT, ARTHUR L. *ADR Principles and Practice*. Sweet & Maxwell, London, 1993, pp. 84–85.
[98] *Trust and Money*, 32. See also on RIBA's opposition to adjudication, KLEIN, RUDI. Is JCT up to the Job?, 29 March 1996, 36.
[99] Clause 90.2 ECC.
[100] See discussion clause 90 and the adjudication table.

England and Wales today it is now a contractual right under the HGCRA.[101]

Combining procedures

It has been noted that the ECC assumes subcontracting to be the norm and thus full provision is made for addressing main contract and subcontract disputes together. Clause 91.2 in the unamended Second Edition provides:

> If a matter disputed under or in connection with a subcontract is also a matter disputed under or in connection with this contract, the *Contractor* may submit the subcontract dispute to the *Adjudicator* at the same time as the main contract submission. The *Adjudicator* then settles the two disputes together and references to the Parties for the purposes of the dispute are interpreted as including the Subcontractor.

In the amended Second Edition version of this clause the term 'settles' is replaced with the phrase 'gives his decision on'. This is an unusual amendment and may suggest less confidence in the adjudicator's ability to resolve disputes. The same amendment is made in clause 92.1. In clause 92.2 'settle' is replaced with 'decide on'; while in clause 92.2 'had not been settled' is replaced with 'a decision had not been given'.

In England the courts have the power to consolidate actions heard in court based upon similar facts or between the same parties. However, until recently this power did not extend generally to arbitrations. Willingness today to consolidate multiparty disputes, or in 'combining procedures',[102] according to contractual provisions runs contrary to this past judicial reluctance. It is a progressive step that reinforces consensualism and party autonomy.[103]

Clause 91.2 is equally as broad as the categories of actions that are referable under clause 90.1. To reach this conclusion, 'matter' in clause 91.2 should be construed as including actions and inactions of the project manager. This follows from the interpretation of 'actions' and 'inactions' in clause 90.1 as matters, and given that in the first column, third row of the adjudication table, it is 'Any *other* matter' that is used as a sweep-up phrase (emphasis added). The drafting of clause 91.2 and the operative clause 'disputed under or in connection with' is identical to that in clause

---

[101] 'A party to a construction contract has a right to refer a dispute arising under the contract for adjudication under a procedure complying with this section': section 108(1) HGCRA.

[102] See clause 91 of the amended 2nd ECC.

[103] See DORE, ISAAK I. *Theory and Practice of Multiparty Commercial Arbitration.* Graham & Trotman, London; Martinus Nijhoff, Dordrecht, 1990, pp. 2–3 for some reasons behind the judicial reluctance. See also DEVITT, T. Multiparty Controversies in International Construction Arbitrations. *International Lawyer*, 1983, **17**, 669 on the civil law position. Cf the strong critique of the unamended Second Edition provisions on the basis of privity of contract by CORNES. The Second Edition of the New Engineering Contract. *International Construction Law Review*, 1996, 111–114.

90.1. The intention of the drafters in using identical words is to address all matters that can be expressed similarly.[104] Hence, in determining which matters arise under or in connection with the subcontract and the main contract, precise symmetry need not be required. This has the effect of broadening the types of disputes that can be heard together and overcoming some limitations that have existed in this regard in the past. Those cases where subcontractors have not been able to have similar disputes determined at the same time as they arose and heard in relation to the main contract will be less likely to arise in any event under the ECC given the bias toward the use of the ECSC or other compatible conditions. The provisions in the clause should also reduce the incentive to litigate where there are more than two parties to the dispute and alleviate the consequent risk of inconsistent findings made by different forums. By reducing the risk of inconsistent findings one of the principal grounds on which courts often refuse to stay proceedings in breach of an arbitration agreement is also removed. The wording is also important in terms of the coherence of the contract documents. That is, because a very large number of disputes are not between the employer and the contractor but between others in the contractual chain or even other performance relationships, a contract system such as the NEC which is fully interlocked and anticipates this should be more effective.[105]

Adjudicator

Under the unamended Second Edition the adjudicator gives a decision on the dispute as an independent adjudicator and *not* as an arbitrator.[106] The express exclusion of the adjudicator serving as an arbitrator likely precludes any settlement by the adjudicator being enforced as an arbitration award.[107] This conclusion is also reinforced by the wording of the clause which provides: 'His decision is enforceable as a matter of contractual obligation between the Parties and not as an arbitral award'.[108] Therefore, any failure to respect the decision is a breach of contract. Both the importance and necessity of the need for a contractual obligation to obey the decision of the adjudicator has been pointed out.[109] On a theoretical level this gives rise to a paradox inherent in legal

---

[104] The New Engineering Contract: Need For and Features, Consultation Document, 15.

[105] For example under clause 92.1 ECC. See also SWEET, JUSTIN. Judging Contracts: Some Reflections on the Third International Construction Law Conference. *International Construction Law Review*, 1994, 425.

[106] Clause 92.1 amended 2nd ECC. Under the unamended Second Edition version 'settle' stands in place of the phrase 'gives his decision on'.

[107] See *A Cameron Ltd* v. *John Mowlem & Co plc* (1990) 52 BLR 24, CA; see generally Arbitration Act 1950 section 26. See for a critique on this issue under the HGCRA, WINTER, J.B. Enforcement of Adjudicator's Awards. *Construction Law*, 1997, **8**(4), 161.

[108] Clause 92.1 ECC.

[109] By WALKER QC, RONALD and SPEAIGHT QC, ANTHONY. Adjudication: Can Contracts Be Drafted so as to Stop Lawyers Wrecking It: A paper given at a meeting of the Society of Construction Law in London on 11 March 1997.

enforcement of contractual remedies. That is, according to Scott, 'it is both a threat and a temptation [and as] ... a result any enforcement standard that sufficiently deters evasion by one party will inevitably invite evasion by the other'.[110] The key, in Scott's analysis, is to seek *flexible* performance standards, whether common law or contractual; for example, as in the case of 'substantial' performance. However, while the doctrine reduces opportunistic claims by removing opportunities by one party to exploit inadvertent breaches, it presents a dilemma in that by reducing the clarity of the performance standard opportunities for evasion of the risk bearer are increased.[111] He restates his thesis in this way:

> The tension between the tough standards needed for effective enforcement of the initial distribution of risks, and the flexible enforcement necessary to encourage cooperative adjustment is inherent and inevitable in the legal regulation of long-term contracts ... If legal rules are to facilitate a cooperative equilibrium, they must strike a balance between the poles of tough and flexible enforcement of contractual obligations. Where the legal doctrines are formulated in binary terms – perform in full or excuse entirely – such a balance may only be achievable by trading off a flexible general rule with a tough enforcement policy in individual cases ... Contractual relationships require both well-defined legal rules and an array of extra-legal mechanisms in order to stabilize patterns of reciprocal cooperation.[112]

In the case of the ECC the same flexibility is introduced with precisely the same term as in Scott's example. Thus, the term 'substantial' or 'substantially' used in seven of the reasons for termination is much better understood against the background of Scott's thesis. Justin Sweet writes the 'common law substantial performance doctrine, whilst usually thought of as a doctrine to prevent forfeiture and unjust enrichment, can be considered as an implied term'.[113]

The amended version of the Second Edition re-words the obligation of the adjudicator to act independently to comply with the HGCRA and changes its legal content as a result. Thus, under clause 90.8 the adjudicator acts impartially[114] and may take the initiative in ascertaining the facts and the law. It may be thought that bestowing some role involving initiative upon the adjudicator suggests more 'civilian' than 'common law' traditions and that it might somehow be inappropriate in this regard. However, if a comparison of the two traditions were

---

[110] SCOTT, ROBERT E. 51 (ns. omitted).
[111] *Ibid.*, 94, n. 118.
[112] *Ibid.*
[113] SWEET, JUSTIN. Planning for Delays in American Complex Long-Term Construction Contracts: Correcting Bad Law, Removing Ambiguities or Exercising Bargaining Power? In *Complex Long-Term Contract Structures* (ed. NICHLISCH), p. 329.
[114] See section 108(2)(e) HGCRA.

undertaken it would be seen that they do indeed share a great deal in common.[115] The Latham Report endorsed the trend toward not only impartial adjudicators but also impartial referees and experts.[116] A similar duty to act impartially is also imposed on the arbitrator under section 33 of the Arbitration Act 1996. The Arbitration Act 1996 came into force on 30 January 1997 and applies to all arbitral proceedings commenced on or after 31 January 1997 no matter when the agreement was made. Independence in the unamended version suggests no relationship with the parties but impartiality does not. In the absence of any supplementary obligation to be independent in the AC the contractor may now need to pay additional attention to this issue and the employer's nomination of an adjudicator. The employer will normally appoint the adjudicator in the first instance and name the adjudicator in part one of the Contract Data. Some criticism has been made of leaving the decision to the employer rather than mutually at the outset.[117] The capacity of the arbitrator to take the initiative in ascertaining the facts and the law would appear to extend to whether to adopt an adversarial or inquisitorial approach, the mode and presentation of the case and defence and the types of procedure and rules of evidence to be followed.[118] It may amount to a *carte blanche* for the adjudicator to determine these issues subject only to such controls as would exist at common law.

The adjudicator's powers include reviewing and revising any action or inaction of the project manager or supervisor.[119] A.A. Kwakye sees this as advantageous: '[t]he increased powers of an adjudicator limits the use of arbitrators in the solution of contractual disputes and this encourages parties to settle their commercial disputes amicably'.[120] The choice of this language, one assumes, was intentional. It is the language of arbitration provisions in various standard forms regarding the power of the arbitrator to review and revise certificates; e.g. clauses 41.4 of the JCT 80 and 67.3(b) of the FIDIC 4th 'open up, review and revise'. It has been observed that clause 67 of the FIDIC conditions has proved problematic

---

[115] See generally LAWSON, F.H. *A Common Law Lawyer Looks at the Civil Law.* University of Michigan Law School, Ann Arbor, 1953; MERRYMAN, J.H. *The Civil Law Tradition.* Standford University Press, Stanford, 1969; GORLA, GINO and MOCCIA, LUIGI. A 'Revisiting' of the Comparison between 'Continental Law' and 'English Law' (16th–19th Century). *Journal of Legal History*, 1981, **2**, 143–156; DOLINGER, JACOB. A Civil Law Lawyer Looks at a Common Law Lawyer's Views on Civil Law: John Henry Merryman's 'The Civil Law Tradition'. *Brooklyn Journal of International Law*, 1991, **17**, 557.

[116] Latham Report, paragraph 5.18(11), 37.

[117] COTTAM, GUY 'An employer-appointed adjudicator is hardly likely to strike confidence into the heart of the contractor': see n. 44 above, 13.

[118] JOYCE, RAYMOND. *A Commentary on Construction Contracts, Part II of Housing Grants, Construction and Regeneration Act 1996.* Thomas Telford, London, 1996, p. 32.

[119] Clause 92.1 ECC.

[120] KWAKYE, A.A. *Construction Project Administration in Practice.* Addison Wesley Longman, Harlock; CIOB, Ascot, 1997, p. 105.

based upon a majority of ICC references under those conditions raising matters of compliance with that clause.[121] The exercise of this power by arbitrators is recognized; however, it has been problematic until recently with the courts themselves holding that they have not had the power to substitute their discretion for the arbitrator's.[122] While there has been this hesitancy on the part of the courts in the past to intervene, more recent decisions have demonstrated a new willingness to do so particularly in cases of unfairness.[123] In the context of an adjudicator's decision under the ECC any lacunae comparable to that under which courts have laboured have been overcome at least insofar as the tribunal is concerned.

Thus the tribunal's powers expressly *include* the power to review and revise any decision of the adjudicator. It is also significant that in both instances the term used is 'include' which thus leaves the availability of other remedies open. This confirms that other powers exist and that this controversy was important enough to address with explicit language. Beyond the adjudication and tribunal the parties could agree to grant the court the same powers conferred on the adjudicator or tribunal including the power to review and revise actions or inactions of the project manager or supervisor.[124]

It has been noted that the powers of the Adjudicator and the tribunal include the power to review and revise any action or inaction of the project manager or supervisor related to the dispute.[125] It may be asked whether this wording excludes the right to review and revise disputes that fall into the third category of dispute, namely those regarding 'any other matter'. It is submitted that it does not and that this power is illustrative only of a wider range of powers which the adjudicator and tribunal exercise. A court, for instance, has power to confirm, vary or set aside, or remit an award.[126] Notwithstanding the absence of inherent jurisdiction in the adjudicator and the tribunal when compared to the courts it seems reasonable that one does not seek to imply limitations which are not

[121] See UFF, JOHN and JEFFORD, NERYS, see n. 55 above, 130, n. 38.

[122] *Northern Regional Health Authority* v. *Derek Crouch Construction Co Ltd* [1984] QB 644, [1982] 2 All ER 175, CA; *Ashville Investments Ltd* v. *Elmer Contractors Ltd* [1989] QB 488 at 495, [1988] 2 All ER 577 at 582, CA. Cf *Partington & Son (Builders) Ltd* v. *Tameside Metropolitan Borough Council* (1985) 32 BLR 150. See now *Beaufort Developments (NI) Ltd* v. *Gilbert-Ash (NI) Ltd* (1998) 88 BLR 1 (HL) overruling the *Crouch* case.

[123] Four cases may be noted: *University of Reading* v. *Miller Construction Ltd and Sharp* (1995) 75 BLR 91 (OR); *Balfour Beatty Civil Engineering Ltd* v. *Docklands Light Railway Ltd* (1996) 78 BLR 42; (1996) 12 Const LJ 261 (CA); *John Barker Construction Ltd* v. *London Portman Hotel Ltd* (1996) 12 Const LJ 277 (OR); and *Tarmac Construction Ltd* v. *Esso Petroleum Ltd* (1996) 51 Con LR 187, commented on by McINNIS, J.A. Recent Developments in Arbitration and Construction. *Law Lectures for Practitioners*. Hong Kong Law Journal, Hong Kong, 1997, p. 84.

[124] For example, under Supreme Court Act 1981, section 43A added by amendment through the Courts and Legal Services Act 1990, section 100 in the United Kingdom.

[125] Clauses 92.1 and 93.2 ECC.

[126] For example, under the Arbitration Act 1979, section 1.

present. The broadening of their jurisdiction is given further impetus with wording that the respective action or inaction need only be 'related to the dispute'. Hence it need not concern the dispute directly.[127] The only express limitation on this under the unamended Second Edition is that which exists in the first instance; namely the dispute arises under or in connection with the contract. It has been suggested that the Second Edition amendments adding the phrase 'any dispute arising under or in connection with this contract' rendered the references to actions and inactions 'unnecessary'.[128] If accepted, the deletion of this phrase in the amended Second Edition reaffirms leaving in the categories of disputes.

In the absence of agreed immunity an adjudicator can be sued for negligence.[129] The absence of immunity for adjudicators which arbitrators[130] have generally has resulted in the inclusion of a specific clause on immunity in the HGCRA, and in turn in the amendments to the Second Edition. Thus, 'The *Adjudicator* is not liable for anything done or omitted in the discharge or purported discharge of his functions as adjudicator unless the act or omission is in bad faith and any employee or agent of the *Adjudicator* is similarly protected from liability'.[131] The standard of bad faith that has been set will thus allow considerable latitude for errors or omissions on the part of the adjudicator. However, challenges to adjudicators' decisions have been subject to a fairly high standard in any event.[132] The extension of the protection to employees or agents of the adjudicators appears to be a greater change than that to the standard itself.

Review by the tribunal

The second tier of dispute resolution under the Second Edition and the third tier of dispute resolution under the amended Second Edition is review by the tribunal. This is a somewhat novel provision in that the precise nature of the 'tribunal' is left to be decided by the parties. In some ways the clause thus anticipates a move away from arbitration as the norm for a final tier of dispute resolution by parties to construction contracts. Several cases lately illustrate a tendency to prefer litigation or the courts as the final tier for dispute resolution over arbitration. Thus arbitration

---

[127]   One analogy could be that of a magistrate who has the power to convict upon an offence which is not before him or her but which nevertheless appears to have been committed on the evidence!

[128]   CORNES, see n. 103 above, 114.

[129]   See *Arenson* v. *Casson Beckman Rutley & Co* [1977] ACC 405, [1975] 3 All ER 901, HL, involving an expert.

[130]   See generally *The Immunity of Arbitrators* (ed. LEW, JULIAN D.M.). Lloyd's of London Press, London, 1990.

[131]   Clause 90.12 amended 2nd ECC.

[132]   See generally *Dixon's Group plc* v. *Jan Andrew Murray-Oboynski* (1998) 86 BLR 16; *Jones* v. *Sherwood Computer Services plc* [1992] 2 All ER 170, [1992] 1 WLR 277, CA; *Campbell* v. *Edwards* [1976] 1 All ER 785, [1976] 1 WLR 403; *Nikko Hotel (UK) Ltd* v. *MEPC* (1991) 28 EG 86; and *Cape Durasteel Ltd* v. *Rosser and Russell Building Services Ltd* (1996) 46 Con LR 75.

clauses are at times being deleted from standard forms of contract.[133] The parties may thus choose the courts, arbitration, or some third option such as a dispute review panel. The release of amendment 18 to JCT 80 (prior to the consolidated release in JCT 98) providing an optional litigation clause and the choice of the court as the review tribunal under the NEC will have been some impetus by the decision of the House of Lords in *Beaufort Developments (NI) Ltd* v. *Gilbert-Ash (NI) Ltd* overruling *Northern Regional Health Authority* v. *Derek Crouch Construction Co Ltd.*[134] The choice is made by the parties and inserted in the Contract Data. In this regard the '*tribunal*' is an identified term. It may also be noted that an optional statement in part of the Contract Data allows the parties to specify the arbitration procedure if the tribunal is arbitration. Even if the choice were not arbitration the parties may still wish to use an amended optional statement to specify any procedure they wish to govern. Thus while arbitration has been left open as a strong possibility for the choice of tribunal it need not be the chosen mode for review.

However, according to Ian R. Macneil, in 'terms of arbitration, its very existence is a practical recognition of relational contract'.[135] This affords a strong reason for the choice of arbitration as the review tribunal. The drafters recommend in no circumstances should an individual be named.[136] Although no reasons are given for this advice perhaps voluntary respect for the tribunal decision would decrease if it were an appeal from a decision of one individual only to another individual, particularly if the decisions were inconsistent.

Either party may invoke the tribunal procedure. Consideration by the adjudicator of the matter would appear to be a condition precedent to invoking the procedure although the adjudicator need not have given a decision. Thus, in either case where the adjudicator has given a decision, or simply failed to do so, within the time provided under the contract, a party can proceed to the tribunal.[137] It is interesting that the procedures contemplate 'dissatisfaction' on the part of the referring party, when the unamended clause 90 made no reference to dissatisfaction. However,

---

[133] See e.g. *Balfour Beatty Civil Engineering Ltd* v. *Docklands Light Railway Ltd* (1996) 78 BLR 42 where clause 66 ICE 5th was deleted; *Tarmac Construction Ltd* v. *Esso Petroleum Co Ltd* (1996) 51 Con LR 187 again under the ICE 5th where clause 66 was deleted and in its place substituted 'to require that the matter be determined by litigation'; and in *John Barker Construction Ltd* v. *London Portman Hotel Ltd* (1996) 12 Const LJ 277 (OR) arising under JCT 80 clause 41 was deleted and replaced by 'the proper law of the Agreement shall be English law and the English Courts shall have jurisdiction'.

[134] *Beaufort Developments (NI) Ltd* v. *Gilbert-Ash (NI) Ltd* (1998) CILL 1386; *Northern Regional Health Authority* v. *Derek Crouch Construction Co Ltd* [1984] QB 644, [1984] 2 All ER 175, CA.

[135] MACNEIL, IAN R. Barriers to the Idea of Relational Change. *Complex Long-Term Contract Structures*, (ed. NICHLISCH), p. 46.

[136] Guidance notes NEC on clause 93.1 ECC, 78.

[137] See clause 93.1 ECC.

following the amendments to clause 90, it is a 'notice of dissatisfaction' that begins the first tier of the dispute resolution. As such, in strict terms, clause 93.1 now deals with *continuing* dissatisfaction although it is not expressed in these terms. Once the condition precedent is satisfied a party would notify the intention to refer the disputed matter to the tribunal. A time bar operates to preclude the party intending to refer the matter unless the notification is made within four weeks of the adjudicator's decision, or any other time agreed by the parties for such notification and whichever period is earlier.[138] The earlier period would be that agreed by the parties as the '*period for reply*' to a communication and inserted in part one of the Contract Data. This follows from the characterization of the notification as a communication within the meaning of clause 13. The tribunal proceedings will not start either before completion of the whole of the works or termination. The termination referred to is that following under clause 94. This provision mimes those in other standard forms that preclude any arbitration until completion of the works.[139]

It has been stated above that consideration by the adjudicator of the matter would appear to be a condition precedent to invoking the procedure. Given that clause 93 operates as a *de facto* arbitration clause the question this raises is whether it will also operate to preclude any attempt by a party to circumvent the adjudicator's jurisdiction and proceed direct to the tribunal or, if not the tribunal, direct to the court.

This question has most often arisen in arbitration cases in relation to applications for stays of proceedings and has been an exceedingly difficult area in the arbitration jurisprudence. While it cannot be stated with certainty how a court will thus decide the question it is submitted that the trend is to give greater weight to the parties' choice of forum and the order in which they appear to have elected to proceed to those fora. Lord Mustill in *Channel Tunnel Group Ltd* v. *Balfour Beatty Construction Ltd* states:

> I would endorse the powerful warnings against encroachment on the parties' agreement to have their commercial differences decided by their chosen tribunals, and on the international policy exemplified by the English legislation that this consent should be honoured by the courts given by Parker LJ in *Home and Overseas Insurance Co Ltd* v. *Mentor Insurance Co (UK) Ltd* and Saville J in *Hayter* v. *Nelson* ...'.[140]

---

[138] See clause 93.1 ECC.

[139] See e.g. clause 41.3 JCT 80. However, under the JCT 80 provision, only certain decisions are so limited, and with reference to practical completion, or termination, as well as alleged termination or abandonment.

[140] Lord Mustill in *Channel Tunnel Group Ltd* v. *Balfour Beatty Construction Ltd* [1993] AC 334 at 356, [1993] 1 All ER 664 at 681, HL; and referring to Parker LJ in *Home and Overseas Insurance Co Ltd* v. *Mentor Insurance Co (UK) Ltd* and Saville J in *Hayter* v. *Nelson* [1990] 2 Lloyd's Rep 295.

Saville J's approach finds expression in the Arbitration Act 1996, section 9 reinforcing party choice and which was upheld in one of the earliest decisions to consider it.[141]

The tribunal is essentially put forward as the final arbiter of the parties' dispute. Thus, the tribunal 'settles' the dispute referred to it. This settlement power of the tribunal has been underscored with the recent amendments to clauses 90, 91 and 92, which substituted prior references to 'settle' with the term 'decide'. Once again, the former suggests a less conclusive or final outcome than the latter. The unamended version of clause 9 uses both the terms 'decision' and 'settles' and appears to use them equivalently. While it was open to the drafters in making amendments to clause 9 to prefer the term 'settlement' in lieu of 'decision', the fact that they did not and left only the original use of the term in the clause dealing with review by the tribunal may reinforce this interpretation that 'settle' implies a more definitive outcome than 'decide'. The powers of the tribunal are exceedingly broad and extend to reviewing and revising any decision of the adjudicator and any action or inaction of the project manager or the supervisor related to the dispute.[142] While broad, the necessity on this wording for it still to 'relate to the dispute' serves as a constraint. In practice, as in arbitral or judicial proceedings in general, the parties must therefore be cognizant of this limitation and the importance of the careful pleading or presentation of one's case to avoid it being unintentionally circumscribed. Parties are not limited, in contrast to the adjudication proceedings, to the information that was put before the adjudicator. Further, the parties are not limited for that matter to evidence or argument put to the adjudicator.[143]

The effect of this wording is to provide the fullest basis upon which the tribunal may come to its decision. It leaves it open to the tribunal to admit late information etc. that was either not available or not permitted to be introduced before the adjudicator. It overcomes, from an evidentiary and arguably procedural point of view, the limitations that might otherwise exist to the admission of such information if it were before a court. However, while this may be the intent, if the parties have chosen a court as their tribunal it would be unlikely that a court would readily override what it sees as evidentiary or procedural protection or requirements solely on the basis of this clause. This too may be a factor, therefore, for the parties in deciding upon the choice of tribunal.

Termination

The provisions on termination are contained in clauses 94 to 97 of the ECC. As with so many topics in the ECC the provisions both resemble and do not resemble exemplars from other forms of contract.[144] The ECC

---

[141] See *Halki Shipping Corpn* v. *Sopex Oils Ltd* [1997] 3 All ER 833 per Clarke J.

[142] Clause 93.2 ECC.

[143] Clause 93.2 ECC.

[144] Cf clause 27 determination by employer, clause 28 determination by contractor, and clause 28A determination by employer or contractor under JCT 80 and JCT 81; clause 69.1 default of employer FIDIC 4th; and clause 63.1 ICE 6th.

differs in how the provisions are presented and ordered. At the outset
there is no general statement of which parties have a right to terminate the
contract; rather the question of procedure introduces the subject. Thus
clause 94.1 begins: 'If either Party wishes to terminate, he notifies the
Project Manager giving details of his reason for terminating. The *Project
Manager* issues a termination certificate promptly if the reason complies
with this contract'. Thus one begins with what are in essence the
'procedures *for* termination', which, in most cases, only become operative
after a warning or advance notice of the alleged reason has been given and
should be contrasted with the 'procedures on termination' in clause 96. A
general statement of each Party's rights to terminate the contract follows
this, but in clause 94.2. It seems, notwithstanding the flow charting of the
termination procedures, that more attention could have been paid to the
logical order in which topics are addressed: setting out first, the existence
of the right, and secondly, the timing and manner in which it is exercised.
The drafting of clause 94 reverses this and is unexplained. Whether a right
to prior notice of an event of default exists varies under different standard
forms. Thus under clause 63.1 of the FIDIC 4th only a single notice of
termination is stipulated, while under clause 27 of the JCT 80 a double
notice requirement is imposed: notice of the default, a grace period to
remedy the default, and subsequent notice of termination.

Clause 94 also provides a form of introduction to the issues that are
addressed in subsequent clauses and the order in which they arise. The
clauses exhibit symmetry in this regard, however. Hence notice, reasons,
procedures and payment in clauses 94.1, 94.2, 94.3 and 94.4 respectively
are followed by reasons, procedures and payment in clauses 95, 96 and 97
respectively. Lastly, clause 95 introduces the convention of a letter suffix
'R' and number to abbreviate listed reasons; 21 listed reasons are
abbreviated as R1 to R21. The convention is followed through with letter
prefixes and numbers for procedures for termination, P1 to P4, in clause
96, and letter prefixes and numbers for any amount due, A1 to A5, in
clause 97.

Typically, in construction contracts, provisions stipulate the grounds
upon which a right to termination arises, the procedure for termination
and the effects of termination upon the rights and obligations of the
parties, although it is unusual to enable both employer and contractor to
bring their contractual obligations to an end simply upon notice.[145] The
ECC provisions conform to this model. The grounds or reasons for
termination are both summarized in a 'Termination Table' and listed in
full.[146] The procedures for and on termination are set out in clauses 94 to
96, and the effects are noted in various clauses.[147] The clauses are
discussed in turn below.

---

[145] The JCT/MW form uses the heading 'Break provisions – Employer or Contractor' in
       section 8 although this is exceptional.
[146] Clauses 94.2 and 95 respectively ECC.
[147] Clauses 35 and 97 ECC.

The provisions on termination do not address the difficult relationship that exists between the parties' rights of determination under the contract and their rights of repudiation at common law.[148] Thus it is unclear whether a breach of contract which constitutes a reason for termination under the contract, *viz.* R1 to R21, will also amount to a repudiatory breach of the contract; and, whether it excludes the right of either party to end the contract by accepting a repudiatory breach of contract by the other.

The correct answer to the latter question at least may turn upon whether the parties have made some provision to the contrary;[149] and, that answer may be different for the employer and the contractor. There is no limitation on the reasons for which the employer may determine the contract;[150] conversely, the contractor's right to determine is 'only for a reason identified in the Termination Table'. The question this difference raises is whether the limitation on the contractor's rights operates to exclude the contractor's normal right to accept any repudiation of the contract by the employer and thus to end the contract in this way. While a view may be taken of the result in law, the better course would have been for the drafters to have expressly ruled in or out the contractor's rights at common law in this instance. The relationship between express contractual rights and common law rights was considered in *Lockland Builders Ltd* v. *Rickwood*.[151] Until *Lockland* was decided it was generally thought that express contractual rights of termination did not limit common law rights of termination unless there was a provision to the contrary, for instance under *Architectural Installation Servies Ltd* v. *James Gibbons Windows Ltd*.[152] However, that view has been changed with the *Lockland* decision and, as a result, it is more likely today than before under the common law that contractual procedures will be viewed exclusively in matters of termination.[153]

In more general terms either party to a contract may bring it to an end when one party commits a repudiatory breach and the other party elects to accept the repudiation.[154] Various examples of repudiatory breaches in general include: a breach of a term of the contract which the parties have expressly or impliedly agreed to be a condition of the contract;[155] a

---

[148] See generally KEATING QC, DONALD. Employer's Remedy for Delay: Termination. In *The Liability of Contractors* (ed. LLOYD), pp. 57–70 who sets out the common law position and under JCT 80, ICE 5th and GC/Works/1.

[149] See *Gilbert Ash (Northern) Ltd* v. *Modern Engineering (Bristol) Ltd* [1974] AC 689, [1973] 3 All ER 195, HL; *Architectural Installation Services Ltd* v. *James Gibbons Windows Ltd* (1989) 46 BLR 91 at 100, 16 Con LR 68 at 73.

[150] Clause 94.2 ECC: 'The *Employer* may terminate for any reason'.

[151] *Lockland Builders Ltd* v. *Rickwood* (1995) 77 BLR 38, 46 Con LR 92, CA.

[152] *Architectural Installation Servies Ltd* v. *James Gibbons Windows Ltd* (1989) 46 BLR 91, 16 Con LR 68.

[153] See editor's comments, (1995) 77 BLR 38 at 40.

[154] *Heyman* v. *Darwins Ltd* [1942] AC 356, [1942] 1 All ER 337, HL.

[155] *Suisse Atlantique Société d'Armement Maritime SA* v. *NV Rotterdamsche Kolen Centrale NV* [1967] 1 AC 361, [1966] 2 All ER 61, HL. See Diplock LJ in *Hong Kong*

fundamental breach of the contract by one party which effectively deprives the other party of the whole benefit of the contract;[156] or total refusal by one party to perform or continue to perform their obligations under the contract.[157] Contractual termination provisions do not normally limit the right to determine at common law for fundamental breach.[158]

The classification of a contractual term as either a condition or a warranty has important consequences with regard to remedies. Traditionally, a warranty is seen as a subsidiary or minor term of a contract, the breach of which entitles the other party to damages only without any additional right to repudiate the contract. In contrast, a breach of condition entitles the party not in breach either to terminate performance of the contract and recover damages for losses suffered as a result of the other parties' breach, or to affirm the contract and recover damages for the breach. Although the classification of contractual terms is a matter of some academic interest, with occasional differences of opinion, for present purposes the traditional classification will be adhered to.

Thus, from the employer's perspective, if the contractor wholly abandons the works the contractor will have committed a repudiatory breach.[159] It is unlikely that delay without more would amount to a repudiatory breach as the contract contemplates delays in completion.[160] However, this may only be true up to a point; for instance that point when delay to the works becomes so great that the employer is forced to take over the works.[161]

A similar analysis may be made with regard to defects in the works. Thus, as express provision may be made for low performance damages[162] in contracts amenable to such an assessment, a number of defects or measurable standard of defective work may be excluded from those breaches, which would necessarily amount to repudiation. This analysis accords with the general law where the presence of defects or omissions without more does not amount to a repudiatory breach.[163]

Fir Shipping Co Ltd v. *Kawasaki Kisen Kaisha Ltd* [1962] 2 QB 26, [1962] 1 All ER 474, CA; *Bovis Homes Ltd* v. *Oakcliff Investment Corpn* (unreported, 30 March 1994, Ch D).

[156] *Photo Production Ltd* v. *Securicor Transport Ltd* [1980] AC 827 at 849, [1980] 1 All ER 556 at 566, HL, per Lord Diplock.

[157] *Freeth* v. *Burr* (1874) LR 9 CP 208 at 214; *Mersey Steel and Iron Co* v. *Naylor Benzon & Co* (1884) 9 App Cas 434, HL.

[158] See *Lubenham Fidelities and Investments Co Ltd* v. *South Pembrokeshire District Council* (1986) 33 BLR 39, 6 Con LR 85, CA; *J M Hill & Sons Ltd* v. *London Borough of Camden* (1980) 18 BLR 31, CA but cf *Lockland Builders* case and discussion above also.

[159] *Marshall* v. *Mackintosh* (1898) 78 LT 750.

[160] For example, clause R1 ECC on delay damages.

[161] Under clause 35 ECC.

[162] Clause S1 ECC

[163] *Hoenig* v. *Isaacs* [1952] 2 All ER 176, CA; cf *Bolton* v. *Mahadeva* [1972] 2 All ER 1322, [1972] 1 WLR 1009, CA.

Three matters may take one outside this analysis. First, the omission of the relevant low performance (or delay) damages clause from the parties' agreement; secondly, a breach which amounts to a substantial failure on the part of the contractor to comply with the contractor's obligations;[164] and thirdly, the nature and seriousness of the defects may confirm that the contractor either will not or cannot perform obligations under the contract.[165] Examining breaches from the contractor's perspective, if the employer wrongfully evicts the contractor from the site, renders completion impossible,[166] or issues a deliberate and unjustified instruction not to complete[167] the works, repudiatory breaches of contract arise.

The ECC makes no distinction between terms and whether they are either conditions or warranties. It is difficult to say which if any of the terms in the ECC may constitute conditions in the strict sense and which would entitle termination without more. It is not unlike other forms, which adopt a similar approach to contractual terms. Any characterization, which could be said to be given by the parties, is not conclusive of the true nature of a term in any case,[168] and the proper classification of the term is a matter of interpretation for the court.

The time frames for correcting a breach in the ECC also detract from making a finding that any given term has the status of a condition. Many of the most serious breaches may be remedied within a period of four weeks after notification.[169] In the case of some breaches, which do not allow the contractor a notice or grace period to rectify the situation, they may be either beyond the contractor's control or would operate as a matter of law to release the contractor from his or her obligations without a notice period.[170]

Returning to the actual wording of clause 94.1, if either party wishes to terminate the contract then the project manager must be notified and given details of the reason for terminating. The matter of notification is expressly governed and must comply with clause 13. The clause 13 requirements are minimal. While the court will construe these requirements strictly,[171] beyond them it will not seek to impose additional formal requirements provided the intention to determine the contract is

---

[164] Clause 95.2 ECC.

[165] See *Sutcliffe* v. *Chippendale & Edmonson* (1971) 18 BLR 149 at 161.

[166] *Roberts* v. *Bury Improvement Comrs* (1870) LR 5 CP 310, Ex Ch; *Felton* v. *Wharrie* (1906) 2 *Hudson's BC*, 4th edn. 398, CA.

[167] *Cort* v. *Ambergate, Nottingham and Boston and Eastern Junction Rly Co* (1851) 17 QB 127; *Carr* v. *J A Berriman Pty Ltd* (1953) 27 ALJ 273.

[168] *L Schuler AG* v. *Wickman Machine Tool Sales Ltd* [1974] AC 235, [1973] 2 All ER 39, HL.

[169] See e.g. clause 95.2 ECC. Cf the seven day notice period to terminate the contractor under clause 63(1) ICE 6th. However, the seven-day notice period may be extended to remedy the default.

[170] See e.g. clause 95.5 ECC.

[171] *Roberts* v. *Bury Improvement Comrs* (1870) LR 5 CP 310, Ex Ch.

manifest.[172] In fact, the courts have actually been lax in validating notices which for some reason infringed the contractual requirements.[173] It must also comply with any requirement for a warning or advance notice in the contract. These terms are not used in the ECC but a reading of its provisions indicates that warnings or notices in advance of termination are required in numerous cases. The notice period is often four weeks, e.g. clause 95.2, 95.3; or thirteen weeks, clauses 95.4, 95.6 but may be absent in limited cases, e.g. clause 95.5. The terms of any advance notice must be explicit in regard to the breach[174] and the termination certificate issued on taking over should pertain to the reason which was given in the advance notice.[175]

If the notice were deficient in some respect it might still operate as the acceptance of a repudiatory breach of contract.[176] Whether this could occur would depend upon the reason for the deficiency and whether or not the termination provisions were specifically invoked.[177] Clause 94.1 itself requires 'details of [the] reason for terminating' to be given. It is an open question as to the detail or sufficiency of the reasons required and whether the restatement of one of the 21 reasons in clause 95 is sufficient.

Upon notice being given in accordance with the contract the project manager issues a termination certificate promptly if the reason complies with the contract.[178] There will eventually be debate in the courts whether this casts an affirmative and mandatory duty upon the project manager to act and issue a termination certificate in this situation or whether the project manager has any residual discretion in the matter. In part the question will arise as a result of the drafting of the clause and the omission of 'may' or 'shall' from it. Only clause 10.1 uses the term 'shall'; all other clauses are drafted in the present tense. Having made this prediction, however, in deference to the choice of the drafters, the importance of the issue would have almost inevitably resulted in the wording of the clause being tested in the courts whether or not one or the other of the omitted words had been included in the clause.

The contractor may terminate only for a reason identified in the termination table while the employer may terminate for any reason.[179] By comparison JCT 81, clause 7.10 grants the employer the power also to

172 *Roberts* v. *Davey* (1833) 4 B & Ad 664; *Marsden* v. *Sambell* (1880) 28 WR 952; *Drew* v. *Josolyne* (1887) 18 QBD 590, CA; *J M Hill & Sons Ltd* v. *London Borough of Camden* (1980) 18 BLR 13, CA.

173 See *Goodwin & Sons* v. *Fawcett* (1965) 175 Estates Gazette 27; *Central Provident Fund Board* v. *Ho Bock Kee* (1981) 17 BLR 21 (Sing CA).

174 See *Pauling* v. *Dover Corpn* (1855) 10 Exch 753.

175 See *Architectural Installation Services Ltd* v. *James Gibbons Windows Ltd* (1989) 46 BLR 91 at 98, 16 Con LR 68 at 71.

176 *Architectural Installation Services Ltd* v. *James Gibbons Windows Ltd* (1989) 46 BLR 91, 16 Con LR 68.

177 See *E R Dyer Ltd* v. *Simon Build/Peter Lind Partership* (1982) 23 BLR 23 at 33.

178 Clause 94.1 ECC.

179 Clause 94.2 ECC.

Table 4   Termination Table

Terminating party	Reason	Procedure	Amount due
The Employer	A reason other than		
	R1–R21	P1 and P2	A1, A2 and A4
	R1–R15, R19	P1, P2 and P3	A1 and A3
	R17, R18, R21	P1 and P3	A1, A2 and A5
The Contractor	R1–R10, R16, R20	P1 and P4	A1, A2 and A4
	R17, R18, R21	P1 and P4	A1, A2 and A5

determine the employment of the management contractor at will; it is noteworthy the clause itself describes their relationship as one of 'employment'. The broad grant of a unilateral right to terminate for any reason in some ways renders the reasons that are specifically listed superfluous. In general one should seek to reduce superfluousness in drafting and improve the conciseness in drafting so far as possible and as a means of reducing risk associated with the conditions.[180] A general statement of the procedures that follow and the amounts due upon termination are referred to in clause 94.2 as well. Table 4 summarizes certain issues in relation to termination: which party, the permissible reasons, the procedure and any amount due.

It has been noted that the employer may terminate for any reason;[181] as such the inclusion of a summary of the reasons in this regard may serve rather to indicate the procedures which follow and the amount that becomes due more than anything else. Clause 94.1, while stating that the employer may terminate for any reason, does not state whether that reason even has to be communicated to the contractor. An argument could be put forward which would underscore that no reason need be communicated to the contractor. If it were accepted it would mirror the JCT 87 determination at will procedure in clauses 7.10 to 7.13 which does not require a reason to be given by the employer to the management contractor.[182] Lastly, groups of reasons are associated with various procedures, some of which are mutually exclusive.

The procedures themselves are to be implemented immediately after the issue of the termination certificate by the project manager.[183] The procedures, abbreviated to P1 to P4, are set out in detail in clause 96. The amounts due, either by the employer to the contractor or vice versa, are abbreviated to A1 to A5. They are also set out in detail in clauses 97.1 and 97.2. The project manager will certify a final payment to or from the

---

[180]   See BUBSHAIT, ABDULAZIZ A. and ALMOHAWIS, SOLIMAN A. Evaluating the General Conditions of a Construction Contract. *International Journal of Project Management*, 1994, **12**(3), 134.

[181]   Clause 94.2 ECC.

[182]   The argument is based on the maxim *expressio unius est exclusio alterius*, 'expression of one thing is the exclusion of the other': Co Littleton 210a, and clause 13.1.

[183]   Clause 94.3 ECC.

contractor within 13 weeks of termination. As with a final payment certificate under other standard forms, the assessment of the amount due is less the total price of previous payments or what would be interim certificates under those other forms of contract.[184]

A long period of time often lapses between the date of termination and any final reckoning or payment under the contract under numerous standard forms. This is to permit time to assess more effectively the effects of termination and the cost consequences. Under the ECC the time lapse is 13 weeks, while under clause 63.3 of FIDIC 4th there is no payment until after the expiration of the defects liability period. After the termination certificate has been issued the contractor does no further work necessary to complete the works.[185]

Reasons for termination

The reasons for termination, although the employer is said to be entitled to terminate for any reason,[186] are set out in detail in clause 95. There are in total 21 reasons listed but which may be roughly grouped into 6 categories. Most of the reasons do not differ materially from those grounds given in some of the other leading forms.[187] Depending upon the category the employer, the contractor, or either party to the contract may be able to terminate if the other party has fulfilled one of the reasons or its equivalent. This wording is typical short form ECC drafting replacing what may have more traditionally read 'permitted, suffered, allowed, acquiesced in ...' etc. It may be noted that, as the ECC is intended to operate in different jurisdictions under various legal systems, these precise acts or events may only have equivalents in those other jurisdictions. If no equivalent does exist it cannot be relied upon as a basis for termination at least under this clause.

Bankruptcy or insolvency[188]

Clause 95.1 lists 10 of the 21 recognized reasons ('Rs') for termination. Thus, under paragraph (a), either party may terminate if the other party is an individual and has:

1. presented a petition for bankruptcy (R1). A petition for bankruptcy is normally presented to the court in accordance with the provisions of Part IX of the Insolvency Act 1986. A 'bankruptcy petition' means a petition to the court for a bankruptcy order (Insolvency Act 1986, section 381(2), (3)).

---

[184]   Clause 94.4 ECC; cf clauses 27.4, 36.6.2, 30.8.2 JCT 80.
[185]   Clause 94.5 ECC.
[186]   Clause 94.2 ECC.
[187]   See e.g. clause 63.1 FIDIC 4th and clause 63(1) ICE 6th.
[188]   See generally BURNETT, ROBERT B. *Insolvency and the Sub-contractor*. CIOB, Ascot, 1991, Occasional Paper 48; and DAVIS, RICHARD *Construction Insolvency*. Chancery Law Publishing, London, 1991.

2. had a bankruptcy order made against them (R2). A 'bankruptcy order' means an order adjudging an individual bankrupt (Insolvency Act 1986, section 381(1), (2)).
3. had a receiver appointed over their assets (R3). The clause leaves open whether it includes the Official Receiver or an interim receiver as those terms are used within the meaning of the Insolvency Act 1986.
4. made an arrangement with creditors (R4). For instance, under Part VIII of the Insolvency Act 1986; namely a composition in satisfaction of the individual's debts or a scheme of arrangement of the individual's affairs.

Under paragraph (b), either party may terminate if the other party is a company or partnership and has:

5. had a winding-up order made against it (R5). The High Court (concurrent with county courts where the amount of a company's share capital does not exceed £120,000) may make a winding-up order on a long list of grounds: (Insolvency Act 1986, section 122).
6. had a provisional liquidator appointed to it (R6). The court may appoint a provisional liquidator as a contingent means of protection of a company's assets after the presentation of a winding-up petition but before a winding-up order is made, under the Insolvency Act 1986 section 135(1).
7. passed a resolution for winding up (other than in order to amalgamate or reconstruct) (R 9). Under the Insolvency Act 1986, section 84(2) this would include resolutions passed in general meeting, special resolutions, and extraordinary resolutions under section 84(1)(a), (b), and (c) respectively.
8. had an administration order made against it (R8). This contemplates administration orders under the Insolvency Act 1986, section 8(2).
9. had a receiver, receiver and manager, or administrative receiver appointed over the whole or a substantial part of its undertaking or assets (R7). For the most part this provision contemplates the appointment of receivers etc. under a security document such as a debenture or trust deed in certain specified events. Under the Companies Act 1985 or the Insolvency Act 1986, unless provision is made to the contrary, any reference to a receiver contemplates a reference to a receiver or manager. By comparison, the appointment of an administrator or receiver without more under clause 27.3 of the JCT 80 are not reasons for termination of the contractor and unlike the corresponding provisions in R7 and R8 in clause 95.1 of the ECC. The ability of the parties to reinstate their agreement under the JCT provision may also operate in practice similarly to the discretion which is afforded either party not to terminate under clause 95.1. Clause 29.2 of DOM/1 and clause 17 of FCEC operate

similarly to the JCT provision in that the stipulated insolvency events alone do not automatically operate to determine the subcontractor's employment but rather it is left to the contractor to make that decision. The ECC may thus be taking too traditional a view of the grounds or reasons for termination in this regard.

10. made an arrangement with its creditors (R10). This contemplates the type of arrangement made under the Insolvency Act 1986, Part I and whether as a composition or a scheme of arrangement.[189]

Contractor defaults

The second category of reasons for termination broadly deals with certain contractor defaults. Thus clause 95.2 lists three defaults that entitle the employer to terminate the contractor. The clause requires the project manager to notify the contractor of the specific default and that the contractor has not put the default right[190] within four weeks of the notification. The defaults are that the contractor has:

11. substantially failed to comply with his or her obligations (R11);
12. not provided a bond or guarantee which this contract requires (R12);
13. appointed a subcontractor for substantial work before the project manager has accepted the subcontractor (R13).

The language of 'fundamental breach' is suggested in R11 of clause 95.2 when it provides that termination may be ordered if the contractor has 'substantially failed to comply with his obligations'.[191] Apart from the question of proper interpretation to be given to the term 'substantially', the wording of the clause also gives rise to further issues of interpretation.[192] First, the wording may be contrasted with that in clause 95.2; that is, the contractor must 'put the default right' within four weeks. Here the operative wording not only presupposes default but that the contractor has 'not stopped defaulting'. This wording implies, at least in the 'health or safety' context, that the breach is of a continuing nature. In the health and safety context[193] breaches of regulations are often subject to fines for individual periods of time during which they continue, e.g. per hour or per day etc. Each new period of time is subject to another fine or even an increasing level of fine.

---

[189] See *March Estates plc* v. *Gunmark Ltd* [1996] 2 BCLC 1.

[190] Clause 95.2 ECC uses the wording 'not put the default right', seemingly a plain or ordinary way of stating that the contractor has not corrected the default.

[191] Clause 95.2 (R11) ECC.

[192] See also clause 95.5 ECC, 'substantially affected the *Contractor's* work', and cf the use of the term 'substantial' in another context in clause 95.6.

[193] Cf the wording here with that used in clause 18.1 ECC and see also the discussion in relation to the clause above.

While this interpretation is logical in this context, it seems out of place in relation to the hindering of the employer or others unless the hindrance was meant in a quasi-criminal way. It is submitted that was not the intent; rather the drafters were seeking to underscore the *magnitude* of the breach. Even if this was the intention, however, the drafting poses problems in determining when any given act of hindrance may have ceased to continue and thus which, of any new acts of hindrance, would require a separate notice and recommencement of the four-week advance notice period.

Pursuant to R12, failure of the contractor to provide a bond or guarantee that the contract requires is a ground for termination upon notice;[194] however, case law has held that such a failure, at least in the case of a performance bond, is not a repudiatory breach of contract.[195] Thus the contractual right appears to exceed that at common law.

The last provision in the clause provides one further reason as a ground for termination. Therefore, under R13 the appointment of a subcontractor for substantial work before the project manager has accepted the subcontractor is also a ground for termination upon notice.[196] Once again 'substantial' is used to attenuate the breach. It is an open question how the term will be construed; qualitatively or quantitatively. However, in at least one case unauthorized subcontracting or subletting of the works was held not to be repudiatory.[197]

Contractor continuing defaults

Pursuant to clause 95.3, the employer may terminate if the project manager has notified that the contractor has defaulted in either of two ways and not stopped defaulting within four weeks of the notification:

14. substantially hindered the employer or others (R14);
15. substantially broken a health or safety regulation (R15).

Clause 95.3 begins with the familiar qualification to the interdicted actions, namely that they must be substantial. Reason 14 expressly interdicts or circumscribes the contractor 'hindering' the employer or others. If one adopts J.F. Burrows'[198] analysis of the duty of co-operation as involving interference, hindrance would be encompassed within its meaning.

Burrows examines co-operation under two broad headings: interference with enjoyment of subject matter, and interference with performance of promises. The second head is further divided between a duty not positively to obstruct and a duty to co-operate actively. Burrows' duty not to obstruct is examined both under the heading of 'total

---

[194] Clause 95.2 (R12) ECC.
[195] *Swartz & Son (Pty) Ltd* v. *Wolmaransstadt Town Council* 1960 (2) SA 1. check cite.
[196] Clause 95.2 (R13) ECC.
[197] *Thomas Feather & Co (Bradford) Ltd* v. *Keighley Corpn* (1953) 52 LGR 30.
[198] BURROWS, J.F. Contractual Co-operation and the Implied Term. *Modern Law Review*, 1968, **31**, 396–402

prevention' as well as 'mere hindrance'. This would invoke the jurisprudence relating to co-operation discussed above and it is submitted provides a sanction against non-co-operative behaviour. In this regard, it is the counterpart to clause 10.1 and, to a lesser extent, clause 25.1. However, the sanction operates only with regard to hindrance on the part of the contractor. As the duty to act co-operatively is imposed on both employer and contractor under clause 10.1 it would be more appropriate if this sanction were available in the event of the hindrance of either party. Turning to R15, the elevation of a health or safety regulation to a ground for termination seems warranted with the increasing attention being paid to this area. Standard forms are generally undergoing amendment to ensure correspondence with the new regulations and the regulations are intended to address the causes of industry health and safety problems.[199]

Non-payment

16. The contractor may terminate if the employer has not paid an amount certified by the project manager within 13 [thirteen] weeks of the date of the certificate (R16).[200]

At common law a party does not have an unequivocal right to suspend performance for late payment.[201] A decision to suspend performance carries a high degree of risk as the suspension could be regarded as repudiatory. In such a case it would be open to the employer to accept the repudiation and sue for damages for breach of contract. To overcome this uncertainty many standard forms of contract have now conferred on the contractor an express contractual right to suspend performance.[202] The HGCRA gives an equivalent right by statute. Section 112 of the HGCRA provides:

> Where a sum due under a construction contract is not paid in full by the final date for payment and no effective notice to withhold payment has been given, the person to whom the sum is due has the right ... to suspend performance of his obligations under the contract to the party by whom payment ought to have been made.[203]

Under the statutory right the HGCRA affords pursuant to section 112(4) the completion date under the ECC is effectively delayed by any period of

---

[199] See NATTRASS, STUART Chief Inspector of Construction. Health and Safety Executive's Overview. At *CDM: The Issues Grasped*. Proceedings of a conference in London on 7 June 1997 by the Construction Industry Council and Global Conferences. Construction Industry Council and Global Conferences, London, 1997.

[200] Clause 95.4 ECC.

[201] See *Lubenham Fidelities and Investments Co Ltd* v. *South Pembrokeshire District Council* (1986) 33 BLR 39, 70, CA.

[202] See e.g. clauses 28.1 JCT 80 and 69.4 FIDIC.

[203] See JOYCE, RAYMOND, n. 118 above, pp. 54–59. See for expressions of concern on the payment provisions, PRICE, JENNY. Paying the Piper. *Legalese Special Report: Construction 1997*. Legalese and the Society of Construction Law, London, 1997, pp. 5–6.

suspension. This would, in practice, be any period up to the 13-week grace period which R16 stipulates assuming the contractor then wished to take advantage of R16. If full payment were made anytime prior to the 13-week grace period expiring the contractor would again have to continue with his or her obligations under the ECC. This assumes that the contractor is not in breach and with reference to the HGCRA, sections 110(2) and 111 were concurrently satisfied. Amendments to the ECC under secondary option Y (UK) 2 following the passage of the HGCRA have added an additional compensation event to address any additional costs of the contractor arising out of the suspension. Clause 60.7 of the amended Second Edition provides: '[s]uspension of performance is a compensation event if the *Contractor* exercises his right to suspend performance under the Act'. It may be significant that the contractor has to suspend performance 'under the Act' for a compensation event to arise. Otherwise it is open to the employer to argue, if the HGCRA's notice provisions were not satisfied, that it is not compensable as least as a compensation event.[204]

Force majeure

According to clause 95.5, either party may terminate in the following cases:

17. war or radioactive contamination has substantially affected the contractor's work for 26 weeks [twenty-six] (R17); or
18. the parties have been released under the law from further performance of the whole of this contract (R18).

Clause 95.5 is described here as and resembles the structure of *force majeure* clauses in other forms for several reasons. This contradicts the characterization given to the clause by Brian Eggleston[205] as a 'frustration clause' as well as his description of R21 in clause 95.6 as a '*force majeure*' clause.[206] First of all, the clause is drafted essentially in two parts.[207] The first part, R17 lists two specific events that allow termination: war, and radioactive contamination as described. While radioactive contamination is relatively new as a ground for termination, war has been considered on occasion.[208] These two grounds also appear in

---

[204] See generally NICKLISCH, F. Quantifying Suspension and Wrongful Termination Claims. *International Construction Law Review*, 1989, 77.

[205] EGGLESTON, see n. 11 above.

[206] See generally on the nature of both clauses McINNIS, J.A. Frustration and Force Majeure in Building Contracts. 195; TREITEL, GUNTHER H. *Frustation and Force Majeure*. Sweet & Maxwell, London, 1994; and BRUNER, P.L. Force Majeure under International Law and International Construction Contract Model Forms. *International Construction Law Review*, 1995, 274.

[207] See CARTOON, BERNARD J. Drafting an Acceptable *Force Majeure* Clause. *Journal of Business Law*, 1978, 230; and YATES, DAVID. Drafting Force Majeure and Related Clauses. *Journal of Contract Law*, 1991, **3**, 186.

[208] See e.g. *Tennants (Lancashire) Ltd* v. *C S Wilson & Co Ltd* [1917] AC 495, HL; *Peter Dixon & Sons Ltd* v. *Henderson, Craig & Co* [1919] 2 KB 778, CA.

clause 80.1. However, there are significant omissions, that is, civil war, rebellion, revolution, insurrection, military or usurped power – apart from strikes, riots and civil commotion which are dealt with separately. As a matter of interpretation, if these events occur, it would be difficult to argue successfully that they are also grounds for termination under R17 although they could be better argued under R18. As a general matter the caution of Lord Porter may be recalled in *The Coxwold*: '[t]he fact is that there is no form of words in which underwriters and insured can express themselves so as to convey with precision what they mean to include in war risks'.[209] Secondly, R18 adds a general ground that purports to address all other grounds that might allow release from further performance. Thus there is considerable scope under the general ground for parties to allege events that permit termination.[210] Lastly, the first part of clause 95.5 allows for a period of time for which the event must endure, *viz.* 26 weeks, prior to recognizing it as a ground of termination. This practice too accords with current usage under typical *force majeure* clauses.[211] Hence, although clause 95.5 may not appear initially to be a *force majeure* clause, upon closer examination a case can be made that it will operate as such. Read with clause 19.1 on illegality and impossibility it serves to reinforce the fairness and co-operative spirit underlying the form. Thus, while excusing events are broadly defined in the second part of clause 95.5, the ability of the project manager to instruct the contractor to overcome those events entailing impossibility, and at the same time the entitlement of the contractor to be compensated for his or her actions, is both progressive and practical.

Suspension of work

The final category of reasons for termination broadly addresses suspension of the work. Thus, if the project manager has instructed the contractor to stop or not to start any substantial work or all work and an instruction allowing the work to restart or start has not been given within 13 weeks:

19. the employer may terminate if the instruction was due to a default by the contractor (R19);
20. the contractor may terminate if the instruction was due to a default by the employer (R20); and
21. either party may terminate if the instruction was due to another reason (R21).

---

[209] Lord Porter, *Yorkshire Dale SS Co Ltd* v. *Minister of War Transport, The Coxwold* [1942] AC 691 at 714, HL.

[210] See e.g. *Matsoukis v Priestman & Co* [1915] 1 KB 681 (strikes); *Walton (Grain and Shipping) Ltd* v. *British Italian Trading Co Ltd* [1959] 1 Lloyd's Rep 223 (export licence restrictions); *Nichols* v. *Marsland* (1876) 2 Ex D 1 (floods); *River Wear Comrs* v. *Adamson* (1877) 2 App Cas 743, HL (storms).

[211] See again CARTOON, BERNARD J., n. 207 above, 230.

No general time limit is imposed on the above reasons and they should operate immediately or without the necessity for any period of advance notice or warning.[212] However, it should be noted that while these reasons for termination operate immediately, there are other reasons that require periods of advance notice or warning. The periods of advance notice or warning pertain only to termination on the part of the employer. Clause 95 does not impose any advance notice or warning requirement on the part of the contractor although there may be periods of delay alone before the contractor can terminate the contract. Thus, under clause 95.4, for instance, the contractor may terminate if the employer has not paid an amount certified by the project manager within 13 weeks of the date of the certificate; a period of delay. However, clause 95.4 imposes no advance notice or warning requirement as such on the part of the contractor. As a result, neither the project manager nor the employer is given an opportunity to rectify the default to pay the certificate within the 13-week delay. The contractor may have reasons for not bringing the default to the attention of the project manager; e.g. the contractor's own entitlement to interest on the certificated amount in any case combined with a desire to end the contract. No obligation appears to arise nor is it incumbent upon the contractor to give notice of this default under the clause 16 early warning provisions. In comparison, clause 28.1 of JCT 81 similarly provides for a single notice of determination by the contractor and without the necessity for advance notice or warning to the employer of a previous default. It is an open question whether the deliberate omission on the part of the contractor to give the contractor advance notice of an intention to terminate for this reason would amount to a breach of the general obligation to act in a spirit of mutual trust and co-operation under clause 10.1 of the ECC.

It may be asked what is the situation if a party acting in good faith terminates the contract for one of the reasons stated but finds that the reason given did not exist in fact? The ECC does not address what the result should be in this case and whether it still amounts to a repudiatory breach by the terminating party. There is, in addition, little guidance in the case law and as a result the parties, it seems, are quite likely to be placed in a dispute situation.[213] One factor, which is relevant to the result, is the action of the innocent party; that is, whether the repudiation is accepted, or rejected and the contract affirmed. If the repudiation is rejected and the innocent party affirms the contract, the decision cannot then later be revoked;[214] both parties remain bound to fulfil all

---

[212] Cf the complicated FIDIC clause 40.3 suspension procedure that commences after 84 days.

[213] See *Lodder* v. *Slowey* [1904] AC 442, PC; *Canterbury Pipe Lines Ltd* v. *Christchurch Drainage Board* (1979) 16 BLR 76 (NZCA); *Woodar Investment Development Ltd* v. *Wimpey Construction (UK) Ltd* [1980] 1 All ER 571, [1980] 1 WLR 277, HL; *Architectural Installation Services Ltd* v. *James Gibbons Windows Ltd* (1989) 46 BLR 91, 16 Con LR 68.

[214] *Bentsen* v. *Taylor Sons & Co (No 2)* [1893] 2 QB 274, CA; *Hain Steamship Co Ltd* v. *Tate & Lyle Ltd* [1936] 2 All ER 597, 41 Com Cas 350, HL.

outstanding contractual obligations.[215] Conversely, if the repudiation is accepted by the innocent party, both parties will be released from any further requirement to perform any remaining contractual obligations which are not due under the contract,[216] although they remain bound to fulfil those contractual obligations which are due at the time of the acceptance of the repudiation.[217] A total failure of consideration would nevertheless relieve the parties of the necessity to fulfil even those contractual obligations which are then due.[218]

The issue of repudiation and innocent parties' right to affirm the contract raises an interesting question of interpretation as a result of the duty of the parties to act in a spirit of mutual trust and co-operation.[219] As noted an innocent party has the right to affirm the contract.[220] However, as the parties must also co-operate in the performance of the contract, repudiation and subsequent affirmation places the terminating party in a difficult position where there are in effect, competing demands. Ultimately, issues involving repudiation and affirmation of the contract are always difficult to resolve and carry a high degree of risk. The duty to act co-operatively in the ECC now provides a new incentive, indeed contractual obligation, for the parties to work toward resolution of the issues if they may. It will certainly not always be enough but it must offer at least additional pause for reflection.

Procedures on termination

The procedures on termination are set out in detail in clause 96. In addition to the procedures on termination the ECC also addresses payment on termination in clause 97. The convention begun in clause 95 is followed through with letter prefixes and numbers for procedures for termination, P1 to P4, in clause 96. The clause is essentially divided into two parts reflected by the two subclauses in clause 96. Thus, under subclause 96.1 in every case of termination the employer is given the right to complete the works or employ others to do so as well as use any plant and materials that the employer has title to.

Apart from this entitlement as a procedural matter, and depending upon the reason for termination, either one or two additional procedures may be

---

[215] *R V Ward Ltd* v. *Bignall* [1967] 1 QB 534, [1967] 2 All ER 449, CA; *Harbutt's Plasticine Ltd* v. *Wayne Tank and Pump Co Ltd* [1970] 1 QB 447 at 464, [1970] 1 All ER 225 at 233, CA, per Lord Denning MR.

[216] *Heyman* v. *Darwins Ltd* [1942] AC 356, [1942] 1 All ER 337, HL.

[217] *McDonald* v. *Dennys Lascelles Ltd* (1933) 48 CLR 457 at 476; *Johnson* v. *Agnew* [1980] AC 367 at 396, [1979] 1 All ER 883 at 892, HL, per Lord Wilberforce; *Hyundai Heavy Industries Co Ltd* v. *Papadopoulos* [1980] 2 All ER 29, [1980] 1 WLR 1129, HL.

[218] *Rover International Ltd* v. *Cannon Film Sales Ltd* (*No 3*) [1989] 3 All ER 423, [1989] 1 WLR 912, CA; and see *Ferguson & Associates* v. *Sohl* (1992) 62 BLR 95, CA.

[219] Clause 10.1 ECC. See also clause 25.1 ECC.

[220] See *White and Carter (Councils) Ltd* v. *McGregor* [1962] AC 413, [1961] 3 All ER 1178, HL.

invoked. Thus P1 applies in every case of termination either by the employer or contractor. However, in other circumstances, and once again according to the reason for the termination, the following other combinations are possible:

(1) P1, P2 and P3;
(2) P1 and P3;
(3) P1 and P4; and
(4) P1 and P5.

The procedures are abbreviated as P2 to P4 in clause 96.2 as follows:

1. P2 – the employer may instruct the contractor to leave the site, remove any equipment, plant and materials from the site and assign the benefit of any subcontract or other contract related to performance of the contract to the employer;
2. P3 – the employer may use any equipment which he has title to;
3. P4 – the contractor leaves the working areas and removes the equipment.

Looking at the procedures individually, P2 is common to many standard forms.[221] In the ordinary course the provision will not serve to vest the plant and materials in the employer such that the employer acquires absolute property to them. Rather, the normal tests will apply with respect to them; thus, the only plant and materials[222] that will vest in the employer are those incorporated in the works. Clause 11.2(10) defines 'Plant and Materials' as those items which are to be included in the '*works*'. It has been noted that this may mark a change from use of the term 'plant' in other contexts where it would not normally include items incorporated in the works.[223] Equipment[224] will not vest at all in the employer and will pass back to the contractor when it is removed with the project manager's permission or it is no longer needed.[225] The latter part of P2 gives the employer a clear right to require the assignment of the benefit of any subcontract or other contract related to performance of the main contract to him or her. Although the effect of termination of the contractor upon the subcontractor is not otherwise dealt with in the provisions on termination in the ECC, such termination is referred to in and is listed as a ground for termination in the ECSC.[226] This applies whether or not the termination involved default on the part of the

---

[221] See e.g. clause 63(2) ICE 6th; cf and contrast provisions in standard forms which entitle the employer to undertake work outside the contract either directly or through another contractor; e.g. clause 29 JCT 80.
[222] Clause 11.2(10) ECC.
[223] See *Re Winter, ex p Bolland* (1878) 8 Ch D 225.
[224] Clause 11.2(11) ECC.
[225] Clauses 70.2 and 72.1 ECC. See generally *Ranger* v. *Great Western Rly Co* (1854) 5 HL Cas 72, HL; *Hart* v. *Porthgain Harbour Co Ltd* [1903] 1 Ch 690.
[226] Clause 95.1 R7 ECSC. Assignment is also expressly prohibited on both the contractor's and subcontractor's parts under clause 26.1 ECSC.

subcontractor. The fact of termination serves to render P2, regarding the assignment of the benefit of any subcontract, of little value if the subcontracts end automatically.[227]

Clause P3 simply recognizes the right of the employer to use any equipment that the employer has title to. The critical issue here is establishing the employer's title to the equipment. This is accomplished under clause 70 in either of two cases and depending upon whether the equipment is either *inside* or *outside* the working areas. 'The Working Areas are the *working areas* unless later changed in accordance with this contract' under clause 11.2(8) while the '*working areas*' is an identified term in part two of the Contract Data and is inclusive of the 'Site' and is especially important to the application of clauses 70 and 71. By comparison, JCT 80, clause 16.1 and JCT 81, clause 15 use a broader concept in their distinctions than the working areas encompassing that area 'adjacent to the Works' as well.

In the case of equipment *outside* the working areas it must be marked – or appropriated – by the supervisor as belonging to the contract and title passes to the employer in this way. With equipment *inside* the working areas, no specific marking is required and rather title passes to the employer once it is brought within a working area. Therefore, prior to the return of any title to the contractor, the employer may use that equipment to which the employer has title, e.g. only when it is removed from the working areas with the project manager's permission under clause 70.2.

Under the fourth procedure outlined, P4, the contractor leaves the working areas and removes the equipment. This seeks to ensure there is no overholding on the part of the contractor following a contested termination and reinforces characterization of the contractor's interest as merely a licence to occupy the site not giving rise to any interest in land. The licence classification is supported by *Hudson's* while the contrary position finds support in the case of *Hounslow London Borough Council* v. *Twickenham Garden Developments Ltd.*[228] The *Hounslow* decision was not followed in *Mayfield Holdings Ltd* v. *Moana Reef Ltd, Cowell* v. *Rosehill Racecourse Co Ltd* and *Porter* v. *Hannah Builders Pty Ltd.*[229] These two latter cases are both preferred in *Hudson's* to *Hounslow* while more recent case authority supports a licence classification.[230]

---

[227]   See *E R Dyer Ltd* v. *Simon Build/Peter Lind Partnership* (1982) 23 BLR 23.

[228]   *Hudson's*, vol. 2, 1301–1302; and *Hounslow London Borough Council* v. *Twickenham Garden Developments Ltd* [1971] Ch 233, [1970] 3 All ER 326.

[229]   *Mayfield Holdings Ltd* v. *Moana Reef Ltd* [1973] 1 NZLR 309; *Cowell* v. *Rosehill Racecourse Co Ltd* [1937] 56 CLR 605 and *Porter* v. *Hannah Builders Pty Ltd* [1969] VR 673.

[230]   *Surrey Heath Borough Council* v. *Lovell Construction Ltd and Haden Young Ltd* (1988) 42 BLR 25, upheld on appeal on other grounds (1990) 48 BLR 108, CA; *Tara Civil Engineering Ltd* v. *Moorfield Developments Ltd* (1989) 5 Const LJ 308; and *Chermar Productions Pty Ltd* v. *Pretest Pty Ltd* (1992) 8 Const LJ 44 following the *Porter* and *Cowell* cases above.

Payment on termination

In addition to the procedures on termination the ECC also addresses payment on termination in clause 97. The clause is divided into two parts that in effect describe the assessment procedures to be followed. Following the convention begun in clause 95 with a letter suffix and clause 96 with a letter prefix, a letter prefix, 'A' for amount, is also given to alternative amounts that may be due on termination. Clause 95 sets out 21 reasons for termination with the suffix letter 'R' for reason; clause 9 introduces the letter prefix 'P' for procedure; and clause 97 uses the letter prefix 'A' for amount. Hence in every case of termination a base amount, designated A1 will be due on termination following taking into account any relevant deductions. This can be seen from the termination table as well which includes 'A1' as part of the amount due in every case. In addition, depending upon the reason for the termination, a further amount, comprising one or more of those described as A2 to A5, may also be due. The A1 amount includes the following.[231]

1. An amount due assessed as for normal payments.[232]
2. The actual cost for plant and materials within the working areas, or which the employer has title to and the contractor accepts for delivery; – 'Actual Cost' is an identified term in each main option and would be determined with reference to section 3 of the applicable SCC. With regard to the plant and materials which the employer has title to this would presume that the plant and materials are outside the working areas, and either marked for delivery, or prepared for marking for delivery to the working areas, and which the contractor will allow ('accepts for delivery') to the working areas.
3. Other actual costs reasonably incurred in expectation of completing the whole of the works; – as this is not indicated to be a deduction it is not intended as such or with regard to any additional costs that the employer would incur in completing the works following termination of the contractor. The drafter's intention is for this provision to include costs which the contractor can show have not been recovered with the normal amount due.[233] The provision may also be contrasted with A3 below. In this regard the provision operates as a savings provision for the normal measure of damages that would be awarded with regard to the contractor's 'expectation' interest in completing the contract. The theoretical explanation for such provisions has been given by Professor Ewan McKendrick: 'The basis of such a claim is that the plaintiff's expectations, engendered by the promise of the defendant that he will perform his contractual obligations, have not been fulfilled and that damages should compensate him for his disappointed expectations by putting him

---

[231] Clause 97.1 ECC.
[232] See discussion clause 50.1 ECC.
[233] Guidance notes NEC on clause 97.1 ECC, 81.

"in as good a position as he would have occupied had the defendant performed his promise"'.[234]

4. Any amounts retained by the employer; – amounts may be retained by the employer under secondary option P and thus this amount would have to be paid on termination.

5. Any deductions of unrepaid balances of advanced payments; – advanced payments would have been made under secondary option J. The contractor is under an obligation to repay advances under clause J1.3 in agreed instalments; and in the event of these remaining on termination they would be deducted from any amount due to the contractor.

The further amount, comprising one or more of those described as A2 to A5, may also be due or deducted as follows.[235]

1. A2 – the forecast actual cost of removing equipment; – by referring to the termination table the contractor would not be paid the forecast actual cost of removing equipment if any of the 21 reasons for termination set out in clause 95 were relied upon by the employer for termination. The interpretation placed upon the termination table in this regard follows from a close reading of the table. It may be noted that this involves the only instance of a negative formulation of listed reasons; e.g. 'A reason other than R1–R21' in column 2, row 2.

2. A3 – a deduction of the forecast of the additional cost to the employer of completing the whole of the works; – this is the counterpart to item 3 above under A1. It is not unusual for an employer to seek to deduct or set off anticipated additional costs for completing the works particularly arising out of any breach of contract on the contractor's part.

3. A4 – the fee percentage applied: for options A, B, C, and D, to any excess of the total of the prices at the contract date over the price for work done to date; or, for options E and F, to any excess of the first forecast of the actual cost for the works over the price for work done to date less the fee; – this follows from clause 52.1 which deems all the contractor's costs which are not included in the actual cost to be included in the fee percentage. Hence the fee percentage may be used as a general multiplier for discrepancies between the total of the prices and the PWDD in respect of the first four main options, and the excess of the first forecast of actual cost over PWDD less the fee.

4. A5 – one-half of A4; – this serves to apportion equally between the employer the amount arrived at under A3 when neither party is responsible for the termination and in those cases arising under R17, R18, and R21.

---

[234] McKENDRICK, PROFESSOR EWAN *Contract Law*. MacMillan Professional Masters, London, 1990, p. 242.
[235] Clause 97.2 ECC.

Once again the amounts in A2 to A5 depend upon the particular ground, R1 to R21, set out in clause 94 and the termination table. Similar provisions are set out in the ECSC. The ECSC sets out in effect the same amounts due on termination although in a slightly different format. Clauses 97 in both the First Edition of the NEC and ECSC do not describe clause 97.1 as A1 and thus the abbreviations used for amounts due, A1 to A4, are set out only in clause 97.2 of the First Edition. A change is introduced in the Second Edition of the ECC and clause 97.1 is now described as A1, while A2 to A5 are described in clause 97.2. Additional provisions allow for changes when termination takes place under main options A, C or D. Thus, under main option A, the amount due is assessed without taking grouping of activities into account,[236] while under main options C and D involving target price contracts, some allowance is made to address the effect of the contractor's share provisions in clause 53. Thus the project manager will assess the contractor's share using the PWDD at termination and the total of the prices for the work done before termination according to clause 97.4 of the ECC. The grouping of activities is relevant under main option A in assessing the PWDD under clause 11.2(24) of the ECC although would not be when termination occurs.

---

[236] Clause 97.3 ECC.

15. Conclusion

We may be approaching a critical road junction in the history of the law of contract. Will we adhere to the traditional adversarial model of the contract in which each party is free to pursue its own rights as self-interest dictates without regard to the detriment caused thereby to the other party? Or will we move to a co-operative concept of contract in which the exercise of rights and powers will be moderated by the good faith doctrine and purposive interpretations based on the co-operative concept and notions such as abuse of power?

Sir Anthony Mason,
Review of *Good Faith and Fault in Contract Law*

General

Contractual documentation has fulfilled an important role throughout time. From the simplest medieval contracts to today's complex construction management agreements contracts have influenced the ways parties build, relate to each other and further the peculiarities of the construction process. Alfred A. Hudson referred to some of those 'peculiarities' over 100 years ago in his seminal text[1] while E.J. Rimmer also used the term is an influential paper over 70 years ago, *The Conditions of Engineering Contracts*, to describe a range of circumstances that differentiate engineering contracts from other contracts.[2] Over time turning points occur. It is often difficult, however, to tell precisely when these occur. One of the leading engineering historians A.W.B. Simpson has put it this way. 'It is in general possible to differentiate between the introduction of new doctrine, and the operation and elaboration of old, even though in a traditional system of law one cannot put a precise date to the reception of new material'.[3] The question

[1] HUDSON, ALFRED A. *The Law of Building and Engineering Contracts and of the Duties and Liabilities of Engineers, Architects and Valuers: With an Appendix of Precedents and an Appendix of Unreported Cases.* Waterlow and Sons, London Wall, London; Stevens and Haynes, Bell Yard, 1891, p. 3 refers to nine peculiarities.

[2] RIMMER, E.J. *The Conditions of Engineering Contracts. ICE Journal*, February 1939, **2**, Paper 5203, 3.

[3] SIMPSON, A.W.B. Innovation in Nineteenth Century Contract Law. *Law Quarterly Review*, 1975, **91**, 247.

that has essentially been posed here is whether the NEC marks a similar turning point or indeed a paradigm shift. A fundamental aspect of this question concerns the role that the NEC plays in relation to contractual documentation as it has evolved and should continue to evolve. It has been seen that the answer to the question is inseparable from how parties build and relate to each other during the construction process. Viewed historically the process of change in construction has been gradual for centuries but began to quicken through the era of industrialization, separation of the professions, emergence of the general contract system and the development of standard forms. The pace of acceleration has now become perhaps its most significant hallmark and it could fairly confidently be stated that change during the last two decades alone has been the most dramatic in history. Klaus Schwab of the Davos World Economic Forum observed: 'We have moved from a world where the big eat the small to a world where the fast eat the slow'.[4]

In a very short time the widest possible range of changes has come about including:

- new legislation, notably the Housing Grants, Construction and Regeneration Act 1996;
- new forms of procurement, e.g. design and build, construction management and management contracting;
- new management techniques, e.g. total quality management, business process re-engineering, value engineering and value management;
- new compulsory modes of dispute resolution, e.g. mandatory adjudication under the Housing Grants, Construction and Regeneration Act 1996;
- new training perspectives, e.g. through the Construction Industry Board;[5]
- new concepts such as buildability[6] and constructability;[7] buildability has of late even been seen to have been a factor in the reasoning of the courts in general terms in two recent cases, *George Fischer Holding Ltd (formerly George Fischer (GB) Ltd)* v. *Multi Design Consultants Ltd* and *Department of National Heritage* v. *Steenson Varming Mulcahy (a firm)*;[8]

---

[4] Klaus Schwab quoted in FRIEDMAN, THOMAS. *The Lexus and the Olive Tree.* Harper Collins Publishers, London, 1999, p. 171.

[5] See e.g. *Training the Team,* and *Educating the Professional Team.*

[6] See generally CIRIA. *Buildability: An Assessment.* CIRIA Publications, London, 1983, Special Publication 26; BISHOP, D. *Buildability: The Criteria for Assessment.* CIOB, Ascot, 985; ADAMS, S. Practical *Buildability.* Butterworths, London, 1989.

[7] *Constructability in Building and Engineering Projects.* Macmillan, London, 1995; and GRIFFITH, A. and SIDWELL, A.C. Development of Constructability Concepts, Principles and Practices. *Engineering, Construction and Architectural Management,* 1997, **4**(4), 295–310.

[8] *George Fischer Holding Ltd (formerly George Fischer (GB) Ltd)* v. *Multi Design Consultants Ltd* (1999) 61 Con LR 85; and *Department of National Heritage* v. *Steenson Varming Mulcahy (a firm)* (1998) 60 Con LR 33.

- new collaborative forms of working, such as partnering and alliancing;[9] and
- information technology.

Combined with other forces shaping the industry as a whole such as the trend toward specialist trade contracting; the creation of new roles among the project participants both at the site and delivery levels; single-point responsibility; and sophisticated risk analysis and finance structures,[10] change itself has become the driving force in industry and made it almost immeasurably complex. On top of these changes have come new industry bodies and configurations that must be taken into account. The most significant changes have followed upon the recommendations made by Sir Michael Latham in *Constructing the Team*[11] which included an Implementation Forum as one possible delivery mechanism to carry out his suggested recommendations and which subsequently became the Construction Industry Board. The Construction Industry Board, not even in existence a few years ago, now has 6 member bodies: Construction Industry Employers Council; the Government through various bodies; the Construction Clients Forum; the Alliance of Construction Suppliers; the Constructors Liaison Group and the Construction Industry Council representing some 140 other bodies.

In sum during the last two decades alone the construction industry has witnessed a revolution in its management, organization and method of work that is unparalleled in its history. What is more, amidst this tumult serious questions have also been raised about the nature and role that contracts should continue to play. Divergent views have been expressed on the topic and yet, despite the changes wrought within industry, contracts too have changed. Diverse new forms of procurement have evolved which now show change in a new light. Hitherto fresh perspectives and analyses are being taken up seeking better to understand both the relationship and importance of contracts to industry and vice versa. What is remarkable about the changes is that they have all shaped industry and also that they have all shaped the NEC. Once again a key question raised here has been whether a turning point has been reached. Much of the discussion in the preceding chapters has sought to address not simply this question but more importantly whether we should *turn away from* these changes or *toward* them. The unequivocal answer reached here is that we must turn toward change and embrace new paradigms. The

---

[9] See generally PIETROFORTE, ROBERTO. *Building International Construction Alliances: Successful Partnering for Construction Firms*. E & FN Spon, London, 1996.

[10] See generally SCRIVEN, JOHN. A Funder's View of Risk in Construction. In *Risk, Management and Procurement in Construction* (eds UFF, JOHN and ODAMS, MARTIN A.). Centre of Construction Law and Management, King's College, London, 1995, p. 71 and CHECKEN, JOHN C. Approach of Financial Institutions to Risk Assessment. In *Managing Risks and Decisions in Major Projects*. Chapman & Hall, London, 1994, pp. 19–33.

[11] Latham Report.

remainder of this chapter brings out some of the central features of the developing paradigm with regard to forms of contract and in particular the contribution the NEC is making to it.

A management imperative

If one characteristic can be said to be defining with regard to the NEC in contrast to traditional forms it is the *management philosophy* which pervades the form. John G. Perry called *management* 'the most important characteristic of NEC'.[12] As Barnes has remarked: '[t]he management of projects has become a science with its own set of rules, techniques and words which are not even mentioned in the existing standard forms'.[13] Others share his view.[14] Barnes' statement, however, was made many years ago. Since that time the NEC has helped to make the statement less applicable to subsequent new forms of contract.[15] The emergence of management as a science and project management as a specialization in relation to it has been noted.[16] The background and research interests of the principal drafters demonstrates their understanding of both concepts. The NEC expresses much of the learning that has taken place with respect to management precepts and how they pertain to construction projects. Until quite recently little attention had been focused on the application of management models to construction activities. It has been shown how this contrasts with the attention devoted to understanding and applying the models to other industries. The most notable illustration is that of the automobile industry and the lessons it may hold for the construction industry; however, examples of resistance to the adoption of project management concepts may also be illustrated.[17] The rousing of the construction industry to both management precepts and models can be seen in the return to a large private sector role during the 1970s. The changes during that decade produced ideal conditions for the creation of a new class of professionals – project managers – alone who could manage the increasingly complex construction process.

---

[12] PERRY, JOHN G. The New Engineering Contract: Principles of Design and Risk Allocation. *Engineering, Construction and Architectural Management*, 1995, **2**(3), 200.

[13] BARNES, DR MARTIN *et al.* Towards Simpler Contracts. BARNES *et al.* introducers. Reported by BARBER, J.N. In *Proceedings of the Institution of Civil Engineers*, June 1986, 80, part 1, 818.

[14] See in particular John Uff's paper Overview: The Place of Management in Construction. *Management and Construction Law*. A one-day seminar on 23 March 1990 by the Centre of Construction Law and Management. King's College, London, 1990, p. 3.

[15] Notably PSA/1 and the new GC/Works 1998 forms.

[16] See GRIFFIN, R.W. *Management*, 3rd edn. Houghton Mifflin, Boston, 1990, pp. 29–55.

[17] See DE HEREDIA, R. Barriers to the Application of Project Management Concepts Outside Entrepreneurial Systems. *International Journal of Project Management*, August 1993, 131–134.

Privatization in government departments and policy guidance underscoring project management in the delivery of new works furthered the growth and interest in project management as conceptualized and carried out by this new class since then; many of the Central Unit on Procurement guidance notes reveal a strong project management leaning. In part in response to these changes new forms of contract came into play. Parallel developments ranging from training and qualification to recognition of the emerging project manager also had to occur. In some ways addressing these and other issues were conditions precedent to the development of the NEC and what is, in some ways, perhaps the first *project management form*. Recognition of the unique position of the NEC in assigning a central role to both project management and project managers has been picked up by John Woodward as well as John Dingle.[18] The appearance of the management contract was similarly a likely necessary precursor to the appearance of the NEC, for the management contract in effect stands somewhere between traditional contracts and design and build forms. However, while the management contract shares the project management role between architect or engineer and contractor, the NEC *assigns* that role exclusively to the project manager. In so doing the NEC has innovated upon both traditional and modern forms to create something unique. If one stands back from this change and looks by comparison at the much longer periods of time that were required for comparable developments in creating and defining the architect's and engineer's role and eventual origin of discrete standard forms of contract reflecting those roles, the pace of change once again can be seen to be remarkable. Perhaps as interesting to note is that, while the professions' representative bodies, the RIBA and ICE, both played roles in developing the traditional standard forms, *no equivalent body* on behalf of project managers participated in developing the NEC. However, Martin Barnes has been the president of the Association of Project Managers. This is a telling distinction and calls into question some of the historical assumptions that existed with regard to the necessary role of profession-specific bodies in the creation of matching standard forms of contract.

Today a host of management principles relevant to the delivery of a construction project have largely been accepted and recognized as quantifiable. John Woodward, for instance, includes among them scope, procurement, planning and progress, time, cost, quality, people, risk, project success/failure and facilities.[19] The NEC can easily be explained with reference to these criteria, in part because it was premised upon certain key tenets in its drafting and consciously works towards their exposition. Michael O'Reilly tersely made the point: '[t]he principal innovations of the Engineering and Construction Contract include its use

---

[18] WOODWARD, JOHN. *Construction Project Management Getting it Right First Time.* Thomas Telford, London, 1997, p. 188; DINGLE, JOHN *Project Management Orientation for Decision Makers.* Arnold, London, 1997, p. 174.

[19] WOODWARD, JOHN, see n. 18 above.

and *promotion* of management principles ...'.[20] Some of these principles referred to in the discussion above have included foresight applied collaboratively to mitigate problems and reduce risk, and clear division of function and responsibility to improve accountability and motivation of people.[21] For example, throughout the NEC, management principles pertaining to time, cost and quality as well as explicit risk management, new roles and clear open communications have been integrated in the NEC and been placed at the forefront of project delivery. The means, range and techniques by which these management principles have been deployed have been discussed above and include the following.

- The choice of contract strategy in procurement in relation to the main options.
- The use of incentives in relation to the cost reimbursable main options C, D, E and F primarily through the definitions of 'Actual Cost' and 'Fee' as well as the contractor's share provisions. Incentives were also discussed in relation to the project manager's handling of both unforeseen events as well as uncertainties.
- Variable and clear risk alternatives in contract strategy in relation to the main options.
- Early warning procedures in relation to compensation claims, which according to Justin Sweet, is an example of good faith and fair dealing that, if accepted and used properly as an adjustment mechanism, can avoid the breakdown of a relationship and the economic dislocation cost associated with it.[22]
- Programming in relation to time.
- Compensation events in relation to risk management.
- Co-operative management in relation to dispute avoidance.[23]
- Adjudication in relation to dispute resolution.[24]

Other important illustrations include the provisions in the NEC regarding 'key people' under clause 24.1 of the ECC and part two of the Contract Data, as well as the clear relationships outlined between tenders and information provided to tenderers.

The techniques have been shown to be a more effective means to control, manage and deliver projects than under traditional contracts. Thus the NEC differs from traditional forms of contract not only in how far it has moved away from them to embrace management principles or tenets in the first instance but rather in how meaningfully, constructively and actively it has sought to *implement* and *apply* the principles as well in

---

[20] O'REILLY, MICHAEL *Civil Engineering Construction Contracts*. Thomas Telford, London, 1996, p. 316, emphasis added.

[21] See PERRY, JOHN G., n. 12 above, 201 and discussion in Chapter 3 above.

[22] SWEET, JUSTIN. Judging Contracts: Some Reflections on the Third International Construction Law Conference. *International Construction Law Review*, 1994, 428.

[23] See discussion of clauses 10.1, 25.1, 26.3 ECC.

[24] See clauses 10, 11.2(2), 51.3, (90, 91, 92, unamended and amended 2nd ECC) and 93 ECC.

contrast to traditional forms. In short, this is one of the most significant contributions of the NEC and has unquestionably set the stage for further re-engineering of the construction sector.[25]

The NEC delivers upon the management imperative it has set for itself through a variety of *means* and *tools*. One of the most important of these tools and which is the cornerstone of the NEC is the requirement to prepare and use a *programme* as a stimulus to good management. The flow charts are also central to one of the key drafting objectives of the NEC; that is, clarity and simplicity in the use and operation of the contract system. This use and elevation in importance of the programme stands in marked contrast to the way programmes have been dealt with under many traditional forms of contract. For example, JCT 80 requires the contractor to provide the architect with a 'master programme' for execution of the works, while ICE 6th requires the contractor to submit a programme showing the order for carrying out the works. FIDIC 4th goes further than either of these other two forms and imposes a duty on the contractor to submit 'a programme, in such form and detail as the Engineer shall reasonably prescribe, for the execution of the works'. The NEC choice is bold given that programming is still a relatively new discipline.[26] Ultimately, the NEC has overcome much of the legal and on site ambivalence toward programmes by permitting the parties to include the programme as one of the contract documents in the Contract Data and actually to use it in delivering the work.

The NEC programming provisions have moved best practice forward by introducing changes and underlining the importance of both *pre-project planning* and accurate *risk analysis* in the process. The programme provisions have also been seen to underscore many of the drafting principles upon which the form proceeded as well as the interdependent nature of what takes place on site. For instance, each participant must plan their progress with regard to the roles and responsibilities of others. The programme provides the axis around which these responsibilities importantly revolve. The true dependence of one upon the other to fulfil their obligations on site thus becomes evident by means of the programme. In this way the programme has become more than a management progress planning and control technique[27] to become rather a way of *improving relations* among the participants. This can be seen in the important values that are promoted through the programme. Take, for example, the best practice value dictating that problems and a range of different solutions should be explored and evaluated before

---

[25] See generally FLANAGAN, ROGER *et al*. *A Bridge to the Future*. Profitable Construction for Tomorrow's Industry and its Customers. Thomas Telford, London; Reading Construction Forum, Reading, 1998.

[26] See KUMLIN, ROBERT R. *Architectural Programming: Creative Techniques for Design Professionals*. McGraw-Hill, New York, 1995, pp. 3–6.

[27] See generally DAY, D.W.J. *Project Management and Control*. Macmillan, Basingstoke, 1994; and LANIGAN, MIKE. *Engineers in Business, The Principles of Management and Product Design*. Addison-Wesley, Wokingham, 1994, pp. 197–198.

resources are committed to a particular course of action.[28] In this way programming and planning are enabling more accurate estimates of the scarce resources to be employed in evaluating outcomes. Another value that NEC programming and planning tools are serving to promote is *motivation*. In general, it can be expected that individuals involved in something will take ownership in it. As such those involved in the preparation of a programme are being motivated to work toward project objectives and goals as a result of them now being shared.

One of the most important characteristics of the NEC is its understanding of and approach to *risk*. The allocation of risk in a construction project is in part a function of the standard form that will be chosen and in part the method of procurement itself. The NEC, through its various main options, allows some basic *choices* to be made at the outset regarding these issues. Each main option assumes the identification, classification and allocation of identified risks. Based upon the choices that have been made in these regards through various main options, a contractor is able to carry out the project in the most suitable way. The outcomes may be further influenced through a mix of secondary option clauses that also address risk. Aside from the core and secondary option clauses, risks are also being attenuated through other risk allocation tools such as sureties, bonds, guarantees, indemnities and insurance. In these ways the NEC regulates both the construction process and a wide variety of construction risks.[29]

However, for the most part the documents which comprise these risk allocation tools are outside the NEC contract system and it is a key recommendation here that they should be fully integrated and their drafting harmonized with the system as a whole. It may be noted once again that considerable emphasis has been laid upon the characterization of the NEC as a *contract system* – taken here to be 'a set of elements connected together which form a whole ... showing properties which are properties of the whole, rather than properties of its component parts'.[30] A systems approach overall has been advocated here as one of the more effective means to move forward on some of the broader objectives that the NEC drafters have articulated.

The NEC approach to risk involves a comprehensive vision. Through attention to risk management and risk allocation principles both in drafting individual clauses on indemnity, consequential damage, compensation events and the like, in addition to the contract system as a whole, *fair* and *equitable* choices have been made that positively impact both project performance and the owner-contractor working

---

[28] See e.g. Chartered Institute of Building. *Programmes in Construction – a Guide to Good Practice*. CIOB, Ascot, 1984.

[29] See generally ABRAHAMSON, MAX. Risk Management. *International Construction Law Review*, 1984, 241–244.

[30] CHECKLAND, P. *Systems Thinking, Systems Practice*. John Wiley, Chichester, 1981, p. 3.

relationship.[31] Put simply, under the NEC model risk allocation is *full*, *fair* and *explicit*. It is *full* in the sense that a complete list of risk events are addressed (primarily in clause 6 compensation events, but also in clause 8 risks and insurance, and clause 9 ECC disputes); it is fair in that it takes both cost and time effects into consideration[32] and it is *explicit* in that it is premised upon a set of verifiable principles.[33] The subject of risk in the NEC is clearly not only defining in terms of the form but is also the best evidence of its progressive outlook.

It has been shown in this book how the *choice of contract* or *procurement strategy* can be understood and the project managed in terms of risk. However, while empirical research has increasingly shown both the importance and relevance of this relationship, traditional standard forms of contract have made few concessions toward it. The failure of traditional forms in this regard has been noted[34] at the same time that the NEC has been hailed as the best and most obvious example of having taken risk into account.[35] The explanation in large part why this occurred is due to the close association of several of the NEC drafters and proponents to the pioneering of risk theory in relation to construction contracts. Leaving aside the details of the principles[36] that were developed, how they operate and specific illustrations of their application at this juncture, the drafters' approach was informed overall by broad intangible goals as well. Thus the NEC drafters sought to improve the management of construction projects and serve the long-term interests of the industry.

The drafters believe that the promotion of these goals is most likely to be achieved or facilitated through risk allocations and procedures for risk assessment which are *equitable*.[37] This premise has been examined critically in this book and found to be supportable and meritorious. It has been seen how the NEC is premised and builds upon both *fairness* and *co-operation*; specifically this book once again has sought to show how this

---

[31] See ASHLEY, DAVID B. *et al. The Impact of Risk Allocation and Equity in Construction Contracts: An Overview of Indemnification, Consequential Damages, Differing Conditions and Delay Claims.* A Report to the Construction Industry Institute. The University of Austin, Austin, Texas, November 1988, p. ii.

[32] See LANIGAN, MIKE. *Engineers in Business, The Principles of Management and Product Design.* Addison-Wesley, Wokingham, 1994, p. 198.

[33] See PERRY JOHN G., n. 12 above, 205 and discussion below; and NORRIS, C. *et al. Project Risk Analysis and Management.* The Association of Project Managers, London, April 1991, p. 89.

[34] See FURMSTON, PROFESSOR MICHAEL. The Liability of Contractors: Principles of Liability in Contract and Tort. *The Liability of Contractors* (ed LLOYD, HUMPHREY). Centre for Commercial Law Studies, Queen Mary College, Longman, London, 1986, 13.

[35] MORRIS, DR PETER. Current Trends in the Organisation of Construction Projects. In *Future Directions in Construction Law.* Proceedings of the Fifth Annual Conference of the Centre of Construction Law and Management. King's College, 1992, p. 191. See also Latham Report nos 2, 6, 7 and 12, 37.

[36] See generally PERRY, JOHN G., n. 12 above, 204–205 and discussion above.

[37] *Ibid.*, 204.

perspective can operate to achieve the drafters' intent to improve the management of construction projects and serve the long-term interests of the industry. This focus in the NEC not simply upon the parties' individual self-interests but on the wider issue of *industry* interests is arguably a departure from traditional forms. It would appear that John Uff, as early as 1991, speculated that if such an emphasis were to succeed it would be a remarkable achievement.[38] In more ways than not, the evidence with respect to whether this has occurred is not in yet[39] but signs of a shift toward its importance has begun.[40] Despite the absence of a complete empirical picture it would appear fairly indisputable that the NEC has still succeeded in promoting the *discussion* of the widest possible industry issues, how both contractual and project relationships bear upon them and how culture is relevant to the debate. The current culture of the industry nevertheless remains a significant challenge to the success of the NEC.[41]

Integration

The last 150 years saw primarily consolidation and perpetuation of a very similar set of principles underlying traditional general contracting. Whether the forms were public or private, civil engineering or building they shared certain common *characteristics*. Primarily, work was completed for fixed lump sums agreed in advance, architects and engineers played central roles in the administration of the contracts, and design and construction were dealt with separately. However, while these characteristics have been the central features underlying traditional general contracting throughout this period, it has been shown in this book how they have increasingly been called into question. The issue that has arisen for traditional forms of contract exhibiting these characteristics is what contribution do they really make to the well being of the construction industry.

The NEC has come at a time when the divisions between the building and engineering sectors have significantly diminished. Many building projects, for example, already contain large engineering components. In theory this fact and thus the necessity to work together should encourage *integration*. Working with mutual forms of contract should logically further facilitate it in turn. However, rather than having this occur the traditional forms of contract have actually slowed integration in

---

[38] UFF QC, JOHN Figaro on ICE – the ICE 6th Edition and the New Engineering Contract. *Construction Industry Law Letter*, 1991, 654.

[39] See COX, PROFESSOR ANDREW and THOMPSON, IAN. Is the NEC Going to Succeed? – An Examination of the Engineering and Construction Contract. (Alias the NEC 2nd Edition). *International Construction Law Review*, 1996, 327; BROOME, JON C. and PERRY, J.G. Experiences of the Use of the New Engineering Contract. *Engineering, Construction and Architectural Management*, 1995, **2**(4), 275.

[40] BROOME, JON C. *The NEC Engineering and Construction Contract: A User's Guide*. Thomas Telford, London, 1999.

[41] See ROOKE, JOHN and SEYMOUR, DAVID. The NEC and the Culture of the Industry. Some Early Findings Regarding Possible Sources of Resistance to Change. *Engineering, Construction and Architectural Management*, 1995, **2**(4), 287.

construction. The reasons for this have been suggested rather critically by Dr Peter Morris: 'Part of the reason is obviously the constraining influence of the traditional, JCT/ICE approach to construction procurement ... [and because] civil engineering, being public sector and less affected by commercial pressures, never strayed from the ICE form'.[42] This marks a significant departure from the very newest forms today, which do seek to achieve both integration and mutuality.[43]

From a strictly legal perspective, as law has erased material distinctions between building and engineering forms, perhaps practice should too. The law poses no impediment to this occurring. The NEC has striven to reduce formalistic sectoral divisions between the building and engineering sectors and thus work toward a *flexible multidisciplinary* form thereby underscoring what is common in the industry rather than what divides it; in particular, the divisions arising from traditional professional roles and the notional distinctions between main contractors, subcontractors, and specialist suppliers which the traditional forms have perpetuated. Certain principal factors have been pointed out in this regard, namely, the form applies across traditional sectors or disciplines; design responsibility may be varied; all procurement routes are allowed for and it may be used both domestically in the United Kingdom and abroad. Recognition of this has been achieved, and it is especially significant that the Construction Clients' Forum has endorsed the use of the NEC for *all* forms of construction.[44] In this way the NEC can be seen to be *leading* to a reshaping of both *attitudes* and *practices* in industry. Substituting a project manager in place of the architect or engineer so often cast in the defining role under the contract during the last 50 or 100 years will have manifest implications that have yet to be fully contemplated. Looked at dispassionately in this regard the form reveals *cross-disciplinarity*.[45] One result is that a project manager working under the NEC today can equally be expected to come from either traditional profession (architecture and engineering) and is just as likely to be engaged on substantially building as engineering projects. The new roles are compatible with the designation temporary multi-organization used today to describe construction projects[46] and operate through the NEC to permit a bridging of the previous divides. Conscious choices have been made by the drafters who put industry needs ahead of single professional groups. The choice is

[42] MORRIS, DR PETER, see n. 25 above, pp. 184–185.

[43] For example, PSA/1 and GC/Works 1998. Methods and systems to facilitate integration on projects are outlined by WEARNE, S.H. in *Principles of Engineering Organization*, 2nd edn,. Thomas Telford, London,1993, Engineering Management Series.

[44] Construction Clients' Forum. *Thinking of Building? A 5 Step Guide to Value for Money*. Construction Clients' Forum, London, 1997.

[45] See on the cross-disciplinary aspect PERRY, J.G. and HOARE, D.J. Contracts of the Future: Risks and Rewards. In *Future Directions*, see n. 35 above, pp. 81–97.

[46] See MAK, STEPHEN W. Risk Analysis in Construction: A Paradigm Shift from a Hard to Soft Approach. *Construction Management and Economics*, 1995, **13**, 387 and citing CHERNS, A.B. and BRYANT, D.T. Studying the Client's Role in Construction Management. *Construction Management and Economics*, 1984, **2**, 177–184.

exceptional given the sponsorship role of the ICE in the development of the NEC. This choice is endorsed here as being in keeping with the most progressive elements within the ICE as a whole. The ICE has re-evaluated important aspects of operation and goals at other times. J.G. Watson has noted:

> [t]he Institution moves with the times. Periodically, it has to adjust its method of promoting the acquisition and dissemination of knowledge, and to reassess the standards of qualification it imposes on its members, in the light of advancing technology and social change.[47]

The point then is that the NEC drafters have consciously adopted an industry or sectorally neutral approach in their drafting and one that can usefully serve as a harbinger for other drafting organizations.

The changes the NEC thus brings differ from much that has changed in the past. Too often the changes that have occurred in industry appeared only to be ad hoc and more in the interests of certain limited segments or individual constituencies than the industry as a whole. There has been an inability, fuelled in part by the admitted complexity which characterizes construction, to address industry needs at once and despite the argument that comprehensive reform would be the best way to proceed. Many of the existing and traditional forms of contract as well have simply been too closely associated with one sector or another, and with one specific constituency or another, to reconcile the industry's conflicting demands. A fully multi-partisan effort, or in its absence, a unilateral effort that can still attract support of the majority of partisans, has been required for reform to take root. While the NEC was a unilateral effort it has sought to appeal to a plethora of views. It has not received the support of everyone but the endorsement that it received from Latham, as well as its conscious attempt to address industry needs as a whole, still remain among the best reasons for others to support it. It is conceded that overall acceptability of the NEC might have initially been enhanced had there been broader representation from industry in its drafting and yet it should also be noted that the past has also clearly shown that achieving consensus itself can be a critical obstacle to reform.

The lack of integration in construction may be discussed along other lines. It may arise in terms of design construction interface; lack of shared knowledge or buildability, fragmentation[48] or even lack of cohesion. The design construction interface may be taken as an example. The NEC has departed from the dichotomous choices that traditional forms of contract present in terms of the design construction interface.[49] The lack of

---

[47] *A Short History: the Institution of Civil Engineers*, 2nd edn. Thomas Telford, London, 1988, p. 3.

[48] *Fragmentation* is considered by HARVEY, R.C. and ASHWORTH, A. *The Construction Industry of Great Britain*. Butterworth-Heinemann, Oxford, 1993.

[49] See MOORE, D.R. Buildability: A Problem of Managing the Transfer of Construction Process Knowledge. *Campus Construction*, 1995, **3**(2), 17–20; and MOORE, D.R.

cohesion is seen as a factor negatively impacting buildability. However one wishes to characterize issues of *division* the solution that is generally put forward is to increase integration as a whole both within industry and on the jobsite. Overcoming the breach between separation of design from construction has figured in many of the past reports on the construction industry and so too have certain of these other aspects. The various factors including the breach between separation and design have been summarized by Roger Flanagan *et al.* in *A Bridge to the Future. Profitable Construction for Tomorrow's Industry and its Customers.*[50] The reason is straightforward: the breach can lead to problems of responsibility and control. While traditional forms of contract have sought to make a contribution toward greater integration, in fact they detracted more from it. It is paradoxical that the NEC form, which has been contrasted to traditional contracts throughout this book, actually returns to a custom of close co-operation pre-dating traditional standard forms to facilitate integration. Yet, while this integration has been pursued, unlike traditional forms themselves, the NEC has skilfully accommodated more recent *organizational changes* within the industry, notably in terms of greater *choice in procurement strategy*; recognition of the growth and importance of *subcontracting*;[51] and the impact of *new management theories*. Taken together and in these ways the NEC has sought and successfully combined both the best traditions of and innovations in construction and contracting. A successful foundation has accordingly been laid by the NEC for still further integration and with the most sophisticated integrative tools.[52]

Structures and tools

The structure of the NEC is unique: a contract system comprising an interlocking family of forms premised upon the same drafting objectives, roles and responsibilities. The NEC is designed to operate on a fully *interlocking*[53] basis. This is a major difference from other standard forms and one of the principal advantages of the NEC. The absence of significant differences between the main and subcontract forms is one aspect of a true interlocking form. Dr Martin Barnes states: '[t]he text of the subcontract differs from the main contract only in the names of the parties and in a few details in the areas of payment and notice periods,

---

Buildability Assessment and the Development of an Automated Design Aid for Managing the Transfer of Construction Process Knowledge. *Engineering, Construction and Architectural Management*, 1996, **3**, 29–46.

[50] FLANAGAN, ROGER *et al.*, see n. 25 above.

[51] This has been measured in terms of value of all contract work according to firm size; falls in the total numbers of employees working under general builders and building and civil engineering contractors. See on the actual statistics COONEY, E.W. Productivity, Conflict and Order in the British Construction Industry: A Historical View. *Construction History*, 1993, **9**, 74–75.

[52] See generally BRESNEN, M. *Organising Construction: Project Organisation and Matrix Management*. Routledge, London, 1990.

[53] See Latham Report paragraph 5.18(3), 37.

insurance requirements and title to equipment, plant and materials'.[54] The uniqueness of the NEC is also in how it has affirmed[55] the importance of interlocking conditions across the project by encompassing consultants' terms of engagement as well. The importance of clear connections founded on good co-operative relationships will serve to reduce the potential number of claims themselves. The interlocking nature and logic of the contract system is reinforced from clause to clause (with references to incorporate the works information, site information, Contract Data, SSC and SSCC) and contract to contract (with core clauses presenting just nine essential issues to be dealt with by the parties). The integrity of the contract system as a whole is further reinforced through prescribed actions and agreed or programmed activities tied together through a set of common drafting objectives. Lastly, the stated objectives for the design of the NEC contract were to make improvements under three main headings: flexibility, clarity and simplicity and stimulus to good management.[56]

It has been shown how actions are at the heart of the NEC. Indeed, if the saying 'actions speak louder than words' is taken literally in this context then much of the force of the criticism directed toward the choice of language used in the form would dissipate. NEC actions are logical and focused upon clearly assigned responsibility for individual tasks. This intent simplifies procedures and will reduce disputes. The parallels to project management theory are evident: that is, being goal oriented and focused upon clear objectives to be accomplished by named individuals. The NEC makes these goals express in contrast to traditional forms. The discussion in this book has sought to show how the NEC is ultimately reducible to a sequential series of actions proceeding from the most general to specific. It has been seen how the NEC moves from broad statements in outline regarding the work through to tasks and subtasks thereby breaking the project, its management and delivery down into more and more manageable packets. Breaking down the work into packages and assigning individual activities to participants are further evidence of the embodying of project management principles within the form. *Actions,* as has been noted, are the most discrete form of activity. Placing the accent upon activities in this way could significantly change some of the assumptions made in traditional construction decision-making models and operations.[57]

[54] BARNES, DR MARTIN. The New Engineering Contract – An Update. *International Construction Law Review*, 1996, 90.

[55] See also UFF, JOHN and JEFFORD, NERYS. European Harmonisation in the Field of Construction. *International Construction Law Review*, 1993, 126.

[56] Guidance notes NEC, 1. John Perry provides a more specific elaboration of the drafting objectives – see n. 12 above, 200.

[57] See the conclusions drawn by ANGELIS, DIANA ISAZA. The Effects of Activity-Based Costing on Traditional Operations Research Models. Inventory, Lot Size, Scheduling, Break Even. PhD dissertation, University of Florida, 1996.

The NEC departs from traditional forms of contract in the reliance that it has placed upon *flow charts* and how they are situated at the centre of the drafting and administrative procedures. While it is true to say that flow charts also can and do play a part in the explication of other forms of contract today it is only the NEC which truly seems to have begun with and ended upon them. The NEC flow charts have not come as an afterthought. They have not been published separately by authors or been created independently of the original contractual procedures. Instead, the flow charts informed the drafting process throughout each successive stage and gave rise to the contractual procedures themselves. As a result of the choice to put the flow charts at the centre of the procedures there are no *culs de sac* in the use of the NEC. Each contractual procedure has a clear start and end point that can be found regarding every single action in the contract. This is a remarkable fact when one contemplates the myriad of actions and interactions that comprise construction operations. This book has shown that it is not just communication that is a problem in construction but communication in relation to the contract.[58] Thus, when the contract is not understood effective communication between the parties is inhibited. In general the use of flow charts in the NEC serves to promote best practice in the administration of the contract as well as foster open communication and understanding of the procedures across party lines. In summary, good communications are central to the success of both projects and the implementation of the NEC. Research has shown that projects are more likely to be successfully completed where open communication is facilitated among the parties. The NEC builds on sound management principles, formal and informal co-operation, specific rules and well-defined roles as federative mechanisms to overcome the rigid or closed communicative mechanisms and hierarchical provisions in traditional standard forms.[59]

The NEC distinguishes itself by setting out clear *drafting objectives* from the very beginning. The intention of the drafters was to improve contracts with regard to their flexibility,[60] clarity, simplicity and management.[61] The flexibility of the ECC has been seen to derive from four principal factors:

(1) the contract system is intended for engineering and construction work across traditional disciplines such as civil, electrical, mechanical and building work;
(2) the contract system can be used whether the contractor has some design responsibility, full design responsibility or no design responsibility;

---

[58] HIGGIN, G. and JESSOP, N.
[59] PIETROFORTE, ROBERTO. Communication and Governance in the Building Process. *Building International Construction Alliances: Successful Partnering for Construction Firms.* E & FN Spon, London, 1996.
[60] Guidance notes, 1.
[61] Guidance notes NEC, 1.

(3) it provides all the normal current options for types of contract such as competitive tender, target contracts, cost reimbursable contracts and management contracts;

(4) it can be used in the United Kingdom and other countries.[62]

The main means whereby clarity and simplicity have been sought to be introduced in the NEC has been through the ordinary or plain language drafting used in the form.[63] It has been argued here that several verifiable features of the NEC support the drafters' view that a greater measure of clarity and simplicity was achieved in the NEC than in traditional forms. Hence, for instance, there are fewer clauses used as a general rule than under other forms; the sentences are shorter; guidance notes have been introduced; flow charts facilitate use and understanding; and it is arranged and organized in a structure which should help users to gain familiarity with its contents. Recognition has come lately with the award of a 'winning document' seal of approval by the Plain Language Commission for the July 1999 release of the Short Contract.

It has been seen how the NEC also respects a series of more specific design objectives or principles that are central to the operation of the contract system.[64] These design objectives revolve around a choice of contract strategy;[65] varying levels of contractor design;[66] specific risk allocation in the secondary options;[67] maximum use of core clauses;[68] separate roles for key tasks;[69] motivations for collaborative working;[70] tight response periods;[71] specific rules for decisions;[72] early warning of potential problems;[73] one procedure to compensate for change/risk events;[74] advance quotations for compensation events;[75] compensation event payments based on actual cost and current programme;[76] methods and resources in the programme;[77] and speedy dispute resolution.[78] Taken individually, any one of these objectives in itself may not have a dramatic

---

[62] Guidance notes, 1.

[63] See generally BARNES, DR MARTIN et al., see n. 13 above, 818–821.

[64] These design objectives have been set out by John Perry: see n. 12 above, 200.

[65] See discussion main options.

[66] See discussion clauses 11.2(15), 14.1, 20.2, 21, 22.1, 23.1, 27.1, 60.1(1) and M1.1 ECC.

[67] See discussion secondary option clauses.

[68] It is recommended that all the core clauses be used unamended.

[69] For example, the separation of the roles of project manager, supervisor, and adjudicator.

[70] See e.g. clauses 10.1, 16, 13, 25, 26.3, 31.2, 31.1, 32.1, 36, 61.3, 61.5, 63.4 ECC.

[71] See e.g. clauses 13.3, 13.4, 13.5, 16, 17.1, 31.1, 31.3, 32.2, 35.2, 35.4, 36.2, 43.2, 45.1. 50, 51, 61, 62.3, 62.5 ECC.

[72] See e.g. clause 16.4, 60.1(7), 61.1, 62.3, 63.4, 64.1 ECC.

[73] See clauses 11.2(29), 11.2(30), 16, 32.1, 61.5, 63.4 ECC.

[74] See discussion compensation events.

[75] See discussion quotations for compensation events.

[76] See again discussion compensation events.

[77] See clauses 31.2, 32.1, 35.3 and 54.2 ECC.

[78] See discussion disputes and termination.

impact upon the operation of the contract, but, *taken as a whole*, they cannot help but have such an effect.

The timing of the embrace of these drafting objectives too must be understood and is deserving of mention. Most date to the drafters' thinking circa the beginnings of work on an NEC Consultation Document many years ago. At that time few of these objectives were really appreciated. However, since then, most have moved into the mainstream especially during the last few years. Some of the greater willingness to accept the assumptions upon which these design objectives have been based would undoubtedly have come from more empirical work of a cross-disciplinary nature in the intervening time as well as the greater penetration of project management tenets into construction theory. However, the point can still be made emphatically that the NEC too appears to have made a lasting contribution to their acceptance.

Fair exchange

The NEC redefines notions of risk and reward in terms of a *fair exchange*. The *quid pro quo* that parties to contracts expect has often fallen short. The NEC solution breaks with tradition in many ways. One of the best examples of this is the notion of compensation events. The concept is new and at the true core of the operation of the contract system itself.[79] By consciously choosing to compensate the contractor for *both* the time and cost effects of the occurrence of these stated events or risks, the NEC has made a significant departure from traditional standard forms, which typically deal with time and cost consequences as mutually exclusive alternatives. The concept challenges conventional wisdom and the way in which risks have been viewed and carried by employers and contractors alike. To reiterate, in the case of contractors, a contractual right to recover for both the time and cost effects of certain events has been conferred upon them; albeit neither would be awarded without proof of loss or entitlement. The choice was premised upon accepting that the occurrence of certain events entail both time and costs or expense. It was assumed from a risk allocation perspective that the contractor should be indifferent to the event and that upon its occurrence employers should be expected to pay for it in full.

The introduction of the compensation event gave rise to other important choices, namely, how any entitlement to time and money should be valued.[80] The drafters adopted a policy that assessment of a risk event would be based upon the forecast affect on the contractor's actual costs and programme.[81] It would follow a bidding or quotation procedure

---

[79] Compensation events are one of the three pillars on which unexpected risk allocations are made along with risk allocation by insurance, and risk allocation by termination.

[80] CORBETT, EDWARD. FIDIC 5th or a New Style Red Book? *International Construction Law Review*, 1993, 289 views it as important in the NEC that there are no neutral events in terms of risk allocation which would allow the contractor only time but no money thus leaving losses where they fall.

[81] PERRY, JOHN G., n. 12 above, 206.

– a form of negotiated agreement – before valuation was finalized. In this way the employer has been given greater control later in the process of adjustment than under traditional forms. The employer can ask for alternative quotations and prefer either cost or time oriented solutions. The objective is better to ascertain the true costs involved in addressing the event than simply through the use of tendered rates under traditional forms. In this way the NEC has moved toward an open book approach to pricing and valuation.[82]

In summary, the compensation event provisions break with past traditions where changes and variations among other risk events have been dealt with variably and perfunctorily.[83] It has been seen that one inevitable result of such past approaches has been an increased number of disputes. The NEC, by seeking fully, fairly and realistically to address these events or risks has moved closer to one of the drafters' key goals of reducing their incidence. Likewise, by openly acknowledging that change during the course of a project occurs[84] and addressing the actual or full time and cost implications of risk events through the compensation events provisions both parties to the contract have become better informed and more realistic about them.

The payment risk is one of the most problematic in construction and accordingly preoccupies contracting parties in many situations.[85] The NEC has been shown to be innovative in terms of its *payment mechanisms*. The NEC moves well beyond traditional forms of contract by effectively providing six distinct payment mechanisms. The emphasis is upon the *process* of pricing the works rather than the price. The NEC drafters appreciated the importance of the distinction here, and as a result stipulated the widest possible range of alternatives by providing in effect a single contract strategy with six different payment mechanisms. Designing and conceptualizing the NEC in this way radically simplifies how one regards the choice of form and method of procurement. In short, parties have been given the widest possible choice from the narrowest range of alternatives.

---

[82] See NORRIS, C. *et al.*, n. 33 above, p. 89; and PERRY, JOHN G., n. 12 above, 206; ABRAHAMSON, MAX. Risk Management. *International Construction Law Review*, 1984, 241; PERRY, J.G. and HOARE, D.J. Contracts of the Future: Risks and Rewards. In *Future Directions in Construction Law*. Proceedings of the Fifth Annual Conference of the Centre of Construction Law and Management, King's College, London, 1992, p. 91; and SCHNEIDER, MICHAEL E. Mastering the Interfaces – Construction Contracts Drafting for Dispute Avoidance. *International Construction Law Review*, 1993, 412.

[83] See generally AKINSOLA, A.O. Identification and Evaluation of Factors influencing Variations on Building Projects. *International Journal of Project Management*, 1997, **15**(4), 263.

[84] See LANIGAN, MIKE, n. 32 above, p. 200; and COX, ROBERT E. Managing Change Orders and Claims. *Journal of Management in Engineering*, 1997, **13**(1), 24–29.

[85] GREENWOOD, DAVID and KLEIN, RUDI. Security of Payment in the Light of the Latham Report: An Opportunity to Remove Unacceptable Risks? *Construction Law Journal*, 1995, **11**, 255 citing GREENWOOD, D.J. *Contractual Arrangements*.

Despite the conceptualized framework outlined here, the payment provisions do involve real complexity. Part of the explanation for this stems from differences across procurement modes and part may involve grudging recognition that many disputes raise payment issues and thus unusual detail has been called for in addressing that risk. These reasons could explain why the drafters have thus approached the payment issue with both care and considerable depth. The payment mechanisms have been explained at length in this book; however, at this stage one may step back from these specifics and view the subject more broadly. In doing so it can be seen initially that very little has been left open to interpretation in applying the mechanisms. Explicit definitions across a wide front have been given to terms. These definitions are, in addition to the SCC and SSCC, providing even further detail. One explanation for such detail is to reduce potential areas of disagreement in calculating payment but while the definitions are complex they can also be seen to apply logically according to the type of procurement strategy that is being implemented. The ability to work across the different strategies with often little more than changes to the meanings of the prices or allowed cost for each procurement route will ultimately prove advantageous for those who wish open accessible procurement alternatives to be available to them. This is a worthwhile trade-off for some of this complexity.

There are other reasons for remarking upon the extensive nature of the payment provisions in the NEC. The payment provisions serve several other important purposes as well; they tie together the mechanics of programming (the programme requirements are considered in advance of and stand as effective conditions precedent to the project manager receiving an application for payment) and activities (the activity schedule itself is a means of allocating the parties' respective shares and arriving at payment due), and they serve as a benchmark for controlling changes occurring during the project (in relation to time). Consequently, they implicitly support the drafters' objectives and reinforce the system aspects of the NEC. In these ways the payment provisions serve to foster integration during the construction process.

Much has been made of efforts by the drafters at times to seek to move practice forward. Another specific area where this is also true concerns *security*. The approach of the drafters is novel. Moving away from the style and vocabulary of real property precedents the drafters preferred to address the twentieth century interests that come into play when rights to possession are contested. The drafters' broad use of terms that apply equally across a spectrum of interests both inside and outside the working areas accepts the reality of construction today and the diverse nature of interests in goods that arise. The drafters have sought to situate the contest over those interests in a realistic and practical context and in doing so they have underscored the relevance of their choices. Rights to possession have been combined with rights to security originating under bonds, guarantees and trust funds in complementary ways that also bring out their similarities. The NEC adopts a comprehensive view with regard to security and offers a number of different mechanisms serving to protect the respective parties' interests both during the course of, as well as following, the stoppage of work. Advanced payment bonds, performance bonds and guarantees may seamlessly form part of the overarching contractual framework the parties put in place. Exceptional provisions with regard to trust fund arrangements may further complement that framework. While the bond and guarantee provisions correspond to other precedents in use, the same cannot be said for the trust provisions. These extremely new provisions have given NEC parties the means if they wish to put the fullest possible insolvency protections into place. Despite some criticism that the trust provisions go too far, such regimes have been successfully used in other jurisdictions and also been endorsed by Latham.[86] The NEC made a dramatic statement by including the provisions in the form and it may yet set the future direction for the industry in this regard. As trust funds in general can be structured to take into account general payment risks, if the HGCRA provisions prove unsuccessful in overcoming some of the more egregious abuses surrounding payment, the issue of trust funds may return to the fore once again.

Relationships

The foundation for all parties' actions in the NEC save the adjudicator is *co-operation*. The significance of beginning the contract with an affirmation of co-operation and imposing such an obligation upon the parties in clause 10 cannot be overstated. In the first place it has been shown how co-operative attitudes improve project success.[87] While some may argue that such a clause is devoid of content it has been argued that, on the contrary, it has the fullest possible meaning because it underscores the necessity for action with regard to every single obligation otherwise imposed upon those named in the contract. These have been held out to comprise some 60 or so independent obligations and it is said that this is the proper meaning to be given to the term 'actions' excluding those which are imposed negatively as when requiring an action to be refrained from.

Working back from jurisprudence which has developed the meaning of 'co-operation' in law it has been argued that the NEC case for recognition and inclusion of an express duty of co-operation was not only warranted but also fully justified. It was argued that the duty in clause 10.2 to co-operate takes future cases arising under the NEC out from under narrower interpretations which have implied the term effectively as

---

[86] The Second Edition of the NEC contains the trust fund provision following a recommendation to this effect in the Latham Report in paragraph 5.18(10), 37; see generally GREENWOOD, DAVID and KLEIN, RUDI, *Ibid.*, 255; and JENKINS, JANE. The Latham Trust Fund Proposals. *Construction Law Journal*, 1995, **11**, 262.

[87] See the discussion above and the reference to MORRIS, P.W.G. and HOUGH, G.H. *Preconditions of Success and Failure in Major Projects*. Major Projects Association, Oxford, 1986, Technical Paper 3.

one necessary only to ensure the fulfilment of preconditions to performance.[88] The express duty to co-operate in the form permits one to make use of co-operative jurisprudence that may be helpful to elaborate upon the meaning of the term as well as circumvent those limitations inherent in the cases. It can be expected that situations will arise in construing the NEC where it will be unclear who bears a particular risk and even the extent to which it should be borne if a shared risk. In these situations it has been argued that resort may be had to important *norms* based upon *co-operation*, *fairness* and even *good faith* to clarify these responsibilities in a *relational* context. It is quite likely that when the drafters fixed upon the concept of co-operation they were unaware of the growing influence of these topics in relation to it as theoretical constructs for modern models of the law of contract(s)[89] when models which emphasize co-operative and relational conduct over long periods of time and which involve not only the interests of the parties to the contract but those of others as well. The NEC has been situated in the context of these models and evaluated as a tool of co-operation in particular with the aim of achieving results in accordance with the purposes of the contract, the goals of the management model it prescribes and the industry in which it is used. The NEC is a precursor to what are forecast here to be wider similar trends in industry.[90]

A relational emphasis may be seen in the NEC which prioritizes values over hard and fast rules. In the close analysis of the provisions in the NEC time and again, whether through the activity schedules, the programme requirements or otherwise, the *interdependence* of individuals in social and economic relationships has come out. Similarly, to work in these relationships, it has been shown how *trust* and *mutual responsibility* are essential. The key elements in the context of the NEC once again are those of co-operation, fairness and good faith. Indeed, the Latham Report and much of what passed into law pursuant to the HGCRA has been

---

[88] For example, *Mackay* v. *Dick* (1881) 6 App Cas 251, HL; *Luxor (Eastbourne) Ltd* v. *Cooper* [1941] AC 108, HL; *Barque Quilpué Ltd* v. *Brown* [1904] 1 CLR 632 at 647; and *London Borough of Merton* v. *Stanley Hugh Leach Ltd* (1985) 32 BLR 51.

[89] See notably WILHELMSSON, THOMAS. Questions for a Critical Contract Law. *Perspectives of Critical Contract Law* (ed. WILHELMSSON, THOMAS). Dartmouth, Aldershot, 1993, pp. 17–21. MORRIS, PETER W.G. *The Management of Projects*. Thomas Telford, London, 1994, forecasts '[c]ontracting may begin to become less exclusively focused on the short term and concern itself more with the greater benefits that can result from longer term 'relationship' contracting', 291.

[90] ALGASOFF, S.A. and McDERMOTT, P. Relational Contracting: A Prognosis for the UK Construction Industry? In *East meets West*. Proceedings of CIB W 92 Procurement Systems in Hong Kong, 4–7 December, 1994, by the Department of Surveying, Hong Kong University. Hong Kong University, Hong Kong, 1994, p. 16 have suggested, relying upon work by ECCLES, R.G. The Quasi Firm in Construction. *Journal of Economic Behaviour and Organisation*, 1981, 2 that relational contracting is at work in the house building sector and that it is set to expand to other sectors if adversarialism in the industry is better addressed.

premised upon the need for greater fairness.[91] Good faith and fairness play a significant role in law in many jurisdictions currently and their influence can be expected to increase. The construction contract is more amenable to invoking notions of good faith and fairness than other contracts because of its long-term character. In the case of the NEC the express obligation to co-operate call both concepts of fairness and good faith in aid.[92] The concepts have been shown to be consistent with both the institution of contracting as well as the duty of co-operation at law. They could have been used to explain why the contract is binding and yet still provide a worthy justification for it. This view transcends once again subjective views of fairness basing it instead in the mutually agreed co-operative venture set out in clause 10 of the NEC. The perspective is consistent with the central role given to the contract here.

The NEC makes intelligent choices with regard to the *avoidance and management of disputes*. The discussion has shown how a diverse number of choices have been made by the drafters that should serve both these ends. In the first instance, the conscious attempt by the drafters to purposefully address these objectives began the distancing of the NEC from many traditional forms.[93] When greater co-operation, clearer allocation of risk, simpler language, clearer communication, and management procedures were added to these goals the NEC moved well beyond them. While these were the broad contours which the drafters pursued across the form as a whole, additional, discrete choices removed the NEC further from many other forms; choices ranging from the introduction of the schedules of cost components through to the use of activity schedules and removal of legal content to the works information. The combination of both general and specific choices by the drafters will serve to significantly diminish the role of conflict on site. Once again the NEC was premised upon such objectives. The discussion here has shown how these goals are supported by some commentators through their opinions and by others through their research. It is true this support and research is not always unequivocal or without qualification but the foundation has been laid in the process for a more empirical and rational assessment of the choices that have traditionally been made only in the

---

[91] It has been argued that both the Scheme for Construction Contracts and the HGCRA legislation itself clearly serve to emphasize a greater interest in the issue of fairness.

[92] A theoretical framework outlined for the NEC can be postulated in terms of both co-operation – the express statement thereof in clause 10.1 – and good faith and fairness impliedly influencing the interpretation and application of the form.

[93] Some commentators see disputes as more likely arising under traditional United Kingdom rather than other forms of contract, see CAPPER, PROFESSOR PHILLIP. Management of Legal Risks in Construction. A paper given to the Society of Construction Law at a meeting in Wales on 21 September 1994, p. 3, citing Thompson and Perry. *Engineering Construction Risks: A Guide to Engineering Construction Risks: A Guide to Project Risk Analysis and Risk Management*. Science and Engineering Research Council, Thomas Telford, Swindon, 1993, p. 36.

abstract. The NEC has moved contract drafting ahead by a generation in this regard.

In general, research suggests that people neither plan as carefully nor pay as much attention to their contractual obligations as has been assumed and rather it is *relations* which influence parties' attitudes toward contractual obligations and performance. It has also shown that people will perform disadvantageous contracts in the hope of maintaining relations or storing credits for the future. That future may be understood in terms of anticipating a subsequent contract with the same party or subsequent conduct within the same contract. People are willing to renegotiate in circumstances where certain risks have occurred and, in practice, a wider range of circumstances is recognized in the research as excusable than most contracts have traditionally provided for. *By keeping the lines of communication open and relationships on track when disputes arise the NEC is profiting from the insights this research has revealed.* These insights are seen not only in the tiered dispute procedures but in other aspects of the contract as well, such as the detailed quotation procedure in the form, the assumptions about equality the procedure makes and how it takes advantage of the parties' willingness to renegotiate in the face of changed circumstances.

Research also suggests that people will perform contracts because of the *relational* sanctions operating. One of the important ways in which these sanctions operate under the NEC is through the role of the adjudicator. Relational sanctions are reflected both in the number of internal remedies for breach available in the contract as well as relational dispute resolution mechanisms. Formerly, this function was largely fulfilled by the independent architect or engineer; however, under the NEC, it is accomplished through the adjudicator. Parties' continuing relationships mean that compromises are arrived at based upon their understood interdependence. The NEC has built upon this process of understanding and now more accurately reflects the relational norms existing in construction. The NEC has been shown to support adjudication in contrast to the traditional contract model of third-party arbitration. The weakness of arbitration in the traditional forms from a relational point of view is that it often cannot be invoked until after the relationship between the parties has been brought to an end. Thus the utility in any relational sanctions that could have been brought to bear in settling the dispute during the course of the enduring relationship will have been lost.[94] The NEC three-tiered dispute resolution and avoidance procedures therefore complement rather than undermine the contractual and social controls thereby serving to promote party co-operation.[95]

---

[94] See MYERS, JAMES J. Why Conventional Arbitration is not Effective in Complex Long-Term Contracts. In *Complex Long-Term Contract Structures* (ed. NICHLISCH), p. 503.

[95] See SCOTT, ROBERT E. Risk Distribution and Adjustment in Long-Term Contracts. *The Complex Long-Term Contract Structures and International Arbitration* (ed. NICHLISCH, FRITZ). C.F. Muller Juristischer Verlag, Heidelberg, 1987, p. 99.

The adjudicatory model that the NEC introduced is a precursor to the introduction of adjudication through the HGCRA. The move away from the quasi-arbitral role of both the architect and engineer in historical terms has been discussed. The NEC took this evolutionary change to a logical conclusion by isolating the adjudicator's role from that role's precursors. Today, in the most recent amendments to the Second Edition of the NEC, the intervention of the adjudicator is preceded by a formal meeting procedure as a first-tier form of dispute resolution. The adjudicator thus enters the setting at the second tier in what is a three-tier process of dispute avoidance and resolution. The adjudication provisions in the NEC were part of an early trend toward alternative forms of dispute resolution in standard forms.[96] However, the NEC has taken the trend further than most. The three-tier process is consistent with the theoretical explanation developed for the NEC. The explanation is posited upon construction projects involving long-term complex relations where parties will often have to continue to perform their substantive obligations under the contract even after disputes have arisen between them. By conceding this and expressly allowing for it in the dispute tiers, the overall objectives of the contract can therefore be safeguarded whilst the parties address their ongoing differences.

Public and private form

The NEC is one of the small number of forms of contract designed to be used unamended on both public and private projects. One question that this raises is whether this should influence the interpretation of the form as a result. In general, with a few exceptions such as tendering, the influence of either public law principles or concepts has been slight on principles of English private contract law. The tendency to regard English private contract law as a singular body of law and thus distinct from other areas of law has reinforced the separation of public law. However, important recent developments, such as privatization[97] and contracting-out, have served to lessen the division between public and private law. That there are tensions between the two areas of law there can be no doubt. One commentator, Jack Beatson, attributes this to the importance contract or private law attaches to certainty versus the more open textured nature of public law concepts such as fairness.[98] In Beatson's view, the line between the two areas will become increasingly blurred. Beatson, relying upon several recent cases[99] that have shown a willingness to

---

[96] See e.g. JCT 81, clauses 4.30–4.37 NSC/C, clause 24 DOM/1 and clause 59 GC/ Works/1 3rd.

[97] For instance in relation to construction through the Private Finance Initiative, see Royal Institution of Chartered Surveyors, *The Private Finance Initiative: The Essential Guide*. RICS Business Services, London, 1995.

[98] BEATSON, JACK. Public Law Influences in Contract Law. In *Good Faith and Fault in Contract Law* (eds BEATSON and FRIEDMAN), pp. 282–284.

[99] *Ibid.*, pp. 269–284 citing *Shearson Lehman Hutton Inc* v. *Maclaine Watson & Co Ltd* [1989] 2 Lloyd's Rep 570 per Webster J; *Interfoto Picture Library Ltd* v. *Stiletto*

invoke public law concepts in private law contexts, submits this is the best approach to take. The topicality of this question is underscored by the recent passage of the HGCRA. The passage of this legislation raises questions of interface. These questions include what affect the legislation will have on common law and whether and to what extent terms other than those provided by default may be implied. The intention here is not to seek to address these questions but to raise them and state that they will increasingly be in issue in construction law. To restate the point, a series of developments is taking place that will promote a re-evaluation of the relationship between public law and private law. The NEC, with its multidisciplinary character and inherent flexibility, is contributing to and should be a beneficiary of any moves to lessen the distinctions between public and private law.

Progress

> [N]ow is an important time for innovation to be high on our national agenda. Changes, for example to contractual relationships imple-mented as a result of Sir Michael Latham's review, could have a profound effect, for good or ill, on attitudes and behaviour. We must get it right.[100]

The NEC has brought to fruition earlier suggestions about how standard forms of contract may be improved. Some years ago at the Construction Contract Policy Conference,[101] participants foreshadowed some of the changes the new form anticipated. At that time a call was made for better management practices,[102] more emphasis upon incentives,[103] and greater attention to risk management.[104] These three factors were initially held out

---

Visual Programmes Ltd [1989] QB 433, CA, per Bingham LJ; and *Woolwich Equitable Building Society* v. *Inland Revenue Commissioners* [1993] AC 70, HL, per Lords Goff and Slynn; but see Beatson's reference to *Blackpool and Fylde Aero Club Ltd* v. *Blackpool Borough Council* [1990] 3 All ER 25, CA, and *R* v. *Lord Chancellor, ex p Hibbitt and Saunders* [1993] COD 326 suggesting a lack of willingness.

[100] BRANSBY, P.L. Towards a New Industrial Realism in Construction Research. *The Unwin Memorial Lecture 1994*. CIRIA, London, 1994. A paper given in London on 12 April 1994.

[101] The Conference was the first organized by the then newly formed Centre of Construction Law and Management at King's College at the University of London and took place 14–16 September in 1988. Papers delivered at the Conference were subsequently published in *Construction Contract Policy, Improved Procedures and Practice* (eds UFF, JOHN and CAPPER, PHILLIP). Centre of Construction Law and Management, King's College, London, 1989.

[102] See BARNES, MARTIN. The Role of Contracts in Management, and WINTER, JEREMY. New Roles in Contracting. In *Construction Contract Policy*, see n. 101 above, pp. 119 and 159 respectively.

[103] WALLACE, IAN DUNCAN. Contract Policy for Money. In *Construction Contract Policy*, see n. 101 above, 202.

[104] ABRAHAMSON, MAX. Risk Problems relating to Construction, and CHAPMAN, C.B. *et al.* Risk Theory for Contracting. In *Construction Contract Policy*, see n. 101 above, pp. 21 and 74 respectively.

as pointing toward a possible improvement in contract practices.[105] Today, with the benefit of hindsight, we can better see the new importance of these changes and how they are *redefining* both construction and contract drafting. However, full recognition of their importance is still not yet complete. The take-up or usage of the NEC was slow, mirroring other precedents, a critical juncture has arguably and plausibly been reached with usage accelerating.[106] Reaching this junction would also appear to coincide with similar tests for the general law of contract itself. In part, the ultimate take-up of the form will be affected by numerous factors outside the drafters' control. These factors include, among others, the availability of alternative forms which build upon and extend NEC features, the effect of the recent changes to the JCT, and even the place of Latham's reforms over time, particularly given how resolutely Latham endorsed the NEC in his report regarding assumptions for a modern form of contract and the recommendations that he made for its adoption.[107] The NEC could eventually only hold a niche place in industry similar to that which the BPF/ACA has come to hold, despite that contract system's promise, if momentum is not carried forward. One dramatic action that could be taken to increase the take-up of the NEC would be for the ICE, if it believed the NEC offered a better vision for the future of contracting, to cease production on new editions of the ICE form. This would send the strongest possible signal to industry that the NEC model is the new way to work in the future. However, in the absence of any empirical research suggesting that ICE form users would move to the NEC or not replace it with FIDIC or another form, the strategy is high risk at best. Nevertheless, it would make a statement. The view expressed here is that, if the NEC were only to occupy a niche position, a significant opportunity would have been missed to build upon the change and innovation the NEC has brought to construction and contracting. So what is the prescription offered here to move the NEC forward and create a true twenty-first century form?

The principal recommendation offered here to move the NEC forward in a constructive way is to develop a fuller complement of documents to extend the contract system. For example, the NEC contains neither a form of instructions to tenderers nor a form of invitation to tender on behalf of the employer and despite the suggestion to the contrary in the Latham Report.[108] While some extension is taking place it is occurring slowly and trails the lead now being set by other forms which have moved to include

---

[105] UFF, PROFESSOR JOHN. Origin and Development of Construction Contracts. *Construction Contract Policy, Improved Procedures and Practice* (eds UFF, JOHN and CAPPER, PHILLIP). Centre of Construction Law and Management, King's College, London, 1989, pp. 15–16.

[106] It was noted above that as of February 1998 some 6000 contracts had been let using the NEC mostly in the United Kingdom with associated subcontracts totalling approximately 200 000 but recent unofficial estimates suggest the NEC now leads the ICE form in usage.

[107] Latham Report, paragraph 5.19, 39.

[108] See the Latham Report, paragraph 5.20(6), 40.

a much wider range of documents.[109] The explanations given by the drafters in not extending the NEC as far as these other forms have are outweighed by the advantages to be gained in ensuring the widest uniformity across the contract system as a whole. The absence of a complete set of forms has been seen to lead to inconsistencies in wording or occasional lapses in terminology.[110] Thus, for example, the form of wording of the agreement both differs from and is inconsistent with the wording of the Sample Form of Tender. The consistent use of terminology should suggest that this not occur. The contractor agrees to provide the works in accordance with parts one and two of the Contract Data in the tender but in accordance with the '*conditions of contract*' in the agreement. As parts one and two of the Contract Data are not synonymous and exclusive only with the conditions of contract, a different agreement is reached depending upon whether the form of agreement or form of tender governs.[111] The uncertainty is exacerbated without a required form of tender, form of agreement, articles of agreement or recitals. This could give rise to a degree of uncertainty over which documents in fact comprise the contract. This uncertainty could be magnified in certain situations involving subcontractors seeking to rely upon the same terms in either the ECC or ECSC. While remedial steps have been suggested here they underscore once again the desirability of the *fullest* complement of documents to support the contract system as a whole. It has been suggested that to alleviate this risk the parties should clearly indicate, in either the sample Form of Agreement or a letter of acceptance, which documents these are.

An excellent counterpoint to the absence of the fullest possible complement of forms in the NEC contract system is one new volume introduced in the second edition of the ENAA Model Form of Contract for Process Plant 1992, volume 4, 'Work Procedures', comprising ten works procedures in total. The procedures are exceedingly diverse and include sample formats, tables, charts and even letters as well as other documents. It is paradoxical that a precedent for the ENAA Works Procedures is provided by those originally set out in the *Manual of the BPF System: The British Property Federation System for Building Design and Construction.*[112] The complement of documents in the BPF System extends to three appendices addressing schedules of responsibilities and duties, checklists, and other BPF System forms. Checklists in particular are deserving of special mention as they reduce the risk of details being left unaddressed by the parties. Checklists could easily be developed from the flow charts in most instances and would serve to overcome

---

[109] See e.g. JCT 80, JCT MW, IFC 84, JCT 81, FIDIC 4th, ICE 6th, NSC/A, DOM/1.
[110] D.G. Valentine has been the most astute and critical observer of the NEC in this regard.
[111] In the list of documents forming part of the agreement in section 3 the contractor's tender is specifically included.
[112] *Manual of the BPF System.*

unintentional omissions. It has been noted[113] that the use of a checklist would help to ensure the most comprehensive coverage of the details to be addressed in the works information and that, on this basis, a form of sample checklist has been prepared and included here. It should be noted that this is a sample checklist (see appendix 5) for consideration of preliminary details that the conditions imply and should be addressed in the works information before work begins. It does not seek to address those changes to the works information which arise after commencement of the works. The NEC form lends itself to the use of checklists – it is recommended here that such checklists should be prepared.[114] In summary, the BPF model presents a fuller picture of the best practice administration of a project and one which compares very favourably with the ENAA Work Procedures. It is submitted that further inspiration should be taken from both the BPF and ENAA models in this regard and with a view to improving upon future editions of the NEC.

The absence of certain documents may have other unintended consequences which can be illustrated by reference to the topic of partnering. It has already been noted that many features of the NEC either lend themselves directly or are similar to partnering;[115] in particular, the commitment to co-operation,[116] early warning procedures,[117] and the pre-pricing of variations.[118] It may even be suggested that what clause 10.1 anticipates itself is the notion of partnering. It was Latham, in his recommendation on partnering, who referred to and endorsed contract conditions that supported partnering. Latham singled out for attention those conditions which imposed a duty on the parties to deal fairly with each other in an atmosphere of mutual co-operation, as well as those imposing firm duties of teamwork; facilitating speedy dispute resolution; interlocking documents and risk allocation choices; predetermined adjudication; and incentives.[119] However, while it can thus be fairly readily concluded that the NEC is both compatible with and supports partnering as a form of organization or relationship management tool, more could still be achieved. A dramatic recent example of such an achievement is the recent release of the NEC Partnering Agreement using both NEC language and drafting conventions.[120] In this way, parties will

---

[113] BAIRD, ANDREW. The New Engineering Contract – A Management Summary for Plant Industry Users. *International Construction Law Review*, 1994, 114 and his suggestion of a checklist and how building upon this suggestion details of one such checklist have been included in an appendix here.

[114] Publications are increasingly promoting checklists, see e.g. the ICE Design and Practice Guides. Thomas Telford, London for examples; or *Briefing the Team*.

[115] See ROE, SALLY. Partnering in Construction. A paper given to the Society of Construction Law at a meeting in London in November 1995, 15.

[116] ECC clause 10.1.

[117] ECC clause 16.

[118] ECC clause 61.

[119] Latham Report, recommendation 19 paragraph 6.47, 62.

[120] More integrated partnering has been called for by some commentators: see e.g. ABRAHAMSON, MAX and WINTER, JEREMY. New Contract Systems –

now be more likely to consider partnering in structuring their relationships and where so acting be put in the best possible position to ensure that those details are consistent with and supported by the other NEC documents.

The recommendation that the complement of forms be further extended can also be considered from another perspective and in another way. One interesting key message for the construction industry that has been drawn from Technology Foresight is that '[d]esign should embrace customized solutions by using standard components which have the flexibility to accommodate a variety of uses and design solutions'.[121] The message can be applied to the way in which the NEC has been drafted or 'designed'. Rephrasing the message, it could thus be said that the 'document design (drafting) should embrace customized (main options) solutions by using standard components (main and secondary option clauses) which have the flexibility to accommodate a variety of uses and design solutions'. The NEC can build even further upon this. The rationale for so doing would be to offer the parties the utmost flexibility in making their choices while preserving at the same time a wholly consistent drafting style. How could this be achieved? If it were felt inappropriate to list further secondary options in each printed contract form or book then it is recommended that a further book, headed Engineering and Construction Contract, 'additional clauses', be prepared. This book could contain sample wording for a wide variety of additional clauses that may be relevant to individual project needs. Once again the premise here is that the availability of such additional clauses would not detract from the NEC contract system but support it.

Technology itself should be a factor when considering how best to extend the NEC. Software programs are currently available to handle the administration or planning aspects of the project bill preparation and contract administration ranging from estimating to construction management.[122] The drafters should similarly move forward independently or jointly to support the development of like programs for the NEC. The near future will require technology to be integrated into every facet of our activities. The NEC has moved toward this with a partial digitized version now available on compact disc. Another mode of delivery could be to permit downloading from either a dedicated Thomas Telford website or perhaps through the NEC Users' Group website for a fee. The complete NEC contract system should be put on a searchable compact

---

Permanent Change or Fashion? *The Building of Construction Law.* A Paper presented at the Tenth Annual Construction Conference on 19 September 1997 by the Society of Construction Law and Centre of Construction Law and Management. King's College, London, 1997.

[121] FLANAGAN, ROGER *et al.*, see n. 25 above, p. 27.

[122] For example, ICEPAC, ICEMATE and CHEOPS software developed jointly by Thomas Telford and CSSP. REISS, GEOFF *Project Management Demystified: Today's Tools and Techniques,* 2nd edn. E & FN Spon, London, 1995, p. 177 notes there are some 150 or so project planning software packages which are now available.

disc. It is recommended this innovation be extended. Notwithstanding the excellent index in the latest edition, a fully searchable compact disc would enable users to customize searches according to their own preferences. A digital format would also facilitate the use of secondary option clauses etc. as the contract could be put together precisely according to the parties' specifications and then printed. No superfluous clauses, for instance, would need to be included. It could also serve to ensure that unintentional gaps were overcome. As a final observation and, admittedly, only a cosmetic one, if the parties wished their contracts to be held in the colour-coded covers the family of forms is currently sold with then such covers could either be sold separately or made available, again digitally, and then output on a laser printer.

Turning from the subject of the complement of documents to another which is likely to continue to remain controversial regarding the NEC, that of language. Criticisms have been made with regard to the language of the NEC and some of them have been agreed with here.[123] The point is that the move toward increasing use of *plain language* conventions may be isolated from some of the legitimate criticisms. These criticisms can be separated from the plain language attributes of the NEC itself.[124] It is submitted here that the benefits of adopting a plain language approach stand apart from occasional weaknesses with regard to the wording of individual clauses. The use of the present tense throughout the NEC remains unusual at best and likewise occasional overuse of bullet points would appear to detract too much from the precision that is sometimes called for, especially in the absence of cross-references as a matter of principle.[125] Future editions of the NEC may have to revisit both issues and consider whether the intended benefits of these drafting practices are outweighed by greater user resistance to the form because of them. The suggestion is not that either plain language or bullet points be done away with, only that some modest changes to them may be needed to address the more legitimate criticisms raised regarding them. In addition, future editions may wish to revisit the effect of certain declarative statements in the conditions which could operate as, or may be more readily clarified if turned into, full definitions. Other more specific recommendations with regard to certain details surrounding the language, format and length have been set out in the commentary above.

The NEC has at times not positioned itself to gain the most profit from its own advantages. Two cases in point may be given. The first concerns *quality management* while the second concerns the Contractor's share provisions and their relationship to *value management*. To take quality in

---

[123] In particular some criticism has been addressed regarding some definitions, italicization, capitalization and identification of terms in Chapters 3 and 7 above.

[124] Notably, shorter sentences, familiar words, active voice, vertical lists for complicated text and minimal cross-references: see generally CUTTS, MARTIN. *The Plain English Guide*. Oxford University Press, Oxford, 1995.

[125] See e.g. clauses 11.2(30) and 80.1 ECC.

the first instance, it can be said that the NEC has made few retreats in its march from Consultation Document through to First and Second Editions. However, one clear exception to this, and where in the view stated here the form has been less progressive than it should have been as a result, pertains to quality management; in particular when quality is such an integral part, and one of the core tenets of, project management.[126] It has been seen in the commentary above that core clause 4 was originally headed 'Quality' rather than the current 'Testing and Defects'. The two headings are distinct and underscore a different orientation; quality suggesting *process* with testing and defects implying *outcome*. Given that the NEC is devoted to procedures it seems incongruous this choice was made and no mandatory quality assurance programme was stipulated. It would seem to be an unnecessary omission when many of the most important principles underlying such programmes remain in the contract system.[127] Further, given the increasing attention being devoted to quality management as a whole in construction[128] and other industries the form should seek to contribute to rather than detract from these developments. Consequently, the NEC provisions now contrast with more progressive provisions in some other forms imposing express quality assurance obligations[129] and in this instance unusually parallel many traditional forms. The central role that programmes play, as well as the stress placed upon dispute avoidance in the NEC contract system, makes the form ideally suited to an express quality management obligation. In summary, while there may be explanations for the ambivalence of both the common law and traditional forms toward quality management[130] it is suggested here that a twenty-first century form should adopt the most proactive stance toward this issue.

The second illustration to be discussed differs in degree. Unlike the issue raised regarding quality management the drafters have not retreated in their stand but merely failed to capitalize fully on the opening they created. It concerns once again the contractor's share provisions and how they could have been better used to reinforce the concept of *value management*. The importance of value management and the increasing attention being given to it is a reflection of the changing nature of the United Kingdom construction industry; it particularly reflects competitive fee bidding for consultants, diversity in procurement routes, redefinition

---

[126] See generally BARBER, J. and ASHFORD, J.L. *Quality Management in Construction – Contractual Aspects.* CIRIA, London, 1992, CIRIA Special Publication 84.

[127] The omission is made more obvious by the express inclusion of quality assurance provisions in clause 40.1 of the PSC First and Second Editions.

[128] Developments furthered through European Union Directives regarding technical harmonization of products; health and safety at work; public procurement and post-construction liability and as discussed above.

[129] See e.g. clause 4.8 FIDIC Orange Book 1st part I.

[130] The ambivalence was noted by UFF, JOHN, in Overview: The Place of Management in Construction. *Management and Construction Law.* A one-day seminar on 23 March 1990 by the Centre of Construction Law and Management. King's College, London, 1990, pp. 11–12.

of roles in industry and moves toward single-point responsibility and management of the total construction process.[131] The NEC implicitly admits of value management through the contractor's share provisions and more emphasis should have been devoted to the subject. This seems like a missed opportunity that could have been used to show how the form supports progressive management tools. Some attention should be given to this in future editions, ideally in the conditions, but alternatively, at least in the guidance notes. It is only by drawing the attention of parties to value management that the best use of and fullest implications from the concept will be realized.[132] The NEC should seek to continue both to shape as well as be shaped by the industry.

The NEC has held itself out as having the ambitious aim of improving the management of construction projects and serving the long-term interests of the industry. A host of factors are influencing the shape of the industry today and many of them have been referred to here. Notwithstanding that influence, it is telling that the NEC itself has become an *agent of reform*. This may be the most significant aspect of the express references that Latham made with regard to the NEC. It may even be why Latham held out the NEC as a model in the way in which he did. That is, in so doing Latham *challenged* existing professional institutions and industry assumptions. Too much should not be read into the fact that the ICE stands behind the form and thus was not meant to be threatened by its ideas for, as has been implied in this book, and perhaps as Latham also saw, the NEC has transcended the ICE as an institution and its message is not weakened by still having the ICE's support. What was the challenge that Latham laid down? It was perhaps not literally to adopt the NEC – but simply to *change*. Latham said, in effect, that if the industry continues to repeat the mistakes of the recent (and distant) past it would be doomed. Latham thus dared the industry to open up to new ideas, fresh outlooks, empirical perspectives, changed methodologies, and novel reconfigurations and in this dare recognized what it is that the NEC truly represents.

The future

If one is trying to anticipate how the construction industry will change as it moves into the 21st century ... what we are likely to see is a wider and more realistic approach to risk identification and allocation; and a greater degree of attention to those features of any particular project which render it different from the 'norm' for which most standard forms are intended.[133]

[131] See KELLY, JOHN and MALE, STEVEN. *Value Management in Design and Construction. The Economic Management of Projects*. E & FN Spon, London, 1993, pp. 4–7.

[132] Express provision for value engineering is made in clause 14.2 of FIDIC Orange Book.

[133] DERING, CHRISTOPHER. Risk Sharing and Contract Forms: Devising Appropriate Contract Terms. In *Future Directions*, see n. 82 above, p. 99.

It is remarkable that it is now many years since the ICE Council decided to lead a fundamental review of 'alternative contract strategies' for civil engineering design and construction.[134] This book has been about whether and to what extent the promise the review held out for best practice in the future has been realized. Surprisingly, not very long ago a general view was held that no single form of contract could deal with every situation.[135] This view contributed to the inappropriate use of traditional forms in many situations when other modes of procurement would have been better advised. Since that time the outcome of the review through the NEC has become known. In the result, the NEC has *encouraged* more wide-ranging views on contract strategy, risk analysis, and project-specific standard form documentation than at any time before. What is more is that these views are now also *better understood* by a wider range of stakeholders in industry than would have been thought possible this past decade. In part, this understanding has come about from a revolution in perspectives, ideals, and practice; however, this understanding has also come about through the NEC itself. The NEC began with vision and through its development has served to move both a new vocabulary and perspective into the mainstream. It has, in a short space of time, taken not only the *surprise* out of the view that no single form of contract could deal with every situation but also removed the qualification that such form would be *alternative*.

---

[134] Guidance notes First Edition, NEC, 1.
[135] KENNEDY, JOHN and DAVIES, ROGER, the preface to *Future Directions*, see n. 82 above, p. iv.

Appendix

Appendix 1. Reports on the construction industry

1. SIMON, E.D. *The Placing and Management of Building Contracts.* HMSO, London, 1944.
2. EMMERSON, SIR H. *The Ministry of Works.* George Allen & Unwin, London, 1956.
3. EMMERSON, SIR H. *Survey of Problems Before the Construction Industries*, Report prepared for the Ministry of Works. HMSO, London, 1962.
4. HIGGIN, G. and JESSOP, N. *Communications in the Building Industry: A Pilot Study,* Commissioned by the National Joint Consultative Committee of Architects, Quantity Surveyors and Builders. Tavistock Institute of Human Relations, London, 1963.
5. BANWELL, SIR HAROLD. *The Placing and Management of Building Contracts for Building and Civil Engineering Works.* HMSO, London, 1964.
6. Tavistock Institute of Human Relations. *Interdependence and Uncertainty: A Study of the Building Industry.* Tavistock Publications, London, 1966.
7. National Economic Development Office. *Action on the Banwell Report.* NEDO, London, 1967.
8. National Economic Development Office. *Contracting in Civil Engineering since Banwell: A Survey of the Implementation of the Recommendations of the Committee under the Chairmanship of Sir Harold Banwell on the Placing and Management of Contracts.* NEDO, London, 1968.
9. National Economic Development Office. *The Professions and their Role in Improving the Performance of Construction Industries – A Feasibility Study.* NEDO, London, 1975.
10. British Property Federation. *Manual of the British Property Federation System for Building Design and Construction.* British Property Federation, London, 1983.
11. FINNISTON, M. *Engineering the Future, Report of the Committee of Inquiry into the Engineering Profession.* HMSO, London, 1980.
12. *Trust and Money, Interim Report of the Joint Government/Industry Review of Procurement and Contractual Arrangements in the United Kingdom Construction Industry.* HMSO, London, December 1993.

13. HAWKE, M. *Mythology and Reality: The Perpetuation of Mistrust in the Building Industry*. CIOB, ASCOT, 1994. CONSTRUCTION PAPER 41.

14. LATHAM, SIR M. *Constructing the Team, Final Report of the Joint Review of Procurement and Contractual Arrangements in the United Kingdom Construction Industry*. HMSO, London, July 1994.

15. LEVENE, P. *Construction Procurement by Government: An Efficiency Unit Scrutiny*. HMSO, London, 1995.

16. HM Treasury. *Setting New Standards: A Strategy for Government Procurement*. HMSO, London, 1995.

17. Audit Commission. *Just Capital: Local Authority Management of Capital Projects*. HMSO, Audit Commission, London, 1996.

18. EGAN, SIR J. *Rethinking Construction: The Report of the Construction Task Force to the Deputy Prime Minister on the Scope for Improving the Quality and Efficiency of UK Construction*. Department of the Environment, Transport and the Regions, London, 1998.

Appendix 2. Original NEC Working Group Members

R.L. Wilson, CBE, BSc(Eng), FEng, FICE, Vice-President, Institution of Civil Engineers; Chairman, Travers Morgan.

Professor Max W. Abrahamson, BA, LLB, FCIArb, Lawyer, Consultant, Baker & McKenzie.

Nael G. Bunni, BSc, MSc, PhD, FIEE, FICE, FIStructE, FCIArb, Senior Director, T.J. O'Connor & Associates.

J.A. Chandler, MA, CEng, FIEI, FICE, FCIArb, Head Contract Services Shell UK Exploration and Production.

L.T. Eames, BSc, FRICS, MCIOB, Commercial Director Costain Civil Engineering Ltd.

F. Griffiths, CEng, FIEE, FInstPS, FBIM, Consultant, Frank Griffiths Associates Ltd, and the Chartered Institute of Purchasing and Supply.

W.S. McAlonan, MSc, FEng, FICE, FIHT, Consultant, formerly Director of Roads, Strathclyde Regional Council.

*T.H. Nicholson, BSc, CEng, FICE, Consultant, formerly Group Manager ICE Fine Chemicals Engineering.

*T.W. Weddell, BSc, CEng, DIC, FICE, FIStrucE, ACIArb, Consultant, Travers Morgan.

*Dr Martin Barnes, BSc(Eng), PhD, FICE, FCIOB, CIMgt, ACIArb, MBCS, FRSA, FEng, FInstCES, FAPM. Currently Dr Barnes is the Executive Director of the Major Projects Association.

*Prof John G. Perry, MEng, PhD, CEng, MICE, MAPM.

S.C. McCarthy, BE, MSc, PhD, MIEI, University of Birmingham assisted in the preparation of the flow charts.

A. Norman, BSc, MSc, CEng, MICE, MAPM University of Manchester Institute of Science and Technology.

P.A. Baird, BSc, CEng, FICE, M(SA)ICE, MAPM, Corporate Contracts Consultant, Eskom South Africa.

L.T. Eames, BSc, FRICS, MCIOB; J Halliday, CEng, MICE; K Lumb, FRICS, ACIArb.

I.M.H. Moore, CBE, Director of External Affairs ICE.
J.J. Lewis Project Manager, June 1991 – January 1992.
R.F. Bell, BSc, CEng, FICE Project Manager.

The members of the drafting team are noted with an asterisk. The last six
individuals listed above were added at the First Edition stage of the NEC.
The Second Edition of the NEC documents was produced by the ICE
through its New Engineering Contract Panel which comprised Dr Barnes
(Chairman), P.A. Baird, L.T. Eames, T.H. Nicholson (Secretary), M.A.
Noakes, Prof. John Perry, N.C. Shaw FCIPS, CEng, MIMechE, and T.W.
Weddell. In addition acknowledgments in the preparation of the Second
Edition were also given to J.C. Broome, BEng, Prof. P.N. Capper, G.C.
Dixon, MA, D.P. Maidment, ACII and A. Norman. The drafting team for
the Professional Services Contract and Adjudicator's contract comprised
Peter Higgins, F. Griffiths, and M. Coleman of the Association of Project
Managers with Dr Barnes advising on co-ordination with the NEC Panel.
The PC was drafted by a Task Group of the NEC Panel whose members
were P.A. Baird, N.C. Shaw, and A.R. Westbrook. A.R. Westbrook was the
only Task Group member who was not also a member of the NEC Panel.
Mr Westbrook, FRICS, O'Brien-Kreitzburg, was formerly with BAA Plc.

Appendix 3. Adjudication Table

Dispute about:	Which Party may submit it to the *Adjudicator?*	When may it be submitted to the *Adjudicator?*
An action of the *Project Manager* or the *Supervisor*	*The Contractor*	Between two and four weeks after the *Contractor's* notification of the dispute to the *Project Manager*, the notification itself being made not more than four weeks after the *Contractor* becomes aware of the action.
The *Project Manager* or *Supervisor* not having taken an action	*The Contractor*	Between two and four weeks after the *Contractor's* notification of the dispute to the *Project Manager*, the notification itself being made not more than four weeks after the Contractor becomes aware that the action was not taken
Any other matter	Either Party	Between two and four weeks after notification of the dispute to the other Party and the *Project Manager*

Appendix 4. Tribunal Clauses[1]

Executive Tribunal for use with Eskom NEC Documents

Purpose	1	To describe the composition and function of the Executive Tribunal referred to by the Contract Data in Eskom NEC documents.
Scope	2	This procedure is the first stage of the *tribunal* referred to in the above named Conditions of Contract. The procedure commences when any Party wishes to exercise its rights in respect of the *tribunal* as stated in section 9 of the Core Clauses and as further identified in the Contract Data provided by the *Employer*.
References	3	The only references that apply are the *conditions of contract* that have been identified in the Contract Data provided by the *Employer* and in particular the Dispute Clauses in section 9 of the Core Clauses, together with all the documentation included in the contract in dispute and the documentation relating to the dispute itself. The references are interpreted in accordance with the conditions of contract.
Definitions	4	The defined and identified terms used in the conditions of contract apply also to this procedure. In addition the following definitions apply for the purpose of this procedure.

(1) Senior Executive is a person employed by a Party who in terms of this employment has a beneficiary interest in the Party and the authority to make decisions on behalf of the Party whether in terms of this contract or otherwise. He is not the *Project Manager*, *Supervisor* or any of the *Contractor's* key people named in this Contract Data.

(2) Support Group is a person employed by either Party as a key witness or legal advisor and may include the *Project Manager*, *Supervisor* or any of the *Contractor's* key people stated in the Contract Data provided by the *Contractor*.

(3) Settlement is an agreement acceptable to the Parties in dispute which terminates the dispute and excludes any right of subsequent appeal to a court of law or arbitration of any subsequent reference to the dispute.

---

1 The tribunal clauses are reproduced with the permission of Andrew Baird [ed: please obtain] from 'Pioneering the NEC System of Documents,' *Engineering, Construction and Architectural Management* 2, no 4 (1995): 249, 267–269 Appendix B.

Actions	5	The Parties, their Senior Executives, the Support Group and the *Project Manager* shall act as stated in this procedure.
Composition of the Executive Tribunal	6	
	6.1	The Executive Tribunal comprises of two Senior Executives from each Party.
	6.2	A neutral third party who is not the Adjudicator may by mutual consent of the Parties assist the Parties as a facilitator.
	6.3	The Executive Tribunal may by consent of all members invite the Support Group to give depositions relating to the dispute during the Executive Tribunal proceedings.
Agreement	7	The Parties in dispute agree, in good faith, to use their best endeavours to reach a Settlement and agree to conduct the Executive Tribunal proceedings in a professional manner.
Project Manager to convene Manager first meeting	8	Within two weeks of a Party giving to the other a notice to refer the dispute for Settlement to the tribunal, or any longer period agreed by the Parties, the Project

- Notifies each Party of the otherís Senior Executives and Support Group who will attend or be available for the purposes of the Executive Tribunal
- Arranges a neutral venue for the Executive Tribunal which is acceptable to the Parties
- Confirms the date and time of the first meeting.

Executive Tribunalís first meeting	9	
	9.1	The Senior Executives and the facilitator (if any), start the meeting by agreeing to an agenda for the meeting and the procedure to be followed during the meeting for hearing presentations by members of the Support Group if required.
	9.2	The Executive Tribunal proceedings are based on the dispute reference, or upon the obstacle to Settlement within the reference.
	9.3	The Executive Tribunal continues during the day(s) agreed until a Settlement is reached, or one Party withdraws, or the facilitator (if any) is of the view that further effort at mediation would not be worthwhile.

Executive Tribunal's second meeting	10	

10.1 If a Settlement is not reached, either at the first meeting or within a period of six weeks thereafter, the Project Manager convenes a second meeting at a venue and time agreed by the Parties.

10.2 At the second meeting the Senior Executives (only) of each Party decide to submit the remaining matter in dispute to

- Expedited arbitration by a single arbitrator conducted according to the rules issued by . . . ., this decision being deemed to be a binding agreement in terms of the Arbitration Act. . .
- full arbitration by a single arbitrator in terms of the *arbitration procedure*
- court proceedings by the . . . Court having jurisdiction

10.3 If no agreement is reached within the day of the second meeting, all Parties reserve their respective rights and the dispute is referred to court proceedings.

The Settlement	11	

11.1 No agreement as to the terms of any Settlement reached during the Executive Tribunal is legally binding unless and until it is reduced to writing and signed by the Senior Executives of both Parties.

11.2 The Parties are legally bound to any Settlement so reduced to writing and signed and undertake to give effect to such settlement in accordance with its terms.

11.3 If a Party fails to give effect to a Settlement within the stated terms, then the other Party is released from the terms of the Settlement if they so wish by written notice to the other Party.

Costs	12	Each Party bears its own cost of the Executive Tribunal. All other costs are borne by the Parties in equal shares.

Appendix 5. Sample Works Information Checklist

No	Item	Section	Employer or Contractor
1.	Has WI been given?	11.2(5)	
1.1	Are works specified and described in WI?	"	
1.2	Are any required constraints stated in WI?	"	
1.3	Is all required information listed in documents in Contract Data?	"	
1.4	Is there any additional information to be given by instruction?	"	
2.	Has WI excluded any equipment?	11.2(11)	
3.	Does WI state work to be done by completion date?	11.2(12) 11.2(13)	
4.	Are all parts of the works capable of measurement in accordance with the WI?	11.2(15)	
5.	Are health and safety requirements stated in WI?	18.1	
6.	Verify WI imposes no illegal or impossible requirements.	19.1	
7.	Have parts of works which contractor to design been stated?	21.1	
8.	Are particulars of contractorís design required to be submitted for acceptance stated?	21.2	
9.	Should WI restrict use of contractor's design by employer for any purpose connected with construction, use, alteration or demolition of the works?	22.1	
9.1	Does employer require consent from contractor for use of his design for other purposes?		
10.	Have requirements for sharing of the working area with others been stated in WI?	25.1	
11.	Is there work of the employer to be shown in WI	31.2	
11.1	Is there work of others to be shown in WI?	"	
12.	Have additional programme requirements been stated?	31.3	
13.	Have facilities to be provided by employer been stated?	33.2	
13.1	Have facilities to be provided by contractor been stated?	"	
13.2	Have services to be provided by employer been stated?	"	
13.3	Have services to be provided by contractor been stated?	"	

No	Item	Section	Employer or Contractor
14.	Should reasons for take over of the works by employer before completion be stated?		
15.	Have all test and inspection requirements been stated in WI?	40.1	
15.1	Does the contractor provide materials for tests and inspections?	40.2	
15.2	Does the contractor provide facilities for tests and inspections?	"	
15.3	Does the contractor provide samples for tests and inspections?	"	
15.4	Does the employer provide materials for tests and inspections?	"	
15.5	Does the employer provide facilities for tests and inspections?	"	
15.6	Does the employer provide samples for tests and inspections?	"	
16.	Are all plant and materials to be tested before delivery stated?	41.1	
16.1	Are all plant and materials to be inspected before delivery stated?	"	
17.	Are conditions to be imposed on work of employer or others?	60.1(5)	
18.	Should contractor prepare any equipment, plant and materials which are outside the working areas be prepared for marking?	71.1	
19.	Should the contractor be given title to materials from excavation?	73.2	
19.1	Should the contractor be given title to materials from demolition?	"	
20.	Have other accounts which the contractor keeps been stated?	C52.2 E52.2	
20.1	Have other records which the contractor keeps been stated?	"	
21.	Should additional acceptance procedures be stated?	C11.2(30) D11.2(30) E11.2(30) F11.2(29)	
21.1	Should additional procurement procedures be stated?	"	
21.2	Are there requirements for how the contractor is to provide the works to be stated?	"	
22.	Will a form of performance bond be set out?	G1.1	
23.	Will a form of parent company guarantee be set out?	H1.1	

No	Item	Section	Employer or Contractor
24.	Will a form of advanced payment bond be set out?	J1.2	
25.	Will any additional conditions of contract refer to the WI?	Z1	

Bibliography of Abbreviated Works

Abu-Hijleh, S. F. and Ibbs, C. W. Schedule-based Construction Incentives. *Journal of Construction Engineering and Management*, 1989, **112**, 430–433.

Abrahamson, Professor Max. Risk Management. *International Construction Law Review,* 1984.

_____, and Winter, Jeremy. New Contract Systems – Permanent Change or Fashion? *The Building of Construction Law*. A paper presented at the Tenth Annual Construction Conference on 19 September 1997 by the Society of Construction Law and the Centre of Construction Law and Management. King's College, London, 1997.

Akinsola, A. O. *et al*. Identification and Evaluation of Factors Influencing Variations on Building Projects. *International Journal of Project Management*, 1997, **15**(4), 263.

Angelis, Diana Isaza. The Effects of Activity-Based Costing on Traditional Operations Research Models. Inventory, Lot Size, Scheduling, Break Even. PhD dissertation, University of Florida, 1996.

Ashley, David B. *et al. The Impact of Risk Allocation and Equity in Construction Contracts: An Overview of Indemnification, Consequential Damages, Differing Conditions & Delay Claims*. A Report to the Construction Industry Institute. The University of Austin, Austin, Texas, November 1988.

Ashford, J. L. *Quality Management in Construction – Certification of Product Quality and Quality Management Systems*. CIRIA, London, 1989, CIRIA Special Publication 72.

Baird, Andrew. The New Engineering Contract – A Management Summary for Plant Industry Users. *International Construction Law Review,* 1994.

_____. Pioneering the NEC System of Documents. *Engineering, Construction and Architectural Management*, 1995, **2**(4).

_____. Adversarialism, Pro-active Management and the NEC. *Commercial Dispute Resolution* (eds ODAMS, MARTIN A. and HIGGENS, JOANNA). Construction Law Press, London, 1996..

Barber, John. *Quality Management in Construction – Contractual Aspects*. CIRIA, London, 1992, CIRIA Special Publication 84.

Barber, P. Title to Goods, Material and Plant under Construction Contracts. *Interests in Goods* (eds PALMER, NORMAN and McKENDRICK, EWAN). Lloyd's of London Press, London, 1993.

Barnes, Dr. Martin *et al*. Towards Simpler Contracts. Barnes *et al*. introducers. Reported by Barber, J.N. In *Proceedings of the Institution of Civil Engineers*, June 1986, **80**, part 1.

_____. The New Engineering Contract. *International Construction Law Review*, 1991.

_____. Risk, Management, Procurement & CCS. *Risk Management and Procurement in Construction* (eds UFF, JOHN and ODAMS, MARTIN A.) Centre of Construction Law and Management, King's College, London, 1995.

_____. The New Engineering Contract – An Update. *International Construction Law Review*, 1996.

Bayton, Ernest J. An Introduction to the Engineering and Construction Contract. A course given at Altrincham on 3 March 1998. Thomas Telford Training, London, 1998.

Beatson, J. Public Law Influences in Contract Law. *Good Faith and Fault in Contract Law* (eds BEATON, JACK and FREIDMANN, DANIEL). Clarendon Press, Oxford, 1995.

Birkby, Gillian. The New Engineering Contract. *Civil Engineering Surveyor Construction Law Review*, 1996.

Blackler, Tony *et al*. *Rowe & Maw, JCT Management Contract. A Comprehensive Analysis of the Contract Package*. Sweet & Maxwell, London, 1989.

Bowcock, John. The FIDIC Contract Forms: The Present and Future. *The Patrick McCreight Memorial Lecture*. A paper given in London on 7 November 1995 by the Society of Construction Law. Society of Construction Law, London, 1995.

British Property Federation. *Manual of the BPF System The British Property Federation System for Building Design and Construction*. British Property Federation, London, 1983.

Brooker, Penny and Lavers, Professor Anthony. Perceptions of Alternative Dispute Resolution as Constraints upon its Use in the UK Construction Industry. *Construction Management and Economics*, 1997, **15**(6).

Broome, Jon and Perry, John G. Experiences of the Use of the New Engineering Contract. *Engineering, Construction and Architectural Management*, 1995, **2**(4).

Bubshait, Abdulaziz A. and Almohawis, Soliman A. Evaluating the General Conditions of a Construction Contract. *International Journal of Project Management*, 1994, **12**(3).

Burkett, John. Building Contracts. *Arbitration*, 1989.

Burrows, J. F. Contractual Co-operation and the Implied Term. *Modern Law Review*, 1968, **31**.

Byrne, The Hon. Mr. Justice. Implied Terms in Construction. *Building and Construction Law*, 1995, **11**.

Capper, Professor Phillip. Management of Legal Risks in Construction. A paper given to the Society of Construction Law at a meeting in Wales on 21 September 1994.

_____. Why are There So Many Disputes for Arbitration in Construction? In *The Building of Construction Law*. A paper presented at the Tenth Annual Construction Conference on 19 September 1997 by the Society of Construction Law and the Centre of Construction Law and Management. King's College, London, 1997.

Carter, J.W. Suspending Contract Performance for Breach. *Good Faith and Fault in Contract Law* (eds BEATON, JACK and FRIEDMANN, DANIEL) Clarendon Press, Oxford, 1995.

_____, and Furmston, Professor M. P. Good Faith and Fairness in the Negotiation of Contracts Part II. *Journal of Contract Law*, 1995, **8**.

Cartoon, Bernard J. Drafting an Acceptable *Force Majeure* Clause. *Journal of Business Law*, 1978.

Centre for Strategic Studies in Construction. *Building Britain 2001*. Centre for Strategic Studies in Construction, University of Reading, Reading, 1988.

Chartered Institute of Building. *Code of Practice for Project Management for Construction and Development*, 2nd edn. Addison Wesely Longman; Ascot: CIOB, Harlow, 1996.

Chase, Richard B. and Aquilano, Nicholas J. *Production & Operations Management A Life Cycle Approach*, 6th edn. Irwin, Homewood, 1992.

Clarke, Malcolm Dr. The Common Law of Contract in 1993: Is There a General Doctrine of Good Faith. *Hong Kong Law Journal*, 1993, **23**.

_____. *The Law of Contract*, 2nd edn. Butterworths, London, 1993.

Checkland, P. *Systems Thinking, Systems Practice*. John Wiley, Chichester, 1981.

Construction Industry Board. *Selecting Consultants for the Team*. Construction Industry Board. Construction Industry Board, Thomas Telford, London, 1996.

_____. *Educating the Professional Team*. Construction Industry Board, Thomas Telford, London, 1996.

_____. *Training the Team*. Construction Industry Board, Thomas Telford, London, 1996.

_____.*Towards a 30% Productivity Improvement in Construction*. Construction Industry Board, Thomas Telford, London, 1996.

_____. *Briefing the Team A Guide to Better Briefing for Clients*. Construction Industry Board, Thomas Telford, London, 1997.

Corbett, Edward. FIDIC 5th or a New Style Red Book. *International Construction Law Review*, 1993.

Cornes, David L. The Second Edition of the New Engineering Contract. *International Construction Law Review*, 1996.

Cottam, Guy. Contract to Suit All Occasions? *Construction News*, 27 May 1993.

_____. Covering All The Options. *Construction News*, 3 June 1993.

Cox, Andrew and Thompson, Ian. Is the NEC Going to Succeed? – An Examination of the Engineering and Construction Contract. (Alias the NEC 2nd Edition). *International Construction Law Review*, 1996.

Cutts, Martin. *The Plain English Guide*. Oxford University Press, Oxford, 1995.

Davis, Langdon and Everest. Contracts in Use: A Survey of Building Contracts in Use During 1995. *Construction Law Journal*, 1997, **13**.

Davis, Richard. Payment Issues and Legislation. *Contemporary Issues in Construction Law, vol. 1 Security for Payment* (eds DAVIS, RICHARD and ODAMS, MARTIN A.) Construction Law Press, London, 1996.

_____, and Odams, A. Martin. *Contemporary Issues in Construction Law, vol. 1 Security for Payment*. Construction Law Press, London, 1996.

Dering, C. Risk Sharing and Contract Forms: Devising Appropriate Contract Terms. In *Future Directions in Construction Law: at Proceedings of the Fifth Annual Conference of the Centre of Construction law and Management*. King's College, London, 1992.

Eggleston, Brian. *The New Engineering Contract, A Commentary*. Blackwell Science, London, 1996.

European Construction Institute. *Implementing TQ in the Construction Industry A Practical Guide*. Thomas Telford, London, 1996.

Evans, John R. Fair and Reasonable? Ordered Variations and the Standard Forms of Contract. MSc dissertation, University of London, Centre of Construction Law & Management. King's College, September 1995.

Fenn, P. *et al.* Conflict and Dispute in Construction. *Construction Management and Economics*, 1997, **15**(6).

Flanagan, Roger *et al. A Bridge to the Future. Profitable Construction for Tomorrow's Industry and its Customers.* Thomas Telford; Reading: Reading Construction Forum, London, 1998.

_____, and Norman, G. *Risk Management and Construction.* Blackwell Scientific Publications, Oxford, 1993.

Future Directions in Construction Law: Proceedings of the Fifth Annual Conference of the Centre of Construction Law and Management. King's College, London, 1992.

Furmston, Professor Michael P. The Liability of Contractors: Principles of Liability in Contract and Tort. *The Liability of Contractors* (ed LLOYD, HUMPHREY). Centre for Commercial Law Studies, Queen Mary College, Longman, London, 1986.

Gallup. Customer Services Poll in *Building.* 28 July 1995.

Godfrey, Patrick S, *et al. Control of Risk A Guide to the Systematic Management of Risk from Construction.* CIRIA, London, 1996, Special Publication 125.

Greenwood, D. J. *Contractual Arrangements and Conditions of Contract for the Engagement of Specialist Engineering Contractors for Construction Projects.* the University of Northumbria at Newcastle, CASEC, Newcastle, 1993.

Greenwood, David and Klein, Rudi. Security of Payment in the Light of the Latham Report: An Opportunity to Remove Unacceptable Risks? *Construction Law Journal*, 1995, **11**.

Hartman, Francis *et al.* Effective Wording to Improve Risk Allocation in Lump Sum Contracts. *Journal of Construction Engineering and Management*, 1997, **123**.

Hellard, Ron Baden. *Project Partnering: Principle and Practice.* Thomas Telford, London, 1995.

Higgin, G. and Jessop, N. *Communications in the Building Industry The Report of a Pilot Study.* Tavistock Publications, London, 1965.

Houghton, Anthony. Milestones and Liquidated Damages. *Construction Law Journal 8*, 1992.

Hudson's Building and Engineering Contracts, 11th edn., vol. 1. Ian Duncan Wallace, ed. London: Sweet & Maxwell, 1994.

Institution of Civil Engineers. *The Need For and Features of the NEC.* Thomas Telford, London, 1991.

Jaynes, Gordon L. Turnkey Contracts: Japan's Model Forms. *International Construction Law Review*, 1993.

_____. Dispute Review Boards: The World Bank is Aboard. *International Construction Law Review*, 1996.

Jenkins, Jane. The Latham Trust Fund Proposals. *Construction Law Journal*, 1995, **11**.

Johnson, Robert E. *The Economics of Building, A Practical Guide for the Design Professional.* John Wiley & Sons Inc, New York, 1990.

Jones, D. S. Philosophies of Risk Allocation – The Case for Foreseeability. *International Construction Law Review*, 1996.

Joyce, Raymond. *A Commentary on Construction Contracts, Part II of Housing Grants, Construction and Regeneration Act 1996.* Thomas Telford, London, 1996.

Justice. *Protecting the Householder Against Defective Building Work.* Justice, London, 1996.

Furyua, Kunihiko. ENAA Revised Model of Contract (1992 edn.). *International Construction Law Review*, 1993.

Kangari, R. Risk Management Perceptions and Trends of US Construction. *Journal of Construction Engineering and Management*, 1995.

Kelly, John and Male, Steven. *Value Management in Design and Construction The Economic Management of Projects*. E & FN Spon, London, 1993.

Kwakye, A. A. *Construction Project Administration in Practice*. Addison Wesley Longman, Ascot: CIOB, Harlow, 1997.

Lanigan, Mike. *Engineers in Business, The Principles of Management and Product Design*. Addison-Wesley, Wokingham, 1994.

Latham, Sir Michael. *Constructing the Team, Final Report of the Joint Review of Procurement and Contractual Arrangements in the United Kingdom Construction Industry*. HMSO, London, July 1994.

Humphrey, LLoyd. *The Liability of Contractors*. Centre for Commercial Law Studies, Queen Mary College, Longman, London, 1986.

Keating on Building Contracts, 6th edn. The Hon. Sir Anthony May. Sweet & Maxwell, London, 1995.

Lock, Dennis. *Project Management*, 4th edn. Gower, Aldershot, 1988.

Loosemore, Martin. Dealing with Unexpected Problems Do Contracts Help? A Comparison of the NEC and JCT 80 Forms. *Engineering, Construction and Architectural Management*, 1994, **1**(2).

Majid, M. Z. Abd and McCaffer, Ronald. Factors of Non-excusable Delays that Influence Contractors' Performance. *Journal of Management in Engineering*, May/June 1998, **14**(3).

Mak, Stephen W. Risk Analysis in Construction: A Paradigm Shift from a Hard to Soft Approach. *Construction Management and Economics*, 1995, **13**.

Management and Construction Law. A one-day seminar on 23 March 1990 by the Centre of Construction Law and Management. King's College, London, 1990.

McGaw, Mark C. Adjudicators, Experts and Keeping Out of Court. *Construction Law Journal*, 1992, **8**.

McGowan, Paul H. *et al. Allocation and Evaluation of Risk in Construction Contracts*. Occasional Paper no. 52. CIOB, Ascot, 1992.

McInnis, J.A. Frustration and Force Majeure in Building Contracts. *Force Majeure and Frustration of Contract*, 2nd edn. (ed McKENDRICK, EWAN). Lloyd's of London Press, London, 1995:.

_____. *Hong Kong Construction Law*. 2 vols. Butterworths, Singapore, 1995.

Minogue, Ann. On the NEC Road Forward. *Construction Legal Times Supplement*, May 1996.

Moore, Richard F. *Response to Change – the Development of Non-traditional Forms of Contracting*. CIOB, Ascot, 1984. Occasional Paper 31.

Morris, Peter W G. *The Management of Projects*. Thomas Telford, London, 1994.

_____. Current Trends in the Organisation of Construction Projects. In *Future Directions in Construction Law: at Proceedings of the Fifth Annual Conference of the Centre of Construction Law and Management*. King's College, London, 1992.

_____, and Hough, G. H. *Preconditions of Success and Failure in Major Projects*. Major Projects Association, Oxford, 1986. Technical Paper 3.

Nassar, Nagla. *Sanctity of Contracts Revisited: A Study in the Theory and Practice of Long-Term International Commercial Transactions*. Martinus Nijhoff Publishers, Dordrecht, 1994.

Netto, A. M. *et al.* Legal Implications of ISO 9000 QMS in Standard Forms of Building Contract. *Training for Quality*, 1997, **5**(4).

Nichlisch, Fritz. *The Complex Long-Term Contract Structures and International Arbitration.* C. F. Muller Juristischer Verlag, Heidelberg, 1987.

Norris, C. *et al. Project Risk Analysis and Management.* The Association of Project Managers, London, April 1991.

Norton, Brian R. and McElligott, William C. *Value Management in Construction A Practical Guide.* MacMillan, London, 1995.

Odams, A. Martin and Higgins, Joanna. *Commercial Dispute Resolution.* Construction Law Press, London, 1996.

O'Reilly, Michael. Risk, Construction Contracts and Construction Disputes. *Construction Law Journal*, 1995, **11**.

_____. *Civil Engineering Construction Contracts.* Thomas Telford, London, 1996.

Patterson, Edwin W. Constructive Conditions in Contracts. *Columbia Law Review*, 1942, **42**.

Perry, Professor John G. and Hayes, R. W. Risk and its Management in Construction Projects. *Proceedings of the Institution of Civil Engineers*, June 1985, **77**, part 1.

_____. Risk and its Management in Construction Projects. *Proceedings of the Institution of Civil Engineers*, June 1986, **80**, part 1.

Perry, Professor John G. and Hoare, D. J. Contracts of the Future: Risks and Rewards. In *Future Directions in Construction Law: at Proceedings of the Fifth Annual Conference of the Centre of Construction Law and Management.* King's College, London, 1992.

Perry, Professor John G. and Thompson, Professor P. A. *Target and Cost Reimbursable Construction Contracts Part A: A Study of Their Use and Implications.* CIRIA, London, 1982. CIRIA Report 85, Part A. (formerly CIRIA Report 56).

Perry, Professor John G. The New Engineering Contract: Principles of Design and Risk Allocation. *Engineering, Construction and Architectural Management*, 1995, **2**(3).

Pietroforte, Roberto. *Building International Construction Alliances: Successful Partnering for Construction Firms.* E & FN Spon, London, 1996.

Priestley, Clive. *British Construction: In Pursuit of Excellence.* A Report to Sir Christopher Foster, Chairman of the Construction Industry Sector Group. Business Round Table, London, February 1994.

Redmond, John. Creative Implication: Implied Terms in Construction Contracts. A paper given to the Society of Construction Law in London on 4 July 1995.

Rooke, John and Seymour, David. The NEC and the Culture of the Industry: Some Early Findings Regarding Possible Sources of Resistance to Change. *Engineering, Construction and Architectural Management*, 1995, **2**(4).

Rowlinson, Steve and McDermott, Peter. *Procurement Systems in Construction: A Guide to Best Practice.* E & FN Spon, London, 1998.

Royce, Darryl. Tugging at the Contract: Some Preliminary Reflections on the JCT Intermediate Form of Building Contract. *Construction Law Journal*, 1984–85, **1**.

Schneider, Michael E. Mastering the Interfaces – Construction Contracts Drafting for Dispute Avoidance. *International Construction Law Review*, 1993.

Scott, Robert E. Risk Distribution and Adjustment in Long-Term Contracts. *The Complex Long-Term Contract Structures and International Arbitration* (ed NICHLISCH, FRITZ). C. F. Muller Juristischer Verlag, Heidelberg, 1987.

Scriven, John. Design Risk and Liability under Design and Build Contracts. *Construction Law Journal*, 1996, **12**.

Shilston, Alan. The Obligation to Co-operate: What does this Involve? *A paper given at a joint meeting of the Society of Construction Law and the Society of Construction Arbitrators in London on 2 June 1992.* Society of Construction Law, London, 1992.

Smith, G. A. Beyond ADR – Dispute Resolution in the Construction Industy through Realistic Contract Risk Allocation. *The Organization of Management of Construction: Shaping Theory and Practice* (eds LANGFORD, D.A. and RETICK, A.), vol. 2. E & FN Spon, London, 1996.

Smith, Robert J. Allocation of Risk – The Case for Manageability. *International Construction Law Review*, 1996.

Stoljar, Samuel J. Prevention and Co-operation in the Law of Contract. *Canadian Bar Review*, 1953, **31**.

Stukhart, G. Contractual Incentives. *Journal of Construction Engineering and Management*, 1984, **110**.

Sweet, Professor Justin. Standard Construction Contracts: Some Advice to Construction Lawyers. *Construction Law Journal*, 1991, **7**.

_____. Standard Contracts for Design and Construction: Comparisons and Advice. *Construction Law Yearbook*, 1994.

_____. Judging Contracts: Some Reflections on the Third International Construction Law Conference. *International Construction Law Review*, 1994.

Teubner, Gunther. Piercing the Contract Veil? The Social Responsibility of Contractual Networks. *Perspectives of Critical Contract Law* (ed WILHELMSSON, THOMAS). Dartmouth, Aldershot, 1993.

Thompson, Professor P. A. and Perry, Professor J. G. *Engineering Construction Risks: A Guide to Engineering Construction Risks: A Guide to Project Risk Analysis and Risk Management.* Science and Engineering Research Council, Thomas Telford, Swindon, 1993.

Uff QC, Professor John. The Place of Law and the Role of Construction. *The Centre of Construction Law and Project Management Lecture: delivered to the Society of Construction Law on 4 October 1988.* London, 1988.

_____. Origin and Development of Construction Contracts. *Construction Contract Policy, Improved Procedures and Practice* (eds UFF, JOHN and CAPPER, PHILLIP). Centre of Construction Law and Management, King's College, London, 1989.

_____. Overview: The Place of Management in Construction. *Management and Construction Law.* A one-day seminar on 23 March 1990 by the Centre of Construction Law and Management. King's College, London, 1990.

_____. Figaro on ICE the ICE 6th Edition and the New Engineering Contract. *Construction Industry Law Letter*, 1991.

_____. Control of Disputes within the Contract Framework. *Future Directions in Construction Law: Proceedings of the Fifth Annual Conference of the Centre of Construction Law and Management.* King's College, London, 1992.

_____, and Jefford, Nerys. European Harmonisation in the Field of Constructon. *International Construction Law Review*, 1993.

_____, and Phillip Capper. *Construction Contract Policy, Improved Procedures and Practice.* Centre of Construction Law and Management, King's College, London, 1989.

_____, and Lavers, Anthony. *Legal Obligations in Construction Revised Conference Proceedings.* Centre of Construction Law and Management, King's College, London, 1992.

Valentine, D. G. The New Engineering Contract: Part 1 – a New Language. *Construction Law Journal*, 1991, **12**.

_____. The New Engineering Contract: Part 2 – Claims for Extensions of Time. *Construction Law Journal*, 1991, **12**.

Wallace QC, Professor I. N. Duncan. *Construction Contracts: Principles and Policies in Tort and Contract.* Sweet & Maxwell, London, 1986.

_____. Defective Work: the New Flavours. *Construction Law Journal*, 1990, **6**.

_____. An Emperor without Clothes – Latham and the DOE. *Contemporary Issues in Construction Law Vol II, Construction Contract Reform: A Plea for Sanity* (ed UFF, JOHN). Construction Law Press, London, 1997.

Williams, David H. Using the NEC: A Client's View. In *New Engineering Contract Conference Proceedings in Hong Kong, 28 November 1994.* Asian Law Journal, Hong Kong, 1994.

Williams, G. Antoinette. Reservation of Title in the Construction Industry: Who Wins? – Some Economic Perspectives on Risk Allocation. *Construction Law Journal*, 1987, **3**.

Williams, Glanville. Language and the Law – IV. *Law Quarterly Review*, 1945, **61**.

Woodward, John F. *Construction Project Management, Getting it Right First Time.* Thomas Telford, London, 1997.

Wright, David. Subrogation: Risk and Responsibility in Construction Contracts. *Construction Law Journal*, 1995, **11**.

Cases

A Bell & Son (Paddington) Ltd v. *CBF Residential Care and Housing Association* (1989) 46 BLR 102.

A Cameron Ltd v. *John Mowlem & Co plc* (1990) 25 Con LR 11, 52 BLR 24, CA.

Acsim (Southern) Ltd v. *Danish Contracting and Development Co Ltd* (1989) 47 BLR 55, CA.

A E Farr Ltd v. *The Admiralty* [1953] 2 All ER 512, [1953] 1 WLR 965.

A E Farr Ltd v. *Ministry of Transport* [1960] 3 All ER 88.

AEG (UK) Ltd v. *Logic Resource Ltd* [1995] CCH Commercial Law Reports 265.

A-G v. *Briggs* (1855) 1 Jur NS 1084.

A-G v. *Chiu Man-lun* [1989] 1 HKLR 99, HKCA.

A Vigers Sons & Co Ltd v. *Swindell* [1939] 3 All ER 590.

Ailsa Craig Fishing Co Ltd v. *Malvern Fishing Co Ltd* 1982 SC, HL.

Alderslade v. *Hendon Laundry Ltd* [1945] KB 189, [1945] 1 All ER 244, CA.

Alexander Corfield v. *David Grant* (1992) 59 BLR 102.

Alfred McAlpine Construction Ltd v. *Panatown* (1998) 88 BLR 67.

Allridge (Builders) Ltd v. *Grand Actual Ltd* (1997) 55 Con LR 91.

Aluminum Industrie Vaassen v. *Romalpa Aluminum Ltd* [1976] 2 All ER 552, [1976] 1 WLR 676, CA.

Amalgamated Building Contractors Ltd v. *Waltham Holy Cross UDC* [1952] 2 All ER 452, CA.

Amec Building Ltd v. *Cadmus Investments Co Ltd* (1997) 51 Con LR 105.

AMF International Ltd v. *Magnet Bowling Ltd* [1968] 2 All ER 789, [1968] 1 WLR 1028.

Anderson v. *Weston* (1840) 6 Bing NC 296.

Anglian Building Products Ltd v. *W & C French (Construction) Ltd* (1972) 16 BLR 1, CA.

Anglian Water Authority v. *RDL Contracting Ltd* (1988) 43 BLR 98.

Anglo Starlite Insurance Co Ltd v. *The Insurance Authority* [1992] 2 HKLR 31.

Appleby v. *Myers* (1867) LR 2 CP 651.

Architectural Installation Services Ltd v. *James Gibbons Windows Ltd* (1989) 46 BLR 91, 16 Con LR 68.

Archivent Sales & Developments Ltd v. *Strathclyde Regional Council* (1984) 27 BLR 98, Ct of Sess.

Arenson v. *Casson Beckman Rutley & Co* [1977] AC 405, [1975] 3 All ER 901, HL.

Arrow Co v. *Tyne Commissioners* [1894] AC 508.

Arterial Drainage Co Ltd v. *Rathangan River Drainage Board* (1860) 6 LR Ir 513.

Ashville Investments Ltd v. *Elmer Contractors Ltd* [1989] QB 488, [1988] 2 All ER 577, CA.

B O C Group plc v. *Centeon LLC* (1999) 63 Con LR 104, CA.

Bolton v. *Mahadeva* [1972] 2 All ER 1322, [1972] 1 WLR 1009, CA.

Bottoms v. *York Corpn* (1892) 2 Hudson's BC 4th edn 208, CA.

Bovis Construction (Scotland) Ltd v. *Whatlings Construction Ltd* 1995 SLT 1339, HL.

Bovis Homes Ltd v. *Oakcliff Investment Corpn* (unreported, 30 March 1994, Ch D).

Bowmakers Ltd v. *Barnet Instruments Ltd* [1945] KB 65, [1944] 2 All ER 579, CA.

BP Refinery (Westernport) Pty Ltd v. *President, Councillors and Ratepayers of the Shire of Hastings* (1977–78) 16 ALR 363, 52 ALJR 20, PC.

Bramall & Ogden Ltd v. *Sheffield City Council* (1983) 29 BLR 73.

Brandt's Sons & Co v. *Dunlop Rubber Co Ltd* [1905] AC 454, HL.

Brian Pty Ltd v. *United Dominions Corporation Ltd* [1983] 1 NSWLR 490

British Eagle International Airlines Ltd v. *Cie Nationale Air France* [1975] 2 All ER 390, [1975] 1 WLR 758, HL.

British Steel Corporation v. *Cleveland Bridge and Engineering Co Ltd* [1984] 1 All ER 504.

British Telecommunications plc v. *James Thomson & Sons (Engineers) Ltd* (1999) 61 Con LR 1, HL.

British Transport Commission v. *Inverness-shire Assessor* 1952 SLT 298.

British Waggon Co and Parkgate Waggon Co v. *Lea & Co* (1880) 5 QBD 149.

Brodie v. *Cardiff Corpn* [1919] AC 337, HL.

Broom v. *Davis* (1794) 7 East 480.

Brown v. *Bateman* (1867) LR 2 CP 272.

Bruno Zornow (Builders) Ltd v. *Beechcroft Developments Ltd* (1990) 51 BLR 16, (1990) 16 Con LR 30.

Brunswick Construction Ltd v. *Nowlan* (1974) 21 BLR 27, 49 DLR (3d) 93.

Bull v. *Robison* (1854) 10 Exch 342, 156 ER 476.

Burbery Mortgage, Finance & Savings Ltd v. *Hindsbank Holdings Ltd* [1989] 1 NZLR 356.

Butterfield v. *Byron* 153 Mass 517 (1890), 27 NE 667 (1891).

Bywaters & Sons v. *Curnick & Co* (1906) 2 Hudson's BC 4th edn 393, CA.

C J Pearce & Co Ltd v. *Hereford Corpn* (1968) 66 LGR 647.

Calvert v. *London Dock Co* (1838) 7 LJ Ch 90.

Callaghan and Welton (t/a R W Construction) v. *Hewgate Construction Ltd* (1995) 75 BLR 11, CA.

Campbell v. *Edwards* [1976] 1 All ER 785, [1976] 1 WLR 403.

Canada Foundry Co Ltd v. *Edmonton Portland Cement Co* [1918] 3 WWR 866, PC.

Canada Steamship Lines Ltd v. *R* [1952] AC 192, [1952] 1 All ER 305, PC.

Canterbury Pipelines Ltd v. *Christchurch Drainage Board* (1979) 16 BLR 76, NZCA.

Cape Durasteel Ltd v. *Rosser and Russell Building Services Ltd* (1996) 46 Con LR 75.

Carr v. *J A Berriman Pty Ltd* (1953) 27 ALJ 273.

Carter v. *Boehm* (1766) 3 Burr 1905, 97 ER 1162.

Caswell v. *Powell Duffryn Associated Collieries Ltd* [1940] AC 152, [1939] 3 All ER 722, HL.

Cementation Piling and Foundations Ltd v. *Aegon Insurance Co Ltd and Commercial Union Insurance* [1993] 1 Lloyd's Rep 526.

Central Provident Fund Board v. *Ho Bock Kee* (1981) 17 BLR 21, Sing CA.

Channel Tunnel Group Ltd v. *Balfour Beatty Construction Ltd* [1992] 1 QB 656, [1993] AC 334, [1993] 1 All ER 664, HL.

Charles Rickards Ltd v. *Oppenheim* [1950] 1 KB 616, [1950] 1 All ER 420, CA.

Chermar Productions Pty Ltd v. *Pretest Pty Ltd* (1992) 8 Const LJ 44.

Chesham Properties Ltd v. *Bucknall Austin Project Management Services Ltd and Ors* (1997) 82 BLR 92.

Church of Scotland v. *Watson* 42 SLR 299.

City of Dublin Steam Packet Co v. *R* (1908) 24 TLR 657.

City of Manchester v. *Fram Gerrard Ltd* (1974) 6 BLR 70.

Clemence v. *Clarke* (1880) 2 Hudson's BC 4th edn 54, CA.

Clydebank Engineering Co v. *Don Jose Ramos Yzquierdo y Castaneda* [1905] AC 6, HL.

CM Pillings & Co Ltd v. *Kent Investments Ltd* (1985) 30 BLR 80, CA.

Coken v. *Young* (1860) 2 F & F 98.

Colley v. *Overseas Exporters* [1921] 3 KB 302, KB.

Collinge v. *Hayward* (1839) 9 Ad & El 633.

Commercial Bank of Australia Ltd v. *Amadio* (1983) 151 CLR 447.

Commercial Cotton Co Inc v. *United California Bank* 209 Cal Rptr 551 (1985).

Commonwealth v. *Verwayen* (1990) 95 ALR 321.

Computer & Systems Engineering plc v. *John Elliott (Ilford) Ltd* (1990) 54 BLR 1.

Comr for Main Roads v. *Reed & Stuart Pty Ltd* (1974) 12 BLR 55.

Comunale v. *Traders & General Insurance Co* 328 P 2d 198 (1958).

Comyn Ching & Co Ltd v. *Oriental Tube Co Ltd* (1979) 17 BLR 47.

Concorde Construction Co Ltd v. *Colgan Co Ltd* (1984) 29 BLR 120, HCHK.

Convent Hospital v. *Eberlin & Partners* (1989) 23 Con LR 112.

Coombe v. *Green* (1843) 11 M & W 480.

Cooper v. *Langdon* (1841) 9 M & W 60; (1842) 10 M & W 785, Ex Ch.

Copthorne Hotel (Newcastle) Ltd v. *Arup Associates* (1998) 85 BLR 22.

Cort v. *Ambergate, Nottingham and Boston and Eastern Junction Rly Co* (1851) 17 QB 127.

Cory Ltd v. *City of London Corpn* [1951] 2 KB 476, CA.

Cosmos Engineering Inc v. *Ministry of Roads and Transportation* (1986 IV) 13 Iran-USCTR 179.

Costain Civil Engineering and Anor v. *Zanen Dredging and Contracting Company Ltd* (1997) 85 BLR 77 QB.

Costain International v. *A-G of Hong Kong* (1983) 23 BLR 54.

County and District Properties Ltd v. *C Jenner & Son Ltd* (1976) 3 BLR 41, [1976] 2 Lloyd's Rep 728.

Courtney & Fairbairn Ltd v. *Tolaini Bros (Hotels) Ltd* [1975] 1 All ER 716, CA.

Cowell v. *Rosehill Racecourse Co Ltd* [1937] 56 CLR 605.

Crabtree v. *Fern Spinning Co Ltd* (1901) 85 LT 549.

Crestar Ltd v. *Carr* (1987) 37 BLR 113, CA.

Croshaw v. *Pritchard and Renwick* (1899) 16 TLR 45.

Croudace Ltd v. *London Borough of Lambeth* (1986) 33 BLR 20, CA.

Currie v. *Misa* (1875) LR 10 Exch 153.

Cutler v. *Close* (1832) 5 C & P 337.

Cutler v. *Wandsworth Stadium Ltd* [1949] AC 398, [1949] 1 All ER 554, HL.

Cutter v. *Powell* (1795) 6 Term Rep 320.

Dallman v. *King* (1837) 7 LJCP 6.

Darlington Borough Council v. *Wiltshire Northern Ltd* [1995] 3 ALL ER 895.

Davies v. *Collins* [1945] 1 All ER 247, CA.

Equitable Debenture Assets Corpn Ltd v. *William Moss Group Ltd* (1984) 2 Con LR 1.

E R Dyer Ltd v. *The Simon Build/Peter Lind Partnership* (1982) 23 BLR 23.

Ess v. *Truscott* (1837) 2 M & W 385 .

Everett v. *Griffiths* [1920] 3 KB 163.

Ex p Dawes, Re Moon (1886) 17 QBD 275, CA.

Fairclough Building Ltd v. *Port Talbot Borough Council* (1992) 62 BLR 82, CA.

Fairclough Building Ltd v. *Rhuddlan Borough Council* (1985) 30 BLR 26, CA.

Felton v. *Wharrie* (1906) 2 Hudson's BC 4th edn 398, CA.

Ferguson & Associates v. *Sohl* (1992) 62 BLR 95, CA.

Fibrosa Spolka Akcyjna v. *Fairbairn Lawson Combe Barbour Ltd* [1943] AC 32, [1942] 2 All ER 122, HL.

Fletcher v. *Ilkeston Corpn* (1931) 96 JP 7.

Franklin v. *Gramophone Co Ltd* [1948] 1 KB 542, [1948] 1 All ER 353, CA.

Frederick Leyland & Co Ltd v. *Compania Panamena Europea Navigacion Limitida* (1943) 76 Ll L Rep 113, CA.

Freeman & Son v. *Hensler* (1900) 64 JP 260, 2 Hudson's BC 4th edn 292, CA.

Freeth v. *Burr* (1874) LR 9 CP 208.

G & T Earle Ltd v. *Hemsworth RDC* (1928) 140 LT 69, CA.

G A B Robins Holdings Ltd v. *Specialist Computer Centres Ltd* (1999) 15 Const LJ 143,

Gammon Building Construction Ltd v. *Cho Hing Yiu (t/a Cho Yiu Kee Construction & Wooden Works)* [1988] HKC 611.

General Dynamics Telephone Systems Center, Inc v. *Iran* (1985 II) 9 Iran-USCTR 153.

General Steam Navigation Co v. *Rolt* (1858) 6 CBNS 550, Ex Ch.

George Fischer Holding Ltd (formerly George Fischer (GB) Ltd) v. *Multi Design Consultants Ltd* (1999) 61 Con LR 85.

George Hawkins v. *Chrysler* (1986) 38 BLR 36, CA.

Gibson v. *Parkes District Hospital* (1991) 26 NSWLR 9.

Gibson v. *Skibs A/S Marina* [1966] 2 All ER 476.

Gilbert v. *Gulliver* [1918] VLR 185.

Gilbert & Partners v. *Knight* [1968] 2 All ER 248, CA.

Gilbert-Ash (Northern) Ltd v. *Modern Engineering (Bristol) Ltd* [1974] AC 689, [1973] 3 All ER 195, HL.

Glenlion Construction v. *The Guinness Trust* (1987) 39 BLR 89.

Glenn v. *Leith* (1853) 1 CLR 569.

Gloucestershire Health Authority and Ors v. *M A Torpy & Partners (t/a Torpy & Partners) and Anor* (1997) 55 Con LR 124.

Gold v. *Patman and Fotheringham Ltd* [1958] 2 All ER 497, [1958] 1 WLR 697, CA.

Gold Star Insurance Co Ltd v. *Graunt* (1991) 3 NZLBC 102.

Golden Horseshoe Estates Co Ltd v. *R* [1911] AC 480, 80 LJPC 135, PC.

Goldsack v. *Shore* [1950] 1 KB 708.

Goldsmith's Co v. *West Metropolitan Railway Co* [1904] 1 KB 1, [1900–03] All ER Rep 667.

Goodyear v. *Weymouth and Melcombe Regis Corpn* (1865) 35 LJCP 12.

Goodwin & Sons v. *Fawcett* (1965) 175 Estates Gazette 27.

GPT Realisations Ltd v. *Panatown Ltd* (1992) 61 BLR 88.

Grafton v. *Easter Counties Rly Co* (1853) 8 Ex 699.

Graham H Roberts Pty Ltd v. *Maurbeth Investments Pty Ltd* [1974] 1 NSWLR 93.

Gray v. *T P Bennett & Son* (1987) 43 BLR 63.

Great Lakes Dredge & Dock Co v. *US* 96 Fed 923 Supp, 924.

Greater London Council v. *Cleveland Bridge and Engineering Co Ltd* (1986) 34 BLR 50, CA.

Green v. *Premier Glynrhonwy Slate Co* [1928] 1 KB 561, 97 LJKB 32, CA.

Groves v. *Lord Wimborne* [1898] 2 QB 402, CA.

Gruenberg v. *Aetna Insurance Co* 510 P 2d 1032 (1973).

H Dakin & Co v. *Lee* [1916] 1 KB 566, CA.

H Fairweather & Co Ltd v. *London Borough of Wandsworth* (1987) 39 BLR 106.

H & N Emanuel Ltd v. *GLC* [1971] 2 All ER 835, 115 Sol Jo 226, CA.

Hadley v. *Baxendale* (1854) 9 Exch 341, [1843–60] All ER Rep 461.

Hain Steamship Co Ltd v. *Tate & Lyle Ltd* [1936] 2 All ER 597, 41 Com Cas 350, HL.

Hall and Tawse South Ltd v. *Ivory Gate Ltd* (1999) 62 Con LR 117.

Halki Shipping Corpn v. *Sopex Oils Ltd* [1997] 3 All ER 833.

Hampshire Insurance Co Ltd [1992] 1 WLR 792, (1992) 60 BLR 26.

Hanak v. *Green* [1958] 2 QB 9, [1958] 2 All ER 141.

Hancock v. *B W Brazier (Anerley) Ltd* [1966] 2 All ER 901, [1966] 1 WLR 1317, CA.

H W Nevill (Sunblest) Ltd v. *William Press & Son Ltd* (1981) 20 BLR 78.

Hall v. *Cazenove* (1804) 4 East 477.

Hamlyn & Co v. *Wood & Co* [1891] 2 QB 488, [1891–94] All ER Rep 168, CA.

Hampshire Insurance Co Ltd [1992] 1 WLR 792, (1992) 60 BLR 26.

Hanrott's Trustees v. *Evans* (1887) 4 TLR 128.

Harbutt's Plasticine Ltd v. *Wayne Tank and Pump Co Ltd* [1970] 1 QB 447, [1970] 1 All ER 225.

Harhischfeger Corporation v. *Ministry of Roads and Transportation* (1984 III) 7 Iran-USCTR 90.

Harris v. *Birkenhead Corpn* [1976] 1 All ER 341, [1976] 1 WLR 279, CA.

Harris v. *Nickerson* (1873) LR 8 QB 286.

Harris International Telecommunications Inc v. *Iran* (1987 IV) 17 Iran-USCTR 31; and (1988 II) 18 Iran-USCTR 292 .

Harrison v. *Walker* [1919] 2 KB 453.

Hart v. *Macdonald* (1910) 10 CLR 417.

Hart v. *Porthgain Harbour Co Ltd* [1903] 1 Ch 690.

Harvela Investments Ltd v. *Royal Trust Co of Canada (Channel Islands) Ltd* [1986] AC 207, [1985] 2 All ER 966, HL.

Hedley Byrne & Co Ltd v. *Heller & Partners Ltd* [1964] AC 465, HL.

Helstan Securities Ltd v. *Hertfordshire County Council* [1978] 3 All ER 262.

Henderson v. *Merrett Syndicates Ltd* [1994] 3 WLR 761, [1994] 3 All ER 506, HL.

Henriksens Rederi A/S v. *P H Z Rolimpex* [1974] QB 233, [1973] 3 All ER 589, CA.

Henry Boot Building Ltd v. *Croydon Hotel & Leisure Co Ltd* (1985) 36 BLR 41, CA.

Heyman v. *Darwins Ltd* [1942] AC 356, [1942] 1 All ER 337, HL.

Hillingdon London Borough Council v. *Cutler* [1968] 1 QB 124, [1967] 2 All ER 361, CA.

Hitchins (Hatfield) Ltd v. *Prudential Assurance Co Ltd* (1991) 60 BLR 51 CA.

Hoenig v. *Isaacs* [1952] 2 All ER 176, CA.

Holland Dredging (UK) Ltd v. *Dredging and Construction Co Ltd* (1987) 37 BLR 1, CA.

Holland Hannen and Cubitts (Northern) Ltd v. *Welsh Health Technical and Services Organisation* (1981) 18 BLR 80; affirmed (1985) 7 Con LR 14, (1985) 35 BLR 1, CA.

Holman v. *Johnson* (1775) 1 Cowp 341.

Holme v. *Brunskill* (1877) 3 QBD 495.

Holme v. *Guppy* (1838) 3 M & W 387.

Home and Overseas Insurance Co Ltd v. *Mentor Insurance Co (UK) Ltd*. [1989] 3 All ER 74, CA.

Home Office v. *Dorset Yacht Co Ltd* [1970] AC 1004, [1970] 2 All ER 294, HL.

Hong Kong Fir Shipping Co Ltd v. *Kawasaki Kisen Kaisha Ltd* [1962] 2 QB 26, [1962] 1 All ER 474, CA.

Hoole UDC v. *Fidelity and Deposit Co of Maryland* [1916] 2 KB 568, CA.

Hopewell Project Management Limited and Hopewell Energy (Philippines) Corp v. *Ewbank Preece Limited* (1997) CILL 1310.

Hospital Products Ltd v. *United States Surgical Corporation* (1984) 156 CLR 41, HC Aust.

Hounslow London Borough Council v. *Twickenham Garden Developments Ltd* [1971] 1 Ch 233; [1970] 3 All ER 326.

House of Spring Gardens Ltd and Ors v. *Point Blank Ltd* [1984] IR 611.

Howard de Walden Estates Ltd v. *Costain Management Design Ltd* (1991) 55 BLR 124.

Humber Oil Terminals Trustee Ltd v. *Harbour General Works (Stevin) Ltd* (1991) 59 BLR 1, CA.

Hunt v. *Massey* (1834) 5 B & Ad 902.

Hudson v. *Ridge Manufacturing Co Ltd* [1957] 2 QB 348, [1957] 2 All ER 229.

Hume v. *Rundell* (1824) 2 S & St 174.

Hutchison v. *Harris* (1978) 10 BLR 19, CA.

Hyundai Heavy Industries Co Ltd v. *Papadopoulos* [1980] 2 All ER 29, [1980] 1 WLR 1129, HL.

ICC award in case no 4761 of 1987 (1987) 114 JD Int's (Clunet) 1012.

I E Contractors Ltd v. *Lloyds Bank plc and Rafidian Bank* [1990] 2 Lloyd's Rep 496, 51 BLR 1, CA.

Independent Broadcasting Authority v. *EMI Electronics and BICC Construction* (1980) 14 BLR 1, HL.

Inserco Limited v. *Honeywell Control Systems* (1998) CILL 1368.

Interfoto Picture Library Ltd v. *Stiletto Visual Programmes Ltd* [1989] QB 433, CA.

International Corona Resources Ltd (1989) 61 DLR (4th) 14, SCC.

IRC v. *Raphael* [1935] AC 96, HL.

Investors Compensation Scheme Ltd v. *West Bromwich Building Society* [1998] 1 WLR 896.

J & J Fee Ltd v. *Express Lift Co Ltd* (1993) 34 Con LR 147.

Jackson v. *Eastbourne Local Board* (1885) 2 Hudson's BC 4th edn 81, HL.

Jackson v. *Hall* [1980] AC 854, [1980] 1 All ER 177, HL.

James Miller & Partners Ltd v. *Whitworth Street Estates (Manchester) Ltd* [1970] AC 583.

Jardine Engineering Corpn Ltd v. *Shimizu Corpn* (1992) 63 BLR 96, [1992] 2 HKC 89, HCHK.

J Crosby & Sons Ltd v. *Portland Urban District Council* (1967) 5 BLR 121.

J F Finnegan Ltd v. *Ford Sellar Morris Developments Ltd* (1991) 53 BLR 38.

London Borough of Camden v. *McInerney* (1986) 2 Const LJ 293.
London Borough of Merton v. *Stanley Hugh Leach Ltd* (1985) 32 BLR 51.
London School Board v. *Jackson* (1881) 7 QBD 502, 50 LJMC 134.
Londonwaste Ltd v. *Amec Civil Engineering Ltd* (1997) 53 Con LR 66.
Lonrho Ltd v. *Shell Petroleum Co Ltd (no 2)* [1982] AC 173, [1981] 2 All ER 456, HL.
Lord Bateman v. *Thompson* (1875) 2 Hudson's BC 4th edn 36, CA.
Lovelace v. *DPP* [1954] 3 All ER 481, [1954] 1 WLR 1468.
Lovell Construction Ltd v. *Independent Estates plc* [1994] 1 BCLC 31.
LRE Engineering Services Ltd v. *Otto Simon Carves Ltd* (1981) 24 BLR 127.
L Schuler AG v. *Wickman Machine Tool Sales Ltd* [1974] AC 235, [1973] 2 All ER 39, HL.
Lubenham Fidelities and Investments Co Ltd v. *South Pembrokeshire District Council* (1986) 33 BLR 39, (1996) 6 Con LR 85, CA.
Luen Yick Co v. *Tan Man Kee Machinery Workshop* [1958] HKLR 405.
Luxor (Eastbourne) Ltd v. *Cooper* [1941] AC 108, HL.
Lyde v. *Russell* (1830) 1 B & Ad 394.
Lynch v. *Thorne* [1956] 1 All ER 744, [1956] 1 WLR 303, CA.
Matthew Hall Ortech Ltd v. *Tarmac Roadstone Ltd* (1998) 87 BLR 96.
Macintosh v. *The Midland Counties Rly Co* (1845) 14 M & W 387.
Mac-Jordan Construction Ltd v. *Brookmount-Erostin Ltd* (1991) 56 BLR 1, CA.
Mackay v. *Dick* (1881) 6 App Cas 251, HL.
Macob Civil Engineering Ltd v. *Morrison Construction Ltd* (1999) CILL 1470.
Maidenhead Electrical Services Ltd v. *Johnson Control Systems Ltd* (1997) 15-CLD-10-01.
Mannai Investment Co Ltd v. *Eagle Star Life Assurance Co Ltd* [1997] AC 749.
Manorlike Ltd v. *Le Vitas Travel Agency and Consultancy Services Ltd* [1986] 1 All ER 573, (1986) 278 Estates Gazette 412.
Manufacturers' Mutual Insurance v. *Queensland Government Railways* (1968) 42 ALJR 181.
Marc Rich & Co AG v. *Bishop Rock Marine Co Ltd* [1996] AC 211, [1995] 3 All ER 307, HL.
March Estates plc v. *Gunmark Ltd* [1996] 2 BCLC 1.
Market Street Associates Ltd Partnership v. *Frey*, 941 F.2d 588, 594, 7th Cir. 1991.
Marsden v. *Sambell* (1880) 28 WR 952.
Marshall and Anor v. *Colonial Bank of Australia* (1903–04) 1 CLR 632.
Marshall v. *Mackintosh* (1898) 78 LT 750.
Maryon v. *Carter* (1830) 4 C & P 295.
Matsoukis v. *Priestman & Co* [1915] 1 KB 681.
Matthew Hall Ortech v. *Tarmac Roadstone* (1998) 87 BLR 96.
Mayfield Holdings Ltd v. *Moana Reef Ltd* [1973] 1 NZLR 309.
McAlpine Humberoak Ltd v. *McDermott International Inc (no 1)* (1992) 58 BLR 1, CA.
McArdle v. *Andmac Roofing Co* [1967] 1 All ER 583, [1967] 1 WLR 356, CA.
McCosker v. *Lovett, Building and Construction Law* 12 (1996): 146.
McDonald v. *Dennys Lascelles Ltd* (1933) 48 CLR 457.
McDonald v. *Workington Corpn* (1892) 2 Hudson's BC 4th edn 228, CA.
McLeod (or Houston) v. *Buchanan* [1940] 2 All ER 179, HL.
Meikle v. *Maufe* [1941] 3 All ER 144.
Mellins v. *Motteux* (1792) 170 ER 113.
Mellows Archital Ltd v. *Bell Projects Ltd* (1998) 87 BLR 26.

Mercers Co v. *New Hampshire Insurance Co* [1992] 3 All ER 57, CA.

Mersey Docks and Harbour Board v. *Henderson Brothers* (1888) 13 App Cas 595, 58 LJQB 152, HL.

Mersey Steel and Iron Co v. *Naylor Benzon & Co* (1884) 9 App Cas 434, HL.

Mertens v. *Home Freeholds Co* [1921] 2 KB 526, CA.

Metcalf v. *Bouck* (1871) 25 LT 539.

Metropolitan Asylum District Managers v. *Hill* (1881) 6 App Cas 193, HL.

Metropolitan Water Board v. *Dick, Kerr & Co* [1917] 2 KB 1, CA.

Metropolitan Water Board v. *Johnson* [1913] 2 KB 900.

Meux v. *Jacobs* (1875) LR 7 HL 481, 44 LJ Ch 481.

Mid-Glamorgan County Council v. *J Devonald Williams & Partner (a firm)* (1991) 29 Con LR 129.

Midland Rly Co v. *Ambergate, Nottingham and Boston and Eastern Junction Rly Co* (1853) 10 Hare 359, 1 WR 162.

Migotti v. *Colvill* (1879) 4 CPD 233.

Milburn Services Ltd v. *United Trading Group (UK) Ltd* (1997) 52 Con LR 130.

Mills v. *Bayley* (1863) 2 H & C 36.

Minster Trust Ltd v. *Traps Tractors Ltd* [1954] 3 All ER 136, [1954] 1 WLR 963.

Mitsui Babcock Energy Ltd v. *John Brown Engineering Ltd* (1996) 51 Con LR 129.

M J Gleeson plc v. *Taylor Woodrow Construction Ltd* (1989) 49 BLR 95.

M J Gleeson (Contractors) Ltd v. *London Borough of Hillingdon* (1970) 215 Estates Gazette 495.

Mona Oil Equipment & Supply Co Ltd v. *Rhodesia Railways Ltd* [1949] 1 All ER 1014, KB.

Money penny v. *Hartland* (1826) 2 C & P 378.

Monmouth County Council v. *Costelloe and Kemple Ltd* (1965) 63 LGR 429, CA.

Moon v. *Witney Union Guardians* (1837) 3 Bing NC 814.

Moorcock, The (1889) 14 PD 64, [1886–90] All ER Rep 530, CA.

Moorgate Tobacco Co Ltd v. *Philip Morris Ltd* (1984–85) 156 CLR 414, HC Aust.

Moores v. *Yakeley Associates Ltd* (1999) 62 Con LR 76.

Morgan v. *Birnie* (1833) 9 Bing 672.

Morgan v. *Ravey* (1861) 6 H & N 265.

Morley v. *Inglis* (1837) 4 Bing 58 .

Morrison-Knudsen International Co Inc v. *Commonwealth of Australia* (1972) 46 ALJR 265.

Morrison Knudsen Company Inc v. *Alaska* 519 P 2d 834 (S Ct Alaska) 1974.

Mottram Consultants Ltd v. *Bernard Sunley & Sons Ltd* (1974) 2 BLR 28, HL.

Munro v. *Butt* (1858) 8 E & B 738, LR 2 CP 651.

Murphy v. *Brentwood District Council* [1991] 1 AC 398, [1990] 2 All ER 908, HL.

National Carriers Ltd v. *Panalpina (Northern) Ltd* [1981] AC 675, HL.

National Trust for Places of Historic Interest or Natural Beauty v. *Haden Young Ltd* (1993) 66 BLR 88, (1994) 72 BLR 1, CA.

NEI Thompson Ltd v. *Wimpey Construction UK Ltd* (1987) 39 BLR 65, CA.

Nene Housing Society Ltd v. *National Westminster Bank Ltd* (1980) 16 BLR 22.

Neodex Ltd v. *Swinton and Pendlebury Borough Council* (1958) 5 BLR 34.

Newfoundland Government v. *Newfoundland Rly* (1999) 13 App Cas 199, PC.

Nichols v. *Marsland* (1876) 2 Ex D 1.

Nikko Hotel (UK) Ltd v. *MEPC* (1991) 28 EG 86.

Nitrigin Eireann Teoranta v. *Inco Alloys Ltd* [1992] 1 All ER 854.

Nokes v. *Doncaster Amalgamated Collieries Ltd* [1940] AC 1014, [1940] 3 All ER 549, HL.

Norta Wallpapers (Ireland) Ltd v. *John Sisk & Sons (Dublin) Ltd* (1977) 14 BLR 49.

Northern Regional Health Authority v. *Derek Crouch Construction Co Ltd* [1984] QB 644; [1982] 2 All ER 175, CA.

North West Metropolitan Regional Hospital Board v. *T A Bickerton & Son Ltd* [1970] 1 All ER 1039, [1970] 1 WLR 607, HL.

Norwich City Council v. *Harvey* (1988) 45 BLR 14, [1989] 1 ALL ER 1180, CA.

Nye Saunders & Partners v. *Brisow* (1987) 37 BLR 92, CA.

Oastler v. *Pound* (1863) 7 LT 852.

Ocean Tramp Tankers Corpn v. *V/O Sovfracht, The Eugenia* [1964] 2 QB 226, [1964] 1 All ER 161, CA.

Opron Construction Co Ltd v. *Alaska* (1994) 14 CLR (2d) 97.

Orr v. *Mitchell* [1893] AC 238, HL.

Outwing Construction Ltd v. *H Randell and Son Limited* (1999) 15 Const LJ 308.

Oval (717) Ltd v. *Aegon Insurance Company (UK) Ltd* (1998) 85 BLR 97.

Overbury v. *Platten*, 108 F (2d) 155, 157 (CCCA 2d 1939).

Oxford University Fixed Assets Ltd v. *Architects Design Partnership (a firm)* (1999) 64 Con LR 13.

Oxford University Press v. *John Stedman Design Group & Ors* (1990) 34 Con LR 1.

P & M Kaye Ltd v. *Hosier & Dickenson Ltd* [1972] 1 All ER 121, [1972] 1 WLR 146, HL.

Page v. *Llandaff and Dinas Powis RDC* (1901) 2 Hudson's BC 4th edn 316.

Pagnan SpA v. *Feed Products Ltd* [1987] 2 Lloyd's Rep 601, CA.

Panamena Europea Navigacion (Cia Lda) v. *Frederick Leyland & Co Ltd* [1947] AC 428, HL.

Paradine v. *Jane* (1647) Aleyn 26, 82 ER 897, Style 47, 82 ER 519.

Parkin v. *Thorvold* (1852) 16 Beav 59.

Partington & Son (Builders) Ltd v. *Tameside Metropolitan Borough Council* (1985) 32 BLR 150.

Pauling v. *Dover Corpn* (1855) 10 Exch 753.

P C Harrington Contractors Ltd v. *Co Partnership Developments Ltd* (1998) 88 BLR 44, CA.

Peak Construction (Liverpool) Ltd v. *McKinney Foundations Ltd* (1970) 1 BLR 111, CA.

Pepper v. *Burland* (1792) 1 Peake NP 139.

Pepper (Inspector of Taxes) v. *Hart* [1993] AC 593, HL.

Percy Bilton Ltd v. *Greater London Council* [1982] 2 All ER 623, HL.

Perini Corpn v. *Commonwealth of Australia* (1969) 12 BLR 62.

Peter Dixon & Sons Ltd v. *Henderson, Craig & Co* [1919] 2 KB 778, CA.

Peter Lind & Co Ltd v. *Mersey Docks and Harbour Board* [1972] 2 Lloyd's Rep 234.

Petrofina (UK) Ltd v. *Magnaload Ltd* (1984) 25 BLR 37, [1984] QB 127, [1983] 3 All ER 35.

Philips Hong Kong v. *A-G of Hong Kong* (1993) 61 BLR 41, PC.

Photo Production Ltd v. *Securicor Transport Ltd* [1980] AC 827, [1980] 1 All ER 556, HL.

Pickering v. *Ilfracombe Rly Co* (1868) LR 3 CP 235.

Pigott Foundations Ltd v. *Shepherd Construction Ltd* (1993) 42 Con LR 98.

Plant Construction plc v. *Clive Adam Associates (a firm)* (1997) 55 Con LR 41.
Pozzolanic Lytag v. *Bryan Hobson Associates* (1999) 63 Con LR 81.
Porter v. *Hannah Builders Pty Ltd* [1969] VR 673.
Potato Marketing Board v. *Merricks* [1958] 2 QB 316.
Pratt v. *George J Hill Associates* (1987) 38 BLR 25, CA.
Public Works Comr v. *Hills* [1906] AC 368, PC.
Queensland Government Railways v. *Manufacturers' Mutual Insurance Ltd*
    [1969] 1 Lloyd's Rep 214.
QuesTech, Inc v. *Iran* (1985 II) 9 Iran-USCTR 107.
R v. *Farmer* [1892] 1 QB 637, [1891–4] All ER Rep 921, CA.
R v. *Gough* [1993] AC 646, [1993] 2 All ER 724, HL.
R v. *Lord Chancellor, ex p Hibbitt and Saunders* [1993] COD 326.
R v. *Peto* (1826) 1 Y & J 37.
R v. *Portsmouth City Council, ex parte Peter Coles, Colwick Builders Ltd and*
    George Austin Ltd (1997) 81 BLR 1, CA.
R v. *Walter Cabott Construction Ltd* (1975) 69 DLR (3d) 542.
R v. *Tao* [1977] QB 141; [1976] 3 All ER 65, CA.
R v. *Ward Ltd* v. *Bignall* [1967] 1 QB 534, [1967] 2 All ER 449, CA.
Raineri v. *Miles* [1981] AC 1050, HL.
Ranger v. *Great Western Rly Co* (1854) 5 HL Cas 72, HL.
Rapid Building Group Ltd v. *Ealing Family Housing Association Ltd* (1984) 29
    BLR 5, CA.
Rayack Construction Ltd v. *Lampeter Meat Co Ltd* (1979) 12 BLR 30.
R D Harbottle (Mercantile) Ltd v. *National Westminster Bank Ltd* [1978] QB
    146, [1977] 2 All ER 862.
Re Bayley-Worthington & Cohen's Contract [1909] 1 Ch 648.
Re Cadogan & Hans Place Estate Ltd, Ex p Willis (1895) 11 TLR 477, CA.
Re Chappell, ex parte Ford (1885) 16 QBD 305, CA.
Re Comptoir Commercial Anversois and Power, Son & Co [1920] 1 KB 868,
    [1918–19] All ER Rep 661, CA.
Re Cosslett (Contractors) Ltd [1996] 4 All ER 46; affirmed [1997] 4 All ER 115,
    CA.
Re De Morgan Snell & Co and Rio de Janiero Flour Mills and Granaries Ltd
    (1892) 8 TLR 292, CA.
Re Follick, ex p Trustee (1907) 97 LT 645.
Re Fuerst Bros & Co Ltd and R S Stephenson [1951] 1 Lloyd's Rep 429.
Re Jartay Developments Ltd (1982) 22 BLR 134.
Re Keen, ex p Collins [1902] 1 KB 555.
Re Nott & Cardiff Corpn [1918] 2 KB 146, 118 LT 487.
Re Nuttal and Lynton and Barnstable Rly Co's Arbitration (1899) 82 LT 17,
    CA.
Re Peachdart Ltd [1984] Ch 131, [1983] 3 All ER 204.
Re Selectmove Ltd [1995] 2 All ER 531, [1995] 1 WLR 474, CA.
Re Trustees of Magdalen Charity, Hastings v. *Shelower* (1968) 19 P & CR
    389.
Re Walker, ex p Barter (1884) 26 Ch D 510, CA.
Re Waugh, ex p Dickin (1876) 4 Ch D 524.
Re Webb [1896] 1 QB 487.
Re Winter, ex p Bolland (1878) 8 Ch D 225.
Re Woods, Woods v. *Woods* [1941] St R Qd 129.
Re Yorkshire Joinery Co Ltd (in liquidation) (1967) 111 Sol Jo 701.
Reeves v. *Barlow* (1884) 12 QBD 436, CA.

Reigate v. *Union Manufacturing Co (Ramsbottom) Ltd* [1918] 1 KB 592; [1918–19] All ER Rep 143, CA.

Renard Constructions (ME) Pty Ltd v. *Minister of Public Works* (1992) 26 NSWLR 234.

Rentokil Ailsa Environmental Ltd v. *Eastend Civil Engineering Ltd* (1999) CILL 1506.

Reynolds v. *John* [1956] 1 QB 650; [1956] 1 All ER 306.

Richardson v. *Buckinghamshire County Council* (1971) 6 BLR 58, CA.

River Wear Comrs v. *Adamson* (1877) 2 App Cas 743, HL.

R M Douglas Construction Ltd v. *Bass Leisure Ltd* (1990) 53 BLR 119.

Robb v. *Green* [1895] 2 QB 1.

Roberts v. *Bury Improvement Commissioners* (1870) LR 4 CP 755; LR 5 CP 310, Ex Ch.

Roberts v. *Davey* (1833) 4 B & Ad 664.

Roberts v. *Watkins* (1863) 14 CBNS 592.

Rosehaugh Stanhope Properties (Broadgate Phase 6) plc and Rosehaugh Stanhope (Broadgate Phase 7) plc v. *Redpath Dorman Long Ltd* (1990) 50 BLR 69, (1990) 29 Con LR 80, CA.

Rotherham Metropolitan Borough Council v. *Frank Haslam Milan & Co Ltd and M J Gleeson (Northern) Ltd* (1996) 78 BLR 1, CA.

Rover International Ltd v. *Cannon Film Sales Ltd (no 3)* [1989] 3 All ER 423, [1989] 1 WLR 912, CA.

Russell v. *Viscount Sa da Bandeira* (1862) 13 CBNS 149.

S Pearson & Son Ltd v. *Dublin Corpn* [1907] AC 351, HL.

Sailing Ship Blairmore Co Ltd v. *Macredie* [1898] AC 593, HL.

Saunders and Collard v. *Broadstairs Local Board* (1890) 2 Hudson's BC 4th edn 164, DC.

Saunders v. *Ernest A Neale Ltd* [1974] 3 All ER 327.

Sauter Automation Ltd v. *Goodman Mechanical Services Ltd (in liquidation)* (1986) 34 BLR 81, Ch D.

Scally v. *Southern Health and Social Services Board* [1992] 1 AC 294, [1991] 4 All ER 563, HL.

Scottish Special Housing Association v. *Wimpey Construction UK Ltd* [1986] 2 All ER 957, [1986] 1 WLR 995, HL.

Scrivener v. *Pask* (1865) LR 1 CP 715.

Scruttons Ltd v. *Midland Silicones Ltd* [1962] AC 466, HL.

Secured Income Real Estate (Australia) Ltd v. *St Martin's Investments Pty Ltd* (1979) 144 CLR 596.

Service Station Association Ltd v. *Berg Bennett & Associates Ltd* (1993) 117 ALR 393.

Sharpe v. *San Paulo Rly Co* (1873) LR 8 Ch App 597.

Shave v. *Rosner* [1954] 2 QB 113, [1954] 2 All ER 280.

Shearson Lehman Hutton Inc v. *Maclaine Watson & Co Ltd* [1989] 2 Lloyd's Rep 570.

Shell UK Ltd v. *Lostock Garage Ltd* [1977] 1 All ER 481, [1976] 1 WLR 1187, CA.

Shepherd v. *Felt and Textiles of Australia Ltd* (1931) 45 CLR 359.

Shirlaw v. *Southern Foundries (1926) Ltd* [1939] 2 KB 206, [1939] 2 All ER 113, CA.

Simmons v. *Woodward* [1892] AC 100, HL.

Sims v. *London Necropolis Co* (1885) 1 TLR 584.

Sir Lindsay Parkinson & Co Ltd v. *Comrs of Works and Public Buildings* [1949] 2 KB 632; [1950] 1 All ER 208, CA.

Tern Construction Group Ltd v. *RBS Garages Ltd* (1993) CILL 844.

Tersons Ltd v. *Stevenage Development Corpn* [1965] 1 QB 37, [1963] 3 All ER 863, CA.

Tesco Stores v. *Norman Hiscox Partnership* (1998) 56 Con LR 42.

Test Valley Borough Council v. *Greater London Council* (1979) 13 BLR 63, CA.

Tharsis Sulphur and Copper Co v. *McElroy & Sons* (1878) 3 App Cas 1040, HL.

Thomas Feather & Co (Bradford) Ltd v. Keighley Corpn (1953) 52 LGR 30.

Thomas v. *Hammersmith Borough Council* [1938] 3 All ER 203, CA.

Thomas v. *Thomas* (1842) 2 QB 851.

Thorn v. *London Corpn* (1876) 1 App Cas 120, HL.

Thornton v. *Place* (1832) 1 Mood & R 218.

Tins Industrial Co Ltd v. *Kono Insurance Ltd* (1987) 42 BLR 110, HKCA.

Tinsley v. *Milligan* [1993] 3 All ER 65, HL.

Token Construction Co Ltd v. *Charlton Estates* (1973) 1 BLR 48, CA.

Tolhurst v. *Associated Portland Cement Manufacturers Ltd* [1903] AC 414, HL.

Tompkinson v. *Parochial Church of St Michael* (1990) 6 Const LJ 319.

Tower Housing Association Ltd v. *Technical & General Guarantee Co Ltd* (1998) 87 BLR 74.

Trade Indemnity Co Ltd v. *Workington Harbour and Dock Board* [1937] AC 1, HL.

Trident General Insurance Co Ltd v. *McNiece Bros Pty Ltd* (1988) 165 CLR 107.

Tripp v. *Armitage* (1839) 4 M & W 687.

Trollope & Colls Ltd v. *North West Metropolitan Regional Hospital Board* [1973] 2 All ER 260, [1973] 1 WLR 601, (1973) 9 BLR 60.

Trollope & Colls Ltd and Holland, Hannen & Cubitts Ltd v. *Atomic Power Constructions Ltd* [1962] 3 All ER 1035.

Trollope & Sons v. *Martyn Brothers* [1934] 2 KB 436.

Turnbull Inc v. *US* 389 F 2d 1007 (CT CL, 1967) 1011.

Tweedle v. *Atkinson* (1861) 1 B & S 393, 30 LJQB 265.

Tyler v. *London & India Docks Joint Committee* (1892) 9 TLR 11.

United Scientific Holdings Ltd v. *Burnley Borough Council* [1978] AC 904, [1977] 2 All ER 62.

United States v. *Spearin* 248 US 132 (1918).

United States Shipping Board v. *Durrell* [1923] 2 KB 739.

University Court of the University of Glasgow v. *William Whitfield and John Laing (Construction) Ltd (Third party)* (1988) 42 BLR 66.

University of Reading v. *Miller Construction Ltd and Sharp* (1995) 75 BLR 91, OR.

US Surgical Corp v. *Hospital Products International Pty Ltd* [1982] 2 NSWLR 766.

Vandyck v. *Hewitt* (1800) 1 East 96.

Victoria Laundry (Windsor) Ltd v. *Newman Industries Ltd* [1949] 2 KB 528, [1949] 1 All ER 997.

Victoria University of Manchester v. *Hugh Wilson & Lewis Womersley (A firm)* (1984) 2 Con LR 43.

Viking Grain Storage v. *T H White Installations Ltd* (1985) 33 BLR 103.

Waghorn v. *Wimbledon Local Board* (1877) 2 Hudson's BC 4th edn 52.

Wain v. *Walters* (1804) 5 East 10

Walford v. *Miles* [1992] 2 AC 128, [1992] 1 All ER 453, HL.

Walker v. *York Corpn* [1906] 1 KB 724, 75 LJKB 413.

Wallace v. *Brandon and Byshottles UDC* (1903) 2 Hudson's BC 4th edn 362, CA.

Wallis v. *Robinson* (1862) 3 F & F 307.

Wallis v. *Superior Court (Kroehler Manufacturing Co)* 207 Cal Rptr 123 (1984).

Walters v. *Whessoe Ltd* (1960) 6 BLR 23, CA.

Walton (Grain and Shipping) Ltd v. *British Italian Trading Co Ltd* [1959] 1 Lloyd's Rep 223.

Waltons Stores (Interstate) Ltd v. *Maher* (1988) 164 CLR 387.

Ware and Jones v. *Lyttelton Harbour Board* (1882) 1 NZLR 191.

Wardens and Commonalty of the Mystery of Mercers of the City of London v. *New Warre* v. *Calvert* (1837) 7 Ad & El 143.

Wates Construction (London) Ltd v. *Franthom Property Ltd* (1991) 53 BLR 23, CA.

Watts v. *Shuttleworth* (1871) 7 H & N 353.

Wayne Tank & Pump Co Ltd v. *Employers' Liability Assurance Corpn Ltd* [1974] QB 57, [1973], 3 All ER 825, CA.

Webb v. *Hughes* (1870) LR 10 Eq 281.

Wellington Corporation v. *Lower Hutt Corporation* [1904] AC 773, PC.

Wells v. *Army & Navy Co-operative Society Ltd* (1902) 2 Hudson's BC 4th edn 346, (1902) 86 LT 764, CA.

Welsh Health Technical Services Organisation v. *Haden Young* (1987) 37 BLR 130.

West Faulkner Associates v. *London Borough of Newham* (1992) 9 Const LJ 232, OR; (1994) 71 BLR 1, CA.

Westminster City Council v. *J Jarvis & Sons* [1970] 1 All ER 943, HL.

Westwood v. *Secretary of State for India in Council* (1863) 7 LT 736.

Wettern Electric Ltd v. *Welsh Development Agency* [1983] QB 796, [1983] 2 All ER 629.

W Hanson (Harrow) Ltd v. *Rapid Civil Engineering Ltd* (1987) 38 BLR 106, 11 Con LR 119.

Wharf Properties Ltd v. *Eric Cumine Associates & Ors (no 2)* (1991) 52 BLR 1, PC.

Wheat v. *E Lacon & Co Ltd* [1966] AC 552, [1966] 1 All ER 582, HL.

White and Carter (Councils) Ltd v. *McGregor* [1962] AC 413, [1961] 3 All ER 1178, HL.

White v. *Weston* [1968] 2 QB 647, [1968] 2 All ER 842, CA.

Widnes Foundry (1925) Ltd v. *Cellulose Acetate Silk Co Ltd* [1931] 2 KB 393, CA.

William Cory & Son Ltd v. *City of London Corpn* [1951] 2 KB 476 CA.

William Lacey (Hounslow) Ltd v. *Davis* [1957] 2 All ER 712, [1957] 1 WLR 132.

Williams v. *Burrell* (1845) 1 CB 402, 14 LJCP 98, 135 ER 596.

Williams v. *Fitzmaurice* (1858) 3 H & N 844.

Williams v. *Roffey Bros and Nicholls (Contractors) Ltd* [1991] 1 QB 1, [1990] 1 All ER 512, CA.

Wilmot v. *Smith* (1828) 3 C & P 453.

Wilsons and Clyde Coal Co Ltd v. *English* [1938] AC 57, [1937] 3 All ER 628, HL.

W Lamb (t/a The Premier Pump & Tank Co) v. *Jarvis & Sons plc* (1998) 60 Con LR 1.

Woodar Investment Development Ltd v. *Wimpey Construction (UK) Ltd* [1980] 1 All ER 571, [1980] 1 WLR 277, HL.

Woolich Equitable Building Society v. *Inland Revenue Commissioners* [1993] AC 70, HL.

X (Minors) v. *Bedfordshire County Council and others* [1995] 2 AC 633, [1995] 3 All ER 353, HL.

Index